GLENCOE

Health

A Guide to Wellness

Teacher's Wraparound Edition

Mary Bronson Merki, Ph.D.
Don Merki, Ph.D.

Contributing Authors

Michael J. Cleary, Ed.D.
Gale Cornelia Flynn

Glencoe McGraw-Hill

New York, New York   Columbus, Ohio   Chicago, Illinois   Peoria, Illinois   Woodland Hills, California

About the Cover

Scull – a light, narrow racing boat for one, two, or sometimes four rowers, each equipped with a pair of oars.

Front cover photograph © by Stephen Wilkes

Back cover inset © Dennis Degnan/Westlight

Glencoe/McGraw-Hill

*A Division of The **McGraw·Hill** Companies*

Send all inquiries to:
Glencoe/McGraw-Hill
21600 Oxnard Street
Suite 500
Woodland Hills, California 91367

ISBN: 0-07-823864-1 (Student's Edition)
ISBN: 0-07-823865-X (Teacher's Wraparound Edition)
ISBN: 0-07-829660-9 (CNN® Video)

Printed in the United States of America.

2 3 4 5 6 7 9   071/043 06 05 04 03 02

Educational Consultants

Nita Auer
Health Educator
North Side High School
Fort Wayne, Indiana

Pamela Connolly
Health and Physical Education
Diocese of Pittsburgh
West Mifflin, Pennsylvania

Justin Cunningham
California Health Framework Writing
   Committee Chair
San Diego, California

Robert Wandberg, Ph.D.
Health Educator
John F. Kennedy High School
Bloomington, Minnesota

Content Reviewers

David Allen, M.D.
Infectious Disease Consultant
Dallas, Texas

Marcella Cook
Health Resource Educator
Charlotte, North Carolina

Roberta Duyff
Nutrition Education Consultant
St. Louis, Missouri

Glen C. Griffin, M.D.
Health Consultant
Mapleton, Utah

Marlene Koch, R.D., L.D.
Nutrition Education Consultant
Dublin, Ohio

Bonnie Mohnsen, Ph.D.
Health Consultant
Cerritos, California

Judy Monroe
Health Educator
St. Paul, Minnesota

Richard L. Papenfuss, Ph.D.
Associate Professor, Health
University of Arizona
Tucson, Arizona

Howard Shapiro, M.D.
Psychiatrist
Los Angeles, California

David Sleet, Ph.D.
Injury Prevention
San Diego, California

Pamela Tollefson, R.N.
Health Education and HIV/STD
   Prevention
Olympia, Washington

Teacher Reviewers

Donna Breitenstein
Director of Health Training Center
Boone, North Carolina

Diana Bruckerhoff
Health Education Coordinator
Columbia, Missouri

Peggy Campbell
Curriculum Supervisor
Huntington, West Virginia

Alisa Debnam
Health Supervisor
Fayetteville, North Carolina

Debra Harris
Health and Physical Education Educator
West Linn, Oregon

Jo Henderson
Health Educator
Seattle, Washington

Gayle S. Jenkins
Health Education Program Specialist
Raleigh, North Carolina

Peggy V. Johns
Supervisor, Pre K-12 Health Education
Largo, Florida

Phyllis Simpson, Ph.D. CHES
Health Supervisor
Dallas, Texas

Deborah Tackmann
Health Educator
Eau Claire, Wisconsin

Betty White
Health Educator
Lexington, Kentucky

CONTENTS

GLENCOE

Health

Glencoe is proud to present the all-new edition of *Glencoe Health: A Guide to Wellness*. Building on years of success and tradition, this new edition continues to provide the solid concept development you expect in a health program. *Glencoe Health* meets your needs with a total teaching program. Here's more about the benefits of *Glencoe Health*.

Thorough Content Coverage and Engaging Presentation

From personal health to injury prevention, from community health to nutrition and fitness; and from alcohol, tobacco, and drugs to personal development and family living, Glencoe has what you're looking for in a health program. The solid, comprehensive coverage of the health content, plus exceptional visuals, result in a student-friendly text that's easy to use and easy to understand. With its short lessons, interactive format, increased emphasis on skill-building, and exciting new visual approach, *Glencoe Health* is a powerful teaching tool to help you reach students of all ability levels.

Outstanding Teacher Support

When it comes to teacher support, the Teacher's Wraparound Multimedia Edition is just the beginning. From performance assessment tips, to videodisc bar codes, the teacher's wraparound edition provides all of the support you need. Print, audio, and technology resources found throughout the teacher's wraparound edition help you manage the wide range of learning styles and ability levels in today's heterogeneous classrooms.

The Teacher Classroom Resources contains more than 20 supplemental materials including health labs, performance assessment activities, lesson quizzes and chapter tests, transparencies, and more – all designed to help you spend less time preparing lessons and more time teaching them.

Engaging, Interactive Hands-On Activities

When it comes to doing activities in the classroom, you need flexibility and choices. That's why we provide a variety of activities designed to provide application, reinforcement, enrichment, and extension. Some of the interactive features include:

1. **Building Health Skills** presents such skills as decision making, goal setting, building self-esteem, communication, refusal skills, and conflict resolution.
2. **Making Responsible Decisions** presents real-life situations students must resolve by using a six-step decision-making process.
3. **Health Lab** offers fascinating learning experiences students can do on their own with minimal equipment.
4. **Overcoming the Odds** uses actual interviews to examine how teens have successfully dealt with adverse situations.

Glencoe Health promotes wellness, health literacy, and positive health behavior, and meets the National Health Education Standards.

Wide Range of Technology Options

Teaching a tough concept? How would you like to simply scan a bar code from your teacher's multimedia edition and have that concept appear instantly as an interactive video on your classroom TV? You can do this with the wide variety of technology options available with *Glencoe Health*.

From video-cassettes and audiocassettes, to videodiscs, Internet, and CD-ROM, the *Glencoe Health* program has all the technology options you need. And, they're specifically created for and directly correlated to the text, with references and bar codes at point of use.

The Student Edition - At a Glance

The *Glencoe Health* student text introduces students to a comprehensive, skills-based health program with a strong emphasis on abstinence. This lays the foundation for building lifelong health skills and reinforces ways to practice skills that help students make positive health choices.

Chapter Opening

Each chapter opens with an engaging and motivational quote, Quick Write activity, and photo related to the chapter's contents. By using the *Self-Inventory* students have the opportunity to evaluate their current health behaviors and attitudes. When they finish the chapter, students see how their attitudes and behaviors have changed by what they've learned in the text.

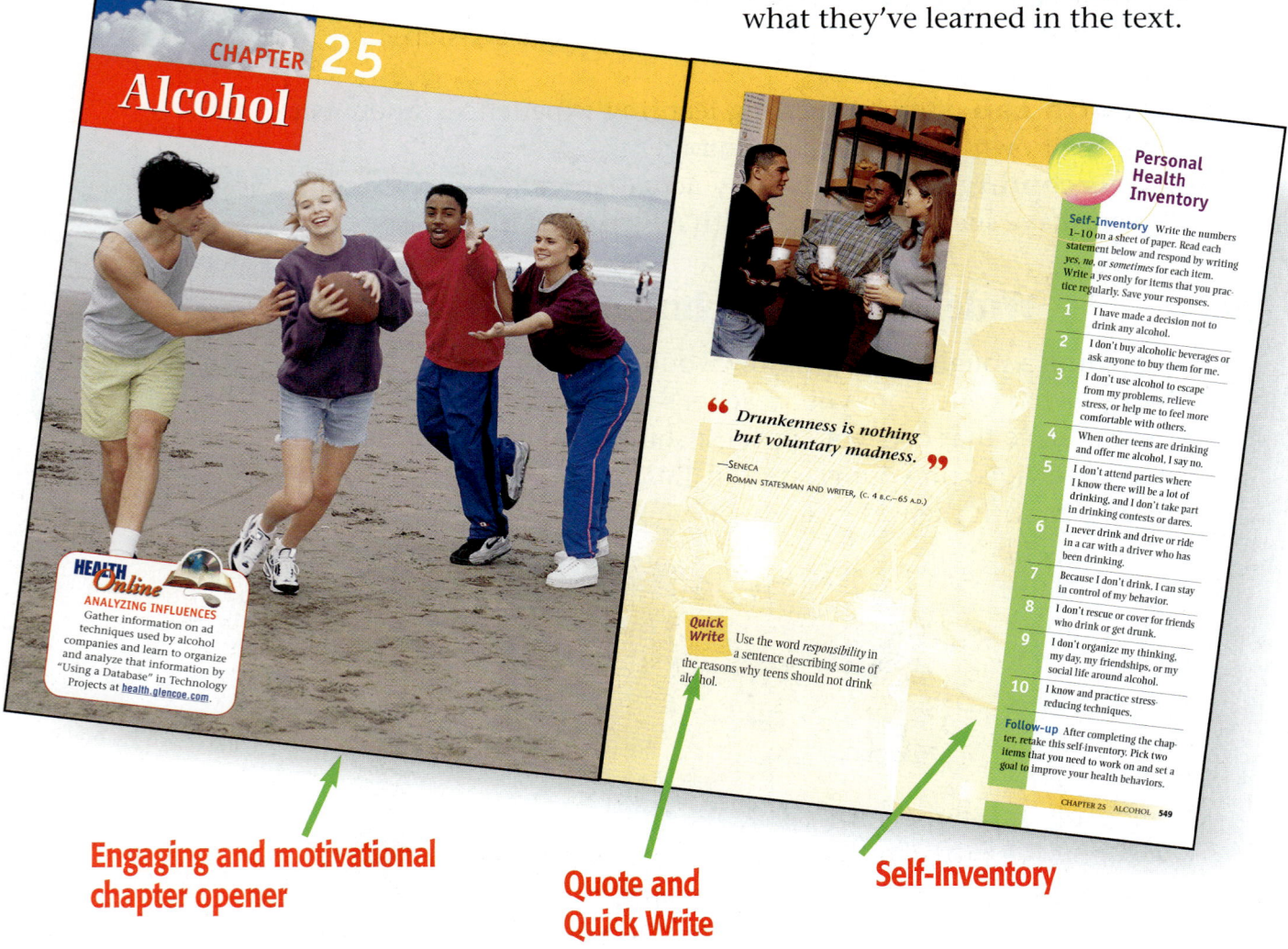

Engaging and motivational chapter opener

Quote and Quick Write

Self-Inventory

Goals and an Action Plan

While goals can differ in the amount of time and degree of effort necessary to reach them, all can be achieved by creating an action plan. Like the decision-making process, an **action plan** is a multi-step strategy for identifying and achieving goals.

Goals for Life

What are your personal goals right now—today? If your answer is that you do not have any, ask yourself why.

If you do not have positive goals, you need to ask yourself: Why? How can I remove the roadblocks that stand in the way of my having positive goals?

Remember, goal setting, like decision making and the other health skills you learned about in this chapter, can move you toward the

Building Health Skills

Setting Goals: Making an Action Plan

AN ACTION PLAN consists of six action-based steps that can help you accomplish your goals. These are:

1. **Select a goal to work on.** In selecting a goal, you need to be specific and realistic. Also, state your goal as something positive. Do not settle for just "not failing." Focus your energies instead on succeeding. This will help motivate you to work toward achieving your goal.

2. **List what you will do to reach the goal.** Look for ways to break your goal down into smaller, more manageable tasks. If your goal is to become a long-distance runner, begin by training yourself to run shorter distances.

3. **Identify sources of help and support.** Sources of support and encouragement are important to achieving any goal. Such sources might include friends, family members, teachers, or neighbors.

4. **Set a reasonable time frame for reaching your goal.** When first setting out toward any goal, you should establish a reasonable time limit for reaching that goal and put it in writing.

5. **Establish checkpoints to evaluate your progress.** As with establishing a time frame, such checkpoints should be reasonable and realistic.

6. **Reward yourself after reaching your goal.** Once you arrive, congratulate yourself and enjoy the personal satisfaction. One way is to buy yourself something you have wanted. Knowing that a reward waits at the end of the journey will help you work that much harder.

keeping Fit

10 Reasons to Work Out

Regular exercise brings benefits to many areas of your life. The following are just some of these benefits:

➤ improved cardiovascular health
➤ better weight control
➤ improved flexibility, muscular strength, and muscular endurance
➤ improved appearance, such as rosy cheeks and well-toned muscles
➤ improved self-esteem
➤ increased productivity
➤ a chance to socialize when you participate in group sports
➤ increased mental alertness
➤ increased ability to handle stress
➤ less fatigue and improved sleep

■ **Muscular endurance.** This is *the ability of the muscles to do difficult physical tasks over a period of time without causing fatigue.*
■ **Cardiorespiratory endurance.** This is *the ability of the heart, lungs, and blood vessels to send fuel and oxygen to the body's tissues during long periods of vigorous activity.*

Each of these components can be measured through various tests and activities. Once you know your strengths and weaknesses, you can take steps to improve your health-related fitness.

Measuring Body Composition

Appearance is probably one of the biggest reasons people exercise and watch what they eat. Since there is a strong relationship between the thickness of lean body tissue and the amount of fat inside your body, a reliable test for body composition is the pinch test. The skin and underlying layer of fat are pinched together on the upper arm and calf. These are measured with an instrument called *calipers*. The measurements are taken three times, then compared with those on a chart for an estimated percentage of body fat. Males with 25 or more percent body fat and females with 30 or more percent body fat are at risk of developing cardiovascular problems. Carrying too much weight also puts added stress on the skeletal system. If you have too much body fat, you can lose some of this fat through moderate physical activity and by reducing the number of calories you take in from food.

Making Responsible Decisions

To Work or to Run?

Rhonda has recently taken a part-time job at a local restaurant. She enjoys the people she works with and the new skills she is learning. She is especially happy about all the things she can do with the money she is earning. The only bad part about the job is that she had to quit running track in order to work the necessary hours. She noticed that since she started working she has been gaining weight and feeling sluggish, probably due in part to her love for the restaurant's famous double fudge sundaes.

What should Rhonda do?

Provide an answer by putting yourself in her place. Then answer the questions below.

What Would You Do?

Apply the six steps of the decision-making process to Rhonda's problem.

1. State the situation.
2. List the options.
3. Weigh the possible outcomes.
4. Consider your values.
5. Make a decision and act.
6. Evaluate the decision.

Building Health Skills

Making Responsible Decisions

Chapter Features

With the increasing attention given to developing skills, students learn and practice ways to make healthy choices. Each chapter includes opportunities for students to apply and practice the health skills of decision making, goal setting, stress management, building self-esteem, communication, and conflict resolution. Through these activities, students learn how taking responsibility for their own health has positive effects not only for themselves but also for others around them. These skills help students learn to choose the behaviors that protect, promote, and maintain health and to avoid dangerous high-risk behaviors.

Other Features of the Student Text

Teens Making a Difference

uses actual interviews to examine how teens have worked in their communities. Follow-up questions emphasize character traits that lead to success in providing service to others.

Health Lab

features science-based health activities and hands-on experiments that require little or no scientific equipment.

Update: Looking at Technology/Looking at the Issues/Our Changing World

provides perspectives on a variety of current health topics and complex social issues, challenging students to apply objective reasoning and critical thinking in today's world.

Health Skills Activities

included at the end of each chapter provides embedded performance assessment activities correlated to the National Health Education Standards.

Connections

provides cross-curriculum activities, reading selections, and critical thinking questions and helps students see how health is related to science, mathematics, language arts, social studies, and physical education.

Internet Connection

gives point-of-use reference to activities on the *Glencoe Health* home page on the World Wide Web.

Character in Action

gives students opportunities to practice and apply Character Education principles they've learned to everyday situations

Also Includes

Keeping Fit provides students with quick, hands-on ideas to apply what they've learned in the classroom to their daily lives.

Hotlinks appear throughout the text highlighted in blue to cross-reference important material in other chapters.

Glossary/Glosario defines each vocabulary term in English format, then separately in the Spanish Glosario.

Support for the Health Teacher

The Teacher's Wraparound Multimedia Edition provides complete lesson plans, teaching suggestions, supplemental information, relevant cross-references, and more—all conveniently "wrapped" around every page of the reduced student text. Teachers will discover that the consistent, easy-to-follow lesson plan format gives a variety of teaching strategies to motivate students; to introduce, teach, and reinforce concepts; and alternative teaching strategies for adapting the program to your own teaching style and to the learning styles of your students.

Teacher's Planning Guide

National Health Education Standards

Block Scheduling

Organized with the Teacher in Mind

Lesson Plans

The teaching material follows a consistent, easy-to-use pattern. The complete lesson cycle—**Focus, Teach, Assess**, and **Close**—make it easy for you to plan a lesson. Included in the lesson plan you will find:

FOCUS

- A list of student objectives
- A Motivator activity to involve students in the lesson
- A Vocabulary activity to help students build vocabulary skills

TEACH

Various activities related to the lesson's content have been identified by one of four codes to give you an idea of their suitability for students of varying learning styles and abilities.

Special Feature – Our Changing World

This feature in the Student Text is supported with teaching strategies and suggestions to guide students through critical changes occurring in today's society and to assist health teachers in addressing local and national crises. Each activity in the Student Text has a corresponding box in the Teacher's Wraparound Edition that provides alternative ways for students to address the hands-on activity.

Assess

Assessment techniques include strategies for reteaching students who have difficulty mastering the important lesson concepts. Enrichment activities are designed for students who are able and willing to explore the content further.

ABC News InterActive™

Barcodes to the video program correlated to chapter content appear at point of use.

Close

An activity that brings closure to the lesson and recaps important concepts from the lesson.

Making Health Accessible for All Students

Teaching strategies in the Meeting Student Diversity boxes incorporate cultural perspectives, strategies for the physically and mentally challenged, and strategies for addressing different learning styles.

MEETING STUDENT DIVERSITY

PROJECT. Have groups of students create a board game to review the body systems discussed in the chapter.

LEARNING STYLES. Students in need of special attention might have a preliminary meeting in which the goals and logistics of the project are discussed. You might arrange for them to work in pairs and small groups during the project.

PHYSICALLY CHALLENGED. Students with physical challenges may wish to serve as consultants on questions specifically geared to care of the body system affected by birth defects or an accident.

Bottom Column Annotations

Boxes at the bottom of the page give you additional information related to the content of the Student Text. This information supplements the core lesson plan by focusing on various areas of interest. The categories include:
- Pathways Through the Program
- Technology Options
- More About. . .
- Personal Health
- School-to-Career
- Home and Community Connection
- Health Literacy
- Promoting Comprehensive School Health
- Your Health Portfolio
- Curriculum Connections
- Meeting Student Diversity
- Answers to Lesson Review

Internet Activity

Each Internet Activity box offers ways for teachers to access and make use of Glencoe's new health Web site. Additionally, the feature offers strategies for implementing safe, educational Internet exploration in the classroom.

•••• PATHWAYS THROUGH THE PROGRAM ••••

Chapter 8 is the first of several chapters that focus on mental and emotional health. During the teenage years, students are beginning to define who they are and what they want out of life. This chapter encourages them to explore their own needs and recognize what shapes their personalities. It helps them to acknowledge the influence that others have on them and that they have on others.

Teens are experiencing a period of rapid change, both physically and emotionally. They seek autonomy but depend on acceptance as a safety net. They often wrestle with their changing perceptions of responsibility and obedience. As students learn to handle their emotions, they learn to respond, not just react. They develop skills and confidence that provide a foundation for healthful maturity.

COOPERATIVE LEARNING

In groups, have students examine shampoo ads in magazines or videotaped commercials. Encourage them to discuss results... for a given shampoo, and analyze the ... for appeal. Discuss techniques used ... products. For example, do ads use testi... trendy or popular images; loaded ...ional words; celebrity endorsement;

transfer, or mentally linking a product with something readers desire, such as a woman surrounded by admirers? Have them compare claims in the ads with ratings in a publication such as *Consumer Reports*, and rank highly rated products in order of cost. Encourage the groups to share their findings.

TECHNOLOGY OPTIONS

ABC NEWS INTERACTIVE You may wish to use *Tobacco* with this chapter. For your convenience, use the separate *ABCNews InterActive™ Bar Code Correlation* that accompanies the *Glencoe Health* program.

MINDJOGGER VIDEOQUIZ

To preview or review chapter content, you may wish to use the *Mindjogger Videoquiz* that accompanies Chapter 24.

SCHOOL-TO-CAREER

MEDICAL ASSISTANT. In an information-based, technologically advanced society, the tests doctors and hospitals run are ever more extensive, and the paperwork required by health care agencies is ever more complicated. More and more, medical assistants are needed to perform these tasks and free doctors and nurses to do the work only they are qualified to do. Medical assistants find career opportunities in hospitals, clinics, emergency centers, and private practice. There they may help physicians examine and treat patients, take blood pressure, check vital signs, and conduct laboratory tests. They may also apply bandages, administer EKG or X rays, answer phones, schedule appointments, keep records, and process insurance forms.

CURRICULUM CONNECTIONS

SOCIAL STUDIES. Have students research foods that are popular in different countries. If possible, bring (or have students bring) to class produce (such as mangoes, pomegranates, etc.) and other foods, and discuss with students the sources of these foods. Also, ask students to locate pictures of foreign foods or recipes from ethnic cookbooks. Discuss how culture and ethnic background affect food traditions and choices.

FAMILY AND CONSUMER SCIENCES. Many students and their families fail to eat breakfast, citing lack of time to prepare it. Invite a family and consumer science teacher to demonstrate and prepare healthy, quick-fix breakfast foods.

STUDENT MODULES

Student modules provide additional information on relevant health issues. They include:

ABSTINENCE is designed to help students take a close look at their choices and decisions they make in their relationships and to recognize the value of practicing abstinence from sexual activity before marriage. The articles provide information about the consequences of high-risk behaviors, and the skills of practicing decision making and effective communication skills, identifying personal, family, and community values, and controlling emotions.

HIV/AIDS and Society is a full-color text that provides current information on HIV infection and AIDS. A Teacher's Annotated Edition is available. A Spanish edition of *HIV/AIDS and Society* student edition is also available.

Education in Sexuality is a full-color text that may be used as a primary text for a human sexuality course or as an extension of *Glencoe Health*. A Teacher's Annotated Edition is available.

The Reality of Drugs provides comprehensive information concerning alcohol, tobacco, and other drugs and their effects on the human body. A Teacher's Annotated Edition is available.

MEDIA AND TECHNOLOGY RESOURCES

Glencoe Health MindJogger Videoquiz

Glencoe Health MindJogger is a videoquiz format available on both videodisc and videocassette. Quizzes combine oral questions, on-screen written questions, and engaging visuals. Can be used for self-assessment or to preview or review chapter content.

ExamView™ Testmaker

This computer software test bank for Macintosh and IBM-compatible computers provides questions in various formats and capabilities to add your own questions.

Audiocassette Program (English, Spanish)

The audiocassettes provide English and Spanish summaries of chapter content for review, reteaching, or for use when you do not have time to teach a particular chapter. Accompanied by a chapter activity and test based on the summaries.

CD-ROM Programs

Glencoe Health CD-ROM
Included together in a four-CD package, these topics are presented with interactive games, movies, and activities to captivate students.
- HIV/AIDS: The Choice is Yours
- Making Decisions About Alcohol and Other Drugs
- Human Sexuality: Taking Responsibility for Myself and Others
- Human Sexuality: A Healthy Me

Nutrition and Physical Activity CD-ROM
An interactive format challenges teens to a two-day virtual experience where they make healthy decisions about nutrition and physical activity.

Transparency Package

The ready-to-use overhead color transparency package contains 72 full-color overhead transparencies. The Teaching Strategies guide provides background information and activity sheets for each transparency to help in guiding discussion.

ABCNews InterActive™ Video Program

Today's teens face important decisions about high-risk behaviors that can cause them to make unhealthy decisions or risk their lives. A unique, effective approach to addressing these issues, the ABCNews InterActive™ series *Understanding Ourselves,* can help teachers positively influence student attitudes and help them change their behavior. *Understanding Ourselves,* the video-based health series, goes beyond just say no. It makes a compelling case to show why not.

The program combines video, text, and activities, and includes eight titles:

Health: AIDS   *Making Responsible Decisions*
Alcohol   *Teenage Sexuality*
Drugs and Substance Abuse   *Tobacco*
Food and Nutrition   *Violence Prevention*

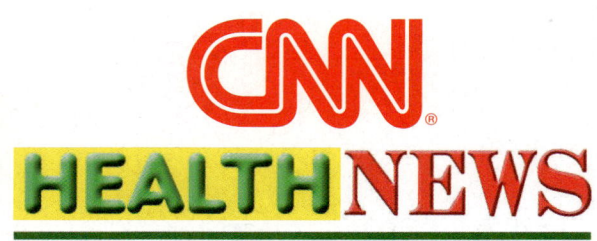

HEALTH NEWS

Glencoe and CNN

Glencoe/McGraw-Hill, the leading publisher of health education materials, has teamed up with CNN, the world's news leader, and Turner Learning, the educational division of CNN and Turner Broadcasting, to create this dynamic feature as a new way to look at and study health issues.

Teaching Strategies

Includes background information on Reliable Resources, Reporting the Story, and Ask the Experts.

Current Articles From CNN

Students meet professionals in the scientific community with expertise and new information on important discoveries. Young people will share their viewpoints about health topics, and news reports investigate issues that include:

* Sports Safety
* School Safety
* Skin Care
* Stress Management
* Technology Advances
* Medical Breakthroughs

Featuring CNN Video Segments

This multimedia program, CNN Health News, updates health topics and practices through CNN video reports. The video is categorized into the following units for ease of use:

Unit 1	Your Health, Fitness, and Nutrition
Unit 2	Mental, Social, and Emotional Health
Unit 3	Your Body, Growth, and Development
Unit 4	Tobacco, Alcohol, and Drugs
Unit 5	Diseases and Disorders
Unit 6	Safety, Consumer, and Environmental Health

GLENCOE HEALTH ONLINE

Health Online

Glencoe Health Online homepage on the World Wide Web provides up-to-date resources and activities to complement Glencoe's comprehensive health program.

Find us at:

health.glencoe.com

For Teachers
- Textbook Resources
- Professional Articles
- National Organizations
- Teaching Today

For Students
- Health Updates
- Career Corner
- Student Activities

For Parents
- Guidelines and tips for using the Internet
- Parent letters in English and Spanish

TEACHER'S CLASSROOM RESOURCES

Activities

Concept Map Activities provide a developmental approach for students to practice concept mapping. They can be used to preview a lesson's content by visually relating the concepts to be learned allowing students to read with purpose. As a review strategy, they reinforce main ideas and clarify relationships. One activity per lesson is provided.

Reteaching Activities allow students who are having difficulty with mastering the major concepts of a lesson to review the concepts from a different perspective. Answers for the teacher are provided at the back of the booklet.

Enrichment Activities allow students the opportunity to explore concepts further. There is one activity for each chapter of *Glencoe Health*. Answers for the teacher are provided at the back of the booklet.

Decision-Making Activities give students an opportunity to practice the decision-making process as they consider a variety of hypothetical situations.

The **Student Workbook** contains a Study Guide and a Vocabulary Activity for each chapter and an Applying Health Skills Activity for each lesson. The Applying Health Skills Activities vary in format and involve conflict resolution, decision making, and life management skills. A Teacher's Annotated Edition is available.

Health Labs give students experience with making observations and hypotheses, collecting and recording data, and forming conclusions based on analysis and interpretations of experimental results. There is one Health Lab for each chapter in the text. Teacher pages provide help and answers to questions.

Also Available as an Electronic TCR on CD-ROM

Cross-Curriculum Activities give students an opportunity to relate health information to the content of other subject areas, including math, social studies, language arts, science, and the arts.

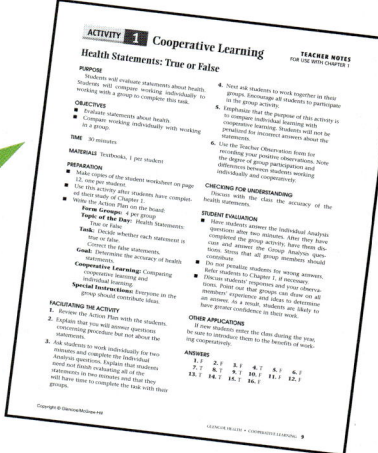

Cooperative Learning Activities promote teamwork, cooperation, and responsibility, as students work in small groups or in teams of three or four, they assist and help each other master skills. In this type of classroom environment, students are encouraged to share ideas, interpret materials, and cooperate to help each other learn.

Health Skills Activities give students additional opportunities to practice and apply the following health skills: communication, decision making, goal setting, conflict resolution, assessing health information, and stress management. Through role-playing, games, and individual and group activities, students develop health skills that lead to positive health behaviors.

Internet Activities is a printed version of the engaging activities found in Students Online at the *Glencoe Health* Internet site. Students will explore up-to-the-minute information and resources as they tap into the benefits of interactive health adventures. Teachers will find instructional guidelines and explanations of the student activities in this booklet.

Assessment

Lesson Quizzes provide a one-page quiz for each lesson in *Glencoe Health*. The quizzes may also be used as a pretest. Answers for the teacher are provided at the back of the booklet.

Performance Assessment Activities assess learning in ways that require a student to manipulate information in flexible and creative ways. Assessment activities are a learning tool for the student and use a variety of strategies to assess student learning. A Teacher's Annotated edition is available.

Chapter Tests provide two forms of tests, A and B. Either or both forms may be used as alternative or makeup tests. Answers for the teacher are provided at the back of the booklet.

Teaching Resources

Reproducible Lesson Plans are provided for each lesson in *Glencoe Health*. The lesson plans follow the teaching cycle—FOCUS, TEACH, ASSESS, and CLOSE—that is developed in the Teacher's Wraparound Edition of *Glencoe Health*. The lesson plans include references to all resources available with *Glencoe Health*.

The *Teaching Transparencies* Binder includes 72 transparencies plus an activity booklet complete with teaching strategies for use with the transparencies.

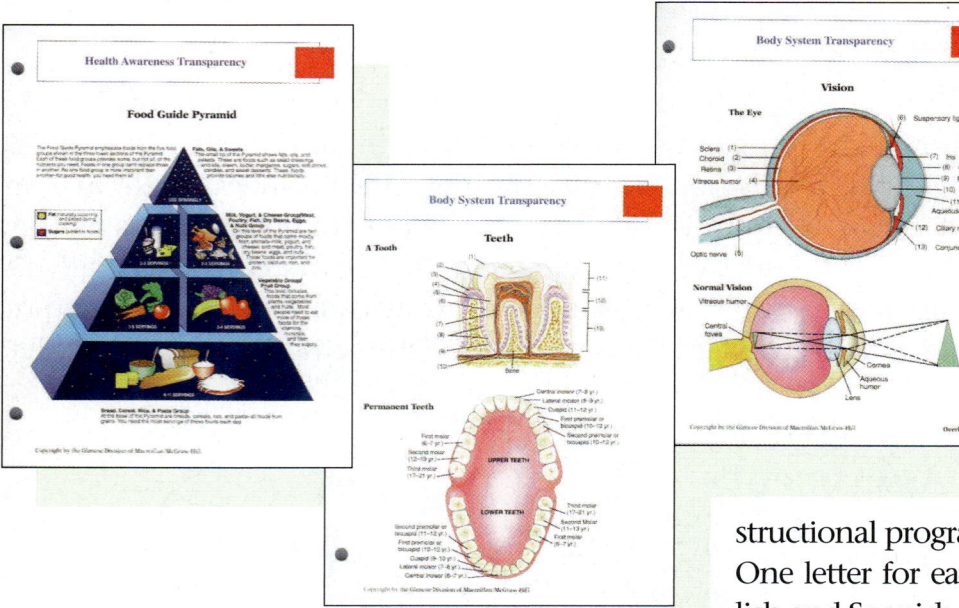

Parent Letters and Activities encourage parental involvement, a critical component of a successful health program. The booklet includes introductory teacher material about how to use these letters to inform parents or guardians of the instructional program and assessment techniques. One letter for each chapter is provided in English and Spanish.

Spanish Resources

Spanish Resources include two booklets: *Parent Letters and Activities, Spanish Summaries and Glossary*. A Spanish edition of *HIV/AIDS and Society (El VIH/SIDA y la sociedad)* student text is also available.

The *Spanish Summaries* are brief summaries of each of the 35 chapters of *Glencoe Health*. The summaries are followed by brief questions and/or statements that help the student grasp the chapter content. Answers for the teacher are provided at the back of the booklet.

Glencoe Professional Health Series

Dealing with Sensitive Issues prepares the educator to discuss issues with students that are generally considered sensitive by providing background information and teaching strategies. Classroom activities are provided for each sensitive issue and cover such topics as depression, eating disorders, abuse, and sexuality.

Promoting a Comprehensive School Health Program has been designed to increase individual and community understanding of what comprehensive school health is and of the need for comprehensive school health programs throughout the United States.

Cultural Diversity in the Health Classroom focuses on how to teach a health education curriculum in a culturally diverse classroom.

Death and the Adolescent is designed to provide teachers with background information and strategies for helping students cope with the grieving process.

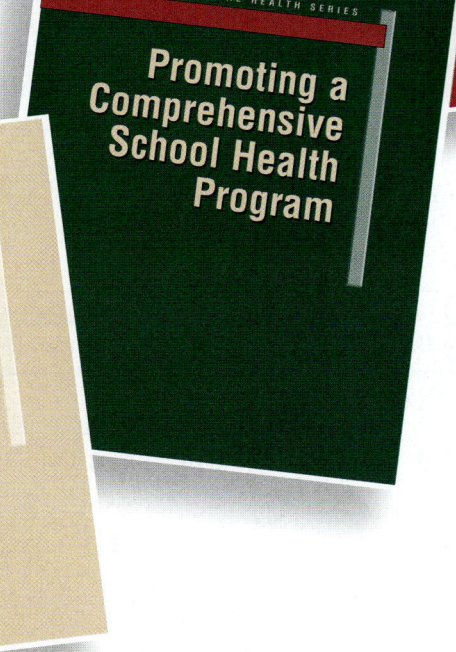

COURSE PRESENTATION

Glencoe Health: A Guide to Wellness is a comprehensive health text with 35 chapters and 108 lessons. The study of this text may extend over the course of one year. This text also is suitable for a semester survey course. Consider the following possible outlines as course work alternatives.

OUTLINE 1 FULL COURSE
One-year (36 week) course, 35 chapters

Unit 1	You and Your Health Chapters 1, 2	2 weeks
Unit 2	Physical Fitness and Nutrition Chapters 3, 4, 5, 6, 7	6 weeks
Unit 3	Mental and Emotional Health Chapters 8, 9, 10	3 weeks
Unit 4	Family and Social Health Chapters 11, 12, 13, 14	4 weeks
Unit 5	Body Systems Chapters 15, 16, 17, 18, 19	5 weeks
Unit 6	Growth and Development Chapters 20, 21, 22,	3 weeks
Unit 7	Medicines and Drugs Chapters 23, 24, 25, 26, 27	5 weeks
Unit 8	Diseases and Disorders Chapters 28, 29, 30, 31	4 weeks
Unit 9	Consumer and Environmental Health Chapters 32, 33	2 weeks
Unit 10	Injury Prevention and Safety Chapters 34, 35	2 weeks

OUTLINE 2 HEALTH SURVEY COURSE
One-semester (18 week) course, 21 chapters

Unit 1	You and Your Health Chapters 1, 2	1 week
Unit 2	Physical Fitness and Nutrition Chapters 3, 4, 5, 6	4 weeks
Unit 3	Mental and Emotional Health Chapters 8, 9	2 weeks
Unit 4	Family and Social Health Chapters 11, 13, 14	3 weeks
Unit 5	Body Systems Chapter 19	1 week
Unit 6	Growth and Development Chapters 21, 22,	1 week
Unit 8	Diseases and Disorders Chapters 28, 29, 30, 31	4 weeks
Unit 9	Consumer and Environmental Health Chapter 33	1 week
Unit 10	Injury Prevention and Safety Chapter 34, 35	1 week

OUTLINE 3 PHYSICAL FITNESS & NUTRITION
One-semester (18 week) course, 24 chapters

Unit 1	You and Your Health Chapters 1, 2	1 week
Unit 2	Physical Fitness and Nutrition Chapters 3, 4, 5, 6, 7	5 weeks
Unit 5	Body Systems Chapters 15, 16, 17, 18, 19	4 weeks
Unit 7	Medicines and Drugs Chapters 23, 24, 25, 26, 27	3 weeks
Unit 8	Diseases and Disorders Chapters 28, 29, 30, 31	3 weeks
Unit 9	Consumer and Environmental Health Chapter 32	1 week
Unit 10	Injury Prevention and Safety Chapters 34, 35	1 week

OUTLINE 4
MENTAL, EMOTIONAL & SOCIAL HEALTH
One-semester (18 week) course, 22 chapters

Unit 1	You and Your Health Chapters 1, 2	1 week
Unit 3	Mental and Emotional Health Chapters 8, 9, 10	2 weeks
Unit 4	Family and Social Health Chapters 11, 12, 13, 14	4 weeks
Unit 5	Body Systems Chapters 16, 17	2 weeks
Unit 6	Growth and Development Chapters 21, 22,	2 weeks
Unit 7	Medicines and Drugs Chapters 24, 25, 26, 27	2 weeks
Unit 8	Diseases and Disorders Chapters 28, 29, 30	3 weeks
Unit 9	Consumer and Environmental Health Chapters 32, 33	2 weeks

MEETS THE NATIONAL HEALTH EDUCATION STANDARDS

The National Health Education Standards were created with the goal of improving educational achievement for students and improving health in the United States through the promotion of health literacy. The Health Standards detail the knowledge and skills essential to the development of health literacy in the form of performance indicators. A lesson by lesson correlation of the *Glencoe Health* student text to the National Health Education Standards demonstrates how *Glencoe Health* meets these criteria. The following is a complete listing of the health standards.

 ## National Health Education Standards

Health Education Standard 1:

Students will comprehend concepts related to health promotion and disease prevention.

Performance Indicators:

As a result of health instruction in Grades 9-11, students will:

1.1 Analyze how behavior can impact health maintenance and disease prevention.
1.2 Describe the interrelationships of mental, emotional, social, and physical health throughout adulthood.
1.3 Explain the impact of personal health behaviors on the functioning of body systems.
1.4 Analyze how the family, peers, and community influence the health of individuals.
1.5 Analyze how the environment influences the health of the community.
1.6 Describe how to delay onset and reduce risks of potential health problems during adulthood.
1.7 Analyze how public health policies and government regulations influence health promotion and disease prevention.
1.8 Analyze how the prevention and control of health problems are influenced by research and medical advances.

Health Education Standard 2:

Students will demonstrate the ability to access valid health information and health-promoting products and services.

Performance Indicators:

As a result of health instruction in Grades 9-11, students will:

2.1 Evaluate the validity of health information, products, and services.
2.2 Demonstrate the ability to evaluate resources from home, school, and community that provide valid health information.
2.3 Evaluate factors that influence personal selection of health products and services.
2.4 Demonstrate the ability to access school and community health services for self and others.
2.5 Analyze the cost and accessibility of health care services.
2.6 Analyze situations requiring professional health services.

Health Education Standard 3:

Students will demonstrate the ability to practice health-enhancing behaviors and reduce health risks.

Performance Indicators:

As a result of health instruction in Grades 9-11, students will:

3.1 Analyze the role of individual responsibility for enhancing health.

3.2 Evaluate a personal health assessment to determine strategies for health enhancement and risk reduction.

3.3 Analyze the short-term and long-term consequences of safe, and risky or harmful behaviors.

3.4 Develop strategies to improve or maintain personal, family, and community health.

3.5 Develop injury prevention and management strategies for personal, family, and community health.

3.6 Demonstrate ways to avoid and reduce threatening situations.

3.7 Evaluate strategies to manage stress.

Health Education Standard 4:

Students will analyze the influence of culture, media, technology, and other factors on health.

Performance Indicators:

As a result of health instruction in Grades 9-11, students will:

4.1 Analyze how cultural diversity enriches and challenges health behaviors.

4.2 Evaluate the effect of media and other factors on personal, family, and community health.

4.3 Evaluate the impact of technology on personal, family, and community health.

4.4 Analyze how information from the community influences health.

Health Education Standard 5:

Students will demonstrate the ability to use interpersonal communication skills to enhance health.

Performance Indicators:

As a result of health instruction in Grades 9-11, students will:

5.1 Demonstrate skills for communicating effectively with family, peers, and others.

5.2 Analyze how interpersonal communication affects relationships.

5.3 Demonstrate healthy ways to express needs, wants, and feelings.

5.4 Demonstrate ways to communicate care, consideration and respect of self and others.

5.5 Demonstrate strategies for solving interpersonal conflicts without harming self or others.

5.6 Demonstrate refusal and negotiation skills to avoid potentially harmful situations.

5.7 Analyze the possible causes of conflict in schools, families, and communities.

5.8 Demonstrate strategies used to prevent conflict.

Health Education Standard 6:

Students will demonstrate the ability to use goal setting and decision-making skills to enhance health.

Performance Indicators:

As a result of health instruction in Grades 9-11, students will:

6.1 Demonstrate the ability to utilize various strategies when making decisions related to health needs and risks of young adults.

6.2 Analyze health concerns that require collaborative decision making.

6.3 Predict immediate and long-term impact of health decisions on the individual, family, and community.

6.4 Implement a plan for attaining a personal health goal.

6.5 Evaluate progress toward achieving personal health goals.

6.6 Formulate an effective plan for lifelong health.

Health Education Standard 7:

Students will demonstrate the ability to advocate for personal, family, and community health.

Performance Indicators:

As a result of health instruction in Grades 9-11, students will:

7.1 Analyze various communication methods to accurately express health information and ideas.

7.2 Express information and opinions about health issues.

7.3 Utilize strategies to overcome barriers when communicating information, ideas, feelings, and opinions about health issues.

7.4 Demonstrate the ability to influence and support others in making positive health choices.

7.5 Demonstrate the ability to work cooperatively when advocating for healthy communities.

7.6 Demonstrate the ability to adapt health messages and communication techniques to the characteristics of a particular audience.

How *Glencoe Health* Meets the National Health Education Standards

The Chapter Planning Guide provides a correlation to the National Health Education Standards for material covered in each lesson.

SCOPE & SEQUENCE

Content Strands	Chapter 1 What Is Health?	Chapter 2 Making Healthful Choices
Personal Health	• Health as combination of physical, mental/emotional, and social well-being (1) • Achieving wellness (1) • Role of lifestyle factors in overall health (1) • Accepting responsibility for your health (3) • Prevention and risk behaviors (3) • Evaluating your health status with the Health Barometer Self-Inventory (3)	• Accessing reliable health info (1) • Making an action plan to accomplish goals (2) • Protecting your health as a guideline for setting goals (2)
Consumer and Community Health	• Advances in technology-based medicine (1) • Being health literate (1) • Importance of health education (1) • Promoting a safe physical and social environment in the community (2) • How your peers affect your health (2) • Taking responsibility for the health of others (3)	• Developing social health skills (1) • Evaluating media sources of health info (1) • Safety and privacy on the Internet (1) • Finding community resources when you need help with a problem (1)
Injury Prevention and Safety	• Examining risks to your physical health (3)	• Using refusal skills to avoid high-risk behaviors (1)
Alcohol, Tobacco, and Other Drugs	• Tobacco, alcohol, and other drugs as high risk behaviors (3)	• Role of refusal skills in declining offers to use tobacco, alcohol, or other drugs (1)
Nutrition	• Role of proper nutrition in maintaining physical health (1) • Eating a nutritious breakfast daily as an important lifestyle factor (1)	
Environmental Health	• How environment influences your health (2) • Influence of air quality, street safety, and access to medical care on one's health (2)	
Family Living	• How heredity influences your health (2) • Understanding your cultural environment (2) • Family support and encouragement as protective factors (3)	• Turning to your parents for help in problem solving (1)
Individual Growth and Development	• Life commitment to wellness (1) • How personal attitudes affect health (1) • Recognizing positive role models and values (3) • Choosing abstinence (3)	• Effective communication skills (1) • Learning refusal skills (1) • Building and improving self-esteem (1) • Learning stress management skills (1) • Making responsible decisions with the decision-making model (2) • Importance of setting goals (2) • Short term vs. long term goals (2)
Communicable and Chronic Disease	• Recent increase in cases of tuberculosis (2)	

Chapter 3 Physical Fitness and Your Health	Chapter 4 Physical Activity for Life	Chapter 5 Nutrition and Your Health
• What it means to be physically fit (1) • Basic components of physical fitness (1) • Benefits of exercise to your physical health (2) • Exercise and weight control (2) • Target heart range (2) • Evaluating an aerobic exercise (2) • Planning a fitness program (3) • Principles of an effective workout (3) • Monitoring your fitness progress (3)	• Understanding sports activities and lifestyle activities (1) • Alternating physical activities (1) • Skills-related fitness—agility, balance, coordination, speed, reaction time, and power (1) • Importance of adequate sleep (2) • Types and treatment of minor (RICE method) and major exercise-related injuries (3)	• Fiber and the digestive system (2) • Average calorie requirements of teens (2) • Understanding cholesterol (2) • Recommended Dietary Allowances (4) • Balancing food intake with physical activity (4) • Choosing healthy eating patterns with the Food Guide Pyramid (4) • Tips for reducing daily fat intake (4)
• Benefits of exercise to your social health (1) • Exercising with others (2)	• Consulting physical education teachers, coaches, or doctors (2) • Health risks associated with chromium picolinate (2) • Drug testing (2)	• Social and cultural influences upon your food choices (1) • Evaluating food advertisements (1) • Sugar and fat substitutes (5) • Analyzing food product label claims (5) • Evaluating the benefits and risks of Olestra (5)
• Considering personal safety when setting a fitness program (3) • Warming up and cooling down before and after exercise (3)	• Preventing heat cramps, heatstroke, frostbite, and hypothermia (3) • Steps for becoming safety conscious (3) • Injury prevention and using proper equipment (3) • Avoiding swimmer's ear (3) • Using protective equipment (3)	• Awareness of open dating and food additives for improved food safety (5)
	• Negative consequences of taking anabolic steroids (2) • Avoidance of alcohol, tobacco, and other drugs to maintain a training program (2)	
• Nutrition and percentage of body fat (1) • Connection between calorie intake, physical activity, and weight control (2)	• Importance of adequate hydration before and during vigorous physical activity (2)	• Understanding nutrients (1) • Carbohydrates as fuel food (2) • Understanding complete and incomplete proteins (2) • Role of fats in health (2) • Water soluble and fat soluble vitamins (3) • The types of minerals and their role in the body (3) • Vital role of water in body functions (3) • Recognizing food additives (5)
• Considering your environment when setting a fitness program (3)	• Cold and hot weather health risks (3)	
	• Heredity and physical ability (2)	• Your family and your food choices (1) • Encouraging your family to adopt healthy cooking habits (4)
• Managing stress through exercise (2) • Aerobic exercise and improved cardiorespiratory endurance (2) • Anaerobic exercise and improved muscular strength and flexibility (2)	• Importance of lifestyle activities (1) • Sexual underdevelopment and steroids (2) • Role of positive mind-set in sports (2) • Developing a healthy attitude about competition (2)	• Recognizing the difference between hunger and appetite (1) • Understanding how emotions affect eating habits (1) • Good nutrition and growth and development in adolescence (1) • Importance of iron and calcium for growth and development (3) • Reading a nutrition label (5)
• Role of exercise in slowing the onset of osteoporosis and building up resistance to disease (2)		• Proper nutrition and disease prevention (1) • High intake of saturated fats and heart disease (2) • Fiber's role in the prevention of heart disease and cancer (4)

Content Strands	Chapter 6 Food and Your Health	Chapter 7 Personal Health
Personal Health	• Determining a healthy weight through the body mass index (1) • Starting a weight control plan (1) • Smart weight gain strategies (1) • Electrolytes and regulating body fluids (3) • Causes and symptoms of foodborne illness (4) • Understanding food allergies and food intolerance (4)	• Functions of the skin and skin hygiene (1) • Proper care for your hair and nails (1) • Parts of the tooth and dental hygiene (2) • Understanding periodontal disease and other mouth and teeth disorders (2) • Parts of the eye and eye care (3) • Understanding vision problems and eye diseases (3) • Parts of the ear and proper ear care (4) • Ear disorders and deafness (4)
Consumer and Community Health	• Recognizing fad diets (2) • Pros and cons of nutrient supplements (3) • Analyzing media messages about food safety (4)	• Health risks of body piercing and tattooing (1) • Comparing health and beauty aids (2) • New technology for eye surgery (3) • Seeing an eyecare professional (3)
Injury Prevention and Safety	• Fasting and other dangerous diets (2) • The physical dangers of anorexia nervosa and bulimia nervosa (2) • Food safety and prevention of foodborne illness (4)	• Preventing skin damage with sunscreen (1) • Preventing or decreasing computer eyestrain (3) • Wearing eye protection equipment (3) • Wearing ear protectors to prevent injury (4)
Alcohol, Tobacco, and Other Drugs	• Avoiding alcohol, tobacco, and other drugs during pregnancy (3)	• Negative effects of smoking and smokeless tobacco on the teeth and mouth (2)
Nutrition	• Understanding calories and the energy equation (1) • Essentials of sports nutrition (3) • Health benefits of vegetarianism (3) • Nutrition and prevention of birth defects (3) • Nutrition and aging (3)	• Strengthening teeth and gums through consumption of foods rich in phosphorus and other vitamins (2)
Environmental Health	• Environmental conditions that promote foodborne bacteria (4)	• Prolonged exposure to loud noise and sensorineural deafness (4)
Family Living	• Role of heredity in obesity (1) • Importance of healthful eating and increased nutrient intake during pregnancy (3)	
Individual Growth and Development	• Tips for staying on a diet (1) • Working exercise into your schedule (1) • Helping a friend with an eating disorder (2) • "Making weight" and sports requirements (3)	• Daily treatment for acne (1) • Communicating with someone who is hearing impaired (4)
Communicable and Chronic Disease	• Vegetarianism and prevention of lifestyle diseases (3)	• The skin as the body's first line of defense against infectious disease (1) • Excessive sun exposure and skin cancer (1) • Contacting HIV or hepatitis from tattooing (1)

Chapter 8 Your Mental and Emotional Health	Chapter 9 Managing Stress in Your Life	Chapter 10 Mental and Emotional Problems
• Assessing your mental fitness (1) • Understanding the link between self-esteem and mental health (1) • Recognizing physical, emotional, aesthetic, and self-fulfilling needs (2) • Fear and sympathetic nervous system (3) • Understanding anger, hostility, and guilt (3) • Coping healthfully with your emotions (4)	• Positive vs. negative stress (1) • Types of stressors (1) • Understanding the three stages of the body's stress response (1) • Low stress tolerance and the brain (2) • Stress and physical health risks (2) • Migraine headaches (2) • Techniques for stress management (3)	• Understanding mental disorders (1) • Types of mental disorders and their characteristics (1) • Recognizing signs of mental health problems (3)
• Giving others a break (1) • The world's homeless population (2) • Importance of empathy for others (3) • New discoveries from brain research (4)	• Seeking support from community leaders, teachers, and friends (3) • Seeking grief counseling (4)	• Helping others who show signs of trouble (2) • Evaluating self-help resources (3) • Types of mental health professionals (3) • Analyzing different viewpoints on chemical therapies (3)
• Safety as a basic physical need (2)	• Resistance as a prolonged stressor can cause physical or mental harm (1) • Illness or injury as a life event stressor (1)	• Prevent injury by recognizing signs of suicide (2)
	• Use of tobacco, alcohol, and other drugs as personal behavior stressors (1)	• Identifying alcoholism as an organic disorder (1) • Substance abuse as a suicide risk factor (2)
• Ranking of nutrition in Maslow's hierarchy of needs (2)	• Poor eating habits, including overeating, as behavioral signs of stress (2)	• Overeating or starving as a sign of mental health problems (1)
• Aesthetic needs and your environment (2) • How environment affects personality (2)	• Environmental stressors (1)	• Explaining seasonal affective disorder (1)
• Role of positive and negative feedback from your family and others (1) • Link between heredity and personality (2)	• Seeking support from your family (3) • Profile of a young man who dealt with the loss of his parents and siblings (4)	• Clinical depression and heredity (1)
• Recognizing roadblocks to mental health (1) • Promoting a positive self-image (1) • Positive self-talk and constructive criticism (1) • Maslow's hierarchy of human needs (2) • Personality and its components (2) • Understanding and identifying your emotions (3) • Emotional changes during adolescence (3) • Suggestions for managing anger (4) • Importance of a positive outlook (4)	• Charting adolescent life changes (1) • Personality type and handling stress (2) • Recognizing signs of stress (2) • Time management and stress reduction (3) • Importance of relaxation and laughter (3) • Stress response to loss (4) • Kübler-Ross' stages of loss and grief reaction (4)	• Understanding personality disorders (1) • Teenage depression and suicide (2) • Recognizing the warning signs of suicide (2)
		• Hypochondria and imagined disease symptoms (1)

SCOPE & SEQUENCE

Content Strands	Chapter 11 Building Healthy Relationships	Chapter 12 Healthy Family Relationships
Personal Health	• Assessing the effects of relationships on your total health (1) • Choosing healthy relationships (1) • Recognizing traits of a healthy relationship (1)	• Evaluating how the family system affects the individual members' health (1) • Strategies for children to cope with their parents' divorce (2) • Tips for obtaining psychological help (3)
Consumer and Community Health	• Identifying your relationships in the community (1) • New "talking machine" technology (2) • Handling disagreements with others (2)	• Impact of families on society (1) • Societal trends affecting families (1) • Analyzing viewpoints about open adoptions (1) • Community services for families in crisis (3) • Counseling and mediation options available (3)
Injury Prevention and Safety	• Role of citizens and community relationships in promoting safety (1)	• Domestic violence may result when families experience extreme stress (2)
Alcohol, Tobacco, and Other Drugs		• Substance abuse and family stress (2) • AA and other support groups (3)
Nutrition	• Using cooperation and teamwork to encourage families to eat together (1)	• Parents provide basic needs that include nutritious foods for their children (1) • Family traditions such as shared meals and celebrations (1)
Environmental Health		
Family Living	• Understanding family relationships (1) • Using constructive criticism with family and friends (2) • Promoting healthy relationships with friends and family through acknowledgments and compliments (2)	• Importance of a healthy family system (1) • Primary functions of the family (1) • Traits of a healthy family (1) • Stressful events a family may face (2) • Understanding separation and divorce (2) • Facts about child and spousal abuse (2)
Individual Growth and Development	• Understanding friendship (1) • Defining the many roles you play (1) • Essentials of effective communication (2) • Developing good listening skills (2) • Understanding non-verbal communication (2) • Obstacles to effective communication (2)	• Responsibilities of the children in the family (1) • Ways to cope with family stress (2) • Ways to strengthen your family ties (3)
Communicable and Chronic Disease		• Serious illness and family stress (2)

Chapter 13 Peer Relationships	Chapter 14 Resolving Conflicts and Preventing Violence	Chapter 15 Your Integumentary, Skeletal, and Muscular Systems
• Acknowledging your dating rights (1) • Being aware of negative peer influence (2)	• Physical and emotional warning signs of conflict (1) • Understanding physical and sexual abuse (3) • Examining rape and date rape (4)	• The functions and structure of the skin (1) • Acne and other skin problems (1) • The function and structure of the skeletal system (2) • Problems of the skeletal system (2) • The function and structure of the muscular system (3) • Serious problems of the muscular system (3)
• Negative aspects of cliques (1) • Cultural rites of passage (1) • Analyzing the effectiveness of teen curfews (2)	• Feuds and gang violence (1) • Importance of tolerance in society (2) • Peer mediation programs (2) • The problem of violence in society (3) • How one teen left the gang lifestyle (3) • TV ratings and violence (3) • Violence in the media (3) • Help for abuse victims and abusers (4)	• Analyzing deodorant claims (1) • New advances in artificial limbs (2)
• Resisting peer pressure to take part in unsafe activities (2)	• Decreasing the odds of falling victim to dating violence (4)	• Use of sunscreen to prevent sunburn • Preventing repetitive motion injury (2) • Preventing back injury through "safe sitting" (3) • Preventing injury-related muscle problems (3)
• Resisting peer pressure to use alcohol (2)	• Alcohol and drug abuse and increased violence (3) • Facts about flunitrazepam—the date-rape drug (4)	
• Sharing meals as part of casual friendship (1)		• Nutrition, minerals and care of the skeletal system (2) • Preventing osteoporosis through exercise and nutrition (2) • Nutrition and maintaining muscle tone (3)
• Volunteering to clean up environment as an example of positive peer pressure (2)	• Territorial tagging damages public property (1)	
• Considering family values when faced with negative peer pressure (2)	• Teaching conflict resolution skills to young children and their families (2) • Shocking statistics on family violence (4)	• Characteristics of the inherited disorder muscular dystrophy (3)
• Kinds of peer relationships (1) • Recognizing positive stereotyping (1) • Dating and learning interpersonal skills (1) • Choosing not to date (1) • Recognizing manipulation (2) • Passive, aggressive, and assertive ways to respond to peer pressure (2) • Using refusal skills (2)	• Understanding interpersonal and internal conflicts (1) • Recognizing and responding to conflict (1) • Respect, rights, and responsibility—tools for conflict resolution (2) • Steps to take when negotiating (2) • How to avoid abuse (4)	• Identifying skin problems (1) • Practicing healthful habits to promote skeletal growth and development (2)
		• Understanding osteoporosis and scoliosis (2)

Content Strands	Chapter 16 Your Nervous and Endocrine Systems	Chapter 17 Your Circulatory and Respiratory Systems
Personal Health	• Functions and structure of the nervous system (1) • Understanding the role of neurons (1) • The divisions of the brain and its complex functions (1) • The role of the autonomic and somatic nervous systems (1) • Glands and the structure of the endocrine system (3) • Disorders of the endocrine system (3)	• The functions and structure of the circulatory system (1) • Understanding the functions of the heart and blood (1) • Functions of the lymphatic system (1) • Understanding blood pressure (2) • Functions and structure of the respiratory system (3) • Problems of the respiratory system (3)
Consumer and Community Health	• How a CT scan works (2)	• Evaluating health information sources (1) • Modern technology to regulate the heartbeat—internal cardiac defibrillators and pacemakers (2)
Injury Prevention and Safety	• Safety measures to protect the nervous system (2) • Preventing head injuries (2) • Preventing in-line skating injuries (2)	
Alcohol, Tobacco, and Other Drugs	• Alcohol, drugs, and nervous system disorders (2)	• Smoking and your circulatory system (2) • Smoking and the respiratory system (3) • Emphysema and tobacco smoke (3)
Nutrition	• Proper nutrition and care of the nervous system (2) • Role of iodine in the prevention of goiters (3)	• Good nutrition and care of your circulatory and lymphatic systems (2) • Iron deficiency and anemia (2)
Environmental Health	• Radiation as a possible cause of cerebral palsy (2)	• Harmful effects of secondhand smoke on the circulatory system (2) • Examining the link between air pollutants and chronic bronchitis (3)
Family Living		
Individual Growth and Development	• Understanding epilepsy and cerebral palsy (2) • Male and female gland differences (3) • Height and growth disorders (3)	• Developing health literacy (1) • Congenital heart disease (2) • Practicing proper breathing through good posture (3)
Communicable and Chronic Disease	• Understanding Parkinson's and Alzheimer's disease, and multiple sclerosis (2)	• Heart disease and being overweight (2) • Understanding leukemia (2) • Immune deficiency, Hodgkins disease, and tonsillitis (2) • Understanding asthma (3)

Chapter 18 Your Digestive and Urinary Systems	Chapter 19 Your Body's Reproductive System	Chapter 20 The Beginning of the Life Cycle
• The structure and parts of the digestive system (1) • The organs that aid digestion (1) • Digestive system problems (2) • Symptoms of gallstones, appendicitis and other digestive disorders (2) • Functions and structure of the urinary system (3) • Urinary tract and bladder infections (3) • Recognizing kidney problems (3)	• Functions and structure of the male reproductive system (1) • Care for the male reproductive system (1) • Understanding hernias and sterility (1) • Functions and structure of the female reproductive system (2) • Infertility and its causes (2)	• Having a healthy pregnancy (1) • Affect of medicines and drugs on pregnancy (1) • Miscarriages and still births (1) • Understanding and identifying genetic disorders (2)
• Comparing antacids (2)	• Sources of help for concerns about sexual maturity (2) • Visiting a gynecologist for a pelvic exam (2)	• Choosing a health professional for prenatal care (1) • Analyzing viewpoints on genetic testing (2) • Television and child development (3)
	• Protecting the external male reproductive organs during strenuous activity (1) • Tampon use safety tips to prevent Toxic Shock Syndrome (2)	• Safety guidelines during pregnancy (1)
• Tobacco smoke and alcohol as potential causes of gastritis (2)	• The link between smoking, cigarettes, and sterility (1)	• Understanding fetal alcohol syndrome (1) • Tobacco and pregnancy (1) • Harmful effects of smoking on the developing fetus (1)
• Importance of eating a variety of foods and drinking plenty of water to maintain a healthy digestive system (2) • Adding fiber to your diet (2)		• Good nutrition during pregnancy (1)
	• Temperature regulation of the testes and sperm production (1) • Environmental hazards and sterility (1)	• Promoting a healthy fetal environment through prenatal care (1)
	• Role of family history in developing cervical cancer (2)	• Role of chromosomes and genes in heredity (2) • Inheriting a genetic disorder (2) • Role of genetic counseling in preventing birth defects (2)
• Lifelong tips for promoting a healthy digestive system (2) • Water intake and a healthy urinary system (3) • Promoting urinary system health through regular physical checkups (3)	• Performing a testicular exam (1) • Steps to becoming a responsible young male (1) • Process of menstruation (2) • Performing breast self-examination (2) • Physical and emotional problems relating to menstruation (2)	• The process of prenatal development (1) • How twins are formed (1) • Stages of the birth process (1) • Difference between dominant and recessive genes (2) • Dealing with birth defects (2) • Four stages of development from infancy to late childhood (3) • Being a positive role model to children (3)
• Overcoming a chronic kidney disease (3)	• Prostate and testicular cancer (1) • Risks of ovarian cysts and cancers of the female reproductive system (2)	

Content Strands	Chapter 21 Adolescence—A Time of Change	Chapter 22 The Life Cycle Continues
Personal Health	• Tips for dealing with acne (1) • Checking your developmental rate (1) • Steps for practicing abstinence from sexual activity (2)	• Steps for conflict resolution through the TALK strategy (1) • Importance of continuing to be physically active in middle and late adulthood (3) • Recognizing the physical transitions of menopause (3)
Consumer and Community Health	• Peer influence on attitudes about sex (2) • Role of society and television in developing attitudes towards sex (2)	• Establishing a place in society (1) • Statistics on teen marriage (2) • Community involvement of older adults (3)
Injury Prevention and Safety	• Evaluating the safety issues of socializing on-line (2)	• Protecting children from harm as a responsibility of parenthood (2)
Alcohol, Tobacco, and Other Drugs	• Choosing abstinence from tobacco, alcohol, and drugs (2)	
Nutrition		• Maintaining good nutrition in late adulthood to promote healthy body functions (3)
Environmental Health	• Developmental tasks of adolescence include social awareness (1)	
Family Living	• Unplanned pregnancies (2) • Family values as a protective factor against sexual activity (2)	• Understanding marriage and commitment (2) • Marital adjustment or adapting to marriage (2) • Understanding parenthood and its responsibilities (2) • Family changes and social transitions of middle adulthood (3) • Aging and family relationships (3)
Individual Growth and Development	• Physical change during puberty (1) • Mental, emotional, and social maturation during puberty (1) • Developmental tasks of adolescence (1) • Forming a personal identity (1) • Sexual activity and adolescence (2) • Using refusal skills to practice abstinence (2)	• Achieving physical and emotional maturity in adulthood (1) • Developmental tasks of adulthood (1) • Achieving self-actualization (1) • Mental, emotional, and physical transitions of middle adulthood (3) • Retirement and the physical, emotional, and social changes of late adulthood (3)
Communicable and Chronic Disease	• Avoiding STDs through abstinence (2) • Understanding AIDS and other STDs (2)	• Reviewing the common diseases of older adulthood (3)

Chapter 23 Understanding Medicines	Chapter 24 Tobacco	Chapter 25 Alcohol
• Understanding the classification of medicines (1) • Medicines for pain relief and cardiovascular problems (1) • Side effects and interaction of medicines (1)	• Hazardous effects of using tobacco (2) • Health benefits of quitting smoking (3) • Weight gain and quitting smoking (3)	• Recognizing the myths about alcohol (1) • Understanding alcohol tolerance and withdrawal (2) • Recognizing binge drinking and traits of the alcoholic (3)
• New medical research on antibiotics (1) • FDA testing process for new medicines (2)	• Reasons teens start to smoke (1) • Cigars, the new smoking fad (1) • Banning tobacco advertising (2) • Nonsmoker rights (2) • Towards a smokefree society (3)	• Teens and alcohol (1) • Analyzing alcohol advertising (1) • Drunk driving organizations MADD and SADD (2) • Costs of alcohol use to society (3)
• Tips for safe use of medicines (1) • How to effectively and safely use antibiotics (1)		• Danger of driving under the influence (2) • Avoiding mixing alcohol with other drugs (2)
• Recognizing signs of physiological dependence on medicines—tolerance and withdrawal (1) • Classifications of the Controlled Substances Act (2)	• Understanding tobacco addiction (1) • Chemicals and other harmful substances in cigarettes (1) • Recognizing the health hazards of specialty cigarettes (1) • Health risks of smokeless tobacco, pipes, and cigars (2) • Techniques for quitting smoking (3)	• Understanding the components and effects of alcohol (1) • Statistics on alcohol consumption and auto accidents (1) • Short-term and long-term effects of drinking (2) • The three stages of alcoholism (3) • Link between sexual activity and alcohol consumption (3)
• Aspirin as a stomach irritant (1)		• Identifying the connection between long-term overuse of alcohol and malnutrition (1)
• Biodiversity of rainforests aids development of new medicines (1)	• Effects of smoking on nonsmokers (2)	• Potential for hypothermia when consuming alcohol in cold weather (2)
• Medicine safety at home (2)	• Health risks to the fetus and mother-to-be linked to smoking during pregnancy (2)	• Fetal alcohol syndrome (2) • Alcohol and the family (3)
• Maintaining an immunization schedule (1) • Recognizing medicine misuse (2) • Understanding medicine labels (2)	• Awareness of advertising and peer pressure to smoke (1) • Fetal growth and development problems associated with smoking during pregnancy (2) • How one teen kicked the smoking habit (3) • Stress management and quitting smoking (3)	• Understanding why young people drink (1) • Decision making skills and choosing not to drink (1) • Using refusal skills to turn down alcohol (2)
• Vaccines, antitoxins, and disease prevention (1)	• Cancer causing chemicals in cigarettes (1) • Link between smoking and chronic bronchitis, emphysema, and lung cancer (2) • Smoking and circulatory system diseases (2)	• The effects of heavy alcohol consumption on the liver (2)

Content Strands	Chapter 26 Illegal Drugs	Chapter 27 Recovering from Addiction and Codependency
Personal Health	• Physical dangers of substance abuse (1) • Medicinal uses of psychoactive drugs (2) • Committing to and understanding the components of a drug-free life (4)	• Understanding the recovery process (1) • Appraising types of professional help for drug and alcohol addiction (1) • Recognizing common traits of codependency (2) • Identifying the difference between codependency and drug addiction (2)
Consumer and Community Health	• Facts about teen drug use (1) • Drug testing debate (1) • Dangers of new designer drugs (3) • Illegal transport of drugs (3) • Drug-free school zones (4) • Community and private programs for drug dependency (4)	• Teen gambling (1) • Examining the high costs of addiction to society (1) • Support groups and other community treatment options (1) • Al Anon and Alateen—community help for codependents (2)
Injury Prevention and Safety		
Alcohol, Tobacco, and Other Drugs	• Understanding substance abuse and drug types (1) • The costs of substance abuse to the individual, their family, and others (1) • Types of psychoactive drugs (2) • Psychological and physiological effects of stimulants, depressants, narcotics and hallucinogens (2) • The use and side effects of anabolic steroids (3) • Marijuana and cannabis derivatives (3) • Understanding inhalants (3)	• Recognizing the warning signs of addiction to alcohol or drugs (1) • Detoxification as the first step towards recovery from alcohol or drug addiction (1)
Nutrition	• Following a healthful nutrition plan as part of living a drug-free life (4)	
Environmental Health		
Family Living	• Examining the health problems of babies born to mothers who used drugs during pregnancy (1)	• Families and the intervention process (1) • Addiction as a family disease (2) • Family counseling and support groups for codependency (2)
Individual Growth and Development	• Reasons teens may start using drugs (1) • Substance abuse and the developing fetus (1) • Being aware of the physical and psychological effects of cannabis (3) • Resisting peer pressure to do drugs (4) • One teen's recovery from alcohol and drug addiction (4)	• Understanding the addiction process (1) • Breaking the cycle of codependency (2) • Helping someone start the recovery process (2)
Communicable and Chronic Disease	• Intravenous drug use and HIV/AIDS (1) • Carcinogenic chemicals in cannabis (3)	

Chapter 28 Infectious Diseases	Chapter 29 Sexually Transmitted Diseases	Chapter 30 HIV and AIDS
• The types of pathogens that cause infectious diseases (1) • Helpful vs. harmful bacteria (1) • Care for the common cold (1) • Importance of lymphocytes in fighting pathogens (1) • The common cold and other respiratory infections (2) • Immunization and vaccines for disease prevention (3)	• Understanding the facts and myths about STDs (1) • Identifying common behaviors of sexually active teens that pose a high risk of contracting an STD (1) • Long-term and short-term effects of STDs (1) • Effects of STDs on your future health (1)	• Identifying risk behaviors known to transmit HIV (1) • Recognizing HIV infection in the symptomatic stage (2)
• Recent rise of tuberculosis (2) • Community immunizations (3)	• The current STD epidemic (1) • Rise in STDs among teens (1) • Social responsibilities of a person infected with an STD (2)	• ELISA and other HIV testing (2) • Global HIV/AIDS statistics (2) • In-home collection kits for HIV testing (2) • AIDS related research and medications (2) • Creating a classroom resource folder for AIDS information (2)
• Reducing infectious disease risk (1)		
• Spread of infectious disease through sharing contaminated needles during intravenous drug use (1)	• Intravenous drug use and STD transmission (1)	• Sharing needles from intravenous drug use and the risk of HIV infection (1) • Abstaining from use of alcohol and other drugs to reduce risks of HIV infection (1)
• Bolstering your immune system with good nutrition (1)		
• Toxic dumping and the spread of pathogens (1) • Food poisoning and the spread of pathogens into the environment (1)		
• Recognizing home kitchens as potential breeding grounds for dangerous bacteria (1)	• Link between STDs and sterility (1) • Health consequences to infants born to mothers with STDs (1)	• HIV transmission through pregnancy and breast feeding (1)
• Immunity and your body's barriers against disease (1) • Your body's passive and active immunity (3) • Basic daily measures to protect against disease (3)	• Practicing abstinence to avoid STDs (1) • Importance of recognizing the signs and symptoms of STD infection (1)	• Understanding the myths about HIV transmission (1) • Sexual intercourse as a high risk behavior (1) • Abstinence as protection against HIV infection (2) • Employing refusal skills to protect yourself against HIV infection (2)
• Transmission of infectious disease through direct and indirect contact (1) • Infectious diseases of the nervous system (2) • Symptoms and treatment of measles, mononucleosis, and hepatitis (2)	• Symptoms and treatment for common STDs—chlamydia, gonorrhea, trichomoniasis, syphilis, genital warts and herpes (2) • Recognizing and treating yeast infections, scabies and other STDs (2)	• Difference between HIV and AIDS (1) • Symptoms and stages of HIV infection (2) • AIDS opportunistic illness (AIDS-OIs) (2) • Common forms of AIDS-OIs (2) • HIV as a retrovirus and the obstacles to finding a cure (2)

SCOPE & SEQUENCE

Content Strands	Chapter 31 Noninfectious Diseases and Disabilities	Chapter 32 Consumer Choices and Public Health
Personal Health	• Making healthful choices to prevent cardiovascular disease (1) • Warning signs of stroke (1) • Differences between benign and malignant tumors (2) • Treatments for a diabetic emergency (3)	• What to expect from a primary care physician (1) • Recognizing the differences between RNs and LPNs (1) • Understanding your health insurance options (1) • Developing patient skills (2) • Being aware of your medical history (2)
Consumer and Community Health	• New surgical procedures and other treatments for cardiovascular disease (1) • Cancer treatments—surgery, radiation, and chemotherapy (2) • Role of society in providing equal rights for the disabled (4)	• Types of health care providers and their services (1) • Health care facilities in your community (1) • Factors to consider when choosing a health plan (2) • Guidelines for choosing a health care provider (2) • Agencies and organizations for health consumers (3) • Public health agencies at local and national levels (4)
Injury Prevention and Safety	• Sunscreen as protection from harmful ultra-violet rays (2)	• Importance of understanding side effects and doctor's instructions when taking prescription medicines (2)
Alcohol, Tobacco, and Other Drugs	• Avoiding tobacco to reduce the risk of heart disease (1) • Smoking, the primary cause of lung cancer (2)	• Role of the FDA in determining whether a medicine should be prescription or over-the-counter (3)
Nutrition	• Good nutrition and the prevention of cardiovascular disease (1) • Connection between cholesterol and arteriosclerosis (1) • Sugar intake and diabetes (3)	• Quackery and weight-loss formulas (3)
Environmental Health	• Environmental risk factors for cardiovascular disease (1) • Carcinogens and cancer (2)	
Family Living	• Heredity as a risk factor for cardiovascular disease (1) • Genetic disorders that induce mental retardation (4)	• Family considerations in choosing a health care provider (2)
Individual Growth and Development	• Reducing the risk of cancer with a healthy lifestyle (2) • Importance of breast self-examination (2) • Physical and mental challenges of living with disabilities (4)	• Shopping for over-the-counter medicines (2) • Lifelong awareness of medical fraud and quackery (3) • Being aware of fraudulent products and remedies (3) • Concern for public health as a developmental task of adolescence (4)
Communicable and Chronic Disease	• Understanding types of cardiovascular disease (1) • Types of cancers (2) • Understanding diabetes and arthritis (3)	• Recognizing the susceptibility of people with chronic illnesses to fraudulent treatments (3)

Chapter 33 The Health of the Environment	Chapter 34 Your Safety and Well-Being	Chapter 35 Providing First Aid and Handling Emergencies
• Health threats of air pollution (1)	• Understanding the accident chain (1) • Treatment for a muscle cramp (2) • Protecting yourself from frostbite (2) • Importance of seeking medical treatment if you become a victim of rape (4)	• First aid for open wounds and severe burns (1) • First aid for swallowing poison and contact poisoning (2) • First aid for snakebite (2) • How to care for animal bites and bee stings (4) • First aid for fractures, sprains, and fainting (4) • Treating weather-related emergencies (4)
• Water pollution from raw sewage and industrial wastes (1) • Environmental hazards of toxic dumping (2) • Dangerous global effects of nuclear waste disposal (2) • Impact of population growth (2) • Social responsibility of conservation (3) • Guidelines for community recycling (3)	• Smoke detectors and fire extinguishers—consumer products for fire safety (1) • OSHA and workplace safety (2) • National and international organizations that provide relief to communities struck by natural disasters (2) • Tips for buying a bicycle helmet (3) • Community services for rape victims (4)	• Emergency medical information tags (1) • Dialing 911 (1) • When and how to contact a poison control center (2)
• Recognizing the effects of toxic and non-biodegradable wastes on water safety (1)	• Tips for handling a fire emergency (1) • Preventing falls (1) • Preventing electric shock (1) • Safety guidelines for water sports, camping and hiking (2) • Exercising vehicular and bicycle safety (3) • Skating safety guidelines (3) • Escaping and surviving a physical attack (4)	• Priority checklist for an emergency (1) • Measures for treating minor burns and nosebleeds to prevent further injury (4)
• Tobacco smoke is a source of carbon monoxide (1)	• Avoidance of alcohol and other drugs to reduce the risk of water-related accidents (2) • Dangers of driving under the influence of alcohol (3)	
• Cooking methods and conservation (3) • Precycling and buying foods in bulk quantities (3)		• Some parts of food plants are poisonous (2)
• Gases and particulates—two main forms of air pollution (1) • Defining the greenhouse effect (1) • How smog is produced (1) • Dangers of deforestation and desertification (2) • Environmental benefits of recycling (3)	• Identifying environmental risk factors that can lead to accidents (1) • Safety tips for surviving natural disasters (2)	• Identifying weather-related health emergencies—frostbite, heat cramps and heatstroke (4)
• Guidelines for conservation in the home (3) • Reducing household wastes through recycling (3)	• Family fire safety guidelines (1) • Family measures for preventing household poisoning (1)	• Safety guidelines for storing household cleaning agents and other poisonous products (2)
• Steps individuals can take to save trees and save energy (2) • Becoming involved in protecting the environment (3)	• Protecting yourself from road rage (3) • Preventive behaviors to reduce the risk of physical violence, sexual assault, and rape (4) • Self-esteem, assertiveness, and other inner tools of self-defense (4)	• Understanding different types of emergencies (1) • Learning first aid to help choking adults and children (3) • Learning rescue breathing for adults and children (3) • Learning CPR for adults and children (3)
• Link between asbestos and lung cancer (1)		

HEALTH RESOURCES

Action on Smoking and Health
2013 H Street NW
Washington, DC 20006

Alcoholics Anonymous
P.O. Box 459
Grand Central Station
New York, NY 10163

Al-Anon/Alateen Family
Group Headquarters
1600 Corporate Landing Parkway
Virginia Beach, VA 23454

Administration on Aging
330 Independence Avenue SW
Washington, DC 20201

American Academy of Pediatrics
141 Northwest Point Road
Elk Grove Village, IL 60007

American Automobile Association,
Foundation for Traffic Safety
1440 New York Avenue NW
Suite 201
Washington, DC 20005

American Cancer Society
1599 Clifton Road
Atlanta, GA 30329

American Dental Association
211 East Chicago Avenue
Chicago, IL 60611

American Heart Association
7320 Greenville Avenue
Dallas, TX 75231

American Institute of Nutrition
9650 Rockville Pike
Bethesda, MD 20814

American Insurance Association, Engineering and Safety Service
85 John Street
New York, NY 10038

American Lung Association
1740 Broadway
New York, NY 10019

American Medical Association
515 North State Street
Chicago, IL 60610

American Optometric Association
243 North Lindbergh Boulevard
St. Louis, MO 63141

American Society of Safety Engineers
1800 E. Oakton Street
Des Plaines, IL 60018-2187

Asthma and Allergy Foundation of America
1233 20th Street, NW
Suite 402
Washington, DC 20036

Centers for Disease Control and Prevention (CDC)
1600 Clifton Road
Atlanta, GA 30341

Council on Environmental Quality
722 Jackson Place NW
Washington, DC 20503

ERIC—Clearinghouse on Teacher Education—Health Education
One Dupont Circle
NW, Suite 610
Washington, DC 20036-1186

Food and Drug Administration
Office of Consumer Affairs
5600 Fishers Lane
Rockville, MD 20857

Juvenile Diabetes Foundation
120 Wall Street
New York, NY 10016

March of Dimes Birth Defects Foundation
1275 Mamaroneck Avenue
White Plains, NY 10605

Mothers Against Drunk Driving
511 East John Carpenter Freeway
Irving, TX 75062

National Arthritis and Musculoskeletal and Skin Diseases Information Clearinghouse
P.O. Box AMS
Rockville Pike
Bethesda, MD 20892

National Association for Mental Health
1790 Broadway
New York, NY 10010

National Association of Sports for Cerebral Palsy
66 East 34th Street
New York, NY 10016

National Cancer Institute, Office of Cancer Communications
Building 31, Room 10A 07
31 Center Drive
Bethesda, MD 20892

National Center for Health Statistics
Centers for Disease Control
6525 Belcrest Road
Hyattsville, MD 20782

National Clearinghouse for Alcohol and Drug Information
P.O. Box 2345
Rockville, MD 20847-2345

National Congress of Parents-Teachers
Association
Alcohol Education Program
330 North Wabash Ave., Suite 2100
Chicago, IL 60611-3690

National Council on Alcoholism and Drug Dependence
12 West 21st Street
New York, NY 10010

National Dairy Council
10255 West Higgins Road
Suite 900
Rosemont, IL 60018

National Fire Protection Association
P.O. Box 9101
Quincy, MA 02269-9101

National Health Information Center
P.O. Box 1133
Washington, DC 20013-1133

National Institute of Allergy and Infectious Diseases
Building 31 Room 7A-50
31 Center Drive MSC2520
Bethesda, MD 20892

National Institute of Mental Health
6001 Exec
Rockville, MD 20857

National Mental Health Association
1021 Prince Street
Alexandria, VA 22314

National Safety Council
1121 Spring Lake Drive
Itasca, IL 60143-3201

National Society for Crippled Children and Adults
2023 West Odgen Avenue
Chicago, IL 60612

National Wildlife Federation
8925 Leesburg Pike
Vienna, VA 22180

Office on Smoking and Health
Centers for Disease Control
Mailstop K 50
4770 Buford Highway NE
Atlanta, GA 30341-5701

Sierra Club
85 Second Street
Second Floor
San Francisco, CA 94105

Students Against Destructive Decisions
P.O. Box 800
200 Pleasant Street
Marlboro, MA 01752

USDA Food and Nutrition Information and Education Resources Center
National Agricultural Library,
U.S. Department of Agriculture
10301 Baltimore Blvd., Room 304
Beltsville, MD 20705

Wheelchair Sports U.S.A.
3595 East Fountain Blvd., Suite L-1
Colorado Springs, CO 80910

GLENCOE

Health

A Guide to Wellness

EIGHTH EDITION

Mary Bronson Merki, Ph.D.

Don Merki, Ph.D.

Contributing Authors
Michael J. Cleary, Ed.D.
Gale Cornelia Flynn

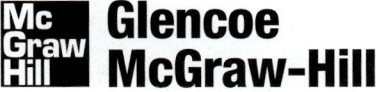

Glencoe
McGraw-Hill

New York, New York   Columbus, Ohio   Chicago, Illinois   Peoria, Illinois   Woodland Hills, California

About the Authors

Mary Bronson Merki, Ph.D., has taught health education in grades K–12, as well as health education methods classes at the undergraduate and graduate levels. As Health Education Specialist for the Dallas School District, Dr. Merki developed and implemented a district-wide health education program, *Skills for Living,* which was used as a model by the state education agency. Dr. Merki has assisted school districts throughout the country in developing local health education programs. Dr. Merki is also the author of Glencoe's *Teen Health* textbook series.

Don Merki, Ph.D., has taught health education for 35 years. He teaches at The University of New Mexico, featuring classes in substance abuse, mental health, adopting a healthy lifestyle, AIDS and sexually transmitted diseases, and stress and life management skills. He has taught students from broad cultural and ethnic backgrounds at every level from elementary to graduate school. Dr. Merki recently served as a consultant to the School of Family Medicine's Alcohol and Substance Abuse Prevention Program at the University of New Mexico, Albuquerque.

Michael J. Cleary, Ed.D., is Professor and School Health Education Coordinator at Slippery Rock University. Dr. Cleary taught at Evanston Township High School in Evanston, Illinois, and later became the Lead Teacher Specialist at the McMillen Center for Health Education in Fort Wayne, Indiana. Dr. Cleary has published and presented widely on curriculum development and portfolio assessment in K-12 health education. Dr. Cleary is the co-author of *Managing Your Health: Assessment for Action.* He is a Certified Health Education Specialist.

Gale Cornelia Flynn is a widely published freelance writer whose work has appeared in many well-known textbooks. Flynn has taught at both junior and senior high school levels. An educational and creative consultant, she now conducts in-service programs in a variety of schools in Delaware. She speaks to students at all levels on subjects ranging from alcoholism to creativity, and runs workshops for parents and teachers.

Glencoe/McGraw-Hill

A Division of The McGraw·Hill Companies

Send all inquiries to:
Glencoe/McGraw-Hill
21600 Oxnard Street, Suite 500
Woodland Hills, California 91367

ISBN 0-07-823864-1 (Student Edition)
ISBN 0-07-823865-X (Teacher Wraparound Edition)
ISBN 0-07-829660-9 (CNN® Video)

Printed in the United States of America.

2 3 4 5 6 7 8 9 0   071/043   07 06 05 04 03 02

Educational Consultants

Nita Auer
Health Educator
North Side High School
Fort Wayne, Indiana

Pamela Connolly
Health and Physical Education
Diocese of Pittsburgh
West Mifflin, Pennsylvania

Justin Cunningham
California Health Framework Writing
    Committee Chair
San Diego, California

Robert Wandberg, Ph.D.
Health Educator
John F. Kennedy High School
Bloomington, Minnesota

Content Reviewers

David Allen, M.D.
Infectious Disease Consultant
Dallas, Texas

Marcella Cook
Health Resource Educator
Charlotte, North Carolina

Roberta Duyff
Nutrition Education Consultant
St. Louis, Missouri

Glen C. Griffin, M.D.
Health Consultant
Mapleton, Utah

Marlene Koch, R.D., L.D.
Nutrition Education Consultant
Dublin, Ohio

Bonnie Mohnsen, Ph.D.
Health Consultant
Cerritos, California

Judy Monroe
Health Educator
St. Paul, Minnesota

Richard L. Pappenfuss, Ph.D.
Associate Professor, Health
University of Arizona
Tucson, Arizona

Howard Shapiro, M.D.
Psychiatrist
Los Angeles, California

David Sleet, Ph.D.
Injury Prevention
San Diego, California

Pamela Tollefson, R.N.
Health Education and
    HIV/STD Prevention
Olympia, Washington

Teacher Reviewers

Donna Breitenstein
Director of Health Training Center
Boone, North Carolina

Diane Bruckerhoff
Health Education Coordinator
Columbia, Missouri

Peggy Campbell
Curriculum Supervisor
Huntington, West Virginia

Alisa Debnam
Health Supervisor
Fayetteville, North Carolina

Debra Harris
Health and Physical Education Educator
West Linn, Oregon

Jo Henderson
Health Educator
Seattle, Washington

Gayle S. Jenkins
Health Education Program Specialist
Raleigh, North Carolina

Peggy V. Johns
Supervisor, Pre K–12 Health Education
Largo, Florida

Phyllis Simpson, Ph.D. CHES
Health Supervisor
Dallas, Texas

Deborah Tackmann
Health Educator
Eau Claire, Wisconsin

Betty White
Health Educator
Lexington, Kentucky

Contents

UNIT 9

Consumer and Environmental Health

Building Health Skills

Making Responsible Decisions

update

CHARACTER IN ACTION

keeping Fit

connections

health lab

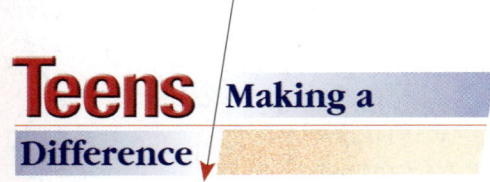

Teens Making a Difference

Drawings, Tables, Charts

Your Health and Wellness

	FEATURES	**CLASSROOM RESOURCES**

LESSON 1

What Is Health?

pages 4–10

"Being Aware of Your Surroundings," *page 9*

- Concept Map Activity 1
- Cooperative Learning Activity 1
- Lesson 1 Quiz
- Lesson Plan 1
- Reteaching Activity 1
- Transparencies 1-3

LESSON 2

Influences on Your Health

pages 11–16

"Caring Across Cultures," *page 13*

"Finding a Cure," *page 15*

- Concept Map Activity 2
- Enrichment Activity 1
- Health Lab 1
- Lesson 2 Quiz
- Lesson Plan 2
- Reteaching Activity 2

LESSON 3

Taking Charge of Your Health

pages 17–21

- Concept Map Activity 3
- Decision-Making Activity 1
- Lesson 3 Quiz
- Lesson 3 Plan 3
- Reteaching Activity 3
- Transparencies 4-6

ACTIVITIES

- ☞ Cross-Curriculum Activity 1
- ☞ Health Lab 1
- ☞ Health Skills Activities 1
- ☞ Parent Letter and Activities 1

ASSESSMENT

- ☞ Chapter 1 Test
- ☞ Performance Assessment Activity 1
- 💾 Testmaker Software

STUDENT ACTIVITIES WORKBOOK

- ☞ Applying Health Skills 1-3
- ☞ Study Guide 1
- ☞ Vocabulary Activity 1

STUDENT DIVERSITY STRATEGIES

- 🎧 Audiocassette Program (English)
- 🎧 Audiocassette Program (Spanish)
- ☞ Spanish Parent Letters and Activities
- ☞ Spanish Summaries, Quizzes, and Activities

MULTIMEDIA COMPONENTS

- 🎧 English Audiocassette Program
- 🎧 Spanish Audiocassette Program
- 🔴 MindJogger Videodisc and VHS program
- 🔴 ABCNews InterActive™ VHS/Videodisc Series

MODULES

- • *The Reality of Drugs,* Student Edition
- • *The Reality of Drugs,* Teacher's Annotated Edition

National Health Education Standards

One of the main goals of the National Health Education Standards is to move students toward "health literacy." Health literacy is the capacity of individuals to obtain, interpret, and understand basic health information and services and the competence to use such information and services in ways which promote health. The health standards were developed by applying the characteristics of a well-educated, literate person within the context of health. The health literate person is:
- • a critical thinker and problem solver • a self-directed learner
- • a responsible, productive citizen   • an effective communicator

Listed below are the Health Education Standards Performance Indicators addressed in each lesson of this chapter.

Lesson	Health Standards Performance Indicators
Lesson 1	1.2, 1.3, 3.1, 4.3
Lesson 2	1.1, 1.4, 1.5, 3.1
Lesson 3	1.3, 1.6, 3.1, 3.3

ONLINE RESOURCES

For a fresh approach to health topics and an in-depth look at health issues, use these online resources found under Teacher Resources at **health.glencoe.com**.

- • **BLOCK SCHEDULE LESSON PLANS** Reinforce health concepts with outside readings selected especially for students. Each reading is accompanied by a lesson plan and activities to enhance
  - • Reading Skills
  - • Cross Curriculum
  - • Media Literacy

- • **TECHNOLOGY PROJECTS** Instructions and suggestions on how to use computer, Internet, and software with health lessons.

- • **HEALTH UPDATES** Timely topics in health news, including late-breaking medical advances and updates on teen risk behaviors.

Out of Time?

If time does not permit teaching this chapter, you may use this feature: Update on page 9.

BLOCK SCHEDULING

Block scheduling provides extended time for hands-on projects and activities. Use the following activities to engage students, provide further depth, and vary your instructional techniques:
- • Update (20–30 minutes) **pg. 9**
- • Teens Making a Difference (30 minutes) **pg. 13**
- • Connections (30 minutes) **pg. 15**
- • Health Skills Activity (60–90 minutes) **pg. 22**

Your Health and Wellness

CHAPTER OVERVIEW

Chapter 1 defines *health* and discusses major influences on an individual's health. Personal responsibility is stressed as a primary means of promoting health.

LESSON 1 Health is the state of total well-being. Although heredity and environment are health factors, your personal health is greatly influenced by the choices and decisions you make. To achieve a high level of health, you must balance the physical, mental/emotional, and social aspects of your health. Developing prevention skills, such as gaining health literacy, should be the focus of everyone's health goals.

LESSON 2 Heredity and environment are influences on your health over which you have little or no control. There is one factor, however, that affects your health over which you have a great deal of control: your behavior. The way you choose to act within your environment and with your inherited abilities has a great impact on who you are and your overall well-being.

LESSON 3 Accepting responsibility for your own health and for the health of others is a positive step toward wellness. A first step is to heighten your awareness of risk factors in your life. A second step is to examine current behaviors and values and to make any necessary changes to reduce risks.

CHAPTER 1

Your Health and Wellness

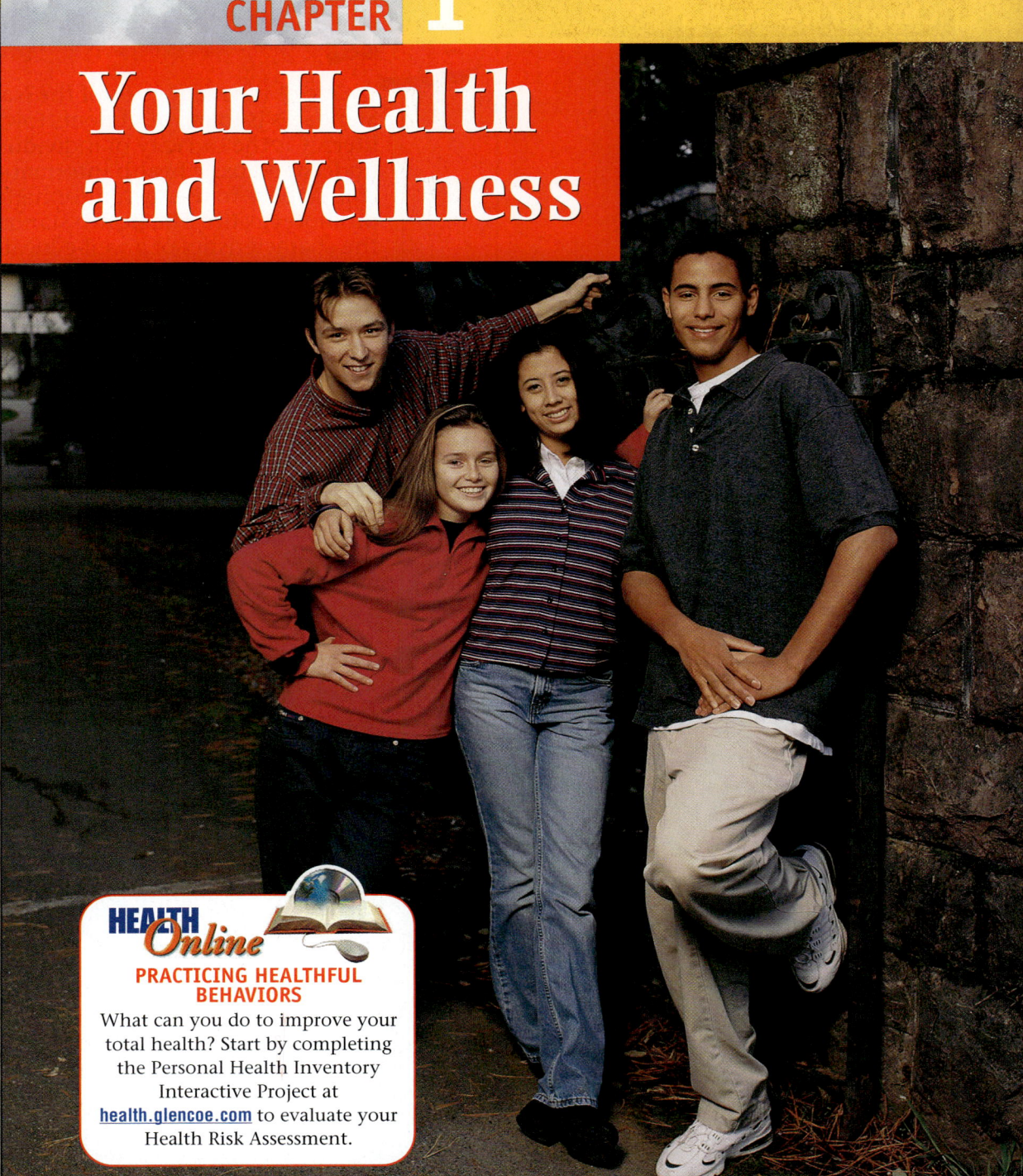

HEALTH *Online*

PRACTICING HEALTHFUL BEHAVIORS

What can you do to improve your total health? Start by completing the Personal Health Inventory Interactive Project at **health.glencoe.com** to evaluate your Health Risk Assessment.

Hands-On Health

TEACHING STRATEGY

Evaluating Health and Wellness Find motivating teaching strategies and activities in the *Hands-On Health: Creative Teaching Strategies* booklet that accompanies the *Glencoe Health* program. Have students examine their own lifestyle choices and how they relate to health and wellness with Activity 2, "A Letter to Yourself."

Time Needed
45 to 60 minutes

Supplies
- "A Letter to Myself" student worksheet
- pen or pencil for each student

> **Whatever I choose to do, I'll try and make it as extraordinary as possible.**
>
> —MARION JONES
> OLYMPIC GOLD MEDALIST, TRACK AND FIELD

Quick Write Make a can-do list of ways to make your life extraordinary each day. Include steps to improve your physical, mental, and social health. Begin each item on the list with the words *I can ...*

Personal Health Inventory

Self-Inventory Write the numbers 1–10 on a sheet of paper. Read each statement below and respond by writing *yes*, *no*, or *sometimes* for each item. Write a *yes* only for items that you practice regularly. Save your responses.

1	I get between seven and eight hours of sleep each night.
2	I eat at least three nutritionally balanced meals each day, beginning with breakfast.
3	I maintain a weight that is right for someone my height and frame.
4	I do at least 20 to 30 minutes of aerobic physical activity three to four times a week.
5	I wear a seat belt in cars and protective gear when bicycling or playing sports.
6	I avoid harmful substances such as tobacco, alcohol, or other drugs.
7	I ask for help when I need it and know where to turn for current and reliable health information.
8	I generally like and accept who I am.
9	I get along well with others.
10	I can express my emotions in healthy ways.

Follow-up After completing the chapter, retake this self-inventory. Pick two items that you need to work on and set a goal to improve your health behaviors.

INTRODUCING THE CHAPTER

Personal Health Inventory

Have students read and respond to the Self-Inventory statements. Assure students that this inventory is entirely for their own use, and encourage them to respond honestly and confidentially.

Remind students to label the page "Total Health" and to save it in their private Health Journals. They will use their responses in a private Follow-up activity at the end of the chapter.

- Ask students: If you had three wishes, what would you wish for? Then ask them to imagine that after they received their wishes, their doctor told them they had an incurable disease. Would their wishes have the same value if their health was taken from them? Why do people often take their health for granted when it is perhaps the most precious gift of all?
- Guide students in discussing the photographs on these two pages. Ask: What does each picture tell you about the teen's health? What health information is not evident? Have students read the introductory quotation on this page, and encourage them to share their responses to the Quick Write. Explain that students will gain a fuller understanding of health, total health, and wellness as they study the lessons in Chapter 1.
- Distribute Parent Letter 1 in the *Parent Letters and Activities* booklet and have students take it home to their parents or guardian. 🖙

TECHNOLOGY OPTIONS

You may wish to use *Making Responsible Decisions* with this chapter. For your convenience, use the separate *ABCNews InterActive™ Bar Code Correlation* that accompanies the *Glencoe Health* program. 🔴

MINDJOGGER
VIDEOQUIZ

To preview or review chapter content, you may wish to use the *MindJogger Videoquiz* that accompanies Chapter 1. 🔴

What Is Health?

FOCUS

LESSON OBJECTIVES

After studying this lesson, students should be able to

- define health.
- describe how the components of health can be represented by a triangle.
- describe the importance of health education and relate wellness to total health.

MOTIVATOR

Ask students to list several of their favorite activities and hobbies. Have them consider how each affects their health.

INTRODUCING THE LESSON

Create three columns on the board labeled *Physical, Mental/Emotional,* and *Social,* respectively. Have several students share their responses to the Motivator activity. Ask students to categorize their responses, placing them in the appropriate column(s). Ask how their activities and hobbies could affect the other aspects of their health.

INTRODUCING HEALTH TERMS

- Ask students to brainstorm synonyms for the word *health.* Have students consider the synonyms and write a one- or two-line definition of *health.* Ask a few volunteers to share their definitions. Introduce the concept of wellness and have students point out similarities and differences between the two terms.
- Ask students to complete Vocabulary Activity 1 and Chapter Study Guide 1 in the *Student Workbook.* ☞

What Is Health?

Although it may not be easy to see, you are in a constant state of change. Think about how your knowledge and skills have expanded in the past few years. What new relationships have you formed? What kind of adult will you become? Many of your answers depend on the choices and decisions you make about your health.

HEALTH TERMS

health

wellness

lifestyle factors

prevention

health education

health literacy

HEALTH CONCEPTS

- Health is the combination of your physical, mental/emotional, and social well-being.
- Wellness is an overall state of well-being, or total health.
- Health literacy is the capacity to obtain, interpret, and understand basic health information and services, and to use these to promote personal health and wellness.

Defining Health

If you were to take a snapshot of your current state of health, how would it look? How are you feeling? Are you alert and well rested? Are you ready to take on whatever challenges the day holds in store for you? Is your outlook positive? Are you getting along well with family members, classmates, and teachers? What about yesterday? Did you eat well and get plenty of physical activity?

Your answers to these and other questions provide a picture of your general level of health. Does that surprise you? If it does, the reason may be that, like many people, you think of health as the absence of sickness. Health, however, is much more than that. **Health** is *the combination of your physical, mental/emotional, and social well-being.* Your personal level of health affects everything about you. It affects how you look, how you feel, even how you act. It affects your

Lesson 1 Resources

TEACHER'S CLASSROOM RESOURCES

☞ **Concept Map** Activity 1

☞ **Cooperative Learning** Activity 1

☞ **Lesson 1 Quiz**

☞ **Lesson Plan 1**

☞ **Parent Letter and Activities 1**

☞ **Reteaching** Activity 1

STUDENT WORKBOOK

☞ **Applying Health Skills 1**

☞ **Chapter Study Guide 1**

☞ **Vocabulary** Activity 1

TRANSPARENCIES

🔖 **Transparencies 1, 2, 3**

attitudes and performance in school, work, and recreation. It affects how you feel about yourself and how successful you are in your relationships. It will probably help determine some of your goals and your ability to accomplish them.

It is important to be aware that health is not an absolute state. Being healthy does not mean that you will never be sick, or that you will be guaranteed a position on the basketball team. Instead, being healthy means striving to be the best *you* can be at any given time.

The Three Elements of Your Health

Notice that people ask, "How are you?" not "Do you have any diseases?" or "Are all of your systems functioning properly?" That is because "how you are doing" involves much more than your physical condition. It also includes how you are doing mentally, emotionally, and socially. To obtain a complete picture of your health, you must take into consideration all of these elements.

Physical Health

In its broadest sense, physical health is the way the parts and systems of your body work together. It means that your body has the ability to cope with the stresses of normal daily life. It means having strength and energy to pursue physical, mental, emotional and social challenges and changes.

To gain or maintain physical health, you need to have proper nutrition, regular physical activity, and enough rest and sleep. You need to practice good hygiene to prevent disease, and get regular medical and dental checkups and treatments when you need them. Good physical health also includes paying attention to what you put into your body. It means resisting harmful substances, such as tobacco, alcohol, and other drugs.

Mental and Emotional Health

Mental and emotional health includes your feelings about yourself, how well you relate to others, and how well you meet the demands of daily life. Mental health also calls for a person to use his or her mind to develop thinking skills. People with good mental health enjoy learning, and they know that striving for information and understanding can be an exciting, lifelong process. They see mistakes as opportunities to learn, grow, and change. They accept responsibility for their actions and stand up for their beliefs and values.

A person with good emotional health is in touch with his or her feelings and expresses

▼ *You can use your talents and skills to help others succeed.*

ACTIVITY *Explain how helping other people learn new skills contributes to your mental health.*

TEACH

L1 Discussing

Ask students to complete the following statement on a sheet of paper: *When you have good health you have…* Ask volunteers to share their answers with the class.

L1 Critical Thinking

Point out that illness can often be prevented, but that health is more than just avoiding illness. It aims toward realizing an individual's potential. Ask students to consider what the term *potential* may refer to when considering physical, mental/emotional, and social health.

L2 Analyzing

Ask students to complete the following statements: *Good health depends on…, A physically healthy person is…, A mentally/emotionally healthy person is…, A socially healthy person is…* Have students discuss their answers with the class.

L2 Class Activity

Draw a large health triangle on the chalkboard. Label the three sides *Physical, Mental/Emotional,* and *Social.* Ask students to list the lifestyle factors and activities that affect health. Have a volunteer write the factors and activities on the board. Ask each student to draw his or her own health triangle on a sheet of paper. Have students put those factors that relate to behaviors in their lives beside each appropriate component on the triangle.

Ask students to determine if their triangles are balanced. Ask them to list behaviors that could be adopted to balance their health triangles.

MEETING STUDENT DIVERSITY

LEARNING STYLES. Teaching strategies that appear throughout the chapter have been identified by one of the following codes.

LD LD strategies are designed for slow learners or students with special needs.

L1 Level 1 strategies should be within the ability range of all students. Full class participation is often required. Teacher direction is usually needed.

L2 Level 2 strategies are for average to above-average students or for small groups. Some teacher direction is needed.

L3 Level 3 strategies are designed for students able and willing to work independently. Minimal teacher direction is needed.

LEP LEP strategies are designed for students with limited English proficiency.

HEALTH Online

Introduce students to Glencoe Health Online and the resources available to them at the Student Site. Preview the Web Links section and familiarize yourself with some of the links and activities provided before you assign students to do the chapter Internet activities.

L1 Cooperative Learning

Have students work in small groups and complete *Cooperative Learning Activity* 1 to analyze health statements. Ask each group to share their ideas with the class.

L2 Cooperative Learning

Have students form groups of three or four. Provide posterboard and magazines. Tell each group to draw a large health triangle on posterboard and label each side with the areas of health. For each side of the triangle, have half the groups make collages of healthy behaviors while the other groups make collages of unhealthy behaviors. Groups should assign individuals to select pictures, cut, and paste the pictures on the poster. Have one student from each group present the group's work to the class. Display the posters in the classroom.

L2 Class Activity

Suggest students track their lifestyles for one week in their private health journals. Ask them to list three positive health behaviors and three negative health behaviors that they took part in each day. Have them identify risks associated with the negative behaviors and describe alternatives to these behaviors.

HEALTH Online

To learn more about the health triangle, visit Glencoe's health home page at **health.glencoe.com**.

▼ *The three elements of your health—physical health, mental and emotional health, and social health—are related to each other and contribute to your total health.*

ACTIVITY *Think about your total health. Identify the activities and behaviors you do to contribute to each side of your health triangle.*

them in appropriate, healthful ways. This type of individual can usually deal with the problems and frustrations of life without being overwhelmed by them. People with good emotional health avoid dwelling on negative thoughts. Instead, they consider their situation and then use positive thoughts and actions to move them through the challenge.

Social Health

Social health involves the way you get along with others. It includes your ability to make and keep friends and also to work and play in cooperative ways, seeking and lending support when necessary. It involves communicating well and showing respect and care for yourself and others.

6 CHAPTER 1 YOUR HEALTH AND WELLNESS

MEETING STUDENT DIVERSITY

VISUAL LEARNERS. To help visual learners understand the concept of balance, obtain a double-pan balance. Place several pennies or pebbles in one pan. Point out the imbalance that exists. Now add pennies or pebbles to the other pan so that the two pans are in balance. Discuss the analogy between balancing the pans and balancing each aspect of the health triangle.

Have students imagine that they are using pennies to balance the sides of their triangles. Encourage them to think in terms of what pennies they would have to add to ensure that all three areas of health are in balance and what behaviors would be correlated to the pennies.

Your Health Triangle

Have you ever been very tired or hungry? Did that feeling affect the way you acted toward others? Did it affect your work? If it continued for a long time, did it affect your physical well-being?

The three elements of health are interconnected, like the sides of a triangle. When one side receives too much or too little attention, the other sides change as well. The whole triangle can become lopsided and unbalanced. To be truly healthy, you need to try to keep all three sides of your health triangle—and your life—in balance.

The Health Continuum

A person with a balanced life is said to have a high degree of **wellness**, *an overall state of well-being, or total health.* It comes from a way of living each day that includes making decisions and practicing behaviors that are based on sound health knowledge and healthful attitudes. Achieving wellness is an ongoing, lifelong commitment to physical, mental/emotional, and social health.

Remember that your health is dynamic. You are constantly being bombarded with messages from advertising and television, and pressures from friends that can affect your health. The fact, however, that your health is dynamic means that it fluctuates along a *continuum*. A continuum is like a yardstick. There are many different points along it where your health can be located at any given time. From day to day and year to year, you experience different levels of total health. In any of the health areas—physical, mental/emotional, or social—there can be a sudden change. By the same token, a person may move from one side of the continuum to the other so gradually that he or she may not be fully aware of the change.

▼ *The continuum shows that your health is on a sliding scale with many degrees of health and wellness in between.*

ACTIVITY *Name three behaviors that would help a person's health move toward the right side of the Health Continuum.*

The Health Continuum

Premature Death	Loss of Health and Wellness		Improved Health and Wellness	High Level of Health
Chronic disorders	Lack of energy, inattention, minor aches and pains		Free from aches and pains	Moderate level of energy	Optimal level of energy, feeling of well-being

People on this side of the continuum usually do not take responsibility for maintaining their own health.

Many people function below the wellness midpoint.

People on this side of the continuum usually exhibit a high degree of responsibility, discipline, and positive direction in life. They accept responsibility for maintaining their own health.

LESSON 1   WHAT IS HEALTH?   **7**

SCHOOL-TO-CAREER

PERFORMANCE ON THE JOB. Have students work individually or in pairs to brainstorm the possible effects of wellness and health choices on an employee's performance. For example, how might job performance be affected by abundance or lack of energy, high spirits or depression, confidence or shyness? What personal choices affect these factors? Tell students to list the brainstormed examples under one of these three heads: *Physical Health, Mental/Emotional Health,* or *Social Health.* Have students form groups to discuss how the items on each list relate to specific occupations, such as postal employee, construction worker, teacher, or sales clerk. Suggest they add to or modify their lists as appropriate.

CHAPTER 1 • LESSON 1

L1 **Discussing**

Ask students to answer the following question: *Is it true that if you are not sick you are healthy?*

L2 **Class Activity**

Review the health continuum in the textbook. Follow up with a discussion of the following question: *Is it possible to be physically, mentally/emotionally , or socially challenged and still show a high level of overall wellness?* Ask students if they have ever been disabled in any way. Explain that with this activity they will experience what it feels like to be physically challenged or handicapped. Provide a wheelchair, crutches, arm slings, splints, earplugs, and blindfolds. Have students choose a partner and participate for approximately 20 minutes as physically challenged individuals. Then have them switch roles with their partners. Ask students to share their discoveries, experiences, and frustrations.

Visual Learning

The Health Continuum

While referring to the health continuum on page 7, tell students a continuum has opposites at either end, with varying degrees in between. In the case of the health and wellness continuum, a high level of health is at one end; premature death is at the other. No one's place on the continuum is permanent. Movement toward (or away from) a high level of health depends on the health habits one chooses to adopt. You may wish to use *Transparency 1* to compare the health triangle and the health continuum.

CHARACTER IN ACTION

Adjusting Your Attitude

Ask students to read the feature. Discuss ways in which practicing an attitude of gratitude may help a person to develop both better character *and* better health. Ask students to share what they are grateful for, beginning with the basics such as air to breathe and water to drink, then branching out from there. Have students write down in their private Health Journals what they are grateful for each day for one week. After the week, ask volunteers to share some of their responses and talk about how doing the exercise has affected their sense of well-being and overall outlook as well as their sensitivity to others' situations and needs.

LEP Class Activity

Ask students to provide three sheets of paper. At the top of each sheet, have them write one component of health (*physical health, mental/emotional health, or social health*). Ask students to cut out pictures from magazines that relate to healthy behaviors in each component of health. Have students tape these on the appropriate sheet of paper. Repeat the procedure with unhealthy behaviors. Allow students to share their work with the class.

L2 Cooperative Learning

Divide the class into small groups. Ask each group to develop a radio announcement that focuses public attention on wellness. Announcements could include "here's how" ideas for listeners to improve their own level of wellness. Have each group appoint a spokesperson to present the announcement.

CHARACTER IN ACTION

Adjusting Your Attitude

Sometimes you can change a situation merely by adjusting your attitude toward it. For example, instead of concentrating on what you lack, or don't have, you might instead decide to concentrate on what you *do* have.

Character Check Try these attitude boosters:

➤ Separate your *wants* from your *needs*.

➤ Notice those in the world who have less or have it tougher than you do.

➤ Learn from people who seem to thrive despite—or even because of—their setbacks.

➤ Recognize that tough times may bring out your greatest abilities and character strengths.

➤ Distinguish between what you can and can't change. Focus on the former. Let go of the latter.

Promoting Your Health

Recent discoveries in medicines and advances in technology have helped wipe out many of the diseases that killed people 100, 50, even 30 years ago. Yet, the way we live today poses new threats to our health and our lives. Millions of people get sick, become disabled, or die each year because of the decisions they make and the way they live. Their decision-making skills and personal behavior are directly related to their deaths. Many of these deaths could be prevented if people practiced a few simple health habits.

Lifestyle Factors

After years of studying many groups of people, experts have identified seven habits that make a difference in people's overall health, happiness, and *longevity*—or how long they live. People who regularly practice these important habits tend to be healthier and live longer. These habits are called lifestyle factors. **Lifestyle factors** are *personal behaviors and habits related to the way a person lives, that help determine his or her level of health.* The following are important lifestyle factors.

■ Get between seven to eight hours of sleep per night.
■ Eat nutritious foods from the various food groups each day.
■ Refrain from smoking and using tobacco products.
■ Eat breakfast daily.
■ Do 20 to 30 minutes of nonstop vigorous activity a minimum of three times a week.
■ Do not use alcohol or other drugs.
■ Maintain your recommended weight.

How many of these basic health habits do you practice regularly? What changes in habits can you make? Keep in mind that not following these guidelines can prove hazardous to your health and take years off your life.

Your Attitudes, Your Health

Practicing good health habits involves much more than just knowing what to do. Your attitudes also affect how well you take care of yourself. For example, in order to practice good health habits, you must believe that there is some benefit for you, and that by not practicing good health habits, problems will develop. You also need to become aware of your overall attitude, or outlook, on life since this can play a major role in both your quality of life and your health.

Studies have shown that optimists, people who tend to see the positive in situations, are less likely to suffer illness and die young than pessimists, those who look for and see the negative in situations. Other studies have concluded that it is not what happens to a person

CURRICULUM CONNECTIONS

SOCIAL STUDIES. Health education was practiced centuries ago. In ancient Greece, boys were sent to education centers known as "gymnasiums," where total health and learning were encouraged. There they engaged in physical activities such as wrestling and running. They also received military and philosophical training. Later, in ancient Rome, physical fitness was taught not so much to promote wellness, but to develop superior soldiers who could win in battle. Ask students to research the health practices of one of these or other past cultures and report their findings to the class.

Our Changing World

Being Aware of Your Surroundings

In the past decade, Americans have witnessed many tragedies. Some were the result of natural disasters, such as Hurricane Andrew and the earthquake in Northridge, California. Other tragedies were deliberate acts of violence, including the shootings at Columbine High School and the terrorist attacks of September 11, 2001.

Although these events were terribly tragic, there are lessons to be learned. For one, we must not take our health and safety for granted, but rather make them a top priority in our daily lives. You can accomplish this task by studying and applying the health skills discussed in this book. Start by being more aware of your surroundings. Let an adult know about anyone who talks about committing acts of violence. Being aware of warning signs and taking action can help prevent a dangerous situation from occurring.

Look for other *Update: Our Changing World* features located throughout this book. In them, you will find important information about health-related concerns that have arisen in today's society.

1. What are some other ways in which being aware of your surroundings can help keep you healthy and safe?

2. Why is it so important to learn from recent tragedies? Is it possible for anything positive to result from a tragedy? Explain your answer.

but the person's attitudes and responding behaviors that determine how well that person will cope and how happy he or she will be.

Wellness and Prevention

A key to your health and wellness is **prevention**, or *practicing healthy habits to keep a person well and free from disease and other ailments*. Wearing seat belts, applying sunscreen, avoiding unsafe areas, and using protective gear when playing sports are just a few preventive measures you can take. What others do you regularly practice?

The Importance of Health Education

Because health is so critical to the quality of your life, learning how to become and stay healthy should be a priority. That is why health education is so important. **Health education** is *the providing of accurate health information in such a way as to influence people to change attitudes so that they take positive action about their health*. Its goal is to help people live long, zestful, and productive lives.

Health education is not just about learning health facts. Its goal is to give students—and that includes you—the tools needed to achieve and maintain total well-being. It is about gaining health literacy.

Our Changing World

Being Aware of Your Surroundings

Let students read the feature title. Ask: Why should you be aware of your surroundings? In what ways can this awareness help you? Do you think this awareness is more essential now than it was years ago? Why or why not? Then let students read the Update feature to learn more about how being aware of their surroundings can help them protect their health and safety. Finally, have students meet in small groups to share and compare their responses to the questions.

L3 ## Research

Ask students to refer to *Healthy People 2010* to evaluate the differences between health issues in the 1990s and health concerns for the year 2010. Have them report their findings to the class.

L2 ## Writing

Tell students that statistics indicate that the three leading causes of death in 1900 were pneumonia and flu, tuberculosis, and inflammations of the digestive tract. Ask students to compare these causes of death with the current leading causes *(heart disease, cancer, and stroke)*. Have them explain in writing some of the possible reasons why these statistics have changed.

L1 ## Analyzing

Use *Transparency 2* and have students evaluate their health and wellness.

MORE ABOUT . . . . .

THE NATIONAL HEALTH EDUCATION STANDARDS. One of the main goals of the National Health Education Standards is to move toward "health literacy." Health literacy is the capacity of individuals to obtain, interpret, and understand basic health information and services and the competence to use such information and services in ways that promote health. The health standards were developed by applying the characteristics of a well-educated, literate person within the context of health. For more information about the National Health Education Standards, contact:

American Association for Health Education
1950 Association Drive
Reston, VA 20191

ASSESS

EVALUATING THE LESSON

Assign and discuss the Lesson 1 Review; then administer, grade, and discuss the *Lesson 1 Quiz* in the TCR. ✏

RETEACHING

- Use *Transparency 3,* "Health Literacy," to analyze and review the categories of being a health-literate individual. 🔖
- Have students clip five health-related articles from newspapers or magazines. Ask students to make a chart with the sections Physical, Mental/Emotional, and Social Health. Have students summarize each article and indicate on the chart which topics related to each area of health.
- Ask students to complete *Reteaching Activity 1* in the TCR. ✏

ENRICHMENT

Many professional and community health organizations have a variety of types of health assessments. Have students call or write to these organizations to obtain copies of health appraisals available. Ask students to complete one health appraisal and to share the appraisals with the class.

CLOSE

Ask each student to draw a health triangle and list three lifestyle choices that support each side of the triangle.

Who says that prevention doesn't work? According to the National Highway Traffic and Safety Administration (NHTSA):

➤ Safety helmets reduce fatalities involving motorcyclists by 38 percent.

➤ Each year, car seat belts save 9,500 lives in the United States alone.

➤ Bicycle helmet use significantly reduces head injuries and deaths from bicycle crashes. Helmets are 85–88 percent effective in preventing head and brain injuries.

Being Health Literate

The fact that you are reading the words on this page means you are *literate*—able to read. Are you "health literate," however? **Health literacy** describes *an individual's capacity to obtain, interpret, and understand basic health information and services and use such information and services in ways that promote his or her health and wellness.*

To be health literate, a person must be:

■ **A critical thinker and problem-solver.** Such an individual is able to evaluate information from reliable sources before making a decision. She or he also knows how to make responsible decisions.

■ **A responsible, productive citizen.** A health-literate person acts in a way that promotes the health of the community, nation, and the world at large. He or she chooses safe, healthful, and legal behaviors that keep with family guidelines and show respect of others and himself or herself.

■ **A self-directed learner.** A self-directed learner is able to gather and use accurate, current health information throughout life. This includes the wealth of information available through newspapers, magazines, and modern technology, including computers, fax, and television.

■ **An effective communicator.** Effective communication is the ability to express one's knowledge, beliefs, and ideas in a variety of forms.

In the lessons and chapters to follow, you will find tools that can help you become a more health-literate person.

LESSON 1 *Review*

Reviewing Facts and Vocabulary

1. In a paragraph, relate the terms *health, wellness,* and *lifestyle factors*.
2. What are the three elements of health?
3. List five lifestyle factors that promote good health.
4. Identify four properties of a health-literate person.

Thinking Critically

5. *Synthesizing.* Review your responses to the Health Barometer Self-Inventory on page 23. Based on your answers, draw your own health triangle. Is it balanced or lopsided? If it is lopsided, what can you do to make the sides more even?
6. *Analyzing.* In your Health Journal list five actions you took in the past week that promote good health.

Applying Health Skills

7. *In Your School.* Make two lists—one of places at school and in the community where health is promoted—and one of places where it is *not* promoted. Compare these lists with those of classmates in a general discussion. Discuss in what ways you and your classmates have taken a step toward increased health literacy.

Lesson 1 Review

Answers to Reviewing Facts and Vocabulary

1. Student paragraphs will vary.
2. Physical, mental/emotional, and social.
3. Any combination of the following: get between seven and eight hours of sleep per night; eat nutritious foods from the various food groups each day; refrain from smoking and using tobacco products; eat breakfast daily; do 20 to 30 minutes of nonstop vigorous activity a minimum of three times a week; do not use alcohol or other drugs; maintain your recommended weight.
4. A health-literate person is a critical thinker and problem solver; a responsible, productive citizen; a self-directed learner; and an effective communicator.

Answers to Thinking Critically

5.–6. Answers will vary.

Influences on Your Health

Imagine that the story of your health were made into a video. The video would portray your health from the day you were born until today. It would show how you felt and functioned at each stage. The uniqueness of your video would be partly a result of the decisions you have made in your life that affected your overall well-being.

HEALTH TERMS

heredity
environment
peers
culture

HEALTH CONCEPTS

- Your health is affected by a number of factors over which you have no control.
- Your heredity, environment, and culture influence your health.
- Your behaviors and the choices and decisions you make can affect your health.

hotlink

heredity For more information on heredity and its impact on health, see Chapter 20, page 461.

Heredity

To some degree, your general level of health was determined before you were born. You are a product of **heredity**. **Heredity** is *all the traits and properties that are passed along biologically from both parents to child*. The most obvious traits are physical ones such as the color of your hair and eyes, the shape of your nose and ears, and your body type and size. You also inherit basic intellectual abilities. Tendencies toward specific diseases can also be inherited.

Environment

Your health is also influenced by your environment. **Environment** is *the sum total of your surroundings—your family, where you grew up, where you live now, and all of your experiences*. Environment includes all

---

FOCUS

LESSON OBJECTIVES

After studying this lesson, students should be able to

- describe heredity, environment, and culture as influences on health over which they have little or no control.
- explain how behaviors and the choices and decisions you make affect your health.

MOTIVATOR

Have students consider what characteristics, likes and dislikes, and interests they have in common with other members of their family.

INTRODUCING THE LESSON

Ask students to share some of the characteristics that they came up with in the Motivator activity. Have them discuss whether the characteristics were due to heredity or to their home environment. Tell students that this lesson will examine influences similar to these that can affect an individual's health.

INTRODUCING HEALTH TERMS

- Have students define the terms and provide examples for each term. Correct any misconceptions.
- Ask students to complete Vocabulary Activity 1 and Chapter Study Guide 1 in the *Student Workbook.* 🗁

Lesson 2 Resources

TEACHER'S CLASSROOM RESOURCES

🗁 **Concept Map** Activity 2
🗁 **Enrichment** Activity 1
🗁 **Health Lab** 1
🗁 **Lesson 2 Quiz**
🗁 **Lesson Plan** 2
🗁 **Reteaching** Activity 2

STUDENT WORKBOOK

🗁 **Applying Health Skills** 2
🗁 **Chapter Study Guide** 1
🗁 **Vocabulary** Activity 1

MULTIMEDIA

🔴 **ABCNews InterActive™ VHS/Videodisc,** *Making Responsible Decisions*

TEACH

L2 Discussing

Introduce the concept of the maternal environment as being part of a person's physical environment. Explain how prenatal care is a major influence on one's development. Explain that good nutrition and a healthy mother enables the baby to fully develop physically, affecting normal body functions and even mental capacity. Ask students to provide examples of good prenatal care, such as seeing a doctor regularly throughout the pregnancy, eating a healthful diet, and avoiding harmful substances such as cigarettes and alcohol.

L3 Research

Have students investigate and report on laws that help regulate a healthful environment in their community, such as laws that regulate smoking, littering, loitering, and curfews.

L3 Research

Have the class find and read recent articles about the influences of heredity and environment on the development of individuals. Let students meet in groups to summarize and discuss the articles.

L2 Personal Involvement

Ask students to find out about the incidence of specific noncommunicable diseases—heart disease, high blood pressure, diabetes, colon cancer, and breast cancer, for example—in members of their extended family.

L2 Health Lab

Distribute *Health Lab 1* and have students investigate which cars produce the most air pollution.

the places you go in a given day and the physical conditions in which you live. It also includes the people in your life—your *social environment.* Yet another aspect of your environment is your culture.

Physical Environment

Your physical environment can affect all areas of your health. How would you describe your environment? Are there parks, jogging paths, and recreational facilities? Is the environment clean and are the streets safe? A person living in this environment may be more likely to enjoy good physical and mental health. In contrast, a person living in an area with a high crime rate, for example, may experience stress and feel threatened for his or her personal safety.

Other aspects of your physical environment that can influence your health include air quality. Pollutants, such as smog and smoke from other people's cigarettes, can increase your chances of developing lung disorders, whereas growing up in a community with clean air lessens your risks of such diseases. Indoor aspects of your environment, such as a frayed electrical cord plugged into a wall socket, can also affect your personal safety.

Access to medical care is another aspect of one's physical environment that influences health. Because of the rising costs of medical care and health insurance in recent years, many people are unable to afford health services. Childhood immunizations are often overlooked, and this has led to a re-emergence of diseases that were once thought to be wiped out.

▼ *Your physical environment influences your total health and contributes to your sense of well-being.*

ACTIVITY *Describe characteristics of your physical environment. What parts contribute to a healthful environment? Are there aspects that pose risks to your health?*

HEALTH LITERACY

RESPONSIBLE CITIZEN. Have students research the major environmental health hazards in their area. Is air, land, or water contaminated by industrial polluters? Is air fouled by millions of cars? Are pesticides applied heavily? Are landfills multiplying and leaking pollution? Are trash and garbage clogging waterways? If students need direction, refer them to the Healthfinder Web site (www.healthfinder.gov) or state and county agencies such as the Department of Public Works, a local water or waste management district, or an air quality board.

Encourage students to list steps they can take to protect their health from the environmental dangers they identified. Next, have them list steps they can take to help reduce pollution or avoid contributing to it.

Teens Making a Difference

...CARING...COMPASSION...RESPECT

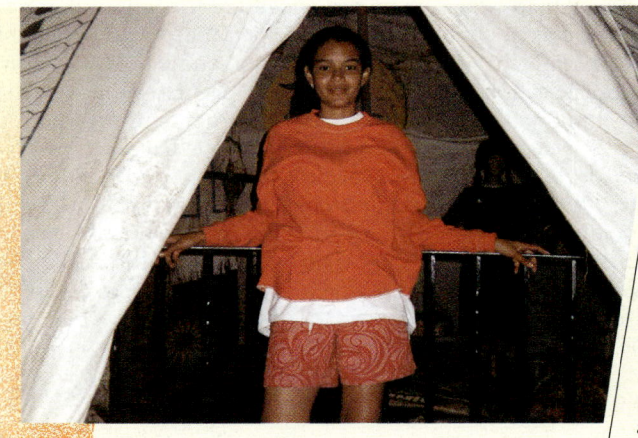

Joceneia, who likes to be called JoJo, is 16. She knows what it's like to move to a new country, have to learn a new language, and try to find her place within a new culture. She is now reaching out to help other young people in the same situation, putting caring and compassion into action and finding joy in the process.

JoJo begins, "I came from Cape Verde, off the coast of Africa, when I was nine. I was having a tough time with English. The teachers taught me and their caring made a big difference. I learned about YouthBuild, an after-school program in Boston that helps students with their homework and other problems. It's held at a drop-in center, and I got the help I needed there. They were kind and caring and took us on field trips and tutored me."

THE GIVE-BACK FACTOR As part of her community service last year, JoJo was a guide with second graders at the Museum of Science. She enjoyed working with children so she decided to give back to the drop-in center that had done so much for her. "I tutor the younger kids as a volunteer. They are kids like me that are in the same situation as I was. I help them after school with English. I make sure they are understanding what they are doing."

She continues, "I'm also in a program called the Summer Search Foundation that helps teens with a desire to travel and learn about other cultures. My first trip was to South Dakota. I stayed on a Native American reservation, and it was the most incredible experience I've ever had because I was with a whole different culture, and I *love* learning about different cultures. Also, the people there were really nice. While we were there, I built a wheelchair ramp for one of the centers. They also have a senior center, and we repainted the whole thing, and I worked at a health clinic filing patients' records. It was fun."

THE "CAN-DO" APPROACH JoJo's positive "can-do" approach keeps her busy and involved. "One of my dreams is to study medicine. I want to be a pediatrician. Coming from what I experienced, I enjoy helping other people a lot. When people help you, you can return that help, and I try to do just that."

JOJO'S STORY
1. Describe how JoJo's story demonstrates both the give-back factor and the can-do approach.
2. How does she also help herself in reaching out to help others?

YOUR STORY
1. What can you do to "give back" to family, friends, your school, or your community?
2. Where can you learn about service projects where you can combine the value of caring with your own interests and career goals?

HOME AND COMMUNITY CONNECTION

CARING IN THE COMMUNITY Have students work individually and compare their experiences to what a person new to the United States may face, including language barriers, cultural differences, and school changes. For example, how might a new culture affect food or exercise options? What differences and opportunities might a person experience? What difficulties would students have in a similar situation?

As a class, discuss organizations in your community that help newcomers in developing physical, mental/emotional, and social wellness as YouthBuild does. How can these groups contribute to a positive experience for new students from other countries? How can teens in your community become involved in organizations such as these?

Teens Making a Difference

Caring Across Cultures

Discussion. Ask students to share experiences in which other people have shown caring to them and how it helped them and made them feel. Have them read the feature and answer the questions that follow it as part of a class discussion. Point out that young people need support and caring in dealing with problems, setting and reaching goals, and putting their highest values into action—just as JoJo did. Ask for examples of ways that teens can get support with each. Have students share examples of times that they have given back to individuals or the community, and how they felt afterward. Brainstorm a list of the Benefits of Giving Back. Ask students how "the give-back factor" and the "can-do approach" each relates to the development of good character. Discuss the concept of giving for the sake of giving rather than giving simply to get back.

Class Activity. Tell students that JoJo is committed to learning about different people, countries, and cultures, including Angola where she has nieces and nephews. Write the following additional quotes by JoJo on the board and ask students to discuss them as they apply to their own lives:
- If you want respect from people different from you, you have to give respect.
- You have responsibility for yourself and for helping others.
- I work to meet expectations and accomplish my goals. I stick with them. I work hard, and when something is really important to me, I go for it!

Answers. *JoJo's Story*
1. Answers will vary.
2. She is working in areas that are related to her own interests, values, and goals.

Responses. *Your Story* 1–2.
1. Answers will vary.

hotlink

peer pressure
Have students provide examples of positive and negative peer pressure and the possible effects of each. Ask how students presently handle negative peer pressure. Tell them that peer pressure will be discussed further in Chapter 13.

L1 Discussing

Help students discuss their social environment. Ask: To what extent can you control your own environment? (*choosing friends, for example*) Which aspects of your social environment are beyond your control? (*your family and neighbors, for example*)

L2 Demonstrating

Suggest that students draw three concentric circles to represent their social environment. In the smallest circle, have them write the names of the people to whom they feel closest and with whom they spend the most time. In the middle circle, have them write the names of individuals or groups with whom they regularly spend time. In the outermost circle, have students write the names of groups and/or individuals with whom they have occasional contact. Then let students meet in small groups to compare and discuss their drawings. Have students ask each other: How do the people and groups in each part of your social environment affect your physical, mental/emotional, and social health?

L2 Guest Speaker

Invite an exchange student to speak with the class about the language, foods, traditions, and religions of his or her home culture.

hotlink

peer pressure For more information on peer pressure and strategies for dealing with it, see Chapter 13, page 304.

▼ *Your peers are an important part of your social environment.*

ACTIVITY *Identify some of the choices and decisions you have made that were influenced by your peers. How does your social environment contribute to positive health behaviors?*

Social Environment

Your social environment includes your family and other people with whom you come into daily contact. A person who is surrounded by individuals who show support, love, strength, and encouragement may have a positive self-image and, as a result, reach out and support others. A healthful, supportive social environment can even help a person to rise above adverse physical conditions, such as poverty. On the other hand, a person from an unhealthful social environment may suffer poor mental and emotional health as a result of rejection, neglect, verbal abuse, or other negative behaviors.

An important part of your social environment, especially during the teen years, is your peers. **Peers** are *people the same age who share a similar range of interests*. Your peers include your friends and classmates. Peers who are loyal and supportive friends can help you grow mentally and socially. At the same time, peers who take part in dangerous, unhealthy, or illegal behaviors like using tobacco, alcohol, or other drugs can put pressure on you to be "part of the group." Standing up to this **peer pressure** can be challenging. One way is by choosing friends who care about their health and yours.

Cultural Environment

Culture is *the collective beliefs, customs, and behaviors of a group.* This group may be an ethnic group, a community, a nation, or an entire section of the globe. The language your family speaks at home, the foods you prefer to eat, and the traditions and religion you practice are all part of your cultural environment.

14   CHAPTER 1   YOUR HEALTH AND WELLNESS

PROMOTING COMPREHENSIVE SCHOOL HEALTH

THE PURPOSE. The primary purpose of a comprehensive school health program is to help your community's school tap into a system of health programming already in place. Most schools have health instruction and physical education classes, counselors, nurses, substance-abuse prevention programs, special education programs, and programs linked with state and local health agencies. Because learning is so closely tied to overall health, a student's physical and mental well-being will receive the priority attention it warrants. To help you develop such a program or to strengthen an existing one, consult *Promoting a Comprehensive School Health Program* in the TCR.

connections

Social Studies

A Values Vocabulary

The actions you take determine who you are. This idea was developed by Greek philosopher Aristotle who lived from 384–322 B.C. By making right choices, showing respect, and caring for yourself and for others, you increase the chances that you will live a longer, more healthful life. Begin by learning to understand and use the following terms.

Values: Your priorities; the ideas, beliefs, or things you cherish above everything else that help guide the way you live.

Character: Characteristics of thinking, feeling, and acting that demonstrate the essentials of who a person is and how he or she functions in the world.

Ethics: Principles of conduct based on objective values or highest moral principles.

Objective Values: The highest values, priorities, or principles; fundamental

laws in the universe, such as *truth* and *justice*.

Core Ethical Values: These are the *highest values*, derived from among the objective values—a group of universal values such as *caring*, *responsibility*, and *respect*. These same highest values exist in many cultures and across many ages.

Good Character: Having traits or characteristics that show or imply feeling, thinking, and acting in terms of objective or core ethical values—your highest values.

1. Think of a time when you or someone close to you made a decision that went against one of the core ethical values. How might this have jeopardized that person's health?

2. If the person making the decision had acted upon the highest values instead, what might have been the result?

connections

Social Studies

Write the words *values, objective values*, and *core ethical values* on the board. Discuss their definitions, similarities, and differences. Make the following important distinctions:
- *Although values are based on priorities, they may not always be based on high ideals. For example, a drug addict may get to the point where the next drug is his or her highest value or priority. Ask students for other examples of values not based on the highest ideals.*
- *Behavior should therefore be based not just on any value but on the highest ideals,* called *objective values* or core ethical values.

Understanding culture can help you understand yourself and get along with others. Culture can help you see what all people have in common. It can help you recognize the variety of ways in which people solve the same basic problems. Finally, your culture gives you a sense of identity as you take your place in a multicultural world.

Behavior

Although you have little or no control over your heredity and environment, you have a great deal of control over one factor affecting your life: your behavior. The way you choose to act within your environment and with your inherited abilities has a very important impact on who you are.

Suppose your family has a history of cardiovascular disease. Does this mean you must "follow in their footsteps"? Not at all! You can reduce your chances of developing this condition through positive

L1 Discussing

Ask students to explain what taking "your place in a multicultural world" involves. Ask: Is our community multicultural? Is our school multicultural? Is your family—or another family you know well—multicultural or at least bicultural? Which cultures are represented in each case?

L1 Analyzing

Have students discuss their responses to these questions: In what ways is taking responsibility for your health the same as taking responsibility for your life? Can you take responsibility for your own life without being health literate? Why or why not?

TECHNOLOGY OPTIONS

VISITING THE VIRTUAL DOCTOR. Someday soon, people may not have to leave their homes to visit the doctor. Instead, patients will arrange "house calls" with their health care providers through interactive computers. The virtual physician will ask questions about medical history and symptoms, diagnose the illness or ailment, and recommend treatment following established guidelines. Consumers will benefit not only by the ways with which they can communicate with doctors, but also by the immediacy of information that will help them make sound health decisions.

ASSESS

EVALUATING THE LESSON

Assign and discuss the Lesson 2 Review; then administer, grade, and discuss the *Lesson 2 Quiz* in the TCR. 🗂

RETEACHING

- Have students create a collage illustrating positive influences on health.
- Ask students to complete *Reteaching Activity 2* in the TCR. 🗂

ENRICHMENT

- Have students research the different wellness programs or assistance programs that employers provide for their employees. What impact have these programs had on the employer, both positive and negative? On the employee?
- To build awareness about some of the ways that personal choices impact personal health and the health of others, have students complete *Enrichment Activity 1*, "Mind and Body: Partners in Good Health," in the TCR. 🗂

CLOSE

Ask students to state the most important concepts in the lesson. Explain that the influence over which they have the most control, behavior, will be discussed further in the next lesson.

---

choices and habits. You can reduce your intake of fried foods and other foods high in fat. You can also develop the positive habit of regularly participating in physical activity and exercise.

Similarly, if you are aware of environmental health influences, you have the ability to take positive action to protect your health. If there is a nonworking smoke detector in your home, you can replace the battery. You can wear sunscreen to protect your skin when you're in the sun. If you know about the dangers associated with cigarette smoke, you can try to avoid being near smokers.

By being aware—by becoming more health literate—you can take positive action to protect your health and the health of others. You can also take advantage of positive hereditary and environmental influences.

Your Behavior, Your Health

Can you recall your health video, discussed at the beginning of this lesson? Imagine that you could keep adding to this video, showing how the decisions you make today will affect your health tomorrow or how the decisions you make tomorrow will affect the rest of your life.

The simple fact is that the remainder of the video is, for the most part, in your hands. True, some factors influencing your health are out of your control, but most of the decisions affecting your health are yours to make. You and nobody else are the video's director. Sit down in the director's chair, and get ready to take responsibility for your health—and your life.

LESSON 2 *Review*

Reviewing Facts and Vocabulary

1. Define *heredity*. Give an example of how heredity can positively influence your health.
2. In your own words, define *physical environment, social environment,* and *cultural environment.*

Thinking Critically

3. *Synthesizing.* A *treatment* is a written description of events and images in a movie or video. Write a two-page treatment for a video of your health to date. Make sure to cover all important highlights.

4. *Analyzing.* Explain how peer pressure can be a positive or negative influence in your life. Why is it sometimes difficult to resist? Tell why it is important to resist the pressure to do something that is dangerous, unhealthy, or illegal.

Applying Health Skills

5. *In Your School.* Identify the resources in your school and community that contribute to the well-being of its citizens. Make a poster or pamphlet describing these resources.

Lesson 2 Review

Answers to Reviewing Facts and Vocabulary

1. Heredity is all the traits and properties that are passed on biologically from parents. Examples will vary.
2. Answers may include: *physical*—neighborhood, water and air quality, size and condition of housing; *social*—peer group attitudes, family structure, relationships; *cultural*—food, clothing, language.

Answers to Thinking Critically

3. The health video treatment should include an assessment of health factors over which one has no control and factors for which one can make healthy decisions.
4. Answers will vary, but should include the importance of self-esteem in choosing healthy behaviors and supportive friends, and in communicating "no" clearly.

Taking Charge of Your Health

You may be responsible for decisions such as buying your own clothes and for managing your schedule. As you move toward adulthood, you become increasingly responsible for more decisions regarding your health. This lesson will help you learn how to make choices to help you live a long and healthy life.

HEALTH TERMS
risk factors
values
abstinence

HEALTH CONCEPTS
- Accepting responsibility for your own health and for the health of others is a positive step toward wellness.
- Risk factors can be offset by behaviors, including making choices and practicing habits that promote good health.
- Abstinence, the conscious decision to avoid harmful behaviors, can increase your chances of a long, happy, and healthful life.

Taking Responsibility for Your Health

Does the prospect of taking on adult responsibilities excite you? Maybe it frightens you a little. Perhaps you are wondering how you get from the teenager you are now to the fully responsible adult you are rapidly becoming.

A first step toward bridging that gap, at least where your health is concerned, is to increase your awareness of risk factors in your life. **Risk factors** are *actions or behaviors that represent a potential health threat*. A second step is to examine your current behaviors and values and to make any necessary changes.

Risk Factors and Teens

The Centers for Disease Control and Prevention (CDC) in Atlanta annually conducts nationwide surveys of America's youth. In the

LESSON 3   TAKING CHARGE OF YOUR HEALTH   **17**

Taking Charge of Your Health

FOCUS

LESSON OBJECTIVES
After studying this lesson, students should be able to
- explain how accepting responsibility for their own health and the health of others is a step toward wellness.
- discuss how risk factors can be offset by healthful behaviors.
- describe how abstinence from sexual activity before marriage and how avoiding tobacco, alcohol, and other drugs can contribute to health.

MOTIVATOR
Have students list the choices they have made in the last few days that have affected their health. Ask them to identify how each choice affected their physical, mental/emotional, or social well-being.

INTRODUCING THE LESSON
Ask a few volunteers to share their responses from the Motivator activity with the class. As choices are revealed, have students discuss whether or not the behaviors were factored toward health and, if so, whether the choices affected their health positively or negatively.

INTRODUCING HEALTH TERMS
- Ask students what this statement means: "You must act responsibly or deal with the consequences."
- Ask students to complete Vocabulary Activity 1 and Chapter Study Guide 1 in the *Student Workbook.*

Lesson 3 Resources

TEACHER'S CLASSROOM RESOURCES
- **Concept Map** Activity 3
- **Decision-Making** Activity 1
- **Lesson 3 Quiz**
- **Lesson Plan 3**
- **Reteaching** Activity 3

STUDENT WORKBOOK
- **Applying Health Skills 3**

- **Chapter Study Guide 1**
- **Vocabulary** Activity 1

TRANSPARENCIES
- **Transparencies 4, 5, 6**

MULTIMEDIA
- **ABCNews InterActive™ VHS/Videodisc,** *Teenage Sexuality*

TEACH

L2 Class Activity

This activity can be used to help relate behaviors that pose risks to students' own health continuum. Instruct students to draw a horizontal line across a sheet of paper. Ask them to put a dot at each end of the line. At the beginning of the line, have them write a zero to represent time of birth, followed by dots at ten-year increments from birth till death. At the end of the life line, have them put the number of years they wish to live or believe they will live.

Listed below are habits or conditions that may cause a person to die prematurely. Read the list to your students. The years given are hypothetical.

- smoking two packs of cigarettes a day (–8 years)
- drinking three or more ounces of alcohol a week (–10 years)
- overeating (more than 2,500 calories per day) (–5 years)
- eating excess fat in your diet (more than 20 percent of fats such as beef, pork, and cheese) (–5 years)
- eating a lot of sugar (pastry, cookies, candy) (–8 years)
- not exercising at least three times a week (–10 years)
- being overweight or obese (–10 years)
- having a lot of stress in your life (–7 years)
- often handling firearms (–3 years)
- often working with or handling toxic chemicals (–3 years)
- often being depressed or unhappy (–5 years)
- driving or riding in a car without wearing seat belts (–3 years)

(continued on page 19)

◆ With what responsibilities have you been entrusted so far? Which responsibilities do you look forward to?

ACTIVITY *List three rights or privileges you have been given in previous years. Next to each, write the responsibility that goes along with that right or privilege.*

most recent survey, questionnaires on personal risk factors were gathered from over 16,000 students and young adults from 151 schools across the nation. The six categories of personal health risk factors covered in the survey are listed below.

- behaviors that contribute to unintentional and intentional injuries
- tobacco use
- alcohol and other drug use
- sexual behaviors
- unhealthy eating behaviors
- physical inactivity

Throughout this program you will learn how teens, like yourself, responded to questions addressing these risk factors. You will also learn about what you can do to reduce or eliminate the risk factors in your life.

Examining Your Habits and Other Behaviors

One finding of the CDC survey is that 33 percent of the teens interviewed smoked cigarettes. Another 36 percent admitted to having been in a physical fight during the previous year. While these numbers may sound alarming at first, they also mean that 67 and 64 percent of the teens surveyed, respectively, *did not* engage in these high-risk behaviors.

MORE ABOUT . . . . .

HEALTH RISK APPRAISAL. To monitor behaviors which place adolescents most at risk for premature mortality, the Centers for Disease Control and Prevention (CDC) developed the Youth Risk Behavior Surveillance System. The YRBSS measures six categories of behaviors: behaviors that contribute to unintentional and intentional injuries; tobacco use, alcohol and other drug use; sexual behaviors that contribute to unintended pregnancy and sexually transmitted diseases, including HIV infection; dietary behaviors; and physical activity. You may wish to visit the CDC website for more information about the 1998 Youth Risk Behavior Survey that allows you to examine youth risk behavior in the six risk categories; compare national, state and local data; create trend graphs; and learn how state and local agencies are using the data.

Where do you fit in? Are you doing everything you can in the interests of your own health and well-being? At the beginning of each chapter in this program, you will find a Health Barometer Self-Inventory like the one on page 3. Through these inventories, you will be able to gauge your behaviors. You will also learn what areas you need to improve.

Cumulative Risks

Cumulative risks are risks that increase gradually and may add up to a total that is greater than expected. Smoking one cigarette is not likely to result in death. Neither is getting one sunburn. If these habits are repeated over time, however, the negative effects *accumulate*, leading to serious health consequences.

Cumulative risks may also be combinations of risk factors whose impact is more serious than that of any component risk alone. Driving over the posted speed limit is a risk factor that can have deadly results. Another is not wearing seat belts when you drive or ride in a car. When these two behaviors occur at the same time, the potential for harm to yourself and to others is greatly magnified. Cumulative risks can and *do* occur in all areas of health and safety. In this program, you will learn strategies for minimizing risks of all sizes.

Taking Responsibility for the Health of Others

Have you ever skipped a stone across the calm surface of a lake or pond and noticed how it creates ripples? In a way, the "ripple effect" you noticed is a metaphor for your actions and behaviors. How you act and behave affects not only yourself, but others around you. A reckless driver risks his or her own life as well as the lives of others.

Taking responsibility for your health includes showing concern for the health of others. Be aware that this responsibility does not end with the people in your immediate environment. It extends, rather, to the community at large.

As you learned in Lesson 1, one of the measures of a health-literate person is responsible citizenship. As you grow older and more mature, you will be expected to behave as a responsible and productive citizen. This includes having a concern for the welfare of the community and a respect for public property and for the property of others. Remember, your environment is a health influence you can help to control. Your health is dependent on your environment's health. So is the health of those around you.

HEALTH *Online*

Visit **health.glencoe.com** and discover six types of risk behaviors. Learn steps to help you adopt healthy habits. Complete the online questionnaire to find out how you could improve your health behavior.

▼ *There are many precautions you can take each day to prevent injuries and reduce the chances of getting hurt.*
ACTIVITY *Identify cumulative risks that can be associated with driving a car. What other cumulative risks can affect your health?*

SPEED LIMIT 55

20%

Traffic collisions are the leading cause of teen deaths.

Have students list on their papers any of these behaviors that they engage in. Ask them to add up the number of years for these behaviors and subtract the total from the projected age they wrote on their life line. Explain that this new number could be their premature age of death due to unhealthy habits.

Have them put another dot on their life lines to indicate their present age. Tell students to write five goals they would like to achieve and the age by which they plan to achieve these goals. Ask them how many of their goals will be affected due to the lost years. Ask students if there are other unhealthy behaviors not on this list that would affect their life line. Suggest they begin a log to chart daily behavioral changes to improve their life expectancy.

L1 Analyzing

Ask students if they or someone they know has ever been involved in a collision in which serious injury occurred. Ask them to analyze risk factors that caused the injury (driving too fast, driving or riding without wearing a seat belt, driving while stressed, driving under the influence). Ask students to analyze the photo and caption and ask them why they think teens as a group have more traffic collisions than older groups. Ask them what can be done about this.

L2 Discussing

Use *Transparencies 4, 5,* and *6* to further explore causes of death among people ages 16–24, risk factors, and protective factors. ♟

PERSONAL HEALTH

QUALITY OF LIFE. Healthy teens tend to base health choices on immediate effects and risks. Projecting consequences 50 years into the future takes long-range vision. However, the decisions teens make about their health can affect the length of their lives. It can also affect the quality of life in their later years. Have students write an imaginary dialogue between a senior citizen and themselves. The senior faces health problems due to health choices he or she made in his/her teens, twenties, and thirties. Students may select a specific health problem such as an injury from an accident, lung cancer, heart disease, or loneliness. What advice would the older individual give? What health choices would he or she suggest the younger person change?

L2 Class Activity

Ask students to write an example of one situation they were involved in during the past week that involved a risk behavior. Have volunteers share their experiences with the class. Allow students to role-play how they would handle each situation.

LEP Class Activity

Ask students to make a class collage using pictures of risk behaviors they find in magazines. Ask students to share the pictures with the class before pasting them into the collage.

L1 Class Activity

Have each student identify one way that he or she could better accept responsibility for his or her actions.

L1 Discussing

Ask students to give examples of movie or music stars, sports figures, politicians, and other prominent individuals who are values role models and who have demonstrated good character by putting core ethical values such as caring, respect, or responsibility into action in their public lives. Now ask for examples of people who profess publicly that they stand for such values but act according to lesser values in their private lives. Ask how this discrepancy makes the students feel. Ask what steps the students can take to ensure that their behavior both in public and in private is based on core ethical values, or the highest ideals. Emphasize that consistency of core ethical values in personal and public behavior is one way to develop good character.

L2 Decision Making

Introduce students to the six step decision-making process presented in Chapter 2. Then have them complete *Decision-Making Activity 1* in the TCR.

Building Character

Building character is an important part of your overall health. You can build good character the same way you would a strong, sturdy building—with planning, practice, and commitment. How can you get started? By taking a look at your values and how you put them into practice.

Whenever you are faced with a decision, it is important that you consider and act on your highest beliefs and principles, or core ethical values. These universal principles and ideals, such as *caring*, *responsibility*, and *respect* are time-tested concepts that still work, not just old-fashioned ideas stored in books on dusty bookshelves. In fact, these values and principles are "living ideas" that can shape your attitudes, guide your behavior, and help you become the best person you can be.

Character education is the deliberate attempt to help people build good character. Just what does that mean for you? It means learning to recognize what these highest values are and finding ways to measure your behavior against them. It means recognizing that what you do and say affects not only your well-being but also the well-being of your family, your friends, and the people in your community.

You can "build good character" by working with only the finest "materials"—the highest values. By identifying, discussing, and coming to understand what the core ethical values are, you can work to put them into practice in all areas of your life. You can, in fact, construct a life that, like a well-built skyscraper, is solid and upright. You will not sway or topple when other lesser values pull at you. You will stand tall.

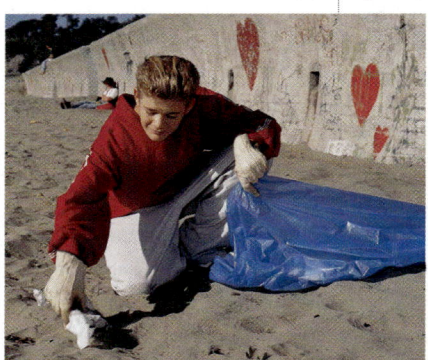

▲ *Values help shape your behavior.*

ACTIVITY *What values might prompt the teen in this photo to donate his time to clean up his environment?*

Protective Factors

You do not have to do this character building alone. Just as you can make a difference in the health of your community, so the people around you—parents, teachers, and others—can help you become a successful adult. The Search Institute, a nonprofit group in Minneapolis, Minnesota, has found that when certain *protective factors* are present in a teen's life, the amount of risk-taking behaviors decreases and the chances for growing up as a healthy, caring, and responsible adult increase. Some of these factors, including having support from the people in your life, are part of your social environment. Other protective factors include positive role models and values.

- **Positive Role Models.** Role models are peers, or others that a young person looks up to. Positive role models inspire you to work harder, to look toward the future, and to choose healthful behaviors. By *being* a positive role model, you can inspire others around you.

- **Positive Values.** Your **values** are *beliefs and standards of conduct that you find important.* Positive values put into practice lead to

---

MORE ABOUT . . . . .

GOOD HEALTH HABITS. *The Surgeon General has determined that cigarette smoking may cause cancer.* Point out to students that this and similar warning labels appear on packages of cigarettes and advertisements relating to cigarettes. Ask: Why, in light of these warnings, do people continue to smoke? Do you think people who smoke are taking a health risk?

Have students discuss risk taking and its relationship to health. Then broaden the discussion to include alcohol, HIV/AIDS, legal and illegal drugs, teen pregnancy, and harmful prenatal substances. Ask students to speculate about how abstinence messages for these concerns might reach teens.

character traits such as honesty, integrity, courage, loyalty, and hard work. The earliest source of values for most people is the family. Your values also reflect to some extent those of society, which is governed by a code of what is right and wrong.

Your values impact your health and the decisions you make. A person who values perseverance, or "stick-to-it-iveness," is more likely to maintain a new exercise program. A person with the courage of his or her own convictions will less likely give in to pressure from peers to participate in high-risk behavior. Instead, he or she will choose abstinence. **Abstinence** is *voluntarily choosing not to do something*.

Abstinence and Your Health

Responsible teens, who value their health, abstain from sexual activity before marriage and from other high-risk behaviors, such as using tobacco, alcohol, and other drugs. As you will learn through this program, abstinence from high risk behaviors is one of the most important health behaviors you can make as a teen.

Although you may not relate your present actions to how they will affect you in the future, it is important to remember that the behaviors you practice now are setting the stage for the health of the adult you will become.

The Three H's

To live a healthful life, you must develop "The Three H's"—good habits of the Head, of the Heart, and of the Hand. Just what does that mean?

➤ **Head** You need to learn to recognize, judge, and understand what is morally right.

➤ **Heart** You need to learn to feel and genuinely care about what is right.

➤ **Hand** You need to learn to act on what you know and feel is right.

Character Check Create a note card or bookmark to remind you to practice "The Three H's."

TEENAGE SEXUALITY (Side 2)

Chapter 10: Deciding Not to Have Sex

Frames 19097-20260

Chapter 15: Fears, Risks and Consequences

Frames 28337-30076

LESSON 3

Review

Reviewing Facts and Vocabulary

1. Explain how protective factors can offset risks.
2. Explain the differences and similarities between attitudes and values with respect to their role in health.

Thinking Critically

3. *Analyzing.* Why might a teen who is informed about health not practice good health habits? Would the teen be considered health literate?
4. *Comparing and Contrasting.* Divide a sheet of paper into two columns. In one column list all the responsibilities you have gained in the past year. In the other column identify the responsibilities that are directly related to your health.

Applying Health Skills

5. *In Your School.* Visit a branch of the public library that maintains back files of newspapers on film. Alternatively, if the classroom computer is hooked by modem to an on-line service that maintains an electronic version of one or more daily newspapers, log on and use the Search command to locate articles having to do with health. Select and read several articles. Conclude by writing a report on the health knowledge you have gained through your research.

ASSESS

EVALUATING THE LESSON

Assign and discuss the Lesson 3 Review; then administer, grade, and discuss the *Lesson 3 Quiz* in the TCR. 🖙

RETEACHING

• Have students create an outline of the lesson using the major heads as Roman numeral headings. Ask students to provide at least two details under each heading.
• Ask students to complete *Reteaching Activity 3* in the TCR. 🖙

ENRICHMENT

Have students write a short essay describing a person who has been a positive role model for them. Ask them to illustrate the positive values this person portrays. Have students include these essays in their health portfolio.

CLOSE

Ask students to state the most important concepts in the chapter. Have students list the behaviors that they would like to change in order to improve their total health.

Lesson 3 Review

Answers to Reviewing Facts and Vocabulary

1. Risk factors are actions or behaviors that represent a potential health threat. One can make choices that reduce or eliminate the risk factors in his or her life. Protective factors include involved parents, teachers, or other positive role models.
2. Values—beliefs and standards of conduct that one considers important. Attitudes— thoughts that determine whether you exercise those values in making healthy decisions.

Answers to Thinking Critically

3. Possible answers: low self-esteem, can't see the connection between present actions and future outcomes, conflict with family values.
4. Answers will vary.

Health Skills Activities

ACTIVITY 1
HEALTH SKILLS

Comprehending Health Concepts, Accessing Health Information

➤ **National Standards**
This activity meets Standards: 1.4; 2.2.

Teach

- Review the definitions of environment, heredity, and culture from Lesson 2. Discuss with students how community health programs can influence an individual's health. Have students explain why communities should offer community health programs to promote health and wellness.

- After students have completed the activity, ask them if the community activities being offered address each side of the health triangle. If not, what side of the health triangle is addressed the least? What are the main populations that are being targeted? Does the community adequately support the health of teens?

ACTIVITY 2
HEALTH SKILLS

Comprehending Health Concepts, Analyzing Influences, Advocacy

➤ **National Standards**
This activity meets these National Health Standards: 1.6; 4.4; 7.6.

Teach

- To ensure privacy, encourage students to complete the Self-Inventory independently, possibly at home prior to the activity. Emphasize that the purpose of the inventory is to identify positive and negative influences that impact behavior.

- If students and groups have difficulty identifying influences, begin the discussion by noting well-known influences, such as friends, the media, parents, etc.

Health Skills Activities

Activity 1: Promoting Health Literacy

So, you've decided to take charge of your health. What health resources are available in your community to help you meet your goal? You are about to find out.

Directions

1. Look through local newspapers for articles, calendars of upcoming health events, and ads for activities that promote health or wellness.
2. List two or three activities or events. Identify the area(s) of health each promotes—physical, social, and/or mental and emotional.
3. Determine the target population for the activity or event (e.g., teens, expectant mothers, senior citizens).
4. Attach a copy of the information about the event to your paper.

Time
30 minutes
Materials
local newspapers, health newsletters, paper

Self-Assessment

✓ Selected two or three community health events and explained how each event selected promotes wellness.
✓ Identified target population for each activity or event.

Activity 2: Awareness, Then Action

Being aware of factors that influence your health is a first step toward becoming the healthiest "you" possible. Find out what influences your health.

Directions

1. Take the Self-Inventory on page 3.
2. Carefully review each of your responses in terms of hereditary and environmental influences that shaped them.
3. With a group, brainstorm ways of decreasing negative influences and maximizing positive ones. You may want to reread Emanuel's story (page 13) for possible ideas.
4. Compile your findings into a group editorial to be submitted to the school newspaper.

Time
one 50-minute period
Materials
pen, paper

Self-Assessment

✓ Demonstrated awareness of how health influences can positively and negatively impact wellness.
✓ Described how knowledge of influences can be used to strengthen health behaviors.

ASSESSMENT SCORING

Using a four-level rubric, the student has achieved a 4 if:

ACTIVITY 1
✔ Student has identified the appropriate areas of health for each community event or activity.
✔ Student has adequately explained how each event or activity promotes wellness.
✔ Student has correctly identified target population for each community event or activity.
✔ The final paper is clear and organized.

ACTIVITY 2
✔ Appropriate positive and negative influences are identified.
✔ The editorial is organized and well-written with appropriate language.
✔ The editorial is grammatically correct and contains no misspellings.
✔ Student describes how knowledge of influences can be used to strengthen health behaviors.

CNN HEALTH NEWS VIDEO

Doctors Learn Diversity

How well do you communicate with your doctor? Do you speak easily and honestly about your health? This communication link is an important part of your health. But communication is never a one-way street. Doctors need to communicate effectively with all of their patients. That can be challenging when dealing with very diverse communities. An unusual program at the Yale School of Medicine helps train doctors to talk to people from different backgrounds. The program also helps medical students learn ways to accommodate a patient's cultural or ethnic background.

Play the Video

Think About It

▶ What is the primary goal of the cultural diversity seminars held at Yale? What strategies do teachers use to achieve these goals?

▶ Give three examples of ways that a patient's cultural background can affect communication with a doctor.

▶ Although most students support the program, some feel that doctors naturally learn the skills taught in this seminar. Do you agree or disagree with this opinion? Why?

CNN HEALTH NEWS **23**

CNN HEALTH NEWS

Doctors Learn Diversity
Video Segment 1 (Time – 2:02)

Objectives. After viewing the video, students should be able to demonstrate how doctors and patients use effective communication to promote health.

Motivator. Write the term *diversity* on the chalkboard. Have students review its definition (variety). Ask "What do we mean when we say a community is *diverse*?" Use Video Segment 1: "Doctors Learn Diversity," to introduce students to an innovative program designed to train doctors to work effectively with people from many backgrounds.

Teach
- Point out that not all communities are diverse—some are homogenous. This means that most people who live there have similar backgrounds. Discuss how the diversity training shown in the video could help all doctors, even those who work in homogenous communities.
- Have students act out a doctor-patient conversation in three ways, each time choosing a different cultural background for the patient, showing how the doctor can communicate effectively with each patient. Help students to select appropriate conversation topics. Consider these possibilities: a doctor asks about a patient's diet; a mother has questions about when to vaccinate her child; a patient wants to know more about a medication's side effects.

Investigate. Encourage students to discuss the concept of diversity training with doctors in their community. Suggest that they prepare a list of 3-5 questions to ask, such as:
- Did you receive any diversity training?
- Do you think a diversity training program is important?
- Has treating a diverse community been a challenge for you? If so, how?

Close. Have students describe the diversity training program to someone who has not seen the video. Make sure student descriptions include key points from the video, including some ways diversity training can improve communication between doctors and patients.

MORE ABOUT . . . . .

RELIABLE SOURCES. The doctor-patient encounter groups depicted in this video began at the Yale School of Medicine. The program developed as a joint effort among the university's Office of Multicultural Affairs, the Office of Education and the Urban Health Program.

Liza Cariaga-Lo, director of the Office of Multicultural Affairs, helped design the seminars. "As medical students become immersed in the courses needed to prepare them for a medical career, it's important that they also become culturally competent," said Cariaga-Lo. "This means being attuned to and understanding the needs of diverse patients, which leads to better diagnosis and more successful doctor-patient relationships."

CHECKING COMPREHENSION

- Assign and discuss the chapter review.
- Use the MindJogger Videoquiz to review the chapter. ●

CHAPTER 1 REVIEW ANSWERS

Using Health Terms

1. health education
2. wellness
3. health literacy
4. health
5. prevention
6. lifestyle factors
7. peers
8. heredity
9. culture
10. environment
11. abstinence
12. risk factors
13. values

Recalling the Facts

1. One measure of physical health is your body's ability to cope with the stresses of normal daily life. Another is having the strength and energy to pursue physical, mental/emotional, and social challenges and changes.
2. Two of the following: enjoys learning, sees mistakes as opportunities to learn and grow, accepts responsibility for his/her actions, stands up for beliefs and values, is in touch with his/her emotions and expresses them in appropriate ways, avoids dwelling on negative thoughts.
3. It reflects a balance of the three elements of total health.
4. The Health Continuum is the full range of levels of total health.
5. Health education is important because it allows people to make decisions that will determine how well and/or how long they will live.

Using Health Terms

On a separate sheet of paper, write the term that best matches each definition below.

LESSON 1

1. The providing of accurate health information in such a way as to influence people to change attitudes so that they take positive action about their health.
2. An overall state of well-being, or total health.
3. An individual's capacity to obtain, interpret, and understand basic health information and services and use such information and services in ways that promote his or her health and wellness.
4. The combination of your physical, mental/emotional, and social well-being.
5. Practicing healthy habits to keep a person well and free from disease and other ailments.
6. Personal behaviors and habits related to the way a person lives that help determine his or her level of health.

LESSON 2

7. People the same age who share a similar range of interests.
8. All the traits and properties that are passed along biologically from parent to child.
9. The collective beliefs, customs, and behaviors of a group.
10. The sum total of your surroundings—your family, where you grew up, where you live now, and all of your experiences.

LESSON 3

11. The conscious decision to avoid harmful behaviors, including sexual activity during the teen years and the use of tobacco, alcohol, and other drugs.
12. Actions or behaviors that represent a potential health threat.
13. Beliefs and standards of conduct that you find important.

Recalling the Facts

Using complete sentences, answer the following questions.

LESSON 1

1. What are two measures of physical health?
2. Name two characteristics of a person who is mentally healthy.
3. Why is a balanced triangle a good symbol of someone's total health?
4. What is the Health Continuum?
5. Why is health education important?

LESSON 2

6. Name two ways you are affected by your physical environment.

7. How can one's behavior have a negative influence on one's health?
8. What can you do to resist pressure from peers?

LESSON 3

9. What are two steps that permit a person to take greater responsibility for his or her health?
10. Describe how cumulative risks affect a person's health.
11. Give an example of how a person can assume responsibility for the health of his or her community.
12. Explain why choosing abstinence is the best health decision a teen can make.

---

6. Living in a clean, safe environment makes you more likely to enjoy good physical and mental health. Living in an area of high crime might make you feel stressed and threatened and less likely to get out and exercise. Pollutants in the air or water can increase your chances of having physical ailments. A home in disrepair can increase your chances of having an accident. Lack of access to medical care increases the risk of illness.
7. You can harm your health by making unhealthy choices in the areas of sexual activity; use of alcohol, tobacco, or drugs; or the use of violence.
8. Possible answers: state your beliefs clearly, care enough about your health to say no, arm yourself with knowledge to educate them on why

Thinking Critically

LESSON 1

1. ***Synthesizing.*** Amy is an honors student, is head of the debate team, and plays first violin in the school orchestra. She also has lots of friends and feels the need to be perfect at everything. In addition, Amy lives almost entirely on fast-food burgers and is 25 pounds overweight. Draw her health triangle.

2. ***Analyzing.*** Consider the seven lifestyle factors. Decide whether each one applies to you always, sometimes, or never.

LESSON 2

3. ***Comparing and Contrasting.*** Divide a sheet of paper into two columns. In one column, list negative hereditary and environmental influences on your health. In the other, list positive influences.

LESSON 3

4. ***Analyzing.*** "I am the master of my fate; I am the captain of my soul." In what way could this quote be applied to decisions about engaging in high-risk behavior?

Making the Connection

1. ***Social Studies.*** In the 1300s, bubonic plague was a serious risk factor to health in Europe. Research this health problem, and compare it to one of the following current health problems: HIV/AIDS, oil spills, and nuclear power by-products. Explain in what ways each period of history has its own health problems.

2. ***Language Arts.*** Write a script for a video titled "A Day in the Life." The video should depict a day in the life of a typical American teen in your community. It should probe the various external risk factors facing this teen, as well as ways in which he or she can respond through behaviors, decisions, and choices.

BEYOND THE CLASSROOM

PARENTAL INVOLVEMENT Ask a parent, guardian, or other adult to tell you about health risks that faced him or her as a teen. Find out how he or she dealt with these risks. What role did values play in the person's success at overcoming these risks? What other factors contributed to overcoming or dealing with the risks?

COMMUNITY INVOLVEMENT Work with classmates to create a survey on health habits and risks. Each class member can then conduct the survey with at least five volunteers in your community or neighborhood. Ask respondents to describe what good health means to them.

SCHOOL-TO-CAREER

Exploring Careers. Health specialists, who work for universities and government agencies such as the Centers for Disease Control and Prevention, specialize in getting at the root of diseases and other issues that threaten the health of the general population. Preparation includes a master's degree in public health.

If you would like to learn more about a future in this exciting health field, contact the American Medical Association, 515 North State St., Chicago, IL 60610, or the American Public Health Association, 800 I St. N.W., Washington, DC 20001-3710.

Thinking Critically

1. Social health is in balance; physical and mental/emotional health are not.
2.–4. Answers will vary.

Making the Connection

1.–2. Answers will vary.

Evaluate

- Use the reproducible *Chapter 1 Test* in the TCR or construct your own using the Testmaker software. 📁 💾
- Use *Performance Assessment Activity 1* in the TCR. 📁

Enrichment

- Ask students to write a brief essay on the changes in health education over the last century, including the transition from an emphasis on disease prevention to the concept of promoting total health. Have them explain why the concept has changed from prevention to total health and include the medical pioneers that have made an impact on disease prevention influencing this change.
- Ask students to complete *Cross-Curriculum Activity 1* in the TCR. 📁

Beyond the Classroom

Keep students involved in the community, and encourage parent participation by assigning the activities on this page for students to work on outside of class.

it's a bad choice, choose friends who care about their health and yours.

9. One step is to increase the awareness of risk factors in his or her life. A second step is to examine current behaviors and values and to make any necessary changes.

10. Cumulative risks increase gradually and may add up to a total that is greater than expected. They may also be combinations of risk factors whose cumulative effect is more serious than that of any component alone.

11. Answers will vary.

12. Abstinence from sexual activity before marriage and from the use of tobacco, alcohol, and other drugs safeguards a teen's health and eliminates the possible results of high-risk behavior.

Making Healthful Choices

	FEATURES	CLASSROOM RESOURCES

ACTIVITIES

- Cross-Curriculum Activity 2
- Health Lab 2
- Health Skills Activities 2
- Parent Letter and Activities 2

ASSESSMENT

- Chapter 2 Test
- Performance Assessment Activity 2
- Testmaker Software

STUDENT ACTIVITIES WORKBOOK

- Applying Health Skills 4, 5
- Study Guide 2
- Vocabulary Activity 2

STUDENT DIVERSITY STRATEGIES

- Audiocassette Program (English)
- Audiocassette Program (Spanish)
- Spanish Parent Letter and Activities 2
- Spanish Summaries, Quizzes, and Activities

MULTIMEDIA COMPONENTS

- English Audiocassette Program
- Spanish Audiocassette Program
- MindJogger Videodisc and VHS program
- ABCNews InterActive™ VHS/Videodisc Series

MODULES

- *Abstinence,* Student Edition
- *Abstinence,* Teacher's Annotated Edition
- *Education in Sexuality,* Student Edition
- *Education in Sexuality,* Teacher's Annotated Edition

National Health Education Standards

One of the main goals of the National Health Education Standards is to move students toward "health literacy." Health literacy is the capacity of individuals to obtain, interpret, and understand basic health information and services and the competence to use such information and services in ways which promote health. The health standards were developed by applying the characteristics of a well-educated, literate person within the context of health. The health literate person is:

- a critical thinker and problem solver
- a self-directed learner
- a responsible, productive citizen
- an effective communicator

Listed below are the Health Education Standards Performance Indicators addressed in each lesson of this chapter.

Lesson	Health Standards Performance Indicators
1	2.1, 4.2, 5.1, 5.6
2	3.4, 6.1, 6.3

ONLINE RESOURCES

For a fresh approach to health topics and an in-depth look at health issues, use these online resources found under Teacher Resources at **health.glencoe.com**.

- **BLOCK SCHEDULE LESSON PLANS** Reinforce health concepts with outside readings selected especially for students. Each reading is accompanied by a lesson plan and activities to enhance
  - Reading Skills
  - Cross Curriculum
  - Media Literacy

- **TECHNOLOGY PROJECTS** Instructions and suggestions on how to use computer, Internet, and software with health lessons.

- **HEALTH UPDATES** Timely topics in health news, including late-breaking medical advances and updates on teen risk behaviors.

Out of Time?

If time does not permit teaching this chapter, you may use these features: Update on page 32; Making Responsible Decisions on page 36; and Building Health Skills on page 38.

BLOCK SCHEDULING

Block scheduling provides extended time for hands-on projects and activities. Use the following activities to engage students, provide further depth, and vary your instructional techniques:

- Health Lab (45 minutes) **pg. 30**
- Update (20–30 minutes) **pg. 32**
- Health Skills Activity (60–90 minutes) **pg. 40**

Making Healthful Choices

CHAPTER OVERVIEW

Chapter 2 presents the health skills that enable students to assume responsibility for their health. Decision-making and goal-setting skills are key to exercising power over one's life.

LESSON 1 Health skills enable you to make better, more informed health choices. Such skills involve communicating effectively, practicing refusal techniques, building self-esteem, managing stress, and accessing reliable information and help. Developing health skills will help you take responsibility for your health and wellness.

LESSON 2 Major decisions in one's life can influence how healthy, happy, and productive a person may be for the rest of his or her life. That is why practicing decision-making skills is essential. A decision-making model can help you develop skills to work through conflicts, recognize health risks and behaviors, consider the consequences of your choices, and make knowledgeable decisions. Setting goals is another skill that empowers you. It is one way to shape your life in a positive direction. An action plan can help you identify and achieve your goals.

CHAPTER 2

Making Healthful Choices

HEALTH Online

GOAL SETTING

Check out Career Corner to discover whether your goals for the future might include a career in sports medicine, health care services, or medical research. Browse through a variety of health careers at **health.glencoe.com**.

Hands-On Health

TEACHING STRATEGY

Sharing Goals Ask students to identify some of their own short- and long-term goals as they catch and return the "question-and-answer ball." See Classroom Management Idea, "Beach Ball," in the *Hands-On Health: Creative Teaching Strategies* booklet. 🔖

Time Needed
10 minutes

Supplies
• beach ball or other soft ball

> ❝ *You have to concentrate on the good things. Life presents as many opportunities for happiness as it does for tragedy.* ❞
>
> —RUDY GIULIANI
> MAYOR OF NEW YORK CITY, 2001

Quick Write Write down one important personal goal to improve your health and list the steps you will take to achieve it.

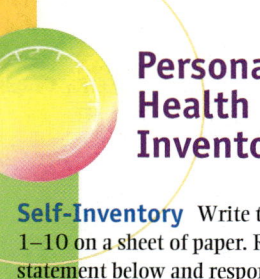

Personal Health Inventory

Self-Inventory Write the numbers 1–10 on a sheet of paper. Read each statement below and respond by writing *yes*, *no*, or *sometimes* for each item. Write a *yes* only for items that you practice regularly. Save your responses.

1 I am able to communicate my thoughts and feelings to others.

2 I am aware of sources of stress in my life and have developed ways of reducing those stresses.

3 I think carefully about media messages before making decisions based on those messages.

4 I can list at least three adults I feel comfortable turning to for help with my problems.

5 I make important life decisions carefully.

6 When faced with a difficult choice, I list my options before going ahead and deciding.

7 Before making a decision, I try to anticipate the short- and long-term consequences.

8 I have thought about the life goals I hope to achieve.

9 I am aware of the short-term goals I will need to reach on the road to achieving my life goals.

10 I have established a time table for reaching my life goals.

Follow-up After completing the chapter, retake this self-inventory. Pick two items that you need to work on and set a goal to improve your health behaviors.

CHAPTER 2   MAKING HEALTHFUL CHOICES   **27**

INTRODUCING THE CHAPTER

Personal Health Inventory

Remind students that the Self-Inventory is a private tool for checking their own current health status. The inventory will be most helpful if they respond to each statement honestly.

After students have recorded their responses, ask them to label their papers "Health Skills" and write today's date. Explain that they will refer back to this page in the Follow-up activity after completing the chapter.

- Have students list the choices they have made over the last few days that have affected their health. Ask them to identify each choice as contributing to their physical, mental/emotional, or social well-being. Ask a few volunteers to share their lists with the class.
- Ask students to read the quotation on this page. Ask for volunteers who can tell the class who Rudi Giuliani is. Explain that he guided New Yorkers and the nation through tragedy with the goal of a strong recovery. Point out how his statement demonstrates the importance of concentrating on the positive, especially in choices regarding health. Have volunteers share experiences in making decisions to reach their own health goals. Tell students they will learn more about making decisions—and about developing other health skills—as they study Chapter 2.
- Distribute Parent Letter 2 in the *Parent Letters and Activities* booklet and have students take it home to their parents or guardians. ✍

TECHNOLOGY OPTIONS

  You may wish to use *Making Responsible Decisions* with this chapter. For your convenience, use the separate *ABCNews InterActive™ Bar Code Correlation* that accompanies the *Glencoe Health* program. 🔴

MINDJOGGER
VIDEOQUIZ

To preview or review chapter content, you may wish to use the *MindJogger Videoquiz* that accompanies Chapter 2. 🔴

Building Health Skills

LESSON OBJECTIVES

After studying this lesson, students should be able to

- explain how health skills contribute to total health.
- describe how effective communication skills and the use of refusal skills can benefit one's health.
- evaluate media messages to make informed, healthful choices.
- access reliable sources of health information.

MOTIVATOR

Write the following on the chalkboard for students to work on while attendance is being taken: *Write a one- or two-line definition of self-esteem.* Ask a few volunteers to share their definitions with the class.

INTRODUCING THE LESSON

Refer to the Motivator. Have students explain how self-esteem can influence behavior. Ask them to list factors that influence self-esteem. Let volunteers share their lists with the class. Explain that building self-esteem is one of the health skills that is central to achieving total health.

INTRODUCING HEALTH TERMS

- Have students discuss how effective communication skills, use of refusal skills, high self-esteem, and stress management promote wellness.
- Ask students to complete Vocabulary Activity 2 and Chapter Study Guide 2 in the *Student Workbook.* ☞

Building Health Skills

Taking responsibility for your health begins with a commitment to take charge of your actions and behaviors in a way that reduces risks and promotes wellness. Once you have agreed to make this commitment, how do you begin making informed decisions? The answer to this question is "by learning and practicing *health skills.*"

HEALTH TERMS

health skills
communication
refusal skills
self-esteem
stress

HEALTH CONCEPTS

- Developing good communication and building self-esteem are health skills central to achieving total health and wellness.
- Learning to evaluate messages from the various media can help you make informed, healthful choices.
- Learning to obtain and evaluate information is an important skill in our fast-paced information age.

What Are Health Skills?

Also known as life skills, **health skills** are *specific tools and strategies that lead to better and more informed health choices.* Health skills are for use not just now, during your teen years, but throughout your entire life. As with other skills you may have mastered, developing health skills takes time and practice. The immediate and long-term benefits to your physical, social, and mental/emotional health, however, make the effort worthwhile.

Social Health Skills

One of the traits of being a health literate person is being an effective communicator. Communicating effectively means being able

---

Lesson 1 Resources

TEACHER'S CLASSROOM RESOURCES

☞ **Concept Map** Activity 4
☞ **Cooperative Learning** Activity 2
☞ **Enrichment** Activity 2
☞ **Health Lab** 2
☞ **Lesson 4 Quiz**
☞ **Lesson Plan** 4

☞ **Parent Letter and Activities** 2
☞ **Reteaching** Activity 4

STUDENT WORKBOOK

☞ **Applying Health Skills** 4
☞ **Chapter Study Guide** 2
☞ **Vocabulary** Activity 2

TRANSPARENCIES

🖐 **Transparencies 35, 36**

to express your knowledge, beliefs, and ideas in many different ways and forms. It also includes the ability to say no to behaviors that threaten your health and well-being. Learning and applying these two skills—communicating and saying no—are essential to good social health.

Communication Skills

You may not think of communicating as a skill. You may be saying to yourself, "I already *know* how to communicate"—but do you? If, in a heated moment, you and a friend shout at each other so loudly that neither of you hears the other, are you communicating? Obviously, there is more to communication than just words. In its deeper sense, **communication** is *a process through which you send messages to and receive messages from others.* Effective communication involves not only making yourself heard but also being a good listener.

The skill of communicating, which is explored more fully in Chapter 11, includes the following:

- **Clearly say what you mean.**
- **Pay attention to *how* you say something.**
- **Be a good listener.**
- **Be aware of your facial expressions and gestures.**

Refusal Skills

Spending time with people who share the same likes and interests, especially during the teen years, is important to your social development. It is equally important to know when another person's needs and desires conflict with your own. Picture a situation where you are asked to do something that compromises your values or that you know or believe is wrong. This may be a high-risk behavior, such as not wearing seat belts, smoking cigarettes, or using alcohol or other drugs.

In such circumstances, a knowledge of refusal skills is vital. **Refusal skills** are *techniques that can help you refuse when you are urged to take part in unsafe or unhealthful behaviors.* This strategy includes the following:

1. **Say no.** Do this calmly at first. Use an expression such as "Sorry, I don't want to" or "I'd rather not."
2. **Explain why you are refusing.** State your feelings. Tell the other person that the suggested activity or behavior goes against your values or beliefs.

▼ *Good communication requires good listening skills.* ACTIVITY *Name three features of a good listener.*

LESSON 1   BUILDING HEALTH SKILLS   **29**

TEACH

◨ Discussing

On the chalkboard, write the following sentence: *Did Maya finally call Noah?* Ask students to take turns reading the sentence, with each student emphasizing a different word. Discuss which of the readings sounded like straightforward questions and which sounded angry or emotional. Encourage students to recognize how tone and inflection can relay emotions.

◨ Critical Thinking

Ask students to remember a time when they may have felt that someone—perhaps a parent, teacher, or a friend—was not listening to them. Have students recall why they believed that the other person was not listening. Suggest students determine how body language may have indicated to them that listening was not taking place.

◨ Discussing

Have students think about someone they know who was unable to communicate effectively because he or she was too shy. Ask: How can you, as a friend, help someone deal with shyness? What measures can a shy person take to improve his or her ability to start conversations?

◪ Synthesizing

Encourage students to make sure that their facial expressions match the words they say. To illustrate, have them demonstrate how an angry face can make even the nicest verbal message seem negative, while a smile can make a serious message seem like a joke. Stress the need to make eye contact during the most important parts of a message.

COOPERATIVE ⟩ LEARNING

COMMUNICATION AND REFUSAL SKILLS. Divide students into groups of three or four to role-play communication and refusal skills. Tell groups to assign one member to come up with a scenario. For example, Nigel wants Sheila to distract a sales clerk while he shoplifts a watch from the counter. The member who thinks of the scenario is to choose two group members to role-play it, with the fourth evaluating the communication and refusal skills. (In a group of three, one member can both create the scenario and evaluate the role-play.)

Tell groups to change roles and repeat the process until every member has performed every task. You may wish to have each group choose one situation to role-play for the class.

health lab

COMMUNICATION STYLES

Time Needed: about 45 minutes

Understanding Objectives:
Students will recognize the importance of intonation in oral communication.

Focus on the Health Lab:
Ask students: When someone is talking to you, how do you receive that person's message? Besides the words the person uses, what do you listen for? What do you look for as the person speaks?

Observation and Analysis:
Let students prepare their own sentences and readings and then work in groups to have others evaluate their messages. If tape recorders are not available, students can speak directly to other group members.

In Conclusion Answers:
1.–2. Answers will vary. **3.** Students may mention tone of voice, gestures, and facial expressions.

Further Investigation:
Suggest that pairs of students plan and present short skits in which teens use effective intonation, as well as tone of voice and body language, to say no to a high-risk behavior.

L1 Discussing

Ask students: How do we form our self-concept? (We judge ourselves based on how we are treated by others; this helps us form a picture of ourselves.) Discuss how and what other people say and do to you affects how you view yourself.

L1 Analyzing

Have students identify and discuss persons whose opinions they value. Ask why these people are significant to them and how often they ask these people for feedback.

---

health lab

COMMUNICATION STYLES

When you communicate, is it through words only? What other methods might you use to express yourself? How do others interpret what you say? In this activity, you will find out.

3. **Suggest alternatives to the proposed activity.** Give a list of safe, healthful activities. Speak calmly.

4. **Back up your words using body language.** Make it clear that you don't intend to back down from your position. Look directly into the other person's eyes.

5. **Leave if necessary.** If the other person continues to put pressure on you, or simply won't take no for an answer, just walk away. Carry money in case you have to call for a ride or take a taxi.

Mental and Emotional Health Skills

Another trait of a health-literate person is being a responsible, productive citizen. This means, in part, respecting yourself and others. Doing this is sometimes easier said than done, especially during the teen years. Two health skills, building **self-esteem** and managing **stress**, can help restore perspective and give you the emotional boost you need during these years.

hot link

self-esteem For more information on self-esteem and its role in good mental health, see Chapter 8, page 188.

stress For more information on stress and strategies for managing stress, see Chapter 9, page 214.

Building Self-Esteem

Think of five words that describe your personality and characteristics. How many of these words paint a positive picture? How many are based on how others see you? How many are based on how you see yourself? Your answers provide a window on your level of self-esteem. **Self-esteem** is *the confidence and worth that you feel about*

COOPERATIVE) LEARNING

BUILDING SELF-ESTEEM. Divide the class into pairs. Ask one student in each pair to interview the other for two minutes. When the time is up, have students reverse roles. Ask each interviewer to list as many positive attributes as possible about the person he or she interviewed. Ask volunteers to read aloud their lists. After each list is read, ask the person whom the report was about to share how he or she felt during the reading.

Conclude by posing the following questions for discussion: Why are we often uncomfortable when someone says nice things about us? How is self-concept related to what people say about us?

What you will need
- Paper and pencil
- Portable audio tape recorder

What you will do
1. Write down a question of five to ten words. Make it the sort heard in everyday conversation. Examples might include "Would you please hand me that pencil?" or "Why don't you have a seat?"
2. Practice reading the sentence aloud. Each time you read it, emphasize or stress a different word. For example: "Why don't you have a *seat?*" and "Why don't *you* have a seat?" Make a recording of yourself saying the sentence five different ways.
3. Find several volunteers to take part in your experiment. Ask each to number a sheet of paper from 1 to 5. Play back a recording of your reading of the sentence the first way, then stop the tape player.
4. Instruct the respondents to write a feeling or attitude they hear in the voice of the speaker. Proceed in a similar fashion for each of the remaining versions of the sentence.

In conclusion
1. How many different emotions did respondents detect in the readings of the sentence? Did the respondents agree in their reactions?
2. Which readings were perceived as sounding negative? Which were seen as positive?
3. What other nonverbal clues can you think of that influence the act of communicating?

---

yourself. Self-esteem affects everything you do, think, feel, and are. A strategy for building or improving self-esteem includes:

- **Examining the messages you send yourself.** Are you one of your own worst critics? If so, stop sending yourself negative messages. If you need to improve in a given area, don't put yourself down. Instead, find a positive way to state your goals.
- **Focusing on the things you do well.** Think about past successes you've had. This will gradually help you build more opportunities for success and expand the range of things you are good at doing.

Stress Management Skills

Your ride to school is late, making *you* late. In class, you realize your history project is due in two days. Situations like these are sources of **stress**, *the body's and mind's reactions to everyday demands.* Stress is an unavoidable part of life. However, when stress threatens to become overwhelming, there *are* solutions. These include:

- **Rechanneling your energy.** Redirect all the pent-up negative energy you are feeling into something positive. Work out your frustrations through physical activity.
- **Relaxing.** Take it easy after a hard day. Try listening to soothing music or taking a warm bath.
- **Laughing.** When things get tough, the tough get laughing. Tune in to your favorite TV sitcom, open a favorite joke book, or get together with friends with whom you have a good time.

LESSON 1 BUILDING HEALTH SKILLS **31**

COOPERATIVE LEARNING

HEALTH RESOURCES. Have students work in groups of three or four to research local agencies and organizations that provide health support and services. Each member may research services and support for each element of health: physical, mental/emotional, and social. Suggest that students search the Web or use resources in the telephone directory, under government agencies, and in the Yellow Pages. Have them choose ten groups or agencies in their respective categories and make a HEALTH RESOURCES chart, with group members completing the section of the chart for their own categories. Bring the groups together. Ask volunteers to propose health problems a teen or community member might face. Challenge other students to find an agency to which they might refer such an individual.

LEP Discussing

Assign students to select books or magazines about teens who have a high level of self-esteem. Also, have them choose a hero or star who exhibits positive signs of self-esteem. Discuss these individuals with the class, asking students to give examples that show that these individuals feel comfortable with themselves, feel positive about other people, and are able to meet the demands of life.

L2 Class Activity

Have students write down three situations or events that might cause "butterflies" (public speaking, preparing for a big test or game, dating, etc.). Let them share their responses. Ask what symptoms often accompany these experiences (dry throat, trembling, feeling flushed, feeling nauseated, etc.). Explain that these are all symptoms of stress and that people can learn to manage stress in their lives.

L1 Analyzing

Let students think of the most stressful day they can remember. Have them list their activities that day, from the time they awoke to the time they went to bed. Instruct them to label any activity that was crucial (such as getting to school on time) with the letter *A*, any activity that was not crucial (such as watching TV) with a *C*, and any activity that was in between (such as helping a friend study for a test) with a *B*. Have students make a chart showing how much time was spent in each category. Ask: Which category of events caused the most stress? How much time was spent in that area? Could better time management have lessened the stress? Discuss other conclusions they could draw from analyzing their stressful days.

L2 Health Lab

Distribute *Health Lab 2* and have students discover how laughter affects stress levels.

update
▶*Looking at Technology*

Accessing Reliable Health Information On-Line

Encourage volunteers to share their own experiences using the Internet. Ask: What do you look for—or find—when you surf the Net? How have you used the Net to find answers to specific questions or to research specific topics? Have you ever found conflicting information from different sources, or found "information" you didn't trust? After students have read the feature, let them summarize and discuss it. Then suggest that they work in groups to identify and list reliable on-line sources of health information.

🔲 Cooperative Learning

Distribute *Cooperative Learning Activity 2* in the TCR and have students analyze the reliability of tabloid news.

update
▶*Looking at Technology*

Accessing Reliable Health Information On-Line

You are in the midst of a digital revolution that is making health information available to anyone with a modem and a connection to the Internet. Just about any health topic, from sunburn to stroke, is a mouse click away.

Is all the information on the World Wide Web equally reliable? According to Dr. George Lundberg, editor of the *Journal of the American Medical Association*, the answer is a resounding *no*. Some information, he warns, is posted on the Internet by unreputable sources that at best have no medical value and at worst can be dangerous to your health.

Mindful of this problem, the U. S. government has added its own home page to the Net. Titled "Healthfinder," the page provides links to hundreds of health-related sites that have been screened for accuracy. The Healthfinder site also enables users to reach state health departments, support organizations, and non-profit health groups.

Total Health Skills

Another trait of a health-literate person is being a self-directed learner—having the ability to gather and use reliable health information. Mastering this skill, and seeking help when you have a problem, can benefit your total health and well-being. Developing an awareness of illness symptoms and staying up-to-date on medical research are habits that can actually help prolong your life.

Accessing Reliable Information

You live in an information age. With the wealth of messages you receive—some are conflicting—how can you tell what to believe and what to disregard? The following strategies can help:

- **Consider the source.** Pay attention to the reputation of a given media source. Is the source widely considered a "popularizer" of fad information or a legitimate provider of documented facts?

- **Consider the "angle."** Are advertisements for products that are "guaranteed to make you look and feel better" as reliable as newspaper reports on health advances? Of course not. When evaluating a media source, ask yourself, "Are the publishers of this information trying to sell me something? Do they have my best interests in mind?" When advisable, proceed with caution.

HEALTH LITERACY

MEDICAL SELF-CARE. The growing medical self-care movement encourages people to take an active role in disease prevention and treatment. With access to health care providers, medical books, journals, and information from computer on-line services, many people who practice medical self-care also stock their homes with the kits necessary to perform diagnostic laboratory tests. Tests that may be performed at home include the detection of pregnancy, presence of blood in stool samples, and measurement of blood glucose and cholesterol. When used as directed, home tests approved by the FDA are accurate and reliable.

Getting Help

Meeting life's demands means facing problems when they arise. When the problems are big, this means being able to reach out and ask for help. When you need help with a problem:

- **Think of people in your life who can offer assistance.** You might turn to a parent, a teacher, a counselor, or a religious leader. Keep a list of such names handy for times when you may need it.

- **Learn about resources in your community.** Many communities offer resources and outreach services for people in need. Many of these can be located in the Yellow Pages of your local phone directory. A health professional in your school may be able to recommend others.

- **Learn about print and electronic resources.** Sometimes, help is only a mouse click away. Yet, caution is needed, especially when using the Internet in search of help. A good starting point for reliable information is Glencoe's Health Web site, which may be found at: **health.glencoe.com**.

keeping Fit

Stay Safe in Cyberspace

Beware! There are many ways that information about you can be stored, shared, or sold on the Internet:

➤ Avoid giving out personal information such as your name, gender, age, interests, phone number, street address, e-mail address, family credit card numbers, or social security number to anyone.

➤ Don't include personal information in a personal home page.

➤ Stay away from discussion logs, which may keep records of your conversations or opinions for years afterward.

LESSON 1 *Review*

Reviewing Facts and Vocabulary

1. Write a paragraph that includes the terms *communication* and *stress*. The first time each of these terms is mentioned, define it in your own words.

2. Divide a sheet of paper into two columns. Label one column *Mental and Emotional Health* and one *Social Health*. Write in the appropriate column the name of a health skill covered in the lesson. Then identify Total Health skills.

Thinking Critically

3. *Analyzing.* Think about your hobbies, pastimes, and other activities you enjoy doing. Describe specific ways in which the activities you named might be used as emotional outlets when you experience stress.

4. *Synthesizing.* Aldo, a freshman, has just become a member of his school's track team. Today in the locker room just before practice, two of the older members of the team offered Aldo a pill that they said would improve his time in the 100-meter dash. Aldo has heard bad things about such pills and does not want to take chances with his health. Explain in detail the steps Aldo can take to refuse the offer.

Applying Health Skills

5. *In Your Home and School.* In your private Health Journal, make a list of adults at home and at school that you could approach if you had a problem. Next to each name, write special qualities that make the person a good source of help (e.g., is a good listener, has 25 years of experience helping teens with troubles).

Stay Safe in Cyberspace

keeping Fit

Ask students if they know what a "cookie" is *(a short text file that Web sites may drop into your hard drive so that you can be recognized when you send information back)*. Discuss how sharing personal information while using the Internet can interrupt privacy or even become dangerous.

ASSESS

EVALUATING THE LESSON

Assign and discuss the Lesson 1 Review; then administer, grade, and discuss the *Lesson 4 Quiz* in the TCR.

RETEACHING

- Have students analyze this statement: *The prime motivation behind all behavior is the maintenance or protection of one's self-esteem.* Have students name common behaviors, negative and positive, that affect our self-esteem. Ask them to list ways to improve self-esteem.

- Ask students to complete *Reteaching Activity 4* in the TCR.

- Use *Transparencies 35* and *36* to review self-esteem and stress management skills.

ENRICHMENT

- Help students evaluate media messages and have them complete *Enrichment Activity 2*, "What You See Is Not All You Get," in the TCR.

CLOSE

Ask students to share ways they will use the health skills presented in the lesson.

Lesson 1 Review

Answers to Reviewing Facts and Vocabulary

1. Communication is the process through which you send messages to and receive messages from others. Stress is the reaction of the body and mind to everyday demands.

2. Possible answers: communication skills, refusal skills, building self-esteem, managing stress. Total health skills include accessing reliable information and obtaining help.

Answers to Thinking Critically

3. Answers will vary.

4. He can say no, then explain that the behavior goes against his beliefs and/or values. He can suggest other activities. He can make it clear that he means what he says. He can leave.

Making Decisions and Setting Goals

LESSON **2**

FOCUS

LESSON OBJECTIVES

After studying this lesson, students should be able to

- identify the steps in the decision-making process.
- explain why it is important to practice decision making.
- develop and implement an action plan for setting a goal.

MOTIVATOR

Write the following on the chalkboard for students to work on while attendance is being taken: *Write a list of all the decisions you made today from the time you woke up until now.* Ask a few volunteers to share their lists.

INTRODUCING THE LESSON

Refer to the Motivator. Ask students to select one of the decisions they made this morning and describe how they went about making the decision, focusing on the process. Tell students they will learn more about problem solving and decision making as they study this lesson.

INTRODUCING HEALTH TERMS

- Have students discuss the difference between realistic and unrealistic goals and describe how setting goals affects self-esteem.
- Ask students to complete Vocabulary Activity 2 and Chapter Study Guide 2 in the *Student Workbook*. ☞

Making Decisions and Setting Goals

Does it seem that people expect a lot of you? The truth is, each time you make a major decision, you are exercising enormous power—power over how healthy, happy, and productive you may be for the rest of your life.

Making responsible decisions and setting meaningful goals are important skills to learn.

HEALTH TERMS

goals

action plan

HEALTH CONCEPTS

- Decision making is a multi-step process that can be used to make responsible health choices.
- Practicing your decision-making skills can prepare you to handle real-life situations.
- Setting and achieving goals is important to the quality of your life.
- A key to effective goal setting is learning to develop and implement an action plan.

Making Responsible Decisions

Imagine finding gift-wrapped boxes at your doorstep along with a note that states, "Whichever box you choose will determine how your life proceeds." Which box would you open? Would you just grab the one nearest to you and hastily tear off the ribbon? Would you instead take your time and carefully inspect each box, looking for subtle clues as to its contents?

Making decisions about major life issues must be done carefully and deliberately. Just as you would slow down and look for approaching cars when arriving at a busy intersection, so you will need to approach life decisions with caution. You will need to "look in all directions" for possible risks, then act decisively and without hesitation once the risks have been identified and weighed.

34 CHAPTER 2 MAKING HEALTHFUL CHOICES

Lesson 2 Resources

TEACHER'S CLASSROOM RESOURCES

☞ **Concept Map** Activity 5

☞ **Decision-Making** Activity 2

☞ **Lesson 5 Quiz**

☞ **Lesson Plan 5**

☞ **Reteaching** Activity 5

STUDENT WORKBOOK

☞ **Applying Health Skills 5**

☞ **Chapter Study Guide 2**

☞ **Vocabulary** Activity 2

TRANSPARENCIES

🖎 **Transparencies 37, 38**

MULTIMEDIA

🔴 **ABCNews InterActive™ VHS/Videodisc,** *Teenage Sexuality*

The Decision-Making Model

One of the traits of a health-literate person is being a critical thinker and problem solver—having the ability to evaluate information from reliable sources and then make a responsible decision. The decision-making model can help you act in a way consistent with this trait. The model is designed to help you make decisions that will protect your rights, health, and self-respect, while respecting the rights, health, and self-respect of others.

There are six basic steps in making an important decision. These are as follows.

▼ *Evaluating a decision you have made will help you make good decisions in the future.*

Step 1 **STATE THE SITUATION**
Examine the situation and ask yourself: What decision needs to be made? Identify others who may be affected by your decision.

Step 2 **LIST THE POSSIBLE OPTIONS**
Ask yourself: What are the possible choices that I could make? Remember, to include "not act at all," if appropriate. Share your options with responsible family members, teachers, or friends. Ask for their advice.

Step 3 **WEIGH THE POSSIBLE OUTCOMES**
Ask yourself if there are both positive and negative results of each choice. Weigh the outcome, or consequence, of each option. Ask yourself: Is this decision healthful, safe, and legal? Does it show respect for myself and others?

Step 4 **CONSIDER YOUR VALUES**
Evaluate whether your course of action is in keeping with the highest values for yourself, your family, and community. Ask yourself: Am I comfortable with the possible outcome? What will my family and other responsible adults think about this decision? What will I feel about this decision in the weeks and months ahead?

Step 5 **MAKE A DECISION AND TAKE ACTION**
Use everything you know at this point to make a responsible decision. You can feel good that you have carefully prepared and thought about the situation and your options.

Step 6 **EVALUATE YOUR DECISION**
After you have made the decision and taken action, reflect on what happened. You might ask yourself: What was the outcome? Was it what I expected? How did my decision affect my health? What effect did my decision have on others? What did I learn? Would I take the same action again?

LESSON 2 MAKING DECISIONS AND SETTING GOALS **35**

HOME AND COMMUNITY CONNECTION

CONSUMER DECISION MAKING. Discuss major purchases for a home such as automobiles, carpet, furniture, refrigerators, or televisions. As items are suggested, ask how the choice of an item may affect physical, mental/emotional, social, or environmental health. For example, choice of an automobile can affect passenger safety, levels of pollution, relationships with people, and for some, self-esteem. Ask what factors should be weighed in deciding. Have students choose a household purchase, list factors they should weigh in making the best selection, and suggest sources of reliable information they can use to investigate these factors. Have students explain why this information is important to know before they make a decision.

TEACH

L1 **Explaining**

Explain that a crucial step in all decision-making is to distinguish between ethical and unethical options. Stress that decisions and actions should only be based on the choices among the *ethical* options. Give examples of ethical and unethical options in making a specific decision—for example, whether or not to drink alcohol. The only ethical decision is for a teen to decide not to drink. Now draw a series of concentric circles on the chalkboard, labeling them respectively from the center outward as follows: *Self, Family, Friends, School*, and *Community*. Explain that our decisions have a "ripple effect" that can extend well beyond our own lives, and deciding among ethical options as opposed to unethical ones can have wide-reaching effects on our own and others' well-being.

LD **Meeting Special Needs**

Have LD students come up with a dilemma and work through the steps of the decision-making process together. Then, assign a problem to be done on an individual basis for reinforcement.

L1 **Explaining**

Explain that there are occasions when we do not have time to use the entire decision-making process. Ask students to give examples of decisions that must be made quickly. Explain what to do in these situations. Allow students time to practice decision-making skills so they will be prepared when they are faced with these situations.

L1 **Discussing**

Use *Transparency 37* to discuss the decision-making process. Use *Transparency 38* to introduce goal setting. ✎

L2 Discussing

Discuss some ways that people can evaluate the results of the choices they make. Ask why it is important to evaluate the consequences of choices.

Making Responsible Decisions

1. Amanda has two commitments for the same afternoon: to take care of her younger brother and to try out for the school play.
2. Amanda could (a) arrange for someone else to care for her brother, (b) skip the play tryouts, or (c) see if she could try out at a different time.
3. Amanda might (a) disappoint her parents but get a part in the play, (b) please her parents but have to miss being in the play she has worked so hard for, or (c) risk being embarrassed about asking for a new tryout time but possibly have a chance to be in the play.
4. Amanda values both her hard work and the trust her parents have placed in her.
5. Responses will vary.
6. Help students consider both the short- and long-term consequences of their decisions.

L2 Decision Making

For more on making responsible decisions, have students complete *Decision-Making Activity 2* in the TCR. ☞

L3 Writing

Ask students to develop, on the computer, models for setting and attaining goals. They should include criteria from the model in the text and add other criteria that would benefit teens in setting and attaining goals. Have students copy and share their models with the class.

CHARACTER IN ACTION

Developing a Moral Compass

Imagine you had a moral compass to guide you in the right direction each time you had to make an important decision. Imagine at the marking for north, the compass said *Right Way,* at the marking for south, *The Wrong Way,* and at east and west, *Possibly the Right Way.* Making ethical decisions would then be easy— you would choose *north* every time.

Character Check To develop a well-defined sense of right and wrong when making decisions:

➤ First, distinguish between ethical and unethical options. Throw out the unethical ones.

➤ Then, choose from among the highest ethical options, those that reflect core ethical values.

Practicing Decision-Making Skills

Practicing the steps in the decision making process will increase your familiarity with the process, along with the likelihood that you will use it the next time a major problem arises. An even more important benefit is that mastering this skill gives you an added measure of control over your total health.

Of course, decision making is not always easy or clear-cut, but remembering to choose only from among ethical options or choices when making a decision will point you in the right direction.

Setting Goals

Do you view your life as a series of events that simply happen to you? Do you see it as a work of art that you are constantly shaping and creating? Think about your plans for the future. What do you want to do with your life? What do you hope to become someday? Do your plans include further education and a family? What type of job do you hope to have? What do you hope to have accomplished by the age of 20? What kind of life do you want to be able to look back on when you are 70?

How you view your life can have major effects on your health and well-being. Having and setting goals is one way to help shape your life in positive directions. A **goal** is *something you aim for that takes*

Making Responsible Decisions

Missing or Making Tryouts

Lately, Amanda has spent much of her free time rehearsing for tryouts for the school play, which are to be held after school on Wednesday. Amanda's mind has been so focused on the tryouts that she has forgotten until now that every Wednesday afternoon she has a standing family commitment to take care of her younger brother. Amanda values hard work, which explains the long hours she has put into rehearsal. However, she also values the trust her parents have placed in her by asking her to take on the responsibility of babysitting. What should she do?

What Would You Do?

Apply the six steps of the decision-making process to Amanda's problem.

1. **State the situation.**
2. **List the options.**
3. **Weigh the possible outcomes.**
4. **Consider your values.**
5. **Make a decision and act.**
6. **Evaluate the decision.**

SCHOOL-TO-CAREER

DECISION MAKING ON THE JOB. Begin a discussion about types of decisions teens and others make in life. Students might begin by quickly jotting down all the decisions they have made that day. Help students distinguish between decisions appropriate for the decision-making model and those that must be made in seconds. Examples of the latter might include whether to brake or swerve to avoid a hazard in the roadway, whether to swim to a drowning victim or wait for emergency services, or other situations where time is of the essence. Have students choose an occupation and list ten examples of decisions this type of employee might make on the job. Tell students to list the examples under one of these heads: *Immediate Decisions* or *Decisions for the Model.* Then have students list other factors to add to the decision-making model when working on the job.

Setting realistic goals and achieving your goals leads to increased self esteem.

ACTIVITY *What goals have you accomplished that contributed to your self-esteem?*

L2 Class Activity

Have students debate this statement: *The only way people learn is by making mistakes.*

L3 Research

Ask students to watch television programs that show people making decisions. List the decisions that were made and discuss whether they were successful.

L2 Writing

Ask the class to collect cartoons featuring decision making. Have them write new captions or dialogue based on information in this lesson. Let them share their cartoons with the class.

L3 Writing

Designate students to develop a board game using behaviors teens engage in. Include the opportunity for players to make choices that will be responsible decisions or ones that will cause some risk. Have them provide results for the students to determine whether or not their choices were correct.

keeping Fit

Recipe for Success

When setting goals, here are some additional pointers that can maximize your chances of success:

➤ **Make your goals *your* goals, not someone else's.** Although other people in your life have hopes and dreams for you, be sure you agree that they match your hopes and dreams.

➤ **Be flexible.** If you do not accomplish your goal the first time, try again. Maybe you weren't realistic enough about how much time it would take. Make a new action plan, and start over.

➤ **Be the best *you* can be.** Although your goals should be realistic, do not be afraid to dream. If your goals are beyond what you can do now, you can sometimes achieve goals you might otherwise not have thought possible.

planning and work. People who identify and work at achieving goals feel more satisfaction with themselves and their lives.

Kinds of Goals

Every goal involves planning, and planning involves time. Some goals can be achieved fairly easily and in a short period of time. Such *short-term goals* include getting your homework done by nine o'clock. Other goals, such as becoming a teacher or a professional dancer, pose a greater challenge. Such *long-term goals* take a longer period—sometimes months or even years—to achieve.

Many long-term goals can be achieved by breaking them down into short-term goals. In order to meet the long-term goal of playing on the school ice hockey team, for example, you must first satisfy the beginning goal of becoming a strong skater. What kinds of short-term goals do you think might be necessary to pursue a career in politics? What short-term goals might help a person work toward the long-term goal of becoming a professional athlete?

Recipe for Success

keeping Fit

Let students brainstorm goals in various areas of their lives. Ask the class to analyze each goal as to whether or not it is realistic, and whether it should be considered a short-term or long-term goal.

HEALTH LITERACY

SELF-DIRECTED LEARNER. Encourage students to examine an advertisement for a product, film, or event. Tell them to list the facts about the product as stated or implied in the ad. Then ask them to identify the message conveyed beyond these facts. Have students compare the message in the ad with that in an objective review of the product, film, or event. For example, they might compare an automobile ad with an evaluation in *Consumer Reports,* or a film ad with a reviewer's comments. Have them write a paragraph comparing and contrasting the message in the ad with the one in the review. If appropriate, they might wish to show their comparison on a Venn diagram. Help students understand the importance in accessing reliable information when making decisions.

L1 Discussing

Explain that it is important to have goals to have a meaningful life. Some goals are easier to attain than others. The difficulty of attaining a goal is not as important as setting one. Individuals differ in the types of goals that they attempt to achieve. Discuss the variables that could exist to determine the types of goals an individual may set. Relate goal setting to self-esteem for all individuals.

Building Health Skills

Making an Action Plan

Skill: Goal Setting

Before students begin reading this feature, help them review the importance of setting goals, and let volunteers identify goals that teens might set for themselves during a school year. For each example, ask: What would a teen need to do to accomplish this goal? Help students recognize the need for a specific plan of action that can help an individual achieve a goal.

After students have read about the first step in making an action plan, let them select (and perhaps revise) one of the goals suggested earlier. Help them use that goal as an example, explaining how they could apply each step of the action plan for meeting that goal.

L2 Parental Involvement

Encourage students to determine five long-term goals they would like to achieve. Have them ask their parents to help them use the goal-setting model. Ask how their parents could help them achieve their goals.

Goals and an Action Plan

While goals can differ in the amount of time and degree of effort necessary to reach them, all can be achieved by creating an action plan. Like the decision-making process, an **action plan** is *a multi-step strategy for identifying and achieving goals.*

Goals for Life

What are your personal goals right now—today? If your answer is that you do not have any, ask yourself why.

If you do not have positive goals, you need to ask yourself: *Why? How can I remove the roadblocks that stand in the way of my having positive goals?*

Remember, goal setting, like decision making and the other health skills you learned about in this chapter, can move you toward the

Building Health Skills

Setting Goals: Making an Action Plan

AN ACTION PLAN consists of six action-based steps that can help you accomplish your goals. These are:

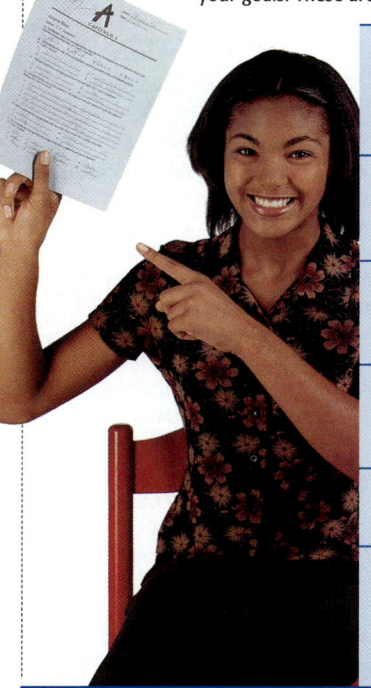

1. **Select a goal to work on.** In selecting a goal, you need to be specific and realistic. Also, state your goal as something positive. Do not settle for just "not failing." Focus your energies instead on succeeding. This will help motivate you to work toward achieving your goal.

2. **List what you will do to reach the goal.** Look for ways to break your goal down into smaller, more manageable tasks. If your goal is to become a long-distance runner, begin by training yourself to run shorter distances.

3. **Identify sources of help and support.** Sources of support and encouragement are important to achieving any goal. Such sources might include friends, family members, teachers, or neighbors.

4. **Set a reasonable time frame for reaching your goal.** When first setting out toward any goal, you should establish a reasonable time limit for reaching that goal and put it in writing.

5. **Establish checkpoints to evaluate your progress.** As with establishing a time frame, such checkpoints should be reasonable and realistic.

6. **Reward yourself after reaching your goal.** Once you arrive, congratulate yourself and enjoy the personal satisfaction. One way is to buy yourself something you have wanted. Knowing that a reward waits at the end of the journey will help you work that much harder.

PERSONAL HEALTH

FUTURE JOURNAL. Encourage students to consider what they hope to have achieved, acquired, or accomplished by age 35. Goals can be personal, professional, philanthropic, financial, or otherwise. For example, students might want a family of a certain size or composition, a successful career, to help the needy, or financial stability. Have them write a journal entry they might write at age 35, reflecting on the moment they set the goal, the steps they took to achieve it, and the rewards of attaining it. Call on volunteers to share their entries with the class.

ultimate goal of total health and wellness. Who would deliberately pass up the chance for improved physical, mental and emotional, and social health; for higher self-esteem; for a better quality of life? Go for it! Start today. Aim for total health!

Other Guidelines for Setting Goals

When setting a goal, keep these additional guidelines in mind:

- Make certain your goal will not harm your health or anyone else's.
- Be sure that your goal shows respect both for you and for everyone else affected by it.
- Set a goal because it will help you grow, not because you want to outdo someone or win someone else's attention.
- If you fail to reach your goal, use what you learn from the failure to set a new goal.

L1 Personal Involvement

Ask each student to think of two goals he or she wishes to reach this week. Have them use the goal-setting model to plan how they will reach one of the goals. Ask them to assess their progress every morning. If they find that they need more time to reach their goal, have them adjust their plans.

ASSESS

EVALUATING THE LESSON

Assign and discuss Lesson 2 Review; then administer, grade, and discuss the *Lesson 5 Quiz* in the TCR.

RETEACHING

- Have students think of a decision they have made in the past year. Ask them to evaluate how they arrived at the decision and to compare their process with the steps given in this lesson: Which of the six steps did they use? Which did they not use? How might the outcome have been different if they had used all six steps suggested?
- Ask students to complete *Reteaching Activity 5* in the TCR.

ENRICHMENT

Have the class investigate sources of health information on the Internet. Ask them to determine reliable sources for information regarding the health skills discussed in the lesson and share them with the class.

LESSON 2 — *Review*

Reviewing Facts and Vocabulary

1. Why are questions about consequences so important when using the decision-making process?
2. Explain the difference between long-term and short-term goals, giving examples of each.

Thinking Critically

3. **Synthesizing.** Write an *interior monologue* (the thoughts of one person written from the "I" point of view) in which a teen uses the decision-making model to decide whether to attend a party where alcohol will be served.
4. **Synthesizing.** Julius, who is 16, has ambitions to become a physician some day. Create an action plan Julius might follow in reaching this life goal.

Applying Health Skills

5. *In Your School.* Goal setting is not limited to individuals. Groups, too, can have goals, such as raising funds for a charity, for another worthy cause, or cleaning up a vacant lot. Think about a goal your class or some other group in your school could work toward achieving. Devise an action plan for this goal. Share your "blueprint" with the school's student council.

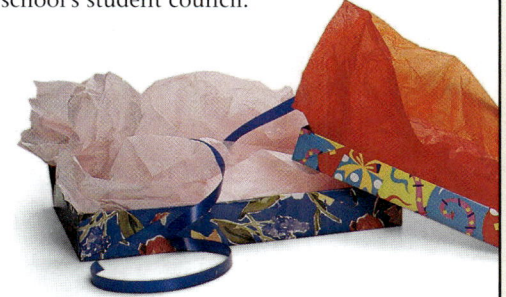

Lesson 2 Review

Answers to Reviewing Facts and Vocabulary

1. They are important because you want to achieve the best possible outcome for your decision.
2. A long-term goal can be broken down into a number of short-term goals that lead you, step-by-step, to the final result. It requires planning and time. A short-term goal takes less planning and less time.

Answers to Thinking Critically

3.–4. Answers will vary.

CLOSE

Have students make a goal map for their lives that covers the next ten years, breaking it down into two-year segments. In each time segment, have them list their goals for family, relationships, education, jobs, hobbies, and physical fitness.

Health Skills Activities

Health Skills Activities

ACTIVITY 1
HEALTH SKILLS
Decision Making

➤ **National Standards**
This activity meets these National Health Standards: 6.1.

Teach

- Walk students through Amanda's story to be sure they understand the order of the decision-making steps.
- Make sure that the scenarios are equally plausible, challenging, and appealing, so as to provide an equal challenge to each of the groups.
- Make sure students understand the importance of considering values when making decisions.
- Insist that students provide concrete, well-thought-out reasons for their ratings.

ACTIVITY 2
HEALTH SKILLS
Analyzing Influences

➤ **National Standards**
This activity meets these National Health Standards: 4.2; 4.4.

Teach

- Instruct students to be aware of the rating symbol that appears on the screen at the beginning of the program and to write this in the network rating box of the media rating sheet.
- As students watch, they should keep in mind the task of summarizing the overall message and may be encouraged to take notes.
- At the end of the broadcast, allow students time to complete their rating sheets. Then proceed with the discussion.

Activity 1 — Responsible Decision Making

Responsible decisions are choices that protect your rights, health, and self-respect. They also respect the health and rights of others. How do you apply decision-making skills?

Directions

1. With a group, review the six steps of the decision-making process on page 35, and practice applying it to Amanda's story on page 36.
2. Next, apply the decision-making model to one of the problems handed out by your teacher.
3. Elect a chairperson to present your solution to the class.
4. Review each groups solution, assigning each a rating of 1 to 5, where 5 is most responsible and 1 is least responsible. Be sure to include reasons.

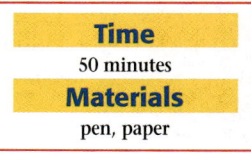

Time
50 minutes
Materials
pen, paper

Self-Assessment

✔ Demonstrated how to apply the decision-making model to solve problems in a way that promotes health.
✔ Discussed how solutions promote or fail to promote health and respect for oneself and others.

Activity 2 — Rating the Media

The TV networks rate programs according to their content (G for General Audience, MA for Mature Audiences Only, etc.). Do these ratings accurately convey the messages these shows are sending? You be the judge.

Directions

1. Prepare a media rating sheet with space for the show's title, type of program (sitcom, action drama), and a brief summary of the overall message (e.g., "glorifies risk-taking," "encourages compromise").
2. At the bottom of the page make two boxes for ratings.
3. View the program your teacher airs in class. Complete your rating sheet. Share your ratings and observations with the class. How do your ratings compare with the network's? How does this show's message compare with that of other shows of the same type? Of other types?

Time
50 minutes
Materials
pen, paper

Self-Assessment

✔ Viewed and rated a TV program using rating sheet.
✔ Analyzed rating and overall message.
✔ Compared personal and class ratings with those of network.

ASSESSMENT SCORING

Using a four-level rubric, the student has achieved a 4 if:

ACTIVITY 1
✔ Student demonstrates a clear understanding of the decision-making model.
✔ Student response shows evidence of having considered values.
✔ Student can identify the consequences, both positive and negative, in making choices.
✔ Student adequately explains reasoning for ratings given.

ACTIVITY 2
✔ Student correctly created media rating sheet.
✔ Student correctly completed rating sheet, giving the TV network rating and his/her own personal rating.
✔ Student summarized clearly and succinctly the overall message of the show.
✔ Student demonstrated an awareness of possible limitations of the current rating system.

HEALTH NEWS VIDEO

The Winning Equation

For those who dream of winning a medal in the Olympics, long hours in the gym are only part of the winning equation. Good nutrition is as important to an athlete's performance as strength or skill. A balanced diet of carbohydrates, protein, and fat has a direct effect on an athlete's energy level and can boost his or her resistance to sickness.

To help the Olympic athletes achieve their goals, experts are on hand to provide guidance in training and nutritional planning. In the end, the athletes know that setting a goal for good nutrition is a key step in getting to the winner's circle.

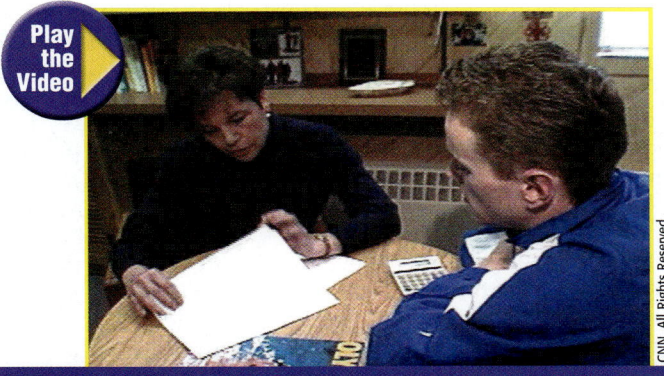

Play the Video

CNN. All Rights Reserved.

Think About It

▶ What are some of the steps these Olympic athletes take to achieve their goal of winning a medal?

▶ What is nutrition's role in helping Olympic athletes to achieve their goals?

▶ Note the serving size of the food in the cafeteria, pointed out by the cafeteria manager. Why do you think it is important for the athletes to get help from experienced resources?

CNN HEALTH NEWS **41**

MORE ABOUT . . . . .

ASK THE EXPERTS. In this video, Olympic athletes depend on nutritionist Judy Nelson to help them devise and monitor a dietary plan for peak performance. Explain to students that to become certified as a nutrition specialist, a person has four options: 1) Registered Dietitians (RD) or Dietetic Technician, Registered (DTR); 2) Certified Nutrition Specialist (CNS); 3) Certified Clinical Nutritionist (CCN); and 4) Certified Nutritionist (CN). While each of these options has different degree requirements and accreditation, all experts in this field must have a variety of science courses as part of their academic studies—biology, anatomy, and chemistry are extremely important throughout a career in nutrition.

The Winning Equation
Video Segment 2 (Time – 2:48)

Objectives. After viewing the video, students should be able to explain how healthful behaviors and getting help from experts can help them reach their goals.

Motivator. Ask students to name Olympic athletes or successful sports figures they admire. Ask: "How do you think these personalities became so successful at their sports." Introduce Video Segment 2, "The Winning Equation" to help students learn more about the preparation involved in achieving such ambitious goals.

Teach

• Have students explain how nutritionists help Olympic athletes train and compete. Discuss how these experts share their knowledge to help others succeed. Then have students list other professionals that are probably part of the team that supports Olympic athletes. Answers include coaches, physical therapists, doctors, sports psychologists, and massage therapists.

• Ask students to create a decision-making scenario for an athlete in the video. They should establish a situation, such as going out to dinner, keeping to a schedule, or choosing a snack for a road trip. Then, have the students show how the athlete could apply the steps of decision making on page 35 to make a healthy decision.

Role Play. Divide the class into teams of two or three students. Have them role-play an athlete talking with either a nutrition expert or a coach. Students should prepare a short skit that raises some of the concerns presented in the video. Have students perform their skits for the class. Follow up with a discussion about how athletes work with experts on goal-setting and nutrition.

Close. Have students tell what experience and characteristics a sports' nutritionist should have, based on the information in this video report.

CHECKING COMPREHENSION

- Assign and discuss the chapter review.
- Use the MindJogger Videoquiz to review the chapter.

CHAPTER 2 REVIEW ANSWERS

Using Health Terms

1. self-esteem
2. communication
3. refusal skills
4. health skills
5. stress
6. action plan
7. goal

Recalling the Facts

1. Health skills can be used throughout your life, and they take time and practice to learn.
2. Correct answers are any three of the following: clearly say what you mean, pay attention to how you say something, be a good listener, be aware of your facial expressions and gestures.
3. Refusal skills are important for resisting pressure to do things you know are wrong or dangerous.
4. Low self-esteem and stress both have a negative effect on decision making.
5. Rechanneling your energy, relaxing, laughing.
6. Radio, TV, movies, music.
7. The source may simply want to manipulate you for a particular or self-serving reason; for example, to make you want to buy something.
8. Answers will vary.
9. It is during the teen years that a person is first confronted with major life issues.
10. State the situation. List the possible options. Weigh the possible outcomes. Consider your values. Make a decision and act. Evaluate your decision.

Using Health Terms

On a separate sheet of paper, write the term that best matches each definition below.

LESSON 1

1. The confidence and worth that you feel about yourself.
2. A process through which you send messages to and receive messages from others.
3. Techniques that can help you refuse when you are urged to take part in unsafe or unhealthful behaviors.

4. Specific tools and strategies that lead to better and more informed health choices.
5. The body's and mind's reactions to everyday demands.

LESSON 2

6. A multi-step strategy for identifying and achieving goals.
7. Something you aim for that takes planning and work.

Recalling the Facts

Using complete sentences, answer the following questions.

LESSON 1

1. In what way are health skills similar to other practical skills you may have learned?
2. What are three steps toward positive communication?
3. Why are refusal skills important during the teen years?
4. Why are having high self-esteem and knowing how to manage stress important?
5. What are three ways of reducing the amount of stress in your life?
6. Name four different media sources.
7. Why is it important to "consider the source" when attempting to determine whether the information received through a particular medium is reliable?
8. Identify three kinds of people you might turn to for help.

LESSON 2

9. Why are decision-making skills so vital, especially during the teen years?

10. What are the six steps in the decision-making process?
11. What are some of the questions you need to ask yourself at Step 2 in the decision-making process? What are some questions you need to ask yourself at Step 3?
12. What are the benefits of practicing decision making?
13. In what way can long-term and short-term goals be interrelated?
14. What are the steps in an action plan?
15. Why is it not a good idea to let someone else set your goals for you?
16. What are some reasons people fail to set personal goals for themselves?
17. What are three ways you can improve your goal-setting skills.

11. What are the possible choices? What are the possible outcomes? Is this solution safe? What risk does it carry? How costly will it be to others? How will it affect my health or the health of others?
12. It gives you an added measure of control over your health and over any situation or dilemma you might confront.

13. Long-term goals can be broken down into manageable, step-by-step, short-term goals. In that way, short-term goals become the means of achieving long-term goals.
14. Select a goal to work on. List what you will do to reach the goal. Identify sources of help and support. Set a reasonable time frame for reaching your

Thinking Critically

LESSON 1

1. ***Analyzing.*** Review the four traits of a health-literate person in Chapter 1 (page 10). Explain how each of these traits emphasizes the importance of one of the following skills: communication, refusal skills, building self-esteem, managing stress, accessing reliable information, obtaining help.

2. ***Synthesizing.*** Beth is constantly being ridiculed and put down by her older sister. Which of the skills covered in the lesson could best help Beth? Explain how she could use this skill to improve her overall health and well-being as well as her relationships with her sister.

LESSON 2

3. ***Synthesizing.*** Explain how the following statement applies to the skill of goal setting: A person's reach should exceed his or her grasp.

Making the Connection

1. ***Math.*** Learn more about flow charts and what the different geometric shapes in them represent. Then create two flow charts, one for a decision you recently made, another for a goal you have achieved. Your flow charts should mirror the decision-making process and action plan steps covered in the chapter.

2. ***Language Arts.*** Working with classmates, gather articles on health breakthroughs from an assortment of print media, including a supermarket tabloid, a magazine ad for a health product or beauty aid, and a newspaper or magazine article. Discuss which source provides the most reliable health information and why.

BEYOND THE CLASSROOM

PARENTAL INVOLVEMENT Ask a parent or other adult at home about a decision he or she has made and what process, if any, was used to make the decision. Share the decision-making model from the chapter, and ask the person whether having access to such a model would have made the decision easier.

COMMUNITY INVOLVEMENT In certain professions—law and teaching, for instance—effective communication is especially critical. Interview an individual from one of these professions and learn about the guidelines he or she uses to ensure good communication.

SCHOOL-TO-CAREER

Technology. Modern technology has reshaped our concept of the mass media. The most recent innovations in this area are on-line communication services and the Internet. This technology enables many industries to process large amounts of information from one place to another more quickly than ever dreamed possible. Learn how health-related industries are using this technology to process health claims and provide information to consumers.

CHAPTER 2 REVIEW **43**

Thinking Critically

1. Answers will vary.
2. The skill of building self-esteem would best help Beth. She can use this skill to give herself positive messages which focus on her best traits and on the things she does well. She can express these messages to her sister and, in so doing, make her sister see her in a positive light.
3. If you set goals that are beyond what you think you can accomplish today and work toward them steadily and with confidence, you will probably surprise yourself by accomplishing more than you thought possible.

Making the Connection

1.–2. Answers will vary.

Evaluate

- Use the reproducible *Chapter 2 Test* in the TCR or construct your own using the Testmaker software.
- Use *Performance Assessment Activity 2* in the TCR.

Enrichment

Ask students to complete *Cross-Curriculum Activity 2* in the TCR.

goal. Establish checkpoints to evaluate your progress. Reward yourself after reaching your goal.
15. Only you know what your real hopes and dreams are, and you are the one who will have to do the work to reach the goal.
16. They may be afraid of failure, of success, of standing apart from their friends, or of being made fun of.

17. Any three of the following: make certain your goal will not harm your health or anyone else's; be sure that your goal shows respect both for you and for everyone else affected by it; set a goal because it will help you grow, not because you want to outdo someone or win someone else's attention; if you fail to reach your goal, use what you learn from the failure to set a new goal.

Physical Fitness and Your Health

	FEATURES	**CLASSROOM RESOURCES**

ACTIVITIES

- Cross-Curriculum Activity 3
- Health Lab 3
- Health Skills Activities 3
- Parent Letter and Activities 3

ASSESSMENT

- Chapter 3 Test
- Performance Assessment Activity 3
- Testmaker Software

STUDENT ACTIVITIES WORKBOOK

- Applying Health Skills 6-8
- Study Guide 3
- Vocabulary Activity 3

STUDENT DIVERSITY STRATEGIES

- Audiocassette Program (English)
- Audiocassette Program (Spanish)
- Spanish Parent Letters and Activities
- Spanish Summaries, Quizzes, and Activities

MULTIMEDIA COMPONENTS

- English Audiocassette Program
- Spanish Audiocassette Program
- MindJogger Videodisc and VHS program
- ABCNews InterActive™ VHS/Videodisc Series

National Health Education Standards

One of the main goals of the National Health Education Standards is to move students toward "health literacy." Health literacy is the capacity of individuals to obtain, interpret, and understand basic health information and services and the competence to use such information and services in ways which promote health. The health standards were developed by applying the characteristics of a well-educated, literate person within the context of health. The health literate person is:

- a critical thinker and problem solver
- a self-directed learner
- a responsible, productive citizen
- an effective communicator

Listed below are the Health Education Standards Performance Indicators addressed in each lesson of this chapter.

Lesson	Health Standards Performance Indicators
1	1.1, 1.2, 1.6, 3.2
2	1.2, 1.3, 3.2, 3.3
3	3.2, 3.4, 6.4, 6.5

ONLINE RESOURCES

For a fresh approach to health topics and an in-depth look at health issues, use these online resources found under Teacher Resources at **health.glencoe.com**.

- **BLOCK SCHEDULE LESSON PLANS** Reinforce health concepts with outside readings selected especially for students. Each reading is accompanied by a lesson plan and activities to enhance
  - Reading Skills
  - Cross Curriculum
  - Media Literacy

- **TECHNOLOGY PROJECTS** Instructions and suggestions on how to use computer, Internet, and software with health lessons.

- **HEALTH UPDATES** Timely topics in health news, including late-breaking medical advances and updates on teen risk behaviors.

Out of Time?

If time does not permit teaching this chapter, you may use these features: Making Responsible Decisions on page 48 and Building Health Skills on page 56.

BLOCK SCHEDULING

Block scheduling provides extended time for hands-on projects and activities. Use the following activities to engage students, provide further depth, and vary your instructional techniques:
- Connections (30 minutes) **pg. 57**
- Health Lab (45 minutes) **pg. 58**
- Health Skills Activity (60–90 minutes) **pg. 66**

Physical Fitness and Your Health

CHAPTER OVERVIEW

Chapter 3 identifies the components and benefits of physical fitness and presents the basics of an exercise program.

LESSON 1 Physical fitness benefits an individual's physical, mental/emotional, and social health. Body composition, flexibility, muscle strength, muscle endurance, and cardiorespiratory endurance are components of fitness. Each component can be measured to determine fitness in that area.

LESSON 2 Regular exercise contributes to physical health by strengthening the body and contributing to the functioning of the nervous, circulatory, and respiratory systems. It also helps control body weight. Exercise can improve aspects of mental and emotional health, reducing stress and contributing to positive self-esteem. It can also improve social health. A variety of exercises contributes to overall fitness.

LESSON 3 To design an exercise program, students should set goals for a program, select appropriate exercises to achieve the goals, and establish when and where to exercise. Each exercise session should include activities that warm up, work out, and cool down the body. Students should check their progress to monitor their exercise program's effectiveness.

Physical Fitness and Your Health

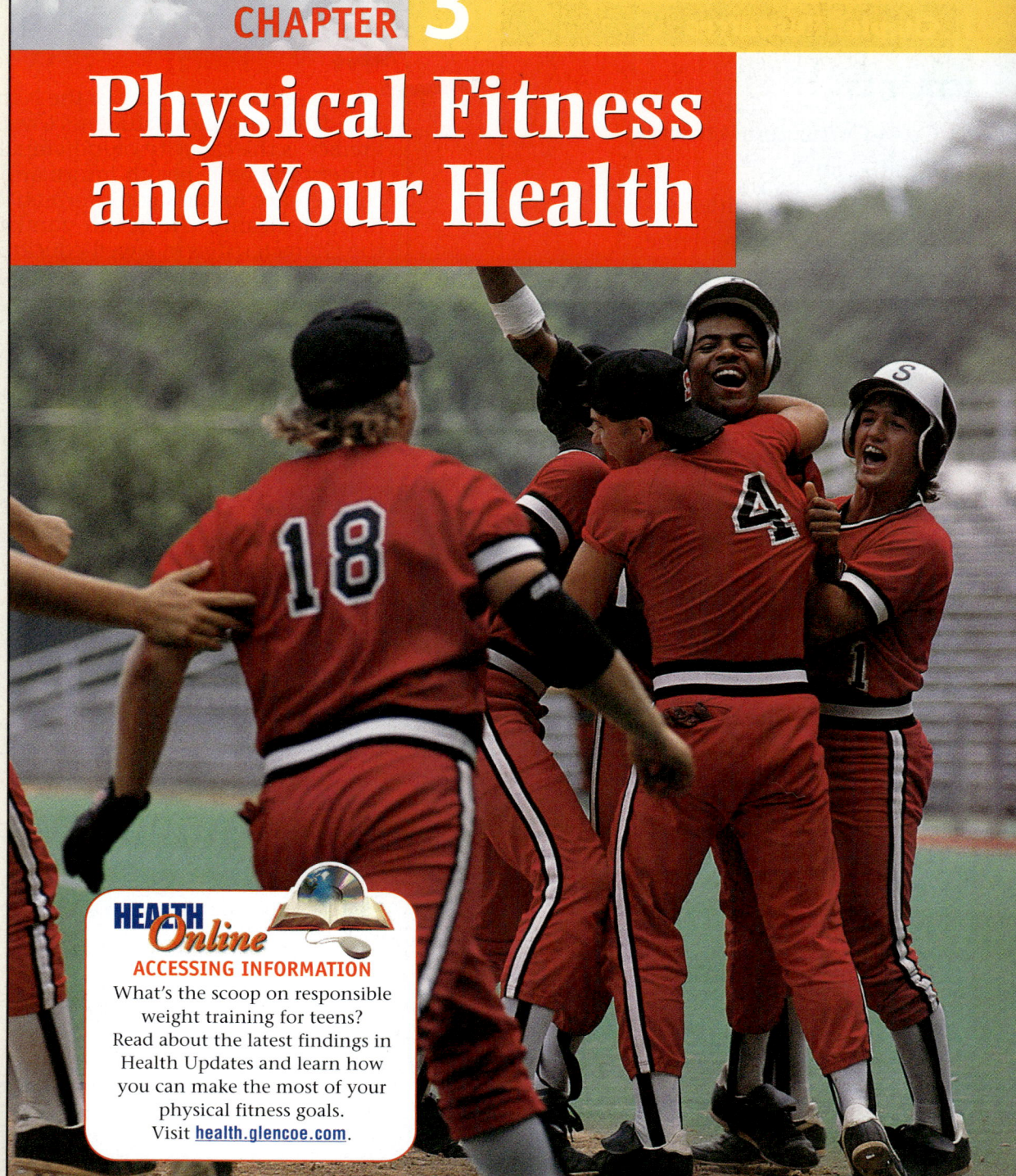

HEALTH Online

ACCESSING INFORMATION

What's the scoop on responsible weight training for teens? Read about the latest findings in Health Updates and learn how you can make the most of your physical fitness goals. Visit **health.glencoe.com**.

Hands-On Health

TEACHING STRATEGY

Reinforcing and Reviewing Bring your health classroom to life with interactive teaching strategies and classroom management techniques that keep your students interested and involved. The unique *Hands-On Health: Creative Teaching Strategies* booklet that accompanies the *Glencoe Health* program offers fun, motivating activities.

The following Classroom Management Ideas can be used to reinforce chapter concepts:

- Beach Ball
- Trivia Questions
- Paper Exchange
- Mental Outburst

Personal Health Inventory

Self-Inventory Write the numbers 1–10 on a sheet of paper. Read each statement below and respond by writing *yes*, *no*, or *sometimes* for each item. Write a *yes* only for items that you practice regularly. Save your responses.

1	I do at least 20 minutes of nonstop vigorous activity that improves the condition of the heart and lungs a minimum of three times a week.
2	I use the stairs instead of escalators or elevators whenever possible.
3	I regularly participate in lifetime sports, such as cycling, swimming or in-line skating.
4	I am more active than I am sedentary.
5	I enjoy a variety of physical activities.
6	I usually warm up before starting an exercise session and cool down after an exercise session.
7	I plan regular times for exercise.
8	I take in about the same number of calories as I burn.
9	I eat nutritious meals and snacks and avoid consuming high-fat foods and snacks.
10	I get at least 8 hours of sleep each night.

Follow-up After completing the chapter, retake this self-inventory. Pick two items that you need to work on and set a goal to improve your health behaviors.

> " *Exercise is absolutely essential to good health. It's a major key to an energetic, long life.* "
>
> —DR. KENNETH H. COOPER
> FOUNDER, COOPER INSTITUTE FOR AEROBIC RESEARCH

Quick Write If exercise is a "major key" to a long and healthful life, list some of the doors this key might help to unlock for you in the near future.

Personal Health Inventory

Let students read and discuss the Self-Inventory statements. Ask: How do the habits suggested by these statements relate to the topic indicated by the chapter title, *Physical Fitness and Your Health?* Then have students record their responses to the inventory statements in their private health journals on a page labeled "My Level of Physical Fitness." Remind students that their responses are private, for their own use only.

- Tell students that physical fitness plays an important role toward achieving and maintaining total fitness or overall health. Exercise is the primary contributor to good physical fitness. It also contributes to mental and social health. Tell them this chapter will present the benefits of exercise, ways to evaluate an individual's level of fitness, and aspects of planning a fitness program.
- Invite volunteers to share with the class some interesting or unique ways they have found to incorporate exercise into their daily lives. Then ask: What immediate advantages do you gain from regular exercise? How can you make sure you participate in some form of physical activity each day?
- Distribute Parent Letter 3 in the *Parent Letters and Activities* booklet and have students take it home to their parents or guardians. 🖅

T E C H N O L O G Y   O P T I O N S

 You may wish to use *Food and Nutrition* videodisc with this chapter. For your convenience, use the separate *ABCNews InterActive™ Bar Code Correlation* that accompanies the *Glencoe Health* program. 🔴

MINDJOGGER
VIDEOQUIZ

To preview or review chapter content, you may wish to use the *MindJogger Videoquiz* that accompanies Chapter 3. 🔴

Physical Fitness and You

FOCUS

LESSON OBJECTIVES

After studying this lesson, students should be able to

- explain the benefits of exercise to their physical, mental/emotional, and social health.
- describe the components of physical fitness.
- describe ways to measure each of the health-related fitness components.

MOTIVATOR

Write the following on the chalkboard for students to work on while attendance is being taken: *Physical fitness consists of five components: body composition, flexibility, muscular strength, muscular endurance, and cardiorespiratory (heart and lung) endurance. Write your own definitions of these five components, and circle the component you think is the most important. Be prepared to discuss the reason for your choice.*

INTRODUCING THE LESSON

Have students share their responses to the Motivator. Point out the role that the components play in physical fitness. Explain that each is important to becoming physically fit.

INTRODUCING HEALTH TERMS

- Have students differentiate the terms *muscular strength* and *muscular endurance* in a paragraph. Ask them to read their paragraphs to the class.
- Ask students to complete Vocabulary Activity 3 and Chapter Study Guide 3 in the *Student Workbook.*

Physical Fitness and You

J erry is a star soccer player. He moves up and down the field with speed and grace. Yet, he isn't very good at doing push-ups. Patty competes on the balance beam but gets completely out of breath after running half a block. Would it surprise you to learn that the physical fitness program of each of these teens is lacking?

HEALTH TERMS

physical fitness
body composition
flexibility
muscular strength
muscular endurance
cardiorespiratory endurance

HEALTH CONCEPTS

- Your level of physical fitness affects your total health.
- A number of tests can be used to measure your health-related fitness levels.
- Reaching a healthy level in all areas of health-related fitness is vital to total health.

What Is Physical Fitness?

A re you able to get through your day easily without tiring? Does your body respond quickly in an emergency? Are you mentally alert in class? Do you feel good about your body? Can you climb five flights of stairs without getting tired?

All of these questions have to do with your level of **physical fitness**, *the ability to carry out daily tasks easily and have enough reserve energy to respond to unexpected demands.* Maintaining a high level of fitness is a lifelong challenge.

Benefits of Physical Fitness

Y our level of physical fitness affects all aspects of your health and life. Your level of physical fitness affects your physical, mental, and social health. It affects how you sleep, eat, and learn. If you are

---

Lesson 1 Resources

TEACHER'S CLASSROOM RESOURCES

- **Concept Map** Activity 6
- **Decision-Making** Activity 3
- **Health Lab 3**
- **Lesson 6 Quiz**
- **Lesson Plan 6**
- **Parent Letter and Activities 3**
- **Reteaching** Activity 6

STUDENT WORKBOOK

- **Applying Health Skills 6**
- **Chapter Study Guide 3**
- **Vocabulary** Activity 3

TRANSPARENCIES

- **Transparencies 8, 9**

fit, you look good, you have energy, and you generally feel good about yourself. Physical fitness has many benefits, including the following:

PHYSICAL HEALTH
- Reduces your chances of acquiring diseases, such as cardiovascular disease, and crippling conditions, such as obesity, that are linked to inactivity.
- Allows you to be more active and capable at any age.
- Gives you higher energy levels for longer periods.
- Improves your posture.

MENTAL/EMOTIONAL HEALTH
- Makes you intellectually more productive.
- Provides relief from stress.
- Helps control depression.
- Gives you a sense of pride and accomplishment for taking care of yourself.
- Contributes to positive self-esteem because you will look and feel better about yourself.

SOCIAL HEALTH
- Reduces stress that can interfere with good relationships.
- Builds self-confidence, making you more able to deal effectively in social situations such as meeting new people.
- Gives you the opportunity to interact and cooperate with others.

Basic Components of Physical Fitness

Not every person's level of physical fitness is the same. A teen who lifts weights probably has good muscular strength but may lack the cardiorespiratory endurance of a classmate who is a long-distance runner. Having total fitness means achieving a healthy level in each of the five areas of *health-related fitness*. These areas, which affect your overall health and well-being, include:

- **Body composition.** This is *the ratio of body fat to lean body tissue, including muscle, bone, water, and connective tissue such as ligaments, cartilage, and tendons.*
- **Flexibility.** This is *the ability to move a body part through a full range of motion.*
- **Muscular strength.** This is *the amount of force a muscle can exert.*

How physically fit is this gymnast?
ACTIVITY *With a partner, discuss the question "Are all athletes physically fit?"*

TEACH

L1 Discussing

Ask students whether they feel they are getting enough exercise. Have students try to develop a single definition of "enough exercise." Afterward, discuss the reasons that make it difficult to reach a consensus. (Many factors are involved, such as age, weight, general health, gender, etc.)

L3 Community Involvement

Choose students to investigate whether there are community sources for determining percentage of body fat by underwater weighing or use of skinfold calipers. If so, assist the students in making an appointment to find out more about measuring body composition. Before the appointment, have students use the library to locate and read current information on the subject.

L1 Speaker

Invite an aerobic dance instructor to demonstrate dance movements and speak to the students about his or her classes. Ask him or her to lead the class in some exercise routines.

L3 Class Activity

Ask for volunteers to create a bulletin board titled "You Can't Be the Picture of Health if You Don't Have All of the Pieces!" Label large jigsaw puzzle pieces with the key concepts from this lesson. Discuss what happens if a piece is missing.

COOPERATIVE LEARNING

ACTIVE CALENDAR. Finding time for exercise is a fitness challenge. Even so, most teens manage to budget time for recreation and socializing. Group students for a discussion of typical teen social activities. These include not only inactive events such as parties, meals, movies, and concerts, often accompanied by junk foods and beverages, but also a variety of sports and other active pastimes. Have groups plan a social calendar for a weekend that includes both daytime and evening exercise. The physical activities may be the focus of the event, such as in tennis dates or dances, or they may be the means of transportation, such as a brisk walk to a movie. Each member should plan an activity for one day or evening.

10 Reasons to Work Out

keeping **Fit**

Have students rank the reasons to work out that are listed. Ask a few students to share their top three reasons. Discuss how rankings differ. Explain how specific interests and concerns help individuals shape their fitness programs. Tell students that they will learn more about making a personal fitness plan in Lesson 3.

Making Responsible Decisions

1. Rhonda has stopped running track to take a part-time job in a restaurant; now she is feeling less fit than before.
2. Rhonda can (a) keep working and not worry about her fitness, (b) quit her job and start running track again, (c) keep her job but cut back on eating sundaes and make more time for regular exercise.
3. Rhonda would probably (a) have spending money but not feel as healthy and alert, (b) regain her fitness but have less spending money and no longer learn or practice work skills, (c) have spending money and feel more fit, though she might have less time for other activities.
4. Rhonda values her health and fitness. She also values spending time with people, learning new skills, and earning her own spending money.
5. Responses will vary.
6. Guide students in considering both the short- and long-term consequences of their decisions.

L2 ## Decision-Making

For more on making responsible decisions, have students complete *Decision-Making Activity 3* in the TCR.

keeping **Fit**

10 Reasons to Work Out

Regular exercise brings benefits to many areas of your life. The following are just some of these benefits:

➤ improved cardiovascular health
➤ better weight control
➤ improved flexibility, muscular strength, and muscular endurance
➤ improved appearance, such as rosy cheeks and well-toned muscles
➤ improved self-esteem
➤ increased productivity
➤ a chance to socialize when you participate in group sports
➤ increased mental alertness
➤ increased ability to handle stress
➤ less fatigue and improved sleep

■ **Muscular endurance.** This is *the ability of the muscles to do difficult physical tasks over a period of time without causing fatigue.*

■ **Cardiorespiratory endurance.** This is *the ability of the heart, lungs, and blood vessels to send fuel and oxygen to the body's tissues during long periods of vigorous activity.*

Each of these components can be measured through various tests and activities. Once you know your strengths and weaknesses, you can take steps to improve your health-related fitness.

Measuring Body Composition

Appearance is probably one of the biggest reasons people exercise and watch what they eat. Since there is a strong relationship between the thickness of lean body tissue and the amount of fat inside your body, a reliable test for body composition is the pinch test. The skin and underlying layer of fat are pinched together on the upper arm and calf. These are measured with an instrument called *calipers*. The measurements are taken three times, then compared with those on a chart for an estimated percentage of body fat. Males with 25 or more percent body fat and females with 30 or more percent body fat are at risk of developing cardiovascular problems. Carrying too much weight also puts added stress on the skeletal system. If you have too much body fat, you can lose some of this fat through moderate physical activity and by reducing the number of calories you take in from food.

Making Responsible Decisions

To Work or to Run?

Rhonda has recently taken a part-time job at a local restaurant. She enjoys the people she works with and the new skills she is learning. She is especially happy about all the things she can do with the money she is earning. The only bad part about the job is that she had to quit running track in order to work the necessary hours. She noticed that since she started working she has been gaining weight and feeling sluggish, probably due in part to her love for the restaurant's famous double fudge sundaes.

What should Rhonda do?

Provide an answer by putting yourself in her place. Then answer the questions below.

What Would You Do?

Apply the six steps of the decision-making process to Rhonda's problem.

1. **State the situation.**
2. **List the options.**
3. **Weigh the possible outcomes.**
4. **Consider your values.**
5. **Make a decision and act.**
6. **Evaluate the decision.**

SCHOOL-TO-CAREER

EXERCISE AND THE JOB. Many modern employers recognize the benefits of physically fit workers. Accordingly, some promote fitness among staff. A few provide exercise equipment or jogging trails on the company grounds. Others provide membership in nearby health clubs. Still others offer showers and lockers for people who want to walk, jog, or bicycle to and from work or during lunch. Have students research some major employers in your community and what, if anything, they do to encourage physical fitness among workers. Suggest that they summarize their findings in a brief oral report. You may wish to give students the alternative of researching an occupation that requires a high level of physical fitness.

Measuring Flexibility

Can you touch your bent knees to your chest? Can you place your palms on the floor while standing or, while sitting, twist at the waist until your shoulders are perpendicular to your feet? If so, you have good flexibility. Flexibility is important because it helps reduce muscle strains and lower back problems.

Although flexibility is specific to each moving joint, the following test gives an idea of your general level of flexibility. Before taking the test, do some light stretching to warm up your muscles.

BODY FLEXIBILITY

1. Position a yardstick on the top of a 12-inch-high box so that it protrudes 9 inches over the edge with the lower numbers facing toward you.
2. Sit on the floor. Fully extend one leg so that the sole of the foot is flat against the side of the box under the yardstick. Bend your other leg with the knee turned out and the foot 2 to 3 inches to the side of the extended leg.
3. Placing the palm of one hand over the back of the other hand, stretch your arms forward over the yardstick. Lean and reach as far as you can.
4. Repeat Step 3 four times. On the fourth try, hold the position for the count of 3, and notice where your fingertips come on the yardstick. Record your score to the nearest inch.
5. To rate your flexibility, find your score on the chart.

Measuring Muscular Strength

Can you lift a heavy stack of books? Activities of this type require muscular strength. Muscular strength is vital to activities that involve lifting, pushing, or jumping. When you have good muscular strength, you are able to perform daily tasks more efficiently. This helps you conserve energy and enables you to get more things done in a typical day.

Because the body has many different muscle groups, there are different measures of muscular strength. Two broad measures are push-ups, which measure upper body strength, and curl-ups, which measure abdominal strength.

▼ *The backsaver sit and stretch measures flexibility of the lower back and hamstrings.*

ACTIVITY *Ask a friend or family member to perform this test, then do it yourself. Is the other person's flexibility measurement similar to yours?*

SCORING (NUMBER OF INCHES)		
MALE	**FEMALE**	**RATING**
8 or more	10 or more	Healthy Range
7 or less	9 or less	Unhealthy Range

L1 Health Lab

Distribute *Health Lab 3* and have students compute their percentage of body fat. ☞

L1 Class Activity

Divide the class into pairs to determine each other's flexibility as discussed on this page.

L1 Discussing

Guide students in discussing the importance of maintaining and improving flexibility. Ask: How does a lack of flexibility limit your activities? How can reduced flexibility affect your strength? What are the best approaches to improving flexibility? Emphasize the importance of regular stretching and remind students of the dangers posed by "bouncing" into a stretch.

L1 Community Involvement

Have several volunteers visit a community center or other local facility that offers exercise or stretching classes for older adults. Ask: Which forms of fitness are emphasized in these classes? How? Why? Let the volunteers discuss what they learned with the rest of the class. Suggest that some students might volunteer to help in these classes for older adults.

L1 Discussing

Ask students to identify sports and other physical activities that require muscular strength. Which focus on upper body strength? lower body strength? both?

HOME AND COMMUNITY CONNECTION

COMMUNITY FITNESS. Have students explore free or low-cost exercise options in their community. Do schools, recreation parks, or churches offer workout facilities? Do many large apartment buildings provide swimming pools or gyms? Does the local YMCA or YWCA have a gym? Are safe bike paths or lanes provided in their area? Do appropriate jogging paths exist?

Is walking, jogging, or cycling safe? Are they near a body of water appropriate for water sports? Do temperatures encourage walking or cycling year-round? Does it snow in the winter? If so, what inexpensive winter sports are available? Encourage students to create a fitness directory based on their findings.

L1 Class Activity

Find an appropriate place, such as a gym, to assess students' upper body strength as discussed on this page. Record and save each student's score. Discuss exercises or activities that will help improve this score. Later in the year, repeat the exercise, and compare each student's previous score.

L1 Class Activity

Divide the class into pairs to determine each other's abdominal strength. Ask them to refer to the instructions and scoring on this page and on page 51.

L1 Critical Thinking

Have students compare the scoring charts for Body Flexibility, Upper Body Strength, and Abdominal Strength. Ask: How do the scoring goals vary for males and females? What do you think accounts for this difference? What do these scores indicate about the flexibility and strength of an individual male compared to the flexibility and strength of an individual female?

UPPER BODY STRENGTH

1. Lie facedown on a mat or carpet with your hands palm-down beneath your shoulders. Your fingers should be spread. Keep your legs straight and slightly apart, toes tucked under.
2. Raise your body until your arms are straight. Lower your body by bending your elbows until your upper arms and forearms are at right angles. Do one push-up every 3 seconds.
3. To rate your upper body strength, find your score on the chart.

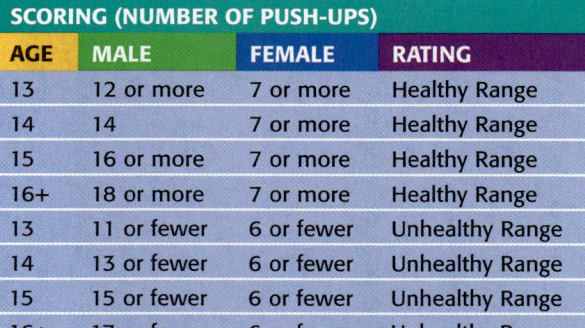

▸ *What part of the body is used when doing push-ups?*
ACTIVITY *List daily activities that require upper body strength and endurance.*

SCORING (NUMBER OF PUSH-UPS)			
AGE	MALE	FEMALE	RATING
13	12 or more	7 or more	Healthy Range
14	14	7 or more	Healthy Range
15	16 or more	7 or more	Healthy Range
16+	18 or more	7 or more	Healthy Range
13	11 or fewer	6 or fewer	Unhealthy Range
14	13 or fewer	6 or fewer	Unhealthy Range
15	15 or fewer	6 or fewer	Unhealthy Range
16+	17 or fewer	6 or fewer	Unhealthy Range

ABDOMINAL STRENGTH

1. Start by lying on your back with your knees at about a 45-degree angle. Your feet should be slightly apart and your arms at your sides.
2. With your heels flat on the floor, curl your shoulders slowly off the ground. As you rise, move the fingers of each hand sideways until your hands are about 8 inches away from your body.
3. Slowly return to the original position. Do one curl-up every 3 seconds.

▲ *Curl-ups measure abdominal strength.*
ACTIVITY *Explain why abdominal strength is beneficial.*

PERSONAL HEALTH

GROUP OR INDIVIDUAL. Some people prefer to exercise on their own schedule and at their own convenience. Others prefer classes or group activities, with the structure of a regular schedule and the stimulation of a group. Ask students to list various types of exercise, including scheduled group, unscheduled group, and solitary activities. Have them rank the activities in order of preference. Then have them list the advantages and disadvantages of each type from their point of view. Finally, students should choose three activities best suited to their personal fitness programs.

4. To rate your abdominal strength, find your score on the chart.

SCORING (NUMBER OF CURL-UPS)

AGE	MALE	FEMALE	RATING
13	21 or more	18 or more	Healthy Range
14+	24 or more	18 or more	Healthy Range
13	20 or fewer	17 or fewer	Unhealthy Range
14+	23 or fewer	17 or fewer	Unhealthy Range

Measuring Muscular Endurance

If you are in the healthy range for doing curl-ups, you probably have not only muscular strength but muscular endurance. People with good muscular endurance generally have better posture and fewer back problems. They are also better able to resist fatigue.

One activity that focuses primarily on muscular endurance is the leg lift.

MUSCULAR ENDURANCE

1. Lie on your stomach on a padded table with both feet planted on the floor. Your body should be positioned so that your thighs are just off the edge of the table.

2. Lift one leg straight out behind you. Hold the leg in the air for the count of one.

3. Slowly lower your leg to the floor. Do one leg lift every 3 seconds.

4. To rate your muscular endurance, find your score on the chart.

 Leg lifts are an indicator of muscular endurance.

ACTIVITY *Explain why it is important to have good muscular endurance.*

SCORING (NUMBER OF LEG LIFTS)	RATING
8 to 25 or more	Healthy Range
7 or fewer	Unhealthy Range

L3 Class Activity

Have students write articles to submit to the campus newspaper. Have them feature classroom activities involving assessment of flexibility, upper body strength, abdominal strength, muscular endurance, and cardiorespiratory endurance. Provide a camera and film for taking photographs of the activities to submit with the articles.

L2 Class Activity

Select a small group of students to design and create a bulletin board titled "Don't Be Confused About the Basic Components of Physical Fitness." Ask them to include major ideas in the lesson. Inform them that the bulletin board will be used to summarize the main ideas for the entire class at the end of the lesson.

L3 Writing

Ask students to write a short story in which two people make different decisions about physical fitness and exercise. Ask them to show how their decisions affect the rest of their lives. Afterwards, select some of the stories to read to the class.

L1 Class Activity

Divide the class into pairs to determine each other's muscular endurance. Ask them to refer to the instructions and scoring on this page.

L2 Class Activity

Divide the class into pairs. Have students assess cardiorespiratory (heart and lung) endurance using the 3-minute step test on page 52. (You will need a sturdy bench and a stopwatch.)

PROMOTING COMPREHENSIVE SCHOOL HEALTH

COMMUNITY SUPPORT. Tapping into local resources is a key to effectively managing a comprehensive school health plan. It is important to involve local health agencies, parents, churches, youth groups, and other organizations. By enlisting local groups and individuals, the committee establishes grassroots support. Community involvement provides the resources and support needed to reduce fragmentation of efforts or duplication of programs. Ongoing collaboration and cooperation between the team and other community members prevents unwarranted controversy. For information about community support, consult *Promoting Comprehensive School Health* in the TCR.

ASSESS

EVALUATING THE LESSON

Assign and discuss the Lesson 1 Review; then administer, grade, and discuss the *Lesson 6 Quiz* in the TCR. 🕮

RETEACHING

- Use *Transparencies 8* and *9* to review components of physical fitness and to have students assess their level of fitness. 🗝
- Have students pair up. Give each pair of students large jigsaw puzzle pieces labeled with the main concepts from the lesson. Assign them to put the pieces together and to explain and discuss each of the concepts with each other.
- Ask students to complete *Reteaching Activity 6* in the TCR. 🕮

ENRICHMENT

Choose students to investigate the use of new high-tech methods to evaluate athletes and their performance.

CLOSE

Ask students to state the most important concepts they learned in the lesson.

🔺 *The number of heartbeats increases during the step test.*
ACTIVITY *Why is endurance important?*

Measuring Cardiorespiratory Endurance

Can you run a mile without stopping? Can you walk all day at the mall without getting tired? If so, you have good cardiorespiratory fitness.

One way to measure cardiorespiratory endurance is to find your pulse recovery rate. This is the rate at which your heart beats following activity. The 3-minute step test determines pulse recovery rate:

STEP TEST

1. Use a sturdy bench about 12 inches high. Step up with your right foot, then your left. Step down with your right foot first. Stepping should be continuous. Fully extend each leg as you step.
2. Step at the rate of 24 steps per minute for 3 minutes.
3. Find your pulse on your wrist. To do this, find a pulse point on your wrist using the first two fingers of the other hand. *Do not use the thumb.* Count the number of pulses you feel for 1 minute.
4. To rate your cardiorespiratory endurance, find your pulse recovery rate on the chart.

SCORING (NUMBER OF HEARTBEATS)	RATING
85–95	Excellent
96–105	Good
106–125	Fair
125 or more	Needs Improvement

LESSON 1 *Review*

Reviewing Facts and Vocabulary

1. What are the benefits of physical fitness?
2. How is lower back flexibility measured?
3. What aspect of health-related fitness do push-ups measure? What do curl-ups measure?
4. What is pulse recovery rate? What test can be used to measure it?

Thinking Critically

5. *Analyzing.* Marcella is 15. Her health-related fitness scores are as follows: flexibility, 14; upper body strength, 5; abdominal strength, 10; muscular endurance, 9; and cardiorespiratory endurance, 106. Describe Marcella's level of overall health-related fitness.

Tell in what areas she needs to improve. What reasons can you give Marcella for wanting to improve?
6. *Evaluating.* Discuss the accuracy of this statement: "Peter is overweight because he eats too much."

Applying Health Skills

7. *In Your Home.* If you are beginning or continuing a personal exercise program, encourage your parents or adult members of your family to join you. Keep an ongoing record of resting heart rate at various times throughout the year. Make a graph of the readings of each family member and analyze improvements as you become more fit.

Lesson 1 Review

Answers to Reviewing Facts and Vocabulary

1. See page 47 for a list of the benefits of physical fitness.
2. By touching the floor with your palms while standing.
3. Push-ups measure upper body strength. Curl-ups measure abdominal strength.
4. The rate at which your heart beats following activity. The step test.

Answers to Thinking Critically

5. Marcella's overall level of fitness is only fair. She needs improvement in all areas except flexibility. Reasons for wanting to improve may vary.
6. Discussion should include a fitness component.

Exercise and Fitness

E ver since the early 1970s, the United States has been in the middle of a fitness boom. At almost any time of day, you can see people of all ages exercising.

How about you? Are you physically active? Are you reaping the benefits of total fitness and health that exercise offers?

HEALTH TERMS

sedentary lifestyle
metabolism
basal metabolism
calories
aerobic exercise
anaerobic exercise
isometric exercise
isotonic exercise
isokinetic exercise

HEALTH CONCEPTS

- A variety of exercises contribute to overall fitness.
- Exercise is essential to the total health of the individual.
- Exercise is a significant contributor to weight management.

Benefits of Exercise

E xercise provides health benefits that last a lifetime. It helps strengthen not only the physical but the mental and social sides of your "health triangle."

Benefits to Physical Health

E xercise improves the physical part of your health by building a strong body. It can help reduce the feeling of chronic fatigue and stiffness, and can improve motor responses. Exercise strengthens the body's muscles, skeleton, and other moving parts and helps slow the onset of osteoporosis, a condition in which bones become brittle and weak. Another important benefit of exercise is that it enhances the body's protection against disease by building up resistance through

---

Lesson 2 Resources

TEACHER'S CLASSROOM RESOURCES
- **Concept Map** Activity 7
- **Lesson 7 Quiz**
- **Lesson Plan 7**
- **Reteaching** Activity 7

STUDENT WORKBOOK
- **Applying Health Skills 7**

- **Chapter Study Guide 3**
- **Vocabulary** Activity 3

TRANSPARENCIES
- **Transparency 10**

MULTIMEDIA
- **ABCNews InterActive™ VHS/Videodisc,** *Food and Nutrition*

Exercise and Fitness

FOCUS

LESSON OBJECTIVES

After studying this lesson, students should be able to

- explain the benefits of exercise to one's physical, mental/emotional, and social health.
- explain the differences between anaerobic and aerobic exercises.
- describe benefits of aerobic exercise.
- distinguish among isometric, isotonic, and isokinetic exercises.

MOTIVATOR

Have students list any fitness-related activities that they have participated in during the last week and describe in what ways they benefitted from the activities.

INTRODUCING THE LESSON

Have students share their responses to the Motivator. Ask them to list the benefits of exercise. Point out that exercise is a major factor of total fitness, and that this lesson will focus on the role that exercise plays in physical, mental/emotional, and social health.

INTRODUCING HEALTH TERMS

- Have each student create a simple crossword puzzle using each of the vocabulary terms. Afterward, ask them to exchange their puzzle with another student. Provide several minutes for them to complete each other's puzzle.
- Ask students to complete Vocabulary Activity 3 and Chapter Study Guide 3 in the *Student Workbook.*

TEACH

L1 Explaining

Talk about the benefits of exercise to bone formation. (Among many other benefits, regular weight-bearing exercise puts stress on bones, which, in turn, stimulates bone formation. Exercise protects from bone loss.)

If students have limited access to the Internet, have them use library resources to gather information about fitness programs. Students might check with physical education teachers to find out how to join school or community workout programs.

L1 Explaining

Stress the fact that being a "couch potato" can be hazardous to one's health. Excessive TV viewing and a reliance on too many labor-saving devices can lead to a sedentary, rather than a healthy, lifestyle.

L2 Class Activity

Encourage students to keep a daily log that calculates the amount of TV they watch during a week. Discuss ways students can replace sedentary activities with activities that build cardiorespiratory fitness.

L1 Explaining

Talk about the importance of exercise in weight loss and weight control. Stress that overweight, which is in most cases caused by eating too much food and not getting enough exercise, can create health problems. Emphasize that "miracle" diets usually promise quick weight loss, but they are nutritionally unsound and some may endanger health. The key to weight control is balance—the amount of food energy eaten balanced by the amount of energy the body uses.

hotlink

nervous system For more information on the nervous system, see Chapter 16, page 364.

circulatory system For more information on the circulatory system, see Chapter 17, page 388.

respiratory system For more information on the respiratory system, see Chapter 17, page 400.

Check out some fun physical fitness activities and learn how your body responds to exercise at **health.glencoe.com**.

hotlink

overweight For more information on overweight and other weight problems, see Chapter 6, page 133.

improving fitness. A strong, toned body is capable of recuperating—or restoring itself—more quickly following an illness.

In addition, exercise contributes to the functioning of the **nervous system**, **circulatory system**, and **respiratory system**.

- **Nervous System.** Exercise can improve your reaction time by helping you respond more quickly to stimuli. This is especially helpful when driving or cycling.
- **Circulatory System.** Regular exercise strengthens the heart. This permits the heart to pump blood more efficiently, so that more work can be done with less effort.
- **Respiratory System.** With regular exercise, your respiratory system begins to work more slowly and efficiently so that you take fewer but deeper breaths. Your lung capacity increases, meaning you do not lose your breath as quickly running to catch a bus.

Exercise and Weight Control

One out of every three American adults and one in five teens is overweight or obese. This situation can be traced to overeating and a **sedentary lifestyle**, *a way of life that requires little movement or exercise.*

YOUR METABOLISM

The problem of **overweight** is related to two concepts:

- **Metabolism** is *the process by which your body gets energy from food.*
- **Basal metabolism** is *the minimum amount of energy required to maintain the life processes in a body.*

You get energy from food, and the energy value of food is measured in *units of heat* called **calories.** Your body requires a minimum number of calories each day in order to maintain itself. Additional calories must be used, or they will be stored in the body as fat.

Your metabolic rate increases during exercise. During exercise, the body burns up more calories than it does when at rest. The number of calories burned up depends on the nature of the activity. The benefit of physical activity remains for a short while even after you stop exercising. Your metabolic rate takes some time to return to normal, so during that time you are still burning more calories than before you began exercising.

Approaches to Everyday Activities	
SEDENTARY	**NON-SEDENTARY**
Taking the car to the store	Walking to the store
Using a golf cart	Walking with your golf clubs
Taking the elevator	Walking the stairs
Playing video games	Playing tennis

HEALTH LITERACY

RESPONSIBLE CITIZEN. Have students work in groups to discuss how technology reduces the physical activity necessary to perform daily tasks. Encourage them to brainstorm a list of inventions or services that deliver fitness benefits to the people delivering them and environmental benefits to global or local ecosystems. Examples might include a shopping or errand-running service on foot or on bicycles, and a gardening service without power mowers, weed-pullers, or leaf-blowers. A sample invention might harness energy generated by people using non-electric treadmills and stationary bikes to power appliances at a gym. Tell students to create an ad for the service or product and display it in the classroom.

YOUR WEIGHT

You are probably familiar with dieting, weight reduction, obesity, and exercise. More information on these topics can be found in Chapter 6. For now, the following statements provide an overview:

- If you take in fewer calories than you burn, you lose weight.
- If you take in more calories than you burn, you gain weight.

If you take in more calories than you can use, the excess calories are stored in the body as fat. One pound (0.5 kg) of fat is equal to about 3,500 calories. A person must control calories to control weight.

Exercise can help a person from becoming obese or overweight by changing the equation. Obesity and overweight have both been linked to heart disease and can be a problem among people of all age groups. Vigorous exercise can help reduce body fat and contribute to weight reduction.

Benefits to Mental and Emotional Health

Exercise can contribute to mental health by helping to reduce emotional stress. A few stretching exercises, for example, can help you relax tense muscles and sleep better. Exercise refreshes people with desk jobs and leads to more productive work time. It may also increase creativity by releasing body chemicals that stimulate the brain's creative centers.

Exercise can be a healthy outlet for tension, anger, or frustration. Being physically fit gives you a sense of pride and accomplishment in taking care of yourself. Getting fit and staying fit contributes to positive self-esteem because you will look better and feel better about yourself.

Benefits to Social Health

Exercise can improve your social health. Are you a member of a recreational or school team? Do you swim laps at a community pool? Do you like hiking or exploring trails in your community? If your answer to

Burning Calories

These activities, performed by a 110-pound woman for 10 minutes, can burn the following numbers of calories:

ACTIVITY	CALORIES BURNED
sitting quietly	11
playing piano	20
dancing	26
walking	41
playing tennis	55
climbing hills	61
swimming	78
running	97

Getting exercise provides opportunities to meet other people.

ACTIVITY *List the friends you have met through physical activities.*

LESSON 2   EXERCISE AND FITNESS   **55**

MORE ABOUT . . . . .

WEIGHT LOSS AND EXERCISE. The expression "burning off calories" is often used, but what does it mean? The process of burning, or combustion, is one form of a reaction called oxidation. This means the uniting of oxygen with other substances. Food that is used by your body for fuel combines with oxygen. This type of oxidation reaction is not as rapid as burning, but it still releases energy. Your body uses this energy for body heat, for automatic processes, and for physical activities. So when you run down the basketball court, dance, go up the stairs, or pound a nail with a hammer, you really are "burning off" calories.

L2 Explaining

Emphasize that the rate of basal metabolism depends on such factors as age, gender (with males slightly higher than females), weight, body fat, amount of sleep (about 10 percent lower during sleep), and surrounding temperature.

L3 Class Activity

Have students record their daily caloric intake versus their energy expenditure for a week. Have students determine whether or not this will lead to weight gain or loss.

L1 Self-Esteem

Ask students to write a paragraph comparing a day in the life of a physically fit person to a day in the life of one who is not physically fit. Ask them to share their paragraphs. Next, describe in detail one individual, perhaps a weight lifter, who works out at a gym five nights a week. Ask the class if this individual is fit. Ask those who volunteer to explain their answers. Explain to the class that being fit means being physically, mentally, socially, and emotionally prepared for what lies ahead. Stress that fitness is more than muscle development. Ask how fitness is related to self-esteem.

L3 Community Involvement

Ask for volunteers to interview an elderly person in their family, extended family, or neighborhood. Have them ask questions such as: How important has exercise been to you in your life? Why? Do you still exercise? If so, what kinds of exercise do you engage in now? What kinds of obstacles to exercising do you encounter? How do you deal with the obstacles? What would you do differently in the area of physical fitness if you had life to live over? Request that students share the results of the interview with the class.

Building Health Skills

Exercise— A Release Valve

Skill: Stress Management

Let volunteers share their responses to these questions: What situations make you feel stressed? How does your body respond to stress? What do you do to relieve stress? When students mention exercising to relieve stress, ask them to identify the specific activities or exercises that they find helpful. After this introductory discussion, let students read the feature to learn more about specific relaxation exercises. Then let volunteers identify and describe other stress-reducing exercises, especially those that students can perform while sitting at their desks. Suggest that students try all the suggested exercises and find those that are best for them.

L3 Class Activity

Choose students to debate the topic: *Everyone should participate in aerobic exercise.*

L2 Class Activity

Have students write public service announcements promoting aerobic exercise. Ask for volunteers to share some of the announcements with the class.

L1 Class Activity

Provide basic art supplies, and have students design logos for T-shirts promoting their favorite kind of aerobic exercise. Choose some of the designs to feature in a display titled "These Aerobic Exercises Rate an A+!"

L1 Discussing

Use *Transparency 10* to introduce students to ways of building their flexibility, strength, and endurance. 🖐

Building Health Skills

Managing Stress: Exercise—A Release Valve

RECHANNELING YOUR ENERGY into exercise is a good way to manage stress. While studying for a test, for example, take a break for some physical activity. Any kind of movement will help, even washing the car or cleaning your room.

Here are some other relaxation exercises for stress management. These exercises are specifically designed to reduce muscle tension:

▲ *To contract your shoulders and upper back, hunch your shoulders to your ears.*
ACTIVITY *Compare your body tension before and after trying this exercise.*

- **Elastic Jaw.** Take a few deep, relaxing breaths. Open your mouth and shift your jaw to the right as far as possible. Hold for a count of three. Repeat to the left. Do this exercise ten times.

- **Sleeper.** Lie on your side with your arms over your head. Stiffen your body, then relax your muscles, and let your body fall where it wants to go, as though you are asleep. Repeat on the other side.

- **Tense-Relax.** Lie on your back in a comfortable position. Make a fist and tense your hand and forearm. Then relax. Repeat with the other hand. You can also tense and relax your upper arm, forehead, shoulders, abdomen, thighs, buttocks, and toes.

any of these questions is *yes*, it is likely that you have met—and possibly formed friendships with—others who share your interests. Because exercise makes you look and feel better and enhances self-esteem, it increases your preparedness to meet new people.

Many find that exercising with a friend or in a group makes the workout more enjoyable. Following a fitness regime with someone else with a similar fitness profile also can help motivate a person to continue with an exercise program.

Improving Your Health-Related Fitness

Sensible exercise is good for you. The more muscles and joints you work, the greater the total health gain. To strengthen the heart and lung capacity, you might consider jogging. To increase muscular strength and endurance, you might lift weights. Chapter 4 provides details of recreational activities, such as hiking, dancing, and skiing, that also help keep the body fit.

Whatever you choose, it is important to add variety to your exercise routine. Doing a variety of exercises develops your overall level of fitness. It also places less strain on certain parts of the body and keeps you from "burning out" through repeating the same activity over and over.

56 CHAPTER 3 PHYSICAL FITNESS AND YOUR HEALTH

CURRICULUM CONNECTIONS

SCIENCE. Have students find their weight in kilograms (weight in pounds ÷ 2.2 = weight in kilograms). Next, have them determine their basal energy needs by applying the following equation: weight in kilograms x 22 (for females) or 24 (for males) = basal calories needed. Then, estimate the percentage of basal calories required for their usual activity level (very sedentary, 20 percent; sedentary, 30 percent; moderately active, 40 percent; very active, 50 percent). Total the calories needed for basal metabolism and activities, then add 10 percent for specific dynamic effect (energy expended to digest and absorb nutrients from food) to find total daily energy needs.

Improving Cardiorespiratory Endurance

Although there are many different exercises you can do, all generally fall into one of two categories, *aerobic* or *anaerobic*. **Aerobic exercise** is *vigorous activity in which oxygen is continuously taken in for a period of at least 20 minutes.* During this time, the heart rate increases, sending more oxygen to the muscles to be used as energy to do more work.

Aerobic exercise increases cardiorespiratory endurance. It raises the lungs' capacity to hold air and strengthens the heart, making it a more efficient pump. Jogging, swimming, dancing, cycling, and brisk walking are examples of aerobic exercise.

Caution: Forcing yourself to go on if you become exhausted while doing aerobic exercise can be dangerous. People with diseases of the heart or lungs should check with their doctors before trying this test.

▲ *Running track is a good form of aerobic exercise.*

ACTIVITY *Describe the aerobic activities you enjoy.*

connections — Math

Finding Your Target Heart Range

Your *target heart range* is the range in which your heart rate should be during exercise for maximum cardiorespiratory endurance. To find your target range:

1. Find your *resting heart rate* by sitting quietly for five minutes and then taking your pulse.

2. Subtract your age from 220 to find your maximum heart rate.

3. Subtract your resting heart rate (the result of Step 1) from the number you arrived at Step 2, your maximum heart rate.

4. Multiply the number you arrived at in Step 3 twice—first by 85 percent and again by 60 percent.

5. Add your resting heart rate to the result from Step 4 when you multiplied by 85 percent; then add your resting heart rate to the number you got when you multiplied by 60 percent.

6. The resulting totals represent your target heart range. Compare your target heart range with other classmates.

connections — Math

You may want to take the class through each of the steps in Finding Your Target Heart Range, using either a volunteer or an imaginary teen. For example: (1) Resting heart rate = 70. (2) Maximum heart rate = $220 - 16 = 204$. (3) $204 - 70 = 134$. (4) $134 \times .85 = 114$; $134 \times .60 = 80$. (5) $114 + 70 = 184$; $80 + 70 = 150$. For the teen in the example, then, the target heart rate is between 150 and 184 beats per minute. After this introduction, let students calculate and compare their own target heart rates.

L1 Class Activity

Lead students in brainstorming a list of exercises. Next, have them categorize and list the anaerobic and aerobic exercises. Discuss the differences between aerobic and anaerobic exercises.

L3 Research

Assign students to design and administer a campus survey of students' total fitness. Stress that students' responses will be anonymous. Afterward, ask students to tally the results and present their findings to the class.

MORE ABOUT . . . . .

BODY WEIGHT. Because the slim, trim look is often considered an ideal, underweight people are usually envied. If underweight people are in good health, a thin body should be of no concern. However, a person who is extremely underweight can have as many health problems as one who is overweight. Underweight people may have poorly developed muscles and poor posture. They lack fat layers, which means they have little insulation. Thus, they tire easily and are more sensitive to cold temperatures. Being underweight has many causes. Frustration and tension can affect the appetite. Some may be so involved in activities that they find little time to eat. Being underweight can also be caused by physical or medical problems.

health lab

EVALUATING AN AEROBIC EXERCISE

Time Needed: about 30 minutes

Understanding Objectives:
Students will gain a clearer understanding of their own responses to aerobic exercise.

Focus on the Health Lab:
Let students recall their own target heart ranges. Ask: How often do you think you get your heart working in that range? What kind of exercise or activity raises your heart rate to that level?

Observation and Analysis:
If possible, conduct the lab activity outdoors or in the school gym. Provide several activity options from which students can choose: running or walking the track and jumping rope, for example. If space is limited, students can run/walk in place.

In Conclusion Answers:
Responses will vary. Let students meet in discussion groups to share and compare their responses.

Further Investigation:
Suggest that students use the same procedure to see whether they reach their target heart ranges when participating in their favorite sports or exercise activities.

An Aerobic Exercise Checklist

keeping Fit

Have students determine what aerobic activities are already a part of their lifestyle. Are their activities meeting the recommendations for effective aerobic exercise? Discuss ways to incorporate more aerobic activity into each day, by exercise and every day actions, like taking the stairs.

health lab

EVALUATING AN AEROBIC EXERCISE

You know that aerobic exercise should raise your heart and breathing rate. How much vigorous exercise is enough for you? How effective is the aerobic activity you are currently doing? You are about to find out.

keeping Fit

An Aerobic Exercise Checklist

Are you considering trying a new sport or making a new physical activity part of your lifestyle? If you are and you want to make sure the activity is aerobic, look for these characteristics:

➤ The activity must be brisk. It should be able to raise the heart rate and breathing rate to within your target zone.

➤ The activity must be continuous. It should be done for 20 to 30 minutes without stopping.

Try *low-impact aerobics*—bicycling, swimming, jumping on a trampoline, and the like—which require less forceful movements.

Improving Muscular Strength, Endurance, and Flexibility

Anaerobic exercise involves *intense bursts of activity in which the muscles work so hard that they produce energy without using oxygen*. Running the 100-meter dash is an example of an anaerobic activity. Calisthenics and weight training are other anaerobic exercises. Resistance training, another type of anaerobic exercise, builds muscles by requiring muscles to resist a force. The more work the muscles do, the stronger they become. Resistance can be provided by using weights or machines, or your own body weight. Resistance training is a good way to tone muscles, improving muscular strength and endurance.

There are three types of resistance training exercises:

■ **Isometric exercise** is *activity that uses muscle tension to improve muscular strength with little or no movement of the body part*. Isometric exercises involve muscles pushing against muscles. Putting the palms of your hands together in front of you and pushing is an example of an isometric exercise.

■ **Isotonic exercise** is *activity that combines muscle contraction with repeated movement*. Push-ups and pull-ups are isotonic exercises. So is lifting weights.

■ **Isokinetic exercise** is *activity that involves resistance through an entire range of motion*. Isokinetic exercises increase the flexibility of the joints, at the same time improving muscular strength and endurance. Pushing or pulling against a hydraulic lever of certain exercise equipment is a type of isokinetic exercise.

58 CHAPTER 3 PHYSICAL FITNESS AND YOUR HEALTH

CURRICULUM CONNECTIONS

READING. Have students read about various organizations that incorporate exercise as part of their fund-raising efforts. Afterward, guide them in working with an organization (such as the March of Dimes) to arrange a walk-a-thon for their class or school.

INDUSTRIAL ARTS. Many aerobic exercise programs use the "step bench" or "box step" as part of their routines. Assign students to research the kinds of step benches currently available and the pros and cons of each. Afterward, ask for volunteers to construct some benches to use in classroom step-bench demonstrations.

What you will need

- Stopwatch or other timing device
- Any equipment as might be needed, such as a jump rope and running shoes
- Your target heart range

What you will do

1. Begin by taking your pulse before you exercise. Find your pulse, at either your wrist or neck. Count the number of beats for 15 seconds and multiply by four.
2. Perform some form of aerobic exercise for 20 minutes. Set a timer so you are sure to continue for 20 minutes. Make sure to exercise briskly and without stopping throughout.
3. Take your pulse again as soon as you stop the exercise. Again, count the number of beats for 15 seconds and multiply by four.
4. Compare your "before" and "after" pulse rates.

In conclusion

1. How many more beats per minute did your heart work after exercise than before exercise?
2. Were you in your target heart range?
3. What can you do when exercising to more closely match your target heart range?
4. Were you surprised by your pulse after exercising? If so, explain why.
5. If your aerobic fitness level is not where it should be, what can you do to improve it?

LESSON 2 *Review*

Reviewing Facts and Vocabulary

1. Describe a sedentary lifestyle.
2. What is *basal metabolism* and how does it relate to calories?
3. Which type of resistance training requires muscles to move against resistance through an entire range of motion?

Thinking Critically

4. **Synthesizing.** Suggest ways that people who need regular exercise and are opposed to it can be encouraged to participate.
5. **Evaluating.** Discuss the accuracy of the statement "Aerobic exercise is better for you than anaerobic exercise."

Applying Health Skills

6. **In Your Home.** Interview family members, teachers, or other adults and ask: How important has exercise been in your life? Why? Do you still exercise? If so, what kinds of exercise do you engage in now? What kinds of obstacles to exercising do you encounter? How do you deal with the obstacles? What would you do differently in the area of physical fitness if you had life to live over?

LESSON 2   EXERCISE AND FITNESS   **59**

EVALUATING THE LESSON

Assign and discuss the Lesson 2 Review; then administer, grade, and discuss the *Lesson 7 Quiz* in the TCR.

RETEACHING

- Have students list the ways they get exercise in a typical week. Then ask them to decide which characteristics each form of exercise has. Does it improve flexibility? improve muscular strength and endurance? increase cardiorespiratory endurance?
- Ask students to complete *Reteaching Activity 7* in the TCR.

ENRICHMENT

- Ask students to design a model showing the heart and ways in which it is strengthened by physical exercise.
- Have volunteers write a short puppet show for elementary students. Have them make two puppets named A. Robic and Anna Robic. The puppets should define, describe, and demonstrate the basics of aerobic and anaerobic exercise. Have students perform their puppet shows for an elementary school class.

CLOSE

Remove the label and top lid from four empty food cans. Write one of the following concepts on each can: *physical health, mental/emotional health, social health, and health-related fitness*. Divide students into four groups, and give each group one of the cans. Give slips of paper to each student. Ask them to see how quickly they can fill their assigned can with slips of paper that review related concepts.

Lesson 2 Review

Answers to Reviewing Facts and Vocabulary

1. A sedentary lifestyle is a way of life that requires little movement or exercise.
2. Basal metabolism is the minimum amount of energy required to maintain the processes in a body. It requires that a certain number of calories be taken in each day.
3. Isokinetic exercise.

Answers to Thinking Critically

4. Answers will vary.
5. Aerobic exercise builds cardiovascular strength. Anaerobic exercise builds and tones muscle groups. For overall long-term health, cardiovascular strength is more important. For overall fitness, a combination of both is best.

LESSON 3

Planning a Fitness Program

FOCUS

LESSON OBJECTIVES

After studying this lesson, students should be able to

- discuss the importance of setting realistic fitness goals.
- identify the basic principles of exercise.
- describe the stages of an exercise session and means of monitoring progress.

MOTIVATOR

Write the following on the chalkboard for students to work on while attendance is being taken: *Make a written list of the benefits of exercise. Next, illustrate and describe a safe warm-up or cool-down exercise.*

INTRODUCING THE LESSON

Refer to the Motivator. Ask volunteers to share their written lists and drawings of warm-up and cool-down exercises with the class. Discuss why the lists are different. Tell students that they will learn in this lesson how to design and begin a personal exercise program and ways to check their progress.

INTRODUCING HEALTH TERMS

- Write the term *resting heart rate* on the chalkboard. Ask students to explain why resting heart rate is an important concept in a fitness chapter.
- Ask students to complete Vocabulary Activity 3 and Chapter Study Guide 3 in the *Student Workbook.*

What are your fitness goals? How fit are you? What special skills do you possess? You'll want to take all of these into account when designing your personal fitness program. If you seldom engage in physical activity, plan a program that is not overly vigorous at first and check with a qualified health professional before beginning.

HEALTH TERMS

cross-training

overload

progression

specificity

warm-up

cool-down

resting heart rate

HEALTH CONCEPTS

- To be effective, the exercise program you choose should address your specific needs and purposes.
- Realistic goals are essential to the success of an exercise program.
- Warming up and cooling down are vital parts of any exercise regime.

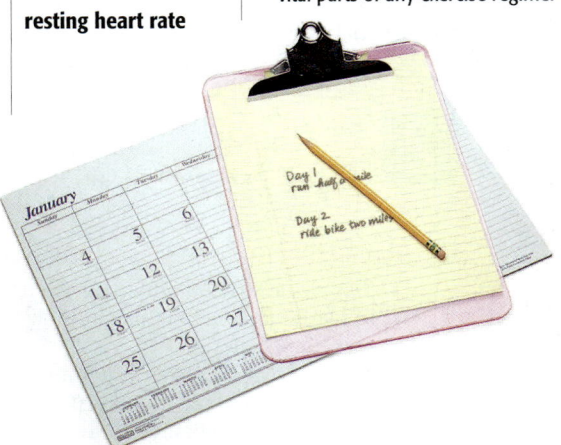

Setting Fitness Goals

Do you "keep meaning to get involved" in physical activity but somehow put it off? Setting fitness goals can help by providing you with a plan for action.

Planning a Fitness Program

If you've started exercise programs before only to stop after a few days or weeks, take some time to assess why you dropped out and what changes you need to make to avoid those pitfalls again. Perhaps you stopped going to an aerobics class because it was difficult to get there on time. To get back on pace, you might as an alternative choose an aerobics exercise such as walking or jogging that you can do on your own time. Another possibility would be to buy or rent an aerobics tape and do the activities in the comfort of your own home.

Lesson 3 Resources

TEACHER'S CLASSROOM RESOURCES
- **Concept Map** Activity 8
- **Cooperative Learning** Activity 3
- **Enrichment** Activity 3
- **Lesson 8 Quiz**
- **Lesson Plan 8**
- **Reteaching** Activity 8

STUDENT WORKBOOK
- **Applying Health Skills 8**
- **Chapter Study Guide 3**
- **Vocabulary** Activity 3

TRANSPARENCIES
- **Transparency 11**

MULTIMEDIA
- **ABCNews InterActive™,** *Food and Nutrition*

Getting Started

Plan your exercise a week ahead of time, and mark the activities and times on a calendar. Set short-term goals at first. If 45 minutes seems too long, start by scheduling only 20 minutes for a warm-up, workout, and cool-down. You can increase duration later when that level of exercise becomes comfortable.

You may want to reward yourself at the end of the week. For example, buy yourself something you have wanted, such as tickets to a concert. After you begin to see benefits from your workouts, you'll eventually become motivated by the results alone.

THE ACTIVITY TRIANGLE

REST OR INACTIVITY
watching TV, playing computer games, sitting for more than 30 minutes at a time

LEISURE ACTIVITIES
golf, bowling, softball, yardwork

FLEXIBILITY AND STRENGTH
stretching, pushups, weight lifting

AEROBIC EXERCISE
brisk walking, cross country skiing, bicycling, swimming

RECREATIONAL
soccer, basketball, martial arts, hiking, tennis, dancing

LIFESTYLE PHYSICAL ACTIVITY
walk the dog, take longer routes, take the stairs instead of the elevator

REST OR INACTIVITY

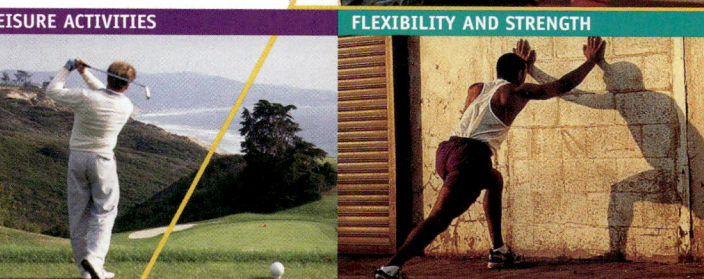
LEISURE ACTIVITIES | FLEXIBILITY AND STRENGTH

AEROBIC EXERCISE | RECREATIONAL

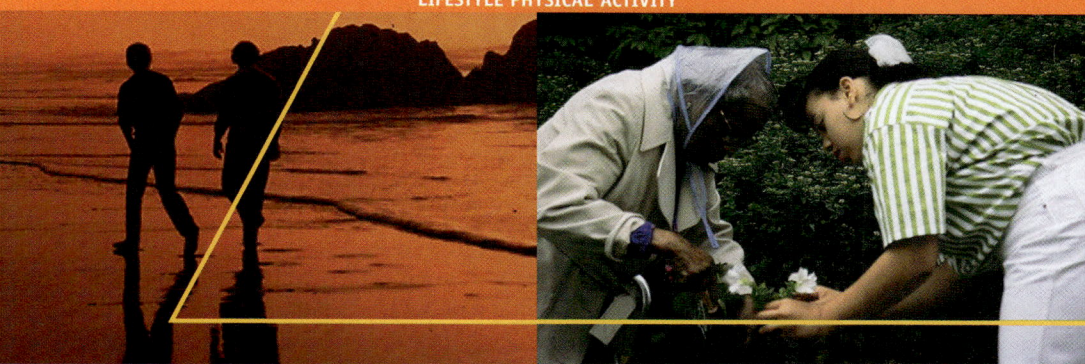
LIFESTYLE PHYSICAL ACTIVITY

Adapted with permission by Park Nicollet HealthSource® Institute for Research and Education.

LESSON 3 PLANNING A FITNESS PROGRAM **61**

TEACH

LEP Class Activity

Ask students to raise their hands to indicate which of them exercises regularly. Then call upon those students to describe how they feel after a good workout. (Students probably will say they feel refreshed, exhilarated, and invigorated after a workout.) Tell students these are natural responses. Next, lead students in a discussion of the advantages of a regular plan of exercise, such as preparing themselves for dealing more effectively with daily life, looking and feeling better, having more energy, reducing body fat, etc.

L1 Self-Esteem

Establish a contract with each student, stating specific fitness goals to achieve by the end of the course. Determine what level of performance will be acceptable for that portion of the student's grade, and discuss this in advance with each student. Discuss how achieving a fitness goal might affect a person's self-esteem.

Visual Learning

The Activity Triangle

Refer students to the Activity Triangle. Explain that this visual tool is one way to help people recognize how to increase physical activity in their lives. They should begin with a strong base (Level 1) and include more daily activity in the form of walking a dog or taking the stairs. Level 2 identifies aerobic and recreational sports they should do 3–5 times a week. Level 3 emphasizes the importance of stretching and strengthening exercises, and the contribution of leisure activities to overall fitness. The top of the Activity Triangle is a visual reminder to make a conscious effort to reduce periods of long sitting and inactivity.

CURRICULUM CONNECTIONS

LANGUAGE ARTS. Ask students to write a short report addressing the following questions: What activity would you enjoy doing as a regular part of your life, now and in the future? How might your ability to perform this activity change as you grow older? How might your ability to continue this activity change as your responsibilities in life change? Would it become more difficult to stick to this activity as time goes by? Ask volunteers to read their reports to the class. Have students look through newspapers and magazines to find examples of older adults who are physically active.

L1 Cooperative Learning

Have students form small groups, each having a leader. Ask the leader to guide the group in choosing an activity, acceptable to all, for a fitness program. Have group members decide on a realistic goal for a period of two weeks. Ask them to discuss ways they can motivate themselves to stick to the program. After two weeks, have group leaders present their group's results to the class.

hotlink

asthma
personal safety
Have students find articles in newspapers and magazines about individuals who participate in sports in spite of medical limitations. Ask them to share some of the articles with the class.

L3 Community Involvement

Select students to interview community members about the kinds of physical exercise activities available to teens and their family members. Have students find out about location, fees, equipment needed, date and time of activity, etc. Ask them to share their information (including any brochures or flyers) with the class.

L2 Class Activity

Have students list a number of fitness activities that they like well enough to do throughout life. Ask them to develop a second list of activities they would like to try. Have them determine what resources would be needed to try these activities. Challenge students to try several of the new activities throughout the course and to share their reactions with the class.

Did You Know?

➤ Each mile you walk or run adds 21 minutes to your life and saves 24 cents in medical costs.

➤ Thirty-three percent of children who watch television more than five hours a day are overweight, compared with only 12 percent of children who watch less than two hours of TV a day.

hotlink

asthma For more on asthma and ways of treating this disease, see Chapter 17, page 404.

hotlink

personal safety For more information on the issues related to personal safety when out alone, see Chapter 34, page 760.

Selecting the Right Activity

A number of factors affect the kind of fitness program you follow. These include:

- **Where you live.** Consider the local terrain. Is the land in your part of the country flat or hilly? To which kinds of activities does the region best lend itself? Temperature—especially extremes in heat or cold—should also be a consideration in selecting an activity.

- **Your range of interests.** Pick activities you like. Remember, exercise should be enjoyable.

- **Your level of health.** A person with **asthma**, a disease of the lungs that can be aggravated by physical activity, will need to take his or her physical condition into account in designing a fitness program. Other health problems also carry risks that will need to be considered.

- **Time and place.** Are you a morning person? If not, do not plan to jog each day at 6 A.M. Instead, pick a time of day when you will be most likely to stick to your goals. Build your program into your daily routine.

- **Personal safety.** Make sure that your plan takes your **personal safety** into account. If you plan to run long distances, avoid high-crime areas or running after dark.

- **Comprehensive planning.** Pick activities that address all five areas of health-related fitness.

Cross-Training

Regardless of which activity you choose, you will probably find yourself engaging in a variety of physical activities. Boxers, for example, use various exercises to get themselves into top physical shape. You have probably seen boxers jumping rope or lifting weights.

Most sports require **cross-training.** This is *combining various exercise routines to help work different body systems.* Jumping rope, swimming, jogging, and cycling are good cross-training activities for athletes.

Basics of an Exercise Program

Every exercise program, whether it is cycling or an aerobics class, should follow the same basic guidelines and include the same basic parts or stages. Consider the following principles for an effective workout:

- **Overload.** This is *working the body harder than it is normally worked.* This might be done by increasing repetitions of a specific exercise or by doing more *sets*—groups of repetitions—of the exercise. Overload builds muscular strength and contributes to overall fitness.

CURRICULUM CONNECTIONS

SOCIAL STUDIES. The popularity of some types of physical exercise differs in various parts of the United States. This is due to differences in temperature, terrain, natural resources, local customs, economic resources, etc. Have students use library resources to identify types of physical exercise commonly enjoyed in various geographical areas of the country (such as snow skiing in the northwest and water skiing in the south). For additional information, direct students to the phone listings for each state's office of tourism.

- **Progression.** Related to overload, progression is *a gradual increase in overload necessary for achieving higher levels of fitness.* As it becomes gradually easier to do an exercise or activity, you increase the number of repetitions or sets. Thus, you take on ever greater challenges.

- **Specificity.** This principle states that *particular exercises and activities improve particular areas of health-related fitness.* Resistance training, as you have seen, contributes to muscular strength and endurance but does little to improve cardiorespiratory fitness. A specific aerobic activity, such as swimming or running, is needed to meet this fitness goal.

In order to derive maximum benefit from an exercise program, you need to include three basic stages. These are the *warm-up*, the *workout*, and the *cool-down*. Each stage needs to be included in every session, even when you are pressed for time.

The Warm-up

Before physical activity, your muscles are stiff. The **warm-up** is *engaging in activity that prepares the muscles for the work that is to come.* The first step is to raise your body temperature with a brisk walk. The second step is to stretch large muscles slowly and smoothly. This increases elasticity and thus prevents injury. The third step is to perform the activity slowly for about five minutes. If you are bicycling, for example, you will ride at an easy pace for five minutes, then increase the pace. Warming up allows your pulse rate to increase gradually. A sudden increase in the pulse rate puts unnecessary strain on the heart and the blood vessels.

The Workout

This part of an exercise program is where you perform the activity at its highest peak. To be effective, the activity needs to follow the *F.I.T.* formula. The letters in this name stand for:

- **Frequency**—how often you do the activity each week.
- **Intensity**—how hard you work at the activity during a session.
- **Time**—how much time you devote to a given session.

Together, these factors determine whether a workout helps you achieve the principle of overload and, ultimately, your workout goal.

FREQUENCY

Workouts should be scheduled three to four times a week, with only one or two days between sessions. Frequency depends on the type of activity you are doing and on your health-related fitness goal.

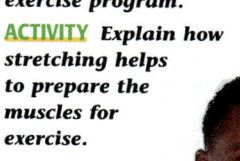

▼ *The warm-up is an important part of any exercise program.*
ACTIVITY *Explain how stretching helps to prepare the muscles for exercise.*

L2 Community Involvement

Have students locate retail outlets that sell reflective clothing and other items for people who exercise at night. Assist students in getting permission to demonstrate the clothing and other items to the class.

L1 Guest Speaker

Invite a physical education teacher or coach to demonstrate exercises that reduce body fat, improve flexibility, condition muscles, and strengthen the heart and lungs. Discuss how a person can judge the potential value of specific exercises. What health and safety considerations should people make in selecting an exercise program?

L1 Demonstration

Ask a weight trainer to come to class and discuss his or her weight-training program and goals. Request that the speaker demonstrate some weight-training exercises.

L1 Explaining

Talk to students about horse races or car races they may have seen. Ask if horses or race cars start cold. (Never. Horses walk, and cars take warm-up laps before racing.) The same is true of professional athletes. They never start a practice or game without a warm-up. The same applies for anyone who is beginning an exercise workout. The body needs time for the muscles to warm up. Ask for volunteers who can explain the difference between warming up and cooling down.

PERSONAL HEALTH

CROSS-TRAINING. Cross-training means varying one's fitness program to include several kinds of exercise. Someone engaged in cross-training might do an intense aerobic dance workout one day, bike the next day, swim the third day, and walk with hand weights the fourth day. As an alternative, he or she might combine within one workout session swimming for the upper body and aerobic dance for the lower body. This variation not only provides a change of pace for the mind, but it also gives muscles and joints most stressed by a particular kind of exercise time to rest. In addition, cross-training helps people achieve a higher level of total body fitness.

LEP Class Activity

Ask students to search through books and current magazines for examples of activities that would be appropriate for warm-up and cool-down exercises. Have them sketch or cut out illustrations of favorite examples as reminders for their fitness journals. Ask for volunteers to demonstrate some of the exercises.

L1 Class Activity

Have students take their resting heart rate in class and record this number on a sheet of paper. Have students create a contract to increase their aerobic activity level in order to improve their level of cardiovascular fitness. Have students keep a diary of their activity level and determine their resting heart rate each day. After six weeks, have students graph their resting heart rate. If the number decreased, it can be assumed that their level of cardiovascular fitness improved over the six-week period.

L1 Parental Involvement

Ask for volunteers to enlist their parents in a joint exercise program. Have students write short reports of their progress to turn in each week.

L2 Cooperative Learning

Distribute *Cooperative Learning Activity 3* and have students invent a sport. 👉

In general, exercising more than three times a week for six months should help get you physically fit. You will then need to keep up your program at least three times a week to maintain your fitness level.

INTENSITY

To improve physical fitness, you need to work your muscles and cardiorespiratory system at a level of intensity that permits you to achieve overload. To accomplish this goal, you must start slowly and build endurance. Doing too much too soon is harmful because it can cause sleeplessness or chronically sore muscles.

In weight training, start with a lighter weight and build to the heavier ones. In aerobics programs, work toward your target heart range. If you're out of shape, give yourself six months to reach it. Target heart range is 60 to 85 percent of your maximum heart rate and the rate in which your heart should beat for optimal exercise benefits.

DURATION

Time spent doing aerobic exercises should be built up gradually. The goal in aerobics is to spend 20 to 30 minutes working at your target heart range. In weight training, do the exercises slowly, taking at least two seconds each time you lower a weight. Rest for one or two minutes between sets, and do a variety of exercises to strengthen your muscles in the full range of motion. An exercise set consists of six to fifteen repetitions.

▼ *A fitness program should always include activities that you enjoy.*

ACTIVITY *List factors you would need to consider in planning your personal fitness program.*

The Cool-Down

The **cool-down** is *engaging in activity to gradually decrease activity.* Just as your body needs to be readied for increased activity, it needs to be returned gradually to a less active state. The reason is that vigorous or prolonged activity causes increased blood flow to the muscles. If you stop suddenly, the blood *pools*—or collects—in those muscles, resulting in less blood flow to the brain. This can lead to dizziness or fainting.

The best way to cool down is simply to slow down as you continue the activity. Slowed activity should be done for about five minutes, followed by five minutes of stretching. You have cooled down adequately when your heart rate is within 20 to 30 beats of your regular heart rate.

MORE ABOUT . . . . .

BASICS OF AN EXERCISE PROGRAM.

Students do not need fancy athletic equipment to get physically fit. They can get an excellent workout just by climbing stairs. Tell students the following: First, find a safe set of well-lighted stairs with limited traffic. Be sure to wear non-slip shoes. Start slowly, remembering to warm up and stretch first. Climb stairs several times a week, aiming to increase both the time you spend climbing and the speed at which you climb. Be certain to tell students that stair climbing is not recommended for people with heart or knee problems.

Monitoring Your Progress

Occasionally, you will want to stop and evaluate your fitness program. Ask yourself these questions: "Do I feel better? Am I walking or bicycling or jogging farther in a shorter amount of time?" If lifting weights, you might ask: "Can I lift more weights for a longer period of time?" Keep in mind, too, that most people will have minor sore or stiff muscles over the first several days of a "new" exercise program. It is important, therefore, to be realistic about your progress. Patience is critical.

Many people keep exercise journals. Begin the journal the day you begin your exercise program. List your goals and keep track of the frequency, intensity, and duration of your workouts. At the end of 12 weeks and every six weeks after that, compare the figures. You'll have a record of your fitness progress!

Your Resting Heart Rate

Another way to monitor your progress is to take your **resting heart rate.** This is *the number of times your heart beats in one minute when you are not active.* A person of average fitness has a resting heart rate of between 72 and 84 beats a minute. After only four weeks of an exercise program, that rate can decrease by five to ten beats a minute. A resting heart rate below 72 beats a minute indicates a good fitness level. A teen at the top of his or her form may have a resting rate as low as 40 beats a minute.

LESSON 3 *Review*

Reviewing Facts and Vocabulary

1. Why do some athletes engage in cross-training?
2. What are the three parts of an exercise program?
3. What do the warm-up and cool-down have in common?
4. How does being physically fit affect your resting heart rate?
5. What can you do to help yourself get started on an exercise program?

Thinking Critically

6. **Evaluating.** Tell how the following weight training session could be improved to include the basics of a good exercise program: stretching— five minutes, lifting heavier weights— 25 repetitions, resting—five minutes, lifting lighter weights—50 repetitions.
7. **Analyzing.** Explain how your resting heart rate is an indicator of your fitness.

Applying Health Skills

8. **In Your Home and School.** Plan your exercise a week ahead of time, and mark the times on a calendar. Keep a record in your Health Journal of the physical activities you actually do at home or school, noting the frequency, intensity, and duration of each workout.

LESSON 3   PLANNING A FITNESS PROGRAM   **65**

CHARACTER IN ACTION

Commit to Be Fit

Ask students to think of the perseverance of one famous athlete and share examples with the class.

ASSESS

EVALUATING THE LESSON

- Assign and discuss the Lesson 3 Review; then administer, grade, and discuss the *Lesson 8 Quiz* in the TCR.

RETEACHING

- Have students make a short videotape demonstrating correct ways to warm up before and cool down after a workout. Ask them to provide commentary on the videotape about what happens to the body during these basic before- and after-exercise techniques as well as what might happen if they are omitted or done improperly.
- Ask students to complete *Reteaching Activity 8* in the TCR.

ENRICHMENT

- Have students analyze advertising claims made about working out on fitness machines by having them complete *Enrichment Activity 3* in the TCR.

CLOSE

Ask students to state the most important concepts learned in the lesson. Have students work in pairs to construct a mobile that illustrates major ideas in the lesson. When completed, have each pair define and explain one concept they have illustrated.

Lesson 3 Review

Answers to Reviewing Facts and Vocabulary

1. To strengthen different muscle groups.
2. The warm-up, the workout, and the cool-down.
3. They allow the pulse rate to adjust gradually to the level of exertion, whether speeding up or slowing down.
4. Being physically fit decreases your resting heart rate.

5. Answers will vary.

Answers to Thinking Critically

6. By lifting lighter weights after stretching and before lifting the heavier weights.
7. A low resting heart rate means the heart muscle is strong, which is an indicator of fitness.

Health **Skills** Activities

Health Skills Activities

ACTIVITY 1
HEALTH SKILLS

Self Management, Health Advocacy

➤ **National Standards**
This activity meets these National Health Standards: 3.4; 7.4; 7.5.

Teach

- Review with students the definition of aerobic exercise (vigorous activity in which oxygen is continuously taken in for a period of at least 20 minutes). Make sure they can differentiate this type of activity from anaerobic types.
- Make sure the performers understand the importance of warming up prior to any strenuous physical activity and of cooling down at the conclusion.

ACTIVITY 2
HEALTH SKILLS

Self Management, Goal Setting

➤ **National Standards**
This activity meets these National Health Standards: 3.5; 6.1.

Teach

Provide students with at least three client descriptions, such as:

- Joel has been dreading his Thursday PE class for two days because his instructor said the class will be practicing chin-ups. Every time Joel has tried to do chin-ups in the past, he could barely do one.
- Raking leaves after school and on weekends allows Renee, age 15, to buy some great looking clothes for her school wardrobe. This September, Renee found herself getting short of breath just raking the neighbor's small yard. The next morning, her arms and back were very stiff and sore.
- Reuben was looking forward to spending time at the lake this summer hanging out with his friends, swimming, and playing volleyball. During the first game of volleyball in June, however, Reuben's legs cramped up and he had to sit out the rest of the games that afternoon.

Activity 1 — Aerobic Workout Video

Experts agree that you are more likely to stick with an aerobic workout if it's one you enjoy. Imagine that you were asked to plan an aerobic workout suited to your fitness level and interests. What kinds of activities would you include?

Directions

1. Working with one or two partners, choose music that you like and that would be appropriate for a workout video.
2. Devise a 20- to 30-minute aerobic workout made up of aerobic exercises or activities that you enjoy. Some possibilities are dance steps, running in place, jumping rope, and kick boxing.
3. As one partner performs the routine, another is to explain safety considerations of each exercise and how it promotes physical fitness. The third partner can manage the videotaping responsibilities.
4. Share your workout video with the class.

Time
Two 50-minute periods

Materials
paper, pen, VCR or CD player, video camera and TV (optional)

Self-Assessment

✓ Exercises and activities selected were aerobic, varied, and filled a 20- to 30-minute workout.
✓ Exercises and activities were demonstrated with personal safety in mind.

Activity 2 — Personal Trainer

Exercise provides physical health benefits. It can also help you perform everyday activities more easily. For this activity, act as a personal trainer to customize an exercise program for a "client."

Directions

1. In small groups or working independently, choose a client from the list your teacher provides.
2. Identify which components of fitness your client needs most to work on.
3. Develop an exercise plan for your client describing specific ways in which he or she can improve in the areas of fitness you have isolated.
4. Share and compare with the class your fitness plan for the client you chose.

Time
One 30-minute period

Materials
none

Self-Assessment

✓ Correctly identified components of fitness client needed most to work on.
✓ Created an exercise plan that would help client achieve his or her fitness goals.

66 CHAPTER 3 PHYSICAL FITNESS AND YOUR HEALTH

ASSESSMENT SCORING

Using a four-level rubric, the student has achieved a 4 if:

ACTIVITY 1

✔ Performers worked well as a group and each participated in the production.
✔ Video communicated a clear message that promoted physical fitness and personal safety.
✔ Student made use of audience evaluation of video.
✔ Audience was supportive and frank in their appraisal.

ACTIVITY 2

✔ Correctly identified components of fitness the client needed most to work on.
✔ Created a fitness plan that would help client achieve fitness goals.
✔ Student understands importance of correctly performing physical activities to avoid injury.
✔ Took an active role during the sharing of plans among classmates.

Supplement Warning

Many products sold as nutritional supplements aren't as safe as you might think. Just because a product is sold in a health store doesn't mean it's healthy.

A supplement called ephedra is a good example. Manufacturers often make many big claims for this herbal supplement. Ephedra, however, can do a lot more than boost your energy. It can give you a heart attack, stroke, or cause complications that can lead to death. The FDA has proposed new warning labels that tell customers exactly how dangerous this unnecessary supplement can be.

The way to develop your physical health is to stick to a healthy fitness program. Skip the supplements in favor of healthy activity.

Play the Video

> HISTORICAL STATEMENT: For over 2000 years, the Chinese have relied upon ma-huang or ephedra in their traditions of using herbs. The plant is a straggly shrub, seemingly leafless to the untrained eye. Extensive research, which has brought about its well-deserved reputation, has been conducted on Chinese ephedra.
> **CAUTION:** This product should NOT be used by individuals with heart disease, high blood pressure, thyroid disease, diabetes, or those who have difficulty in urination. It should NOT be taken concurrently with antidepressant or antihypertensive drugs containing monoamine oxidase (MAO) inhibitors. NOT recommended for children under 12 years of age.
> **DIRECTIONS:** As a dietary supplement, take one to two capsules daily with meals or a glass of water. Store in a cool, dry place.
> **INGREDIENT:** One capsule supplies 375 mg. Chinese ephedra (ma-huang).

CNN. All Rights Reserved.

Think About It

- Why has the FDA requested warning labels for supplements that contain ephedra? What will the labels say?
- Suppose a friend tells you "Anything herbal is safe. After all, it comes from nature." How would you respond?
- What are some safe alternatives to these dangerous supplements?

CNN HEALTH NEWS **67**

MORE ABOUT . . . . .

EPHEDRA. The National Football League recently became the first major professional sports league to ban the use of ephedra. After the deaths of several high school and college athletes were blamed on the use of this dangerous supplement, the league took action to prevent further use of the stimulant.

In addition to preventing misuse of the stimulant within professional sports, the NFL hopes that its ban will send an important message to high school students who might consider using the supplement. Data suggest that the use of supplements by high school and college students is increasing, putting more teens at risk.

Objectives. After viewing the video, students should recognize the benefits of a healthy exercise program for improving fitness rather than using dangerous supplements.

Motivator. Ask: "What products are you likely to find in a health store?" List all responses on the chalkboard. Then ask students to contemplate if every product sold in a health store is actually healthy. Invite students to watch Video Segment 3 to introduce the dangers of one such supplement: ephedra.

Teach

- Use a Word Web to help students summarize what they have learned about ephedra. Write the names ephedra and ma-huang in the center circle. Then create two circles labeled "What is it?" and "What does it do?" Have students complete the chart by adding lines and notes to each outer circle.
- Emphasize the benefits of participating in a healthy exercise program over using unnecessary supplements. Help students generalize to expand the focus of the report to include supplements other than ephedra. Discuss the benefits of a balanced exercise program. Compare the benefits with the potential dangers of using supplements.

Investigate. Have students do field research at a local nutrition store or an Internet site that sells health supplements. Students should collect the names of five supplements, note their ingredients, and list claims made by the manufacturer or store clerks. Then discuss each of the supplements as a class. Invite students to identify the unsupported claims and other persuasive techniques used to make these supplements seem effective. Have students explain how an exercise program can replace any of these unnecessary products.

Close. Have students imagine that a friend tells them about "a new supplement that helps you lose weight and gain muscle without exercising." Ask students to respond, using details from the video in their answers.

CHAPTER 3 *Review*

CHECKING COMPREHENSION

- Assign and discuss the chapter review.
- Use the MindJogger Videoquiz to review the chapter.

CHAPTER 3 REVIEW ANSWERS

Using Health Terms

1. physical fitness
2. flexibility
3. muscular endurance
4. isotonic
5. aerobic
6. isometric
7. basal metabolism
8. cool-down
9. warm-up
10. overload
11. cross-training
12. resting heart rate

Recalling the Facts

1. Your level of physical fitness affects your physical, mental, and social health. It affects how you eat, sleep, and learn. If you are fit, you look good, have energy, and generally feel good about yourself.
2. Strength and endurance.
3. One way to measure body composition is by a "pinch" test, using calipers to pinch the skin on the upper arm and calf.
4. Strength is measured by the number of pull-ups and push-ups one can do; endurance is measured by the number of leg-lifts.
5. Heart and lungs.
6. Exercise can help reduce feelings of chronic fatigue and stiffness and can improve motor responses. It strengthens the body's muscles, skeleton, and other moving parts and helps slow the onset of osteoporosis. A strong body has better protection against disease and recovers faster after disease or injury. It strengthens all the major systems necessary for good health.

Using Health Terms

On a separate sheet of paper, write the term that best matches each definition below.

LESSON 1

1. The ability to carry out daily tasks easily and have enough reserve energy to respond to unexpected demands.
2. The ability to move a body part through a full range of motion.
3. The ability of the muscles to do difficult physical tasks over a period of time without causing fatigue.

LESSON 2

4. Activity that combines muscle contraction with repeated movement.
5. Vigorous activity in which oxygen is continuously taken in for a period of at least 20 minutes.

6. Activity that uses muscle tension to improve muscular strength with little or no movement of the body part.
7. The minimum amount of energy required to maintain the life processes in a body.

LESSON 3

8. Engaging in activity to gradually decrease activity.
9. Engaging in activity that prepares the muscles for the work that is to come.
10. Working the body harder than it is normally worked.
11. Combining various exercise routines to help work different body systems.
12. Number of times your heart beats in one minute when you are not active.

Recalling the Facts

Using complete sentences, answer the following questions.

LESSON 1

1. How does your level of physical fitness affect your total health?
2. What are the two categories used for measuring physical fitness?
3. How is body composition measured?
4. What two activities can be used to measure strength and endurance?
5. What two organs of the body does cardiorespiratory endurance measure?

LESSON 2

6. How are exercise and physical fitness related?
7. How does exercise help the nervous system?
8. How do metabolism and calories relate to a person's weight?

9. Describe ways in which exercise might improve your self-esteem.
10. How does anaerobic exercise differ from aerobic exercise?

LESSON 3

11. Explain the principles of overload, progression, and specificity, and tell how they are important in designing a physical fitness program.
12. What is the significance of the F.I.T. formula? What are the parts of this formula?
13. How is warming up beneficial to a person's heart rate?
14. How long will it likely take for a person who is out of shape to become physically fit when following a good fitness program?

68 CHAPTER 3 PHYSICAL FITNESS AND YOUR HEALTH

---

7. Exercise can improve your reaction time by helping you respond more quickly to stimuli.
8. If you take in more calories than you burn, you gain weight. If you take in fewer calories than you burn, you lose weight.
9. Being physically fit gives you a sense of pride and accomplishment. You will look better and feel better about yourself.

10. Aerobic exercise is vigorous activity in which oxygen is continuously taken in for a period of at least 20 minutes. Anaerobic exercise involves intense bursts of activity in which the muscles work so hard that they produce energy without using oxygen. Aerobic exercise strengthens the cardiovascular system. Anaerobic exercise strengthens different groups of muscles.

Thinking Critically

LESSON 1

1. **Analyzing.** How might body composition affect a person's total fitness?
2. **Analyzing.** Compare the fitness levels of a 75-year-old non-smoking female who bicycles three times a week to a 16-year-old male whose only physical activity is walking three blocks to school.

LESSON 2

3. **Synthesizing.** Participating in an aerobics class will contribute to cardiorespiratory endurance. Some people cannot afford this, or do not want to exercise in front of a group. What would accomplish the same goal and be more private, as well as less expensive?

LESSON 3

4. **Evaluating.** Percy plays football in the fall, hockey in winter, and baseball in the spring and summer. Analyze his program of physical fitness. Tell what is missing and what he could do to make up for these omissions.

Making the Connection

1. **Social Studies.** Soccer, long a popular sport in countries the world over, has developed a big following in the United States in recent years. Write a two-page report about this sport. On the first page, describe soccer, using outside resources if you are familiar with it. On the second, identify the exercise benefits that come from playing the sport.

2. **Science.** Find articles in your local newspaper or magazines that have to do with the costs of poor fitness. Look, in particular, for information on the rise in cardiovascular diseases and overweight and its relationship to sedentary living. Share your findings with the class in a brief oral report.

BEYOND THE CLASSROOM

PARENTAL INVOLVEMENT Observe members of your household for several days, taking note of physical activities done by each member that provide—or fail to provide—some fitness benefit. Afterward, conduct a roundtable discussion with interested family members, sharing suggestions for improvement where needed. Work together to set up a regular plan of family fitness and exercise.

COMMUNITY INVOLVEMENT Call or visit a health spa, physical fitness center, or your local YMCA or YWCA. Find out what kinds of fitness exercises they recommend for teenagers. Discover what types of equipment and facilities are available. Also, find out what other services they provide. Report to your class on your findings.

SCHOOL-TO-CAREER
Exploring Careers. Interview a personal trainer or other expert on careers in the area of health-related fitness. Ask questions to determine what kind of preparation and experience is required for such careers. Also, find out about the various settings in which such professionals work.

11. Refer to pages 62 and 63 for definitions of terms. It's important to challenge the body's performance (overload), to increase the challenge gradually (progression), and to focus on specific fitness goals (specificity).
12. The factors of the F.I.T. formula determine whether a workout helps you achieve your goal in working out. The components of the formula are: Frequency (how often you do the activity), Intensity (how hard you work at the activity during a session), and Time (how much time you devote to a given session).
13. A sudden increase in the pulse rate puts unnecessary strain on the heart and the blood vessels. Warming up increases the pulse rate gradually and safely.
14. Six months.

Thinking Critically

1. The higher the ratio of body fat to lean tissue, the lower the level of overall fitness.
2. Analysis should include discussion of protective factors such as exercise and risk factors such as smoking.
3. Exercise using an aerobics videotape.
4. He's not working on a program geared toward cardiovascular fitness. He needs to add aerobic exercise to his program.
5. The program should include aerobic activities as well as activities geared toward flexibility, endurance, and upper and abdominal body strength.

Making the Connection

1. Reports will vary. Benefits should include improved cardiorespiratory endurance, strength and endurance in leg muscles, and flexibility.
2. Reports will vary.

Evaluate

- Use the reproducible *Chapter 3 Test* in the TCR or construct your own using the Testmaker software.
- Use *Performance Assessment Activity 3* in the TCR.

Enrichment

- Have students complete *Cross-Curriculum Activity 3* in the TCR.

Beyond the Classroom

Keep students involved in the community, and encourage parent participation by assigning the activities on this page for students to work on outside of class.

Physical Activity for Life

	FEATURES	CLASSROOM RESOURCES

Chapter Resources

ACTIVITIES

- Cross-Curriculum Activity 4
- Health Lab 4
- Health Skills Activities 4
- Parent Letter and Activities 4

ASSESSMENT

- Chapter 4 Test
- Performance Assessment 4
- Testmaker Software

STUDENT ACTIVITIES WORKBOOK

- Applying Health Skills 9–11
- Study Guide 4
- Vocabulary Activity 4

STUDENT DIVERSITY STRATEGIES

- Audiocassette Program (English)
- Audiocassette Program (Spanish)
- Spanish Parent Letters and Activities
- Spanish Summaries, Quizzes, and Activities

MULTIMEDIA COMPONENTS

- English Audiocassette Program
- Spanish Audiocassette Program
- MindJogger Videodisc and VHS program
- ABCNews InterActive™ VHS/Videodisc Series

National Health Education Standards

One of the main goals of the National Health Education Standards is to move students toward "health literacy." Health literacy is the capacity of individuals to obtain, interpret, and understand basic health information and services and the competence to use such information and services in ways which promote health. The health standards were developed by applying the characteristics of a well-educated, literate person within the context of health. The health literate person is:

- a critical thinker and problem solver
- a self-directed learner
- a responsible, productive citizen
- an effective communicator

Listed below are the Health Education Standards Performance Indicators addressed in each lesson of this chapter.

Lesson	Health Standards Performance Indicators
1	1.1, 3.1, 3.2, 6.4
2	1.1, 1.7, 3.1, 3.3
3	3.1, 3.4, 3.5, 3.6

ONLINE RESOURCES

For a fresh approach to health topics and an in-depth look at health issues, use these online resources found under Teacher Resources at **health.glencoe.com**.

- **BLOCK SCHEDULE LESSON PLANS** Reinforce health concepts with outside readings selected especially for students. Each reading is accompanied by a lesson plan and activities to enhance
  - Reading Skills
  - Cross Curriculum
  - Media Literacy

- **TECHNOLOGY PROJECTS** Instructions and suggestions on how to use computer, Internet, and software with health lessons.

- **HEALTH UPDATES** Timely topics in health news, including late-breaking medical advances and updates on teen risk behaviors.

Out of Time?

If time does not permit teaching this chapter, you may use these features: Making Responsible Decisions on page 81 and Building Health Skills on page 88.

BLOCK SCHEDULING

Block scheduling provides extended time for hands-on projects and activities. Use the following activity to engage students, provide further depth, and vary your instructional techniques:

- Connections (30 minutes) **pg. 82**
- Health Skills Activity (60–90 minutes) **pg. 90**

Physical Activity for Life

CHAPTER OVERVIEW

Chapter 4 focuses on skills-related fitness and considerations during training to reduce risks of injury and help athletes perform at their best.

LESSON 1 Skills-related fitness enables those interested in sports or recreational activities to perform at their best. Measuring skills and then participating in activities to build specific skills is an effective way to establish consistent performance.

LESSON 2 Most of the risks of physical activity can be reduced through common-sense decisions and practices. Preparing your body and mind for performance also contributes to an individual's athletic success.

LESSON 3 With any movement activity, there is risk of accident or injury. Risks of injury to the skeletal and muscular systems exist due to the nature of the activities. Proper treatment can reduce the extent and duration of these injuries. Weather-related risks also exist. Risks associated with exercise can be minimized.

CHAPTER 4
Physical Activity for Life

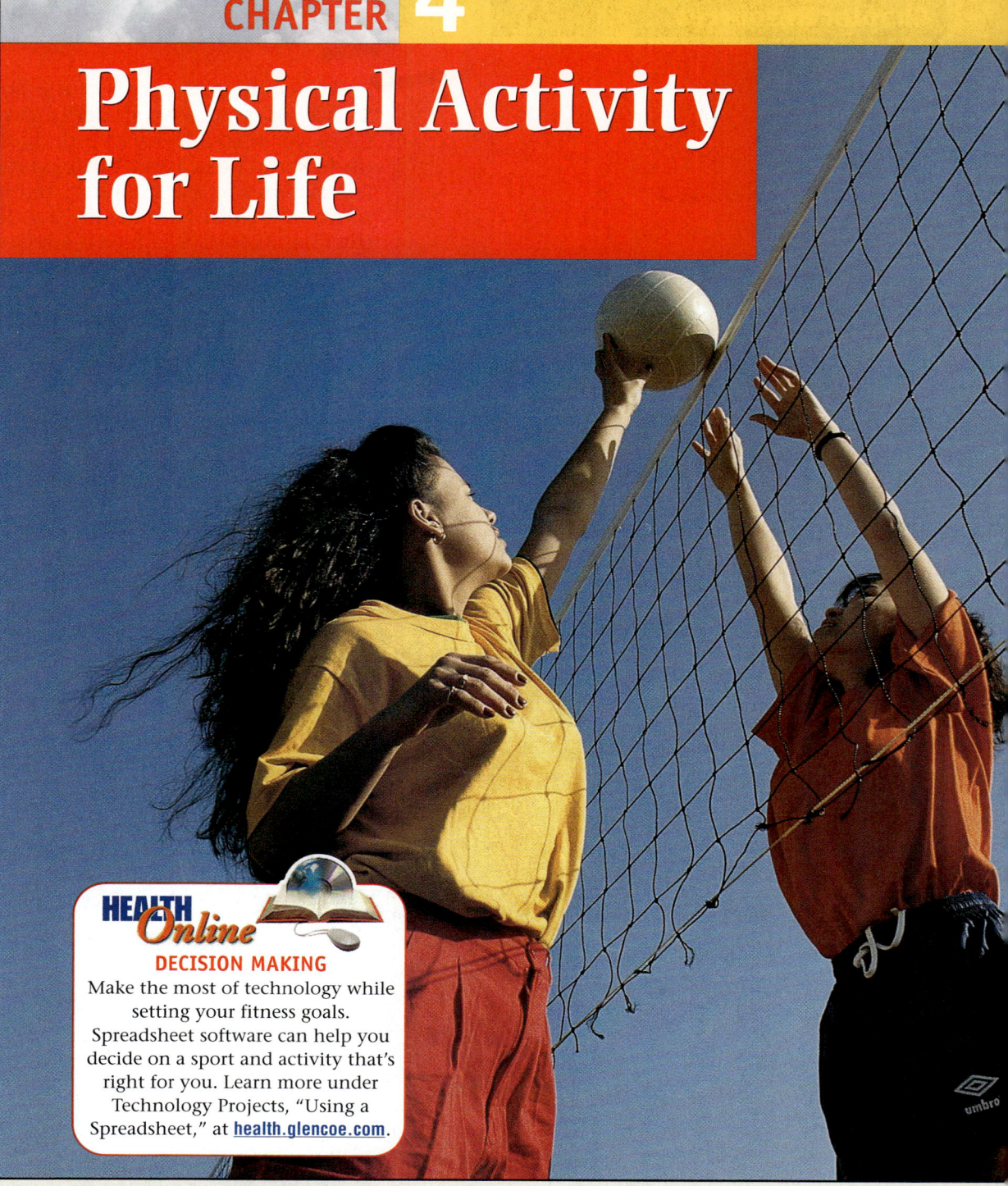

HEALTH Online

DECISION MAKING
Make the most of technology while setting your fitness goals. Spreadsheet software can help you decide on a sport and activity that's right for you. Learn more under Technology Projects, "Using a Spreadsheet," at health.glencoe.com.

Hands-On Health

TEACHING STRATEGY

Reinforcing and Reviewing Bring your health classroom to life with interactive teaching strategies and classroom management techniques that keep your students interested and involved. The unique *Hands-On Health: Creative Teaching Strategies* booklet that accompanies the *Glencoe Health* program offers fun, motivating activities. ☞

The following Classroom Management Ideas can be used to reinforce chapter concepts:

- Beach Ball
- Trivia Questions
- Paper Exchange
- Mental Outburst

Personal Health Inventory

Self-Inventory Write the numbers 1–10 on a sheet of paper. Read each statement below and respond by writing *yes*, *no*, or *sometimes* for each item. Write a *yes* only for items that you practice regularly. Save your responses.

1	I am more active than I am sedentary.
2	I incorporate activities into my life that provide exercise.
3	I use the stairs instead of escalators or elevators whenever possible.
4	I enjoy a variety of physical activities and sports.
5	I regularly participate in sports, such as cycling, swimming, or in-line skating.
6	I take into consideration my unique skills and physical abilities when choosing a sport.
7	I know and follow safety rules for the physical activities I participate in.
8	I follow a nutritious diet, avoid harmful substances such as tobacco and alcohol, and get adequate rest.
9	I avoid "winning at all costs" in sports.
10	I take proper precautions to minimize the risk of injury.

Follow-up After completing the chapter, retake this self-inventory. Pick two items that you need to work on and set a goal to improve your health behaviors.

> **Those who think they have not time for exercise will sooner or later have to find time for illness.**
>
> —EDWARD STANLEY
> 15TH EARL OF DERBY, (1826–1893)

Quick Write List all of the physical activity and exercise you have done in the past three days. Now think about which of these activities you might practice into adulthood or even over a lifetime.

INTRODUCING THE CHAPTER

Personal Health Inventory

Introduce the Self-Inventory and point out that the statements relate to students' physical activities. Have students read the statements and record their *yes, sometimes,* or *no* responses privately. Remind students that the only "right" responses are those that reflect their own habits and attitudes. Have students label their papers "My Participation in Physical Activity" and keep them in their private Health Journals, to be used in the Follow-up Activity at the end of the chapter.

- Discuss with students how good performance in sports and other skills-related physical activities is dependent upon the development of specific skills and the preparation of the body and mind for the challenge of the activity. Tell students that this chapter will focus on these aspects of fitness. It will also discuss injuries associated with physical activity.
- Have students read the chapter opener quotation and look at the photographs in this chapter. Ask: Which physical activities do you consider most enjoyable? Why? Which do you think are most beneficial? Why? Then encourage volunteers to identify the physical activities they engage in regularly and to describe the benefits they notice when they are active. Tell students that, as they study Chapter 4, they will learn more about physical activity and its importance to all aspects of health.
- Distribute Parent Letter 4 in the *Parent Letters and Activities* booklet in the TCR. 📖

TECHNOLOGY OPTIONS

 You may wish to use *Food and Nutrition* with this chapter. For your convenience, use the separate *ABCNews InterActive™ Bar Code Correlation* that accompanies the *Glencoe Health* program. 🔴

MINDJOGGER
VIDEOQUIZ

To preview or review chapter content, you may wish to use the *MindJogger Videoquiz* that accompanies Chapter 4. 🔴

Physical Activity and Skills-Related Fitness

LESSON **1**

Physical Activity and Skills-Related Fitness

FOCUS

LESSON OBJECTIVES

After studying this lesson, students should be able to

- explain the difference between lifestyle activities and sports activities.
- describe the six basic measures of skills-related fitness.
- assess their abilities at each of the skills.

MOTIVATOR

Ask students to make a list of three of their favorite sports or physical activities that require skills. Beside each sport or activity, have them identify the skills involved in the activity.

INTRODUCING THE LESSON

Have students share their responses to the Motivator. Then explain that kinesthesiologists have identified six skills that are common to many physical activities. Tell the students that this lesson will present those skills and describe ways to measure each.

INTRODUCING HEALTH TERMS

- Ask students to define in their own words each of the vocabulary terms listed. Then have them compare their definitions with those provided in the Glossary and correct any misconceptions.
- Have students complete Vocabulary Activity 4 and Chapter Study Guide 4 in the *Student Workbook*. ☞

W hat kinds of physical activities do you enjoy? Do you like to play basketball? Maybe you prefer riding mountain bikes, skiing, or playing volleyball. Whatever your preference, physical activity can provide enjoyable ways of keeping fit.

HEALTH TERMS

physical activity
lifestyle activities
agility
balance
coordination
speed
reaction time
power

HEALTH CONCEPTS

- Physical activity can take place in many forms.
- Recreational activities and sports can help you maintain a high level of physical fitness.
- Skills-related fitness includes those aspects of fitness that help you perform well in sports and other physical activities.
- A number of tests can be used to measure skills-related fitness levels.

Choices for Physical Activity

Physical activity includes *any form of movement—whether purposeful, as in exercise and sports or recreation, or incidental, as when carrying out domestic chores.*

All forms of physical activity provide varying amounts of exercise and benefits to one's overall health and fitness. Since many forms of physical activity involve working or playing with others, it can also be a healthful way to socialize. Generally, physical activities can be grouped into two main classes. These are *lifestyle activities* and *sports activities.*

Lifestyle Activities

You probably already do some physical activity as part of your daily routine, such as biking or playing basketball. Maybe you perform a

Lesson 1 Resources

TEACHER'S CLASSROOM RESOURCES

☞ **Concept Map** Activity 9
☞ **Enrichment** Activity 4
☞ **Lesson 9 Quiz**
☞ **Lesson Plan 9**
☞ **Parent Letter and Activities 4**
☞ **Reteaching** Activity 9

STUDENT WORKBOOK

☞ **Applying Health Skills 9**
☞ **Chapter Study Guide 4**
☞ **Vocabulary** Activity 4

regular task at home, such as raking leaves or walking your dog. These are examples of **lifestyle activities**, *forms of physical activity that are a normal part of your daily routine or recreation and that promote good health throughout a lifetime.*

Lifestyle activities provide many physical and social benefits. Activities associated with camping, such as carrying a backpack, hiking, and setting up tents, for example, all work the body's muscles. Dancing is an excellent aerobics activity, and so is cross-country skiing.

Sports Activities

Sports activities differ from lifestyle activities in that they usually involve competition and are guided by a set of rules. When you think of sports, you may think of team sports such as football, basketball, and hockey, but other possibilities exist.

■ **Individual sports.** These are skills-oriented activities that you can do by yourself, such as swimming, bicycling, or playing golf. Many individual sports also are called lifetime sports, because they are more likely than team sports to become part of a person's routine over a lifetime.

■ **Partner sports.** These are activities carried out with a partner, such as playing tennis or racquetball.

■ **Nature sports.** These are activities in which there is some interaction with one of the elements of nature, such as surfing, rock climbing, and sailing.

Choosing Physical Activities

When selecting new sports or physical activities, it is best not to limit yourself to a single type. Alternating physical activities works different muscles and body systems, thus contributing to different aspects of total fitness. It also helps reduce your chances of injury.

Another reason for varying the activities you do is variety itself. Doing the same routine day in and day out can cause boredom and ultimately may lead you to stop altogether. Even slightly changing your routine can give you more enthusiasm. You might try swimming one day of the week, in-line skating the next, and power walking on still another.

Skills-Related Fitness

Regular physical activity develops skills-related fitness. Like health-related fitness, skills-related fitness contributes to your total physical health. There are six basic measures of skills-related fitness.

▼ **Many people take aerobics classes to stay fit.**

ACTIVITY *What physical activities are part of your routine? Are they individual, partner, or nature sports?*

TEACH

L2 Class Activity

Select students to plan a sporting activity for the class. Ask: What equipment will be needed? Will money be involved? If so, how will students get the money? What permissions may be necessary? Should other students and faculty members be invited to participate? When and where should the event be held? At what time? Assist students in finalizing the plans for the event.

L1 Class Activity

Collect brochures, flyers, and other information about school and community exercise programs. Ask volunteers to make a display of the materials and to discuss with the class some of the information contained in them.

L1 Class Activity

Have students brainstorm a list of exercises/sports. Then ask them to rate the exercises/sports they have tried, from "10" for their favorite to "1" for least favorite. Next, have them answer in writing the following questions: How often have you done each exercise/sport? When? Where? Would you make it part of a lasting exercise program? Why or why not? Lead the class in a discussion of some of the responses.

L1 Writing

Let each student choose a sporting event and write a two-page report about the activity. As part of the report, have them include information about amateur vs. professional participation in the sport and/or a brief profile of a prominent figure in the sport.

MEETING STUDENT DIVERSITY

THE PHYSICALLY AND MENTALLY CHALLENGED. Many individuals who are physically or mentally challenged participate in and enjoy physical activities. Have students research the Special Olympics. Ask for volunteers to interview young people who participate in the Special Olympics and those who volunteer their assistance during the events.

Also, ask students to find articles in newspapers and magazines about athletic accomplishments of individuals who are physically challenged. Survey the community for such individuals, and ask if they would be willing to be interviewed by one or two students.

LEP Class Activity

Ask students to write the name of a sport or physical activity in which they are skilled or would like to be skilled. Ask them to explain in one sentence why the sport or activity is important to them. Write some of the sports and activities they name on the chalkboard, along with their reasons for preferring that sport or activity. Point out that an important part of being healthy is choosing what is right and best for them as individuals, not what is most popular among their peers.

L1 Writing

Suggest that students write private entries in their Health Journals, discussing their confidence (or lack of confidence) in their own skills-related fitness. Ask: Which skills do you think you are best at? Which are most difficult for you? How do your fitness-related skills influence your own choices of sports and other physical activities? Inform students that they will have an opportunity to rate their own fitness-related skills; afterward, they may want to review their journal entries and compare their perceptions with their ratings.

L1 Discussing

Divide the class into small groups, and let each group select a sports activity (baseball, tennis, or in-line skating, for example). Have group members discuss the six basic measures of skills-related fitness. Ask: Which are most important to successful participation in that sport? Let group members work together to rank the six fitness measures from most to least important.

- **Agility.** This is *the ability to control the body's movements and to change the body's position quickly.*
- **Balance.** This is *the ability to remain upright either while standing still or moving.*
- **Coordination.** This is *the ability to use two or more body parts together well, or to use the senses along with the body parts.*
- **Speed.** This is *the ability to move a distance or complete a body movement in a short period of time.*
- **Reaction time.** This is *the rate of movement once a person realizes the need to move.*
- **Power.** This is *the ability to use force with great speed.*

It is important to recognize that different sports require different parts of skills-related fitness. For example, a figure skater needs good agility, but not the power of a linebacker. Most sports require varying degrees of several skills. Some people have more natural ability in skills-related fitness than others. Although you have less control over your levels of physical skill, you can work to improve them. Knowing which skills you do well can help you decide which sports or physical activities are best for you. No matter how you score on the skills-related parts of fitness, you can still enjoy some type of physical activity.

▼ *The side shuttle measures agility.*

ACTIVITY *List several sports in which players use a side shuttle.*

Measuring Your Agility

Have you ever noticed how tennis players slide quickly and gracefully from side to side to reach the ball? These players have a high degree of agility. One test that measures agility is the side shuttle. Preparation for the test includes placing five lines of masking tape on the floor, about three feet apart, as in the picture.

SIDE SHUTTLE

1. Start with your feet outside the first line.
2. Slide over all the lines without crossing your feet, until your outside foot passes over the last line.
3. Then slide back, until your other foot passes over the first line. Only one foot should cross the outside lines.
4. Repeat, sliding across and back as many times as you can in ten seconds. Keep track of your slides.
5. Freeze in place when your partner yells "stop." Count one point for each line you crossed.
6. To rate your agility, find your score on the chart.

SCORING (LINES CROSSED)		
MALE	**FEMALE**	**RATING**
31 or more	28 or more	Excellent
26–30	24–27	Good
19–25	15–23	Fair
less than 19	less than 15	Needs Improvement

74 CHAPTER 4 PHYSICAL ACTIVITY FOR LIFE

COOPERATIVE LEARNING

SPORTS COMMENTARY. Have students work in pairs to read several newspaper or magazine descriptions of sports events such as basketball games. Alternatively, they may record and watch the events on video if the equipment is available at home and school. Tell them to analyze several reported actions of the players and decide which of the six measures of skills-related fitness are most required by each player's move. Then have them role-play a post-game televised discussion of the highlights, commenting on the measures displayed in each event. For example: "Did you see Rutgers jump? What power!" "Yes, but what about Garcia's reaction time when he blocked that shot?"

Measuring Your Balance

If you've ever watched a gymnast on the balance beam, you can see how crucial the skill of balance must be to this sport. The body balance test is one good way to measure balance. You'll need a yardlong piece of wood that's about 1-inch square. The stick balance consists of two parts. To rate yourself, add the scores for both parts together.

BODY BALANCE—PART 1

1. Place the stick on the floor. Stand so that the balls of both feet are on the stick and both heels are on the floor.
2. Raise both heels off the floor while keeping your balance on the stick for 15 seconds. Have a partner time you. Keeping your arms straight out and focusing on an immovable point in front of you will help you keep your balance. Place your heels back on the floor.
3. Repeat Step 2.
4. Score two points if you could balance for 15 seconds on your first try. Score one point if you could balance for 15 seconds on your second try. If you were successful on both tries, your score is three.

BODY BALANCE—PART 2

1. Stand on the stick with your foot running lengthwise on it. Use the foot you would balance on when you kick a ball.
2. Bring your other foot off the floor and balance for 10 seconds. Then rise on your toes and balance for another 10 seconds.
3. Score one point if you balanced for 10 seconds before rising on your toes. Score one point if you balanced for 10 seconds on your toes. Score a bonus point if you were able to maintain your balance for both. The highest score is three.
4. To rate your balance, add your scores from Parts 1 and 2 and find your total score on the chart.

🔻 *The stick balance measures balance.*
ACTIVITY *List several sports figures that you think possess good balance skills.*

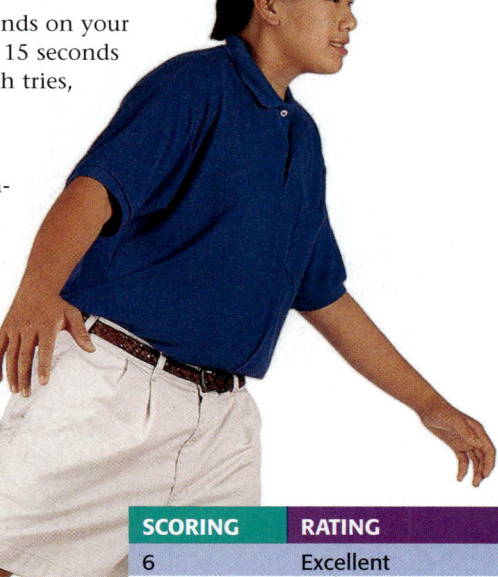

SCORING	RATING
6	Excellent
5	Good
3 or 4	Fair
less than 3	Needs Improvement

L1 Demonstrating

Ask several volunteers to prepare an area in the classroom for the activity designed to measure agility. Then have them demonstrate the activity for the rest of the class. (They will need masking tape, a yardstick, and a stopwatch, a clock, or watch that can measure seconds.) If time and space permit, you may want to have all students work with partners to measure their own agility.

L1 Critical Thinking

Ask students to explain why they think the agility scoring for males is different from that for females. Suggest that students compare class scores for male and female students. Ask: Which group includes the highest score? the lowest score? How do the average scores of the two groups compare?

L1 Class Activity

Have students identify several sports figures who demonstrate good balance skills. Suggest that they list specific sports and other physical activities (such as ballet and other forms of dance) that require especially good balance. Then let several volunteers demonstrate the two body balance activities for the rest of the class to be sure everyone understands the instructions. Finally, let students work with partners to rate their own balance skills.

L1 Discussing

After students have measured their balance, ask students with the highest scores to offer balancing "tips" to those whose rating was *Fair* or *Needs Improvement*. Have volunteers research exercises that would improve balancing skills.

SCHOOL-TO-CAREER

ACTIVE COMMUTING. Have volunteers conduct a poll in your school to find out how many students walk, cycle, or ride in motor vehicles to school. Tell them to record the results in a SCHOOL category. Suggest that they establish a WORK category as well. For the WORK category, have them find out how many students and/or adult members of their household walk, cycle, or ride in motor vehicles to work. Encourage students to tabulate the results and post them in the classroom. Allow time to discuss the findings, as well as ways to encourage use of physical activity as a means of transportation.

L1 Discussing

Ask students who play soccer to describe some of the coordination requirements of the game. Then have students identify other sports in which good coordination skills are needed. Ask volunteers who participate in those sports to demonstrate the Stick Toss and Catch.

L1 Class Activity

Let students work with partners to use the Stick Toss and Catch to measure their own coordination skills. If possible, have students conduct this activity outdoors or in a large, open area, such as the school gym.

L2 Researching

What exercises and activities can students use to improve their coordination? Ask volunteers to research this topic and to share their findings with the rest of the class.

L2 Demonstrating

Invite a student who is skilled in juggling or manipulating a hacky sack with his or her feet to demonstrate his or her skills to the class. Then encourage the guest to explain how he or she started the activity and what process he or she followed to develop the coordination needed.

L1 Group Activity

Have students work in groups to brainstorm a list of sports and other physical activities that require skill in speed. Which group can generate the longest list within a given period of time (four minutes, for example)?

Measuring Your Coordination

A baton twirler in a parade throws the baton high into the air and continues walking. As the baton falls toward him, he reaches out, grabs it, and continues twirling. The twirler has good coordination. Coordination usually involves either the eyes and hands, the eyes and feet, or the hands and feet. People with good eye-hand or eye-foot coordination are good at hitting and kicking games such as baseball, soccer, and golf. A test that measures coordination is the stick toss and catch. This test requires three thin sticks or dowels, each one to two feet long. Give yourself three practice tries before doing this activity for a score.

► *Wand juggling measures the skill of coordination.*
ACTIVITY *Explain why good coordination skills are needed in soccer.*

STICK TOSS AND CATCH

1. Hold two sticks out in front of you, one in each hand. Have a helper place the third stick across the two you are holding.
2. Toss the top stick into the air, causing it to make a one-half turn. Then catch it with the sticks in your hands.
3. Repeat, tossing the stick five times to the right and five times to the left, for a total of 10 tries.
4. Score one point for each time you caught the stick. To rate your coordination, find your total score on the chart.

SCORING	RATING
9–10	Excellent
7–8	Good
5 or 6	Fair
less than 4	Needs Improvement

Measuring Your Speed

A runner moves rapidly toward the finish line. She is demonstrating speed. The short sprint is a test that measures speed. You will need a space of at least 30 yards with a clearly marked starting line and a way to measure distances in yards from that line. To prepare, you may want to mark the starting line and distance lines of 10 to 25 yards with masking tape. Your partner will need a stopwatch and a whistle.

MEETING STUDENT DIVERSITY

THE PHYSICALLY CHALLENGED. Ask students to research the history and activities of the Special Olympics. Have them determine when it began. What was its purpose? Who can participate? What are some of the opportunities for volunteers? In what countries are the Special Olympics held? What does it cost to participate? How are the events funded? When are they held? Invite representatives and/or volunteers from the community to speak with the class about the Special Olympics and how students can get involved.

SHORT SPRINT

1. Start off a few steps behind the starting line.
2. When your partner blows the whistle, signaling "go," begin running as quickly as you can. As your feet cross the starting line, your partner will begin timing you.
3. Your partner will blow the whistle again exactly three seconds later, then mark the spot where you were. At the sound of the second whistle, slow down gradually to a stop.
4. Your score is the distance you covered in the three seconds after crossing the starting line. To rate your speed, find your score on the chart.

SCORING (YARDS RUN)		
MALE	**FEMALE**	**RATING**
24 or more	22 or more	Excellent
21–23	19–21	Good
16–20	15–18	Fair
less than 16	less than 15	Needs Improvement

Measuring Your Reaction Time

Perhaps you've seen runners on blocks, ready to take off as soon as they hear the starting signal. The best runners can take off quickly, and even gain a second or two over their nearest competitor. This is because they have quick reaction time.

The yardstick drop is one good way to measure reaction time. You will need a yardstick for this activity. Try the activity three times and choose your best score.

YARDSTICK DROP

1. Have a partner hold the top of a yardstick between the thumb and index finger.
2. Place your hand around the yardstick at 24 inches, but without touching it. Allow your arm to rest on the edge of a table. Your partner can adjust the yardstick to help you do this.
3. Be alert and focus on the stick. Your partner will drop the yardstick without warning. Catch the yardstick as soon as you can.
4. Your score is the inch marked on the yardstick where you catch it. To rate your reaction time, find your score on the chart.

▼ *The yardstick drop measures reaction time.*
ACTIVITY *Discuss which part of a track or swim race most requires excellent reaction time.*

SCORING (INCHES)	RATING
more than 21	Excellent
19–21	Good
14–18	Fair
less than 14	Needs Improvement

LESSON 1   PHYSICAL ACTIVITY AND SKILLS-RELATED FITNESS   **77**

L1 Class Activity

If possible, set up a convenient location at school where students can complete the Short Sprint activity during a class period. If space and/or scheduling don't permit this kind of class work, have students work with partners to follow the procedure for measuring speed as a homework assignment.

L1 Critical Thinking

Ask: Do you think an athlete's ability to catch a yardstick is a good indicator of his or her ability to begin running as soon as the start of a race is signaled? Why or why not? Encourage students to express and support their own opinions.

L1 Class Activity

Let students work with partners to complete the Yardstick Drop. After both partners have tried the activity three times and recorded their scores and ratings, suggest that partners discuss their approach to noticing and catching the stick. Then let students try the activity again: Can any of them improve their ratings?

L1 Class Activity

After students have read the instructions for the Standing Long Jump activity on page 78, let them discuss the kinds of jumps they have done or watched. Ask: Why is the power involved in this jump different from that required for a triple jump? a high jump? Then let students work with partners to complete the activity and to record their scores and ratings.

MORE ABOUT . . . . .

FITNESS IN THE PAST. During the period of growth and frontier settlement in the United States, most people were very active. Fitness and exercise were a part of everyday life and necessary for survival. Then came the age of labor-saving devices—inventions that ranged from indoor plumbing and the automobile to dishwashers and hair-dryers—making life so easy that many Americans have adopted sedentary lifestyles. Sedentary living is inactive living, a way of life that is devoid of daily physical activity beyond that required for attending school or going to work. This way of life has been shown to be harmful to one's health, leading to a wide variety of circulatory, respiratory, digestive, and other problems, which only goes to show that some things never change—being fit is still a matter of survival!

ASSESS

EVALUATING THE LESSON

Assign and discuss Lesson 1 Review; then administer, grade, and discuss the *Lesson 9 Quiz* in the TCR. ☞

RETEACHING

- Have students analyze three sports to determine which skills are involved in the activity. Then have students compare and discuss their lists.
- Ask students to complete *Reteaching Activity 9* in the TCR. ☞

ENRICHMENT

- Have students investigate a sport that they are unfamiliar with to determine its rules and what equipment, if any, is needed. Encourage them to look into sports that are popular in certain regions of the United States or in different cultures.
- Help students analyze advertising claims about working out on fitness machines by having them complete *Enrichment Activity 4*, "Hi-Tech Pumping Iron," in the TCR. ☞

CLOSE

Tell students that while the development of skills is important to performance, other factors also contribute to one's physical abilities. The next lesson will focus on preparing for performance, both physically and mentally.

HEALTH *Online*

Use the online evaluation tools at **health.glencoe.com** to measure your current fitness levels and to set goals for improving your own physical fitness.

Measuring Your Power

The muscular swimmer moves quickly through the water, pulling with strong arms while kicking rapidly. He has power, the ability to use force with great speed. The standing long jump is one barometer of a person's power. To prepare, make a starting line on the floor with masking tape. Do the standing long jump twice, and record your better score.

STANDING LONG JUMP

1. Begin by standing behind the line. Use your arms to swing yourself forward, and jump as far as you can. Do not hop or run before you jump, and keep both feet together.
2. A partner can use a tape measure to find the distance from the starting line to the spot where you landed. Measure to the spot closest to the starting line where any body part touched the floor.
3. To rate your power, find your score on the chart.

SCORING (INCHES JUMPED)		
MALE	**FEMALE**	**RATING**
87 or more	74 or more	Excellent
80–86	66–73	Good
70–79	58–65	Fair
less than 70	less than 58	Needs Improvement

LESSON 1 *Review*

Reviewing Facts and Vocabulary

1. How do lifestyle activities differ from sports activities?
2. Name the six areas of skills-related fitness.
3. Name three tests that can be used to measure the above areas of skills-related fitness.

Thinking Critically

4. *Analyzing.* How does the skill of agility differ from the health-related fitness of flexibility?
5. *Comparing and Contrasting.* In a chart, show the similarities and differences between the skills-related fitness used to play baseball and hockey.

Applying Health Skills

6. *In Your Home and School.* Make a two-column chart. In the first column, list the physical activities that you engaged in during the past week. Analyze each activity for the different parts of skills-related fitness. In the second column, list which skills are addressed in each activity.

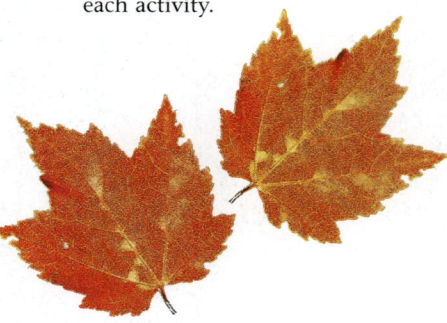

Lesson 1 Review

Answers to Reviewing Facts and Vocabulary

1. Lifestyle activities are part of a daily routine. Sports activities involve competition and have rules.
2. Agility, balance, coordination, speed, reaction time, power.
3. Any three: side shuttle, body balance test, stick toss and catch, short sprint, yardstick drop, standing long jump.

Answers to Thinking Critically

4. Agility refers to the amount of control you have over your body's movements. Flexibility refers to the ease with which your body moves.
5. The primary difference would be that baseball requires all measures of skills-related fitness in short bursts, whereas hockey requires them continuously throughout the game.

Physical Activity and Total Health

Physically active teens are healthy teens. You can try to make physical activity a goal no matter where you are and what you are doing. When you get together with your friends, do something active such as riding bicycles, playing tennis, or taking a walk. These activities add to your total health, and being fit feels great!

HEALTH TERMS

training program

hydration

anabolic steroids

HEALTH CONCEPTS

- Most of the risks of physical activity can be reduced or eliminated through some common sense decisions and practices.
- Preparing your body and learning the rules are important precautions to take before playing sports.

Getting Started

Just as a well-designed exercise program begins with a warm-up, it is wise not to begin a new sport or physical activity without careful preparation. Although professional athletes often have individual trainers, you can consult your physical education teacher, coaches, or family physician to help you set training goals.

Sports and Nutrition

What you eat and drink is an important part of a **training program**. This is *a program of formalized physical preparation for participation in a sport*. Food provides the energy necessary for top performance. You will learn more about nutrition and its role in sports in Chapters 5 and 6. Getting adequate hydration when engaged

LESSON 2   PHYSICAL ACTIVITY AND TOTAL HEALTH   **79**

FOCUS

LESSON OBJECTIVES

After studying this lesson, students should be able to

- describe some important considerations for a training program.
- describe how the mind-body connection affects sports performance.

MOTIVATOR

Ask students to list ways they have prepared for an athletic event.

INTRODUCING THE LESSON

Have students share their responses to the Motivator. Explain how peak performance is dependent not only on skill development, but also on the preparation of body and mind. Discuss how good nutrition, adequate rest, and the ability to relax and concentrate are important.

INTRODUCING HEALTH TERMS

- Ask students to find the definition of the term *anabolic steroids* in the Glossary. Have them discuss why they think this drug is illegal.
- Ask students to complete Vocabulary Activity 4 and Chapter Study Guide 4 in the *Student Workbook.*

Lesson 2 Resources

TEACHER'S CLASSROOM RESOURCES

- **Concept Map** Activity 10
- **Decision-Making** Activity 4
- **Lesson 10 Quiz**
- **Lesson Plan 10**
- **Reteaching** Activity 10

STUDENT WORKBOOK

- **Applying Health Skills 10**
- **Chapter Study Guide 4**
- **Vocabulary** Activity 4

MULTIMEDIA

- **ABCNews InterActive™ VHS/Videodisc,** *Food and Nutrition*

TEACH

L2 Research

Suggest that volunteers read current articles about the specialized sports drinks now on the market. Ask: What benefits do advertisements for these drinks emphasize? What actual benefits—if any—do the drinks offer? Under what circumstances should teens choose sports drinks over water? Let the volunteers share their findings with the rest of the class.

hotlink

anabolic steroids
Discuss with students that there is no legitimate shortcut to improved performance. Ask them to recall the principles of an effective workout and have them discuss how the body responds to overload over a period of time.

L1 Discussing

Ask students to suggest specific reasons for avoiding tobacco, alcohol, and other drugs. Ask: How can the use of such substances affect an athletic training program? What effect is it likely to have on a person's physical health? mental/emotional health? social health?

L1 Discussing

Bring a variety of sports drinks to class. Compare ingredient labels. Ask: What is the primary ingredient in each? Of what benefit are these ingredients to an athlete? What are some alternate sources of these ingredients?

hotlink

anabolic steroids For more information on the harmful effects of anabolic steroids, see Chapter 26, page 586.

▼ *Hydration is important during vigorous physical activity.*

in vigorous activity also is important. **Hydration** is *the addition of body fluids,* which you get through drinking liquids, especially water. During physical activity, the body loses water primarily by sweating and intense breathing. This process, called dehydration, can be a real threat. One of the first signs of dehydration is fatigue. Your body cannot effectively work when it is dehydrated. Thirst is not a good indicator of fluid loss. Exercise can blunt the thirst mechanism. Also, thirst is the body's way of telling you that the body is already depleted. To prepare for activity, an athlete should drink several cups of fluids two hours before, and then 15 minutes before, a heavy workout.

Avoiding Harmful Substances

Avoiding harmful substances such as tobacco, alcohol, anabolic steroids, and other drugs is another part of making healthful decisions and maintaining an athletic training program. **Anabolic steroids** are *chemicals similar to the male hormone testosterone.* They are sometimes taken illegally by athletes to increase muscle mass and

HOME AND COMMUNITY CONNECTION

COMMUNITY EXERCISE FACILITIES. Have students research exercise opportunities in your community. They should look for facilities such as recreation parks, swimming pools, tennis courts, skating rinks, and ski slopes. They should also include organized activity programs such as sports teams, classes, and activity clubs. Instruct them to make a chart using the six measures of skills-related fitness as headings. Under each heading, have students list local opportunities to develop and use the skills. One sport may be placed in several categories. Students may wish to construct the chart on poster board and display it in the classroom.

performance. The negative consequences of taking anabolic steroids are enormous. These include:

- increased risk of cancer and heart disease.
- sterility, or the inability to have children.
- skin problems, such as acne and hair loss.
- unusual weight gain or loss.
- sexual underdevelopment and dysfunction.
- violent, suicidal, or depressive tendencies.

Anabolic steroids mean trouble for athletes in other ways. Illegal distribution of steroids is a felony, and possession of steroids without a prescription is illegal. Athletes who test positive for steroids risk their careers. Purchasing "street steroids" adds risks, because these drugs can be mixed with other dangerous substances. The best choice regarding steroids, as with other illegal drugs, is abstinence.

Adequate Rest

Another important component of training is sleep. The rest that goes along with healthful sleeping helps the body re-energize. Too little sleep disrupts the **nervous system** causing such problems as slowed reaction time, lack of concentration, and depression. On average, teens need between eight and ten hours of sleep each night.

If you have trouble falling asleep at night, it is important to look for a cause. You may also try rearranging your schedule to allow time to unwind before bed. Since physical activity energizes the body, it is best not to exercise for several hours before bedtime. Instead, try

h⊙t link

nervous system For more information on the nervous system, its care and function, see Chapter 16, page 372.

Making Responsible Decisions

Asking a Frank Question

Jerry and his friend Dave are on their school's competitive swim team. The two boys have always shared a commitment to good health and fitness. Recently, Jerry has noticed that Dave seems to be getting more muscular and seems to have become more aggressive. Jerry suspects that Dave may be using steroids. He doesn't know for sure. He wants to confront his friend, but if he is wrong, he could ruin a great friendship. What should Jerry do?

What Would You Do?

Apply the six steps of the decision-making process to Jerry's problem.

1. **State the situation.**
2. **List the options.**
3. **Weigh the possible outcomes.**
4. **Consider your values.**
5. **Make a decision and act.**
6. **Evaluate the decision.**

LESSON 2   PHYSICAL ACTIVITY AND TOTAL HEALTH   **81**

L2 Researching

Assign a group of volunteers to read about current research on the sleep needs of teens, focusing on both the number of hours and the timing of those hours. Let these volunteers summarize their findings for the rest of the class. Then help students discuss how they might adjust their schedules to get the sleep they need.

Making Responsible Decisions

1. Jerry is concerned because he thinks Dave may be using steroids.
2. Jerry can (a) discuss his concerns with Dave, (b) ignore the signs that Dave may be using steroids, or (c) talk with the coach or another adult about his concerns.
3. If Jerry talks with Dave, Dave may become angry; however, if Dave is using steroids, the discussion might help him stop. If Jerry ignores the signs, he will continue to feel concerned about his friend, and Dave—if he is using steroids—might continue to use them. If Jerry talks with the coach or another adult, Dave might get help, but he might also become very angry with Jerry.
4. Jerry values his friendship with Dave. He also values his friend's health.
5. Responses will vary.
6. Encourage students to discuss both the short- and long-term consequences of their decisions.

L2 Decision Making

For further study on making responsible decisions, assign *Decision-Making Activity 4* in the TCR. 📁

MORE ABOUT . . . . .

STEROID ABUSE. Steroids have been used illegally by both athletes and nonathletes since the late 1950s to improve their athletic ability and to look better. The serious, health-destroying side effects of illegal steroid use have been well documented, but did you know that, according to recent studies, adolescent steroid users are also likely to use other drugs and to share needles, thereby increasing the risk of HIV/AIDS infection? Because the largest group to report first use of anabolic steroids is currently under 15 years old, preventive measures should start by the beginning of middle school. These may include peer counseling groups, presentations by physicians, coaches, athletes, school principals, and school health-care officials.

c o n n e c t i o n s
Social Studies

Ask students to share what they know about drug testing in their community. Ask: Which local employers—if any—test for drugs before hiring? Which test employees randomly? What is the school district's policy toward drug testing? After a brief introductory discussion, have students read the feature to learn more about drug testing. Then, in a class discussion, have students explain and support their responses to the feature questions. Suggest that students discuss this issue with their parents or other family members.

L1 Current Events

Suggest that students find, read, and bring to class recent articles (from newspapers or magazines) that describe the behavior of crowds at sporting events. Provide time for students to share and discuss these articles.

L3 Writing

Have each student select and read the biography of a successful athlete. Then have students write essays discussing the attitudes that contributed to the athlete's success.

c o n n e c t i o n s
Social Studies

Drug Testing

According to the National Institute on Drug Abuse, on any given day in the United States, 25 percent of workers between the ages of 18 and 40 would test positive for drugs. Some experts estimate that drug use costs employers over $60 billion a year in decreased productivity, absenteeism, and accidents. Therefore, in the interest of health, safety, and economics, many companies are now testing employees for drug use. The practice is stirring a heated debate.

Presently, drug testing is used in hospital emergency rooms for suspected drug overdoses and when arrests for driving violations suggest drug use. Some schools are now suggesting random drug testing for students.

1. Who, if anyone, do you think should be tested for drugs? Why? In what kinds of situations?

2. What do you think about schools testing students for drugs? Why? Do you think this testing should be random or "across the board"?

▲ *A pep talk before a competition can motivate athletes to do their best.*
ACTIVITY *Name other steps you can take to be prepared to do your best physically and mentally.*

reading or taking a hot bath. Avoid watching stress-producing videos or TV before going to bed. Also, avoid eating before bed or consuming drinks that contain caffeine. The relaxation techniques you learned about in Chapter 3 may also help.

Sports and the Mind

There is more to sports than just playing the game. As you learned in Lesson 1, your levels of skills-related fitness have some impact on your ability to play certain sports. Your thoughts affect your performance as well.

Effort and Ability

We are all born with different physical abilities. Heredity endows some people, for example, with greater speed, others with the endurance to run long distances without tiring.

In choosing a new sport or activity, be realistic about aspects of your natural ability. Does this mean that you should not try out for the sport of your dreams or "give it your all" on the playing field? Of course not. The sports world is full of stories of professional athletes who were once told they didn't have the skills to excel in their sport.

82 CHAPTER 4 PHYSICAL ACTIVITY FOR LIFE

MORE ABOUT . . . . .

EXERCISE PROGRAMS. Dr. Kenneth Cooper, the "father of aerobics," recommends that 14- to 18-year-olds try some of these regular exercise programs to increase their levels of fitness:

• walking 3 miles, 4 times per week, in less than 45 minutes for girls and less than 43 minutes for boys;

• swiming 1,000 yards, 4 times a week, in less than 25 minutes for girls and less than 24 minutes for boys;

• running or jogging 3 miles, 4 times a week, in less than 27 minutes for girls and 24 minutes for boys;

• cycling 8 miles in less than 40 minutes for girls and less than 32 minutes for boys.

Mind-Body Connection

Having a positive mind-set is important in sports, especially in team sports. When you think you can do a particular activity, such as jumping a hurdle in track, you are more likely to be successful than if you doubt your ability to perform. That's why coaches often give "pep talks" to their teams before an important game.

Sports and Competition

Emotions at sporting events often run high. Each team has a strong desire to win. Competition can be a positive force. Wanting to excel to "bring their team to victory" helps motivate many teenagers to develop fitness and perform at their best. It also builds character and generates team spirit and pride, leading team members to become close friends.

An excessive need to win or be first, however, can be harmful to yourself and to others. Remember that sports are games, not life. There cannot be a winner without there also being a loser. Demonstrating good sportsmanship at sports events helps you avoid conflict. It also shows that you have a healthy attitude toward the game.

LESSON 2 Review

Reviewing Facts and Vocabulary

1. What role does training play in sports?
2. How can your thoughts affect your physical performance?

Thinking Critically

3. **Analyzing.** Gilbert, who is trying out for the track team, has heard of a pill that "makes you fly like the wind." Give at least three reasons Gilbert should avoid using this pill.
4. **Synthesizing.** Search sports magazines or the sports section of a daily newspaper for stories that show good sportsmanship. In your private Health Journal, note qualities and traits of the athletes you admire and would like to adopt for yourself.

Applying Health Skills

5. **In Your Home.** Interview at least three relatives to find out about the kinds of sports or physical activities each enjoys. Ask what benefits he or she gains from taking part in this activity. Also, ask about the person's training program and how he or she keeps a positive attitude toward the sport or physical activity. Then answer the same questions for yourself with regard to a sport or physical activity in which you participate.

CHARACTER IN ACTION

Citizenship On and Off the Field

After students have completed the Character Check, ask them to ask themselves the following additional questions:

- Do I consistently show respect for all parties when I am winning a game?
- Do I show respect to the refs, even after a bad call?
- Do I show respect for my opponents after a crushing win?
- Do I show respect for all concerned both before and after the game?

To find the Citizenship Through Sports Alliance homepage, check Glencoe Health Online Web Links at health.glencoe.com.

ASSESS

EVALUATING THE LESSON

Assign and discuss the Lesson 2 Review; then administer, grade, and discuss the *Lesson 10 Quiz* in the TCR.

RETEACHING

- Have students develop an outline of the lesson using the headings as a guide.
- Ask students to complete *Reteaching Activity 10* in the TCR.

ENRICHMENT

- Have students research sports psychology and determine major factors involved in becoming mentally fit to compete.

CLOSE

Ask students to state the most important concepts learned in the lesson.

Lesson 2 Review

Answers to Reviewing Facts and Vocabulary

1. Training prepares you to participate in the sport.
2. You are more likely to succeed when you think that you can.

Answers to Thinking Critically

3. Answers will vary. Possible responses: Gilbert doesn't know what the drug is; he doesn't know what possible side effects it has; there are rules against drug use in competition; use and/or distribution of certain drugs is against the law.
4. Private health journal entries will vary.

Avoiding Injuries

LESSON 3

Avoiding Injuries

FOCUS

LESSON OBJECTIVES

After studying this lesson, students should be able to

- describe the most common injuries that occur during exercise.
- identify weather-related risks when exercising.
- explain ways to avoid risk and injury during exercise.

MOTIVATOR

Write the following on the chalkboard for students to work on while attendance is being taken: *Write a paragraph describing a recent injury that you or someone else suffered as a result of participating in a sport or physical activity.*

INTRODUCING THE LESSON

Have students share their responses to the Motivator. Discuss ways each of the injuries might have been avoided.

INTRODUCING HEALTH TERMS

- Have students write a definition of each of the vocabulary terms, and give an example of how each might occur.
- Ask students to complete Vocabulary Activity 4 and Chapter Study Guide 4 in the *Student Workbook.* 🡢

With any activity that involves movement, there is always a risk of accident or injury. The risk of injury during exercise increases when a person is not in good physical condition or has not sufficiently warmed up and cooled down. Attempting physical activities beyond your level of ability also increases the risk of injury.

HEALTH TERMS

- **muscle cramp**
- **strain**
- **sprain**
- **overexertion**
- **heat cramps**
- **heat exhaustion**
- **frostbite**
- **hypothermia**

HEALTH CONCEPTS

- Physical activities and sports carry an inherent risk of injury.
- Taking proper precautions can minimize the risk of injury.
- Paying attention to the weather is among the most important safeguards you can take against injury from outdoor physical activities.
- Wearing the proper attire and using the proper equipment help protect against injuries.

hotlink

muscular and skeletal systems For more information on injuries of the muscular and skeletal systems, see Chapter 15, pages 344 and 352.

Minor Exercise-Related Injuries

Have you ever had sore muscles after exercising or experienced the pain of a twisted ankle? The most common injuries that occur from exercise are to the **muscular** and **skeletal systems**. These injuries, which usually result from too much stress being placed on a joint or muscle, include the following:

- **Muscle cramp.** This is *a spasm or sudden tightening of a muscle,* usually the result of irritation within the muscle from being tired, overworked, or from dehydration—a lack of water. If you get a muscle cramp, drinking cool water may help to alleviate the problem. Muscle cramps are a danger to swimmers because they could prevent a person from being able to swim, causing drowning.

84 CHAPTER 4 PHYSICAL ACTIVITY FOR LIFE

Lesson 3 Resources

TEACHER'S CLASSROOM RESOURCES

🡢 **Concept Map** Activity 11
🡢 **Cooperative Learning** Activity 4
🡢 **Health Lab 4**
🡢 **Lesson 11 Quiz**
🡢 **Lesson Plan 11**
🡢 **Reteaching** Activity 11

STUDENT WORKBOOK

🡢 **Applying Health Skills 11**
🡢 **Chapter Study Guide 4**
🡢 **Vocabulary** Activity 4

- **Strain.** This is *a condition in which muscles have been overworked.* Strains can occur from participating in strenuous activity you are not used to. To avoid strains, warm up properly and don't go "all out" the first day of exercise.

- **Sprain.** This is *an injury to tissues surrounding a joint.* Ligaments, strong bands or cords of tissue that connect the bones to one another at a moveable joint, may be stretched and torn. A sprain may be accompanied by severe pain, swelling, and difficulty in moving. Warming up properly and using proper equipment can help you avoid sprains. A sprain may take more time to heal than a broken bone, and severe sprains are major injuries that require medical treatment.

Treatment for Minor Injuries

The injuries described above are often minor and, therefore, easily treated. Muscle cramps can be relieved through light massage and by applying heat after 72 hours. Minor strains and sprains can be treated by using the *R.I.C.E.* procedure, a method whose name comes from the first letter of each of its parts:

- **Rest.** Avoid using the affected muscle or joint. This may mean staying in bed for a day or two.

- **Ice.** Ice helps reduce pain and swelling. Place ice cubes in a plastic bag and hold it on the affected area for 20 minutes, remove the ice for 20 minutes, and then apply again for another 20 minutes.

- **Compression.** Light pressure through the use of an elastic bandage can help reduce swelling. The bandage should not be so tight that it cuts off blood flow to the area.

- **Elevation.** Raising the affected limb above heart level helps reduce pain and swelling.

Major Exercise-Related Injuries

When injuries are severe, medical treatment is required. You will learn about first aid procedures for medical emergencies in Chapter 35.

- **Fractures** are any type of break in a bone. Fractures usually require immobilization to heal properly. Fractures in which the two parts of the bone have been separated must be moved back into place. In some cases, the parts may

⚠ *Injuries to the skeletal system can occur during many activities.*
ACTIVITY *Name three common exercise-related injuries.*

LESSON 3 AVOIDING INJURIES **85**

TEACH

L1 Discussing

Ask how many students have ever had a muscle cramp after a game or other vigorous activity: What did it feel like? Did you warm up before the game or exercise session? If so, what kind of warm-up exercises did you do? *(Most students will acknowledge that they did little or no warming up.)* Point out that warming up gets the muscles ready for action and that people who warm up prior to exercise suffer fewer cramps and fewer injuries.

L3 Guest Speaker

Invite an athletic trainer to class to discuss common sports injuries and what is being done to prevent and treat them. Have students prepare a list of questions to ask the speaker.

L1 Discussing

Talk about the differences between a sprain and a strain and ways both might be treated.

L2 Explaining

Talk about reasons why cold packs are applied to sprains and muscle injuries.

L1 Discussing

Have students bring to class articles from newspapers and magazines that describe sporting or athletic injuries. Discuss the consequences of the injuries and ways they might have been prevented.

L2 Community Involvement

Choose several students to develop a list of interview questions to ask a physical therapist. Next, assist them in making arrangements to visit a physical therapist to find answers to the questions. Request that they report their findings to the class.

CURRICULUM CONNECTIONS

PHYSICAL EDUCATION. If your school has a swimming program, have students practice how to safely deal with a severe cramp that occurs in deep water.

LANGUAGE ARTS. Have students do research on an athlete who overcame an injury and write a brief paper summarizing the athlete's experience.

HISTORY. Ask students to find events in history (such as mountain-climbing expeditions) in which individuals experienced weather-related risks and injuries. Have them present an oral report of their findings.

L1 Discussing

Lead a class discussion about the short-term and possible long-term effects of heat cramps, heat exhaustion, heatstroke, hypothermia, and frostbite. Conclude by addressing prevention and treatments.

L2 Cooperative Learning

Pair students and have them develop a scenario of someone with a heat-related injury. Ask each pair to trade stories with another pair, read the histories, and list ways to avoid the injury in the future.

L3 Cooperative Learning

Divide the class into small groups. Have the groups talk with coaches or physical education teachers at the school about ways sporting equipment can decrease injuries. Have each group present a report and demonstrate the use of a piece of equipment that helps prevent injuries.

L1 Discussing

Ask students to identify and evaluate common myths related to the treatment of each injury discussed in the lesson. *(Myths might include treating frostbite with hot water, applying heat to sprains, working through the pain, etc.)*

L2 Cooperative Learning

Assign *Cooperative Learning Activity 4,* "Diagnose an Injury," in the TCR. ✐

need to be held in place with clamps and screws so that the break can heal.

- **Dislocations** result when a bone slips from its normal position at a joint. A doctor must put the bone back into place and immobilize the joint so that the tissue can heal.
- **Tendinitis** is a condition in which the tendons, bands of fiber that connect muscles to bones, are stretched or torn from overuse. This type of injury requires rest, medications, and physical therapy to heal.
- **Blows to the head,** another sports-related injury, can cause swelling of the brain, resulting in unconsciousness and even death. If you experience a headache or dizziness after a blow to the head, report it to your coach or see a physician as soon as possible. You may have suffered a concussion, a temporary disturbance of the brain's ability to function. If you receive two concussions from playing a particular sport, it is recommended that you change sports, as concussions can lead to serious neurological problems. You will learn more about brain injuries in Chapter 16.

▼ *Helmets, knee pads, and gloves are proper equipment when skateboarding.*
ACTIVITY *Explain why protective equipment is necessary.*

Weather-Related Risks

Certain health problems can occur in hot or cold weather. You can avoid weather-related health risks while exercising if you pay attention to how your body is reacting. Do not exercise when temperatures are extremely high or extremely low, and pay attention to the wind-chill factor and smog index.

Hot Weather Health Risks

Many of the risks of hot weather are related to either **overexertion**—*overworking the body*—or dehydration, a lack of fluids. You should not exercise in hot weather without rehydrating. Drink plenty of water, even if you don't feel thirsty. Smog is usually worse in hot weather. Don't exercise outdoors during smog alerts, or damage to the lungs can result.

Heat cramps are *muscle spasms that are the result of loss of large amounts of salt and water through perspiration.* To avoid **heat cramps**, make sure you are drinking plenty of water while doing physical activity in hot weather.

hotlink

heat cramps For more information on heat cramps and how to treat them, see Chapter 35, page 789.

MORE ABOUT . . . . .

WEATHER-RELATED RISKS. Heavy exercise on hot, humid days can be dangerous. Bioclimatologists have developed a heat index that combines heat and humidity values so one can assess the risks of prolonged activity in various conditions. For example, 90° + 60% humidity = a heat index of 100, the apparent temperature; 95° + 65% humidity = a heat index of 119; 100° + 60% humidity = a heat index of 132. What do these numbers mean? A heat index of 80 to 90 means fatigue is possible; 90 to 105 indicates that heat cramps and heat exhaustion are possible; 105 to 130 signifies that heat cramps and heat exhaustion are likely and heatstroke possible; 130 or above means that heatstroke is likely.

Heat exhaustion is *an overheating of the body resulting in cold, clammy skin and symptoms of shock.* It is caused by overexertion in a hot, humid atmosphere. Other symptoms of heat exhaustion include dizziness, headache, shortness of breath, and nausea. If you experience any of these symptoms, move to a cool place and lie down with your feet raised.

Continuing to exercise in hot weather with the symptoms of heat exhaustion and dehydration can lead to a life-threatening condition called **heatstroke**. The body loses its ability to rid itself of excessive heat through perspiration. Body temperature rises, and a person might have difficulty breathing and collapse suddenly. Spectators at sporting events also sometimes experience heatstroke. If heatstroke occurs, call for help immediately, move the person to a cool place, and sponge him or her with cold water until help arrives.

Cold Weather Health Risks

Exercising in cold weather, especially cross-country or alpine skiing, has its own health risks. **Frostbite** is *a condition that results when body tissue becomes frozen.* Dressing warmly in cold weather, covering all exposed skin—especially the head, face, feet, and fingers, where frostbite most often occurs—keeps the body warm and prevents **frostbite**. It also protects the skin from windburn, skin irritated by freezing wind. Dressing in layers is beneficial, because air becomes trapped between the layers, adding to warmth. If you notice a lack of feeling in your toes, fingers, nose, or ears while exercising in cold weather, go indoors to warm up. Don't risk frostbite, which requires medical care.

Hypothermia is *a condition in which body temperature becomes dangerously low.* Although hypothermia is usually associated with cold weather, it can also result from long exposure in windy or rainy weather where the body becomes cold and loses its ability to warm itself. When hypothermia occurs, body temperature becomes dangerously low. The brain cannot function at a low temperature, and body systems shut down. Hypothermia is a serious condition that can lead to death. A person with hypothermia may act disoriented and lose motor control. Seek medical help as soon as possible.

Thinking About Safety

Because of the risk of injury, safety is a major concern in sports programs. Become safety conscious by:

- **Being aware of the people around you.** This includes other players in a sport and spectators, if any.
- **Playing at your skill level.** Know your physical limits and don't exceed them.
- **Obeying rules and restrictions.**
- **Accepting responsibility for your own safety.**

hot link

heatstroke For more information on heatstroke and how to treat this condition, see Chapter 35, page 789.

hot link

frostbite For more information on frostbite and emergency measures for this weather-related health emergency, see Chapter 35, page 788.

LD Class Activity

Have students verbalize symptoms of and care procedures for heatstroke and frostbite.

L1 Class Activity

Ask students to make a written list of 10 sports and exercises. Have them rank each one as to its potential for injury, with "1" representing activities that have the greatest risk of causing injury and "10" representing those with the least risk. Lead a class discussion of the lists and reasons for the rankings.

hot link

heatstroke
frostbite
Tell students that more about how to treat weather-related injuries will be covered in Chapter 35, which focuses on first aid. Discuss how risks for such injuries can be greatly reduced by being prepared for outdoor conditions. Ask students to recall some ways to prepare for excessive heat or cold when exercising.

L3 Guest Speaker

Invite one or more cyclists to demonstrate and speak about new types of equipment designed to promote safety. (Examples might include reflective clothing, rearview mirrors on helmets, high-impact helmets, etc.)

L1 Class Activity

Ask students to bring an item or illustration of a piece of sporting gear that they think offers good value, comfort, and protection from injury during exercise. Have them present the item to the class and discuss the reasons for their choice.

HEALTH LITERACY

SELF-DIRECTED LEARNER. Hypothermia can be a danger in a variety of climates and activities. Even in temperate climates, prolonged exposure to moderately cool temperatures can cause hypothermia. Prolonged immersion in water can result in hypothermia even if the water is not very cold. Have students research hypothermia, the various conditions that can cause it, and its prevention and treatment. How, for example, can people guard against hypothermia when lost in the wilderness with insufficient clothing? How can one conserve body heat after a boating accident far from shore? Tell them to write a feature such as one that might appear in an outdoor survival handbook.

L2 Health Lab

Distribute *Health Lab 4* and have students investigate the importance of wearing athletic shoes when running or jogging.

L2 Class Activity

Display copies of magazines specializing in running, walking, weight lifting, and other activities. Let students use the magazines to find articles about avoiding risk and injury during exercise. Have them write a short summary of the articles. Close with a discussion comparing the information in the magazines with that in the lesson.

Building Health Skills

Safety vs. Personal Conflicts

Skill: Physical Safety

Show students a bicycle helmet, and let volunteers explain why it is such an important piece of safety equipment. Ask students to think about their responses to these questions (without having to indicate their own practices or ideas). Ask: Do you always wear a helmet and other kinds of safety equipment when they are needed? If not, why not? Then let students read the feature to learn more about sports safety, and have them use their private Health Journals to explore their responses.

Avoiding Swimmer's Ear

keeping **Fit**

Ask students what other health concerns a swimmer might have and what can be done to reduce the incidence or severity of the problems. *(For example, eye injury/wear goggles, muscle injury/stretching, etc.)*

You can promote safety by keeping personal safety in mind and using the right equipment or protective gear.

Personal Safety

Risks to personal safety can be minimized by choosing the right time and place to exercise. This is especially true when you will be working out alone. If you are planning to run or jog, choose a well-used park during daylight hours, when plenty of runners and other people are out. Wearing a whistle, which you can blow to attract attention if in danger, is always a good practice.

Using Proper Equipment

Exercise equipment and clothing is big business, but you do not have to spend a lot of money to exercise. If you are starting a new sport, rent or borrow the equipment to see how you like it before buying your own. To avoid injury, make sure that the equipment fits

Building Health Skills

Safety vs. Personal Conflicts

WHEN CHAD SKATEBOARDS, he never wears knee or elbow pads. "They make it hard to move," Chad tells himself. Many teens, like Chad, are inwardly torn over issues such as sports safety. They recognize the risks associated with not wearing a helmet when bicycling, for example, but believe that helmets are only for people who aren't skilled in the activity. The truth is that Chad doesn't really believe that an accident can happen to him.

How about you? Do you secretly avoid using safety equipment because you don't want to appear to your peers as someone who can't do the activity? Do you believe "it won't happen to you"? Here's how to find out how safe you are:

1. **Make a list of activities you do regularly.** Include both sports activities and lifestyle activities. Use a page in your Health Journal for your list.

2. **List protective gear and equipment that should be worn while doing each activity.** Use information provided in this lesson, along with knowledge you already have.

3. **Circle in red each piece of gear or equipment that you do not use.** Be honest with yourself. Do not include items that you own but never use.

4. **Examine your reasons.** Think about the real reasons you fail to take proper precautions against these risks.

5. **Decide how you are going to handle the situation.** If, like Chad in the story above, you are afraid what your peers might think, try talking to them. Maybe they aren't aware of the risks themselves!

88 CHAPTER 4 PHYSICAL ACTIVITY FOR LIFE

PERSONAL HEALTH

SAFETY HANDBOOK. Suggest that students consider the physical activities that require them to use or exert large muscles. Examples will include both lifestyle activities (such as lifting at work, cycling to school, or gardening at home) and sports activities (such as tennis, baseball, or track). Have them choose three in which they engage most often and research the most common injuries associated with those activities. Tell them to write a personal safety manual, detailing precautions to observe while engaged in the activities they listed.

properly and is in good condition. Learn all you can about the proper use of the equipment.

Footwear is an important consideration for many sports. Shoes should have a cushioned heel, good arch support, and ample toe room. Laced shoes are best for proper control of your foot in the shoe. Avoid buying shoes that must be broken in before wearing them.

Choose clothing that is comfortable and doesn't restrict movement. When it's warm outside, dress lightly. When it's cool outside, wear loose-fitting layers of clothes. You can easily remove or add layers to ensure a safe, comfortable body temperature. Always wear socks, to cushion and pull perspiration away from your feet.

Protective Equipment

Many sports require protective equipment such as helmets, mouth guards, and padding. Athletic cups protect the genitals of males during contact sports such as hockey and football. Helmets should also be worn each time you bicycle or skateboard to prevent serious head injuries. Knee and elbow pads are important equipment for bikers, skateboarders, and skaters. Wearing colorful clothing, placing reflective tape on the bicycle, or using a light at night makes bicyclists more visible to drivers and pedestrians.

keeping Fit

Avoiding Swimmer's Ear

Swimmer's ear occurs when bacteria grow in the outer ear. The condition is called swimmer's ear because it happens often to swimmers who get water in their ears. Here's how you can avoid swimmer's ear:

➤ Drain water from your ears after every swim. Do this by gently tapping your head with a flat palm.

➤ Use swimmer's eardrops, or place two or three drops each of rubbing alcohol and vinegar into your ears after every swim.

➤ Avoid putting cotton swabs in your ears after you swim. The cotton removes protective ear wax, and can scratch the skin in the ear canal.

LESSON 3 *Review*

Reviewing Facts and Vocabulary

1. How is a strain different from a sprain?
2. How do heat cramps differ from muscle cramps?
3. What should you watch for when purchasing used athletic equipment?

Thinking Critically

4. **Comparing and Contrasting.** Tell what injury is most likely to result from each of the following situations: (a) Although Josh hasn't played hockey since last season, he pushes himself to perform physically to make a good impression. (b) Jenny is an avid alpine skier. She accepts an invitation to go skiing, even though it is 10 degrees below zero.
5. **Evaluating.** After jogging five miles in 96-degree heat, Flora felt she could not go on. She was perspiring a lot. She became pale, dizzy, nauseated, and had trouble breathing. Tell what injury Flora has suffered and what she could have done to prevent it.

Applying Health Skills

6. **In Your Home.** Talk to your parents or other adult family members about procedures that might be followed in your home in the event of a physical activity-related injury. Then post emergency information, such as your family physician's phone number, the type of medical insurance your family has, and the names and numbers of responsible adults who might be contacted in an emergency.

LESSON 3   AVOIDING INJURIES   **89**

ASSESS

EVALUATING THE LESSON

Assign and discuss Lesson 3 Review; then administer, grade, and discuss the *Lesson 11 Quiz* in the TCR.

RETEACHING

- Have each student develop a quiz about common sports injuries and how they can be prevented. Have students exchange their quizzes as a form of review.
- Ask students to complete *Reteaching Activity 11* in the TCR.

ENRICHMENT

- Have students investigate a specific sport to determine which injuries are common to the sport. Then have students prepare a manual identifying equipment that can be used and steps that can be taken to prevent potential injuries, as well as ways to treat the injuries.
- Ask volunteers to interview someone they know who has had a broken arm or leg in a cast for a number of weeks. Have them find out how the inactivity caused by wearing the cast affected the muscles and previous degree of conditioning. Let students share what they learn with the class.

CLOSE

Remind students that safety should be the priority of any physical activity, regardless of how capable you become in a sport. Your performance and continued participation in the activity rely upon your health and your body's strength, flexibility, and endurance.

Lesson 3 Review

Answers to Reviewing Facts and Vocabulary

1. A strain is overuse of a muscle. A sprain is a tissue injury.
2. A heat cramp is the result of loss of salt and water through perspiration. A muscle cramp is the result of the muscle being overworked.
3. It should fit properly and be in good condition.

Answers to Thinking Critically

4. (a) Strain. (b) Hypothermia.
5. Flora has heat exhaustion. She should have either taken in more water before her run or avoided running in the heat entirely.

Health Skills Activities

ACTIVITY 1
HEALTH SKILLS
Self Management, Goal Setting

➤ **National Standards**
This activity meets these National Health Standards: 3.4; 6.4; 6.5; 6.6.

Teach

- Review with students the steps in an action plan. Be sure student identifies a fitness goal that is realistic and measurable.
- Establish a date for review of plans that will give students a chance to attain one of their performance benchmarks. A period of 4 to 6 weeks should be adequate for this purpose. Make sure each student writes this date down on his or her action plan and identifies interim dates.
- Check back with students periodically (weekly) to make sure they are maintaining their schedule.

ACTIVITY 2
HEALTH SKILLS
Comprehending Health Concepts, Self Management, Health Advocacy

➤ **National Standards**
This activity meets these National Health Standards: 1.1; 3.5; 7.1.

Teach

- Pass out scrap paper first. This will reinforce the importance of preparing first drafts in all areas of school work and will prevent more impulsive students from simply plunging ahead to the final draft of their sign.
- Have students share drafts and provide each other with constructive ideas for improving their signs.
- Encourage students in the class with skills in using graphics software to develop their signs using the computer.

Health Skills Activities

Activity 1 — A Personal Fitness Plan

Becoming and staying fit is essential to good health. It is up to each individual to take charge of his or her own fitness. Start by creating a fitness action plan.

Directions

1. Write your name and today's date at the top of a sheet of paper.
2. Divide the page in half lengthwise to form two columns. In the left column, list the elements of a comprehensive plan to improve and maintain your fitness.
3. In the right column, make a physical fitness action plan (see page 38). Give careful thought to your goals, making sure your objectives are measurable.
4. Carry out your fitness plan, checking your action plan from time to time.
5. On a date specified by your teacher, bring your plan to class for review.

Time
30 minutes for writing plan

Materials
paper, pen or pencil

Self-Assessment

✓ Identified the elements of a comprehensive fitness plan.
✓ Listed at least two realistic goals and an action plan that you can work toward to achieve health-related fitness.

Activity 2 — What's Wrong with This Picture?

To avoid injury related to physical activity, you need to know the causes of such injuries. In this activity, you will raise the consciousness of people in your own school or community.

Directions

1. Create a sign that shows correct and incorrect ways of performing a physical action, such as lifting or stretching. Use international symbols where possible. (For example, to show the proper way to lift heavy objects, you might draw a silhouette of a person bending at the knees with a red slash through it.)
2. Sketch out ideas on scrap paper before transferring them to poster board. Make your sign as colorful and eye-catching as possible.
3. Display your sign in the school hallway or, with permission, in a public place.

Time
40 minutes

Materials
scrap paper, poster board, markers, computer (optional)

Self-Assessment

✓ Created visually appealing signs that communicate proper safety and injury prevention techniques.
✓ Showed at least two clearly correct or incorrect actions.

ASSESSMENT SCORING

Using a four-level rubric, the student has achieved a 4 if:

ACTIVITY 1
✔ Student identified the elements of a comprehensive fitness plan.
✔ Student identified at least two personal realistic, attainable physical fitness goals.
✔ Student developed a physical fitness action plan that follows the action plan format.
✔ Student pursued the plan for the prescribed length of time.

ACTIVITY 2
✔ Student completed signs that were visually appealing and eye catching.
✔ Student completed signs that clearly communicated its message.
✔ Student showed at least two clearly correct or incorrect actions.
✔ Student demonstrated an understanding that advocacy can influence health behaviors.

HEALTH NEWS

Playing It Safer

Sports-related injuries send an average of 2.6 million young people to the hospital each year, according to a new study done by the Centers for Disease Control and Prevention in Atlanta, Georgia. Dr. Michael Busch, of Children's Healthcare of Atlanta, says that the most common injuries are relatively minor.

"A lot of them are simple musculoskeletal injuries," Busch said. "Your traditional sprains and fractures."

Experts estimate two-thirds of all sports injuries are preventable.

In the past, medical training emphasized the treatment of sports injuries. Today doctors are highlighting injury prevention.

"The real key is education," says Busch. "We know a lot more about the importance of equipment, diet, and rules related to safety."

The use of protective equipment is vital. Kneepads, elbow pads, and shin guards help to prevent bruises and abrasions. Although wrist guards can't thwart every wrist fracture, they do prevent hand abrasions and sprains. Bike helmets are essential for rollerblading, skateboarding, scooters, snowboarding and cycling.

"You should never see a child on a bike without a helmet," Busch said.

Read This

How Risky Is Your Favorite Sport?

Which sports put players at the greatest risk? Researchers examined three years of data about young people and sports injuries. This chart shows the sports that were the source of the most emergency room visits.

Sport	Average Number of ER Visits Per Year
Basketball	447,000
Cycling	421,000
Football	271,000
Baseball	245,000
Skating/Skateboarding	150,000
Gymnastics/Cheerleading	146,000
Snow Sports	111,000
Soccer	95,000

Source: CDC

Think About It

1. Give two examples of preventable sports injuries. Explain how someone might avoid each injury.
2. How can you advocate for safe sports at your school?

CNN HEALTH NEWS 91

MORE ABOUT . . . . .

TECHNOLOGY AND SCIENCE. Advances in technology have greatly increased the safety of playing many sports. According to the Bicycle Helmet Safety Institute, modern safety equipment is far more effective than early models. For example, in the early 1900s, bicycle helmets were made of leather and wool padding. These soft helmets did little to protect riders' heads from the impact of falls.

Today, bicycle helmets are lighter and offer far more protection. Current helmets contain layers of high-tech materials, including thin, tough plastics and insulating foams. Designers apply aerodynamics to construct helmet shapes that fit the head comfortably, yet minimize the effects of wind pressure.

CNN HEALTH NEWS

Playing It Safer

Objectives. After reading the article, students should understand the problem of sports-related injuries and identify specific strategies for preventing them.

Motivator. Ask students to predict which sport produces the greatest number of injuries. When students suggest a sport, ask them to explain why they think this sport is risky and to describe the injuries that might be associated with it. Then have students read the article "Playing It Safer," and interpret the data in the chart.

Teach

- Help students evaluate the data about sports injuries by asking them to analyze generalizations based on the article. Students should explain whether the data supports any of the following conclusions:
  1) Basketball and cycling are too dangerous for young people.
  2) Taking healthy precautions can prevent many sports injuries.
  3) Safety equipment cannot prevent most injuries.
- Encourage students to take a class or school poll about the use of safety equipment and sports. The poll should focus on how well students follow safety rules when they play sports or practice sports away from school. Share and analyze poll results as a class.

Decision Making. Have students create a decision-making scenario based on one student's choice to start playing a sport. Students will weigh the possible outcomes, including injury, plus identify strategies to help players remain safe. Have students apply the 6-step decision making model on page 35.

Close. Have students create and present a safety checklist for a sport of their choice. Their lists should include precautions and safety rules to follow when playing this sport, and the required and recommended safety equipment. Students should explain how using these lists could help change the trends identified in the article.

CHAPTER 4 *Review*

CHECKING COMPREHENSION

- Assign and discuss the chapter review.
- Use the MindJogger Videoquiz to review the chapter.

CHAPTER 4 REVIEW ANSWERS

Using Health Terms

1. coordination
2. reaction time
3. lifestyle activity
4. agility
5. physical activity
6. power
7. balance
8. speed
9. training program
10. anabolic steroids
11. hydration
12. frostbite
13. heat exhaustion
14. cramp
15. heat cramps
16. sprain
17. strain
18. hypothermia

Recalling the Facts

1. Biking is a sport that can also be a means of transportation. Basketball and tennis are sports that can also be recreational activities. Running or jogging can be either a competitive sport or part of a daily routine.
2. Agility.
3. Agility, balance, coordination, power.
4. The start.
5. Nutrition fuels the body; rest recharges it.
6. It can cause very damaging side effects.
7. Adequate warm-up and fluid intake before exercising can prevent cramps.
8. Concussions may cause permanent brain damage.
9. Damage to the lungs may result.
10. Frostbite.

Using Health Terms

On a separate sheet of paper, write the term that best matches each definition below.

LESSON 1

1. The ability to use two or more body parts together well, or to use the senses along with the body parts.
2. The rate of movement once a person realizes the need to move.
3. Physical activity that is a normal part of your day-to-day routine or recreation.
4. The ability to control movements and to change the body's position quickly.
5. Any form of movement, whether purposeful, as in exercise and sports, or incidental, as when doing domestic chores.
6. The ability to use force with great speed.
7. The ability to remain upright either while standing still or moving.
8. The ability to move a distance or complete a body movement in a short period of time.

LESSON 2

9. A program of formalized physical preparation for participation in a sport.
10. Chemicals similar to the male hormone testosterone.
11. The addition of body fluids.

LESSON 3

12. A condition that results when body tissue becomes frozen.
13. Overheating of the body resulting in cold, clammy skin and symptoms of shock.
14. Spasm or sudden tightening of a muscle.
15. Muscle spasms that are the result of loss of large amounts of salt and water through perspiration.
16. An injury to tissues surrounding a joint.
17. Condition in which muscles have been overworked.
18. Condition in which body temperature becomes dangerously low.

Recalling the Facts

Using complete sentences, answer the following questions.

LESSON 1

1. Identify three activities that could be either lifestyle or sport activities. Give examples to support your claims.
2. What skills-related fitness does the side shuttle measure?
3. What skills-related fitness does a discus-thrower in the Olympic Games possess?
4. Which part of a swim race most requires excellent reaction time?

LESSON 2

5. How are nutrition and adequate rest beneficial to an athlete?

6. Why are anabolic steroids not part of a good training program for a weight lifter, even though they do increase muscle bulk?

LESSON 3

7. What causes and prevents muscle cramps?
8. Why must players of contact sports take concussions seriously?
9. Why should you avoid exercising outdoors in heavy smog?
10. What medical condition results when body tissue becomes frozen?

Thinking Critically

LESSON 1

1. **Comparing and Contrasting.** List several lifestyle activities that are chores and several that are forms of recreation. Tell which of the measures of physical fitness are supported by each activity.
2. **Evaluating.** Conrad's skill-related fitness scores are as follows: agility, 20; balance, 4; coordination, 2; power, 88; reaction time, 20; and speed, 25. In which skills does he excel? Name three sports that Conrad might have success in.

LESSON 2

3. **Evaluating.** List several questions you could ask about a team's training program to determine if all the aspects of a good training program have been included.

LESSON 3

4. **Analyzing.** Mr. Vasquez had been working for three hours in the sun. Suddenly, he fell to the ground. He was not perspiring, and he felt very hot. His pulse was racing and breathing was difficult. Tell what problem he was suffering.

Making the Connection

1. **Science.** Develop a physical activity program that someone in good health could perform outdoors in each season in your locality. Note any risks of weather-related health problems that might exist when carrying out these activities, as well as precautions that could be taken against each possible risk.

2. **Language Arts.** Jim Abbott has pitched at the professional level for several baseball teams despite missing one hand. Tony Dempsey is a professional football place kicker who lacks toes on his kicking foot. Research one such individual to learn about the special properties that enabled him or her to excel as an athlete.

BEYOND THE CLASSROOM

PARENTAL INVOLVEMENT Some family members may have medical conditions that preclude certain kinds of exercise. If possible, identify someone in your family or a family friend that has, or has had, such a problem. Work with this person to develop a modified exercise program that covers as many of the 11 basic measures of fitness as possible.

COMMUNITY INVOLVEMENT Observe 20 people doing physical activity in your neighborhood. Record your answers to these questions in a chart: How old are they? What are they doing? Are they alone, or with a partner or group? At what time do they participate in physical activities? What conclusions can you draw from the information you gathered?

SCHOOL-TO-CAREER
Interpersonal. Invite a physical therapist to speak to your class for more information on becoming a physical therapist. Find out in what ways physical therapists help people with sports-related injuries, what training you would need, where you might work, and the range of pay. Write a summary of your findings and add the information to a class booklet on careers.

Thinking Critically

1. Raking leaves (coordination, agility, balance), mowing the lawn (coordination, power), washing windows (coordination, balance), walking the dog (speed, coordination), hanging laundry (agility, coordination) are lifestyle activities.
2. He excels in reaction time, power, and speed. He might do well in football, baseball, or track.
3. Questions should include whether nutritional information is included; information on hydration, the avoidance of harmful substances, and adequate rest; and information on the mind-body connection.
4. He is suffering from heatstroke. He should be moved to a cool place and sponged with cold water until help arrives.

Making the Connection

1. Each program should include adequate hydration and warm-up as well as attention to temperature extremes.
2. Reports will vary.

Evaluate

- Use the reproducible *Chapter 4 Test* in the TCR or construct your own using the Testmaker software.
- Use *Performance Assessment Activity 4* in the TCR.

Enrichment

Have students complete *Cross-Curriculum Activity 4* in the TCR.

Beyond the Classroom

Keep students involved in the community, and encourage parent participation by assigning the activities on this page for students to work on outside of class.

Nutrition and Your Health

	FEATURES	**CLASSROOM RESOURCES**

LESSON 1

Food in Your Life
pages 96–100

- Concept Map Activity 12
- Lesson 12 Quiz
- Lesson Plan 12
- Reteaching Activity 12
- Transparencies 12, 13

LESSON 2

Nutrients: Carbohydrates, Proteins, and Fats
pages 101–106

- Concept Map Activity 13
- Enrichment Activity 5
- Lesson 13 Quiz
- Lesson Plan 13
- Reteaching Activity 13

LESSON 3

Nutrients: Vitamins, Minerals, and Water
pages 107–111

- Concept Map Activity 14
- Health Lab 5
- Lesson 14 Quiz
- Lesson Plan 14
- Reteaching Activity 14

LESSON 4

Guidelines for a Healthful Eating Style
pages 112–120

Making Responsible Decisions
"Valuing and Helping Friends,"
page 116

Building Health Skills
"Setting Goals: Improving Your Snacking Habits," *page 118*

- Concept Map Activity 15
- Cooperative Learning Activity 5
- Decision-Making Activity 5
- Lesson 15 Quiz
- Lesson Plan 15
- Reteaching Activity 15
- Transparencies 14, 15

LESSON 5

Being a Smart Food Consumer
pages 121–125

update ▶ Our Changing World
"Safety Inspections: Imported Foods," *page 124*

- Concept Map Activity 16
- Lesson 16 Quiz
- Lesson Plan 16
- Reteaching Activity 16
- Transparency 16

Chapter Resources

ACTIVITIES

- Cross-Curriculum Activity 5
- Health Lab 5
- Health Skills Activities 5
- Parent Letter and Activities 5

ASSESSMENT

- Chapter 5 Test
- Performance Assessment Activity 5
- Testmaker Software

STUDENT ACTIVITIES WORKBOOK

- Applying Health Skills 12–16
- Study Guide 5
- Vocabulary Activity 5

STUDENT DIVERSITY STRATEGIES

- Audiocassette Program (English)
- Audiocassette Program (Spanish)
- Spanish Parent Letters and Activities
- Spanish Summaries, Quizzes, and Activities

MULTIMEDIA COMPONENTS

- English Audiocassette Program
- Spanish Audiocassette Program
- MindJogger Videodisc and VHS program
- ABCNews InterActive™ VHS/Videodisc Series

National Health Education Standards

One of the main goals of the National Health Education Standards is to move students toward "health literacy." Health literacy is the capacity of individuals to obtain, interpret, and understand basic health information and services and the competence to use such information and services in ways which promote health. The health standards were developed by applying the characteristics of a well-educated, literate person within the context of health. The health literate person is:

- a critical thinker and problem solver
- a self-directed learner
- a responsible, productive citizen
- an effective communicator

Listed below are the Health Education Standards Performance Indicators addressed in each lesson of this chapter.

Lesson	Health Standards Performance Indicators
1	1.2, 1.4, 3.1, 4.2
2	1.1, 1.3, 1.6
3	1.3, 1.6, 3.1, 3.3
4	3.4, 6.1, 6.4, 6.6
5	1.7, 2.2, 2.3, 7.1

ONLINE RESOURCES

HEALTH Online

For a fresh approach to health topics and an in-depth look at health issues, use these online resources found under Teacher Resources at **health.glencoe.com**.

- **BLOCK SCHEDULE LESSON PLANS** Reinforce health concepts with outside readings selected especially for students. Each reading is accompanied by a lesson plan and activities to enhance
  - Reading Skills
  - Cross Curriculum
  - Media Literacy

- **TECHNOLOGY PROJECTS** Instructions and suggestions on how to use computer, Internet, and software with health lessons.

- **HEALTH UPDATES** Timely topics in health news, including late-breaking medical advances and updates on teen risk behaviors.

Out of Time?

If time does not permit teaching this chapter, you may use these features: Making Responsible Decisions on page 116; Building Health Skills on page 118; and Update on page 124.

BLOCK SCHEDULING

Block scheduling provides extended time for hands-on projects and activities. Use the following activities to engage students, provide further depth, and vary your instructional techniques:

- Update (30 minutes) **pg. 124**
- Health Skills Activity (60–90 minutes) **pg. 126**

Nutrition and Your Health

CHAPTER OVERVIEW

Chapter 5 identifies the elements necessary for proper nutrition and explains how students can make healthful food choices.

LESSON 1 Food impacts life because it supplies nutrients the body needs to function properly. Food choices are linked to one's physical needs, social and cultural background, and emotions.

LESSON 2 During digestion, food breaks down, and simpler nutrients are released and absorbed to provide energy; to build, repair, and maintain body tissues; and to insulate the body.

LESSON 3 Digestion also breaks down food to release vitamins and minerals, which regulate body processes. Water absorbed from digested foods serves many functions within the body.

LESSON 4 The Dietary Guidelines and the Food Guide Pyramid help individuals choose a healthful diet. A varied, moderate, and balanced diet forms the foundation of a healthy eating pattern.

LESSON 5 Information on food labels and on supermarket shelves can help consumers make wise food choices and purchasing decisions.

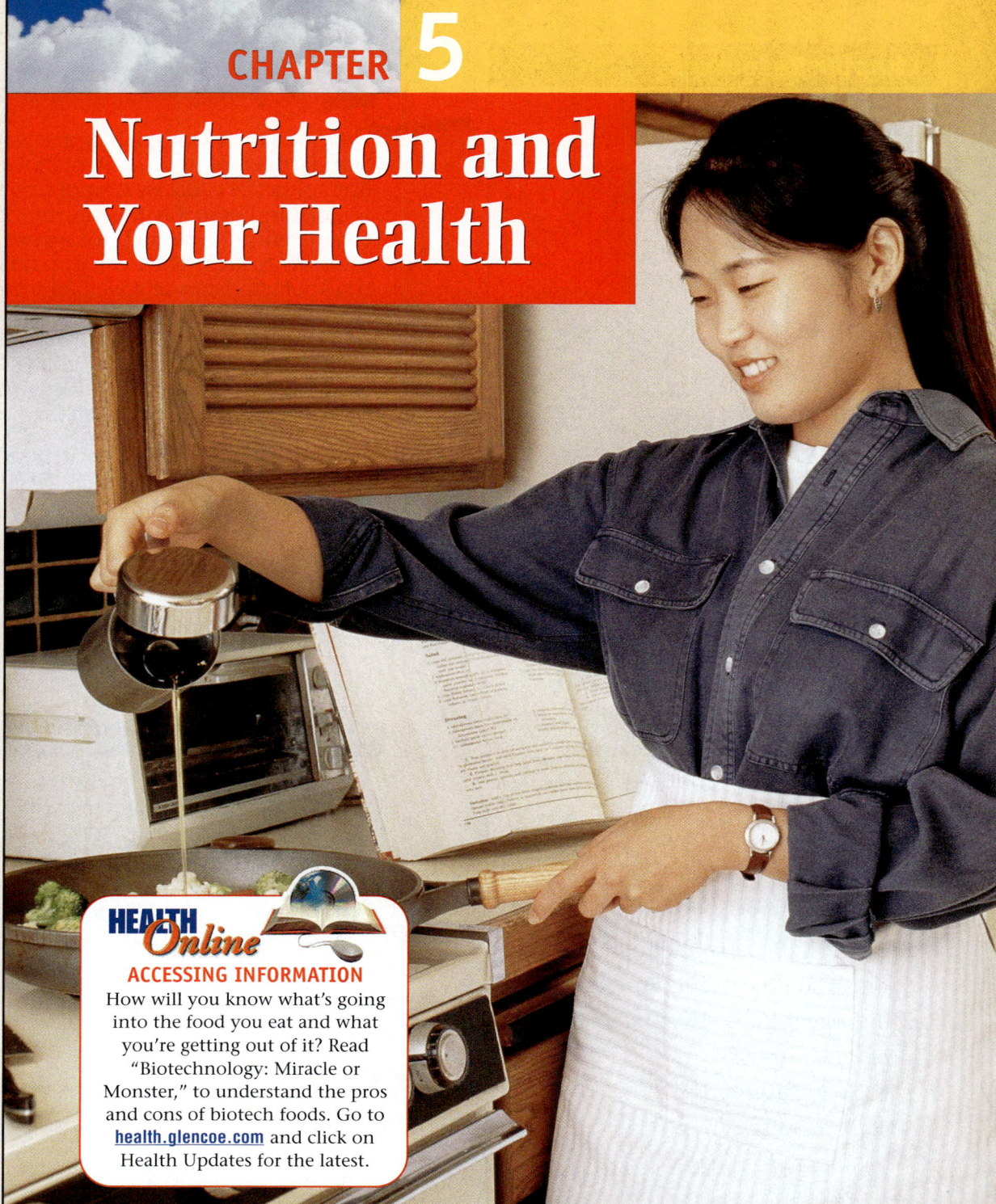

CHAPTER 5

Nutrition and Your Health

HEALTH Online

ACCESSING INFORMATION

How will you know what's going into the food you eat and what you're getting out of it? Read "Biotechnology: Miracle or Monster," to understand the pros and cons of biotech foods. Go to **health.glencoe.com** and click on Health Updates for the latest.

Hands-On Health

TEACHING STRATEGY

Analyzing Popular Snack Foods Encourage students to rate popular snack foods in terms of eye-appeal, taste, calories, fat content, sugar content, and sodium content. See Activity 13, "Rate that Snack Food," in the *Hands-On Health: Creative Teaching Strategies* booklet.

Time Needed
45 to 60 minutes

Supplies
- Selection of popular snack foods
- Nutrition Facts labels from snack foods

Personal Health Inventory

Self-Inventory Write the numbers 1–10 on a sheet of paper. Read each statement below and respond by writing *yes*, *no*, or *sometimes* for each item. Write a *yes* only for items that you practice regularly. Save your responses.

1	I eat a variety of foods that provide nutrients my body needs.
2	I include plenty of fruits, vegetables, and grain products such as pasta, rice, and bread in my eating plan.
3	I cut away visible fat or choose lower-fat meats and remove the skin from chicken.
4	I make an effort to trade off my intake of fried foods and other foods I think might be high in fat with lower-fat foods.
5	I taste food before salting it.
6	I choose nutritious snacks.
7	I eat the recommended servings from the five food groups from the Food Guide Pyramid.
8	I follow a nutritious eating plan at breakfast every day.
9	I know how to read nutrition labels and use that information when shopping.
10	I am able to spot false or misleading claims and promises in food ads.

Follow-up After completing the chapter, retake this self-inventory. Pick two items that you need to work on and set a goal to improve your health behaviors.

> ❝ *Reverse the typical American meal pattern and instead eat like a king for breakfast, a prince for lunch and a pauper for dinner.* ❞
>
> —Jane Brody
> Nutritionist

Quick Write List some of the main ingredients that make up a healthful eating plan for breakfast, for lunch, and for dinner.

Personal Health Inventory

Let students work with partners or in small groups to read and discuss the statements in this Self-Inventory. Ask: How do the activities and habits reflected in these statements relate to good health? Then have students make a private record of their responses to the Inventory statements and label the page "Nutrition." Remind them to keep these responses in their private Health Journals.

- Display a food that is probably unfamiliar to many of your students, such as fresh gingerroot, jicama, or chutney. Allow volunteers to taste the food. Ask the volunteers why they were willing to try something new. What factors influenced their decision? Why were other people less willing to do so? Tell students that they will learn about their reasons for making food choices and about the positive effects of good nutrition as they study this chapter.
- Have students share examples of when they have been invited to go out with friends for a shake or fries and have eaten just to be sociable. Ask: What are your choices in these situations? Let students work together to brainstorm a list of reasons why people eat and or why they choose particular foods.
- Distribute Parent Letter 5 in the *Parent Letters and Activities* booklet in the TCR. 🗂

TECHNOLOGY OPTIONS

ABCNEWS INTERACTIVE™ You may wish to use *Food and Nutrition* with this chapter. For your convenience, use the separate *ABCNews InterActive™ Bar Code Correlation* that accompanies the *Glencoe Health* program. 🔴

MINDJOGGER
VIDEOQUIZ

To preview or review chapter content, you may wish to use the *MindJogger Videoquiz* that accompanies Chapter 5. 🔴

LESSON 1

Food in Your Life

FOCUS

LESSON OBJECTIVES

After studying this lesson, students should be able to

- describe factors that influence one's food choices.
- explain how food choices reflect one's culture, ethnic background, and, perhaps, one's religious beliefs.
- identify ways that family members and friends may affect one's food decisions and preferences.
- explain how time and money influence food choices.

MOTIVATOR

Write the following on the chalkboard for students to work on while attendance is being taken: *List five foods you like and five you dislike. Beside each food, write a reason why you like or dislike it.*

INTRODUCING THE LESSON

Have volunteers share their responses to the Motivator. On the chalkboard, list foods that come up repeatedly. Students may change their minds as they hear others' responses. Ask students to name factors other than taste that influence their choice of foods. Tell them they will learn more about influences on food choices as they study this lesson.

INTRODUCING HEALTH TERMS

- Have students use the terms *nutrients* and *nutrition* in a written paragraph. Ask them to read their paragraphs to the class.
- Ask students to complete Vocabulary Activity 5 and Chapter Study Guide 5 in the *Student Workbook*. 🖘

Picture yourself biting into a crisp, juicy apple or a slice of pizza oozing with cheese and zesty tomato sauce. Which picture appeals to you most? What foods do you enjoy eating?

Not all foods supply the same nutrients in the same amounts. Making informed, healthful food choices is important to your health and to your energy level.

HEALTH TERMS

nutrients

hunger

appetite

nutrition

HEALTH CONCEPTS

- The body has a physical need for food, which is signaled by hunger.
- Many people's eating habits are governed by appetite, rather than by hunger.
- Factors that influence your food choices include culture, family and friends, advertising, lifestyle, and mood.
- Learning the basics of nutrition can help you become a more healthful eater both now and later in life.
- Proper nutrition is a tool in disease prevention.

Why Do You Eat?

The foods you eat are your body's chief source of **nutrients** (NOO-tree-uhnts), the *substances in food that your body needs to function properly to grow, to repair itself, and to supply you with energy.* The nutrients in food affect all sides of your health triangle. They affect how you look, feel, act, grow, and even your abilities—how well you function each day.

Have you ever wondered why you eat and why you make certain food choices? The reasons may be more complex than you realize. Your eating habits stem from both a physical *need* for food and a psychological *desire* for food. Learning to recognize the difference between the two helps you to make more healthful food choices.

Lesson 1 Resources

TEACHER'S CLASSROOM RESOURCES

🖘 **Concept Map** Activity 12

🖘 **Lesson 12 Quiz**

🖘 **Lesson Plan 12**

🖘 **Parent Letter and Activities 5**

🖘 **Reteaching** Activity 12

STUDENT WORKBOOK

🖘 **Applying Health Skills 12**

🖘 **Chapter Study Guide 5**

🖘 **Vocabulary** Activity 5

TRANSPARENCIES

💧 **Transparencies 12, 13**

MULTIMEDIA

🔴 **ABCNews InterActive™ VHS/Videodisc,** *Food and Nutrition*

Your Body's Physical Need for Food

The most basic reason for eating is physical. Food, along with air and water, is one of life's basic needs. Your body tells you through hunger when it needs food. **Hunger** is *a natural drive that protects you from starvation.*

When your stomach is empty, its walls contract, stimulating nerve endings. The nerve endings signal your brain that your body's food supply needs replenishing. Once you have responded to this message, the walls of the stomach are stretched and the nerve endings are no longer stimulated. By eating, you have satisfied your physical need for food. You feel "full."

Your Mind's Desire for Food

Have you ever "made room" for dessert at the end of a big meal? Maybe you have eaten in response to the aroma of fresh-baked cookies, or maybe, like Pete in the story that opened this chapter, you ate to be sociable. In such cases, you have eaten not in response to hunger but to **appetite.** Appetite is *a desire, rather than a need, to eat.*

Appetite is a learned, rather than an inborn, response. It is shaped by factors in your environment and by your emotions.

Your Environment

There are a number of environmental factors that influence your food choices. These include your cultural heritage, your family and social relationships, media messages, and your lifestyle.

CULTURE

What foods do you associate with picnics, county fairs, the movies, baseball games, and holidays such as Thanksgiving, and birthday parties? Your food choices reflect the culture you live in, as well as your ethnic background and perhaps your religious beliefs. Teenagers have a culture of their own, too. What eating practices seem to be part of teen culture?

TEACH

L1 Discussing

Talk about how food is related to common adolescent health concerns such as weight management, cavities, acne, etc. Point out the relationship of diet to overall well-being.

L1 Class Activity

Most newspapers offer a weekly food section. Ask students to begin reading that section to collect questions submitted and answered about nutrition. Use these as a topic of discussion and for collecting additional information throughout the unit.

L1 Class Activity

Invite a representative of the Jewish (or other) faith to describe his or her food customs to the class.

L1 Class Activity

Ask students who have lived in other regions of the United States to present a brief oral report describing the differences in food customs they have found among the various regions.

L1 Community Involvement

Tell volunteers to visit a restaurant with an ethnic cuisine that they have never tried before. Afterward, have them discuss their experience with the class.

LD Discussing

Encourage students to describe one of their family's favorite foods and explain why it is special. (*Examples might include an old family recipe, a food that is served on special occasions, or a food that is part of a cultural tradition.*)

CURRICULUM CONNECTIONS

SOCIAL STUDIES. Have students research foods that are popular in different countries. If possible, bring (or have students bring) to class produce (such as mangoes, pomegranates, etc.) and other foods, and discuss with students the sources of these foods. Also, ask students to locate pictures of foreign foods or recipes from ethnic cookbooks. Discuss how culture and ethnic background affect food traditions and choices.

FAMILY AND CONSUMER SCIENCES. Many students and their families fail to eat breakfast, citing lack of time to prepare it. Invite a family and consumer science teacher to demonstrate and prepare healthy, quick-fix breakfast foods.

Visual Learning

Advertising and Nutrition

Tell students that the chart "Advertising and Nutrition" refers to the amount of advertising time spent on television for food products. Ask them to identify the category that receives the most time *(desserts, snacks, and soft drinks)*. Ask: Which category receives the least amount of time? Have students discuss reasons for this big differentiation.

L1 Discussing

Help students identify the leading factors that affect their food choices. Have them consider questions such as: Do they really love pizza, or do they eat it because their friends do? Do they choose easy-to-make foods for breakfast when they prepare it themselves? How much do they consider the cost of food when eating out?

L1 Discussing

Ask: Is peer pressure a positive or negative influence on food choices? Why? *(It can be both. For example, friends can encourage a sense of adventure by introducing peers to new foods, but they may pressure their friends into poor food choices.)*

FOOD AND NUTRITION (Side 2)

Chapter 5: Food Advertising

Frames 8896-12599

Chapter 7: Food and Folklore

Frames 18054-18179

ADVERTISING AND NUTRITION

62% Desserts, snacks, and soft drinks	**20%** Breads, rolls, pastas, cereals	**8%** Shortening, oil, mayonnaise, sauces	**5%** Meats, processed meats, poultry, fish	**3%** Milk, butter and cheese	**2%** Fruits and vegetables

▲ *Does it appear to you that advertising promotes wellness through good nutrition?*

ACTIVITY *Determine which categories of food products receive the most attention and which receive the least from advertisers.*

FAMILY AND FRIENDS

What you ate as a child, what you learned to like and dislike, and when you ate meals were all influenced by your family. These influences affect your food decisions and preferences now, and they will continue to influence you throughout your life.

As you have grown older, friends have influenced your food choices. Perhaps you tried new foods at their homes or tasted different foods at parties. Because eating can be a social experience, food is the focus of many gatherings.

ADVERTISING

Food ads are everywhere—on television, in magazines, and on billboards. Food advertisements are created to make you aware of certain

MORE ABOUT . . . . .

ADVERTISING. Advertising is regulated by federal and state laws and agencies. The Federal Trade Commission (FTC) oversees truth in advertising. The Food and Drug Administration (FDA) deals with the labeling and advertising material shipped with packages or used as supplements to labels. Radio and television advertising is regulated by the Federal Communications Commission (FCC). State laws for advertising vary widely, although most states have truth-in-advertising laws prohibiting false and misleading advertisements.

foods and, perhaps, to sell you on their benefits. Most importantly, they can shape food decisions. Think about food ads you see and hear on television. Which foods have you bought or tried as a result of such ads?

Many people believe everything they read in newspapers and see and hear on television and radio. While many ads are responsible, others may be misleading. For example, an ad may state that a food is low in fat without stating that it is also high in calories. Advertisers spend millions of dollars on powerful persuasion techniques. Ads may try to persuade you that status, sex appeal, weight loss, or a terrific appearance will be yours if you buy the product. To make informed food choices, you need to know about food and health. You need to listen and judge advertising messages carefully. That way, you—not advertisers—control what foods you buy and eat.

TIME AND MONEY

Taste and nutrition are the two top factors that influence food shopping decisions. Cost, convenience, and food safety come next. With today's busy lifestyles, people rely more on foods they can cook and eat quickly, such as microwavable meals and other convenience foods. To stay healthy, choose some foods that will provide you with essential nutrients and that can be prepared and eaten within the time you have available. Skipping meals cheats your body of the nutrients food provides. Cost can also affect food choices. How has cost affected food decisions you have made?

Your Emotions

Emotions are another factor that affects eating habits. Have you ever headed to the refrigerator just because you had nothing else to do? Do you tend to eat more—or less—when you feel stressed, frustrated, or depressed? Eating to relieve tension or boredom can result in overeating. At the same time, if you lose your appetite when you are upset or bored, you may miss out on getting important nutrients that your body needs.

Your Eating Habits

Choosing foods that taste good *and* provide nutrients without too much fat, cholesterol, and sodium, is one of the most healthful ways to reduce major risk factors for chronic diseases, including **obesity**, high blood pressure, and high blood cholesterol. Why, then, is eating linked to six out of ten leading causes of death in the United States, including heart disease, stroke, and cancer? One answer is that many people are unable to distinguish between appetite and hunger. They eat past the point of feeling full because their appetite continues to be stimulated after their hunger has been satisfied. Unfortunately, many of the foods that stimulate the appetite are also high in fat and calories.

keeping Fit

Managing Your Eating Habits

Here are some tips for managing your eating habits.

➤ **Avoid being influenced by others in making your food choices.** Make choices with *your health* in mind—not just your appetite.

➤ **Pay attention to quantity.** Start off with reasonably sized servings, and, if possible, use a smaller plate. Listen to your body's "hunger clock" rather than to your appetite. When you feel full, set down your fork or spoon and stop eating. Remember, it takes 20 minutes for your stomach to completely signal your body that it is satisfied.

➤ **Make something other than food the focus of everyday social occasions.** If you are getting together with friends, consider a setting other than a restaurant. This might be a park, a community swimming pool, a skating rink, or the home of one of the group members.

hotlink

obesity For more information on obesity and the health risks associated with it, see Chapter 6, page 134.

Managing Your Eating Habits

keeping Fit

Have students recall what they had for lunch the day before. Ask students to consider what influenced their choices and the amount they ate. Ask them to share their responses.

LEP Class Activity

Give each student a food advertisement from a magazine or newspaper and ask them if the ad makes them want to eat the food. Have them give reasons for their answers.

L2 Self-Esteem

Suggest students examine their present diet to determine factors that influence food choices. Ask them to list at least one food they eat because of each of the following influences: childhood preference, family custom, ethnic background, teen culture, peer pressure, role models, advertising, time, money, and personal emotions. Have them think of times when they were feeling low and times when they were feeling good. Did their self-esteem influence their food choices at those times?

Did You Know?

➤ **Living high on the hog** means having a high standard of living, or living comfortably and well. Southern in origin, this saying refers to the fact that the choicest cuts of ham or bacon come from the upper part of the hog's sides.

➤ **To have a hollow leg** means to eat heartily. This saying can first be traced to 1362 when the word *hollow* meant to be hungry or to look starved. There is even some speculation that people with hollow wooden legs may have hidden food inside them.

PERSONAL HEALTH

FOOD CHOICES. In the United States, most people, even those with limited incomes, select foods to some extent based on what they want or like rather than on what they need. Consumers in the United States enjoy a wide range of food choices. In any country, the economic status of the people has a major influence on the foods eaten. Have students list what they have eaten in the last 24 hours and give reasons for each food choice. Then have them conduct research about the food choices of a low-income population in a country where chronic hunger exists. Tell them to write a short paragraph contrasting the reasons for their food choices with what they would be if they were impoverished and lived in an area where food was scarce.

ASSESS

EVALUATING THE LESSON

Assign and discuss the Lesson 1 Review; then administer, grade, and discuss the *Lesson 12 Quiz* in the TCR. 📖

RETEACHING

- Have students make a list of the factors that influence people's food choices. After each factor, ask them to write at least one sentence, summarizing what they learned about that factor in the lesson.
- Ask students to complete *Reteaching Activity 12* in the TCR. 📖

ENRICHMENT

Ask for volunteers to videotape several television food commercials to present to the class. Have the class critique the effectiveness of the ads.

CLOSE

Place seven plates or soup bowls on a table, each labeled with the following concepts: *physical health, cultural, family and friends, advertising, time and money, emotions,* and *nutrition and adolescence.* Divide the class into seven groups, and assign each group one of the seven concepts. Have each group compose a paragraph summarizing the concept. Bring the class together, and select volunteers to read the paragraphs aloud. Briefly discuss whether the paragraphs accurately summarize the concepts.

Nutrition Throughout Your Life

At every stage in life, good nutrition is essential for health. **Nutrition** is *the process by which the body takes in and uses food.* Even before you were born, then as an infant and a child, and now as a teen, nutrients in food provided and continue to provide you with substances you need to grow and develop. At each age you have required the same nutrients. As you have grown and developed, however, you have needed them in increasing amounts.

Getting the nutrients your body needs also enables you to have energy, feel and look your best, and stay mentally alert. Another important benefit of good nutrition is that it can help prevent chronic diseases such as heart disease, certain cancers, diabetes, and stroke.

Next to the first years of life, adolescence is the fastest period of growth a person experiences. For growth and active living, the body uses more energy from food and has higher nutrient needs than ever before. In spite of this, many teens skip meals and make poor food choices. Think about what you have eaten today. Would you describe your food choices as healthful?

LESSON 1 *Review*

Reviewing Facts and Vocabulary

1. Explain the difference between hunger and appetite.
2. What factors influence decisions that affect food choices?
3. Why is good nutrition so important during adolescence?

Thinking Critically

4. *Analyzing.* Give three examples of how your culture and family have influenced your eating habits.
5. *Comparing and Contrasting.* Compare your food habits with those of a friend. What might account for the differences and similarities?
6. *Synthesizing.* In what ways beyond those mentioned in the lesson can emotions affect your food choices?

Applying Health Skills

7. *In Your Home.* Analyze factors that influence your eating patterns. Make a chart showing the food purchased in one grocery shopping trip. Indicate whether foods were selected for reasons of cost, convenience, culture, or any other factor described in the lesson. Analyze the chart, and determine which factors represented the greatest influence on your family's food choices. Share your findings with your family, discussing the impact these choices make on the nutritional value of your meals.

Lesson 1 Review

Answers to Reviewing Facts and Vocabulary

1. Hunger is the body's need for food. Appetite is the mind's desire for food.
2. Cultural heritage, family and social relationships, media messages, and lifestyle influence your food choices.
3. Because it is a time of bodily growth and change.

Answers to Thinking Critically

4. Answers should include family gatherings, holiday traditions, and/or religious beliefs.
5. Answers should include the factors listed in question 2 above.
6. Answers will vary.

Nutrients: Carbohydrates, Proteins, and Fats

In order to survive, the human body needs the nutrients found in food. These nutrients, which perform a number of life-sustaining functions in the body, are divided into six main categories: carbohydrates, proteins, fats, vitamins, minerals, and water. Each has a unique function in the normal growth and functioning of your body.

HEALTH TERMS

carbohydrates
glucose
glycogen
proteins
amino acids
lipid
linoleic acid
cholesterol

HEALTH CONCEPTS

- The nutrients found in food are essential to life.
- Carbohydrates are the body's chief fuel.
- A healthful eating plan includes appropriate amounts of protein to build and repair body tissue.
- Limiting fat and dietary cholesterol is a guideline for health.

Carbohydrates

Do you enjoy eating potatoes, pasta, and bread? These foods are rich in carbohydrates. Made up of carbon, oxygen, and hydrogen, **carbohydrates** are *the starches and sugars found in foods.* Carbohydrates are the body's preferred source of energy, providing four calories per gram.

Depending on their chemical makeup, carbohydrates are classified into one of two types—simple or complex. Health experts recommend that 55 to 65 percent of your daily calories come from carbohydrates, mainly complex carbohydrates.

Lesson 2 Resources

TEACHER'S CLASSROOM RESOURCES

- **Concept Map** Activity 13
- **Enrichment** Activity 5
- **Lesson 13 Quiz**
- **Lesson Plan 13**
- **Reteaching** Activity 13

STUDENT WORKBOOK

- **Applying Health Skills 13**
- **Chapter Study Guide 5**
- **Vocabulary** Activity 5

MULTIMEDIA

- ABCNews InterActive™ VHS/Videodisc, *Food and Nutrition*

LESSON **2**

Nutrients: Carbohydrates, Proteins, and Fats

FOCUS

LESSON OBJECTIVES

After studying this lesson, students should be able to

- define *carbohydrates, proteins,* and *fats* and describe their roles in maintaining good health.
- identify food sources for carbohydrates, proteins, and fats.
- contrast complete and incomplete proteins.
- define cholesterol and explain its relationship to overall health.

MOTIVATOR

Write the following on the chalkboard for students to work on while attendance is being taken: *List the following nutrients on a sheet of paper: carbohydrates, proteins, and fats. Under each nutrient, list as many foods as you can that are good sources of that nutrient.*

INTRODUCING THE LESSON

Have students share their responses to the Motivator. Ask them to save their responses until the end of the lesson to check their accuracy.

INTRODUCING HEALTH TERMS

- Have students make sets of flash cards to review the definitions and functions of each of the vocabulary terms.
- Ask students to complete Vocabulary Activity 5 and Chapter Study Guide 5 in the *Student Workbook.*

TEACH

L1 Discussing

Talk about why carbohydrate foods often are considered fattening. Describe a low-carbohydrate diet. Stress that although omitting or limiting simple carbohydrates can drastically reduce one's caloric intake, complex carbohydrates are essential to a well-balanced diet.

L1 Personal Involvement

Tell students to list all the complex and simple carbohydrates they have eaten in the past 24 hours. Ask each student to compare the two lists and write a summary statement about his or her intake of carbohydrates.

L3 Researching

Have the class research the relationship between carbohydrates and tooth decay. *(Bacteria in plaque act on carbohydrates to form acids that destroy tooth enamel and irritate gums. Frequent consumption of sticky, sugary foods increases the risk of tooth decay.)*

L1 Class Activity

Point out to students that they need 20–30 grams of fiber a day. Bring a variety of breakfast cereals to class, and have students check the nutritional label on each box to calculate how many servings of that cereal they would have to eat to meet the fiber requirement. (Make sure students understand that breakfast cereal is only one source of daily fiber. Have students list on the chalkboard other fiber sources.)

Simple Carbohydrates

Simple carbohydrates, or sugars, are present naturally in fruits, some vegetables, and milk. These sugars are called fructose in fruit, lactose in milk, maltose in grain, and sucrose in table sugar. Sugars are also added to many manufactured food products, such as candy, cookies, soft drinks, and other concentrated sweets. In recent decades, food manufacturers have also begun adding corn syrup and other forms of sugar to soups, salad dressings, breads, and other foods you may not characterize as being sweet.

Complex Carbohydrates

Complex carbohydrates, or starches, are found in great supply in rice and other grains, seeds, nuts, legumes (dried peas and beans), and tubers (potatoes, cassava, yams, taro). Starches are called complex carbohydrates because they are chemically more complex than simple carbohydrates. They are made of many sugars linked together. During digestion, starches break down into sugars.

The Role of Carbohydrates

Before your body can use carbohydrates, it must first convert them to **glucose**, *a simple sugar and the body's chief fuel.* Glucose that is not used right away is stored in the liver and muscles as *a starch-like substance* called **glycogen** (GLY-kuh-juhn). Later, when more glucose is

▼ *Which of these foods do you eat regularly? What other foods do you enjoy eating?*
ACTIVITY *List the foods in the picture that are high in complex carbohydrates.*

MORE ABOUT . . . . .

GRAINS. Grains figure prominently among the relatively few species of plants that furnish people with most of their food worldwide. The most important domesticated species include:

- wheat—domesticated nearly 9,000 years ago in the Near East and today the world's most widely cultivated plant;

- rice—domesticated in Southeast Asia and today the plant that feeds more people than any other;

- maize—domesticated in the Americas and today used chiefly to feed livestock;

- sorghum, barley, rye, oats, and millet— each less important than the first three but still significant food crops in various parts of the world today.

needed, the glycogen is converted back to glucose. When people consume more carbohydrates than their body needs for energy or can store as glycogen, this excess is stored as adipose tissue, or body fat.

Fiber

Found in the tough, stringy part of vegetables, fruits, and grains, fiber is a special form of complex carbohydrate. Although it cannot be digested and used as energy, fiber serves other vital functions. It helps move waste through your **digestive system** and helps prevent constipation, appendicitis, and other intestinal problems. Eating enough fiber throughout your life may reduce your risk of some cancers and heart disease. It is also instrumental in controlling diabetes. Some types of fiber seem to help lower blood cholesterol and control blood sugar, though this connection is only partially understood.

For people watching their weight, fiber offers other benefits. Fiber-rich foods are bulky, so they offer a feeling of fullness. They tend to be lower in fat and calories, and they may take longer to chew, thereby slowing the pace of your meal.

You can increase your fiber intake by eating an abundance of vegetables and fruits, especially those with edible skins and seeds. Other good sources include whole-grain products, such as bran cereals, whole-wheat breads and pasta, whole rye bread, brown rice, oatmeal, corn tortillas, and popcorn. It is recommended that you eat 25 grams of fiber a day.

Proteins

A vital part of every body cell, **proteins** are *nutrients that help build and maintain body tissues.* Muscle, bone, connective tissue, teeth, skin, blood, and vital organs all contain protein. Like carbohydrates, proteins provide four calories per gram. Like both carbohydrates and fats, excess protein calories are converted to fat for storage.

Just as letters of the alphabet are arranged to make different words, proteins are made of chains of building blocks called amino acids. These **amino** (a-MEE-noh) **acids,** *substances that make up body proteins,* can be arranged in numerous ways. Your body can make all but nine of the 20 different amino acids. These nine are called *essential amino acids,* because they must come from foods you eat.

Complete and Incomplete Proteins

Protein-rich foods are categorized into *complete protein* or *incomplete protein* sources depending on the amino acids these foods contain.

- **Complete proteins** are foods that contain all the essential amino acids that the body needs and in the proper amounts. These sources include animal products, such as fish, meat, poultry, eggs, milk, cheese, yogurt, and many soybean products.

hotlink

digestive system For more information on the digestive system and its functions, see Chapter 18, page 412.

Did You Know?

➤ Americans eat their own weight in sugar every year.

➤ The term *protein* comes from a Greek word meaning "of prime importance." The name is fitting because without protein, life could not exist.

L2 Class Activity

Have students find definitions of *whole grain* and give examples. *(Whole grains consist of the endosperm, germ, and bran. Whole-wheat bread contains a whole grain; white bread has only the endosperm.)* Discuss the health benefits of whole grains. *(They have more fiber and more nutrients, especially B vitamins and vitamin E.)*

hotlink

digestive system

Tell students that the majority of digestion and nutritional absorption is achieved in the small intestine, though water is absorbed primarily in the large intestine. The digestive system is discussed in detail in Chapter 18.

L2 Personal Involvement

Ask students to record their diets for 24 hours and then calculate the amount of protein they ate. Have them determine how their diet compares with the Food Guide Pyramid on pages 114–115.

L1 Discussing

Present this case study to the class: Tim, a vegetarian, is coming for a two-day visit. He doesn't eat meat, poultry, or fish. What foods should you offer? Lead students in brainstorming a list of tasty, nutritious foods to offer Tim that stay within the guidelines of his diet.

PERSONAL HEALTH

VEGETARIAN DIETS. Consuming enough complete protein is a challenge for some vegetarians. Lacto-ovo vegetarians avoid only meat, poultry, and fish. They get complete protein from eggs, milk, cheese, and yogurt. Lacto means milk and ovo means eggs. Vegans eliminate all animal sources of food from their diet. Unless they combine foods carefully, their meals will not provide the protein they need. Three equations help create vegetarian meals with complete protein:

- Legumes + Grains = Complete Protein
- Legumes + Nuts or Seeds = Complete Protein
- Any Plant Protein + Eggs or Dairy Products = Complete Protein

L1 Discussing

Talk about why fats are important in the body. Then ask students to identify the dangers of having too much fat in their diets. *(Diets high in fat may be high in calories, which can lead to obesity. For many people, high-fat diets increase the risk of heart attacks and strokes.)*

L1 Discussing

Ask: Is it healthy to cut fat out of your diet? If not, why not? *(Among other functions, fat carries vitamins through the bloodstream, provides energy, and becomes part of cell membranes.)*

L2 Cooperative Learning

Divide the class into six groups. Using food composition charts, have students investigate differences in fat content among these foods: (1) whole, 2 percent, and skim milk; (2) cheddar and skim-milk mozzarella cheese; (3) ice cream and frozen yogurt; (4) chicken with and without skin; (5) butter, margarine, and lard; and (6) bologna and lean lunch meat.

Visual Learning

Protein Combinations

Help students understand the concept of combining foods to create complete proteins with foods that contain incomplete proteins. Point out that each of the puzzle pieces puts together a grain product with either beans or nuts. (Tofu is a soybean product; tortillas are made from corn or flour.) Explain that grains by themselves cannot provide the necessary protein because they do not contain all of the essential amino acids. By combining foods, such as putting peanut-butter onto a slice of wheat bread, they will have all of the amino acids that make up a complete protein. Ask students to give other examples they include in their eating plans.

■ **Incomplete proteins** are foods that lack some of the essential amino acids. Such sources are foods derived from the seeds of plants: legumes, nuts, whole grains, and the seeds themselves. Eating various incomplete protein sources—legumes with grains, for example—yields the equivalent of a complete protein. They need not be eaten at the same meal as long as the day's meals supply both of them. The illustration below shows some examples of complete proteins from incomplete sources.

▼ *By combining incomplete protein sources over the course of a day, you can be sure your body is getting complete sources of protein.*

ACTIVITY *Look at the puzzle pieces and identify as many of the seeds pictured as you can. They represent foods you can combine to get complete proteins.*

The Role of Proteins

During each of the normal periods of marked growth—infancy, childhood, adolescence, and pregnancy—amino acids build new body tissues. Throughout life, new proteins form constantly to replace damaged or worn-out body cells.

Proteins in enzymes, hormones, and antibodies also help regulate many body processes. Enzymes are substances that control the rate of thousands of biochemical reactions in your body cells. Hormones regulate reactions. Antibodies help identify and destroy bacteria and viruses that cause disease in the body.

PROTEIN COMBINATIONS

Incomplete Proteins

1 slice of bread + 2 oz. of peanut butter

2 oz. of tofu + 1 cup of rice

1 tortilla + 1 cup of beans

Complete Proteins

CURRICULUM CONNECTIONS

SOCIAL STUDIES. Invite several adults who follow vegetarian diets to come to class and describe what they eat and discuss reasons for their food choices. Follow up by asking volunteers to try a vegetarian diet for several days. Have them report to the class their reactions to the experience. Ask the students if it was difficult to avoid meat. Were they hungrier than usual? How did their family and friends react? Would they consider becoming vegetarians?

FAMILY AND CONSUMER SCIENCE. Have students gather recipes for vegetarian sandwiches and meals. Prepare some of the foods, and have a food-tasting session.

Fats

You have no doubt seen the following words printed on food packages: *"Now with less fat." "Reduced fat." "Low fat." "No fat."* With all the media attention that fat has received in recent years, you might wonder why it is considered a nutrient at all. Although consuming too much fat is unhealthful, as these labels may indicate, the fact is your body needs some fat. Fats represent the most concentrated form of energy available. Gram for gram, fats deliver more than twice the energy of either carbohydrates or proteins.

Chemically, fats are a type of **lipid** (LIP-uhd), *a fatty substance that does not dissolve in water.* Like carbohydrates, fats are composed of carbon, hydrogen, and oxygen atoms. Fats are made of fatty acids. Fats are generally classified as either saturated or unsaturated, depending on their chemical composition. Fats are a combination of both types.

Saturated Fats

A fatty acid is said to be saturated when the fatty acid holds all the hydrogen atoms it can. Animal fats and tropical oils, such as palm oil, palm kernel oil, and coconut oil, have a high proportion of saturated fats. Fats in beef, pork, egg yolks, and dairy foods are higher in saturated fatty acids than fats in chicken and fish. Foods high in saturated fats are usually solid or semi-solid at room temperature. High intake of saturated fats is associated with an increased risk of heart disease.

Unsaturated Fats

A fatty acid is described as unsaturated when it is missing one or more pairs of hydrogen atoms. Most vegetable fats, including olive, canola, soybean, corn, and cottonseed oils, contain a higher proportion of unsaturated fatty acids. Such fats become liquids, or oils, at room temperature. Unsaturated fats have been associated with a reduced risk of heart disease. Be careful, however, when selecting products made with vegetable oils since processing can change a fat's characteristics. Hydrogenation—the adding of missing hydrogen atoms—makes them more saturated and firmer in texture. Margarine, for example, is vegetable oil but in hydrogenated form.

The Role of Fats

Besides providing nine calories per gram of energy, fats are integral to other important health functions as well. They carry vitamins A, D, E, and K into your blood and serve as sources of **linoleic** (lih-noh-LAY-ik) **acid.** This is *an essential fatty acid not made in the body but which is essential for growth and healthy skin.* Fats in food add flavor, and they help satisfy hunger since they take longer to digest than

Olive oil   Canola oil   Vegetable oil

▲ *More and more, Americans are switching to less saturated forms of fat in their diets.*

ACTIVITY *Can you think of other trends that show Americans are becoming more health-conscious?*

L2 Class Activity

Using a food composition table, have the class compare the fat content of one serving of each of the following: French fries, potato chips, and a plain baked potato. Ask: What accounts for the differences? What happens to the fat content of a baked potato when sour cream or butter is added?

L1 Class Activity

Suggest students read current consumer health articles on fat and cholesterol in newspapers and magazines. Ask them to share the main ideas of the articles with the class. Lead students in evaluating the reliability of the information.

LD Explaining

On the chalkboard, list the terms *carbohydrates, proteins,* and *fats.* Next to each, write one source of the nutrient and, in one simplified sentence, describe the body's uses for it. Have LD students copy this information into their class notes for later review.

L2 Parental Involvement

Ask volunteers to investigate their family history of serum cholesterol levels and cardiovascular disease. Request that they find out whether family members changed their diets or lifestyles to lower serum cholesterol, and if so, in what ways. Remind students that family history is one risk factor in determining their own health. Other risk factors include obesity and smoking.

SCHOOL-TO-CAREER

NUTRITION IN THE CAFETERIA. In most institutional settings, meals are planned to provide a balanced selection of healthy foods. Have students interview the food manager of a cafeteria in a school, child care center, or other institution. If your cafeteria uses a caterer, students may wish to contact the catering company. Tell them to ask how the food manager applies the information in this chapter when planning weekly menus. Ask where planners obtain the nutritional information they need to plan balanced meals. Students may then write a menu for an institutional meal and explain the nutritional need met by each item.

ASSESS

EVALUATING THE LESSON

Assign and discuss the Lesson 2 Review; then, administer, grade, and discuss the *Lesson 13 Quiz* in the TCR. 🖝

RETEACHING

- Make up some advice column-type questions that can be answered at least partially with information from the lesson. Have students work individually to compose response letters.
- Ask students to complete *Reteaching Activity 13* in the TCR. 🖝

ENRICHMENT

- Have volunteers read the labels on a variety of bread packages. Have one group compile a list of the names, weights, and prices of whole-grain bread. Have the second group make a list of non-whole-grain breads names, weights, and prices. Tell students to decide whether each bread is whole grain by looking at the first ingredient listed on the label. Have them discuss their findings with the class.
- To inform students of the National Cancer Institute's national campaign called "5 a Day for Better Health," ask them to complete *Enrichment Activity 5*, "More Than an Apple a Day," in the TCR. 🖝

CLOSE

Have students summarize the major concepts of the lesson by analyzing a typical fast-food meal (burger, fries, milkshake).

HEALTH Online

Using a research tool at **health.glencoe.com**, become familiar with good sources of each nutrient. Record what you have eaten in the last three meals and check which nutrients the foods contain. Are you lacking important nutrients?

---

carbohydrates and proteins. Body fat plays a different role than dietary fat does. Body fat surrounds and cushions your vital organs, protecting them from injury, and it insulates your body against excessive heat and cold.

Your body needs only a moderate amount of dietary fat each day. The average teenage girl, who needs about 2,200 calories daily, should have no more than 66 grams of fat daily. Teenage boys, who use an average of 2,800 calories daily, should have no more than 84 grams of fat daily. Too much fat is linked to obesity, heart attacks, and other health problems. The *Dietary Guidelines for Americans* and other reports from advisory groups recommend that most Americans cut their fat intake to no more than 30 percent of calories. These groups further suggest replacing some saturated fats with unsaturated fats.

Cholesterol

Cholesterol is *a fatlike substance produced in the liver of all animals and, therefore, found only in foods of animal origin*—meats, poultry, fish, eggs, and dairy products. Your body needs some cholesterol, like fat, but it can make what it needs. Cholesterol is instrumental, for example, in the production of the sex hormones, of vitamin D (in the presence of sunlight), and of the protective sheath around nerve fibers. At the same time, like fat, elevated blood cholesterol levels in the blood constitute a major risk factor for heart and other circulatory diseases. Consumption of dietary fat, especially saturated fat, tends to raise blood cholesterol levels. Limiting these fats may reduce the risk.

LESSON 2 Review

Reviewing Facts and Vocabulary

1. What three nutrients provide energy?
2. What is protein? What does it do?
3. Name three functions of fats.

Thinking Critically

4. **Synthesizing.** What other products besides those mentioned in the lesson do you think might contain hidden sugar?
5. **Evaluating.** How would you distinguish a healthful meal from an unhealthful one?

Applying Health Skills

6. **In Your Home and School.** Think back to the meals you ate over the last two or three days. Divide a sheet of paper into three columns labeled *Carbohydrate-rich Foods, Protein-rich Foods,* and *High-fat Foods*. Identify which foods you ate that belong to each of these categories. Which changes in your eating patterns, if any, do you need to make?

Lesson 2 Review

Answers to Reviewing Facts and Vocabulary

1. Carbohydrates, proteins, and fats.
2. Protein is a nutrient that builds and maintains body tissues.
3. They provide energy; carry vitamins A, D, E, and K into the blood; and serve as a source of linoleic acid.

Answers to Thinking Critically

4. Answers will vary.
5. A healthful meal delivers a high ratio of nutrients per calorie. An unhealthful meal is high in calories and low in nutrients.

Nutrients: Vitamins, Minerals, and Water

Some of the body's most essential nutrients are every bit as important as carbohydrates, fats, and proteins. These important nutrients are vitamins, minerals, and water. In this lesson you will learn about the unique function of each one and the best food sources of these nutrients.

HEALTH TERMS

vitamins

minerals

HEALTH CONCEPTS

- Healthful eating includes consuming ample amounts of vitamins and minerals.
- Water is the body's most essential nutrient.

Vitamins

Vitamins are *compounds that help regulate many vital body processes, including the digestion, absorption, and metabolism of other nutrients.* Vitamins are known as *micronutrients* because they are needed in small amounts. Although vitamins do not supply calories, some of them speed up reactions that produce energy in body cells.

Of the 13 vitamins that play a key role in good nutrition, only one—Vitamin D—is manufactured by the body. The rest must be derived from food. Vitamins are classified into two groups: *water-soluble* and *fat-soluble*.

Water-Soluble Vitamins

Water-soluble vitamins include Vitamin C and the eight vitamins in the Vitamin B complex. As their name suggests, water-soluble

LESSON **3**

Nutrients: Vitamins, Minerals, and Water

FOCUS

LESSON OBJECTIVES

After studying this lesson, students should be able to

- define *vitamins* and *minerals* and describe their roles in maintaining good health.
- discuss properties of water-soluble vitamins and fat-soluble vitamins.
- describe the role of water in maintaining good health.

MOTIVATOR

Ask students to write in their private Health Journals several facts regarding vitamins and minerals.

INTRODUCING THE LESSON

Have students share their responses to the Motivator. List their responses on the chalkboard. Tell students to verify their statements or correct misconceptions as they read the chapter.

INTRODUCING HEALTH TERMS

- Have students identify several examples of vitamins and minerals.
- Discuss the meanings of *water-soluble* and *fat-soluble*.
- Ask students to complete Vocabulary Activity 5 and Chapter Study Guide 5 in the *Student Workbook.*

Lesson 3 Resources

TEACHER'S CLASSROOM RESOURCES

- **Concept Map** Activity 14
- **Health Lab 5**
- **Lesson 14 Quiz**
- **Lesson Plan 14**
- **Reteaching** Activity 14

STUDENT WORKBOOK

- **Applying Health Skills 14**
- **Chapter Study Guide 5**
- **Vocabulary** Activity 5

MULTIMEDIA

- **ABCNews InterActive™ VHS/Videodisc,** *Food and Nutrition*

TEACH

L1 Class Activity

People need fruits and vegetables rich in vitamins C and A every day. Have students use classroom sources to find out what foods are good sources of these vitamins. Encourage them to discuss their findings with the class.

Cooking Good!

keeping Fit

Demonstrate the correct cooking method for several fresh vegetables, and allow students to taste the properly cooked dishes.

L3 Guest Speaker

Ask a family and consumer sciences teacher to demonstrate and discuss ways to cut down on vitamin loss in the handling of fruits and vegetables.

L2 Discussing

Have students debate whether vitamin supplements are necessary for healthy individuals. Ask them to collect information to support their position. Hold a class debate, with each student having 30 seconds to present his or her supportive evidence. Establish a rule that students cannot repeat, as part of their debate, what anyone else has said. At the end, have students draw conclusions about vitamin supplements and current consumer information regarding them.

Water-Soluble Vitamins

VITAMIN	ROLE IN BODY	FOOD SOURCE
C (ascorbic acid)	Protects against infection; helps with formation of connective tissue; helps wounds heal; maintains elasticity and strength of blood vessels; promotes healthy teeth and gums.	Citrus fruits, cantaloupe, tomatoes, cabbage, broccoli, potatoes, peppers
B_1 (thiamine)	Changes glucose into energy or fat; helps prevent nervous irritability; necessary for good appetite.	Whole-grain or enriched cereals, liver, yeast, nuts, legumes, wheat germ
B_2 (riboflavin)	Is essential for producing energy from carbohydrates, fats, and proteins; helps keep skin in healthy condition.	Milk, cheese, spinach, eggs, beef liver
Niacin	Important to maintenance of all body tissues; helps in energy production; needed by body to utilize carbohydrates, to synthesize human fat, and for tissue respiration.	Milk, eggs, poultry, beef, legumes, peanut butter, whole grains, and enriched and fortified grain products
B_6	Essential to amino acid and carbohydrate metabolism. Helps turn the amino acid tryptophan into serotonin (a messenger to the brain) and niacin.	Wheat bran and germ, liver, meat, whole grains, fish, vegetables
Folic acid	Necessary for the production of RNA and DNA and normal red blood cells; reduces risk of birth defects.	Nuts and other legumes, green vegetables, orange juice, folic acid-enriched breads and rolls, liver
B_{12}	Necessary for production of red blood cells and normal growth.	Found in animal products, such as meat, fish, poultry, eggs, milk, other dairy foods, some fortified foods
Pantothenic acid	Functions in the breakdown and synthesis of carbohydrates, fats, and proteins; necessary for synthesis of some of the adrenal hormones.	Milk, cheese, poultry, wheat germ, whole-grain cereals and breads, legumes, green vegetables

keeping Fit

Cooking Good!

Foods containing water-soluble vitamins need to be cooked carefully so that the vitamins are not destroyed by heat or lost through steam or in cooking water. Follow these tips:

➤ Cook fruits and vegetables quickly, or steam them.

➤ Cover food during cooking.

vitamins dissolve in water and thus pass easily into the bloodstream in the process of digestion. Excess amounts are excreted in urine. Since these vitamins are not stored in the body, you need to replenish your supply of them regularly through the foods you eat. Foods that contain these vitamins need to be cooked carefully so that only a minimum amount of vitamins are lost. Adding variety to the foods you eat will also ensure that you obtain these nutrients.

Fat-Soluble Vitamins

Fat-soluble vitamins—vitamins that are absorbed and transported by fat—include Vitamins A, D, E, and K. Your body obtains Vitamin A in two ways: directly from plant-eating organisms and by manufacturing it from carotenoids in plants such as *beta-carotene*, a substance found in carrots, broccoli, spinach, and other vegetables.

Myths & Realities

MYTH. Everyone should take a nutrient supplement each day.

FACT. The use of nutrient supplements is often unnecessary, costly, and sometimes unsafe. Supplements often keep people from getting medical attention they need and, despite some claims, supplements will not improve athletic performance, relieve menstrual cramps, provide "insurance" against emotional stress, or serve as a pick-me-up for tired, run-down people. Instead, the extra food athletes eat provides the added nutrients they need; no evidence proves that vitamin B_6 supplements relieve menstrual cramps, although large doses may cause nerve damage; so-called stress vitamins are not needed, but rest and recreation are; and vitamin B_{12} does not provide extra energy.

Fat-Soluble Vitamins

VITAMIN	ROLE IN BODY	FOOD SOURCE
A	Maintenance of epithelial tissue; strengthens tooth enamel and promotes use of calcium and phosphorus in bone formation; growth of body cells; keeps eyes moist; helps eyes adjust to darkness; possible aid in cancer protection.	Milk and other dairy products, green vegetables, carrots, deep-orange fruits, liver
D	Promotes absorption and use of calcium and phosphorus; essential for normal bone and tooth development.	Fortified milk; eggs; fortified breakfast cereal; sardines; salmon; beef; margarine; produced in the skin upon exposure to ultraviolet rays in sunlight
E	May relate to transporting oxygen through blood and longevity; may be a protection against red blood cell destruction.	Widely distributed in foods; vegetable oils, legumes, nuts, seeds, and wheat germ
K	Essential for blood clotting; assists in regulating blood calcium level.	Spinach, broccoli, eggs, liver, cabbage, tomatoes; produced by intestinal bacteria

Unlike water-soluble vitamins, which are eliminated through the urine, fat-soluble vitamins are stored in the body's fatty tissue, the liver, and the kidneys. Excess buildup of these vitamins can have a toxic or other damaging effect on the body. People who take nutrient supplements with very large doses of fat-soluble vitamins are especially vulnerable to these effects.

Minerals

Minerals are *inorganic substances that the body cannot manufacture but that act as catalysts, regulating many vital body processes.* Like vitamins, minerals are micronutrients. Despite the small amounts your body needs, each mineral has its own unique function in health.

Your body requires larger amounts of some minerals than others. So-called *trace* minerals—the ones your body needs in tiny, or trace amounts—include iron, iodine, copper, and others. During the teen years, when growth is rapid, iron is especially important. It is essential for the hemoglobin in your blood, which carries oxygen throughout the body. Without ample iron, you may feel tired and have little endurance.

Another important mineral to the body is calcium. Giving structure to your bones, calcium helps develop and maintain bone strength. It also aids muscle contraction, blood clotting, and the proper functioning of the nervous system. Milk and most other dairy products, some leafy green vegetables, and canned salmon are good sources of calcium. When you fail to get enough calcium through foods such as these, your body draws upon deposits of the mineral in the bones and sends these to the muscles, blood, and nerves. This

▲ *The best source of vitamins and minerals is in the foods you eat.*

ACTIVITY *Identify which nutrients are in these foods.*

L1 Explaining

Point out that taking extra fat-soluble vitamins may be dangerous. The vitamins can accumulate in the body's fat tissues, and excess build-up can be toxic.

L2 Explaining

Explain how eating healthful foods contributes to the physical health side of the health triangle by describing the role of antioxidants. Tell students that these chemical compounds, which include vitamins C and E, rid the body of free radicals. Explain that free radicals, which are formed in numerous metabolic reactions, trigger destructive chemical reactions, destroy genes, and destroy cells. Add that scientists believe damage by free radicals is one cause of cancer and of aging itself. Ask students if they know what foods are rich in antioxidants. *(primarily fruits and vegetables)*

LEP Defining

On the chalkboard, list the categories of nutrients presented in this lesson. Next to each, write one source of the nutrient and, in one simplified sentence, describe the body's uses for it. Have LEP students copy this information into their class notes for later review.

Did You Know?

Here is why you should eat your spinach. It's a good source of beta-carotene, which helps prevent heart disease, cancer, and cataracts. It is also a good source of magnesium, which helps keep blood cholesterol down. It's also rich in fiber.

MORE ABOUT . . . . .

DIET AND NUTRITION. According to research, the average American drinks more soft drinks than water, milk, or juice. This is especially true of teenagers!

In the past, soft drinks were snack beverages. Today they accompany many fast-food meals. Young people who drink large amounts of soft drinks typically have diets low in calcium, riboflavin, and vitamins A and C, just when their needs are highest. Unless they are sugar-free, soft drinks promote tooth decay. Each sip bathes teeth with sugar.

Phosphates in soft drinks provide phosphorus, but too much phosphorus without adequate calcium throws off the balance of these nutrients needed for bone health.

L3 Cooperative Learning

Have students work in groups to develop a lesson for an elementary class on the importance of nutrients. Groups might write skits, design games, or produce a video. Arrange to have one or more lessons presented to a grade school class, Scout meeting, etc.

L3 Community Involvement

Choose students to interview a social service agency representative. Have them ask about nutritional deficiency problems in the local community. Request that students find out what programs are available to alleviate nutritional deficiencies and what role is played by volunteers. Have students compile a list of qualifications for volunteers and share the list with the class.

L1 Class Activity

Have students examine the Minerals chart on this page. Direct them to create a new chart with four columns. Label the first column "Mineral" and list each of the minerals again. Label the second column "Food Items in My Diet." Have students list all the food items they currently include in their diet that contain each mineral. Label the third column "Effects of Deficiency," and have students do some research to discover what the effects would be for each mineral. Finally, label the fourth column "Effects of Overdose." Have students do research to discover what these effects would be. After the students have completed their charts, discuss with them whether their charts look balanced. Encourage students to brainstorm other foods that they could include or remove from their diet to help them balance their intake of minerals.

L2 Health Lab

Distribute *Health Lab 5* and have students answer the question "Do Fruit Juices Contain Iron?"

Minerals

MINERAL	PRIMARY FUNCTION	FOOD SOURCE
Calcium	Building material of bones and teeth (about 99 percent of body calcium is in your skeleton); regulation of body functions: heart muscle contraction, blood clotting.	Dairy products, leafy vegetables, canned fish with soft, edible bones, tofu processed with calcium sulfate
Phosphorus	Combines with calcium to give rigidity to bones and teeth; essential in cell metabolism; helps to maintain proper acid-base balance of blood (calcium and phosphorus are the most abundant minerals in the body).	Milk and most other dairy foods, peas, beans, liver, meat, fish, poultry, eggs, broccoli, whole grains
Magnesium	Enzyme activator related to carbohydrate metabolism; aids in bone growth and muscle contraction.	Whole grains, milk, dark green leafy vegetables, legumes, nuts
Sodium	Regulates the fluid and acid-base balance in the body; aids in transmission of nerve impulses.	Table salt, prepared sauces, soy sauce, milk, processed foods, foods in a brine such as pickles
Potassium	Part of the system that controls the acid-base and liquid balances; thought to be an important enzyme activator in the use of amino acids.	Legumes, potatoes, bananas, oranges, meat, milk
Sulfur	Component of the hormone insulin and some amino acids; builds hair, nails, skin.	Nuts, dried fruits, barley, oatmeal, eggs, beans, cheese
Chloride	Associated with sodium and its functions; a part of the gastric juice, hydrochloric acid; also functions in the starch-splitting system of saliva.	Table salt, milk, meat, fish, poultry, egg whites
Iron	Part of the red blood cells' oxygen and carbon dioxide transport system; important for use of energy in cells and for resistance to infection.	Meat, shellfish, poultry, legumes, peanuts, dried fruits, egg yolks, liver, fortified breakfast cereal, enriched rice
Iodine	Essential component of the thyroid hormone, thyroxin, which controls the rate of cell oxidation; helps maintain proper water balance.	Iodized salt, saltwater fish
Zinc	Function still under study; a component of many enzyme systems and an essential component of the pancreatic hormone insulin; essential for growth; promotes cell reproduction and repair.	Shellfish, meat, milk, eggs
Selenium	Works with Vitamin E to prevent cell damage.	Grain products, milk, eggs, meat, kidney, liver, seafood
Copper	An essential ingredient in several enzymes; needed for development of red blood cells.	Beans, Brazil nuts, whole-meal flour, lentils, seafood, kidney, liver
Fluoride	Essential to normal tooth and bone development and maintenance.	Fluoridated water, fish with edible bones
Manganese	Enzyme activator for carbohydrate, protein, and fat metabolism; also important in growth of cartilage and bone tissue.	Whole-grain products, nuts, green leafy vegetables, kidney, liver, beans, Brazil nuts, lentils

110 CHAPTER 5 NUTRITION AND YOUR HEALTH

MORE ABOUT . . . . .

STUDENT ATHLETES. "Athletic" drinks designed to replace salts lost in perspiration are not necessary unless an individual loses more than 3 quarts of water (about 6 pounds of weight) during an activity. Sweat has a lower concentration of salts than blood, so people lose proportionately more water than salts when they perspire. The most pressing need is to replace the lost water. If a person exceeds 3 quarts of replacement fluid, she or he may add about ½ teaspoon of salt for each quart thereafter. Salt tablets are not recommended, and concentrated salt should not be consumed unless large quantities of water are drunk at the same time.

can result in weakening of the skeleton and can increase your body's susceptibility to bone **fractures**. A lack of calcium in the teen years can lead to poor bone density and later in life to osteoporosis, a condition in which bones become brittle and weak.

Three other important minerals—sodium, chloride, and potassium—belong to a group of minerals known as *electrolytes*. They are called this because they become electrically charged when in solution, as they are in the body fluids. Sodium and potassium help maintain the balance of fluid within body cells. You probably get enough sodium in the form of salt—sodium chloride. Bananas and orange juice are excellent sources of potassium.

hotlink

fractures For more information on fractures and other problems of the skeletal system, see Chapter 15, page 344.

Water

If you were asked to guess which nutrient makes up the greatest percentage of your body, what would you say? If your answer was "water," you would be right.

Water is a regulator and is vital to every body function. It carries nutrients to and transports waste from your cells, mainly through the plasma in your blood. Water lubricates your joints and mucous membranes. It enables you to swallow and digest foods, absorb nutrients, and eliminate wastes. Through perspiration, water helps your body cool down and prevents the buildup of internal heat.

Your body uses about 10 cups (2.4 liters) of water a day. If you perspire from fever, hot weather, or strenuous exercise, you use more. Some water can be replaced by drinking fluids such as juice, milk, or water itself—about six to eight cups (1.4 to 1.9 liters) daily. Food is also a source of water. On average, fruits, vegetables, and milk products contain about 75 percent water.

LESSON 3 *Review*

Reviewing Facts and Vocabulary

1. Write a short paragraph that defines the terms *vitamin* and *mineral* and explains the chief importance to the body of these micronutrients.
2. Compare and contrast water-soluble and fat-soluble vitamins.

Thinking Critically

3. *Analyzing.* Since few foods naturally contain Vitamin D, manufacturers fortify milk with this vitamin. Why do you think milk was the food chosen for this purpose?

4. *Evaluating.* Consider the validity of the statement *Water should not be considered a nutrient because it does not provide calories or energy.*

Applying Health Skills

5. *In Your School.* Some critics claim that lunches offered on school campuses could be more healthful. Take a position on this issue with respect to your school's own options for lunch. Back up your views with information from the lesson.

ASSESS

EVALUATING THE LESSON

Assign and discuss the Lesson 3 Review; then administer, grade, and discuss the *Lesson 14 Quiz* in the TCR. 🖘

RETEACHING

- Have students copy the section headings (written in bold print in the textbook) into their notebooks. Ask them to leave two to three lines after each heading. Instruct students to write an original summarizing sentence for each heading in the appropriate space.
- Ask students to complete *Reteaching Activity 14* in the TCR. 🖘

ENRICHMENT

Assign volunteers to research the problems caused by deficiency or overconsumption of one of these minerals: calcium, phosphorus, magnesium, chlorine, potassium, sodium, iron, iodine, or zinc.

CLOSE

Display numerous pictures of foods rich in vitamins or minerals. Divide the class into small groups. Have each group determine which vitamins or minerals each food provides.

Lesson 3 Review

Answers to Reviewing Facts and Vocabulary

1. Paragraphs will vary.
2. Water-soluble—pass easily into the bloodstream; aren't stored in the body, so they must be replenished regularly. Fat-soluble—are absorbed and transported by fat; excess amounts are stored in the body and can be damaging.

Answers to Thinking Critically

3. Because milk contains high levels of calcium, and vitamin D helps the body use calcium.
4. Since nutrients are the substances you take in that allow your body to function, and the body can't function without water, water must be a nutrient, even though it doesn't supply calories or energy.

Guidelines for a Healthful Eating Style

Guidelines for a Healthful Eating Style

Guidelines for a Healthful Eating Style

LESSON OBJECTIVES

After studying this lesson, students should be able to

- explain the meaning and role of Recommended Dietary Allowances.
- name the five food groups and recommended servings for each.
- describe the guidelines for maintaining body weight.
- describe tips to control fat, sugars, and sodium in foods.
- explain the use of food groups to develop healthy eating patterns.

MOTIVATOR

Write the following on the chalkboard: *Divide a sheet of paper into three lengthwise columns. In the left column, list the five food groups. In the center column, name at least three foods that belong in each group. In the right column, rank the five groups according to how often you eat these foods, with 1 for most-eaten to 5 for least-eaten.*

INTRODUCING THE LESSON

Have students share their responses to the Motivator. Talk about the importance of each group and the need to eat a variety of foods from each group.

INTRODUCING HEALTH TERMS

- Ask students to complete Vocabulary Activity 5 and Chapter Study Guide 5 in the *Student Workbook.* 🖛

Having information about nutrition is an important and necessary step toward healthful eating. Yet, it is only a start. Think about the thousands of food products lining supermarket shelves. Which of these items will you choose to get the nutrients and food energy your body needs? How do you make healthy food choices?

HEALTH TERMS

Recommended Dietary Allowances (RDA)

HEALTH CONCEPTS

- The *Dietary Guidelines for Americans* help you make healthful food choices.
- Varying the foods you eat based on availability, affordability, and personal taste adds to the enjoyment of eating.
- Balancing the types of foods and nutrients consumed over the course of several days is part of a sound eating plan.
- Moderation—the controlling of portion size as well as the fat, saturated fat, cholesterol, sugars, and sodium in your food choices—can also make you a more healthful eater.

Dietary Guidelines for Americans

To help you meet this challenge to healthful eating, the U.S. Department of Agriculture (USDA), with the support of the Department of Health and Human Services, has published a booklet titled *Nutrition and Your Health: Dietary Guidelines for Americans.* This booklet spells out the **Recommended Dietary Allowances (RDA)**— *the amounts of nutrients that will prevent deficiencies and excesses in most healthy people*—for Americans two years old and older. These recommendations may be seen as nutritional standards against which you can evaluate—and, where needed, modify—your eating habits.

Following the *Dietary Guidelines* will help decrease your risk of getting eating-related chronic diseases now and in the future. It will also help ensure variety, balance, and moderation among the foods you choose.

Lesson 4 Resources

TEACHER'S CLASSROOM RESOURCES

- 🖛 **Concept Map** Activity 15
- 🖛 **Cooperative Learning** Activity 5
- 🖛 **Decision-Making** Activity 5
- 🖛 **Lesson 15 Quiz**
- 🖛 **Lesson Plan 15**
- 🖛 **Reteaching** Activity 15

STUDENT WORKBOOK

- 🖛 **Applying Health Skills 15**
- 🖛 **Chapter Study Guide 5**
- 🖛 **Vocabulary** Activity 5

TRANSPARENCIES

- 🖈 **Transparencies 14, 15**

MULTIMEDIA

- 🔴 **ABCNews InterActive™,** *Food and Nutrition*

Eat a Variety of Foods

No single food provides all of the nutrients your body needs in the right amounts. To eat healthfully, you need to eat a variety of foods. Varying your food choices based on what is available, affordable, and personally enjoyable to you also helps make eating a more pleasurable experience.

THE FOOD GUIDE PYRAMID

The Food Guide Pyramid on page 114 is a graphic tool for expressing the *Dietary Guidelines*. The Food Guide Pyramid categorizes foods into five food groups, indicating a range of servings for each that a person is advised to eat daily. Notice that these recommendations are not meant to apply just to one food or to a single meal but to all the foods you eat over the course of several days—your eating pattern.

The Pyramid's food groups are presented in different sizes. In general, the greater the number of servings recommended from a food group, the larger the group in the Pyramid.

Notice that the ranges of servings are broad. This is because specific nutritional needs vary depending on age, gender, physical condition, body size, and activity level. Teenage boys and active men usually need the most servings, whereas young children generally require less. Except for additional iron and calcium needed by females (ages 12–50), eating the recommended number of servings should supply all the nutrients most healthy people need.

Balance the Foods You Eat with Physical Activity

Balancing the foods you eat with physical activity can help you stay at or reach a weight that is right for you. Follow these guidelines:

- **Balance the amount of energy in food with the amount of energy your body uses.** Many teens lead a too-sedentary life, spending far too much time in front of the television or the computer. Counter some of this inactivity by getting enough physical activity.

- **Be aware that controlling body fat is more important to health than controlling body weight.** The location of body fat can be a risk factor. In particular, excess fat in the abdomen poses a greater health risk than excess fat in the hips and thighs.

- **Keep in mind that all calories add up in the same way, no matter what their source.** Calories count. Excess calories, whether from carbohydrates, fats, or proteins, are converted into fat for storage.

▼ *Good nutrition habits are important throughout life.*
ACTIVITY *Name and list some good nutrition habits that you can follow.*

LESSON 4   GUIDELINES FOR A HEALTHFUL EATING STYLE   **113**

PERSONAL HEALTH

HOW MANY CALORIES DO YOU NEED IN A DAY? Here's one way to get a rough idea of your daily calorie needs. If you are extremely inactive, you need about 12 calories per pound to stay at your current weight. If you are involved in light activity, you need 15 calories per pound. When you're moderately active, you need up to 20 calories per pound. So if you are a moderately active person weighing 140 pounds, your needs are 140 x 20 = 2,800 calories a day.

TEACH

L1 Cooperative Learning

Divide the class into five groups, and assign each one a food group. Have students compete to see which group can list the most examples of foods in their group. Give students two minutes to complete their lists. At the end of the two minutes, have each group share its list. Ask the rest of the class to add to each list and name the recommended number of servings from each group per day for a teen.

L1 Class Activity

Distribute seven index cards to each student, and ask them to keep the cards throughout the week. Have them label each card with their name and one of these food groups: Milk, Meat, Fruit, Vegetable, Bread, Combination, and Other. Ask them to write down everything they eat, listing each food on the appropriate card. Tell students that if the food contains partial servings from more than one group, they can list it on the Combination card. At the end of the week, have students deposit their cards in boxes labeled with the above seven groups. Select volunteers to count the cards in each box and record the results on the chalkboard.

Next, ask the class: Did you eat foods from each of the five main food groups? From which group did you eat the most foods? Why? From which did you eat the least? Why? Which foods were a combination? What foods did you list on the "Other" card?

L1 Explaining

Stress the value of selecting low-fat foods in the milk and meat groups, low-fat and low-sugar preparation methods for the fruit and vegetable groups, and high-fiber and whole-grain foods in the bread and cereals group. To confirm that students can identify low-fat, low-sugar, high-fiber and whole-grain foods on their own, have them give examples of each.

L1 Discussing

Many foods that are naturally low in fat often are prepared with considerable added fat. Fried and creamed dishes, dressings, and condiments often make some of the lowest-fat foods into some of the highest-fat meals. Ask students to suggest at least one high-fat and one low-fat method of preparing each of the following: chicken, fish, potatoes, corn, and apples.

L2 Class Activity

Gather containers of various fats and oils. Have students place them on a continuum from most to least for each type of fatty acid: saturated, monounsaturated, and polyunsaturated. Remind students that diets high in fat, especially saturated fat and cholesterol, increase the risk for heart disease, obesity, and some cancers.

L3 Class Activity

Divide students into small groups. Provide each group with a variety of food labels, and ask students to determine each food's percentage of calories from fat. Have them summarize their findings in a chart, ranking each food from highest to lowest in percentage of fat.

L1 Explaining

Note: According to the USDA, 1/2 cup cooked dry beans or peas, 1 egg, or 2 Tbsp. peanut butter can substitute for 1 oz. of lean meat. Remind teens that they should limit their intake of foods that are high in fat and cholesterol.

Food Guide Pyramid
A GUIDE TO DAILY FOOD CHOICES

FATS, OILS, AND SWEETS
Nutrients: Fats, Carbohydrates

MILK, YOGURT, AND CHEESE
Nutrients: Protein, calcium, Vitamins A, D, B₂, and phosphorus

MEAT, POULTRY, FISH, BEANS, EGGS, AND NUTS
Nutrients: Protein, iron, B vitamins, and phosphorus

VEGETABLES
Nutrients: Vitamins A, C, and K, calcium, iron, magnesium, fiber, and carbohydrates

FRUITS
Nutrients: Vitamins A, C, magnesium, and potassium, fiber, and carbohydrates

BREAD, CEREAL, RICE, AND PASTA
Nutrients: Complex carbohydrates, fiber, iron, B vitamins

114   CHAPTER 5   NUTRITION AND YOUR HEALTH

CURRICULUM CONNECTIONS

SOCIAL STUDIES. Have students interview foreign students or use library resources to learn about eating patterns in different countries. Ask them to find answers to questions about a country such as: How many meals are eaten each day? What are some typical meals? Do foods tend to be high (or low) in fat, sugar, and salt? Are snacks an important part of the diet? What percentage of meals are eaten at home? Are fast foods popular?

Daily Serving Equivalents

FATS, OILS, AND SWEETS
Servings: Use sparingly.
Found in: candy, soft drinks, butter, margarine, salty snack foods such as chips, mayonnaise, salad dressing, jams and jellies

MILK, YOGURT, AND CHEESE
Servings: 2–3
SINGLE SERVING EQUIVALENTS:
- 1 cup of milk or yogurt
- 1½ ounces of natural cheese
- 2 ounces of processed cheese

MEAT, POULTRY, FISH, BEANS, EGGS, AND NUTS
Servings: 2–3
SINGLE SERVING EQUIVALENTS:
- 2–3 ounces of cooked lean meat, poultry, or fish
- 1 egg
- ½ cup of cooked dry beans
- 2 tablespoons of peanut butter

◀ *The Food Guide Pyramid shows the types of foods you need and in which amounts.*
ACTIVITY *Determine single serving equivalents within particular sections of the pyramid.*

VEGETABLES
Servings: 3–5
SINGLE SERVING EQUIVALENTS:
- 1 cup of raw leafy vegetables
- ½ cup of other vegetables, cooked or raw
- ¾ cup of vegetable juice

FRUITS
Servings: 2–4
SINGLE SERVING EQUIVALENTS:
- 1 medium apple, banana, or orange
- ½ grapefruit or melon wedge
- ¾ cup of 100-percent fruit juice
- ½ cup of berries
- ½ cup of canned fruit, water or natural juice pack
- ½ cup of dried fruit

BREAD, CEREAL, RICE, AND PASTA
Servings: 6–11
SINGLE SERVING EQUIVALENTS:
- 1 slice of bread
- ½ hamburger bun or English muffin
- 1 small roll or biscuit
- 3 to 4 small crackers
- 1 ounce of ready-to-eat breakfast cereal
- ½ cup of cooked cereal
- ½ cup of cooked rice
- ½ cup of cooked pasta

Choose Plenty of Grain Products, Vegetables, and Fruits

Why do vegetables, fruits, and grain products get special attention? It is because they are excellent sources of complex carbohydrates and fiber. They are usually low in fats and calories, and they provide essential vitamins and minerals.

A high intake of fiber and complex carbohydrates has been shown to decrease the risk for heart disease, obesity, and some cancers. The National Cancer Institute recommends 20 to 35 grams of fiber a day, in contrast to the 10 to 15 grams currently consumed daily by most Americans.

Choose an Eating Style Low in Fat, Saturated Fat, and Cholesterol

The top section of the Food Guide Pyramid contains foods you are advised to use sparingly—fats, oils, and sweets. At present, fat makes

HEALTH Online

Visit **health.glencoe.com** to learn about the five food groups and the Food Guide Pyramid.

⬛1 Explaining

Point out that sugar comes in many forms. Among the most common are sucrose, lactose, galactose, fructose, dextrose, and maltose. Encourage students to look for these sugars on food package labels. Also, remind them to look for identifying words such as sugar, brown sugar, honey, corn syrup, corn sweeteners, and concentrated fruit juice.

⬛2 Cooperative Learning

Divide the class into small groups, and have them resolve this case study: Imagine their younger brother has a sweet tooth and loves to snack on candy. What alternatives might they suggest? How might they help change his food habits? Ask the members of each group to share their suggestions with the class.

⬛1 Discussing

Have students brainstorm a list of sources of dietary fat. Talk about ways to control fat in one's diet.

FOOD AND NUTRITION (Side 1)
Chapter 4: The Energy Balance

Frames 6751-9875

Chapter 6: The Food Pyramid

Frames 14276-18521

Chapter 7: The Vegetable Eaters

Frames 18562-21919

Chapter 8: Fast Foods

Frames 21939-25111

HOME AND COMMUNITY CONNECTION

Young people with a family history of cardiovascular disease are advised to know their serum cholesterol levels. (Serum cholesterol is found in blood; dietary cholesterol, in food.) Cholesterol screening is one way to identify people with an increased risk of cardiovascular disease. In fact, some doctors believe it is wise to get this baseline data while a person is young so doctors can monitor changes. Because the body makes cholesterol, elevated serum cholesterol is not necessarily associated with consuming large amounts of dietary cholesterol.

L1 Discussing

Remind students that high sodium intake is linked to high blood pressure. Sodium is found in processed foods in the form of monosodium glutamate (MSG), soy sauce, sodium bicarbonate, and salt (sodium chloride). Distribute a variety of food labels, and have students list high-sodium ingredients.

Making Responsible Decisions

1. Denise is having trouble maintaining a healthful diet when she spends time with her closest friends.
2. Denise could (a) discuss her eating plan with her friends and ask for their help, (b) continue to spend time with them—including at the fast-food restaurant—and try to resist the pressure she feels, (c) suggest other activities the three can enjoy together, or (d) spend less time with Rae and Yvonne and try to develop new friendships.
3. Denise might (a) get support from her friends—or risk having them disagree with or even embarrass her, (b) improve her resistance to the pressure—but probably still have trouble and possibly feel resentment toward her friends, (c) help her friends enjoy other activities and improve their health, or risk having them disagree and perhaps begin to avoid her, or (d) miss her old friends, but perhaps develop close new friendships.
4. Denise values both her good health and her friendship with Rae and Yvonne.
5. Responses will vary.
6. Guide students in considering both the short- and long-term consequences of their decisions.

L2 Decision Making

For further study on making responsible decisions, assign *Decision-Making Activity 5* in the TCR.

Did You Know?

➤ The number of food shoppers claiming that fat content in food is their biggest concern rose 600 percent—from 8 percent to 48 percent—in the last eight years.

➤ A 12-ounce carbonated soft drink contains 9 to 12 teaspoons of sugar. Diet drinks are exceptions.

➤ Americans consume 76 pounds of sugar on average from soft drinks alone each year.

➤ Foods containing sugar substitutes are not necessarily lower in calories than similar products made with sugar. You need to read the label to find out the number of calories.

up about 34 percent of the calories in the average American diet. This is well in excess of the no more than 30 percent of calories from fat called for in the *Dietary Guidelines*. Eating styles high in fat are linked to obesity and some cancers. A diet high in saturated fat and cholesterol also contributes to increased cholesterol levels, a risk factor for heart disease.

To control the amount of fat you eat:

- Cut off the fat you see on meat.
- Eat lean meat and poultry.
- Remove the skin from chicken and turkey.
- Eat more fish, including oilier fishes such as salmon or halibut. Omega-3 fatty acids, a polyunsaturated fat in fish, have been linked with a decreased risk of heart disease.
- Occasionally, perhaps one or two times a week, have a meal based on dried beans or other legumes instead of meat.
- Choose lower-fat milk, cheese, and yogurt.
- Eat less salad dressing and mayonnaise. Spread only a little margarine or butter on bread or potatoes.
- Substitute vegetables, fruits, and whole-grain snacks for foods with a high fat content.
- Cut down on fried foods, including french fries. Eat roasted, baked, broiled, or grilled meat, poultry, or fish instead. Choose vegetables that are steamed, boiled, or baked.

For most people, including teens, many of the above tips help control cholesterol as well as fat. For individuals with a tendency toward

Making Responsible Decisions

Valuing and Helping Friends

Denise is watching her intake of fat, added sugars, and salt. Yet, every time she goes out with her closest friends, Rae and Yvonne, the three end up at the same fast-food restaurant. Rae and Yvonne always order shakes and fries, and Denise feels pressured to order the same as her friends. Denise wants to suggest a different plan, but she has known Rae and Yvonne since the second grade and doesn't want to seem like a troublemaker. At the same time, she doesn't want to compromise her health and nutrition goals. What can Denise do?

What Would You Do?

Apply the six steps of the decision-making process to Denise's problem.

1. **State the situation.**
2. **List the options.**
3. **Weigh the possible outcomes.**
4. **Consider your values.**
5. **Make a decision and act.**
6. **Evaluate the decision.**

CURRICULUM CONNECTIONS

FAMILY AND CONSUMER SCIENCES. Place 10 breakfast cereals with varying sugar contents in small cups—1 cup of each cereal for each student. Arrange each type on a separate tray. Number each tray and the corresponding cereal box. Remove the boxes. Ask students to taste and rate each cereal, using a scale of 1 to 10, with 10 being the most favored. Then have them rate the sugar content. Ask if there is a correlation between perceived sweetness and tastiness. Was there general agreement among students? Did their perceptions of sweetness correspond with the label information?

high blood cholesterol levels, additional precautions may need to be taken. These include increasing one's awareness of and limiting foods high in dietary cholesterol such as egg yolks, organ meats like liver, and even some low-fat foods, such as shellfish.

Choose an Eating Style Moderate in Sugars

Americans eat sugar in many forms, and most like its taste. Healthy people can eat a moderate amount of sugar. As with fats, the guideline is to watch the size and frequency of foods with added sugars, such as sweet desserts, candy, and soft drinks, and to balance these with foods that provide the amounts of nutrients your body needs.

Some tips for using sugar in moderation are:

- Become aware of your intake of foods with added sugars but few nutrients. If you drink a lot of soda, reach instead for a natural fruit juice or even plain water. Substitute fruit for doughnuts, candy, or other sweets made with added sugar.
- Learn to identify added sugars by their names on product packages, such as corn syrup, honey, and sucrose.
- Choose canned fruits packed in water or juice rather than in heavy syrup.
- Eat sweets as part of a meal, rather than as between-meal snacks. Other foods in the meal may help neutralize damaging acids from carbohydrates that build up on the teeth. When sweets are eaten, be sure to brush your teeth afterward, using a fluoride toothpaste, and floss daily.

Choose an Eating Style Moderate in Salt and Sodium

Sodium is one of the body's essential minerals. It helps transport nutrients into your cells and helps wastes move out. It also helps maintain normal blood pressure and nerve function. Yet, most Americans consume far more than the amount advised: 2,400 mg or less sodium a day.

Where does all the sodium come from? About 10 percent is naturally present in foods. The remainder comes from table salt—sodium chloride—and processed foods. In fact, about 75 percent of the sodium we eat is derived from processed foods. The remainder comes from the salt shaker. Too much sodium may put some people at risk of high blood pressure, although body weight, genetics, and amount of physical activity are some other factors that affect this condition.

Follow these tips to ensure a moderate intake of sodium and salt:

- Become "sodium-literate." The Nutrition Facts panel on food labels identifies the sodium content. Learn to look for and read this information when you buy processed foods.

Sweet desserts and sugary snacks provide little nutritional value. Instead, substitute with melon, grapes, and other fresh fruits.

ACTIVITY What nutrients are found in these fruits?

L1 Class Activity

On paper plates, have students shake a salt shaker as if they were salting a serving of French fries. Then have them use measuring spoons to measure the salt. About how much sodium is that? *(Five grams equal 1 teaspoon.)* Talk about ways they can reduce their intake of salt and sodium.

L3 Community Involvement

Select students to interview a dietitian, nurse, or doctor to learn ways to modify the amount of saturated fat, sugars, and sodium in the diet. Have students write the recommendations in their own words and share them with the class.

L2 Class Activity

Choose volunteers to try various salt substitutes and alternative sweeteners and decide which ones they might consider using on a regular basis. Ask them to consider taste, cost, relative nutritional value, and safety in making their decisions.

L2 Class Activity

Encourage students to plan a breakfast menu that includes at least one nontraditional breakfast food. Stress that the menu should be well balanced and supply about one-third of the day's calories. Discuss the completed menus. Ask volunteers to list nontraditional breakfast foods that they enjoy.

LD Class Activity

Have the class create a healthy meal plan for one day and discuss the role each food plays in the plan.

L2 Cooperative Learning

Assign *Cooperative Learning Activity 5,* "Restaurant for Teens Only," in the TCR.

PERSONAL HEALTH

NUTRITIOUS SNACKS. To add protein to the diet, try hard-boiled eggs, pieces of cheese, chunks of tuna, or slices of leftover roast or steak.

To add vitamin C to the diet, try strawberries, other berries, melon, tomatoes, citrus fruits, raw pineapple, or nectarines.

To add vitamin A to the diet, eat carrot sticks, raw broccoli, green pepper rings, or dark green vegetables. Also, try yellow fruits and vegetables.

To add calcium to the diet, try any dairy product, frozen yogurt, cheese chunks, custard, cottage cheese, or fruit.

To add B vitamins and minerals to the diet, eat whole-grain or enriched breads and cereal, dairy products, nuts, or raisins.

Building Health Skills

Improving Your Snacking Habits
Skill: Goal Setting

Ask students to share their own ideas about snacks. What part, if any, do you think snacks should play in your eating plan? Why? What changes do you think you ought to make in the number of snacks you eat? in the kinds of snacks you eat? After a brief introductory discussion, let students read the feature to find out more about improving—but not eliminating—their snacks. Have students record their action plan responses as private journal entries, and suggest that they review these entries occasionally to remind themselves of their snacking goals.

L1 Community Involvement

By law, school lunch programs must serve meals representing the five food groups. Using the weekly school lunch menu, have students break down the meals into the five food groups.

L3 Class Activity

Instruct selected students to videotape a lunch period in your school cafeteria. Have them interview students and teachers as to their food choices. Play the video for the class. Ask whether or not students generally make sound nutritional choices. Do teachers eat differently than students? What can students do to eat more nutritiously at school?

- Season foods with herbs and spices rather than salt, and encourage the family member who prepares meals at home to use less salt in cooking.
- Taste foods before you salt them. If you must add salt, shake once, then taste again.
- Go easy on the salty snacks you eat—such as chips and pretzels.

Healthful Eating Patterns

Whether you eat three meals a day, or four, five, or six "mini-meals," *variety, moderation,* and *balance* are the foundation of a healthful eating plan. Meals and snacks with adequate servings from all five food groups in the Food Guide Pyramid provide the nutrients and energy you need.

Building Health Skills

Setting Goals: Improving Your Snacking Habits

BECAUSE THE BODY continues to grow throughout adolescence, your nutritional and caloric needs right now are at a high point. One way of meeting the increased needs is through smart snacking. As with other aspects of health, you can become a smarter snacker. In order to do this, you have to make up your mind that a change is in order, then follow a logical plan of action.

1. **Make a list of your current favorite snacks.** Divide a page of your private Health Journal into three columns. Write the names of your favorite snacks in the first column. Include any food consumed between meals, including beverages such as soda or milk. Be as thorough as possible.

2. **Determine where each listed item belongs on the Food Guide Pyramid.** Fruits and vegetables are self-evident. Yogurt and cheese belong in the Milk, Yogurt, and Cheese group. Crackers, pretzels, and popcorn belong in the Bread, Cereal, Rice and Pasta group. Soft drinks and candy belong with the Fats, Oils, and Sweets group. Write this information in the second column next to the corresponding items in Column 1.

3. **Identify the nutrients the snack provides.** Again, refer to the Food Guide Pyramid on page 114. Look in particular for foods that provide calcium, iron, protein, and vitamins A and C. All of these are nutrients that are especially important to consume in adequate amounts. Note your findings in Column 3.

4. **Review your list.** Which snacks belong with the Fats, Oils, and Sweets group? To what food groups are your combined snacks contributing most? What foods might you change to moderate fat, sugar, or sodium intake or to add more food variety?

HOME AND COMMUNITY CONNECTION

HEALTHY ALTERNATIVES. Have students pretend they are planning a party and want to offer healthy foods and beverages. Tell them to list healthy foods and beverages they can make or buy, including finger foods. Each food should provide important nutrients. Foods or beverages with excessive fat, sugar, or sodium should be avoided. The refreshments should include foods from several groups. At a party, the food and beverages need to appeal to a variety of tastes. Encourage students to share their lists, and have the class choose the best three party menus. Students may wish to compile the lists into a booklet and make copies to take home.

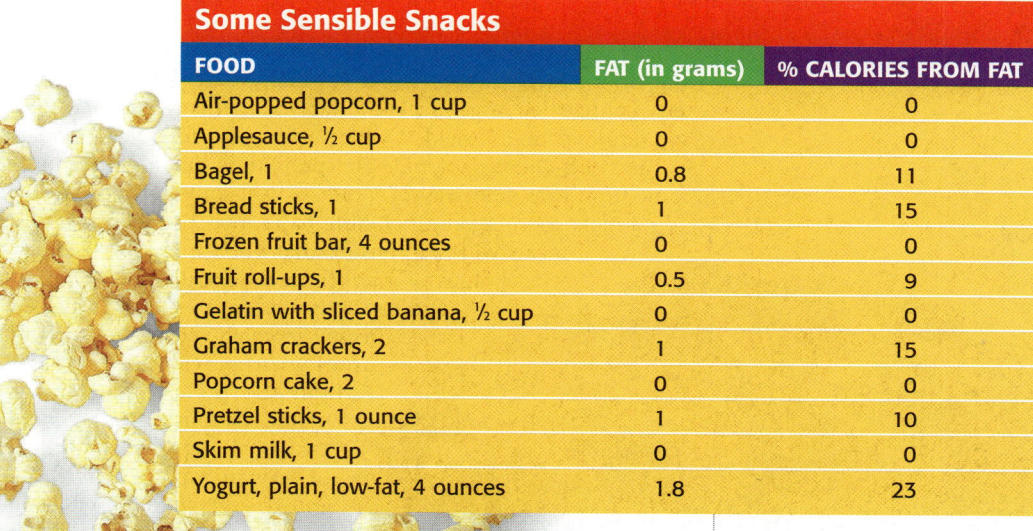

Some Sensible Snacks

FOOD	FAT (in grams)	% CALORIES FROM FAT
Air-popped popcorn, 1 cup	0	0
Applesauce, ½ cup	0	0
Bagel, 1	0.8	11
Bread sticks, 1	1	15
Frozen fruit bar, 4 ounces	0	0
Fruit roll-ups, 1	0.5	9
Gelatin with sliced banana, ½ cup	0	0
Graham crackers, 2	1	15
Popcorn cake, 2	0	0
Pretzel sticks, 1 ounce	1	10
Skim milk, 1 cup	0	0
Yogurt, plain, low-fat, 4 ounces	1.8	23

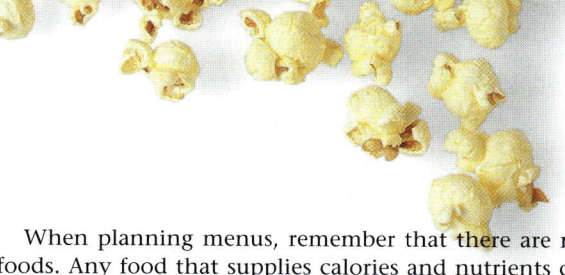

What other foods that you enjoy eating would make healthful snacks?

ACTIVITY *Which of the foods listed contain the least fat? Which contain the lowest percentage of calories from fat? Which do you think are sources of the following nutrients: Carbohydrates? Calcium? Protein?*

When planning menus, remember that there are no good or bad foods. Any food that supplies calories and nutrients can be part of a nutritious eating style. Nutrition guidelines apply to all your food choices for a day or more, not for just a single meal or food.

Breakfast

Breakfast may be your most important meal. After 10 to 14 hours without fuel, your body needs to be recharged. According to breakfast studies, eating a nutritious morning meal is linked with better mental and physical performance in late morning. Those who ate breakfast also reacted faster and experienced less muscle fatigue than those who skipped breakfast.

As with other meals, a key to successful breakfast planning is variety. This helps break some of the monotony of the same traditional breakfast foods; a varied meal provides a variety of nutrients. You might choose peanut butter on toast, pizza, or even a stuffed tomato for a healthful and eye-opening beginning. To get enough vitamin C during the day, add a citrus juice or fruit or tomato juice for breakfast. Breakfast is also a good time to get one calcium-rich serving of milk, cheese, or yogurt and a perfect opportunity to add needed fiber by eating a high-fiber cereal.

L1 Discussing

Snacking is a typical teenage eating pattern. Have students list on the chalkboard snack foods in each food group, including the "empty-calorie group." Ask them to identify which snacks are the most nutritious.

LD Class Activity

Select students to create a bulletin board illustrating nutritious snacks. Title the board "Super Snack Selections."

L2 Personal Involvement

Have students plan a daily menu, including snacks, that appeals to them and that provides an adequate number of servings from the five food groups. Display and discuss some of the examples.

L1 Personal Involvement

Have students select one area of their diet that needs improvement and write down a goal to improve it. Help students analyze their progress at the end of a week.

L3 Community Involvement

Select students to interview local restaurant owners about their efforts to control sugar, fat, and sodium in the food they serve. Ask students to share their findings with the class.

COOPERATIVE LEARNING

ACTIVITY. Some people rely on fast food when they are away from home at mealtimes and do not have time or money to eat at restaurants with the healthiest food options. However, many fast-food restaurants offer healthy options. Group students. Have each group member collect menus and nutrition brochures from two fast-food sources in your area. From each fast-food establishment, have the group choose one of the healthiest items and one of the unhealthiest items. Have them discuss whether they would be willing to choose the healthiest foods. Of the foods they are willing to eat, which is the healthiest at each establishment? Students may wish to publish their recommendations for interested classmates.

ASSESS

EVALUATING THE LESSON

Assign and discuss the Lesson 4 Review; then administer, grade, and discuss the *Lesson 15 Quiz* in the TCR. ☞

RETEACHING

- Ask for volunteers to bring in a menu from their favorite restaurant. Have them identify the food groups represented by the various menu items, including food combinations.
- Ask students to complete *Reteaching Activity 15* in the TCR. ☞

ENRICHMENT

Have students keep a 24-hour record of everything they eat and drink, including amounts. Then ask them to exchange their food records and pretend they are dietitians working with a client. Provide food composition tables, and ask them to calculate the nutrients and calories in the partners' food record. Next, ask them to compare these values to the RDA and write a short paper analyzing their client's diet. Have them meet with each other, suggesting changes the other might make.

CLOSE

Play a game of nutritional bingo. Using construction paper, create grids to serve as bingo cards. Let the middle spot of the bingo cards be a free space. Think of 24 different nutrition-related questions and write them on index cards. Write the answers to the questions on the bingo cards in a different order. Students can use small paper clips to mark the correct responses on their cards as the questions are read.

Lunch and Dinner

Typically, Americans eat a sandwich or something similar for lunch and then a large dinner. Other cultural groups follow a reverse pattern, eating their large meal at midday. Either way, the focus of lunch and dinner should provide a variety of foods from several food groups in the Food Guide Pyramid. The protein at lunch or dinner might come from eggs, a lean meat, poultry, fish, some form of legumes, or a dairy food. Again, including pasta, rice, or bread at both these meals will help ensure that you satisfy the 6 to 11 servings of grain from the Food Guide Pyramid that many active teenagers need. A turkey and cheese sandwich piled high with lettuce and tomato provides one serving each from the protein, dairy, and vegetable sections of the pyramid and two from the grain group. A slice of vegetarian pizza with steamed or grilled vegetables provides similar nutrient benefits.

LESSON **4** *Review*

Reviewing Facts and Vocabulary

1. Name the six sections of the Food Guide Pyramid, and identify the recommended serving ranges.
2. How are the terms *variety, balance,* and *moderation* important in any eating plan?

Thinking Critically

3. *Analyzing.* What are some of the health problems that can arise from unhealthful eating patterns? How might you benefit if you improved your eating pattern?
4. *Evaluating.* Which foods do you eat on a regular basis that may be high in sodium or salt? Which are high in fat, especially saturated fat? How could you tell?

Applying Health Skills

5. *In Your Home and School.* Keep a food diary of the foods you eat over a period of several days. Analyze your choices by making a list of the five food groups and organizing the foods you ate into the appropriate groups. (Some foods such as pizza may represent more than one food group.) What does the chart tell you about your eating habits? Discuss it with a family member and identify how you could add more balance to your eating habits.

Lesson 4 Review

Answers to Reviewing Facts and Vocabulary

1. Refer to the Daily Serving Equivalents table on page 115.
2. Variety keeps us from getting bored with our eating pattern, balance ensures we get all the nutrients we need, and moderation keeps us from eating too many foods that provide little nutritional benefit.

Answers to Thinking Critically

3. Health problems include obesity, high blood pressure, heart disease, nutrient disorders such as rickets or thyroid disease, and lack of energy. Benefits include greater energy, fewer colds and illnesses.
4. Answers will vary. You can tell by reading the Nutrition Facts panel or product label.

Being a Smart Food Consumer

The Food Guide Pyramid is one way of evaluating the nutritional contribution of a food or several foods to your overall eating pattern. This task becomes more challenging when you shop for prepared and packaged foods.

To help food shoppers, all food products now carry a standardized Nutrition Facts panel.

HEALTH TERMS

food additives

enriched food

fortification

unit pricing

HEALTH CONCEPTS

- The Nutrition Facts panel found on almost all packaged food products can help you judge whether a prepared or packaged food product meets your nutritional needs.

- Part of health literacy is learning to understand and judge claims made on food packages.

- Knowing what you are buying is as important as knowing what you are eating.

Nutrition Label Basics

The Nutrition Facts panel on food labels indicates the nutrient and calorie content of foods. This information helps you find good sources of nutrients, compare nutrients and calories among similar products, and choose foods that meet special dietary needs. Specifically, each label contains:

- serving size;
- servings per container;
- calories per serving and calories per serving from fat;
- grams of total fat, saturated fat, total carbohydrate, fiber, sugars, protein, and milligrams of cholesterol and sodium per serving;
- percentage of the Daily Value (DV) the product supplies of the above nutrients (except sugars and protein), plus some important minerals and vitamins in one serving.

LESSON 5   BEING A SMART FOOD CONSUMER   **121**

Being a Smart Food Consumer

FOCUS

LESSON OBJECTIVES

After studying this lesson, students should be able to

- list the information required on a nutrition information label.
- name reasons why additives are used in food.
- explain the difference between enriched and fortified foods.
- interpret open-dating information on food labels.
- compare food prices by using unit pricing.

MOTIVATOR

Write the following on the chalkboard for students to work on while attendance is being taken: *In the grocery sack at the front of the class is an ordinary can of corn. List five items of information that are printed on the can's label.*

INTRODUCING THE LESSON

On the chalkboard, list students' responses to the Motivator. Tell students they will learn about information that is required on food labels and how to use the information to make wise food choices.

INTRODUCING HEALTH TERMS

- Have students design a "Help Wanted" advertisement for a dietitian. Ask them to use as many vocabulary terms as possible in their ad.
- Ask students to complete Vocabulary Activity 5 and Chapter Study Guide 5 in the *Student Workbook.*

Lesson 5 Resources

TEACHER'S CLASSROOM RESOURCES
- **Concept Map** Activity 16
- **Lesson 16 Quiz**
- **Lesson Plan 16**
- **Reteaching** Activity 16

STUDENT WORKBOOK
- **Applying Health Skills 16**

- **Chapter Study Guide 5**
- **Vocabulary** Activity 5

TRANSPARENCIES
- **Transparency 16**

MULTIMEDIA
- **ABCNews InterActive™ VHS/Videodisc,** *Food and Nutrition*

TEACH

L1 Class Activity

Ask students to bring nutrition information labels (from cereal boxes, snack foods, and other processed foods) to class. Collect the labels, read aloud the nutrient content from one label, and ask the class to guess the type of food. Discuss why many packaged foods are calorie-rich but nutrient-poor.

L2 Cooperative Learning

Divide the class into two teams. Give food labels with nutrient information to each team. Have one team call out a nutrient listed on a package. In 15 seconds, the other team must name one function and one food source of the nutrient to receive one point. The first team to reach 20 points wins.

L3 Writing

Have students research any current legislation being considered to improve the nutritional content of school lunches. Then help them draft a letter to their congressperson asking where the individual stands on the matter. Request that students share the response, when it is received, with the class.

L1 Class Activity

Either photocopy the content information or copy the ingredients from several food labels listing many additives. Distribute the information to the class and ask students to guess what type of food contains these ingredients. Ask them what purposes they think the additives serve.

Some nutrient labels have two lists. If a food is eaten with another food—for example, cereal with milk—nutritional information is given for the product alone and with the other food.

Foods that do not need to carry the Nutrition Facts panel include:

- food served in restaurants;
- plain coffee and tea;
- some spices and other foods that contain no nutrients;
- fresh meat, poultry, and fish;
- fresh fruits and vegetables;
- food produced by very small companies or offered in very small packages.

 The Nutrition Facts on the food label provide easy-to-read nutrition information "at the source."
ACTIVITY *How many calories from fat are contained in this product?*

Ingredients List

Almost all food labels must have an ingredient list. Labels list ingredients by weight in descending order. The ingredient in greatest amount is listed first. Food labels with several similar ingredients may be confusing. For example, when three sweeteners—corn syrup, sugar, and honey—are used in the same product, each is listed separately and lower on the list than if they were listed totally as one ingredient.

Nutrition Facts title signals that the label contains the new required information.

Serving sizes are more consistent across product lines and reflect the amounts people actually eat.

List of nutrients covers those most important to the health of today's consumers.

Daily Values are based on a daily diet of 2,000 and 2,500 calories.

Label shows calories per gram of fat, carbohydrates, and protein.

Calories from fat help consumers meet dietary guidelines that recommend people get no more than 30 percent of their calories from fat.

% Daily Value shows how a food fits into the overall daily diet.

Nutrition Facts

Serving Size ½ cup (114g)
Servings Per Container 4

Amount Per Serving

Calories 90		Calories from Fat 30

	% Daily Value*
Total Fat 3g	5%
Saturated Fat 0g	0%
Cholesterol 0mg	0%
Sodium 300mg	13%
Total Carbohydrate 13g	4%
Dietary Fiber 3g	12%
Sugars 3g	
Protein 3g	

Potassium	0%	Thiamin	0%
Vitamin A	80%	Riboflavin	0%
Vitamin C	60%	Niacin	0%
Calcium	4%	Vitamin B 6	0%
Iron	4%	Folate	0%
Vitamin D	0%	Phosphorus	0%

* Percent Daily Values are based on a 2,000 calorie diet. Your daily values may be higher or lower depending on your calorie needs:

		2,000	2,500
Calories		2,000	2,500
Total Fat	Less than	65g	80g
Sat Fat	Less than	20g	25g
Cholesterol	Less than	300mg	300mg
Sodium	Less than	2,400mg	2,400mg
Potassium		3,500mg	3,500mg
Total Carbohydrate		300g	375g
Dietary Fiber		25g	30g

HEALTH LITERACY

SELF-DIRECTED LEARNER. Food labels list ingredients in descending weight order but can be deceptive. Fat, sodium, or sugar may be added in several forms. On a jar of plum jam with 3 ounces of plums, 2¾ ounces of cane sugar, and 2¼ ounces of corn syrup, the ingredients read "plums, cane sugar, corn syrup," suggesting the jam contains more fruit than sugar when the amounts are almost the same. Fats such as soybean oil, partially hydrogenated corn oil, and canola oil are also listed separately. Have students examine labels in a supermarket; find five products that list more than one type of sugar, fat, or sodium; copy the list of ingredients and total grams of fat, sugar, and sodium; and report their findings to the class.

FOOD ADDITIVES

Additives must be listed on food labels. **Food additives** are *substances added to food intentionally to produce a desired effect.* They are used to:

- add nutrients,
- lengthen storage life and keep it safe to eat,
- give flavor or color,
- maintain texture,
- control food's acidity,
- help age foods, such as cheese.

Foods can also be enriched or fortified to improve nutrient value. An **enriched food** is *a food in which nutrients that were lost in processing have been added back.* Breads, pastas, and rice made of refined grains are enriched with B vitamins and iron. **Fortification** is *the addition of nutrients that are not naturally present.* Because vitamin D helps deposit calcium in bones, milk is fortified with vitamin D.

The U.S. Food and Drug Administration (FDA) and the USDA regulate most foods that cross state lines. This includes foods with additives. If food manufacturers want to use regulated additives in their products, they must prove to the appropriate government agency that the additives are safe in the amounts used.

Some additives, such as sugar and salt, are termed *generally recognized as safe (GRAS).* Because they have been used safely for years, these 700 or so additives can be used without permission.

SUGAR AND FAT SUBSTITUTES

The food industry has responded to many consumer concerns about nutrition. In many cases, the industry has been very creative in substituting ingredients that lower either the caloric count or the fat content.

Fructose, natural fruit sugar, is used as a sugar substitute. Because it is sweeter than table sugar, less is needed, so it supplies fewer calories. A noncaloric sweetener, *aspartame,* is commonly added to soft drinks and frozen desserts and is considered safe for most people when used in moderation. You can also buy aspartame in powdered form.

In response to the public's recent concern about fat, the food industry has begun developing fat substitutes. They have the potential for widespread use in processed foods, fried foods, and home cooking.

Food Product Label Claims

The food labeling regulations permit labels of certain foods to claim possible benefits in combating a disease or condition. For example, labels on products that are high in calcium can claim to be a possible help in preventing osteoporosis. Labels on foods high in fiber, low in fat, or high in vitamins A and C can claim they "may help" to lessen the risk of cancer.

If you see the word "organic" on a label, it means the food product was made from foods grown without pesticides or synthetic fertilizers.

keeping Fit

Sensitive to Additives?

Food manufacturers in the United States use almost 3,000 additives in their products, and all of them have been approved as safe by the government. However, a small percentage of people have reactions to colorings, flavorings, and preservatives in foods. Learning which ones they are sensitive to can sometimes mean the difference between feeling fit and having unpleasant reactions. Monosodium glutamate, or MSG, for example, is a food additive safe for most people but may cause discomfort to others. In the case of sulfite sensitivity, the reaction can be life threatening.

L3 Class Activity

Point out that food additives, including artificial flavors, dyes, taste enhancers, and preservatives, are very common. Then have students study labels on prepared foods (such as hot dogs, luncheon meats, cereals, ice cream, yogurt, powdered drinks, etc.) to compile lists of chemical additives to foods. Ask students to use library resources to research each of the additives and give a brief report to the class about their advantages and disadvantages.

Sensitive to Additives?

keeping Fit

Ask students if any of them are sensitive to any additives in foods. Discuss ways to avoid certain additives, for example, by reading labels, asking restaurant servers about the additives, requesting that it not be added, avoiding certain foods, etc.

L2 Class Activity

Select students to create a poster or bulletin board featuring foods that are fortified or enriched.

L1 Discussing

Ask students what would happen to the food supply if all additives were banned. *(Although banning food additives might reduce cancer risks, consumers would be limited to local food sources or to transported and stored foods that might lack quality and appeal. In some cases, foods without additives could be dangerous.)*

CURRICULUM CONNECTIONS

SCIENCE. Divide the class into three groups. Have each group conduct one of the following demonstrations to explore the functions of food additives. Let each group compare the results and draw conclusions to be discussed in class. (1) Flavor. Have students make oatmeal cookies with and without salt and vanilla.

(2) Appearance. Have students cut an apple in half and brush one half with citric or ascorbic acid. Let both halves sit for several minutes. (3) Preservation. In separate plastic bags, store bakery bread without additives and supermarket bread with additives. Let the bread sit for several days at room temperature.

up|date
▶*Our Changing World*

Imported Food

Ask students: Why is the U.S. government concerned about the safety of imported food? Which government agencies are responsible for protecting our food supply? How do these agencies ensure that imported food is safe for consumers? Then have students read the Update feature to learn more about safety inspections of imported food. Let students form small discussion groups in which they can explain and support their responses to the questions. As a follow-up, ask volunteers to research and report on the latest information on the safety of imported food.

L3 Researching

Provide food labels from various manufacturers that contain toll-free telephone numbers. Have several students call the numbers, requesting classroom information on food labeling, food additives, and sugar and fat substitutes. When the material is received, have students display and discuss the information with the class.

ABCNEWS
INTERACTIVE™

FOOD AND NUTRITION (Side 2)

Chapter 8: Evaluating Your School Lunch Program

Frames 18859-21591

Chapter 9: Participating in Your School Lunch Program

Frame 21600-24394

---

up|date
▶*Our Changing World*

Safety Inspections: Imported Food

The safety of imported food is an ongoing concern in the United States, where 3.7 million food shipments arrive each year. The FDA inspects imported food when it enters the country, but the percentage of food inspected has dropped in recent years as the volume of imported food has risen.

In addition to the FDA food inspections, the USDA also inspects crops and livestock as they enter the United States. In the past few years, these inspections have successfully prevented mad cow disease and foot-and-mouth disease—both livestock diseases—from crossing the U.S. border.

Following the terrorist attacks in September 2001, safety concerns over imported food have been heightened. President Bush asked Congress for emergency funding for national security and recovery. His request included money that would be allocated to fund more frequent and thorough inspections of imported food.

1. Do you think that the United States should limit the amount of food imported from other countries? How might this action benefit food consumers? What problems might it cause?

2. Research the latest information on safety inspections of imported food.

Other terms that may appear on food product labels and their meanings are:

- **Healthy:** The food is low in fat and saturated fat and contains limited amounts of cholesterol and sodium—no more than 360 mg per serving. In addition, if it is a single-item food, it provides at least 10 percent of one or more of the following: Vitamin A or C, iron, calcium, protein, or fiber.
- **Light:** The calories have been reduced by at least a third, or the fat or sodium by at least half.
- **Less:** The food contains 25 percent less of a nutrient or of calories than a comparable food. Similarly, if a food label claims *more*, the food contains 10 percent more of a nutrient than the Daily Value for that food.
- **-free:** The product contains no amount, or only a slight amount, of fat, cholesterol, sodium, sugars, or calories.
- **Fresh:** The food is raw, unprocessed, contains no preservatives, and has never been frozen or heated.

CURRICULUM CONNECTIONS

FAMILY AND CONSUMER SCIENCES. Ask students to make a list of 5 to 10 of the additives most commonly found in foods in the food lab or at home. Have them write a letter to a consumer advocacy group requesting information on the safety of these additives.

SCIENCE. Ask students to research and write about: (1) the chemical properties shared by pepper and mustard that make them useful in retarding food spoilage (have them explain the chemical nature of these preservatives); or (2) the chemical properties that make emulsifiers useful in preventing salad dressing and other oil mixtures from separating.

■ **Natural:** This term is reserved for meat and poultry only. According to the USDA, it means the food is minimally processed with no artificial or synthetic ingredients.

Open Dating

Many food products are open dated with a system that consumers can easily interpret. Look for these dates on labels:

■ **Expiration Date**—last date you should use the product
■ **Freshness Date**—last date a food is thought to be fresh
■ **Pack Date**—the date on which the product was packaged
■ **Sell Date**—Also known as the pull date, this term denotes the last date the product—for example, milk—should be sold. Note that you can store a product past its sell date.

Shelf Labeling

In recent years, stores have begun including vital information of their own to help shoppers. The best-known and perhaps most important information of this kind is **unit pricing**, *a strategy for recognizing the relative cost of a product based on the cost of a standard unit, such as an ounce or gram.* An 8-ounce can of corn that costs 88¢, for example, has a unit price of 11¢ per ounce. If a 12-ounce can of the same brand costs $1.04, it would have a unit price of 8.7¢ per ounce. Buying the larger can would give you more corn for your money. The one caution is that, before buying a larger size of a product, it is wise to determine whether you can use the extra amount.

▼ *Unit pricing labels appear below most products on supermarket shelves. Note that this helpful pricing policy is not confined to food products but applies to health and beauty aids as well.*

ACTIVITY *What other factors do you consider in making a choice besides the price?*

Review

Reviewing Facts and Vocabulary

1. What do the terms *enriched* and *fortified* mean?
2. What are four reasons food additives are used in food?
3. What do *open dating* and *unit pricing* mean?

Thinking Critically

4. *Analyzing.* Review your own buying and shopping practices. What is at the root of your decisions?

5. *Evaluating.* Have you used the Nutrition Facts panels on foods? If not, how could this information prove helpful to you in the future?

Applying Health Skills

6. *In Your Home.* Compare two similar food products in the kitchen of your home. Use information from the products' Nutrition Facts panel, other claims made on the packaging, and any open dating codes.

Lesson 5 Review

Answers to Reviewing Facts and Vocabulary

1. *Enriched* means nutrients that were lost in processing have been added back. *Fortified* means nutrients that were not naturally present have been added.
2. Any four: to add nutrients, lengthen storage life, add flavor or color, maintain texture, control acidity, help age certain foods.

3. *Open dating* tells you how long the product will remain fresh and/or usable. *Unit pricing* helps you compare the cost of different sizes of packages.

Answers to Thinking Critically

4.–5. Answers will vary.

ASSESS

EVALUATING THE LESSON

Assign and discuss the Lesson 5 Review; then administer, grade, and discuss the *Lesson 16 Quiz* in the TCR. ☞

RETEACHING

- Divide the class into five groups, and assign each group one of the main food groups. Have them design a food label for a food product from that group. Tell them to include required information, such as nutrients, calories, ingredients, and other facts to inform and assist the consumer. Display and discuss the completed labels.
- Ask students to complete *Reteaching Activity 16* in the TCR. ☞

ENRICHMENT

Ask for volunteers to bring to class packaged food items from other countries. Display the items and have students compare the labels with those on products produced and packaged in the United States.

CLOSE

Divide the class into groups of two. Give each group labels from cans, packages, or boxes of food. Briefly go through the lesson, having students identify required information on the labels, as well as any health claims or additional information. Also, ask them to identify and explain open-dating information.

Health Skills Activities

Health Skills Activities

ACTIVITY 1
HEALTH SKILLS
Comprehending Health Concepts, Accessing Health Information, Self Management

➤ **National Standards**
This activity meets these National Health Standards: 1.1; 2.2, 3;4.

Teach
- Collect and distribute Nutrition Facts panels among various groups.
- Display the formula used to compute the percentage of calories from fat. Total fat calories ÷ total calories per serving = percentage of calories from fat. Help students recognize that this formula will yield a fractional result, which can be expressed as a percentage. (For example, if a snack cracker provides 160 calories per serving, 60 of those from fat, then the percentage of calories from fat is 60 ÷ 160 = .38 or 38 percent. This is higher than the 30 percent recommended limit.)
- Have groups share their findings, then reconvene to discuss lower-fat alternatives to the higher-fat foods.

ACTIVITY 2
HEALTH SKILLS
Comprehending Health Concepts, Accessing Health Information, Self Management

➤ **National Standards**
This activity meets these National Health Standards: 1.5; 2.4; 3.4.

Teach
- Prior to class, gather—or ask students to gather—nutrition pamphlets from fast-food restaurants in the community.
- Review with students the general nutrition guidelines described in the chapter, emphasizing those areas where teens need to be especially aware, such as getting plenty of calcium and iron in their eating plan. Some students may require help locating areas of the data you are using that correspond to these needs.

Activity 1 — Life of the Party

Directions

One key to healthful eating is to limit the fat calories in your eating plan to 30 percent or less. Is it possible to plan heathful foods for a party? You are about to rise to that challenge.

1. With a group, list foods and food combinations you associate with entertaining (for example, crackers, chips and dip).
2. Match the foods on your list with the Nutrition Facts labels provided by your teacher. Figure out what percent of the calories come from fat. (See the Nutrition Facts panel on page 122.)
3. Brainstorm creative lower-fat alternatives to any foods that are over the limit.
4. Share your findings with those of other groups. If possible, hold an in-class party featuring nutrient-dense treats.

Time
50 minutes (30 minutes for activity, 20 minutes for party during a later class)

Materials
paper, pen or pencil, computer with printer (optional), Nutrition Facts panels from a variety of high- and low-fat snack-type products

Self-Assessment
✔ Identified the fat calories of foods and computed the percentage based on total calories.
✔ Provided lower-fat alternatives to higher-fat snack foods.

Activity 2 — Fast-Food Report Card

Directions

Many restaurants—including fast-food chains—now offer separate foods and menus for people aware of the importance of good nutrition. How do various fast-food restaurants in your community stack up when it comes to nutrition?

1. As a class, make a checklist of criteria to use in evaluating a restaurant menu. Develop your criteria in terms of the Food Guide Pyramid (page 114).
2. Working as part of a smaller group, rate the menu of a particular fast-food chain. Use the nutrition pamphlets supplied by your teacher.
3. Share your findings with classmates.
4. Discuss with the class whether the results from this project will make a difference in the eating habits of class members.

Time
40 minutes

Materials
paper, pen or pencil, computer with Internet access (optional)

Self-Assessment
✔ Included at least three items in your criteria list for evaluating menus.
✔ Noted at least two findings in your results.

ASSESSMENT SCORING

Using a four-level rubric, the student has achieved a 4 if:

ACTIVITY 1
✔ Student demonstrated ability to correctly read Nutrition Facts labels.
✔ Student understood and applied the mathematical formula for computing percentage of fat.
✔ Student determined what types of snack foods were high in fat.
✔ Student correctly identified some lower-fat alternatives.

ACTIVITY 2
✔ Student contributed to developing criteria for the class checklist.
✔ Student ensured there were at least three items in criteria list for evaluating menus.
✔ Student correctly interpreted and applied the numerical data in the source used.
✔ Student played a supportive and helpful role in the group to which he or she was assigned.

CNN HEALTH NEWS ARTICLE

The Skinny on Healthy Eating

If you're heading to the soccer field, remember the shin guards . . . and four glasses of milk. You'll need both to protect your bones.

Calcium is an important nutrient in a teenager's diet, but it's not the only one. A balanced diet is essential. Health professionals often talk about what effect poor eating habits will have later, but solid nutrition is important now.

Growth occurs during adolescence. Teens who eat poorly could grow into adults with health problems. An inadequate diet could lead to poor school performance, weak bones, a lack of energy, and disease.

"Doctors talk about eating right to prevent disease later. Well, disease is starting now," said Kris Rudolph, a registered dietitian at Cincinnati's Teen Health Center Adolescent Nutrition Program.

"We're seeing an increase in diabetes, high blood pressure, and elevated cholesterol levels in teens," she said. "That's happening now. It's not waiting until they are 40."

A healthy diet includes servings from the milk, meat, vegetable, fruit, bread and fat groups. The heaviest concentration should come from the bread and cereal group. Fats should be limited. Teens should eat two to three servings of fruits each day and three to four servings of vegetables.

Read This ▼

Diets Out of Balance

What are teens eating today? The results of a recent study by the American College of Cardiology revealed many poor eating habits. Careless food choices already are having dangerous effects on these teens' health:

- 80% included more than the recommended amount of fat in their daily diets
- 49% had high cholesterol levels
- 11% had high blood pressure

Researchers also point out that fat-heavy diets greatly increase the chance that these students will develop heart disease.

Think About It

1. Explain three ways that a balanced diet can prevent disease.
2. Eating wisely one day won't make you healthy if you eat poorly the rest of the week. What strategies do you think will really help teens establish daily balanced diets?

CNN HEALTH NEWS **127**

MORE ABOUT . . . . .

REPORTING THE STORY. Discuss the role that media plays in raising public consciousness about health issues. Point out that articles like the one included in this lesson draw readers' attention to important new information that can help them make healthy decisions.

Public service announcements (PSAs) are commercials, radio ads, posters, or other media that do not sell products. Instead, they communicate messages to help inform the public. Government agencies, corporate sponsors, or private individuals usually pay for these announcements. Topics for health-related PSAs range from the importance of eating a balanced diet to the dangers of using drugs and tobacco.

CNN HEALTH NEWS

The Skinny on Healthy Eating

Objectives. After reading the article, students should be able to explain the benefits of a balanced diet as a protection against certain noninfectious diseases.

Motivator. Write the phrase *Food is Fuel* on the chalkboard. Have students discuss how food is used to fuel the body. Then point out that food also can protect us from harm or disease. Have students read "The Skinny on Healthy Eating" to focus on how food protects the body.

Teach

- Draw a chart on the chalkboard to compare and contrast healthy and unhealthy diets. Invite students to list characteristics, under each heading, of healthy and unhealthy diets and identify some possible effects of each diet. Emphasize that healthy diets can promote wellness and resistance to some diseases.
- Have teams of three or four students work together to create a print ad, commercial, or radio spot that strongly makes the connection between poor eating habits and disease. Each team member should have a specific role in producing the public service announcement, such as writer, actor, director, or technician. Teammates should share their final announcements with classmates.

Role Play. Have students role play situations in which they need to make healthy food choices, such as:
- ordering food in a restaurant
- planning a meal for a class picnic
- selecting foods for a school cafeteria

Discuss how each choice can help promote a balanced diet and prevent disease.

Close. Ask students to explain the connection between a teenager's diet and disease. Make sure they can identify specific diseases and conditions (diabetes, high blood pressure, elevated cholesterol levels) that are increasingly affecting teens with poor eating habits.

CHECKING COMPREHENSION

- Assign and discuss the chapter review.
- Use the MindJogger Videoquiz to review the chapter. 🔴

CHAPTER 5 REVIEW ANSWERS

Using Health Terms

1. appetite
2. nutrients
3. hunger
4. nutrition
5. proteins
6. glycogen
7. carbohydrates
8. glucose
9. amino acids
10. minerals
11. Recommended Dietary Allowances
12. fortifying
13. additives
14. enriched food
15. unit pricing

Recalling the Facts

1. Cultural and ethnic factors influence food choices. What you eat and when you eat are influenced by family and friends. Media messages can be a strong influence on food choices.
2. Examples will vary.
3. They are a better energy source.
4. Fiber helps move waste through the digestive system. It may reduce the risk of some cancers and heart disease and helps control diabetes. Fiber gives a feeling of fullness, so you tend to eat less.
5. A necessary building block of proteins in the body that must come from the food you eat.
6. Fat-soluble vitamins can be stored in the body; water-soluble vitamins must be replenished regularly.

Using Health Terms

On a separate sheet of paper, write the term that best matches each definition below.

LESSON 1

1. A desire, rather than a need, to eat.
2. Substances in food that your body needs to function properly, to grow, to repair itself, and to supply you with energy.
3. A natural drive that helps protect you from starvation.
4. The process by which the body takes in and uses food.

LESSON 2

5. Nutrients that help build and maintain body tissues.
6. A starchlike substance stored in the liver and muscles.
7. The starches and sugars found in foods.
8. A simple sugar and the body's chief fuel.
9. Substances that make up body proteins.

LESSON 3

10. Inorganic substances that the body cannot manufacture but that act as catalysts, regulating many vital body processes.

LESSON 4

11. The amounts of nutrients that will prevent deficiencies and excesses in most healthy people.

LESSON 5

12. The addition to food of nutrients that are not naturally present.
13. Substances added to food intentionally to produce a desired effect.
14. A food in which nutrients that were lost in processing have been added back.
15. A strategy for recognizing the relative cost of a product based on the cost of a standard unit, such as an ounce or gram.

Recalling the Facts

Using complete sentences, answer the following questions.

LESSON 1

1. How does your environment affect your food choices?
2. Give two examples of how eating is tied to emotions.

LESSON 2

3. Why are complex carbohydrates more beneficial than simple carbohydrates?
4. What are some benefits of foods high in fiber?
5. What is an essential amino acid?

LESSON 3

6. What is the difference between water-soluble and fat-soluble vitamins?

7. Describe whether vitamin and mineral supplements should be used as substitutes for food.

LESSON 4

8. Explain the importance of variety, moderation, and balance in your eating pattern?
9. List four ways of reducing your intake of fat. Explain which would be the most effective for you, and why.

LESSON 5

10. What is required on a Nutrition Facts panel of a food label?
11. How are ingredients listed on food labels?

128 CHAPTER 5 NUTRITION AND YOUR HEALTH

7. Because vitamins and minerals are necessary to help the body use food in digestion and are not foods themselves, they can't be used as food substitutes.
8. Variety keeps you from getting bored with your eating pattern, moderation keeps you from eating too much, and balance ensures that you get all the nutrients you need.

9. Any four: Eat more fresh fruits and vegetables; remove fat from meat before cooking; remove skin from poultry before cooking; eat roasted, baked, broiled, or grilled meat, fish, or poultry; eat more fish; substitute beans or legumes for meat; use less salad dressing, mayonnaise, and butter; steam, boil, or bake vegetables; avoid fried foods; read labels to avoid

Thinking Critically

LESSON 1

1. **Analyzing.** How might a limited budget influence your food choices?
2. **Synthesizing.** How do boredom, stress, and happiness affect eating habits? Give examples to support your claims.

LESSON 2

3. **Synthesizing.** Create a persuasive advertisement for a nutritious food.

LESSON 3

4. **Comparing and Contrasting.** In what ways are vitamins and minerals similar to other nutrient groups? In what ways are they different?

LESSON 4

5. **Evaluating.** What parts of the Food Guide Pyramid should provide most of the calories you currently take in?

LESSON 5

6. **Evaluating.** When Pete shops for food, he always looks for the terms *healthy* and *light*. Is Pete using enough information to make good food shopping decisions? Why or why not?

Making the Connection

1. **Language Arts.** Read a magazine or newspaper article about a nutritional issue. Summarize the article in writing.
2. **Social Studies.** Learn about the foods served by Native Americans of the Pacific Northwest in the rituals known as *potlatches*. In your research, determine how these foods are prepared. Publish a short booklet on the classroom computer that contains recipes for or descriptions of at least three of the dishes, noting which essential nutrients each provides.

BEYOND THE CLASSROOM

PARENTAL INVOLVEMENT Find recipes in cookbooks for the prepared foods you most enjoy eating. Take note of the hidden fats and sugars. Explore with family members easy-to-make alternatives that are more nutritionally balanced. Write about your discoveries and experiences with such alternative recipes.

COMMUNITY INVOLVEMENT With several classmates, create a guide to restaurants in your community that summarizes the variety on their menu. You might create a separate section for establishments that feature dishes designated "heart healthy" by the American Heart Association. In your guide, include the price range for dishes, along with such vital information as each restaurant's address, telephone number, and hours of operation. Share copies of your guide with other classes and community members.

SCHOOL-TO-CAREER

Exploring Careers. Interview the school dietitian or another registered dietitian in your community about the possibilities of a career in nutrition. Determine what preparation, including schooling and training, is necessary, the various settings in which dietitians work, and the types of interpersonal skills needed for various jobs. Share your findings with the class.

Thinking Critically

1. Answers will vary.
2. Boredom, stress, and happiness will either increase or decrease appetite. Examples will vary.
3. Answers will vary.
4. They are similar in that they help the body repair itself, function, and grow. They are different in that they are needed only in small amounts and they don't provide energy to the body.
5. Grains.
6. He should be looking for the total balance of nutrients in the foods he buys.

Making the Connection

1. Summaries will vary.
2. Booklets will vary.

Evaluate

- Use the reproducible *Chapter 5 Test* in the TCR, or construct your own using the Testmaker software.
- Use *Performance Assessment Activity 5* in the TCR.

Enrichment

- Have students complete *Cross-Curriculum Activity 5* in the TCR.

Beyond the Classroom

Keep students involved in the community, and encourage parent participation by assigning the activities on this page for students to work on outside of class.

processed foods with a high fat content.

10. Serving size; servings per container; calories per serving and calories per serving from fat; grams of total and saturated fat, total carbohydrate, fiber, sugars, protein, and milligrams of cholesterol and sodium per serving; percentage of the Daily Value the product supplies of the above nutrients and important minerals and vitamins in one serving.

11. By weight, in descending order.

Food and Your Health

	FEATURES	CLASSROOM RESOURCES

LESSON 1

Managing Your Weight
pages 132–138

c o n n e c t i o n s
Math

"Determining Your Body Mass Index," *page 135*

- Concept Map Activity 17
- Health Lab 6
- Lesson 17 Quiz
- Lesson Plan 17
- Reteaching Activity 17

LESSON 2

Fad Diets and Eating Disorders
pages 139–144

Teens Making a **Difference**

"Fulfilling Dreams," *page 143*

- Concept Map Activity 18
- Cooperative Learning Activity 6
- Enrichment Activity 6
- Lesson 18 Quiz
- Lesson Plan 18
- Reteaching Activity 18

LESSON 3

Nutrition for Individual Needs
pages 145–150

Making Responsible **Decisions**

"Is Making the Right Weight Right?" *page 147*

up date ▶ *Looking at Technology*

"Nutrient Supplements, Pro and Con," *page 149*

- Concept Map Activity 19
- Decision-Making Activity 6
- Lesson 19 Quiz
- Lesson Plan 19
- Reteaching Activity 19

LESSON 4

Protecting Yourself from Food Problems
pages 151–155

Building Health *Skills*

"Analyzing Messages About Food and Food Safety," *page 152*

- Concept Map Activity 20
- Lesson 20 Quiz
- Lesson Plan 20
- Reteaching Activity 20
- Transparency 17

Chapter Resources

ACTIVITIES

- Cross-Curriculum Activity 6
- Health Lab 6
- Health Skills Activities 6
- Parent Letter and Activities 6

ASSESSMENT

- Chapter 6 Test
- Performance Assessment Activity 6
- Testmaker Software

STUDENT ACTIVITIES WORKBOOK

- Applying Health Skills 17-20
- Study Guide 6
- Vocabulary Activity 6

STUDENT DIVERSITY STRATEGIES

- Audiocassette Program (English)
- Audiocassette Program (Spanish)
- Spanish Parent Letters and Activities
- Spanish Summaries, Quizzes, and Activities

MULTIMEDIA COMPONENTS

- English Audiocassette Program
- Spanish Audiocassette Program
- MindJogger Videodisc and VHS program
- ABCNews InterActive™ VHS/Videodisc Series

National Health Education Standards

One of the main goals of the National Health Education Standards is to move students toward "health literacy." Health literacy is the capacity of individuals to obtain, interpret, and understand basic health information and services and the competence to use such information and services in ways which promote health. The health standards were developed by applying the characteristics of a well-educated, literate person within the context of health. The health literate person is:

- a critical thinker and problem solver
- a self-directed learner
- a responsible, productive citizen
- an effective communicator

Listed below are the Health Education Standards Performance Indicators addressed in each lesson of this chapter.

Lesson	Health Standards Performance Indicators
1	3.1, 3.2, 3.4, 6.4
2	2.1, 2.2, 4.2, 6.4
3	3.3, 3.4, 6.1, 6.4
4	1.4, 3.1, 3.2, 3.4

ONLINE RESOURCES

HEALTH Online

For a fresh approach to health topics and an in-depth look at health issues, use these online resources found under Teacher Resources at **health.glencoe.com**.

- **BLOCK SCHEDULE LESSON PLANS** Reinforce health concepts with outside readings selected especially for students. Each reading is accompanied by a lesson plan and activities to enhance
  - Reading Skills
  - Cross Curriculum
  - Media Literacy

- **TECHNOLOGY PROJECTS** Instructions and suggestions on how to use computer, Internet, and software with health lessons.

- **HEALTH UPDATES** Timely topics in health news, including late-breaking medical advances and updates on teen risk behaviors.

Out of Time?

If time does not permit teaching this chapter, you may use these features: Making Responsible Decisions on page 147; Update on page 149; and Building Health Skills on page 152.

BLOCK SCHEDULING

Block scheduling provides extended time for hands-on projects and activities. Use the following activities to engage students, provide further depth, and vary your instructional techniques:

- Connections (30 minutes) **pg. 135**
- Teens Making a Difference (30 minutes) **pg. 143**
- Update (30 minutes) **pg. 149**
- Health Skills Activity (60–90 minutes) **pg.156**

Food and Your Health

CHAPTER OVERVIEW

Chapter 6 discusses weight management, eating disorders, and the specific dietary concerns of such individuals as athletes and vegetarians. Food safety is also addressed.

Lesson 1 Weight management is really an issue of energy intake and expenditure. A smart weight-control plan doesn't require a diet, but rather eating wisely and exercising throughout life.

Lesson 2 Fad diets and other quick weight-loss strategies carry certain risks, while an obsession with thinness, along with psychological pressures, can lead to the eating disorders known as anorexia nervosa and bulimia nervosa. These disorders require medical assistance and counseling.

Lesson 3 Many individuals have specific needs, some of which require special dietary considerations. Participating in sports may cause individuals to modify their diets. This should not be necessary if a balanced eating plan is already in place. Following a vegetarian diet requires greater nutritional awareness. Certain population groups can benefit from nutritional supplements if dependable sources of vitamins and minerals are needed.

Lesson 4 Food safety is a major health issue. Protecting oneself from foodborne illness comes with knowing the causes and ways to keep food safe.

CHAPTER 6

Food and Your Health

HEALTH Online

ANALYZING INFLUENCES

Body image and weight management are issues teens deal with all the time. Create an electronic slide show with Presentation Software to demonstrate how you think males as well as females are influenced by society's expectations. See the Technology Projects at **health.glencoe.com**.

Hands-On Health

TEACHING STRATEGY

Facing Up to Hidden Fats Help students "see" the "hidden fats" in popular fast-food sandwiches. See Activity 15, "Fat on a Bun," in the *Hands-On Health: Creative Teaching Strategies* booklet. 🖐

Time Needed
10 to 15 minutes

Supplies
- hamburger buns
- lard (or butter)
- tablespoon
- wax paper or napkins

> **The American diet is too loaded with fats and sweets and too deficient in fruits, vegetables and grains.**
>
> —Dr. David Satcher
> U.S. Surgeon General

Quick Write   List ten of your favorite foods that you enjoy eating. What food groups are most represented in your list?

Personal Health Inventory

Self-Inventory Write the numbers 1–10 on a sheet of paper. Read each statement below and respond by writing *yes*, *no*, or *sometimes* for each item. Write a *yes* only for items that you practice regularly. Save your responses.

1	I try to keep my weight within a healthy range.
2	I try to eat a variety of nutritious foods, even when I am attempting to lose or gain weight.
3	If I had a weight problem, I would be satisfied with losing or gaining ½ to 1 pound a week.
4	I exercise at least 20 or 30 minutes on most days of the week.
5	I would not fast or go on a quick weight-loss or weight-gain diet.
6	If I compete in athletics I follow a balanced eating plan with a variety of foods.
7	I drink plenty of water before, during, and after exercise.
8	I do not substitute nutrient supplements, such as vitamin pills, for a sensible eating style.
9	I avoid leaving perishable foods standing at room temperature for more than 2 hours.
10	I wash my hands before and after handling food.

Follow-up After completing the chapter, retake this self-inventory. Pick two items that you need to work on and set a goal to improve your health behaviors.

INTRODUCING THE CHAPTER

Personal Health Inventory

Let students read and briefly discuss the statements in the Self-Inventory: How do the attitudes and habits identified in these statements contribute to a high level of wellness? Then have students record their responses to the statements in their private Health Journals. Have them label their papers "Food and Health" and remind students that these responses are for their own personal use and will be referred to during the Chapter Review.

- Display as many diet books in your classroom as you can. Ask students why they think there are so many books written on this subject. Ask each student to select one book and read about the author's professional training and experience. Discuss the levels of training in nutrition for various professionals. Point out that nutritionists are the most highly trained in this field. Tell students they will learn more about weight management in this chapter.
- Allow students to read and discuss the quotation on this page. Ask: Why do you think American teens might not have the most healthful eating habits? Then let students recall instances in which they made food choices due to influences other than their health and well-being. How could their choices have been different if they were considering their nutrition and health?
- Distribute Parent Letter 6 in the *Parent Letters and Activities* booklet. ▱

TECHNOLOGY OPTIONS

ABCNEWS INTERACTIVE You may wish to use *Food and Nutrition* with this chapter. For your convenience, use the separate *ABCNews InterActive™ Bar Code Correlation* that accompanies the *Glencoe Health* program. ●

MINDJOGGER
VIDEOQUIZ

To preview or review chapter content, you may wish to use the *MindJogger Videoquiz* that accompanies Chapter 6. ●

LESSON 1

Managing Your Weight

FOCUS

LESSON OBJECTIVES

After studying this lesson, students should be able to

- explain calories, their role as the body's fuel, and how they affect body weight.
- contrast overweight and obesity and identify the impact of obesity on overall health.
- describe the health risks related to being underweight.
- discuss healthful weight-loss and weight-gain strategies.

MOTIVATOR

Write the following on the chalkboard for students to work on while attendance is being taken: *List all of the methods you can think of that people use in trying to lose weight. Then write down the results you might expect from each.*

INTRODUCING THE LESSON

Refer to the Motivator. Ask a few volunteers to share their lists of how people try to lose weight. Make a master list on the chalkboard. Discuss students' impressions of expected outcomes. Point out that exercise is just as important as food intake in maintaining a desired level of weight.

INTRODUCING HEALTH TERMS

- Have students use the vocabulary terms in a short story about a teen having problems with food. Ask them to read their stories to the class.
- Ask students to complete Vocabulary Activity 6 and Chapter Study Guide 6 in the *Student Workbook*. ☞

To be truly fit, you need to maintain a healthy weight—now and throughout your lifetime. Your own healthy weight probably will not be the same as the weight of a high-fashion model, a bodybuilder, or your best friend. You can use some general guidelines, however, to judge your weight and to keep it within a healthy range.

HEALTH TERMS

overweight

obesity

underweight

undernutrition

body mass index (BMI)

nutrient-dense

HEALTH CONCEPTS

- Being obese, overweight, or underweight poses risks to your total health.
- Physical activity is an important part of weight management and maintenance.
- The only way to lose weight is by burning more calories than you consume. You need to consume an adequate number of calories for someone your height and age, and include physical activity in your life.

Calorie Basics

In order to understand weight management, you need to understand calories—what they are, where they come from, and how they affect body weight. When people hear the word *calories,* they often think of fattening foods. Calories, or more correctly, kilocalories, are simply a unit to measure energy. Calories are a measure of the energy in food and the energy your body burns. Calories are not nutrients.

Calories: Their Source

Some foods have more calories than others. The specific number of calories depends on the amount of carbohydrate, fat, and protein in the food as well as the portion size. The way a food is prepared or cooked also affects the calorie count.

Lesson 1 Resources

TEACHER'S CLASSROOM RESOURCES
- ☞ **Concept Map** Activity 17
- ☞ **Health Lab 6**
- ☞ **Lesson 17 Quiz**
- ☞ **Lesson Plan 17**
- ☞ **Parent Letter and Activities 6**
- ☞ **Reteaching** Activity 17

STUDENT WORKBOOK
- ☞ **Applying Health Skills 17**
- ☞ **Chapter Study Guide 6**
- ☞ **Vocabulary** Activity 6

MULTIMEDIA
- 🔴 **ABCNews InterActive™ VHS/Videodisc,** *Food and Nutrition*

In the previous chapter you learned about three nutrients that supply energy, or calories. Carbohydrate, the main source, and protein each supply four calories per gram. Fat supplies more than twice as much—nine calories per gram. For this reason, even small amounts of fat in a food significantly increase its caloric content.

Calories to Burn

How many calories do you need? Several factors play a role, such as rate of growth, body size, gender, age, and metabolic rate. For example, some people have a higher metabolic rate than others, so they need more calories. Children and teens need more calories than adults do because they are still growing. Taller and bigger people need more calories than shorter and smaller people do. A person's activity level also plays a major role. Active people need more calories than sedentary people do in order to remain active.

Balancing the Energy Equation

Keeping a healthy weight is an issue of energy balance. Simply stated, calories consumed must equal calories burned. You gain or lose weight by tipping the balance. By taking in fewer calories than you expend, you lose body weight. When you take in more calories than you expend, you gain. Your body stores the extra calories as body fat.

Each pound (0.5 kg) of body fat equals about 3,500 calories. To lose 1 pound (0.5 kg) a week, which is a realistic, healthy goal, you need to consume 500 fewer calories than normal each day. Here is the calculation you can use: 500 calories per day x 7 days = 3,500 calories = 1 pound (0.5 kg) of body fat. What will happen if you also burn 250 extra calories a day through physical activity?

Weight Problems: Risky Business

Being too heavy or too thin increases the risk of developing health problems later on. In the meantime, weight problems can certainly affect the quality of life.

Body Fat versus Body Weight

Although we use the terms *overweight* and *obesity* interchangeably, these conditions are not the same. **Overweight** means *weighing more than 10 percent over the standard weight for height;* **obesity** means *excess body fat, or adipose tissue.* Usually obesity and overweight go together.

From a health standpoint, being overweight or being obese is risky. However, in

▼ *People come in all different ent shapes and sizes.*

ACTIVITY *Explain how to determine whether or not you are overweight or underweight.*

LESSON 1   MANAGING YOUR WEIGHT   **133**

TEACH

L1 Explaining

Remind students that adding 100 extra calories to their daily food intake will add 12 pounds in a year if their activity levels remain the same.

LD Class Activity

Show LD students how to use calorie counters. Have them plan a week's worth of healthful meals within a certain calorie limit.

L2 Class Activity

Have students survey the contents of any vending machine at school and make a list of the foods and beverages offered. Tell them to analyze the nutrients in the foods and beverages as well as the number of calories in each. Ask them to report their findings to the class.

LEP Class Activity

Provide food-related magazines for students to collect pictures of high-calorie foods and drinks that total about 3,500 calories. Explain that this is the amount of calories (or food) that students would have to cut out each week to lose one pound (0.5 kg) if dieting alone was used to lose weight.

L3 Cooperative Learning

Ask students to pretend that they own a chain of fast-food restaurants. Have students work in groups to decide on a restaurant name, a nutritionally balanced menu featuring low-calorie fast foods, and a promotional campaign. Have them present their ideas to the class for feedback.

SCHOOL-TO-CAREER

ENERGY FOR WORK. People's daily calorie requirements vary by occupation. In some occupations, workers exercise vigorously for most of the day. Instruct students to choose an occupation such as dancer, professional athlete, construction worker, window washer, or farm laborer. Have them find the number of calories burned while engaged in specific movements similar to those used in the work performed. Suggest they use their research to calculate how much the workday calorie requirement of such a worker exceeds that of a word processor of the same size, age, and gender.

L1 Class Activity

Guide students in creating a bulletin board contrasting overweight people with excess body fat and those with increased muscle mass.

hot link

sedentary lifestyle

Ask students to provide examples of sedentary and nonsedentary approaches to everyday activities. Discuss the impact of these lifestyles on weight management.

L1 Explaining

Tell students that pinching a fold of skin and measuring its thickness is one way of telling if a person has too much fat. This is because extra fat is stored under the skin. Average male bodies are made up of about 12½ percent fat, and average female bodies are made up of 20 percent fat.

L1 Discussing

Have students think about people they know who are unhappy with their weight. Ask students whether they think these individuals really need to lose (or gain) weight or are reacting to pressure from society, friends, and family. Talk about ways that pressure is applied from outside the individual.

hot link

sedentary lifestyle For more information on factors that contribute to a sedentary lifestyle, see Chapter 3, page 54.

▼ *Regular physical exercise is a key to maintaining your proper weight.*

ACTIVITY *Describe two other benefits of a regular exercise program.*

certain situations, being overweight might not be a risk. A football player or bodybuilder may be overweight because of excess muscle, not excess fat. Body composition, rather than weight, is often a better measure of fitness.

Obesity: A Hazard to Health

Obesity is a common health risk in the United States. Excess body fat strains the body frame and increases the workload of the heart and the lungs. Obese people have a higher risk of health problems, including hypertension, diabetes, high blood cholesterol, atherosclerosis, and some cancers. Also, obese people are often inactive, which increases their health risks even more.

Adolescent obesity is increasing. Besides the health risks later in life, excess body fat during adolescence may affect self-esteem and social health. Unfortunately, many teens who are overweight or obese as adolescents continue to be so through adulthood.

Why do people gain too much weight? There are two main reasons:

- **sedentary lifestyle**
- poor food habits

Interestingly, studies show that many obese people actually eat less than normal-weight people who exercise more.

The causes of obesity may be more complex, however. Heredity may play a role, but the exact relationship is unclear. Some scientists believe that obese people have more fat cells, which may get smaller but never go away. Other researchers are exploring the set point theory. This theory says that each person has a biological set point for weight and body fat. The body works to maintain that point by lowering the metabolic rate when caloric intake goes down. Then it is hard to lose weight and keep it off.

Underweight: A Health Risk

Being underweight can sometimes pose health risks. With so much attention placed on obesity, we sometimes forget the health risks related to being **underweight**, or *being 10 percent or more below normal weight.* Being too thin means that a person has little body fat as an energy reserve, and perhaps less of the protective nutrients the body stores. This makes it harder for an overly thin person to fight off infection and increases the risk of health problems if surgery is needed.

Underweight people may be undernourished, too. **Undernutrition** is *not consuming enough essential nutrients or calories for normal body functions.* Among other health

MORE ABOUT . . . . .

WEIGHT-LOSS STRATEGIES. For students trying to lose body fat, here are some healthful hints: (1) Be patient. Don't try to lose weight in a hurry. Change your eating habits gradually. (2) If you have setbacks, don't panic or give up. Stay calm and analyze the situation. If you find yourself unwrapping a big chocolate bar, stop. Don't criticize yourself; instead ask yourself why you want to eat that candy bar. Sometimes old cravings win out, but they can be dealt with if you are willing to face them. Take charge of the situation. Be determined to eat healthful foods. Throw out that chocolate bar and go for a walk or call a friend—anything to take your mind off eating.

risks, underweight people have a greater chance of developing iron-deficiency anemia.

Managing Body Weight

How many people do you know who have tried to lose weight? How many lost weight, only to regain it shortly afterward? Why? Perhaps they did not follow realistic and effective weight-control strategies.

Determining a Healthy Weight

Height and weight charts are often used to determine a person's proper weight. However, the range of weights listed on these charts can vary a great deal when accounting for different body frames. For example, two people who are the same height can have very different weights. A large-boned person will weigh more than a small-boned person of the same height.

Measuring a person's body composition is a more accurate way to determine a healthy weight.

The chart shown on page 136 provides an indicator for acceptable weight. This chart determines **body mass index (BMI).** This is the ratio of weight to height. BMI is a better measure of disease risk than body weight alone. Certain groups, however, should not use BMI as a predictor of health risk. These include athletes, such as body builders, and pregnant women, both of whom have abnormally high BMIs.

Health Risk Based on BMI

BMI CATEGORY	HEALTH RISK
Under 25	Minimal
26–27	Low
28–30	Moderate
31–34	High
35–39	Very High
40 and higher	Extremely High

connections Math

Determining Your Body Mass Index

There are several quick and easy ways to compute your BMI. One is to use the chart on the next page. A second is the following formula:

1. Multiply your weight in pounds by 703 (e.g., for a person weighing 149 pounds, this would be $149 \times 703 = 104,747$).

2. Multiply your height in inches times itself (e.g., for a person 65 inches tall, this would be $65 \times 65 = 4,225$).

3. Divide the answer in Step 1 by the answer in Step 2 (e.g., $104,747 \div 4,225 = 24.8$, or 25 when expressed as a rounded number).

Refer to the table on this page titled "Health Risk Based on BMI" to see the risk category associated with your BMI. How do you rate?

LESSON 1 MANAGING YOUR WEIGHT **135**

L1 Explaining

Emphasize that ideal body shape is influenced by culture. Mention that ideal proportions vary from country to country and from one generation to the next.

L2 Discussing

Ask students why males of a certain height and frame size weigh more than females of the same height and frame size. *(Males' small frames are larger than females' small frames. Males tend to have more muscle tissue, which is dense. Females have more fat tissue, which is less dense.)*

connections Math

Review with students the importance of knowing one's own BMI. Then read the feature with the class, and guide students in following each step of the example. Point out the range of numbers: In Step 1, the product is likely to be in the tens or hundreds of thousands. In Step 2, the product will probably be in the thousands. Ask students to calculate their own BMI (using calculators if they want) and to record their ratings in their private Health Journals.

CURRICULUM CONNECTIONS

MATH. Have students compute how many calories they need to maintain their present weight. Ask them to compare this figure to the total number of calories they eat in a day.

HISTORY. Ask students to research how society's view of the ideal figure has changed through the years. Have them create a display or time line illustrating their findings.

FAMILY AND CONSUMER SCIENCES. Have students individually plan a week's worth of menus to meet their personal goals to gain, lose, or maintain weight. Also, have them suggest ways to add calories to commonly eaten foods to promote weight gain.

CHARACTER IN ACTION

Consideration and Respect

Have students suggest healthful tips for a weight-loss plan. Remind students to think positively when attempting to lose weight and to focus on progress, not setbacks or media images of the "perfect" body. Also have students suggest ways to show support for friends and family trying to manage their weight in healthful ways.

L1 Discussing

Talk about the value of consulting a doctor, nurse, or dietitian before starting a program to lose or gain weight.

L1 Explaining

Point out that some fast-food businesses have responded to people's increasing concerns about healthful food choices. (Many now offer salad bars, broiled chicken, and baked potatoes.) Discuss how these may be good alternatives as long as they are not covered with fat-laden salad dressings or margarine, butter, and cheese.

L2 Guest Speaker

Invite a school nurse or dietitian to class to talk about reaching and maintaining a healthy weight. Encourage students to prepare a list of questions to ask the speaker.

L1 Explaining

Stress that slow, steady weight loss (or gain) is healthier and more likely to be permanent than rapid, variable weight loss (or gain).

L2 Health Lab

Distribute *Health Lab 6* and have students investigate the amount of fat in butter and margarine. ☞

YOUR ACCEPTABLE WEIGHT

This chart provides a fairly simple way to determine whether you have too much body fat. Find your weight in the left-hand column (lb.) and your height in the right-hand column (in.). Then put a ruler between the two numbers. If the line falls within the acceptable range, in the middle of the chart, your weight is all right. If the line falls in the overweight or obese range, consult a physician.

This chart can only let you know whether you are overweight. It is not a scientific measure of healthful weight. Even if you come out in the acceptable range on the chart, talk with your physician if you think you may have a weight problem.

🔺 *You can improve your overall health by staying within your acceptable weight range.*

ACTIVITY *Find your own acceptable weight on the chart. What can you do to maintain your acceptable weight?*

Starting a Weight-Control Plan

The true meaning of the word *diet* is everything a person eats and drinks, not a restrictive eating plan. The truth is teens especially need the nutrients from all the food groups for growth and should not consider restricting their food intake. A healthy eating plan and physical activity are often all you need to do to get to an appropriate weight.

These steps can get you started if you are considering a weight-control plan:

- **Target your weight.** Based on your body frame, choose a target weight that is within a healthy range and not too thin. Ask a health care professional what range is healthy for you.

- **Set smart goals.** Losing or gaining one-half to one pound (0.2 to 0.5 kg) a week is realistic, attainable, and safe.

- **Make a personal plan,** preferably one that includes both a nutritious eating plan and regular physical activity. Consider your own food preferences and lifestyle. Choose activities you will enjoy doing. It is easier to follow a plan that you create yourself.

136 CHAPTER 6   FOOD AND YOUR HEALTH

PERSONAL HEALTH

In the United States, many health problems result from dietary excess. People eat for many reasons, only one of which is hunger. The sight or smell of food may be tempting, or a social function may involve food. In some parts of the world, people eat whatever is available, and most health problems result from hunger or dietary deficiency. Have students list reasons they have eaten in the past 24 hours. Suggest they consider hunger, temptation, boredom, stress, scheduled meals, social occasions, enjoyment, and comfort. Have them speculate about how their reasons would differ if food were scarce, hard to obtain, and less appealing.

- **Put your goal and plan in writing.**
- **Stick to your plan.** To help, keep a diary of what you eat and when, so that you become more aware of your food habits. Focus on eating a variety of foods with at least the minimum number of servings from the Food Guide Pyramid. Avoid meal skipping; try to eat three or more meals a day.
- **Think positively.** If you slip up occasionally, that is okay. Focus on your progress, and get back on track.
- **Evaluate your progress, but avoid weighing yourself every day.** Instead, weigh yourself once a week at the same time of day.
- **Recognize that plateaus are normal.** Plateaus are a period of time when your weight does not change.

Smart Weight-Loss Strategies

The best weight-loss strategies are easily summed up as follows:

- Eat fewer calories (and make them nutrient dense). **Nutrient-dense** foods are *foods high in nutrients relative to their caloric content.*
- Burn more calories through exercise.
- Better yet, do both.

This advice is the same no matter how much you need to lose—5, 15, even 50 pounds (2.3, 6.9, even 22.7 kg). These strategies can help your weight-loss plan work for you:

- As a teen, eat at least 1,400 to 1,600 calories daily. Otherwise, you may miss out on essential nutrients.
- Eat mainly low-calorie foods from the five food groups, including fruits and vegetables.
- Eat foods you like. If your favorites are high in calories, have just a tiny portion from time to time.
- Make meals last. Take small bites.
- If you are tempted to snack, choose low-calorie snacks such as carrots or celery.

Smart Weight-Gain Strategies

Some people want to gain weight to look better; others want to gain to participate in sports. Smart weight gain includes physical activity and an eating plan that is higher in calories. Without exercise, extra food calories turn mainly to body fat. Consider these tips:

- Increase caloric intake, especially with foods high in complex carbohydrates, such as bread, pasta, rice, and potatoes.
- Eat more frequently. Take second helpings.
- Eat nutritious snacks, but space them two to three hours before meals to avoid spoiling your appetite.

Learn the basics of weight management from Shape Up America, including strategies for decreasing food intake and increasing physical activity, at **health.glencoe.com**.

CHARACTER IN ACTION

Consideration and Respect

Weight management is an important part of your overall health. It is common for people to be sensitive about some aspect of his or her appearance. Yet each person, *whatever* his or her weight, build, or overall appearance, deserves basic dignity and **respect**.

You can demonstrate respect by considering the feelings of others and showing kindness toward people who may seem self-conscious about the way they look, speak, or move.

Character Check Practice respect toward those whose appearance may be different from your own. Imagine what it is like to be that person. Vow never to make fun of other people. Discourage other people from doing it, too.

As students plan their own fitness programs, have them check the Web Links for ways to evaluate their own physical fitness levels. These resources will provide them with weight management tips and safe workout practices.

L2 Personal Involvement

Have students use a calorie chart to determine how many calories are burned through their daily activities.

L2 Class Activity

Have students act out the following case studies to show how they might support others who are trying to lose weight: (1) Three teens go to a fast-food restaurant for an after-school snack. (2) Several teens get together for a 10-mile bike trip. One teen is obese and cannot keep up with the group. Have students discuss how they would deal with the two situations.

L1 Class Activity

Ask students to brainstorm a list of nonfood rewards they would find motivating during a weight-control program.

Myths & Realities

MYTH. A person can lose weight simply by dieting.

FACT. Most people cannot permanently lose weight by dieting alone. The human body tries to maintain a fixed weight, or set point; when one diets, the body thinks it is starving. It has a built-in safeguard to protect it from the famines human beings have had to face throughout history. As soon as an individual reduces the calories he or she consumes, the metabolic rate slows down, and the body begins to use fewer calories for all of its processes. However, a small amount of exercise added to daily activities can help speed up the metabolic rate and thereby lower the person's set point.

ASSESS

EVALUATING THE LESSON

Assign and discuss the Lesson 1 Review; then administer, grade, and discuss the *Lesson 17 Quiz* in the TCR. ☞

RETEACHING

- Make up some advice-column type questions that can be answered at least partially with information from the lesson. Have students work individually to compose response letters.
- Ask students to complete *Reteaching Activity 17* in the TCR. ☞

ENRICHMENT

Have students apply their understanding of sound nutrition to create menus for a restaurant for people who are watching their weight. The menus might include calorie information; tips for calorie trimming; and/or symbols for low-sugar, low-sodium, and low-fat foods.

CLOSE

Have students close their textbooks and write an outline of the lesson's major concepts. Ask them to write a summarizing sentence beside each concept. Afterward, request that they open their textbooks to check the accuracy of their outlines. Conclude with a brief discussion of the most important concepts learned in the lesson.

---

hotlink

exercise For more information on exercise and its importance to good physical health, see Chapter 3, page 53.

Physical Activity and Weight Management

People can lose body fat just by dieting, but increased physical activity helps them reach their target weight faster, easier, and, over the long run, more effectively. Whether you need to lose, gain, or maintain weight, you need physical activity. Consider the following benefits of regular **exercise:**

- It burns calories, which promotes loss of body fat.
- It tones and builds muscles to give a firm, lean body shape. Without exercise, the weight lost may be lean tissue as well as body fat.
- It helps promote a normal appetite response, which helps anyone trying to gain, lose, or maintain weight.
- It helps relieve the stress that often leads to overeating or undereating.
- It helps increase metabolic rate, so the body burns more calories for several hours, even while resting. It takes more calories to maintain muscle tissue than body fat. Exercise may help lower your set point.
- It increases self-esteem, which helps keep your plan on track.

To build muscles and spend calories, you really need to work your muscles on a regular basis. Adding exercise to your daily routine, such as using stairs instead of an elevator or walking instead of driving, helps. To set up a realistic, yet effective, exercise program, refer to Chapter 4.

LESSON 1 *Review*

Reviewing Facts and Vocabulary

1. Discuss the relationship between maintaining a healthy weight and energy balance.
2. Name three health risks related to obesity.
3. What role does physical activity play in weight management?

Thinking Critically

4. *Analyzing.* Compare being obese to being overweight.
5. *Synthesizing.* Suppose you want to lose 1 pound (0.5 kg) per week for the next five weeks. How would you change the amount of calories you eat and the amount of calories you burn through exercise to reach that goal?

Applying Health Skills

6. *In Your Home.* Has anyone in your family gone on a weight-loss or weight-gain diet? Interview this person about his or her eating and physical activity plan. Discuss whether the plan was successful in achieving permanent weight change.

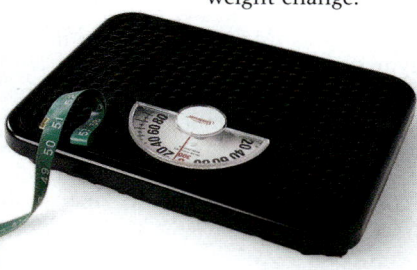

138 CHAPTER 6 FOOD AND YOUR HEALTH

Lesson 1 Review

Answers to Reviewing Facts and Vocabulary

1. Calories consumed must equal calories burned to maintain weight. To lose weight, calories consumed must be less than calories burned.
2. Any three: hypertension, diabetes, high blood cholesterol, atherosclerosis, and some cancers.
3. Physical activity increases the number of calories burned in a day.

Answers to Thinking Critically

4. Overweight is a measure of pounds. Obesity is an excess of body fat. They generally go together.
5. You could decrease the number of calories you eat by 250 per day and increase the amount of exercise you do to burn 250 calories per day.

Fad Diets and Eating Disorders

"Miracle Pill Burns Off Fat!" "Melt Fat Away While You Sleep!" You have probably seen headlines like these. They appear in ads in magazines, subways and buses, and on billboards. They promise quick and easy solutions to weight problems.

In this lesson, you will examine the risks of fad diets and other quick weight-loss strategies.

HEALTH TERMS
weight cycling
anorexia nervosa
bulimia nervosa

HEALTH CONCEPTS
- Weight control requires self-discipline and commitment. There are no shortcuts.
- Be wary of any diet or weight-loss scheme that promises to take off pounds in an abnormally short time period or without any effort.
- Eating disorders are symptoms of other problems.

Weight control products

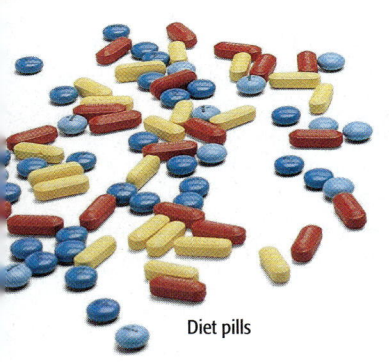
Diet pills

Fad Diets

Look up the term *diet* in the dictionary, and you will find it refers to everything you eat and drink. In this society in recent decades, however, the term *diet* has come to be associated with the idea of losing weight. Fad diets—approaches to weight control that are popular for a short time—come and go but rarely have any lasting effect. Many of these diets limit food variety and certain nutrients. They have names that tell all, such as the "grapefruit diet" or the "cabbage soup" diet. As a rule, these diets are hard to stick to for very long.

Some fad diets cost a lot of money. Others are far more costly, causing problems with one's health. As a health consumer, you need to be aware of the health risks associated with such practices and products.

Lesson 2 Resources

TEACHER'S CLASSROOM RESOURCES
- **Concept Map** Activity 18
- **Cooperative Learning** Activity 6
- **Enrichment** Activity 6
- **Lesson 18 Quiz**
- **Lesson Plan 18**
- **Reteaching** Activity 18

STUDENT WORKBOOK
- **Applying Health Skills 18**
- **Chapter Study Guide 6**
- **Vocabulary** Activity 6

MULTIMEDIA
- **ABCNews InterActive™ VHS/Videodisc,** *Food and Nutrition*

Fad Diets and Eating Disorders

FOCUS

LESSON OBJECTIVES
After studying this lesson, students should be able to

- evaluate popular diets and diet gimmicks.
- contrast anorexia nervosa and bulimia nervosa.

MOTIVATOR
Write the following on the chalkboard for students to work on while attendance is being taken: *In your own words, define the terms* eating disorder, anorexia nervosa, *and* bulimia nervosa. *List several reasons or factors that might result in an eating disorder.*

INTRODUCING THE LESSON
Have students share their responses to the Motivator. Talk about why some teens develop eating disorders or poor eating patterns.

INTRODUCING HEALTH TERMS
- Ask students to create and share a public service announcement about eating disorders using the terms *anorexia nervosa* and *bulimia nervosa.*
- Write the following on the chalkboard: Anorexia means *"without appetite,"* nervosa means *"of nervous origin."* Have students use the dictionary to find the definitions of *anorexia nervosa* and *bulimia nervosa.* Then ask them to contrast the disorders.
- Ask students to complete Vocabulary Activity 6 and Chapter Study Guide 6 in the *Student Workbook.*

TEACH

L1 Explaining

Tell students that weight cycling, a chronic process of on-again, off-again weight loss, is often associated with fad dieting. Stress that most people regain the weight they lost from a fad diet or quick weight-loss diet. Often they will gain back more than they lost as soon as they return to their regular eating habits.

L2 Cooperative Learning

For more on fad diets, assign *Cooperative Learning Activity 6* in the TCR. 👝

L1 Class Activity

Direct students to locate a variety of newspaper and magazine advertisements or headlines regarding weight loss. Discuss the reasons for such a large number of different programs or techniques. Ask students what many of the claims have in common. *(They promise to be quick, easy, painless, and successful.)*

L2 Class Activity

Have students locate examples of dieting tips from magazines and newspapers and discuss the relative merits of the different plans. Ask them if any of the advice seems dangerous (such as an extremely low-calorie diet) and which of the plans seems most sensible.

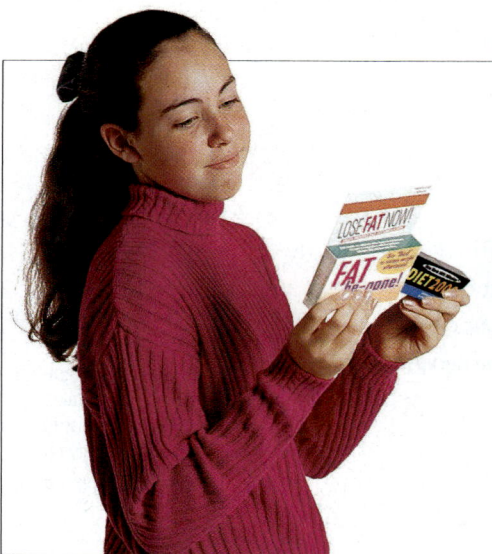

Let the Dieter Beware

Beware of any diet or product that:

- involves eating only one food.
- claims that you can eat anything you want or as much as you want.
- promises quick results.
- supplies too few calories—below 1,400 calories a day—for energy and health.
- requires a weight-loss aid, such as a vitamin pill, a body wrap, a liquid shake, or an appetite suppressant, or the purchase of books, videos, or tapes.
- promises spot reducing—an unrealistic claim because weight loss occurs all over.
- does not teach a person how to make lifestyle changes to achieve permanent weight loss.

🔺 *There is no safe way to take weight off quickly, no matter what claims and promises the ads make.* ACTIVITY *List the key words on the product packages that are clues to false and misleading claims.*

Weight Cycling

"Lose Pounds Fast!" At first, some diets seem to live up to claims like this. However, since the weight loss is usually from water, not body fat, the pounds lost are quickly regained. These rapid ups and downs in weight are all part of **weight cycling.** This is *the cycle of losing, regaining, losing, and regaining.* Other names are "seesaw dieting" and "yo-yo dieting."

Weight cycling may be less healthy than being slightly overweight. Why? Lean body tissue lost along with body fat is replaced by more body fat. Because body fat burns fewer calories than muscle does, the person continues to require fewer and fewer calories to maintain weight. Therefore, losing weight becomes harder and harder.

Other Risky Weight-Loss Strategies

Other weight-loss approaches not only fail to achieve permanent weight loss, but they can be dangerous and even fatal. These include:

- **Fasting.** Avoiding food, or *fasting,* is dangerous even for a short time. For health, growth, and energy, you need a fresh supply of nutrients daily. For example, without enough food energy, the body uses its own muscle tissue for energy.
- **Liquid Protein Diets.** High-protein, low-carbohydrate liquid diets can have such serious side effects that the U.S. Food and Drug Administration (FDA) requires a warning label on these products. Using them as the only source of nutrients can result in serious health problems, even death. Using them as an approach to weight loss should only be done under medical supervision.

140 CHAPTER 6 FOOD AND YOUR HEALTH

CURRICULUM CONNECTIONS

LANGUAGE ARTS. Encourage students to become consumer reporters and investigate the following approaches to weight control: diet candies, diet pills, liposuction, liquid meals, weight-control clubs, intestinal bypass surgery, and a currently popular diet. Have them write a "Consumer Update" describing the approach, effectiveness, cost, and safety of each. Make copies of their reports to distribute to the entire class.

MATH. Have students find the calories in a single serving of their favorite snacks. (Help students to understand what constitutes a serving size.) Ask volunteers to compile the calorie information into a one-page handout for the class.

■ **Diet Pills.** Some diet pills claim to "burn," "block," or "flush" fat from the system. However, science has yet to come up with a low-risk pill that does this. Diet pills may help control the appetite, but they can have very serious side effects. Some cause drowsiness, while others may produce anxiety. Some diet pills may even be addictive.

Eating Disorders

Today's society is obsessed with being thin. The average female high-fashion model is about 5 feet 8 inches (1.7 m) tall and weighs less than 110 pounds (50 kg). Does this model represent an accurate picture of a healthy, typical female figure? In truth, no, but many people compare themselves to these models.

An obsession with thinness, along with psychological pressures and perhaps genetic factors, can lead to two eating disorders: anorexia nervosa and bulimia nervosa. Thousands of people in the United States, mainly females, suffer from these disorders.

▼ *Throughout history, each era has had its own standard for the ideal male and female form.*

ACTIVITY *Describe the ideal body image represented by male and female models in advertisements today.*

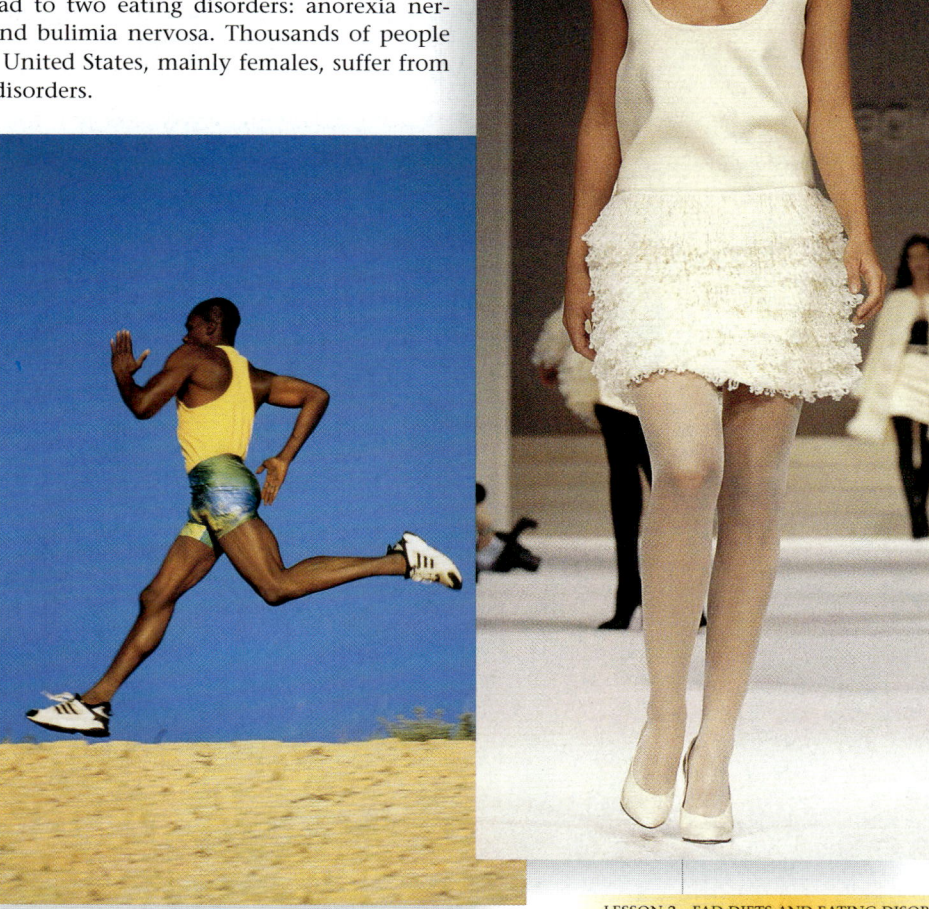

LESSON 2   FAD DIETS AND EATING DISORDERS   **141**

L2 **Explaining**
Stress how fad diets make it difficult to maintain an ideal weight once it is attained, since they do not teach new ways of eating.

L1 **Discussing**
Display photographs and advertisements from magazines and newspapers to represent the association between people's values and their food decisions. Examples might include pictures of food and people that emphasize physical fitness, family togetherness, friendship, community, and self-esteem. Ask volunteers to identify some of the values portrayed in the pictures. Emphasize that food decisions reflect people's values and the way they feel about themselves and others.

L1 **Discussing**
Ask students to recall messages they were given about eating while they were growing up. Examples might include giving candy or other sweets as a reward, persuading children to eat vegetables even if they don't like them, requiring that children clean their plates before leaving the table, or disciplining children by sending them to bed hungry. Discuss the impact of those early experiences on their present food choices and behaviors.

L1 **Explaining**
Talk about how common it is for many people to respond to stress or anxiety by not eating or by overeating. Emphasize that these actions can ultimately result in long-term eating disorders and do not eliminate stress. Explore with them ways of effectively dealing with stress.

HOME AND COMMUNITY
C O N N E C T I O N

EATING DISORDERS. People who have eating disorders often seek the support of self-help organizations. Overeaters Anonymous is a group that helps people who eat compulsively get control of their lives. The OA program relies on the same steps of recovery followed by groups such as Alcoholics Anonymous. Like those programs, it respects confidentiality. More information is available in the white pages of the phone book.

L1 Discussing

Ask the class what some of the health risks associated with bulimia nervosa are. Ask: Why is bulimia nervosa not considered a disease?

L1 Discussing

Have students describe the food choices they make when they are angry, sad, or frustrated. Ask them if the choices are different from the choices they make when they are happy, excited, or content. If so, have them describe how their choices are different and why they think this is so.

L3 Community Involvement

Ask volunteers to research community sources of help for individuals suffering from anorexia nervosa and/or bulimia nervosa. Have them prepare a list of survey questions to ask about the kinds of treatments available, the length of most kinds of treatments, fees, training, and qualifications of personnel. Request that students share materials from the community programs and their findings with the class.

FOOD AND NUTRITION (Side 2)

Chapter 12: Eating Disorders: Anorexia and Bulimia

Frames 35557-41864

Chapter 13: Eating Disorders: Binge Eating

Frames 41903-43765

Chapter 14: Eating Disorders: Facing the Problem

Frames 43776-47076

---

keeping Fit

Helping a Friend with an Eating Disorder

If you have a friend who has an eating disorder, you can help by following these tips:

➤ First, listen.

➤ Use your active listening skills and encourage your friend to share feelings honestly.

➤ If you think the problem is serious, help your friend find adult or professional help.

➤ *People with eating disorders should seek professional medical help.*

ACTIVITY *Explain the consequences a teen might face by not dealing with an eating disorder.*

Anorexia Nervosa

Anorexia nervosa is *a disorder in which the irrational fear of becoming obese results in severe weight loss from self-induced starvation. Anorexia* means "without appetite." *Nervosa* means "of nervous origin." Anorexia nervosa is a psychological disorder with emotional and physical consequences. It relates directly to an individual's self-concept and coping abilities. Outside pressures, high expectations, the need to achieve, and the need to be accepted help lead to this disorder.

Each person with anorexia is different, but the following behaviors and emotions are typical: extremely low caloric intake, an obsession with exercising, emotional problems, unnatural interest in food, unrealistic or distorted sense of body image, and denial of an eating problem. Most people with anorexia are females in their teens or twenties. This disorder is not typically associated with males, but they can be at risk as well as females.

A person with anorexia has physical symptoms related to malnutrition and starvation. These include extreme weight loss, constipation, hormonal changes, heart damage, impaired immune function, and decreased heart rate. In females, the menstrual cycle may stop because of low body fat. In severe cases, anorexia can result in death.

COOPERATIVE) LEARNING

Teens may become obsessed with weight or body image by comparing themselves unfavorably to models in advertisements, characters in fiction, and celebrities in the media. Have students collect and share several magazine ads or describe television commercials that project unrealistic images against which teens might measure themselves. Ask them to examine the ads and brainstorm a list of celebrities that teens often wish to emulate. What unrealistic qualities do the ads project? Overly slender bodies? Bulgng muscles? Ballooning breasts? Have them role-play a panel of experts discussing the role of the media in eating disorders and other unhealthy behaviors.

Teens Making a Difference

...RESPONSIBILITY...CARING ...CITIZENSHIP

Yennifer, 15, knows the value of food. Though she has never experienced prolonged hunger herself, she has listened to the stories of how her parents and sister suffered from hunger when they lived back in El Salvador. "When my sister was little, before I was born, my mom and dad were so poor that my sister did not have food sometimes," she begins. She has taken these stories to heart. Now a student at Lakewood High School in Florida, she is working hard to collect canned foods and make further plans to help people in need both locally and in El Salvador, the place of her birth.

FOOD FOR PEOPLE, FOOD FOR THOUGHT When a series of earthquakes hit El Salvador, Yennifer took action. "I went to my counselor at school to talk about the earthquakes in El Salvador and to see what I could do. The counselor sent me to Aspira." Aspira, a national organization, works to help Latino teens stay in school and go on to college. "Aspira helped me to find specific ways to help other people," Yennifer continues. "They gave me instruction on how I could help the earthquake victims. Along the way, they also gave me new goals. We are collecting canned foods and other things through the whole school for the earthquake victims. We have placed boxes all over for the foods, and we are having success," she says with pride. "Right now we are collecting for El Salvador," she says, "but we know there is hunger and need around us here in Florida, too, and we are planning to make more new projects to get food to the hungry right here."

LEARNING SKILLS, EARNING FRIENDS Yennifer has learned many skills along the way. "We have made posters and speeches to tell others what we are doing and what we need from them. I am drawing posters," she says. "I like to do that. No, I *love* it. We've also had to talk to the principal and teachers and other people like that and get hooked up with the community. We found churches willing to help send the boxes to El Salvador," she says in an empowered voice. "And I feel better about myself because I can reach out and do something to make a difference. You can, too."

YENNIFER'S STORY

1. What values has Yennifer put into action?
2. How did listening to other people's stories of hunger inspire Yennifer to reach out to help others?

YOUR STORY

1. What steps can you take to address hunger in your own school or community? What support might you need to help you to accomplish this goal?
2. What skills and benefits to your self-esteem can you gain in the process of helping others?

TEENS MAKING A DIFFERENCE **143**

Teens Making a Difference

Fulfilling Dreams

Discussion. Encourage students to share their reactions to Yennifer's story. Inform students that Yennifer, a freshman in high school, grew up in El Salvador and has vivid memories of seeing kids hungry on the streets. Fueled by these images and her parents' stories, she has plans to help people in the future. She would like to be a scientist or a doctor. She would like to get involved with foundations and organizations like Aspira that help teens set goals and overcome difficulties.

Next, read the following additional quotes from Yennifer aloud and ask for students to react to each and apply her words to their own lives or experience.

- I don't want to be a doctor or scientist to have money but because I want to help my people and other peoples, too.
- I want to thank all the people who work in Aspira or foundations like that who are helping teens, hungry and otherwise, because they are doing a great job. They help us if we need orientation on how we can do things. They help us find ways to reach our goals and to make our dreams come true.

Class Activity. Have students cut out pictures of starving or malnourished people from magazines or newspapers. Ask each student to write a story about how these people can be helped through caring and compassion.

Answers. *Yennifer's Story*
1. Any or all of the following: caring, responsibility, compassion, concern, generosity, kindness, initiative, and civic duty.
2. Her parents' stories inspired her, moving her to help others.

Responses. *Your Story* **1.–2.** Answers will vary. Encourage students to discuss their ideas with other classmates before writing their responses to these questions.

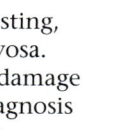

PERSONAL HEALTH

SIGNS OF ANOREXIA NERVOSA. Fasting, if uncontrolled, can lead to anorexia nervosa. This eating disorder may result in severe damage to one's health or even in death. Early diagnosis and care improve the chance for recovery, although recovery is long. Some signs of anorexia nervosa are low caloric intake, extreme interest in food, obsessive involvement in strenuous activity, intense fear of being obese, inaccurate image of one's body, attitude of extreme perfectionism, emotional problems, extreme weight loss, constipation, and, for females, absence of menstrual periods.

Helping a Friend with an Eating Disorder

keeping Fit

Select students to develop a plan for a campaign to encourage teens who suffer from eating disorders to get professional help. The plan might include posters, guest speakers, and newspaper articles. Encourage students to carry out the campaign.

ASSESS

EVALUATING THE LESSON

Assign and discuss the Lesson 2 Review; then administer, grade, and discuss the *Lesson 18 Quiz* in the TCR. ☞

RETEACHING

- Have students identify products that claim quick and easy weight loss. Ask: Why are these claims likely to be false?
- Ask students to complete *Reteaching Activity 18* in the TCR. ☞

ENRICHMENT

- Tell students to find out how starvation (from anorexia) or dehydration (from bulimia) affects the body. Have them determine why lack of food or water ultimately causes death.
- Impress upon students the need to avoid self-destructive behaviors in an attempt to meet unrealistic beauty standards and have them complete *Enrichment Activity 6*, "The Dangers of Fad Diets," in the TCR. ☞

CLOSE

Encourage students to recognize and understand the factors that influence an individual's body image. Discuss ways to deal with peer pressure and media messages that are related to body image.

Bulimia Nervosa

Bulimia nervosa is *a disorder in which cycles of overeating are followed by some form of purging or clearing of the digestive tract.* Often the person with bulimia follows a restrictive diet, then binges—or quickly eats large quantities of food—when hungry. This behavior is followed by self-induced vomiting or purging through abuse of laxatives. After a binge a person may try to follow a severely restrictive diet in order to restore a sense of control and avoid the possibility of weight gain.

The desire to become thin, more attractive, and more physically perfect can be overwhelming until vomiting or purging becomes a daily routine. Associated with this behavior may be the misguided notion that once the perfect figure is attained, everything in life will be fine. Bulimics are often secretive, but know they have a problem.

Bingeing, purging, or fasting should never be viewed as a smart way to control weight. Bulimia can lead to serious health problems—even death. Vomiting and diarrhea can lead to dehydration, kidney damage, and irregular heartbeat. Chronic vomiting erodes tooth enamel, causes tooth decay, and damages tissue of the stomach, esophagus, and mouth. Because laxative abuse interferes with digestion and absorption, nutrient deficiencies may occur. Laxative abuse can also lead to serious damage of blood composition.

Anorexia and bulimia are not diseases; they are symptoms of other problems. Both are psychological in nature. People suffering from these disorders need medical help and qualified counseling immediately. Recovery is a long process, but early diagnosis and care improve the chance of recovery.

If you believe a friend has symptoms of anorexia or bulimia, advise your school nurse, or, in a caring way, encourage your friend to get help. Do not try to counsel your friend yourself.

LESSON 2 *Review*

Reviewing Facts and Vocabulary

1. Give three examples of an unhealthful weight-loss plan.
2. Describe what is meant by the term *weight cycling*.

Thinking Critically

3. *Analyzing.* What influences do you think might lead a person to be at risk for anorexia?
4. *Synthesizing.* If you had a friend who might have an eating disorder, what could you do to help?

Applying Health Skills

5. *In Your School.* Using library resources, write a research report on eating disorders. Consider reading about celebrities who have struggled with such problems and how they deal with them. Share your findings with the class.

Lesson 2 Review

Answers to Reviewing Facts and Vocabulary

1. Eating only one food, fasting, liquid protein diets, diet pills.
2. Weight cycling is the cycle of losing, regaining, losing, and regaining weight.

Answers to Thinking Critically

3. Media images, genetic factors, social pressures, low self-esteem.
4. Encourage your friend to share her or his feelings, and then help your friend find adult or professional help.

Nutrition for Individual Needs

Are you physically active? Do you engage in sports in and out of school and in other physically demanding activities? In this lesson you will explore the special nutritional requirements of athletes, vegetarians, and two other groups of people with special nutritional needs—aging persons and pregnant women.

HEALTH TERMS

electrolytes

rehydration

carbohydrate loading

vegans

nutrient supplements

megadoses

HEALTH CONCEPTS

- Nutrient-dense foods contribute to an athlete's diet by providing energy as well as nutrients.
- The vegetarian diet offers a number of benefits, although vegetarians need to ensure that they get all the necessary nutrients.
- Aging persons and pregnant women have special dietary needs.

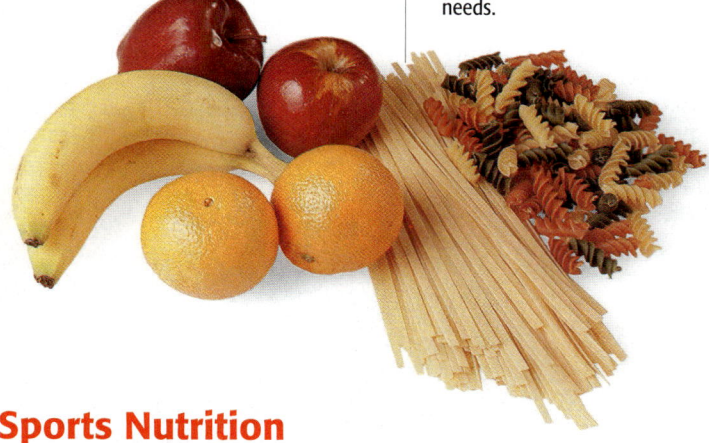

Sports Nutrition

Are you a serious athlete? Do you engage in basketball or tennis? Do you swim for fun and relaxation? No matter what type of athlete you are, good nutrition can help you do your best. Smart food choices can help you reach your top physical performance.

The Training Diet

No one food or nutrient builds muscles or increases speed. The best training diet is balanced, moderate, and varied. Athletic training does not significantly alter the body's requirements for protein, vitamins, or minerals. The main difference is the athlete's increased need for calories, or food energy. Nutrient-dense foods are the best sources of energy and nutrients together.

LESSON 3   NUTRITION FOR INDIVIDUAL NEEDS   **145**

Lesson 3 Resources

TEACHER'S CLASSROOM RESOURCES

- **Concept Map** Activity 19
- **Decision-Making** Activity 6
- **Lesson 19 Quiz**
- **Lesson Plan 19**
- **Reteaching** Activity 19

STUDENT WORKBOOK

- **Applying Health Skills 19**
- **Chapter Study Guide 6**
- **Vocabulary** Activity 6

MULTIMEDIA

- **ABCNews InterActive™ VHS/Videodisc,** *Food and Nutrition*

Nutrition for Individual Needs

FOCUS

LESSON OBJECTIVES

After studying this lesson, students should be able to

- discuss special problems related to athletics and nutrition.
- identify and explain sports nutrition myths.
- discuss the possible benefits and risks of a vegetarian diet to one's health.
- identify health conditions or stages of life when nutrient supplements may be beneficial as well as the risks associated with some supplements.

MOTIVATOR

Write the following statement on the chalkboard: *Athletes should eat differently than nonathletes.*

INTRODUCING THE LESSON

Ask students if they agree or disagree with the statement provided in the Motivator. Let a few volunteers support their reasoning. Tell students that the dietary concerns of athletes and other individuals with specific concerns, such as vegetarians, will be discussed in this lesson.

INTRODUCING HEALTH TERMS

- Have students write a paragraph using the terms *electrolytes* and *rehydration* that advises athletes about a healthful training diet.
- Distribute and have students complete Vocabulary Activity 6 and Chapter Study Guide 6 in the *Student Workbook.*

TEACH

L2 Discussing

Ask the class why there is so much misinformation regarding athletes and dieting. *(People look for quick, easy answers to gain more speed, strength, etc.)*

L1 Explaining

Let students explain what being an athlete involves. Ask: Is a training diet appropriate only for teens who participate in organized sports? Encourage students to clarify and support their answers.

L1 Personal Involvement

Encourage students to consider their own fluid intake before, during, and after their workouts. What could they do to help maintain a healthy level of hydration? How might those changes improve their workouts and their overall feelings of good health?

L2 Researching

Ask volunteers to research the specific symptoms and dangers associated with dehydration and with heatstroke. How are the two different? How can these conditions be recognized? How should they be treated? Let the volunteers discuss their findings with the rest of the class.

L1 Class Activity

Have students brainstorm a list of sports or other activities in which weight is considered important; record their ideas on the board. Then, let students divide the activities into two lists: one in which participants strive to keep their weight down, and the other in which participants try to keep their weight up.

Physical activity requires an increase in fluids, especially during hot weather, to prevent dehydration and heatstroke. Dehydration leads to an imbalance of **electrolytes.** These are *minerals that become electrically charged when in solution*—as they are in bodily fluids. Examples of electrolytes include sodium, potassium, and chloride. Electrolytes play an important role in regulating body fluids.

Electrolyte balance requires that the intake of water and electrolytes equal the amounts eliminated through perspiration and body wastes. For an athlete, this means drinking several cups of fluid two hours, and then 15 minutes, before a heavy workout. **Rehydration**, or *restoring lost body fluids*, is important after exercise or competition. Drink two cups of fluid for every pound of body weight lost through sweat. Water is the best source of fluid to replenish losses experienced during exercise.

"Making Weight"

In some sports, maintaining a certain body weight is important. Wrestlers, for example, compete in a specific weight class. In contact sports, a little extra body weight may offer some advantages. Wise athletes meet their weight requirements in a healthful way.

Trying to compete in a weight class that is below your healthy weight can be dangerous. Fasting, crash dieting, or trying to sweat off extra weight before weigh-in can cause dehydration and can compromise performance. Over time, these practices may result in loss of muscle

▶ Following a varied, balanced diet is an essential part of achieving athletic performance.
ACTIVITY List some special concerns an athlete might have in maintaining good nutrition.

MORE ABOUT . . . . .

ATHLETES AND BODY WEIGHT. Body weight is important in many sports. Extra weight is an advantage in football, for example, but sports such as wrestling have weight restrictions. Being lean with good muscle mass is essential for all sports.

Athletes' weight should match their desired weight and remain stable. Crash diets and sweat baths before a weigh-in are unhealthy. They result in fatigue, dehydration, muscle loss, and poor performance. Athletes who need extra weight for contact sports need a slow, steady program of weight gain. Building extra muscle takes time and exercise. Extra body fat, which can be gained more quickly, does not improve strength.

Making Responsible Decisions

Is Making the Right Weight Right?

Terry's boyfriend, Carlos, is the star of the school's varsity wrestling team and a top prospect for a college scholarship. Terry loves the excitement of the sport and is proud of Carlos, but she has mixed emotions. Carlos's natural weight is about 10 pounds over the 157 pounds at which he wrestles. To lose weight before wrestling season,

he severely limits his food intake, exercises, and tries various other tricks. Terry knows that this is not healthy. While trying to lose weight, Carlos becomes irritable, sullen, and sometimes mean. He is counting on winning the scholarship in order to be able to attend college. His coach believes that he would not be successful wrestling in a higher weight class. Terry has spoken to

Carlos about her concerns. He says he has the situation under control, but he really doesn't. What should Terry do?

What Would You Do?

Apply the six steps of the decision-making process to Terry's problem.

1. **State the situation.**
2. **List the options.**
3. **Weigh the possible outcomes.**
4. **Consider your values.**
5. **Make a decision and act.**
6. **Evaluate the decision.**

---

mass, too. If you must lose weight, follow the sensible plan—one-half to one pound (0.2 to 0.5 kg) a week.

Athletes who train to gain weight need to eat in a healthful way and to exercise to build muscle mass. Extra calories should come mainly from nutrient-dense foods. Slow, steady weight gain, no more than two pounds (0.9 kg) a week, is best. Using hormones such as steroids to increase muscle mass is not healthy. Hormones may stunt growth and damage the body's reproductive system.

Eating Before Competitions

Many athletes ask, "What should I eat before competing, and how far ahead of the event?" Eating three to four hours before an event allows the stomach to empty, yet keeps the athlete free from hunger pangs while competing.

Before competing, choose a meal high in carbohydrates and low in fat and protein. Fats and proteins stay in the digestive tract too long. Good sources of carbohydrates are pasta, rice, breads, vegetables, and fruits. Drinking plenty of fluids before a workout is important, too.

Carbohydrates are stored in the body in the form of glycogen. Athletes who participate in endurance sports, such as cross-country running or long-distance bicycling, may benefit by **carbohydrate**

CURRICULUM CONNECTIONS

FAMILY AND CONSUMER SCIENCES. Team up with a food and nutrition class for a demonstration of nutrient-dense vs. empty-calorie foods. Also, have students gather recipes for pre-competition meals and nutritious fluids.

SCIENCE. Have students research the ingredients in sports drinks and report their

findings to the class. Ask them to contrast the use of sports drinks and water in providing necessary fluids for athletes.

LANGUAGE ARTS. Help students write letters to their favorite athletes, asking about their training diets and pre-competition meals.

Making Responsible Decisions

1. Terry is concerned that her boyfriend's efforts to keep his weight down for wrestling are jeopardizing his health.
2. Terry can (a) try to put more pressure on Carlos, (b) ignore the problem, or (c) talk with Carlos' coach or another trusted adult.
3. Terry might (a) find that Carlos resents her pressure but she also might succeed in getting Carlos to improve his health, (b) continue to worry that Carlos is hurting his own health, but avoid stirring up his anger or resentment, (c) succeed in getting an adult to help Carlos change his habits, but risk making Carlos angry at her intrusions.
4. Terry values her relationship with Carlos; she also values his health.
5. Responses will vary.
6. Remind students to evaluate both the short- and long-term consequences of their decisions.

L2 Decision Making

For further study on making responsible decisions, assign *Decision-Making Activity 6* in the TCR.

L1 Discussing

Ask students to identify specific nutrient-dense foods. Ask: Which of these foods do you like? How can you incorporate more of these foods into your daily diet? Are nutrient-dense foods good only for athletes who are training to gain weight? Why or why not?

L2 Class Activity

Let students form small cooperative groups, and have each group select a competitive sports event, such as a track meet, a volleyball game, or a gymnastics competition. Have group members work together to plan a specific meal for an athlete to eat before the competition.

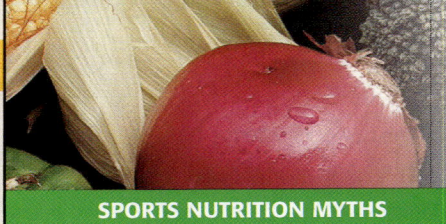
L2 Researching

Have students do library research to refute these common sports nutrition myths: (1) Honey provides immediate energy. (2) Sucking ice before a workout will prevent dehydration. (3) Taking a salt tablet will help prevent dehydration.

L1 Discussing

Help students identify and discuss the reasons people give for accepting or rejecting vegetarianism. Encourage students to share their responses to each suggested reason. Ask volunteers to explain their own reasons for following (or for choosing not to follow) a vegetarian diet.

L2 Demonstrating

Let interested students work together to write a weeklong eating plan for a vegetarian (or vegan) teen. Encourage students to include a variety of foods that provide a balanced diet and include adequate amounts of iron, zinc, and B vitamins.

L3 Researching

Ask volunteers to read about heart-healthy programs that advocate a very low-fat vegetarian diet (for example, that described by Dr. Dean Ornish). Ask: What are the other essential elements of the program? What results has the program recorded? What problems, if any, are associated with the program?

L1 Discussing

Have students share their responses to these questions: Do you think vegan parents should limit the diets of their very young children to exclude all nonplant foods? Why or why not?

loading, or *storing extra glycogen in the muscle,* before strenuous exercise. Several days ahead, the athlete eats a high-carbohydrate diet to store plenty of muscle glycogen. At the same time, training is tapered and often eliminated the day before the event to allow for maximum glycogen storage. Carbohydrate loading is not advised for teen athletes. Growing bodies are still developing and need an even balance of nutrients. Glycogen storage upsets this necessary balance.

SPORTS NUTRITION MYTHS

MYTH Vitamin pills give extra energy.
FACT Because vitamins do not supply calories, extra amounts will not give extra energy.

MYTH Consuming extra protein or taking amino acid supplements build extra muscle.
FACT The only way to build muscle mass and strength is through exercise.

MYTH Eating a high-fat, high-protein meal before competition improves performance.
FACT A high-fat, high-protein meal will not digest as quickly as one high in carbohydrates and will lower performance.

MYTH Eating a candy bar before a workout provides quick energy.
FACT Energy for physical activity comes from foods you ate several days, not an hour or so, before a workout.

MYTH Drinking tea, colas, or coffee before a workout will improve performance.
FACT All three beverages contain caffeine, which can cause headaches, stomach upset, nervousness, irritability, and diarrhea.

hotlink

lifestyle diseases For more information on lifestyle diseases, as well as their causes and dangers, see Chapter 31, page 676.

Vegetarianism

More and more Americans, including teenagers, are choosing to follow a vegetarian eating pattern. Those who avoid eating meat, fish, and poultry but eat dairy foods and eggs are called lacto-ovo vegetarians. *Lacto* refers to milk, and *ovo* refers to eggs. Some people turn to vegetarianism out of concern for the environment or for the conditions under which food animals are raised and slaughtered. Others have a belief in nonviolence or a desire for a healthier lifestyle.

Vegetarian eating can have health benefits. By reducing saturated fats and cholesterol from animal products, vegetarians may reduce the risk of **lifestyle diseases** such as heart disease, high blood pressure, and some forms of cancer. Be aware, however, that vegetarians still need to watch fat intake.

At the same time, following a vegetarian food style requires greater nutritional awareness. Vegetarians must take care to consume incomplete proteins in a way that will yield complete protein during the day. It is not necessary to have the combinations at one meal as once believed, but just sometime during the day. Vegetarians must also be sure they are getting enough iron, zinc, and B vitamins. The key to a healthful vegetarian diet is to eat a wide variety of foods in adequate amounts, including fruits, vegetables, leafy greens, whole-grain products, nuts, seeds, and legumes, as well as dairy foods and eggs.

Vegans

Most vegetarians eat dairy products and eggs. The type of vegetarians known as **vegans** (VEE-gunz)—*vegetarians who eat only foods of plant origin*—do not. Because animal products are the only food sources of vitamin B_{12}, vegans must supplement their food choices with vitamin B_{12}. Since vegans do not use milk or other dairy products, they must make sure to get adequate vitamin D and calcium from other sources.

148 CHAPTER 6 FOOD AND YOUR HEALTH

PROMOTING COMPREHENSIVE SCHOOL HEALTH

THE TEAM. Under the comprehensive school health program, each campus would have a site-based decision-making committee comprised of teachers, campus staff, parents, community members, and business representatives. In addition to academic performance objectives, plans related to students' physical and psychological needs must also be addressed. Schools might already have a drop-out prevention committee working together with school/community drug prevention committees. These committees can also focus on the students' academic performance as related to health. For more detailed information about developing such a program, consult *Promoting a Comprehensive School Health Program* in the TCR.

Nutrient Supplements

Will the time ever come when people can get all the nourishment they need from pills? Probably not, but nutrient supplements *can* provide dependable sources of some vitamins and minerals. **Nutrient supplements** are *pills, powders, liquids and other nonfood forms of nutrients.* Under some health conditions or during certain stages of life, some groups of people may benefit from nutrient supplements. These groups include pregnant women and the elderly.

▶ *Looking at the Issues*

Nutrient Supplements, Pro and Con

Annual sales of nutrient supplements have more than doubled during the last decade. This growth has spurred a debate among nutrition experts and supplement manufacturers.

ANALYZING DIFFERENT VIEWPOINTS

▶ **Viewpoint One**

Most nutrition experts are in agreement that basic nutritional needs for most people can be met by following the guidelines of the Food Guide Pyramid. Foods, they argue, also contain substances your body requires that supplements do not provide, such as fiber and phytochemicals, including beta carotene, lycopene, and others. Eating some vegetables such as broccoli and cabbage, appear to lessen the risks of some types of cancer. No nutrient supplements can make the same claim. Moreover, some supplements, such as melatonin, are potentially dangerous. At present, labeling of nutrient supplements is regulated by the FDA for the protection of the consumer. However, the FDA is not responsible for determining the effectiveness of supplements.

▶ **Viewpoint Two**

Supplement manufacturers note that antioxidant vitamins—vitamins C and E and beta carotene—may help reduce the risk of diseases and illnesses such as some cancers, heart disease, cataracts, and even the common cold. Yet, they say, to get the amount of antioxidants needed through food, a person would have to consume many more servings of fruits and vegetables than most people consume. The only way they say to ensure an adequate amount is through taking nutrient supplements.

EXPLORING YOUR VIEWS

1. Do you agree that healthful eating can give you all the vitamins and other nutrients you need, or do you feel that you should also take nutrient supplements? Explain your response.

2. A spokesperson for the American Dietetic Association has stated: "If you decide you have met your nutritional needs by taking a few tablets in the morning, you may not pay attention to how you eat the rest of the day." Do you agree or disagree?

▶ *Looking at the Issues*

Nutrient Supplements, Pro and Con

Ask students to indicate, by a show of hands, whether they took a vitamin pill or other nutrient supplement this morning. Let volunteers explain why they do—or do not—take such supplements regularly. Then have students read the feature to learn more about nutrient supplements and about attitudes toward them. Ask students to write their responses to the two Views questions and compare their opinions with those of other students.

L1 Family Involvement

Suggest that students discuss their own ideas about nutritional supplements with other family members. Which family members—if any—should be taking supplements regularly? Why? Which family members should be encouraged to follow a balanced eating plan and avoid nutritional supplements?

L1 Guest Speaker

Invite a local obstetrician or nurse-midwife to speak to the class, explaining the dietary recommendations he or she usually makes to pregnant patients. If the health care provider gives dietary lists or handouts to patients, ask that these be shared with students. Also, ask the health professional to explain whether and why he or she recommends prenatal vitamins for most patients.

HEALTH LITERACY

CRITICAL THINKER. Assign students to examine articles in general-interest and home-oriented magazines for a period of four weeks. Tell them to pay particular attention to the magazines displayed in supermarket lines. Have them record the number of featured articles about nutrient supplements, as well as features giving recipes for nutrient-rich foods. Encourage them to compare the frequency of these types of articles with the frequency of articles on any other topic. Have them write up their conclusions about the public's relationship with nutrition and food.

Direct students to the site on nutrients in Web Links for this chapter. Have students work in groups. Assign each group a nutrient to find out its benefits, common food sources, and note the symptoms of deficiency or toxicity warnings.

ASSESS

EVALUATING THE LESSON

Assign and discuss the Lesson 3 Review; then administer, grade, and discuss the *Lesson 19 Quiz* in the TCR. 📖

RETEACHING

- Have students identify the specific dietary concerns of athletes and how these concerns are best met.
- Have students describe the health benefits of a vegetarian diet. Why must vegetarians have a greater awareness of nutrition?
- Ask students to complete *Reteaching Activity 19* in the TCR. 📖

ENRICHMENT

Direct students to plan a day's menu for a vegetarian diet. Ask them to highlight the combinations of foods that would provide a complete protein.

CLOSE

Remind students that a diet that meets the guidelines provided by the Food Guide Pyramid will meet the majority of their needs. Emphasize that nutrition supplements generally are not needed except under certain health conditions and during certain stages of life.

To learn more about food and your health, including facts about nutrient supplements, visit **health.glencoe.com**.

Nutrition During Pregnancy

Healthful eating is an important aspect of prenatal care, along with avoiding tobacco, alcohol, and other drugs. Pregnant women have somewhat increased nutritional needs because they are supplying nutrients for the developing fetus as well as their own additional needs. In particular, they may need more iron, calcium, and folic acid.

Nutrition and Aging

A Tufts University study on nutrition and aging reveals that people 60 and older may need even more of certain vitamins—B_6 and vitamin D, for example—than young adults do. Older adults may not be able to process and synthesize vital nutrients as efficiently as younger people. In addition, some medications commonly prescribed for the elderly can interfere with nutrient absorption. Nutrient supplements may therefore be beneficial for older adults.

Risks Associated with Nutrient Supplements

With vitamins, as with nutrition as a whole, moderation is the key. **Megadoses**, or *very large amounts of nutrient supplements*, are potentially dangerous. Excess amounts of the fat-soluble vitamins A, D, E, and K, for example, stay in the body and become toxic. Too much vitamin A can lead to liver damage, hair loss, blurred vision, and headaches. Excess vitamin C puts a heavy strain on the kidneys.

Throughout the teen years and much of adulthood, the safest and most healthful approach to getting the micronutrients you need is through the foods you eat.

LESSON 3 *Review*

Reviewing Facts and Vocabulary

1. What types of foods should be included in the best training diet for athletes?
2. Compare the lacto-ovo vegetarian and vegan eating patterns.
3. Give three examples of situations in which nutrient supplements might be beneficial.

Thinking Critically

4. *Evaluating.* Describe the diet of a vegetarian, an athlete, and a pregnant female. Decide whether or not it is healthful and explain why.

5. *Evaluating.* Determine whether or not doubling protein intake is a good method of building muscles.

Applying Health Skills

6. *In Your School.* From what you know about nutrition and the Food Guide Pyramid, plan a sample one-day menu to be followed by a member of one of your school's athletic teams who is in training. Find out the athlete's average level of calorie expenditure and food preferences.

Lesson 3 Review

Answers to Reviewing Facts and Vocabulary

1. Nutrient-dense foods are the best for athletes.
2. Lacto-ovo vegetarians eat dairy foods and eggs. Vegans eat only foods of plant origin.
3. Nutrient supplements can be beneficial for pregnant women, for the elderly, and during illness when it might not be possible to consume an adequate, balanced diet.

Answers to Thinking Critically

4. Answers will vary.
5. An increase in the amount of protein you eat won't build muscles. Muscles are built by exercise and a balanced, nutritious diet.

Protecting Yourself from Food Problems

Most of the foods you eat have food labels to help you make informed food choices and reduce health risks associated with certain foods. Yet, some risks are not reflected on these labels. How can you be sure the food you eat is safe? In this lesson, you will learn ways to protect yourself from food-related problems.

HEALTH TERMS

foodborne illness
contaminant
pasteurized
perishable
cross-contamination
food allergy
food intolerance

HEALTH CONCEPTS

- Foodborne illness can be caused by bacteria.
- Specific safety measures can be taken to limit the spread of foodborne pathogens and to help avoid cross-contamination.
- Food allergies stem from additives as well as from various kinds of foods.

Food Safety

Food safety has been described as one of the major health problems. Foodborne illness is on the rise. More than 6 million Americans suffer from foodborne illness each year, and the incidence may be much higher.

Foodborne Illness

Foodborne illness, or *food poisoning*, often comes from eating food that has come in contact with a **contaminant**, *a substance that spoils or infects.* In most cases, the contaminant is a bacteria, a parasite, or virus. These bacteria cannot be seen, smelled, or tasted. The best protection against foodborne illness is knowledge of the causes of contamination and ways to keep food safe.

LESSON 4   PROTECTING YOURSELF FROM FOOD PROBLEMS   **151**

Lesson 4 Resources

TEACHER'S CLASSROOM RESOURCES
- **Concept Map** Activity 20
- **Lesson 20 Quiz**
- **Lesson Plan 20**
- **Reteaching** Activity 20

STUDENT WORKBOOK
- **Applying Health Skills 20**

- **Chapter Study Guide 6**
- **Vocabulary** Activity 6

TRANSPARENCIES
- **Transparency 17**

MULTIMEDIA
- **ABCNews InterActive™ VHS/Videodisc,** *Food and Nutrition*

Protecting Yourself from Food Problems

FOCUS

LESSON OBJECTIVES

After studying this lesson, students should be able to

- identify symptoms of foodborne illness.
- describe ways to select and handle food safely.
- differentiate food allergy from food intolerance.

MOTIVATOR

Write the following on the chalkboard for students to work on while attendance is being taken: *Describe a time when you, a family member, or a friend experienced a foodborne illness. Name the cause, the symptoms, and the treatment.*

INTRODUCING THE LESSON

Have students share their responses to the Motivator. Tell them that they will learn more about food safety and food sensitivities in the lesson.

INTRODUCING HEALTH TERMS

- Instruct students to find newspaper and magazine articles that use as many of the vocabulary terms as possible. Select some of the articles to have students read to the class.
- Ask students to complete Vocabulary Activity 6 and Chapter Study Guide 6 in the *Student Workbook.*

TEACH

LD Explaining

Due to high-level vocabulary, LD students may have difficulty reading this lesson independently. Point out specifics that you expect them to learn during class discussions.

L1 Class Activity

Arrange with the school cafeteria manager for the class to tour the cafeteria. Ask students to prepare a list of questions pertinent to food safety prior to the tour. After the tour, discuss their observations, and ask for volunteers to send a note of appreciation to the manager.

L1 Discussing

Use *Transparency 17* to review procedures of keeping food safe.

Building Health Skills

Analyzing Messages about Food and Food Safety
Skill: Accessing Reliable Information

Introduce this feature by showing (or describing) two magazine articles that present different points of view on the same food product, such as bran. Ask: Which of these articles are you more likely to believe and act on? Why? Then have students read the feature to learn more about evaluating such information and the sources of that information. As a follow-up, ask students to bring to class newspaper or magazine articles about food and food safety; let them work in groups to discuss and evaluate the information in each article.

Causes and Symptoms of Foodborne Illness

There are two main ways that food can become contaminated:

■ Animals raised or caught for food may harbor disease organisms in their tissues. If meat or milk from such an animal is eaten without being thoroughly cooked or **pasteurized**—*treated by a process of heating to destroy or slow the growth of pathogens*—the organisms may cause illness.

■ Food may be contaminated with bacteria spread from an infected person or animal.

Foodborne illnesses related to food spoilage are commonly caused by bacteria: *Salmonella, Staphylococcus aureus, Clostridium perfringens, Escherichia coli (E. coli),* and *Clostridium botulinum.* The last, which

Building Health Skills

Analyzing Messages About Food and Food Safety

NEWSPAPER, MAGAZINE, TELEVISION, and radio reports advise people about food and food safety on an almost daily basis. Trying to sort through all these messages can be confusing. Sometimes reports from different sources contain conflicting information. How can you tell whether the information is reliable? Which warnings should you pay attention to? The following tips can help you decide.

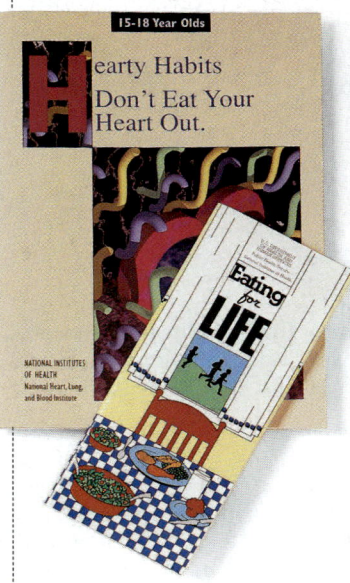

1. **Consider the source.** Where does the message come from? Information from sources such as the FDA or U.S. Department of Health are likely to be more reliable than information from a manufacturer trying to market a product. Reliable sources, such as the FDA, often have authority. They generally use scientific evidence to back up the information or warning.

2. **Consider the risk group.** Are you at risk, or is the problem limited to a specific group, such as aging people, or to a certain area of the country? For example, if you might have food that has been shipped from an area with a problem, such as contaminated strawberries from California, you need to check the source of the food.

3. **Consider the specifics.** Sometimes manufacturers recall batches of a product that may be unsafe. Most manufactured products, such as canned goods, have lot numbers. If there is a problem with a specific batch, you need to check lot numbers and discard or return any items with the lot number that is being recalled.

4. **Consider the nature of scientific research.** Messages about food and food safety can change as researchers discover new information. Early findings can be contradicted by later findings. Different researchers might even interpret the same findings in different ways! Look at their conclusions as guidelines, not established fact.

152 CHAPTER 6   FOOD AND YOUR HEALTH

CURRICULUM CONNECTIONS

SCIENCE. Working with the science department, provide slides or pictures of the bacteria that cause food poisoning. Ask students to describe these bacteria and compare their properties.

SOCIAL STUDIES. Food safety standards vary from country to country. Let students research foodborne illnesses occurring in various parts of the world. Have them create a bulletin-board exhibit, using a world map to point out places where these illnesses are most prevalent. Ask students to locate newspaper and magazine articles about food safety and foodborne illnesses to use as part of their exhibit.

causes botulism, is found in improperly canned or preserved food. Botulism is especially dangerous, because it can be fatal.

Common symptoms of foodborne illness include nausea, vomiting, diarrhea, fever, and body aches. Since many of these symptoms are similar to those of the flu, foodborne illness is sometimes hard to diagnose. Most people recover from the symptoms in a few days. For the elderly, very young, and individuals who are malnourished or have problems with their immune system, however, foodborne illness can be serious.

Minimizing Risks of Foodborne Illness

Bacteria need three conditions for growth: nutrients, moisture, and warmth. Bacteria in food multiply rapidly between 40° and 140° F (4.4° and 60° C). At these temperatures, bacteria double in number in 30 minutes.

You can keep food safe by selecting and handling it with care. The U.S. Department of Agriculture has identified six critical control points that can limit foodborne illness:

1. **Buying.** Do not buy or eat food with damaged packaging, dents, cracks, bulging lids, or popped safety buttons. Make sure meat and poultry products are refrigerated when purchased. Keep packages of raw meat and poultry separate from other foods. Refrigerate foods that are **perishable,** or *liable to spoil,* within one hour.

2. **Home Storage.** Refrigerate or freeze meat and poultry immediately. Wash your hands before and after handling any raw meat, poultry, or seafood. Store foods according to package instructions.

3. **Pre-preparation.** Thaw meat in the refrigerator, *never* at room temperature. Bacteria can grow rapidly at certain temperatures. Avoid **cross-contamination**—*the spreading of bacteria from one food to another*—by washing your hands before and after handling food. In addition, wash work surfaces and utensils immediately after use. Do not let juices from raw meat, poultry, or seafood come in contact with cooked foods or foods that will be eaten raw.

4. **Cooking.** Always cook food thoroughly. Use a meat thermometer to determine whether food has reached a safe internal temperature. Cook food thoroughly, then refrigerate and reheat it if necessary.

Washing cutting boards and other equipment in hot, soapy water can prevent cross-contamination of foods.

ACTIVITY *Explain why juices from raw meat, poultry, or seafood should not come in contact with other foods.*

LESSON 4   PROTECTING YOURSELF FROM FOOD PROBLEMS   **153**

LEP **Class Activity**

Allow a volunteer to demonstrate correct hand-washing techniques and how to avoid cross-contamination of food. Have other students critique the demonstration.

L1 **Discussing**

Hands can be carriers of contamination. Lead students in brainstorming a list of other sources of kitchen contamination, such as pots and pans, towels, aprons, countertops, cutting boards, hair, insects, etc.

L2 **Community Involvement**

Request permission for a small group of students to visit a local food market. Have the group observe the precautions taken in the market to prevent foodborne illness. Ask students to share their findings with the class and to discuss whether or not some precautionary techniques they observed should be improved.

L3 **Community Involvement**

Select volunteers to visit several local restaurants. Have them learn what precautions are taken by restaurants to decrease the likelihood of foodborne illness or contamination. Ask them to find answers to questions such as: What government agency is involved locally in regulating food production and cleanliness? What procedure is used to determine how clean a restaurant is? What state guidelines exist that govern procedures and standards of food cleanliness and safety?

FOOD AND NUTRITION (Side 1)
Chapter 10: Kitchen Survival Skills

Frames 28651-33042

L1 Cooperative Learning

Divide the class into three groups. Ask each group to plan a meal for a barbecue, a family holiday, or a formal dinner. After the menus are selected, have students identify what measures they would take with each food or dish to prevent foodborne illness. Discuss each group's menu and precautions.

L1 Personal Involvement

Ask volunteers to check the temperature in their refrigerators and freezers at home. Have them find out if the temperatures are adequate to prevent foodborne illness and food spoilage.

L2 Community Involvement

Have several students visit a supermarket to survey the ingredient lists of packaged cookies and crackers. Ask them to list specific products (if any) that someone with an allergy to wheat could eat. Request that they share their findings with the class.

L1 Discussing

Have volunteers discuss allergic reactions they have had to food products. Ask: Did you know what caused the reaction? How did you find out? How long have you had the allergy?

5. **Serving.** Keep hot foods hot (above 160° F; 71.2° C) and cold foods cold (below 40° F; 4.4° C). Never leave perishable foods at room temperature for more than two hours.

6. **Handling Leftovers.** Refrigerate leftovers within two hours of cooking. Put dates on containers before refrigerating. When reheating leftovers, reheat thoroughly. Throw away suspicious foods without tasting them. Remember, if in doubt, throw it out!

Food Sensitivities

Many people experience abnormal reactions to a food substance or food additive. These reactions may stem from a sensitivity to certain foods or from a specific physiological response to a food or food additive.

Food Allergies

Do you have itchy eyes and sneeze during hay fever season? Have you ever developed a raised welt from an insect bite? These are signs of an *allergy*. An allergy is the body's reaction to an irritating substance or a toxin. Foods can also cause an allergic reaction in some people. With a true **food allergy**, *the body's immune system overreacts to substances in some foods*. These substances, called allergens, are usually proteins. The immune system responds to them as it would to **pathogens**, or foreign invaders. The body produces antibodies for defense against these substances.

hotlink

pathogens For more information on pathogens and their role in infectious diseases, see Chapter 28, page 620.

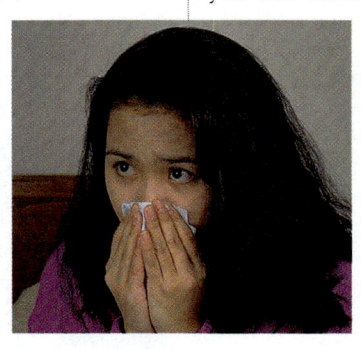

▶ *Foods such as bleu cheese, soy sauce, milk, eggs, nuts, and wheat can cause allergic reactions.*

ACTIVITY *How would you advise a person to find out about a reaction to a particular food item?*

154 CHAPTER 6 FOOD AND YOUR HEALTH

HOME AND COMMUNITY CONNECTION

Encourage students to evaluate their kitchens at home for precautions against food-borne illness. Are different cutting boards used both for animal foods and for foods that are to be eaten raw? Are raw meats kept separate from other foods? Are nonporous, quick-drying items used for cleaning dishes and surfaces whenever possible? Are cleaning cloths washed in the washing machine with hot water after each use? Do family members avoid the use of items such as sponges that are porous and remain wet long enough to breed microorganisms? Do those in the family who cook wash their hands after handling raw meat and before handling other foods? Are hot foods kept hot and cold foods cold? Are leftovers refrigerated promptly?

The foods that cause most food allergies are nuts, eggs, wheat, and soy. Fish, shellfish, chicken, and tomatoes may also cause problems. Sulfites, or food additives that help preserve food, and certain nutrients, such as monosodium glutamate (MSG), cause allergic reactions in some people. To identify an allergy, doctors ask patients to eliminate certain foods from their diet one at a time or to keep a food diary. They may also conduct tests for antibodies.

Some people with food allergies show no symptoms. Others may experience one or more reactions. These include rash, hives, or itchiness on the skin; vomiting, diarrhea, or abdominal pain; and hay fever-like symptoms in the respiratory tract. In the most serious cases, food allergies can be deadly. If, after eating a food, you experience any of the symptoms described, be sure to consult a health care professional.

Food Intolerance

Food allergy should not be confused with food intolerance. **Food intolerance** is *a negative reaction to a food or an ingredient in food that is not related to the body's immune system or to food poisoning.* It is sometimes caused by irritants such as food additives. It may also be associated with certain foods, such as green peppers or fried foods. Food intolerance can also be caused by an inborn or acquired defect, such as the inability to digest the lactose in milk, called **lactose intolerance**.

hotlink

lactose intolerance For more information on lactose intolerance, see Chapter 18, p. 416.

ASSESS

EVALUATING THE LESSON

Assign and discuss the Lesson 4 Review; then administer, grade, and discuss the *Lesson 20 Quiz* in the TCR.

RETEACHING

- Choose students to make a video of someone pretending to be working in the food service industry. Have them display as many poor food safety habits as possible. Present the video to the class and ask, "What's wrong in this situation?"
- Ask students to complete *Reteaching Activity 20* in the TCR.

ENRICHMENT

Have each student make a checklist that an inspector might use to monitor restaurants for food safety violations.

CLOSE

Divide the class into six groups, and assign each group one of the tips for safe food selection and handling. Have each group rephrase their tip and provide several examples or situations that exemplify their tip.

LESSON 4 *Review*

Reviewing Facts and Vocabulary

1. Define the term *foodborne illness*.
2. What are the common symptoms of foodborne illness?
3. How does the body react in a case of food allergy?

Thinking Critically

4. *Analyzing.* Explain why some people may be more vulnerable to foodborne illness than others.
5. *Synthesizing.* Describe how a doctor might find out whether you are allergic to peanut butter.

Applying Health Skills

6. *In Your Home.* Inspect the contents of your refrigerator at home, and make a list of foods that have sell dates. Next to each item, note how often it is used in your household and whether any product is past its date of use. Discuss with family members a strategy for ensuring that all such purchases are used within the prescribed time frame after purchase.

LESSON 4   PROTECTING YOURSELF FROM FOOD PROBLEMS   **155**

Lesson 4 Review

Answers to Reviewing Facts and Vocabulary

1. Food poisoning caused by bacteria, a parasite, or a virus.
2. Nausea, vomiting, diarrhea, fever, body aches.
3. Rash, hives, itchiness; vomiting, diarrhea, abdominal pain; hay fever-like symptoms in the respiratory tract.

Answers to Thinking Critically

4. Answers will vary.
5. He would tell you not to eat peanut butter for a while to see if symptoms continue. If they stop, he would then tell you to eat it and observe whether symptoms return.

Health **Skills** Activities

Health Skills Activities

ACTIVITY 1
HEALTH SKILLS
Comprehending Health Concepts, Accessing Health Information, Self Management

➤ **National Standards**
This activity meets these National Health Standards: 1.3; 2.1; 4.2; 3.3.

Teach
- Provide students with the promotional information of a well-known weight-loss plan.
- Students should sign up for groups based on individual strengths and areas of interest. Some of the tasks to be represented in each group include Analyst (responsible for leading the group in its assessment of the weight-loss plan), Writer (responsible for doing written and final drafts of the report), and Public Relations Specialist (responsible for working with members of other groups to get the pamphlet into the public eye).

ACTIVITY 2
HEALTH SKILLS
Comprehending Health Concepts, Health Advocacy

➤ **National Standards**
This activity meets these National Health Standards: 1.3; 7.4.

Teach
- Have students identify the similarities and differences among nutrient needs of teens who play sports and those who do not. One way of doing this would be in a Venn diagram, two large overlapping circles, the intersection of which represents similarities.
- While the coach is present in the class, you may want to have him or her talk briefly about dietary recommendations he or she makes to team members. Use this opportunity to explore any misconceptions students may have about the nutrient needs of teen athletes (such as carbohydrate loading, which is not recommended for teens).

Activity 1 — Diet Mania

Today, you see ads for countless weight-loss diets on television and printed in publications. Diet specialists and diet centers everywhere boast plans to "take the weight off." Do these diets really work?

Directions
1. As a small group, examine the weight-loss plan your teacher provides. Note the claims made, along with features such as total calories, food choices, number of meals per day, and so on.
2. Write a report of your findings, describing any health risks and benefits of the plan.
3. Combine your report with those of classmates into a pamphlet titled "The Skinny on Weight-Loss." Offer to leave copies of your pamphlet in the school library and other high-visibility locations in the community.

Time
50 minutes plus outside research and writing time

Materials
library or Internet resources, paper, pen or pencil, computer

Self-Assessment
✓ Analyzed a weight-loss plan using information from the book.
✓ Identified risks and benefits.

Activity 2 — Nutrition for the "Teen Team"

As you have learned, athletes need to watch what they eat in order to achieve peak performance. In a sense, you are a member of a team with special nutrition needs—the "teen team." Prepare a pep talk and eating plan for your team members.

Directions
1. Using your book, review the nutrient needs of teens and teen athletes. Note similarities and differences in terms of the amounts of protein, carbohydrates, and other key nutrients. (Don't forget water—one of the most important, and neglected, nutrients.)
2. Prepare a pep talk, urging members of the teen team in your school to make healthful food choices. Explain the benefits to mental and physical performance in all areas.
3. Distribute copies of your pep talk, or arrange to deliver it over the school PA system.

Time
40 minutes

Materials
paper, pen or pencil

Self-Assessment
✓ Explained at least three performance benefits of healthful eating.
✓ Identified healthful foods consistent with the Food Guide Pyramid.
✓ Provided a clear message using effective persuasive communication strategies.

156 CHAPTER 6   FOOD AND YOUR HEALTH

ASSESSMENT SCORING

Using a four-level rubric, the student has achieved a 4 if:

ACTIVITY 1
✔ Student executed the responsibilities associated with the task chosen.
✔ Student worked cooperatively with group members at carrying out their tasks.
✔ Student correctly analyzed weight-loss plan according to information provided in the text.
✔ Student identified risks and benefits of the weight-loss plan.

ACTIVITY 2
✔ The pep talk produced focuses on the importance of healthful eating for all teens.
✔ Student explained at least three performance benefits of healthful eating.
✔ Food recommendations in the talk were consistent with the Food Guide Pyramid.
✔ The speech has the proper tone and energy associated with pep talks.

Anorexia Warning

Today, Gina has a healthy appetite and a strong self-image. But that wasn't always true. She nearly died from anorexia nervosa. Surprisingly, Gina says she didn't always feel terrible, even though she was starving herself. She often felt like she was "on top of the world."

These feelings are one reason it can be difficult to help people with anorexia. They feel good, even though they aren't getting enough nutrition. Gina says she felt like she was addicted to not eating.

Scientists are studying why anorexia can create feelings of happiness. They are also learning more about why anorexia tends to run in families. This knowledge will help people combat this critical eating disorder.

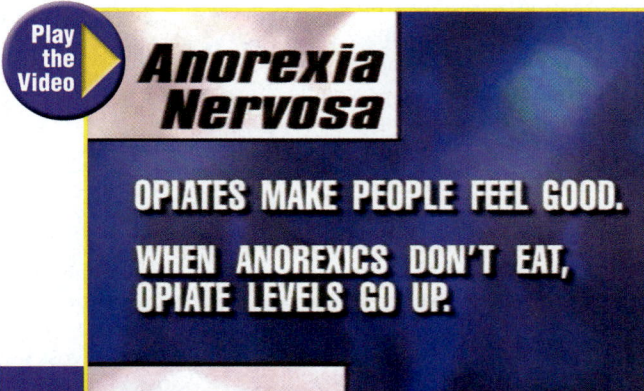

Play the Video

Anorexia Nervosa

OPIATES MAKE PEOPLE FEEL GOOD.

WHEN ANOREXICS DON'T EAT, OPIATE LEVELS GO UP.

CNN. All Rights Reserved.

Think About It

- How did Gina feel when she was anorexic? How did she learn to manage this disorder?
- How can anorexia affect chemicals in the body?
- According to the researcher in the video, what factors do most scientists agree lead to anorexia?
- Why is it important for people with anorexia to get treatment, even if they feel well?

CNN HEALTH NEWS **157**

Anorexia Warning
Video Segment 4 (Time – 2:26)

Objectives. After viewing the video, students should be able to recognize the health dangers of eating disorders and understand the impact these disorders have on a person's life.

Motivator. Begin discussion by talking about how personal histories can help us understand essential health issues. Invite students to consider the difference between reading the facts about a disease and reading a profile about a person who has that disease. Emphasize that both forms of information are necessary to gain a full picture. Then have students view Video Segment 4, "Anorexia Warning," a profile of one student who suffered and recovered from this deadly eating disorder.

Teach

- Have students consider how this video might affect two different audiences: 1) an audience of junior high school students; and 2) an audience of people who have suffered from anorexia
- Point out that both audiences could gain information as well as comfort from the viewing.
- Encourage students to research the warning signs of anorexia. Suggest that they use library and/or Internet sources to compile a list of warning signs to share with classmates.

Role Play. Ask students the following question: "What strategies would you use to help a friend or classmate who shows warning signs of anorexia?" You may wish to have students role play monologues to illustrate their responses. Students can imagine they are talking on the telephone or face to face with a friend or classmate who shows the warning signs of anorexia. Encourage them to improvise ideas freely while a partner jots them down. Then both students can evaluate the list to decide which statements are sensitive and effective.

Close. Have students explain why the video producers decided to do a profile of Gina. Ask students to identify the goal of the report and tell if they think the goal was accomplished.

MORE ABOUT . . . . .

REPORTING THE STORY. The reporter who created this video chose Gina as a case study to give viewers insight into how anorexia affects real people. Such news items are sometimes called human interest stories because they focus on news at a personal, human level.

Have students consider what criteria the reporter used when selecting Gina as a subject for the video. Ask: "What factors make her story universal? What is unique about her story?"

Have students suggest three other health topics that could be reported at the human level. Ask them to tell how reporters might find and select people to profile.

CHECKING COMPREHENSION

- Assign and discuss the chapter review.
- Use the MindJogger Videoquiz to review the chapter. 🔴

CHAPTER 6 REVIEW

Using Health Terms

1. nutrient-dense
2. obesity
3. overweight
4. body mass index
5. undernutrition
6. bulimia nervosa
7. weight cycling
8. anorexia nervosa
9. rehydration
10. megadoses
11. nutrient supplements
12. vegans
13. carbohydrate loading
14. dehydration
15. food allergy
16. pasteurized
17. cross-contamination
18. perishable
19. foodborne illness

Recalling the Facts

1. Excess body fat creates a higher risk of hypertension, diabetes, high blood cholesterol, atherosclerosis, and some cancers.
2. Sedentary lifestyle, poor food habits.
3. Little energy reserves, higher risk for anemia, too few stored protective nutrients to fight off infection or disease.
4. It helps to bring into balance calories consumed vs. calories burned.
5. Lean body tissue lost with body fat is replaced by more body fat, which burns fewer calories than muscle does. The person then requires fewer calories to maintain weight, and losing weight becomes harder.
6. Any four: extremely low caloric intake, an obsession with exercising, emotional

---

Using Health Terms

On a separate sheet of paper, write the term that best matches each definition below.

LESSON 1

1. High in nutrients relative to calories provided.
2. Excess body fat, or adipose tissue.
3. Weighing more than 10 percent over the standard weight for height.
4. The ratio of weight to height.
5. Not consuming enough essential nutrients or calories for normal body functions.

LESSON 2

6. A disorder in which cycles of overeating are followed by some form of purging and clearing of the digestive tract.
7. The cycle of losing, regaining, losing, and regaining.
8. A disorder in which the irrational fear of becoming obese results in severe weight loss from self-induced starvation.

LESSON 3

9. Restoring lost body fluids.
10. Very large amounts of nutrient supplements.
11. Pills, powders, liquids and other synthetic forms of nutrients.
12. Vegetarians who eat only foods of plant origin.
13. Storing extra glycogen in the muscle for athletic activity.
14. The loss of excess body fluids.

LESSON 4

15. Condition in which the body's immune system overreacts to food substances.
16. Treated by a process of heating to destroy or slow the growth of pathogens.
17. The spreading of bacteria in food.
18. Liable to spoil.
19. Food poisoning.

Recalling the Facts

Using complete sentences, answer the following questions.

LESSON 1

1. Why is obesity considered a health risk?
2. What are two main reasons why people might be obese or overweight?
3. What health risks are associated with being underweight?
4. How does physical activity promote healthy weight?

LESSON 2

5. Why does weight cycling make permanent weight loss difficult?
6. What are four signs of anorexia nervosa?
7. What are the behavioral differences between anorexia and bulimia?

LESSON 3

8. Name some benefits of a vegetarian diet.
9. What is the best high-performance diet for sports?
10. Name one risk and one benefit associated with nutrient supplements.

LESSON 4

11. What conditions promote the growth of bacteria in food?
12. Name four steps that should be taken to avoid cross-contamination of foods.
13. What are three symptoms of a food allergy?

---

problems, unnatural interest in food, unrealistic or distorted sense of body image, denial of an eating problem.
7. In anorexia nervosa, a person starves oneself. In bulimia nervosa, overeating is followed by vomiting or purging with laxatives.
8. Reduced risk of heart disease, high blood pressure, and some forms of cancer.

9. A nutrient-dense, balanced diet.
10. Answers will vary.
11. Nutrients, moisture, and warmth.
12. Any four: don't buy foods with damaged packaging, keep packages of raw meat separate from other foods, refrigerate or freeze meat immediately, wash hands before and after handling raw meat or fish, thaw meat in the refrigerator, don't let juices from raw

Thinking Critically

LESSON 1

1. **Synthesizing.** Besides overeating, what personal habits could lead to obesity?
2. **Evaluating.** How can a healthy eating plan improve your life?

LESSON 2

3. **Comparing and Contrasting.** Compare the causes, behaviors, and effects of anorexia nervosa and bulimia nervosa.

LESSON 3

4. **Analyzing.** Why is it necessary for vegetarians to pay special attention to such nutrients as iron, zinc, and B vitamins?

LESSON 4

5. **Analyzing.** Why do food service establishments post signs that say, "Wash hands before returning to work"?
6. **Evaluating.** How would you decrease the risk of foodborne illness at an afternoon barbecue?

Making the Connection

1. **Science.** After it was discovered during the 1950s that diet pills containing the stimulant drug dextroamphetamine did not work and could even become habit-forming, the FDA issued a series of warnings. Learn more about appetite suppressants now being developed, their chemical composition, and the health risks involved. Share your findings in a brief oral report.

2. **Social Studies.** In developed countries, foodborne illnesses are controlled or prevented by adequate sanitation and sewage treatment, regulations that govern food production and distribution, and generally high standards of hygiene. Choose an area of the world where illnesses such as typhoid and cholera, are still prevalent. Research the causes, the public health consequences, and solutions.

BEYOND THE CLASSROOM

PARENTAL INVOLVEMENT Survey family members to determine a physical activity plan they could do together. After the family members have shared the results of their ideas, analyze the plan and offer additional suggestions of how the plan could be implemented.

COMMUNITY INVOLVEMENT Overeaters Anonymous is a group of individuals who support one another in their attempts to overcome eating problems. Contact a branch of this organization in your community. Find out what services OA provides and how "sponsors" are used to help

people through recovery. Share your findings in a brief report.

SCHOOL-TO-CAREER
Exploring Careers. Write to The American Dietetic Association, 216 West Jackson Blvd., Suite 800, Chicago, IL 60606, for information on a career as a dietetic technician. Determine what schooling, in-service training, and interpersonal skills are necessary. Share your findings with the class in the form of an oral or written report.

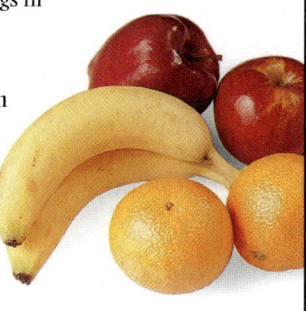

Thinking Critically

1. Answers will vary.
2. It can prevent disease and increase your energy; make you look better and, thus, increase your self-esteem and improve your social life; give you a sense of greater control over your life.
3. Review pages 142–144 for answers.
4. Because animal products are the only natural sources of these nutrients.
5. Because unclean hands are a common source of food contamination.
6. Proper refrigeration of food, washing of hands before and after handling food, washing of utensils to prevent cross-contamination of foods, use of separate utensils for separate foods, etc.

Making the Connection

1.–2. Reports will vary.

Evaluate

- Use the reproducible *Chapter 6 Test* in the TCR or construct your own using the Testmaker software.
- Use *Performance Assessment Activity 6* in the TCR.

Enrichment

Have students complete *Cross-Curriculum Activity 6* in the TCR.

Beyond the Classroom

Keep students involved in the community, and encourage parent participation by assigning the activities on this page for students to work on outside of class.

---

meat or fish come in contact with other foods.

13. Rash, hives, itchiness, vomiting, diarrhea, abdominal pain, hay fever-like symptoms.

Personal Health

	FEATURES	CLASSROOM RESOURCES

LESSON 1
Healthy Skin, Hair, and Nails
pages 162–166

Making Responsible Decisions
"Should I Suntan?" *page 164*

- Concept Map Activity 21
- Decision-Making Activity 7
- Lesson 21 Quiz
- Lesson Plan 21
- Reteaching Activity 21
- Transparency 53

LESSON 2
Healthy Teeth and Mouth
pages 167–170

Building Health Skills
"Comparing Health and Beauty Aids," *page 168*

- Concept Map Activity 22
- Cooperative Learning Activity 7
- Lesson 22 Quiz
- Lesson Plan 22
- Reteaching Activity 22
- Transparency 54

LESSON 3
Healthy Eyes
pages 171–175

update ▶ Looking at Technology
"New Laser Eye Surgeries," *page 174*

- Concept Map Activity 23
- Enrichment Activity 7
- Health Lab 7
- Lesson 23 Quiz
- Lesson Plan 23
- Reteaching Activity 23
- Transparency 55

LESSON 4
Healthy Ears
pages 176–179

- Concept Map Activity 24
- Lesson 24 Quiz
- Lesson Plan 24
- Reteaching Activity 24
- Transparency 56

ACTIVITIES

- Cross-Curriculum Activity 7
- Health Lab 7
- Health Skills Activities 7
- Parent Letter and Activities 7

ASSESSMENT

- Chapter 7 Test
- Performance Assessment Activity 7
- Testmaker Software

STUDENT ACTIVITIES WORKBOOK

- Applying Health Skills 21–24
- Study Guide 7
- Vocabulary Activity 7

STUDENT DIVERSITY STRATEGIES

- Audiocassette Program (English)
- Audiocassette Program (Spanish)
- Spanish Parent Letter and Activities
- Spanish Summaries, Quizzes, and Activities

MULTIMEDIA COMPONENTS

- English Audiocassette Program
- Spanish Audiocassette Program
- MindJogger Videodisc and VHS program

National Health Education Standards

One of the main goals of the National Health Education Standards is to move students toward "health literacy." Health literacy is the capacity of individuals to obtain, interpret, and understand basic health information and services and the competence to use such information and services in ways which promote health. The health standards were developed by applying the characteristics of a well-educated, literate person within the context of health. The health literate person is:

- a critical thinker and problem solver
- a self-directed learner
- a responsible, productive citizen
- an effective communicator

Listed below are the Health Education Standards Performance Indicators addressed in each lesson of this chapter.

Lesson	Health Standards Performance Indicators
1	2.3, 3.3, 3.4, 6.1
2	2.3, 2.6, 3.3, 3.4
3	2.3, 2.6, 3.4, 4.3
4	1.4, 1.6, 3.1, 3.4

ONLINE RESOURCES

For a fresh approach to health topics and an in-depth look at health issues, use these online resources found under Teacher Resources at **health.glencoe.com**.

- **BLOCK SCHEDULE LESSON PLANS** Reinforce health concepts with outside readings selected especially for students. Each reading is accompanied by a lesson plan and activities to enhance
  - Reading Skills
  - Cross Curriculum
  - Media Literacy

- **TECHNOLOGY PROJECTS** Instructions and suggestions on how to use computer, Internet, and software with health lessons.

- **HEALTH UPDATES** Timely topics in health news, including late-breaking medical advances and updates on teen risk behaviors.

Out of Time?

If time does not permit teaching this chapter, you may use these features: Making Responsible Decisions on page 164; Building Health Skills on page 168; and Update on page 174.

BLOCK SCHEDULING

Block scheduling provides extended time for hands-on projects and activities. Use the following activities to engage students, provide further depth, and vary your instructional techniques:

- Update (30 minutes)   **pg. 174**
- Health Skills Activity (60–90 minutes)   **pg. 180**

Personal Health

CHAPTER OVERVIEW

Chapter 7 discusses the structure, functions, and care of the skin, teeth, mouth, eyes, and ears. Problems associated with each body part are also presented.

LESSON 1 The functions and care of the skin are presented in this lesson. Proper grooming of the hair and nails is also discussed.

LESSON 2 The structure of teeth, their functions, oral hygiene, and problems associated with teeth and gums are presented in this lesson.

LESSON 3 Of all the special sense organs, our eyes provide us with the greatest amount of information about our environment. Their structure, functions, associated problems, and ways to care for them are discussed in this lesson.

LESSON 4 The structure and functions of the ear, proper ear care, and problems associated with ears are presented in this lesson.

INTRODUCING THE CHAPTER

- Tell students that we often take for granted the abilities of our body. Our skin serves as protection and helps regulate body temperature. Our teeth allow us to eat a variety of foods and even help us enunciate many words. Our eyes allow us to perceive our surroundings in color and depth. Our ears allow us to differentiate a wide range of sounds that hold meaning for us. These abilities are not only basic to our everyday functioning, but they also enable us to experience our diverse environment. Ask students to consider how not having just one of these abilities would affect their lives.

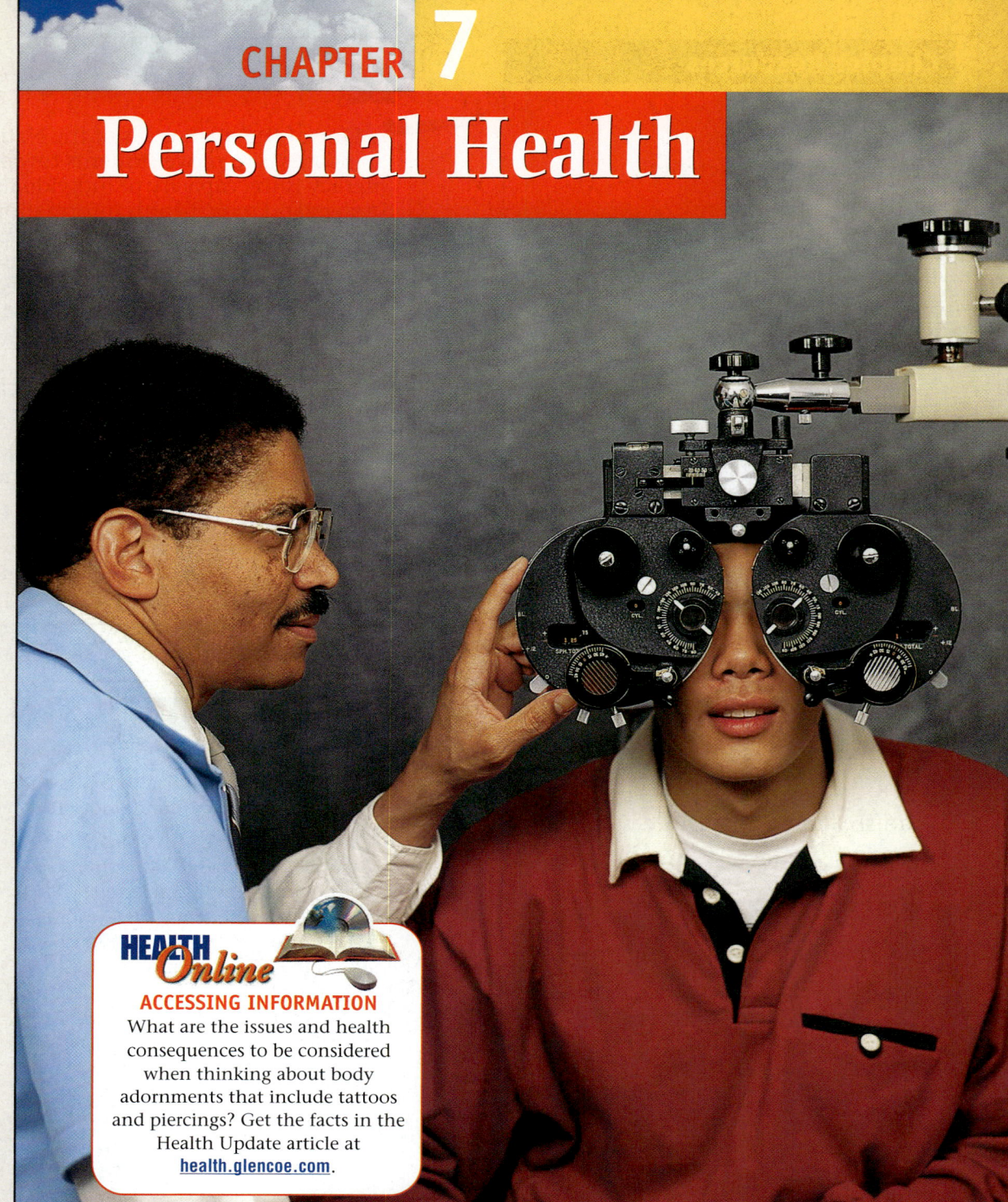

CHAPTER 7
Personal Health

HEALTH Online

ACCESSING INFORMATION

What are the issues and health consequences to be considered when thinking about body adornments that include tattoos and piercings? Get the facts in the Health Update article at **health.glencoe.com**.

Hands-On Health

TEACHING STRATEGY

Reinforcing and Reviewing Bring your health classroom to life with interactive teaching strategies and classroom management techniques that keep your students interested and involved. The unique *Hands-On Health: Creative Teaching Strategies* booklet that accompanies the *Glencoe Health* program offers fun, motivating activities.

The following Classroom Management Ideas can be used to reinforce chapter concepts:

- Beach Ball
- Trivia Questions
- Paper Exchange
- Mental Outburst

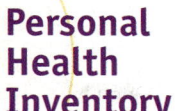

Personal Health Inventory

Self-Inventory Write the numbers 1–10 on a sheet of paper. Read each statement below and respond by writing *yes, no,* or *sometimes* for each item. Write a *yes* only for items that you practice regularly. Save your responses.

1	I wash my face twice daily.
2	When I am in the sun, I use appropriate sunscreen.
3	I keep my hair clean.
4	I keep my nails clean and evenly trimmed.
5	I brush my teeth more than once a day and floss regularly.
6	I have regular dental checkups.
7	When reading or studying for long periods of time, I rest my eyes periodically.
8	I have my eyes checked by a professional on a regular basis.
9	I avoid extremely loud noises— 85 decibels or more.
10	I wear some type of ear protection when I know I will be around loud noises.

Follow-up After completing the chapter, retake this self-inventory. Pick two items that you need to work on and set a goal to improve your health behaviors.

Personal Health Inventory

Let students read the Self-Inventory statements and discuss how each statement relates to good health. Then have students label the page "Personal Health," and respond to the statements in their private Health Journals. Encourage students to use this inventory as a tool for evaluating and improving their own health by responding honestly to each statement.

- Let volunteers describe the photographs on this page: How does each item or activity relate to a teen's personal health? Then have students read the quotation and discuss the importance of taking the time to care for your health and appearance. Conclude this brief discussion by telling students they will learn more about taking care of themselves and developing their own health habits as they study the lessons in Chapter 7.
- Distribute Parent Letter 7 in the *Parent Letters and Activities* booklet.

> 66 *A man (or woman) too busy to take care of his health is like a mechanic too busy to take care of his tools.* 99

—SPANISH PROVERB

Quick Write Write the following words in a vertical list: *hair, skin, nails, eyes,* and *ears.* Next, jot down one step you can take to improve the health, hygiene, or care of each. Estimate the amount of time that each of these caretaking steps might actually take up on an average day.

TECHNOLOGY OPTIONS

MINDJOGGER
VIDEOQUIZ

To preview or review chapter content, you may wish to use the *MindJogger Videoquiz* that accompanies Chapter 7.

Healthy Skin, Hair, and Nails

LESSON **1**

FOCUS

LESSON OBJECTIVES

After studying this lesson, students should be able to

- describe the structure and functions of the skin.
- identify ways to maintain healthy skin, hair, and nails.

MOTIVATOR

Ask students to consider what they notice first about an individual when meeting him or her for the first time.

INTRODUCING THE LESSON

Have students share their responses to the Motivator. Explain that first impressions are largely based on a person's grooming, and that the condition of a person's skin, hair, and nails is most apparent. Ask students to list things that they do daily to enhance their appearance. Tell them that appearance is only one aspect of good grooming, and that care of the skin, hair, and nails also serves to protect these parts of the body.

INTRODUCING HEALTH TERMS

- Have students define each term in their own words and then verify their definitions using the Glossary. Tell them to write sentences using each vocabulary term.
- Ask students to complete Vocabulary Activity 7 and Chapter Study Guide 7 in the *Student Workbook*. 📁

Healthy Skin, Hair, and Nails

Y ou probably know the expression "Put your best foot forward." Your physical appearance has a great effect on the people you meet. Whether you are talking to a new person at school or applying for a job, your appearance influences how people react to you. Taking care of yourself makes you feel better, too.

HEALTH TERMS

sweat glands
acne
sebaceous glands
follicles
dandruff

HEALTH CONCEPTS

- The health of your skin, hair, and nails affects the way people respond to you.
- Healthy skin, hair, and nails can be achieved through simple daily hygiene, such as bathing and washing, as well as through periodic maintenance.
- The way an individual takes care of skin, hair, and nails is often an indication of how that person feels about himself or herself.

hot link

integumentary system For more information on the integumentary system and its chief organ, the skin, see Chapter 15, page 340.

infectious diseases For more information on the body's defense against infectious diseases, see Chapter 28, page 632.

Functions of the Skin

W hat do you see when you meet another person for the first time? One of the first features people notice about you is your skin. Together with your hair and nails, your skin forms the basis of one of your body's main systems, the **integumentary system**. In fact, the skin itself is the body's single largest organ!

Every living organism is protected by some kind of protective cover. In humans, that function is served by the skin. The skin also helps cushion your internal tissues and organs and is your body's first line of defense against **infectious diseases**. The skin provides protection against the ultraviolet rays of the sun. Another important

Lesson 1 Resources

TEACHER'S CLASSROOM RESOURCES
📁 **Concept Map** Activity 21
📁 **Decision-Making** Activity 7
📁 **Lesson 21 Quiz**
📁 **Lesson Plan 21**
📁 **Parent Letter and Activities 7**
📁 **Reteaching** Activity 21

STUDENT WORKBOOK
📁 **Applying Health Skills 21**
📁 **Chapter Study Guide 7**
📁 **Vocabulary** Activity 7

TRANSPARENCIES
🧴 **Transparency 53**

function of the skin is the regulation of the body's temperature. Your skin has an enormous supply of tiny blood vessels just beneath the surface. When your internal temperature rises, circulation to these blood vessels increases. As internal heat is circulated through these surface blood vessels, it is lost through the process of radiation. You start to perspire, and as the perspiration evaporates, your skin cools. This last function is accomplished by means of the **sweat glands**, *structures within the skin that secrete perspiration through ducts to pores on the skin's surface.* When your body gets hot, sweat glands become more active and produce perspiration through pores onto your skin to cool the body down.

Healthy Skin

Every morning and every evening, you should wash your face with soap and water. If the skin on your face is very oily, wash it once more during the day. Pat your skin dry with a clean towel. If you use creams and cosmetics, select them carefully and avoid greasy preparations. Eat a well-balanced diet. Vitamin A helps promote healthy skin. Milk, egg yolks, liver, green leafy and yellow vegetables, and yellow fruits are good sources of vitamin A. Get plenty of rest and exercise. Try to keep your hands away from your face.

Skin and the Sun

Understanding the sun's effect on the skin and knowing some protective steps to take can help you better care for your skin. The sun does not have the same effect on everyone. Some people tan more easily than others. Some people with fair skin may never tan; they may just burn.

Ultraviolet (UV) rays are light rays that come from the sun. Two types of ultraviolet rays are important in considering the sun's effects on the human body. The shorter rays, which are most intense in the middle of the day, are the main cause of sunburn. The longer rays, in the morning and late afternoon, are less strong.

Do not be fooled on a hazy or cloudy day. Up to 80 percent of ultraviolet rays can penetrate haze, light clouds, or fog. Ultraviolet rays can also be reflected upward from the ground, sand, and water. Snow is an excellent reflector, sending back more than 85 percent of the rays.

The most important thing you can do for your skin is to keep it clean.

ACTIVITY *Name other ways you can keep your skin healthy.*

TEACH

L1 Researching

Ask students: What conditions, other than heat, stimulate the sweat glands? *(pressure, anxiety, nervousness)* Have a volunteer find out how and why these emotional conditions trigger this physical reaction.

L1 Explaining

Emphasize that UV rays affect all kinds and shades of skin. Individuals with dark skin also need to protect themselves from the sun.

L2 Researching

Let students work with partners or in small groups to read about melanin: What is it? Where and how is it produced? How does it function in the body? What other organisms produce melanin? Ask students to write short essays summarizing their findings.

L1 Discussing

Ask the class to identify sporting activities during which it is especially important to protect skin from the harmful effects of the sun. Be sure they include sports that take place in or on water and those that take place on snow.

L1 Analyzing

Ask students how they would respond to a teen who says: "I'm already 17 years old, and I've spent every day of every summer out in the sun. The damage has already been done—there's no point in starting to protect my skin from the sun now."

MORE ABOUT . . . . .

SUNBLOCKS. For adequate sun protection, a sunblock with an SPF (sun protection factor) of 15 or greater is recommended. SPF, which is rated from 2 to 15 or greater, indicates how long a person can stay in the sun without becoming burned. If you normally burn (unprotected) after 15 minutes in the sun, for example, an SPF of 8 will allow you to stay out for 8 times 15, or 120 minutes (2 hours). A 15 SPF will increase the time you can remain outside to more than 3 hours. Using a sunblock, regardless of SPF rating, does not mean that you will only tan but not burn. You will burn if you remain in the sun without protection beyond the protected length of time.

L2 Discussing

Have a group of students investigate prices and collect information on sunscreens that are available in stores in their community. Ask the students to share their findings. Discuss sunless tanning products as a healthful alternative to tanning beds or exposure to the sun.

Making Responsible Decisions

1. Now that Jessica has learned about the dangers of ultraviolet rays, she wonders whether she should start protecting her skin from the sun.
2. Jessica could (a) ignore the warnings and continue to tan, (b) protect her skin from the sun, (c) protect her skin and encourage her friends to do the same.
3. Jessica might (a) risk developing skin cancer but enjoy feeling attractive with a tan right now, (b) guard against the risk of skin cancer but sometimes feel uncomfortable because she doesn't have a tan and doesn't participate in tanning with her friends, (c) guard against the risk of skin cancer and help her friends make a similar choice—though some or all may reject her suggestions.
4. Jessica values her own good health. She also values looking attractive and looking like her friends.
5. Responses will vary.
6. Encourage students to consider both the short- and long-term consequences of their decision.

L2 Decision Making

For further study on making responsible decisions, assign *Decision-Making Activity 7* in the TCR.

⚠ *No matter what your skin type is, it is important to use sunscreen to prevent damage from UV rays.*
ACTIVITY *Name other ways this teen could protect herself from sun damage.*

You should not judge a sunburn by how red you look while you are still out in the sun. It takes about two to eight hours after exposure for a sunburn to show. The pain from the burn is greatest about six to 48 hours after exposure.

In addition to causing sunburn, exposure to the sun's ultraviolet rays can permanently destroy the elastic fibers that keep the skin tight. This causes the skin to age prematurely, or before its time. The layers of skin cells also thicken with repeated sun exposure, giving the skin a hard, leathery texture.

Ultraviolet radiation also damages deoxyribonucleic acid (DNA), the genetic material in skin cells. Accumulated DNA damage can result in the formation of cancerous cells. Excessive sun exposure is the primary cause of certain types of skin cancer. Therefore, you should protect your skin. Use a sunblock if you are going to be in the sun for a prolonged period of time. Sunblocks stop the sun's rays by reflecting them.

The effects of the sun on your skin may not show up for years and cannot be stopped with any cosmetic ointments. These effects are cumulative, or build up over time, and the damage is irreversible. The healthiest behavior is prevention. Avoid overexposure to the sun's ultraviolet rays.

Making Responsible Decisions

Should I Suntan?

In the past, Jessica has always taken pride in having a deep tan. However, after learning about the dangers of ultraviolet rays and their relationship to skin cancer, she is having second thoughts about her tanning habits.

On the one hand, she thinks she looks healthier and more attractive with a tan, and a lot of her friends have tans. On the other hand, she does not want to develop skin cancer later on in life. What should Jessica do?

What Would You Do?

Apply the six steps of the decision-making process to Jessica's problem.

1. **State the situation.**
2. **List the options.**
3. **Weigh the possible outcomes.**
4. **Consider your values.**
5. **Make a decision and act.**
6. **Evaluate the decision.**

164 CHAPTER 7 PERSONAL HEALTH

📖 SCHOOL-TO-CAREER

SKIN CARE. Have students interview a person who works all or most of the day in the sun. For example, they might speak to lifeguards, physical education teachers or coaches, farm laborers, gardeners, or construction workers. Have them ask what effects these workers experience from sun exposure, and what steps they take to protect themselves.

Encourage students to research preventive measures by contacting unions or occupational health and safety agencies. Tell them to write handbooks for workers in a given occupation, or create posters that could be posted in the workplace, listing the precautions that might protect workers from sun damage.

Body Piercing and Tattooing

Do some of your friends wear eyebrow or nose rings? Maybe some have tattoos. People have been decorating their bodies for thousands of years. Some decorations, such as blush and other facial cosmetics, are temporary. Others, such as body piercing and tattooing, are not.

Both body piercing and tattooing pose health risks. Each involves puncturing the skin. This can permit pathogens to enter if the equipment used is not sterile or if follow-up care of the wound is inadequate. A special concern is the risk of hepatitis or **HIV** infection from dirty needles during tattooing.

Tattooing and piercing threaten not only your physical health but also your social health. A tattoo that has a current girlfriend's or boyfriend's name may not be appreciated by future dates. A nose ring or other piercing may make a poor first impression on a potential employer. Before going along with fads like these, consider the long-term consequences.

Skin Problems

Many problems of the skin are not life-threatening. They can, however, affect a person's self-image. Following healthy habits may help eliminate some of these problems. One common skin problem during adolescence is **acne**. This is *a clogging of the pores of the skin.* Some adults get acne as well. The **sebaceous** (sih-BAY-shuhs) **glands** are *structures within the skin that produce an oily secretion called sebum.* When these glands enlarge, they produce excess sebum. During adolescence, the increase in hormone production causes these glands to enlarge and produce more sebum, making the skin oily. The oil becomes trapped in a pore and plugs it, allowing bacteria to multiply and causing the area to become inflamed.

Keeping the skin clean is the most important treatment for acne. Wash the skin twice daily. Medicinal lotions and creams may also help relieve the condition. Picking at or squeezing pimples can spread the infection and cause scarring.

Your Hair

Humans have hair present on almost all the skin surfaces of their bodies. You have between 100,000 and 200,000 hairs on your head alone! The roots of hairs are made up of living cells. These grow out of **follicles**, *tiny pits in the skin.* The upgrowth of dead cells and keratin—a protein that also makes up nails and the outer skin layer—from the root forms the hair. Your hair affects your appearance greatly. Taking proper care of your hair is an important part of total health. So is wearing a style that fits your features.

Proper care includes washing your hair regularly. Brushing your hair daily keeps dirt from building up and helps distribute the natural hair oils evenly. These oils keep the hair soft and give it its shine.

hotlink

HIV For more information on how HIV is spread, see Chapter 30, page 656.

keeping Fit

Perspiration

Many people think perspiration causes body odor. Perspiration itself is not the cause. Bacteria interacting with perspiration create the odor. Sweat glands are numerous under the arms, which is the reason body odor tends to be a problem in that area. A routine of regular bathing and use of an antiperspirant will help control perspiration problems. Using deodorant will help mask the body odor.

Learn techniques for improving your personal health and hygiene at **health.glencoe.com**.

keeping Fit

Perspiration

Discuss the growing number of antibacterial soaps and detergents that are available. Have a group of students investigate the effectiveness of some of these products by contacting consumer agencies or looking at consumer publications. Ask the students to prepare a brief presentation of their findings.

L1 Analyzing

Tell students that in many American communities, ear piercing is accepted and even common for females, but other forms of piercing are uncommon and often unacceptable, at least to adults. Ask: What do you think accounts for these different attitudes? How do you think adults' disapproval of certain kinds of piercing might affect teens' attitudes toward those same types of piercing?

L1 Class Activity

Divide the class into three groups, and assign each group one kind of product: acne skin cleansers, dandruff treatments, or shampoos for controlling head lice. Let group members work together to compare at least three different brands of their assigned product, noting differences in price, ingredients, and advertising claims.

HEALTH Online

Discuss physical problems associated with adolescence (e.g., acne). Then divide the class into groups and have each explore a different area of hygiene such as hair care, skin care, or nail care. Set aside class time for students to share information on their topic, including safe and effective treatments for problems and ways of promoting hygienic health.

COOPERATIVE) LEARNING

ACTIVITY. In groups, have students examine shampoo ads in magazines or videotaped commercials. Encourage them to discuss results promised for a given shampoo, and analyze the ads' bases for appeal. Discuss techniques used to sell products. For example, do ads use testimonials; trendy or popular images; loaded or emotional words; celebrity endorsement; transfer, or mentally linking a product with something readers desire, such as a woman surrounded by admirers? Have them compare claims in the ads with ratings in a publication such as *Consumer Reports,* and rank highly rated products in order of cost. Encourage the groups to share their findings.

EVALUATING THE LESSON

Assign and discuss the Lesson 1 Review; then administer, grade, and discuss the *Lesson 21 Quiz* in the TCR. ☞

RETEACHING

- Ask students to create concept maps portraying ways to care for the skin, hair, and nails.
- Ask students to complete *Reteaching Activity 21* in the TCR. ☞
- Use *Transparency 53,* "The Integumentary System," to review parts of the skin. ♨

ENRICHMENT

Have students investigate products available to both boys and girls that help maintain healthful hair and skin. Ask them to interview cosmetologists at department stores to determine the benefits of their products.

CLOSE

Use the lesson objectives listed on page 162 of the Teacher's Wraparound Edition to review the lesson's concepts.

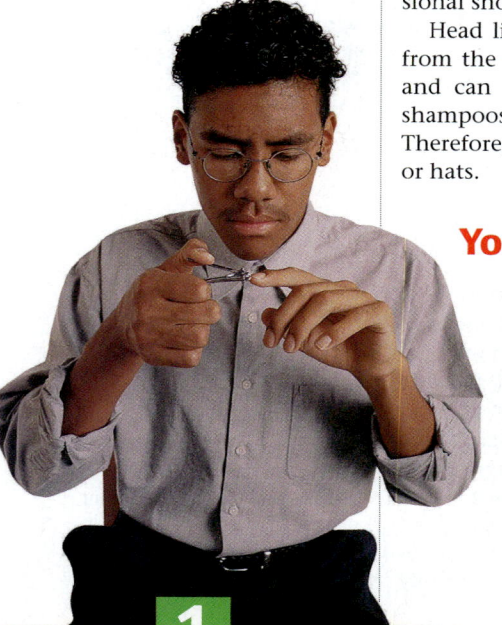

▽ *Clean, trimmed nails add to your overall appearance.*
ACTIVITY *List other personal hygiene habits that contribute to a healthy appearance.*

Hair Problems

Dandruff, *a condition in which the outer layer of dead skin cells is shed from the scalp,* is one common hair and scalp problem. It becomes noticeable when white flakes of skin cling to the hair or are shed onto the collar and shoulders of clothes. Regular, thorough washing of hair—especially with anti-dandruff shampoos—can control ordinary dandruff. If itching and scaling persist, a health professional should be consulted.

Head lice are small, wingless insects that live on and suck blood from the scalp. Their bites make the scalp itchy and uncomfortable and can cause infection. Lice can usually be killed by medicinal shampoos. Head lice can be spread from one person to another. Therefore, it is wise not to use other people's combs, brushes, towels, or hats.

Your Nails

Your fingernails and toenails are dead cells that grow from the outer layer of your skin. Living cells extend from the root of the nail, below the skin, to just above the base of the nail. As living cells die and are replaced, they are pushed up, forming the rest of the nail. Good nail care includes keeping nails clean and evenly trimmed. Keep your cuticles pushed back and clip hangnails with a nail clipper. You should cut toenails straight across, leaving the nail just at or slightly above skin level. If you cut the nails too low, you increase your risk of skin infection and ingrown nails.

LESSON **1** *Review*

Reviewing Facts and Vocabulary

1. What is the relationship between an overactive sebaceous gland and acne?
2. What effect does the sun have on skin?

Thinking Critically

3. ***Analyzing.*** Your cousin who lives in another state has written to tell you she is thinking of having her lower lip pierced, insisting that it is "all the rage." What advice might you write back to her?
4. ***Synthesizing.*** Explain how your overall appearance makes a statement about how you feel about yourself.

Applying Health Skills

5. ***In Your Home.*** Think of the healthy grooming habits that are part of your morning or evening routines. Which are the most important to you? Which are your least favorite? Consider how you might make these activities more balanced so as to give equal time to each area.

Lesson 1 Review

Answers to Reviewing Facts and Vocabulary

1. An overactive sebaceous gland causes the blockage of pores, resulting in acne.
2. The sun can tan or burn the skin, causing premature aging, and possibly causing skin cancer.

Answers to Thinking Critically

3. She is putting herself at risk for hepatitis, HIV, and other infections. She will probably get tired of it once it's no longer "the rage." She will have a harder time finding employment.
4. Your overall appearance indicates whether you take the time to care for yourself.

Healthy Teeth and Mouth

What is the most common noninfectious disease in the United States? If you guessed tooth decay, you are right. Most Americans have or have had tooth decay. Yet, this is also one of the most preventable diseases. In this lesson, you will learn about the function and structure of the teeth and how to prevent tooth decay.

HEALTH TERMS

periodontium

pulp

plaque

periodontal disease

tartar

HEALTH CONCEPTS

- Regular oral hygiene can help you have clean, healthy teeth and breath.
- Oral hygiene is an important step in preventing periodontal disease.

Your Teeth

Your teeth are the single most noticeable contributor to the appearance of your mouth and face. Teeth not only allow you to chew food, but they also form the shape and structure of your mouth.

Parts of the Tooth

The area immediately around the teeth is called the **periodontium** (per-ee-oh-DAHN-tee-uhm). It is made up of the gums, periodontal ligament, and the jawbone. Together these structures support the teeth.

LESSON 2   HEALTHY TEETH AND MOUTH   **167**

Lesson 2 Resources

TEACHER'S CLASSROOM RESOURCES

- **Concept Map** Activity 22
- **Cooperative Learning** Activity 7
- **Lesson 22 Quiz**
- **Lesson Plan 22**
- **Reteaching** Activity 22

STUDENT WORKBOOK

- **Applying Health Skills 22**
- **Chapter Study Guide 7**
- **Vocabulary** Activity 7

TRANSPARENCIES

- **Transparency 54**

Healthy Teeth and Mouth

FOCUS

LESSON OBJECTIVES

After studying this lesson, students should be able to

- describe the structure and functions of the teeth and mouth.
- define periodontal disease and explain its causes and methods of prevention.

MOTIVATOR

Make a "Q-sort" by dividing an 8½ x 11-inch sheet of paper into five sections. In each section, write one term pertaining to the mouth and teeth found in the vocabulary list. Make enough copies to give each student one sheet. Write the following on the chalkboard for students to work on while attendance is being taken: *Tear the sheets into five sections. Then sort the terms into the following categories: parts of the tooth, parts of the mouth, and mouth and tooth disorders.*

INTRODUCING THE LESSON

Refer to the Motivator. Have volunteers share their categorized terms with the class. Discuss reasons for any differences. Explain to students that this lesson will contain information on the mouth and teeth.

INTRODUCING HEALTH TERMS

- Ask students to complete Vocabulary Activity 7 and Chapter Study Guide 7 in the *Student Workbook.*

TEACH

L2 Demonstrating

Bring an anatomical model of the teeth to class. Explain and point out to the class the eight incisors, 20 molars, and four canine teeth on the model. Bring in dental X rays to show the class cavities or fillings.

L2 Discussing

Discuss why some teens need to have their wisdom teeth removed. Explain the difference between impacted wisdom teeth and ones that have broken through the gum line.

LEP Class Activity

Ask some students to make a collage with pictures of things important for good dental health. Have other students make a collage showing images of less-than-perfect smiles.

Building Health Skills

Comparing Health and Beauty Aids
Skill: Assessing Reliable Information

Display several colorful ads (cut from magazines, for example) for different toothpastes. Ask students to react to the ads and to explain which of the ad claims they believe, if any. Then have students read the feature to learn more about examining and evaluating advertising claims. You may want to have pairs of students select and evaluate an ad for a dental care product. Let partners present their ads to the rest of the class, explaining how each of the first three steps can be applied in evaluating the claims of the ad.

The tooth itself is divided into three major parts: the root, the neck, and the crown. The crown is the visible part of the tooth. The **pulp** is *the living tissue inside the tooth.*

CROSS-SECTION OF A TOOTH

Cusp
Enamel
Dentin
Gum
Gingiva
Cementum
Pulp cavity with nerves and vessels
Periodontal ligaments
Periodontal membrane
Root canal
Bone

Crown
Neck
Root

▶ *A tooth is a living structure made up of many parts.*
ACTIVITY *Describe the structures within each of the three parts of the tooth and explain the different functions of different teeth.*

Building Health Skills

Comparing Health and Beauty Aids

"BREAKTHROUGH PRODUCT bleaches teeth whiter, faster." "Now—whiter, brighter teeth!" "Unique formula lightens teeth to a dazzling white." With all the claims being made, how do you know which product to buy? Here are a few pointers:

1. **If it sounds too good to be true, it probably is.** Manufacturers sometimes make claims that are false or misleading. Beware of products that promise radical changes in short periods of time. Watch for "cures" for something that science does not have a cure for.

2. **Be alert to key words.** Promoters of health and beauty aids may use key phrases such as *one-time offer, scientific breakthrough, unique formula,* or *secret ingredient.* This is a typical marketing technique used to attract and deceive consumers.

3. **Read the fine print.** Just how different are the various products? Check and compare the list of ingredients on the labels.

4. **Consult a dental professional.** Ask your dentist or dental hygienist for his or her recommendation.

HEALTH LITERACY

CONSUMER HEALTH. Some toothpastes and mouthwashes contain additives that are said to fight dental disease. Fluoride, for example, is reported to make teeth more resistant to cavity-causing acids. Other substances, such as sanguinaria extract, inhibit plaque formation. Encourage students to examine ads for toothpastes and mouthwashes and to read labels of various brands in the stores. Have them list substances represented as cavity fighters or plaque inhibitors and note which brands have their claims supported by the American Council on Dental Therapeutics. Suggest that they also research negative effects of such substances, and decide whether they want to use dental products containing these ingredients.

Healthy Teeth and Mouth

Good, regular oral health care is necessary for healthy, clean teeth. Because a toothbrush often misses hard-to-reach spots, flossing is also important. Flossing removes **plaque**, *a sticky, colorless film that acts on sugar to form acids that destroy tooth enamel and irritate gums.* Flossing also removes food particles stuck between teeth and between teeth and gums.

Fluoride has been shown to be effective in helping to prevent tooth decay. Today, 60 percent of the nation's drinkable water supply has been treated with fluoride. Dentists may treat children's teeth by painting on a fluoride solution or by briefly holding a fitted tray filled with fluoride gel against the teeth. Fluoride mouthwashes and toothpastes can be purchased for daily use at home.

Besides regular brushing and flossing, regular visits to a dental care professional are the next most important part of oral dental health. The food choices you make are also important. Frequent consumption of sugary foods contributes to tooth decay. If you eat sweets, it is important to brush your teeth as soon as possible. Eating foods rich in phosphorus and vitamins C and D, meanwhile, can strengthen teeth and gums. Avoid smoking and the use of smokeless tobacco, which can lead to oral cancer. Smokeless tobacco causes white patches or leukoplakia, which is a forerunner to mouth cancer.

Periodontal Disease

More than 20 million Americans have lost most or all of their teeth. The culprit is **periodontal** (per-ee-oh-DAHN-tuhl) **disease**, *an inflammation of the periodontal structures.* It is almost entirely preventable.

Periodontal disease is primarily the result of the destructive action of bacteria in the mouth. Bacteria form plaque. Unless plaque is removed once every 24 to 36 hours, it can harden into **tartar**, or calculus. Either name refers to *a hard, crustlike substance.* Tartar irritates both the underlying bone and the surrounding gums.

Decay begins as the plaque eats into the enamel and then spreads to the dentin. Your tooth will become more sensitive as the decay reaches the pulp. You will get a toothache when the decay reaches the pulp and exposes the nerve. If it is not treated, the bacterial infection can spread.

A tooth becomes abscessed when decay progresses to the stage where pus collects in, and tissue becomes inflamed around, the bone sockets of a tooth. Infection from an abscessed or badly decayed tooth in the upper jaw can spread into the sinuses.

Brushing Up

Removing plaque from teeth requires two minutes of proper brushing. Most people, however, brush for a maximum of 45 seconds. To make sure you brush long enough, play a radio in the background. Brush through the entire length of one song.

Here are more tips:

➤ Hold the bristle tips at a 45-degree angle against the gumline.

➤ Brush back and forth in very short strokes. Use a gentle, scrubbing motion.

➤ Brush the outer surfaces of each tooth, the inside surfaces and, finally, the chewing surfaces.

➤ To clean the inside surfaces of the front teeth, tilt the brush vertically and make up-and-down strokes.

➤ Brush your tongue to help freshen breath and remove bacteria.

Flossing reaches areas your toothbrush cannot get to, such as gaps between teeth and around the gums. See techniques on page 170.

ACTIVITY *Describe what might happen if a person does not floss in addition to brushing.*

Brushing Up

Share the following recommendations from the American Dental Association: Brush at least twice a day. Change the position of the toothbrush frequently, moving slowly across every tooth. Use a brush that has soft, rounded bristles. Replace your toothbrush every three to four months. Throw away your toothbrush after you have strep throat or upper respiratory infection.

L2 Cooperative Learning

Have students complete *Cooperative Learning Activity 7*, "Personal Health," in the TCR.

PERSONAL HEALTH

PERSONAL HEALTH. Have students find evaluations of toothbrushes in publications such as *Consumer Reports*. What types and brands of toothbrushes are recommended? Suggest they call their dentists or a school of dentistry and ask for recommendations about shape and type of bristles, and other suggestions. Encourage them to compare their answers. Do the dentists agree on all points? Invite students to check *Consumer Reports* to see if the ratings align with dentists' recommendations. Have them use their research to decide what type of toothbrush to buy when they replace the one they are using now.

ASSESS

EVALUATING THE LESSON

Assign and discuss the Lesson 2 Review; then administer, grade, and discuss the *Lesson 22 Quiz* in the TCR.

RETEACHING

- Have students make a poster showing the progression of periodontal disease and how to prevent it.
- Ask students to complete *Reteaching Activity 22* in the TCR.
- Use *Transparency 54* to review the parts of a tooth.

ENRICHMENT

Ask student volunteers to interview a dentist to find out the most common dental problems he or she sees in the teenage population. Have them ask questions such as: What are the primary causes of these problems? How might they be prevented? How can they be treated once they occur? Have the volunteers summarize their findings and share them with the class.

CLOSE

Summarize the most important concepts in this lesson. Explain that responsible health habits such as brushing, flossing, and visiting the dentist annually will prevent dental complications later in life.

keeping Fit

Proper Flossing Technique

Take care of your teeth and gums by following these steps:

➤ Break off an 18- to 24-inch length of floss. Wrap the ends around a finger of each hand.

➤ Hold the floss taut. Slip it gently between two teeth until it touches the gum. Using an up-and-down motion, rub the side of each tooth with the floss. Use a clean section of floss for each pair of teeth.

Other Problems of the Teeth and Mouth

In addition to periodontal disease, several other tooth and mouth disorders can occur. These are often caused by poor oral health care, but they may also result from poorly aligned teeth.

Halitosis

Halitosis is the medical term for bad breath. This condition can be caused by such factors as decayed teeth, eating certain foods, smoking, and mouth infections. Mouthwashes and mints may temporarily cover up the odor. However, if halitosis is caused by tooth decay or other infections, the only way to cure it is to treat the underlying cause of the problem.

Gingivitis and Periodontitis

Gingivitis is a disorder in which the gums become red and swollen and bleed easily. The inflammation may be caused by dental plaque, misaligned teeth, or deposits of decaying food. A dentist must determine the cause of the inflammation in order to treat this condition.

If gingivitis goes untreated, a more serious form of gum disease can develop. Called *periodontitis,* this disease results in swollen, tender, or bleeding gums. Bone surrounding the teeth is gradually destroyed, causing teeth to become loose and possibly fall out. As with gingivitis, good oral health care prevents this disease.

Malocclusion

Malocclusion is a condition in which the teeth of the upper and lower jaws do not align properly. Malocclusion can lead to decay and disease. It can also affect a person's speech and ability to chew. Orthodontics is the area of dentistry that corrects malocclusion.

LESSON 2 *Review*

Reviewing Facts and Vocabulary

1. How can you protect and maintain your teeth?
2. Describe the causes of tooth decay.

Thinking Critically

3. *Synthesizing.* Develop a headline for a poster aimed at people who do not regularly brush or floss their teeth.
4. *Evaluating.* How might you be able to distinguish between a person who practices good oral health and one who does not?

Applying Health Skills

5. *In Your Home and School.* Locate three ads for dental health products and analyze the claims these ads make. Then, create your own ad on how to practice good dental health using one of the health products. Share it with your family and the class.

Lesson 2 Review

Answers to Reviewing Facts and Vocabulary

1. A good diet, daily flossing and brushing, regular dental checkups.
2. Causes of tooth decay include unchecked bacteria in the mouth, malocclusion, and frequent consumption of sugary foods.

Answers to Thinking Critically

3. Answers will vary.
4. By the condition of his or her teeth.

Healthy Eyes

Imagine video equipment that provides images so convincingly three-dimensional and lifelike that you feel as though you are in the middle of the action. Such wonders exist, although they cannot be found in any store. In fact, you already own a set. They are your eyes.

HEALTH TERMS

lacrimal gland

sclera

cornea

choroid

retina

HEALTH CONCEPTS

- The parts around the eyes provide protection for the eye.
- Measures can be taken to protect the eyes.
- Many vision problems can be corrected with professional help.

Your Eyes

More than 80 percent of the information you receive about the environment around you comes by way of your eyes. Your eyes have more than a million electrical connections and can distinguish nearly 8 million differences in color!

Situated within bony sockets in the skull, your eyes are surrounded by protective structures. These include the eyebrows, eyelids, and eyelashes, all of which keep out foreign matter. Another important structure is the **lacrimal** (LAK-rih-mul) **gland.** This is *the gland responsible for producing tears.* Tears are made mostly of water and a small amount of salt and mucus. The salt gives the tears an antiseptic effect, which helps them fight pathogens. Tears keep the eyeballs moist and help remove foreign particles from the eyes.

LESSON 3   HEALTHY EYES   **171**

Lesson 3 Resources

TEACHER'S CLASSROOM RESOURCES

- **Concept Map** Activity 23
- **Enrichment** Activity 7
- **Health Lab** 7
- **Lesson 23 Quiz**
- **Lesson Plan 23**
- **Reteaching** Activity 23

STUDENT WORKBOOK

- **Applying Health Skills** 23
- **Chapter Study Guide** 7
- **Vocabulary** Activity 7

TRANSPARENCIES

- **Transparency 55**

Healthy Eyes

FOCUS

LESSON OBJECTIVES

After studying this lesson, students should be able to

- label the parts of the eye.
- explain the process of seeing.
- discuss eye care.
- describe common vision problems.

MOTIVATOR

Write the following on the chalkboard for students to complete while attendance is being taken: *Why do people wear glasses? List as many reasons as you can.*

INTRODUCING THE LESSON

Refer to the Motivator. As students share items from their lists, write a composite list on the chalkboard. Have students categorize the reasons as either medical or fashion.

INTRODUCING HEALTH TERMS

- Have students look at the illustration of the eye on page 172. Distribute several colors of clay. Direct students to create a model of the eye using different colors to represent the different structures. Upon completion, have students share their models and discuss the structures included as well as the functions.
- Distribute and have students complete Vocabulary Activity 7 and Chapter Study Guide 7 in the *Student Workbook.*

TEACH

L1 Health Lab

This experiment will show if students are right- or left-eye dominant. Give students the following directions:

1. Point your index finger up and hold it out in front of you.
2. Line it up with an object across the room.
3. Close your left eye. Now open your left eye and close your right.
4. At which time does your finger appear to jump to the side? If your finger stays lined up with the object when your right eye is open, you are right-eye dominant. If it stays lined up when your left eye is open, you are left-eye dominant.

L2 Discussing

Have students bring pictures of optical illusions to class to test other students. Discuss how our brain interprets what we see.

Computer Sense

keeping Fit

Tell students that they should be aware of how much time they spend in front of the computer. Encourage them to limit their computer sessions to short periods or to schedule frequent breaks to avoid eye strain. Forming healthy habits now will help them in the future as they use computers more and more.

L2 Demonstrating

Use an anatomical model of the eye to differentiate parts of the eye. Explain how light enters the eye and signals what is actually seen.

L2 Discussing

Discuss how sight develops and how we learn to use our eyes.

keeping Fit

Preventing Computer Eyestrain

To prevent or decrease the problem of computer eyestrain, remember to:

➤ Place the screen just below your line of vision.
➤ Place the screen 20 to 24 inches from your face.
➤ Avoid glare by placing the screen away from a window.
➤ Use a glare-filtering cover.
➤ Adjust the brightness of the screen, neither too bright nor too faint.
➤ Rest your eyes by looking away from the screen, focusing on a distant object, about every 15 minutes.

Tears reach the surface of the eye through tiny ducts. Some of the tears evaporate from the eye's surface. Those that do not evaporate are drained into the nasal cavity by two tear ducts located at the inner corner of each eye. These ducts open into larger ducts that run down into the nose. When the production of tears increases, the ducts are not able to carry away the extra quantity, and the tears will flow over the lower lid.

Parts of the Eye

The eye is made up of two main parts. One of these, the optic nerve, is a cable that connects the eye with the brain. The second, the eyeball wall, is itself made up of three layers.

■ The **sclera** (SKLEHR-uh) is *the tough, white outer coat of the eye.* It protects the inner structures of the eye from injury and helps maintain the eye's spherical shape. The rounded front part of the sclera forms the transparent **cornea.** This is *the main lens that performs most of the eye's focusing.*

■ The **choroid** (KOHR-oid) is *the middle layer of the eyeball wall.* Among the structures it contains is the iris, the colored part of the eye.

■ The **retina** is *the light-sensitive membrane on which images are cast by the cornea and lens.* The retina contains millions of light-sensitive receptors. These are classified, depending on their shape, as either *rods* or *cones.* The rods are highly sensitive to light but not to color. The opposite is true of the cones.

Within the shallow space formed by the cornea and lens is a watery fluid known as the *aqueous humor.* This fluid is continuously formed and drained to help maintain pressure within the eye. A second fluid, the *vitreous humor,* is a clear jelly that fills the eyeball behind the lens. The vitreous humor keeps the eyeball firm.

➤ *The eye is a complex organ.*
ACTIVITY *Name the major parts and functions of the eye.*

THE EYE

Sclera — Cornea — Iris — Pupil — Lens — Optic Nerve — Retina

MORE ABOUT . . . . .

SUNGLASSES. Most sunglasses we buy do not indicate on their labels whether they are safe for exposure to UV radiation. UV radiation is a part of sunlight. It can damage the eyes if they are not protected by sunglasses that block or absorb the full range of UV-B and UV-A (290–380 nm). Such protective sunglasses should be worn in bright sunlight to prevent radiation damage. Prescription sunglasses will provide the necessary lenses to block or absorb UV radiation. However, it can be difficult to determine which nonprescription sunglasses have adequate UV protection.

Vision

Vision starts in the retina. As light rays pass through the cornea and aqueous humor, they are bent and directed through the pupil. The light rays then pass through the lens, which adjusts to focus the light on the retina. The lens bulges to accommodate objects that are near and flattens to accommodate objects that are distant.

The rods and cones in the retina change this "visual information" into **nerve impulses**. These impulses are passed along the optic nerve to the brain, where they are fused into a single image. Because each eye has a slightly different view of a given object, the brain must interpret depth. This "stereoscopic" vision, as it is called, is important in judging distance.

In normal vision, a sharp image is produced. If you stand 20 feet (6 m) from an eye chart and can read the top eight lines, you have 20/20 vision. If you can read at 20 feet (6 m) what a person with normal vision can read at 40 feet (12 m) you have 20/40 vision. A person who has less than 20/200 vision and who cannot see the letter at the top of the chart is considered legally blind.

Healthy Eyes

Sensible eye care begins with regular checkups by a trained eye care professional. If corrective lenses have been prescribed for you, wear them. Take breaks from using your eyes for long periods of time, especially when working at a computer. It is important to read and watch television in a well-lighted room. Avoid rubbing your eyes. Avoid direct sun or bright light, or wear sunglasses. Wear protective goggles or glasses when engaging in an activity or sport that could cause an eye injury.

Eye Problems

Even with regular care, problems of the eye can occur. Eye problems can be divided into two general types: vision problems and diseases of the eye.

Vision Problems

The two most common vision problems are nearsightedness and farsightedness.

Nearsightedness, or *myopia*, is a condition in which light rays are focused in front of the retina rather than on it. Objects close up are seen clearly, but distant objects are blurred. Concave corrective lenses make the rays focus farther back. Myopia can now be corrected by a surgical procedure called *radial keratotomy*. (See Update, page 174.)

Farsightedness, or *hyperopia*, occurs when the light rays are focused behind the retina. Distant objects can be seen clearly, but close objects are blurred. Convex lenses correct this condition.

hotlink

nerve impulses For more information on nerve impulses and their function, see Chapter 16, page 364.

▼ *Regular examinations by an eye-care professional are important in early detection of eye problems.*

ACTIVITY *Can you read the number shown in this simple test for color-blindness?*

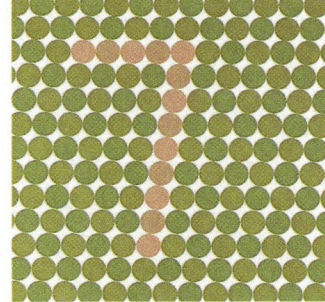

L1 Class Activity

Read the following statement aloud and ask students to write down the missing words: *Vision occurs when light rays pass through the (cornea) and (aqueous humor). The image is magnified. Light rays then penetrate the (lens), which adjusts to focus the light on the (retina), which sends impulses from the (optic nerve) to the occipital lobe of the (brain), which interprets the light rays as an image.*

L2 Discussing

What should you do if you get something in your eye? Discuss recommended techniques for removing foreign objects from the eye. Demonstrate first-aid techniques for eye injuries, including chemical burns.

L1 Discussing

Discuss adjustments a person would have to make after losing his or her sight. Explain the difference between being blind and having a visual impairment.

L1 Discussing

Poll the class to determine how many of the students wear contacts. What are some of the varieties of eyeglasses and contact lenses now available? Ask students what vision problems their corrective lenses correct.

L2 Health Lab

Distribute *Health Lab 7* and have students learn how images are projected on the retina. ☞

PERSONAL HEALTH

EYE CARE. Pinkeye, or conjunctivitis, may result from allergic reactions, from exposure to cosmetics or chlorinated water, or from a bacterial infection or virus. Should a student get pinkeye, he or she should follow these steps:

• Don't touch the eye.

• Use tissues when wiping away pus and crust.

• Don't wear eye makeup.

• Don't wear contact lenses until the condition has cleared up.

• Don't use other people's washcloths and towels, and warn them not to use yours.

• Use a warm washcloth compress on each eye to cleanse and soothe.

• If your eyes are light-sensitive or feel painful, call your doctor.

L1 Guest Speaker

Ask the school nurse to talk to the class about vision problems and school requirements for testing the vision of all students.

L2 Class Activity

Make arrangements for the class to observe a Braille writer, talking books, and other specialty products developed for people who are blind or have a visual impairment.

HEALTH Online

Invite a group of volunteers to use the quiz questions as the basis of a peer survey involving other students in the school. Urge the group to publish its findings in the form of a graph or chart with accompanying text. The information might be sent to a local or school newspaper.

up date
▶ *Looking at Technology*

Laser Eye Surgery

Have students respond to these questions with a show of hands: How many of you are nearsighted? How many of you wear glasses? How many wear contact lenses? How many would be willing to have surgery if it would correct your vision completely? Would you be more willing to have the surgery if it were done with bursts of light rather than with a scalpel? Let students share their reactions to this kind of eye surgery, and then have them read the feature to learn more about new developments in laser surgery.

HEALTH Online

Visit **health.glencoe.com** to learn how to care for your eyes and protect them from injury. Then take the interactive quiz on eye care facts and myths at the American Academy of Ophthalmology Web Link.

Other vision problems include the following:

- **Astigmatism.** In this condition, the curvature of the lens is uneven. As a result, the light rays focus at different points, causing the entire image to be blurred. Astigmatism can be corrected with lenses shaped to the correct curvature.

- **Strabismus.** In this condition, the muscles of both eyes do not work together. The eyes may appear crossed or one eye may appear to turn outward. A person with strabismus may have double vision since the brain cannot fuse the input from each eye into a single image.

- **Amblyopia.** If strabismus goes undetected or untreated, it may lead to *amblyopia,* or reduced vision in an eye that otherwise appears to be normal. The unused eye loses some ability to see. Treatment of amblyopia may include covering the stronger eye with a patch, wearing corrective lenses, or corrective surgery.

Most vision problems can be corrected with the use of prescription glasses or contact lenses.

up date
▶ *Looking at Technology*

Laser Eye Surgery

Throughout history, doctors have looked for ways to correct imperfect vision. One early advancement was RK or Radial Keratotomy—a surgical operation to improve nearsightedness by changing the curve of the cornea over the pupil. The surgeon made several deep incisions in the cornea in a radical or spoke-like pattern. Then with the advent of laser technology, in the 1980s, PRK (Photo Refractive Keratectomy) was introduced. In PRK, a computer-guided laser is used to precisely sculpt the surface of the cornea.

One of the latest advancements in laser eye treatments, developed in the 1990s, is LASIK (Laser in Situ Keratomileusis). In this procedure, a small flap in the cornea is created using a device called a micokeratome. Then, a cold (excimer) laser beam is used to either trim or to build up the surface of the cornea depending on whether the patient is nearsighted or farsighted. The entire procedure takes approximately 60 seconds and is guided by a preprogrammed computer.

There are, however, risks involved with corrective laser eye surgery. This can include sensitivity to light or scarring of the cornea, and it is not suitable for correcting some vision problems. Researchers are continuing to make advancements to reduce the risks involved in laser eye treatments.

MEETING STUDENT DIVERSITY

DIABETICS. Diabetic retinopathy is a condition that damages the small blood vessels nourishing the retina and occurs as a result of the inadequate or faulty insulin production caused by diabetes. It is essential for all persons with diabetes to pay attention to any of the following warning signs: loss, distortion, or dimness of vision; pain in or around the eyes; excessive tearing or discharge from the eye; swelling of the eyelids or protrusion of the eye; double vision; flashes of light, halos around lights, or floating spots; a sudden crossing or deviation of one eye; a change in color of an eye.

Diseases of the Eye

Diseases of the eye range from easily treated infections to disorders and conditions that can threaten sight. Among the more common but less serious diseases are sty and pinkeye. A sty is an inflamed swelling of a sebaceous gland near the eyelash. Pinkeye, or *conjunctivitis,* is an eye infection of the sclera or related tissues, causing redness, discomfort, and discharge. Both conditions can be treated with **antibiotics**.

More serious diseases of the eye include:

- **Cataracts.** This is a clouding of the lens, which causes blurring or hazy vision and problems with night vision. The only treatment is to remove the lens surgically and restore the eye's vision with an artificially implanted lens or with special contact lenses.
- **Glaucoma.** Glaucoma is a condition in which pressure of the fluid in the eye is so high that it damages the optic nerve and may result in blindness.
- **Detached Retina.** The retina may become separated from the outer layers of the eye as a result of natural degeneration—or wearing out of the tissue—or from injury.

hotlink

antibiotics For more information on the class of medications called antibiotics and the kinds of infections they are used to treat, see Chapter 23, page 512.

Wear protective goggles or glasses when engaging in an activity that could cause eye injury.

ACTIVITY *List different sports activities that require eye protection equipment.*

LESSON 3 Review

Reviewing Facts and Vocabulary

1. Describe the main functions of the three layers of the eyeball wall.
2. Explain the roles of the rods and cones in vision.
3. How do cataracts affect vision?

Thinking Critically

4. *Evaluating.* Do you think it is important for school-aged children to have their vision tested on a regular basis? Why or why not?
5. *Comparing and Contrasting.* Create a Venn diagram with two overlapping circles to show similarities among and differences between nearsightedness and farsightedness. Similarities should be placed in the area where the two circles overlap, differences in the nonoverlapping areas.

Applying Health Skills

6. *In Your Home and School.* Research the costs of various types of eyewear, both eyeglasses and contact lenses of different types. Identify factors that are responsible for the price differences. Share this information with your family and the class.

Lesson 3 Review

Answers to Reviewing Facts and Vocabulary

1. Refer to page 172, *Parts of the Eye.*
2. Rods and cones are the retina's receptors. Sensitive to light and color, they transmit nerve impulses to the optic nerve.
3. They cloud the lens, causing blurred or hazy vision and problems with night vision.

Answers to Thinking Critically

4. Children should be tested regularly because their bodies are constantly changing.
5. Similarities: Both are caused by the failure of the lens to focus the image exactly on the retina, and the result for both is blurred vision. Difference: For nearsightedness, distant objects appear blurred, and for farsightedness, nearby objects are blurred.

ASSESS

EVALUATING THE LESSON

Assign and discuss the Lesson 3 Review; then administer, grade, and discuss the *Lesson 23 Quiz* in the TCR. 🖜

RETEACHING

- Have students make posters of eye charts and eye tests. Under each, have them describe in their own words the purpose of the chart or test as it relates to eye health.
- Ask students to complete *Reteaching Activity 23* in the TCR. 🖜
- Use *Transparency 55* to review the parts of the eye. 🧪

ENRICHMENT

- Have students write a book for grade-school children that creatively presents some basic information about eye structure and eye care. For example, students might make the main character of the book a private eye named Investigator Sight, who is better known as I. Sight. This character might take readers on a secret journey through a giant eyeball to uncover the many mysteries of vision.
- Help students keep up-to-date with one of the most common products of vision technology by having them complete *Enrichment Activity 7,* "Contact Lenses," in the TCR. 🖜

CLOSE

Summarize the most important concepts in this lesson. Ask students what health behaviors they will adopt to take care of their eyes.

Healthy Ears

FOCUS

LESSON OBJECTIVES

After studying this lesson, students should be able to

- label the parts of the ear.
- explain the process of hearing.
- discuss ear care.
- describe common hearing problems.

MOTIVATOR

Write the following on the chalkboard for students to work on while attendance is being taken: *Explain the difference between being partially hearing impaired and being totally hearing impaired.*

INTRODUCING THE LESSON

Discuss student responses to the Motivator. Explain that many factors, including loud noises, can cause vibrations in the inner ear and damage hearing. Some individuals are born with a total hearing impairment and are deaf. Others develop a partial or total hearing impairment from external factors, including noises or diseases, that affect hearing. This lesson will provide information on how sounds or messages are transmitted through the ear to the brain and how external factors can determine the extent of hearing loss.

INTRODUCING HEALTH TERMS

- Conduct a spelling bee with the vocabulary terms for the chapter.
- Ask students to complete Vocabulary Activity 7 and Chapter Study Guide 7 in the *Student Workbook.* ☞

LESSON **4**

Healthy Ears

I f you thought ears were only for hearing, think again. If it were not for the role ears play in balance, you could not sit upright or walk. In this lesson, both these roles will be explored. You will also learn about ways of protecting these vital sense organs.

HEALTH TERMS

external auditory canal

ossicles

labyrinth

otosclerosis

tinnitus

HEALTH CONCEPTS

- Hearing is the result of sound waves moving through the structure of the ears.
- There are effective measures to care for the ears.
- Hearing loss can be prevented by avoiding exposure to excessively loud noise.

Parts of the Ear

T he ear extends deep into the skull and has three main parts. These are:

- **The Outer Ear.** Known technically as the *auricle,* this is the familiar fleshy, curved part attached to each side of the head. It is made up of fatty tissue and cartilage. The auricle collects sound waves and directs them into the ear. Visible within the auricle is the **external auditory canal,** *a passageway about one inch (2.5 cm) long that leads to the eardrum.* This canal is lined with fine hairs and tiny wax-producing glands that protect the ear by trapping dust and other foreign substances. At the inner end of the auditory canal is the tympanic membrane, better known as the eardrum.

176 CHAPTER 7 PERSONAL HEALTH

Lesson 4 Resources

TEACHER'S CLASSROOM RESOURCES

☞ **Concept Map** Activity 24
☞ **Lesson 24 Quiz**
☞ **Lesson Plan 24**
☞ **Reteaching** Activity 24

STUDENT WORKBOOK

☞ **Applying Health Skills 24**
☞ **Chapter Study Guide 7**
☞ **Vocabulary** Activity 7

TRANSPARENCIES

⬛ **Transparency 56**

INNER, MIDDLE, AND OUTER EARS

INNER EAR (LABYRINTH) — MIDDLE EAR — OUTER EAR

AUDITORY OSSICLES

Semicircular canals
Stapes
Incus
Malleus
Auricle

Cochlear nerve
Vestibule
Cochlea
Round window

Eustachian tube

Eardrum
Oval window
Mastoid process
Temporal bone
External auditory canal

▼ *The standard unit for measuring the intensity of sound is the decibel (dB).*

ACTIVITY *List at least three activities during which hearing protection should be worn.*

- **The Middle Ear.** Behind the eardrum are the **ossicles** (AH-si-kuhlz), which are *three small bones linked together that connect the eardrum with the inner ear.* The malleus is the first bone. It is attached to the eardrum and is the largest of the three bones. The incus is the middle bone. It connects the malleus and the innermost bone, the stapes. The stapes is stirrup-shaped and attaches to the inner ear. It is the smallest bone in the body. The ends of the stapes are attached by ligaments to a membrane called the oval window, which leads to the inner ear.

- **The Inner Ear.** The **labyrinth** (LAB-uh-rinth), or *inner ear,* consists of a maze of winding passages divided into three parts. The cochlea, the outermost part, turns sound vibrations into nerve impulses for transmission to the brain. The central and innermost parts, the vestibule and semicircular canals, contain structures critical to the sense of balance.

Hearing

Your ears transform sound waves—vibrations in the air—into nerve impulses that your brain interprets as sounds. Sound waves entering the external auditory canal cause the eardrum to vibrate. These vibrations are carried across the middle ear by the ossicles and into the inner ear. There they are converted into nerve impulses that are then sent to the brain.

Slight differences in how sounds arrive at each ear can indicate the direction a sound is coming from. This is called *binaural hearing.* A sound is slightly louder in the ear that is closer to the

TEACH

🔲 Demonstrating

Use an anatomical model of the ear to explain the path of sound to the brain, where the message is interpreted. Ask students to form groups of five to make a collage of external factors that affect hearing.

🔲 Class Activity

Bring a level to class. Point out how the level is used to determine the horizontal angle of a surface. Have students use the level on different objects to see if each one is balanced. Explain how the small bulb, which is partially filled with water, works. *(The slightest change causes the bubble to shift.)* Demonstrate to the class the similarities of the level to the ear in maintaining balance. Explain with charts or drawings how the liquid in the semicircular canals constantly shifts to compensate for movement.

🔲 Discussing

Talk about how one's ears pop in elevators or on planes. *(This is due to a change in air pressure in the Eustachian tube.)* What are some common remedies for dealing with this type of discomfort? *(swallowing, yawning, chewing gum.)* Why do these methods work? *(They force the valve at the throat end of the Eustachian tube to open and release or admit air as needed.)*

MORE ABOUT . . . . .

ACUITY AND RANGE OF HUMAN HEARING. When the energy of audible sound waves is compared with the energy of visible light waves, human hearing is about 10 times more sensitive than human vision. In fact, if our hearing were much more acute, it would result in our experiencing a constant buzzing or hissing sensation.

Human ears can detect sound waves from about 20 to 20,000 cycles per second (or hertz), which is a range of over 10 octaves. Human voices range from about 500 to 4,000 hertz, so it's not surprising that our greatest acuity falls within that range, occurring between about 1,000 and 2,000 hertz.

L1 Discussing

How do closed-captioned TV programs for the hearing impaired work? Have students develop a list of TV programs they watch that are closed-captioned. What conclusions can students draw from this quick research about the variety of TV programs available for those with a hearing impairment?

L1 Demonstrating

Have the school nurse demonstrate the audiometer for the class. Ask students to discuss hearing devices that are available for the hearing impaired.

L2 Personal Involvement

Instruct students to keep an inventory of loud sounds they hear outside the classroom. Which are potentially detrimental to hearing? What can be done to lessen this problem?

L1 Guest Speakers

Invite several people to talk about personal experiences with hearing loss. What has been the most difficult situation they faced because of difficulty hearing? What is the funniest thing that ever happened because of miscommunication? Ask the speakers to offer additional guidelines for communicating with a hearing-impaired person. Hold a class discussion for additional questions and comments.

CHARACTER IN ACTION

Worth Hearing

Have students work in small groups to practice lip-reading. What did they observe about this experience? What do they think it would be like to rely on this means of communicating with other people? How can they honor the needs and dignity of the hearing-impaired?

---

sound source and reaches that ear a fraction of a second sooner than it does the other ear. Your brain notices these differences in loudness and time and uses them to determine the direction from which the sound comes.

Balance

The semicircular canals in your ears provide much of the brain's information about balance. At one end of each canal is an organ called a *crista*. The crista contains many tiny hairs bathed in a fluid. As the head moves, the fluid shifts, bending the hairs and stimulating nerve impulses. Some of these hairs are sensitive to gravity. Others respond to positions and movements—up and down, side to side, back and forth. Nerve fibers send information about changes in position to the brain. The brain then signals the muscles to make the necessary adjustments to maintain balance.

Healthy Ears

To keep your ears healthy, it is important to clean them regularly and to protect them against weather, especially the cold. Clean the outer ears with a cotton swab. Use the soft head of the swab to remove dirt and earwax, but do not push the swab into the ear. Never use pencils or other sharp items to clean your ears.

Avoiding loud noises is another measure you can take to protect the health of your ears. When you are listening to music or the TV, keep the sound at a reasonable level. When you operate noisy machinery, wear ear protectors. Exposure to loud noise over time can lead to temporary, and sometimes permanent, hearing loss. If your school offers hearing tests, have one performed on you. Early diagnosis of problems is important.

Problems of the Ear

Deafness is a complete or partial inability to hear. Total deafness is rare and is usually congenital, or present from birth. Partial deafness, ranging from mild to severe, is most commonly caused by an ear disease, injury, or the aging process.

All deafness is one of two types. These are known as *conductive* and *sensorineural*.

Conductive Deafness

In conductive deafness, sound waves are not passed from the outer to the inner ear. This can be caused by damage to the eardrum or the ossicles or by earwax blocking the auditory canal. Middle-ear infections may lead to rupture of the eardrum. Persistent buildup of fluid within the middle ear, often due to infection, is the most common cause of hearing difficulties in children.

▲ *Having regular checkups helps ensure healthy ears.*

ACTIVITY *List situations in which you would need to take steps to protect your hearing.*

HOME AND COMMUNITY CONNECTION

THE HEARING IMPAIRED. Encourage students to investigate how their community provides for individuals with impaired hearing. Are signers present to translate at town meetings or meetings of the city council and other city and district agencies? Are signers present at other community events, such as plays and celebrations, or are captions provided? Do most public telephones have volume adjustments? How easy is it to contact community agencies through access operators for the hearing impaired? Have students write a letter to the editor of a local newspaper, commending community provisions for the hearing impaired or suggesting needed changes.

A less common cause of conductive deafness is **otosclerosis** (OH-toh-skluh-ROH-suhs)**.** This is *a hereditary disorder in which an overgrowth of bone causes the ossicles to lose their ability to move.* Otosclerosis is usually progressive. This means its severity increases with time. Surgery can be used to treat this condition.

Sensorineural Deafness

In sensorineural deafness, sounds that reach the inner ear are not sent to the brain. This is the result of damage to the cochlea, to the auditory nerve, or to part of the brain. Sensorineural deafness can be caused by many factors. These include prolonged exposure to loud noise, some medicines such as streptomycin, increased fluid pressure in the labyrinth, viral infections, and tumors.

Have you ever experienced a ringing noise in your ears? **Tinnitus** (TIN-uh-tuhs) is *a condition in which a ringing, buzzing, whistling, hissing, or other noise is heard in the ear in the absence of external sound.* Tinnitus is usually a symptom of damage to the ear. It can also be a reaction to medication, or a symptom of a physical condition, such as hypertension. About 50 million Americans have tinnitus. Overexposure to loud noise is the most common cause of tinnitus.

You can do something about hearing loss and tinnitus. Take these steps to protect your ears:

- Lower the volume of the source of the noise.
- Wear earplugs in a noisy environment.
- Limit the length of time you are exposed to loud noise. It will reduce the chance of permanent ear damage.

CHARACTER IN ACTION

Worth Hearing

One way to show care and respect is to be **considerate** of others' specific needs.

Character Check When communicating with someone who is hearing impaired, follow these guidelines.

➤ Face the person, speak clearly.

➤ Speak loudly, but do not shout.

➤ Speak slowly, but do not talk "down" to the person in terms of content.

➤ Keep lip movements and facial gestures normal.

➤ Keep your hands away from your mouth when you speak.

➤ Show the same dignity toward the hearing impaired that you do toward all people.

LESSON 4 Review

Reviewing Facts and Vocabulary

1. What is the function of the auditory canal?
2. Identify the parts of the labyrinth.
3. Describe the proper method for cleaning the ears.

Thinking Critically

4. **Analyzing.** Analyze the ear as a source of balance.
5. **Evaluating.** What has been the impact of this lesson on your willingness to care for your ears?

Applying Health Skills

6. **In Your School.** Think about areas in and around your school where noise is

a problem. Write a letter to the school's administration proposing remedies for this problem. Find out whether your community is one of the growing number nationwide that has ordinances— or laws—to control loud noises from car stereos and other sources.

LESSON 4 HEALTHY EARS **179**

ASSESS

EVALUATING THE LESSON

Assign and discuss the Lesson 4 Review; then administer, grade, and discuss the *Lesson 24 Quiz* in the TCR.

RETEACHING

- Ask students to make a drawing of the ear. Tell them to label each part and trace the path of sound through the ear. Have them explain how hearing loss or damage occurs and what the causes are.
- Ask students to complete *Reteaching Activity 24* in the TCR.
- Use *Transparency 56* to review the parts of the ear.

ENRICHMENT

Have students read about Gallaudet University in Washington, D.C., the nation's only institution of higher learning for the deaf. What particular resources does it offer its hearing-impaired students? In what ways is it like other liberal arts colleges? What do you think the advantages of attending such a school might be for the hearing impaired?

CLOSE

Summarize the most important concepts in this lesson. Have students list five rules for ear care they are willing to follow for life.

Lesson 4 Review

Answers to Reviewing Facts and Vocabulary

1. It transmits sound waves to the eardrum.
2. Cochlea, vestibule, and semicircular canals.
3. Use a cotton swab to remove dirt and earwax from the outer ear.

Answers to Thinking Critically

4. Organs in the ear, that are sensitive to gravity and motion, transmit messages to the brain to help send messages to keep the body structure in balance.
5. Answers will vary.

ACTIVITY 1
HEALTH SKILLS

Comprehending Health Concepts, Accessing Health Information

➤ **National Standards**
This activity meets these National Health Standards: 1; 2.1.

Teach

- At least one week before you carry out this activity, instruct students to begin keeping track of what they eat on a daily basis. If possible, remind students again later in the week to keep track of their diet.
- Review the role of vitamins in healthy skin, covered in Lesson 1.
- Bring to class any health articles you discover that detail how vitamins influence personal health.
- Refer students to page 108 in the text to carry out the activity.

ACTIVITY 2
HEALTH SKILLS

Analyzing Influences, Health Advocacy

➤ **National Standards**
This activity meets this National Health Standard: 5.1; 7.6.

Teach

- Distribute the children's books to students. Suggest that the students look at the types of illustrations featured and the language—especially the length of sentences and word choice.
- Follow up the outside reading of the completed children's books with a discussion of how successful the books were in delivering the intended message. What would students do differently if they planned to write an additional children's health book?

Health **Skills** Activities

Activity 1 — Vitamins for Health

Adjusting your diet or taking vitamin supplements can help to ensure that you are getting all the vitamins you need to maintain your personal health. Evaluate your diet to see if it lacks any of the essential vitamins that you need.

Directions

1. For one week, keep track of all the foods and beverages you intake. Include everything you eat—breakfast, lunch, dinner, and even snacks.
2. Bring in the diet information that you have been recording for the last week. Refer to page 108 in your health text.
3. Compare the foods you have been eating with the foods listed in the chart. List all the vitamins that are included in your diet for each day. Make note of any vitamins you are missing or that you receive in small amounts.
4. Next to the list of any vitamins your diet may be lacking, record what role those vitamins play in your body. Determine whether you need to add any foods or supplements to your diet.

Time
one week out of class and 50 minutes in class

Materials
paper, pen or pencil

Self-Assessment

✓ Recorded your diet for at least one week.
✓ Correctly compared diet to chart on page 108 and identified any vitamins that may be deficient in your diet.

Activity 2 — Promoting Personal Health Care

Teachers of elementary children are always looking for interesting ways of teaching their students about the proper care of the eyes, teeth, and hair. What creative ideas do you have about the best ways to teach personal health care to young children?

Directions

1. Create a booklet to teach young children about the care of the eyes, teeth, and/or hair. Read several children's books for ideas.
2. Make a storyboard, plotting out illustrations, and then outline the text. Complete your storyboard, making it colorful and appealing. Focus on the best way to positively influence your target age group.
3. Read your completed story to a young child—maybe a brother or sister—or to a class at a local elementary school. Ask for feedback on what was learned about improving hygiene habits.

Time
two 50-minute periods

Materials
children's books, storyboard, paper, pen or pencil, markers

Self-Assessment

✓ Described appropriate personal care of eyes, teeth, and/or hair illustrated with pictures.
✓ Created messages appropriate to age group of younger children.

180 CHAPTER 7 PERSONAL HEALTH

ASSESSMENT SCORING

Using a four-level rubric, the student has achieved a 4 if:

ACTIVITY 1
✔ Student recorded his/her diet for the time allotted.
✔ Student correctly compared diet to chart.
✔ Student identified any vitamins that were deficient in his/her diet.
✔ Student identified ways those deficient vitamins could be incorporated either through foods or supplements.

ACTIVITY 2
✔ The student made a storyboard and/or a preliminary draft of a children's book.
✔ The student communicated appropriate personal care of eyes, teeth, or hair.
✔ The students showed creativity in communicating health ideas.
✔ The student followed with the reading of the book for an elementary audience.

HEALTH NEWS

ARTICLE

Harmful Rays of Light

If you weren't born with a tan, the Centers for Disease Control and Prevention says you should think twice about trying to get one.

Since tanning now can lead to skin cancer later, the federal government is directing its skin cancer prevention message toward young people. The "Choose Your Cover" campaign includes upbeat, youth-oriented TV, radio, and print advertisements. The ads tell children and teenagers to use sunscreen, wear wide-brim hats and avoid the midday sun.

"Young people need to know that the risk of getting skin cancer later can be greatly reduced if they start protecting their skin from the sun now," CDC Director Jeffrey P. Koplan said.

"The effects of the sun are cumulative," said Mary Kay Sones, a spokeswoman for the CDC. "Most of a person's lifetime sun exposure occurs before 18," she said.

The CDC recommends that individuals take personal responsibility for their skin. Protective measures include wearing a hat, remaining in the shade, slathering on sunscreen with an SPV of at least 15, donning sunglasses, and covering skin with lightweight clothing.

If possible, people should avoid going outside between the peak hours of 10 a.m. and 4 p.m., when the sun's rays are most powerful.

Read This

Take the Quiz: Are You at Risk?

1. What is your skin complexion?
   - Fair
   - Dark
2. Do you have a family history of skin cancer?
   - Yes
   - No
3. Do you have freckles?
   - Yes
   - No
4. How often are you exposed to the sun?
   - Everyday
   - Only on vacation
   - Never
5. Do you use sunscreen with an SPF rating of 15 or higher?
   - Yes
   - No

Think About It

1. Do you always wear sunscreen? Why or why not?
2. Do you think you could be at risk for skin cancer?
3. Does the statement from CDC Director Jeffrey P. Koplan motivate you to be more cautious in the sun?

CNN HEALTH NEWS **181**

MORE ABOUT . . . . .

RELIABLE SOURCES. The Centers for Disease Control and Prevention (CDC) is recognized as the leading federal agency for protecting health and safety. One of the major components of the Department of Health and Human Services, with approximately 8,500 employees in 170 occupations, the CDC develops and applies disease prevention and control, environmental health, and health promotion and education activities designed to improve the health of the people of the United States.

Challenge students to discover more about the CDC as a reliable source of information about skin cancer and prevention. Students can use the Glencoe Web Links at health.glencoe.com to connect with the CDC online.

HEALTH NEWS

Harmful Rays of Light

Objectives. After reading the article, students should be able to identify the risks of skin cancer and explain the precautionary measures teens can take to decrease these risks.

Motivator. Discuss the results of the quiz "Are You at Risk?" Explain that the risk of skin cancer increases if you have fair skin that freckles or burns, if there is a family history of the disease, and if you do not wear sunblock with SPF 15 or higher. While consistent exposure to the sun is a major risk factor in all types of skin cancer, it takes only intermittent exposure to the sun to increase the risk of developing melanoma.

Teach
- Have students brainstorm reasons why young people do not wear sunscreen. Discuss whether they think the current message being conveyed by the federal government dubbed "Choose Your Cover" will be effective with teens.
- Students can apply their understanding by working in groups to design a sun-friendly playground that educates young children about sun risks and prevents sun damage at the same time. Some examples include placing canopies over play equipment, making sunblock readily available, or building a sundial so children will know when the sun is the strongest.

Investigate. Have students interview family members about a family history of skin cancer and any preventive measures their parents or guardians took to protect them from the sun. Students can ask family members how frequently and to what extent they were exposed to the sun without protection. Ask: "Now that you know about your past exposure to the sun, will you change your current behaviors?"

Close. Help students to explain the goals of the "Choose Your Cover" campaign. Invite them to describe the element of the program they believe will most likely be effective.

CHECKING COMPREHENSION

- Assign and discuss the chapter review.
- Use the MindJogger Videoquiz to review the chapter. 🔴

CHAPTER 7 REVIEW ANSWERS

Using Health Terms

1. sweat glands
2. dandruff
3. acne
4. sebaceous glands
5. follicle
6. pulp
7. tartar
8. plaque
9. periodontal disease
10. periodontium
11. lacrimal gland
12. retina
13. choroid
14. cornea
15. sclera
16. otosclerosis
17. ossicles
18. tinnitus

Recalling the Facts

1. Cushions internal tissues and organs; regulates body temperature; protects against infections, diseases, and ultraviolet rays.
2. Skin cancer.
3. Regular cleansing, use of sunscreen.
4. Removes dirt, distributes natural oils.
5. Keep them clean and evenly trimmed.
6. Chew food, form shape and structure of the mouth.
7. Gums, periodontal ligament, and jawbone. Together, they support the teeth.
8. By the removal of plaque.
9. In malocclusion, the upper and lower teeth don't align properly. It can be treated by orthodontics.

Using Health Terms

On a separate sheet of paper, write the term that best matches each definition below.

LESSON 1

1. Structures within the skin that secrete perspiration through ducts to pores on the surface of the skin.
2. A condition in which the outer layer of dead skin cells is shed from the scalp.
3. A clogging of the pores of the skin.
4. Structures within the skin that produce an oily secretion called sebum.
5. Tiny pits in the skin.

LESSON 2

6. The living tissue inside the tooth.
7. A hard, crustlike substance.
8. A sticky, colorless film that acts on sugar to form acids that destroy tooth enamel.
9. An inflammation of the periodontal structures.

10. The area immediately around the teeth.

LESSON 3

11. The gland responsible for producing tears.
12. The light-sensitive membrane on which images are cast by the cornea and lens.
13. The middle layer of the eyeball wall.
14. The main lens that performs most of the eye's focusing.
15. The tough, white outer coat of the eye.

LESSON 4

16. A hereditary disorder in which an overgrowth of bone causes the ossicles to lose their ability to move.
17. Three tiny, linked, movable bones.
18. A condition in which a ringing, buzzing, whistling, hissing, or other noise is heard in the ear in the absence of external sound.

Recalling the Facts

Using complete sentences, answer the following questions.

LESSON 1

1. Name three functions of your skin.
2. What can be a serious result of excessive exposure to the sun over a period of time?
3. What basic procedures can keep skin healthy?
4. How does regular brushing benefit your hair?
5. What are some basic procedures to follow for good nail care?

LESSON 2

6. What functions do teeth serve?
7. What are the parts of the periodontium, and what function do they serve together?

8. How can periodontal disease be stopped in its early stages?
9. What is malocclusion, and what are its effects?

LESSON 3

10. How does the lens of the eye change, and for what purpose does it change?
11. What part does the brain play in vision?
12. Name three things that you can do to protect your eyes.

LESSON 4

13. What is binaural hearing?
14. What is the function of the semicircular canals?
15. Name four steps you can take to protect your ears.

10. The lens bulges to adjust to nearby objects and flattens to adjust to distant objects.
11. The brain interprets the nerve impulses that are sent through the optic nerve from the eye.
12. Regular checkups, wear glasses or contact lenses if they've been prescribed, take breaks when working at a computer, read and watch TV in a well-lighted room, don't rub your eyes, avoid direct sun or wear sunglasses, use safety goggles when appropriate.
13. The way the brain uses signals from both ears to determine the direction a sound comes from.
14. They provide information about balance.
15. Answers will vary.

Thinking Critically

LESSON 1

1. **Analyzing.** Analyze the sense of the statement: "To avoid the sun, I'm going to a tanning salon."
2. **Comparing.** Describe the differences between gingivitis and periodontitis.

LESSON 2

3. **Synthesizing.** Conduct a survey of the number of people in your class and other grades in your school who wear braces or dental retainers. What might these numbers indicate?

4. **Analyzing.** What snack foods would you recommend for a person who wanted healthy teeth and who was trying to eliminate tooth decay?

LESSON 3

5. **Synthesizing.** What activities would require protective eyewear? When is it appropriate to wear protective eyewear?

LESSON 4

6. **Analyzing.** Consider the statement: "Walkmans and headsets cause more problems than they are worth."

Making the Connection

1. **Science.** Ask a science teacher to help you use a sound level meter to measure the noise levels in various parts of the school. Compare readings against approved safety levels. Make recommendations about improving unhealthful situations to the school administration or student council.

2. **Music.** The great German composer Ludwig van Beethoven lost most of his hearing before he died. Learn about Beethoven and other hearing-impaired composers. Write a brief report summarizing your findings.

BEYOND THE CLASSROOM

PARENTAL INVOLVEMENT Invite family members to take part in an experiment to determine how well brushing and flossing remove plaque from teeth. Get two disclosing tablets for each family member from your dentist or dental hygienist. Each person chews one tablet without swallowing, spits into a sink, and rinses his or her mouth with water. Dark spots on teeth and gums show where plaque has formed. Have each person brush and floss carefully, then use the second disclosing tablet. Compare and discuss the differences in the amount of plaque that is seen.

COMMUNITY INVOLVEMENT Take a sign language class or borrow a book on American Sign Language from your local library. Practice with a friend.

SCHOOL-TO-CAREER

Exploring Careers. The eye care field includes a variety of professions, including ophthalmologist, optometrist, optician, and optometric technician. For each career, determine the educational background and training, duties and responsibilities.

Thinking Critically

1. The cause of tanning, the skin's protective reaction to UV rays, is the same whether you are in the sun or a tanning salon; therefore, the damage will be the same.
2. Gingivitis is an inflammation of the gums only. Periodontitis is a more advanced disorder that also can affect the bones and ligaments that support the teeth.
3. Answers will vary.
4. Fresh fruits and vegetables, sugar-free snacks.
5. Athletic activities, construction or industrial jobs, etc.
6. Answers will vary.

Making the Connection

1. Findings and recommendations will vary.
2. Reports will vary.

Evaluate

- Use the reproducible *Chapter 7 Test* in the TCR or construct your own using the Testmaker software.
- Use *Performance Assessment Activity 7* in the TCR.

Enrichment

Have students complete *Cross-Curriculum Activity 7* in the TCR.

Beyond the Classroom

Keep students involved in the community and encourage parent participation by assigning the activities on this page for students to work on outside of class.

Your Mental and Emotional Health

	FEATURES	CLASSROOM RESOURCES

ACTIVITIES

- Cross-Curriculum Activity 8
- Health Lab 8
- Health Skills Activities 8
- Parent Letter and Activities 8

ASSESSMENT

- Chapter 8 Test
- Performance Assessment Activity 8
- Testmaker Software

STUDENT ACTIVITIES WORKBOOK

- Applying Health Skills 25–28
- Study Guide 8
- Vocabulary Activity 8

STUDENT DIVERSITY STRATEGIES

- Audiocassette Program (English)
- Audiocassette Program (Spanish)
- Spanish Parent Letters and Activities
- Spanish Summaries, Quizzes, and Activities

MULTIMEDIA COMPONENTS

- English Audiocassette Program
- Spanish Audiocassette Program
- MindJogger Videodisc and VHS program
- ABCNews InterActive™ VHS/Videodisc Series

National Health Education Standards

One of the main goals of the National Health Education Standards is to move students toward "health literacy." Health literacy is the capacity of individuals to obtain, interpret, and understand basic health information and services and the competence to use such information and services in ways which promote health. The health standards were developed by applying the characteristics of a well-educated, literate person within the context of health. The health literate person is:

- a critical thinker and problem solver
- a responsible, productive citizen
- a self-directed learner
- an effective communicator

Listed below are the Health Education Standards Performance Indicators addressed in each lesson of this chapter.

Lesson	Health Standards Performance Indicators
1	1.2, 1.4, 5.2, 5.4
2	1.1, 1.2, 1.3, 1.4
3	1.2, 1.3, 3.1, 3.2
4	1.2, 3.1, 5.3, 6.1

ONLINE RESOURCES

For a fresh approach to health topics and an in-depth look at health issues, use these online resources found under Teacher Resources at **health.glencoe.com**.

- **BLOCK SCHEDULE LESSON PLANS** Reinforce health concepts with outside readings selected especially for students. Each reading is accompanied by a lesson plan and activities to enhance
  - Reading Skills
  - Cross Curriculum
  - Media Literacy

- **TECHNOLOGY PROJECTS** Instructions and suggestions on how to use computer, Internet, and software with health lessons.

- **HEALTH UPDATES** Timely topics in health news, including late-breaking medical advances and updates on teen risk behaviors.

Out of Time?

If time does not permit teaching this chapter, you may use these features: Building Health Skills on page 188; Making Responsible Decisions on page 205; and Update on page 206.

BLOCK SCHEDULING

Block scheduling provides extended time for hands-on projects and activities. Use the following activities to engage students, provide further depth, and vary your instructional techniques:

- Connections (30 minutes) **pg. 195**
- Update (30 minutes) **pg. 206**
- Health Skills Activity (60–90 minutes) **pg. 208**

Your Mental and Emotional Health

CHAPTER OVERVIEW

Chapter 8 describes the characteristics of mental health. Students are introduced to Maslow's hierarchy of needs; the emotions that most impact thinking, behavior, and relationships; and how to deal with emotions in healthful ways.

LESSON 1 Though it is difficult to identify specific standards for evaluating a person's mental health, some general characteristics of good mental health exist. Self-esteem can greatly affect mental health and is directly related to one's general level of wellness. High self-esteem promotes good mental health.

LESSON 2 Maslow's hierarchy of needs ranks what human beings must have to survive and thrive. As individuals progress through their hierarchy of needs, they move toward reaching their full potential, and in the process, develop a richer quality of life.

LESSON 3 Your emotions influence everything you do, affecting your thinking, behavior, and relationships. Patterns of negative emotions can greatly affect your physical health. Learning to recognize emotions is a first step toward learning how to deal with them.

LESSON 4 Being able to feel and deal with a variety of emotions and situations is a key to good mental health. Learning to cope with emotions in healthful ways is important to good mental health.

CHAPTER **8**

Your Mental and Emotional Health

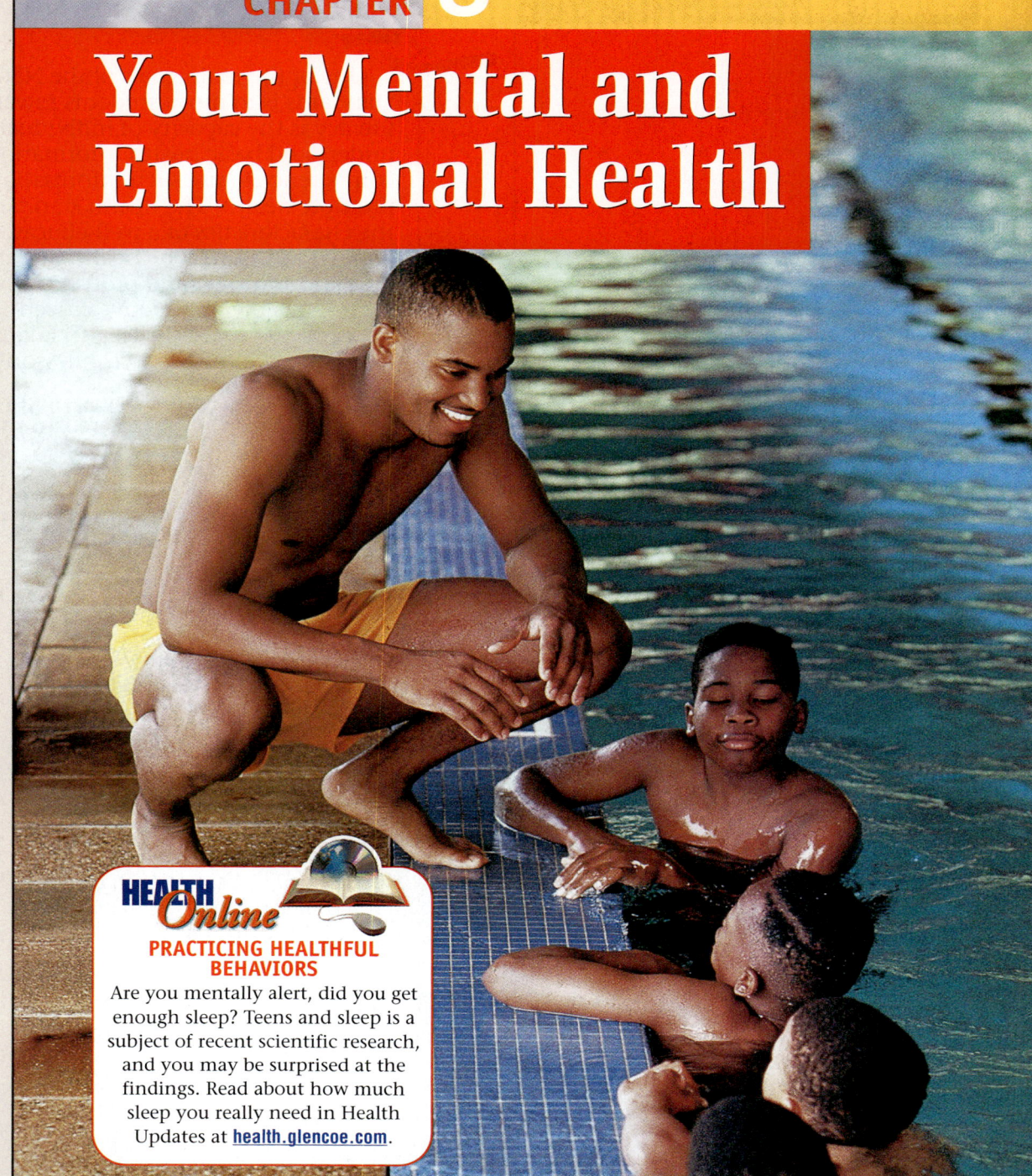

HEALTH Online
PRACTICING HEALTHFUL BEHAVIORS

Are you mentally alert, did you get enough sleep? Teens and sleep is a subject of recent scientific research, and you may be surprised at the findings. Read about how much sleep you really need in Health Updates at **health.glencoe.com**.

Hands-On Health

TEACHING STRATEGY

Identifying Personal Strengths Guide students in identifying their own positive personality traits and achievements, as well as areas that need improvement, in an art-based activity. See Activity 7, "My Coat of Arms," in the *Hands-On Health: Creative Teaching Strategies* booklet. ☞

Time Needed
30-45 minutes

Supplies
- "My Coat of Arms" student worksheet
- colored pencils, markers

Personal Health Inventory

Self-Inventory Write the numbers 1–10 on a sheet of paper. Read each statement below and respond by writing *yes*, *no*, or *sometimes* for each item. Write a *yes* only for items that you practice regularly. Save your responses.

1	I have a generally positive outlook on life.
2	Overall, I like and accept who I am.
3	I recognize my strengths and weaknesses.
4	I try to learn from my mistakes.
5	I am interested in and get along well with others.
6	I can cope with challenges and face problems rather than avoid them.
7	I take responsibility for my personal behavior.
8	I understand my needs and try to get them met in healthful ways.
9	I express my emotions in positive ways.
10	I am usually in control of my emotions more than they are in control of me.

Follow-up After completing the chapter, retake this self-inventory. Pick two items that you need to work on and set a goal to improve your health behaviors.

> 66
> *Positive attitudes—optimism, high self-esteem, an outgoing nature, joyousness, and the ability to cope with stress—may be the most important bases for continued good health.* 99

—HELEN HAYES
INSPIRATIONAL WRITER, (1900–1993)

Quick Write Think of someone you know who has a positive attitude. Summarize in a few sentences how other people react to the person. How does being around that person make *you* feel?

INTRODUCING THE CHAPTER

Personal Health Inventory

Point out that all the statements in this Self-Inventory identify habits and attitudes related to mental and emotional health. Explain that students will find this activity most helpful if they respond to each statement openly and honestly, and reassure them that their responses are completely confidential. Ask students to record their responses in their private Health Journals and label their page "My Level of Mental and Emotional Fitness." They will refer to this page in the chapter follow-up.

- William Glasser provides a model on the psychology of strength vs. weakness. He discovered that the most effective way to develop strength, happiness, and positive emotional health is to apply the following pathways consistently: (a) giving and receiving love, (b) becoming self-disciplined, (c) gaining worth and recognition, and (d) having fun. Have students brainstorm ways they can accomplish each pathway at home and at school.
- Have students read the quotation and do the Quick Write on this page. Ask volunteers to share what they write about positive attitudes. Explain to students that as they read the lessons in Chapter 8, they will learn more about identifying, accepting, and expressing emotions.
- Distribute Parent Letter 8 in the *Parent Letters and Activities* booklet.

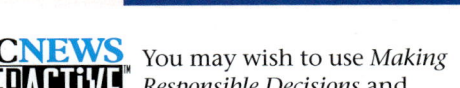

TECHNOLOGY OPTIONS

ABCNEWS INTERACTIVE You may wish to use *Making Responsible Decisions* and *Violence Prevention* with this chapter. For your convenience, use the separate *ABCNews InterActive™ Bar Code Correlation* that accompanies the *Glencoe Health* program.

MINDJOGGER
VIDEOQUIZ

To preview or review chapter content, you may wish to use the *MindJogger Videoquiz* that accompanies Chapter 8.

What Is Mental Health?

LESSON OBJECTIVES

After studying this lesson, students should be able to

- explain how good mental health means much more than not being mentally ill.
- discuss the varying levels of mental health.
- describe how self-esteem is directly related to an individual's general level of wellness.

MOTIVATOR

Write the following on the chalkboard for students to work on while attendance is being taken: *Write as many words as you can think of that describe a person with good mental health.*

INTRODUCING THE LESSON

Have students share their responses to the Motivator. Ask students whether they think good mental health is something that some people are born with or something that is achieved. Tell students that mental health is an important part of the health triangle, and that in this lesson they will learn some ways of achieving it.

INTRODUCING HEALTH TERMS

- Have students write statements that use the vocabulary words in correct context. Their statements should be relevant to their own lives. Ask volunteers to share their responses.
- Ask students to complete Vocabulary Activity 8 and Chapter Study Guide 8 in the *Student Workbook.* 🖙

What Is Mental Health?

Close your eyes. Quickly think of three images that suggest positive mental health. Do you see someone smiling or chatting with friends? Do you see someone attacking a project or problem with a "can do" attitude? Do you see yourself?

HEALTH TERMS

mental health
feedback

HEALTH CONCEPTS

- Mental health means much more than not being mentally ill.
- There are varying levels of mental and emotional health.
- Self-esteem is central to mental and emotional wellness.

Your Mental Health

As with physical health, mental health is much more than the absence of sickness. **Mental health** is *generally having a positive outlook, being comfortable with yourself and others, and being able to meet life's challenges and demands.* Being mentally healthy means being able to cope, adapt, and thrive on many levels. Someone who is mentally healthy can usually handle a wide variety of feelings and situations. He or she will usually make wise and safe choices that demonstrate both strong values and responsible behavior.

Lesson 1 Resources

TEACHER'S CLASSROOM RESOURCES

🖙 **Concept Map** Activity 25
🖙 **Health Lab 8**
🖙 **Lesson 25 Quiz**
🖙 **Lesson Plan 25**
🖙 **Parent Letter and Activities 8**
🖙 **Reteaching** Activity 25

STUDENT WORKBOOK

🖙 **Applying Health Skills 25**
🖙 **Chapter Study Guide 8**
🖙 **Vocabulary** Activity 8

TRANSPARENCIES

🧴 **Transparency 18**

This is not to say that people with a high degree of mental health are never unhappy. Like Seth in the chapter-opening story, everyone's level of mental health has its ups and downs. You can have good physical health yet suffer from an occasional cold or a sore muscle. Likewise, you can have good mental health and still have a bad day or even a bad week once in a while. By the same token, just as you can work consciously at becoming more physically fit, you can also work at improving your "mental fitness."

Assessing Your Mental Fitness

As a health-literate person, your first step toward improving your mental health is to assess your general level of mental fitness. Think back to the health continuum you learned about in Chapter 1. Where on this sliding scale is your mental health at this very minute? How about during recent weeks and months? How many of the signs of mental health in the box below describe you?

How you see yourself may have a lot to do with how others see you.

ACTIVITY *Write down three adjectives that others might use to describe you and three that you would use to describe yourself.*

Signs of Good Mental Health

In general, people with good mental health:

- are realistic about their strengths and weaknesses.
- are responsible for their personal behavior.
- avoid high-risk behaviors, such as using tobacco, alcohol, or other drugs.
- are open-minded and flexible.
- are fun-loving and able to relax alone or with others.
- respect both their own and others' needs.
- respect everyone's value as a human being—including their own.
- express their emotions in ways that do not hurt themselves or others.
- invest time and energy into nourishing relationships.
- put their talents and abilities to good use.
- view change as a challenge and an opportunity.

TEACH

L2 Class Activity

Ask volunteers to give examples of statements people might make that would indicate they felt good about themselves. Let other volunteers give examples that would indicate the people did not feel good about themselves.

L1 Explaining

Tell students that being or pretending to be happy all the time is not necessarily mentally healthy. An array of emotions is healthy for everyone, as long as one emotion does not dominate the others or is not expressed inappropriately.

L3 Class Activity

Have each student create a list of behaviors that indicate mental wellness and behaviors that may indicate a need for help. The lists should be as specific as possible.

LEP Discussing

Making friends when you cannot speak their language is difficult at best. Ask students to consider how it might feel to be in a school where they didn't understand the language. How would they want others to treat them? What might students do to help LEP students feel welcome? How might they help LEP students learn English?

L1 Discussing

Use *Transparency 18* and have students rate their level of mental health wellness.

MORE ABOUT . . . . .

MENTAL FITNESS. In France, there is a long history of doing mental exercises to stimulate the brain, memory, and imagination. Formal workshops, courses, and programs in clubs and clinics are now giving the middle-aged and elderly in France new formal and challenging mental puzzles and exercises to keep their minds working in top form. Among the mental aerobics they routinely do: finding synonyms and antonyms for words and memorizing the names of people, train schedules, and poems.

Remind students that to keep their minds in top-notch form both today and long into the future, they should give their brains a workout every day.

L1 Personal Involvement

Tell students that sometimes people feel down for no particular reason. For example, some people find that they feel bad after eating certain foods, overeating, not eating anything, getting too much sleep or having sleep interrupted, not getting any exercise, or just before their menstrual periods.

Students can make a mood map to determine a pattern of these episodes. Have them start by getting a blank calendar and writing down what their basic moods are each day and what their eating, drinking, sleeping, exercising, and other habits are that may account for how they feel. After a month, see if they can establish both a pattern and a cause for their mood shifts. However, if their bad feelings continue, increase in severity, or are incapacitating, they should seek help from a trusted adult, counselor, or friend.

L1 Cooperative Learning

Divide the class into four groups composed of students with differing ability levels. Select a scribe for each group and a task master to keep the group focused. Have two groups develop a list of things a person might hear as he or she grows up that would enhance self-esteem. Have the other two groups develop a list of things that would inhibit or lower self-esteem. Give the groups 10 minutes to complete the exercise. Next, have the groups with the same assignments work together to compare lists and select the best items from each. There must be a consensus on each item, not just a majority. Ask representatives to share results.

L2 Health Lab

Distribute *Health Lab 8* and have students research the role of positive feedback in relation to performance. ☞

CHARACTER IN ACTION

Forgiveness

Forgiveness means letting go of the misdeeds and mistakes of others.

Character Check Can you think of someone you hold a grudge against? Remind yourself that people make mistakes. Try to understand the feelings behind the person's behavior. Wish for something good to happen to that person, despite your resentment. Take responsibility for your part in what went wrong. Be forgiving and let go of the rest.

Can you find patterns in the ways you react to different situations and people? Are there certain conditions under which you feel more alive, positive, and able to cope? The more you identify such factors, the better able you may be to control them.

Roadblocks to Mental Health

On the road to improved mental health, you may run into obstacles in your own thinking, attitudes, or behaviors. By becoming aware of these roadblocks, you can learn to bypass them. Among these roadblocks are the following:

- **All-or-nothing thinking.** Many situations have "shades of gray." Learn to recognize and accept these subtle degrees of difference.
- **Expecting the "worst" in others or yourself.** Look for the good, and you will be more likely to find it.
- **Being a perfectionist.** Trying to be perfect or thinking you can do it all often leads to failure and frustration. Remind yourself that no one is perfect. Don't be afraid to ask for help when you need it.
- **Letting your actions or words betray your values.** Stand up for what you believe in and know is right.

Building Health Skills

Promoting a Positive Self-Image

IT IS NEVER too late to begin improving your self-esteem and, in turn, your mental health. Try the following suggestions:

1. **List your assets or strengths.** Include your mental, emotional, and physical strengths. Read this list every day for a week.

2. **Surround yourself with positive, supportive people.** Choose friends who support you, believe in you, and respect your individual rights and needs.

3. **Find something that you love to do, and do it frequently.** If you're always too busy to do the things you enjoy, you're not fully taking care of yourself. Make time for your favorite activities and pastimes.

4. **Stop making life a contest.** Recognize that there will always be people more and less able than you in all areas of life. Be content with doing the best you can in all areas that really matter to you.

5. **Help someone else.** One way to feel good about yourself is to see the positive effects of your own words or actions on someone else's life.

188   CHAPTER 8   YOUR MENTAL AND EMOTIONAL HEALTH

MEETING STUDENT DIVERSITY

THE PHYSICALLY IMPAIRED. Ask volunteers to write a skit, poem, or song about their personal experiences with a physical impairment. Have them share their viewpoints on dealing with life's challenges. Ask them to portray how positive support from others helps, and how negative responses can hurt. Also have them portray how they deal with personal feelings of negativity or depression.

Self-Esteem and Your Mental Health

Self-esteem—the confidence and worth that you feel about yourself—is directly related to your general level of wellness. How you feel mentally and physically and how you take care of yourself—your health habits—are all affected by what you think of yourself. Teens with high self-esteem are better able to take failure in their stride and move forward. They often tend to have specific long-term goals and aspirations for their future. Having high self-esteem promotes good mental health.

The Role of Positive and Negative Feedback

How is self-esteem formed? Over the years you have received **feedback**—*messages from others that indicate who they think you are or what they think you are like.* You have received positive or negative feedback from many sources—from your parents or guardians, other adults who first took care of you, as well as from your siblings, your extended family, teachers, coaches, friends, and your peers.

From the moment you were born, you began to receive, process, and store these messages, which came mostly from your family. Some messages were nonverbal. People hugged you, patted you, and smiled at you. Perhaps they frowned at or ignored you. All of these actions made deep and lasting impressions on you. These first caregivers gave you verbal messages, too, like "Oh, what a cute baby!" or "Bad boy!" With all of these verbal and nonverbal messages that you received, you began to develop your self-esteem.

By the time you reached school age, other factors started to play a role in how you viewed yourself. Now, in addition to your family, your feelings were influenced by how friends, neighbors, and teachers reacted to you. During the teen years, feedback from peers takes on a new and greater importance. Messages from the media about what you as a teenager *should* be like have also directly or indirectly begun to shape and influence your self-image.

So what does self-esteem have to do with overall mental health? A person who has received mostly positive feedback will generally have high

▼ *Participating in community projects and volunteering your skills and talents can contribute to positive mental health.*

ACTIVITY *Over the next month, learn a new skill or try a new and healthful recreational activity. Record your progress in your private Health Journal.*

Building Health Skills

Promoting a Positive Self-Image
Skill: Self-Esteem

Ask how students would respond to a teen who says the following: *It's too late for me to have any real self-esteem. I had a miserable childhood—my parents didn't even want me, and they let me know it!* After several volunteers have shared their ideas, let students read the Building Health Skills feature to learn more about how anyone—at any age—can improve his or her self-esteem. Have students meet in groups to discuss their ideas about the specific suggestions listed in the feature. Then ask students to write private Health Journal entries, identifying what they can do to improve their own self-esteem.

L3 Researching

Many schools have established peer-to-peer helpers. These student volunteers are trained by a counselor to work with students who express a need to "talk." The peer counselors learn how to assist their friends in problem-solving ten common issues. Have students find out how to start peer helper groups in your school.

CHARACTER IN ACTION

Forgiveness

Ask students to role-play situations where an individual has his or her feelings hurt by a friend, discusses these feelings in healthful and honest ways, and eventually forgives the friend's behavior. After the skit, discuss the emotional benefits to the person doing the forgiving.

PERSONAL HEALTH

MEDIA AND SELF-ESTEEM. Many people lower their self-esteem by comparing themselves unfavorably to others, especially models in advertisements, characters in fiction, celebrities, and others in the media. Have students select several ads from magazines or television that project unrealistic images that could be mistakenly accepted as standards of reference.

What unrealistic qualities do these images project? Perfect beauty? Wealth? Superstar status? Encourage students to examine fictitious characters on television or in literature that have become role models. In what ways might people feel inferior if they compared themselves with these characters?

h⊙t link

constructive criticism
Discuss how constructive criticism fosters a positive outlook and goal orientation. Ask students to note in their journals a personal situation where constructive criticism would have helped them get through a difficult situation.

ASSESS

EVALUATING THE LESSON

Assign and discuss the Lesson 1 Review; then administer, grade, and discuss the *Lesson 25 Quiz* in the TCR. ✐

RETEACHING

- Ask students to write a test question based on the lesson. Divide the class into two teams and ask them the questions, awarding points for correct answers. Repeat the questions that were answered incorrectly.
- Ask students to complete *Reteaching Activity 25* in the TCR. ✐

ENRICHMENT

Ask students to speak to five people they usually don't speak to. Instruct them to watch for nonverbal responses from these people and draw conclusions from their observations. Then ask students to observe the nonverbal and verbal responses of five close friends. Students should record their conclusions in both situations.

CLOSE

Provide students with a summary of what they should have learned as a result of this lesson by reviewing the lesson objectives.

self-esteem. Someone who has received lots of negative feedback may be more likely to have low self-esteem and fragile mental health. This person may also misinterpret the feedback she or he gets from others, and may assume messages are negative even when they are not.

Self-Talk

Feedback comes not just from others but also from yourself. Are you too hard on yourself when you do something wrong or make a mistake? Do you go overboard in focusing on your own limitations or weaknesses? *Negative self-talk*—hurtful or non-constructive messages that you send yourself—can erode your self-esteem as much and sometimes even more than negative feedback from others. Positive feedback on the other hand, can do just the opposite. If someone continually tells you you can do whatever you set out to do, you may start to believe that person—and in yourself.

Listen to the messages you send yourself, and replace any negative self-talk with **constructive criticism**. When you make a mistake, accept it as part of being human and try to learn and grow from the experience. This is one way of reducing the chances of making the same mistake in the future. Get into the habit, moreover, of giving yourself a verbal pat on the back from time to time. Tell yourself "Good job" or "Way to go" when you've done something deserving of praise. Your self-esteem and mental health will benefit.

h⊙t link

constructive criticism For more information on constructive criticism and its benefits to social and overall health, see Chapter 11, page 209.

LESSON **1** *Review*

Reviewing Facts and Vocabulary

1. Name three signs of positive mental health.
2. Name two factors that influence a person's self-esteem.

Thinking Critically

3. *Analyzing.* Make two lists, one of positive feedback and one of negative feedback that you received in your childhood. Describe how you think each kind of feedback affected your self-image.
4. *Evaluating.* Over the next week, keep track of each time you hear a "put-down" from a peer. Take note of when and where the put-down is delivered, how it is received, and how it seems to affect

the self-esteem of its recipient. See if you can find a relationship between the level of self-esteem of the people who deliver put-downs and the frequency with which they use them.

Applying Health Skills

5. *In Your Home.* Think of a caring adult in your family who has been important in your life and has given you positive feedback. Write a letter to this person, thanking him or her for caring. Indicate in the letter how this positive feedback has affected your feelings of self-worth.

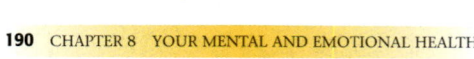

Lesson 1 Review

Answers to Reviewing Facts and Vocabulary

1. Having a positive mental outlook, being comfortable with yourself and others, and being able to meet life's challenges and demands.
2. Positive feedback and negative feedback about yourself.

Answers to Thinking Critically

3.–4. Answers will vary.

Your Needs, Your Personality

Have you ever been so thirsty for a drink of water that nothing else seemed to matter? Like all people, you usually try to get your most basic needs met first. This is true not only for physical needs, but also for emotional and social needs. Getting your needs met in positive ways is essential for your total health.

HEALTH TERMS

hierarchy of needs
aesthetic
self-actualization
personality
psychologists
modeling

HEALTH CONCEPTS

- All human beings have basic needs.
- When basic needs are continuously not met, physical and mental illness may occur.
- Personality is shaped by three main factors: heredity, environment, and behavior.
- The factor over which you have the most control is your personal behavior.

A Pyramid of Needs

There are many theories that try to explain or describe human behavior and development in terms of needs. One famous theory is that of Abraham Maslow, who organized human needs into the form of a pyramid. Maslow maintained that although everyone has needs, some are more basic than others. These lower needs must be satisfied before higher-level needs can be met. Maslow's **hierarchy of needs** is *a ranked list of those needs essential to human growth and development presented in ascending order from the most basic to the most fulfilling or satisfying.*

People who do not have their needs met in healthful ways may be motivated to get them met in unhealthful or inappropriate ways. Think of the child who is constantly being scolded for misbehaving. That child has probably learned that one sure way to get attention is

---

LESSON | 2

Your Needs, Your Personality

FOCUS

LESSON OBJECTIVES

After studying this lesson, students should be able to

- recognize that all human beings have basic needs.
- describe Abraham Maslow's hierarchy of needs pyramid.
- state three main factors that influence the development of one's personality.

MOTIVATOR

Write the following on the chalkboard for students to work on while attendance is being taken: *List 25 needs you have and categorize them under the appropriate levels in Maslow's hierarchy of needs.*

INTRODUCING THE LESSON

Refer to the Motivator. Have students identify the categories under which they listed most of their needs. Ask why people tend to think in terms of physical needs rather than emotional or aesthetic needs. Explain that as people get older, their needs change.

INTRODUCING HEALTH TERMS

- Ask the class to write definitions for the vocabulary terms in their own words. Have students then read their definitions to a partner, who should respond with the appropriate term and give feedback on whether the definition could be improved.
- Ask students to complete Vocabulary Activity 8 and Chapter Study Guide 8 in the *Student Workbook.*

Lesson 2 Resources

TEACHER'S CLASSROOM RESOURCES

- Concept Map Activity 26
- Lesson 26 Quiz
- Lesson Plan 26
- Reteaching Activity 26

STUDENT WORKBOOK

- Applying Health Skills 26
- Chapter Study Guide 8
- Vocabulary Activity 8

TRANSPARENCIES

- Transparency 19

TEACH

Invite interested students to complete the assignment as a group and present their findings in the form of a mock documentary. Some group members are to represent mental health professionals, while others conduct interviews, and so on. If possible, the documentary should be videotaped and broadcast on school TV.

L1 Writing

Have students visit a store that sells greeting cards and read the messages on cards with friendship or caring themes. (Suggest that students seek out a store clerk if they need help locating such cards.)

Students should then compose an original greeting card that meets an emotional need of someone they care about. If they wish, they may give it to the person.

L3 Reading

Have students locate and read magazine articles or newspaper clippings that discuss individuals whose basic needs are unmet for some reason, such as during war, civil unrest, or due to social problems such as homelessness. Ask them to be prepared to discuss their readings in class.

Your emotional needs are an important part of your good mental health. Follow the Web Links at **health.glencoe.com** to the National Institute of Mental Health and learn how mental health professionals study mental disorders.

Every human being feels the need to belong.

ACTIVITY *Name three places or groups where you feel that you belong.*

to act up. How do you think this child might act as an adolescent or as an adult in order to meet the need to be recognized? At any time such people can be shown more healthful ways to get their needs met. With help, they can often overcome some of the damage that may have resulted from being neglected or deprived earlier in life.

Physical Needs

At the bottom of Maslow's pyramid are physical needs. Among these are the need to satisfy hunger, thirst, sleep, and so on. People who are denied these become physically weak. A lack of essential nutrients the body needs also interferes with the normal functioning of the brain, which in turn affects a person mentally. Many people in our society take for granted that these needs are easily satisfied for everyone. They may overlook the fact that there are great numbers of people for whom food, clean water, and shelter are scarce or unavailable.

Emotional Needs

Emotional needs include the need to be loved, to belong, and to be valued and recognized. After we meet our physical needs, most of our behavior is an attempt to meet emotional needs.

- **The need to be loved.** Everyone needs to give love and to feel that he or she is valued and loved in return. Babies who are denied both physical and emotional attention may be stunted physically and mentally. They may fail to thrive. Some even die.
- **The need to belong.** Everyone has the need to belong. Human beings are social beings; that is, they need to be with and interact with people. We need to feel like we belong to and are a valued member of a group. When we are mentally healthy, we meet these needs in positive ways that benefit ourselves and those to whom we are connected. When we are not mentally healthy, we may isolate ourselves from others.
- **The need to be valued and recognized.** Another emotional need that all human beings have is feeling that they have personal value or worth. We have a need to achieve—to have ourselves and others recognize that we are competent at something and that we can make a positive contribution to the world. We must have something we can do well, and we need recognition from others.

Aesthetic Needs

At the next level of Maslow's pyramid are **aesthetic**, or *artistic,* needs. The word *aesthetic* means artistic; it applies to our response to or appreciation of

MEETING STUDENT DIVERSITY

THE EMOTIONALLY CHALLENGED. The Federation of Families for Children's Mental Health believes that young people with emotional, behavioral, or mental disorders

- have special needs that require individualized services.
- must be respected for their rights, likes and dislikes, values, strengths, and cultural and racial backgrounds.
- are entitled to full citizenship in their communities.
- must get what they need to achieve their full potential.
- belong with families and need ongoing relationships with adults.
- make contributions to their families, and must receive the help they need to stay at home with their families when possible.

MASLOW'S HIERARCHY OF NEEDS

Need for self-actualization

SELF-FULFILLING

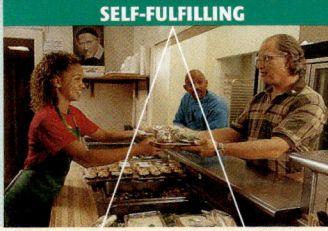

Need to know, to explore, to understand

AESTHETIC

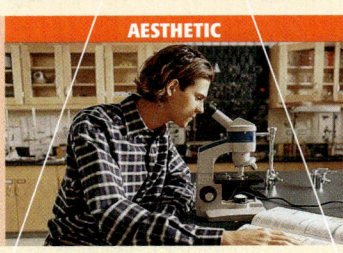

Need to achieve, to be recognized

EMOTIONAL

Need to belong, to love and be loved

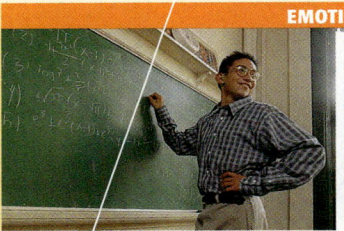

Need to be secure and safe, out of danger

PHYSICAL

Need to satisfy hunger, thirst, sleep, etc.

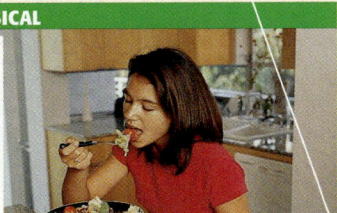

that which is beautiful. We feel the need to appreciate beauty in its many forms, and we also feel the desire for order and balance in our lives. Our senses are constantly stimulated by the rhythms, forms, and colors around us, which can, in turn, affect our behavior and mental health.

Self-Fulfilling Needs

At the top of Maslow's pyramid is the need to reach one's full potential as a person. This quest for **self-actualization**—*the striving to become the best that you can be*—includes having goals that motivate and inspire you. Self-actualization is a lifelong process.

▲ *Basic needs speak the loudest.*
ACTIVITY *Describe a time when you needed food, water, or sleep, and this need overshadowed everything else.*

LEP ## Cooperative Learning

Assign students to small groups. Have them make or select a gift—such as a poem, a card, or a collage—that could bring a smile to a resident of a mental health center or a local nursing home. Before the gifts are presented, display them for the rest of the class.

L1 ## Class Activity

Divide students into groups of five or less. Provide each group with three sheets of paper in different colors. Ask the groups to write the emotions or feelings each color evokes from them on the corresponding color paper. Put the colored papers on the walls and have each group select a reporter to share the group's responses with the class. Circle the emotions that are the same but are evoked by responses to different colors. Discuss why similar reactions may come from different colors.

L3 ## Class Activity

Ask students to plan a color scheme for a children's hospital, a home for the aging, a psychiatric center, or a hospice. All rooms and areas of these facilities need to be considered. Have students develop the sequence of steps they will need to follow in order to plan the various color schemes.

L1 ## Discussing

Use *Transparency 19* to introduce, reinforce, and discuss Maslow's hierarchy of needs.

HEALTH LITERACY

EFFECTIVE COMMUNICATOR. One person can boost or crush another's self-esteem at times. Pair students to brainstorm a list of situations that hold the potential for one person to affect another's self-esteem, such as these examples: One teen asks another for a date, a player beats another at tennis before an audience, a friend constantly borrows things and does not take care of them. Have students role-play the situations twice, first handling them in ways that damage self-esteem, then handling them in ways that protect self-esteem.

L2 Writing

Ask students to visit an art exhibit at a local museum or gallery. Different types of artworks will usually be displayed. If no exhibit is available, borrow a selection of paintings or artwork to bring into the classroom. Ask students to describe in a brief written report which pieces of art they found pleasing and why.

Visual Learning

The Domino Effect

Have students examine the dominoes shown and ask them to describe the reaction that occurs when one domino in a row is touched. (You may wish to set up a demonstration with real dominoes.) Discuss how this domino effect is experienced as students learn about personality development. Ask students to picture each domino as a step or a thought that brings them closer to a goal in their journey toward self-actualization. Have them describe how one step taken now can have a positive, or negative, effect on the future as students work toward achieving their goals.

During the teen years, working toward self-actualization may involve volunteering to help others, making specific education and career goals, and beginning to work toward these goals. What goals have you begun to work toward?

It is important to note that not all of your needs can be met all of the time. You may have some needs met only partly and still strive to satisfy the higher ones. Even people raised in extreme conditions can create lives for themselves that reach toward self-actualization.

Understanding Your Personality

Think about words you have heard to describe other people—for example, "quiet," "pushy," or "outgoing." Words like these may describe some characteristics of a person's personality. **Personality** is, in fact, *a complex set of characteristics that makes you unique and sets you apart from everyone else.* It includes your emotional makeup, attitudes, thoughts, behaviors, and more.

Psychologists, *professionals with doctoral degrees who diagnose and treat emotional and behavioral disorders,* view personality as one window on a person's mental health. Over the years, they have isolated a

▼ *Just as one domino can knock into another, making all three fall, one positive thought, feeling, or behavior can have a positive "domino effect" on the other two.*
ACTIVITY *Think of a time when a positive feeling or thought had a positive "domino effect" on your behavior.*

194 CHAPTER 8 YOUR MENTAL AND EMOTIONAL HEALTH

PERSONAL HEALTH

HUMAN DEVELOPMENT. Point out to the class that humans begin life concerned only with their own needs at the bottom levels of the pyramid. Later they develop a need for approval and begin to put someone else's wishes or directives ahead of their own in order to get along.

Have students write private health journal entries discussing the role of group acceptance in their behavior and decision making. Suggest that they give examples from their experience and that of their peers, and identify each as a positive, negative, or neutral influence.

number of different personality traits and investigated these in depth. Maslow's hierarchy, explained earlier in this lesson, is one model of personality.

Foundations of Personality

Your personality began taking shape before you were actually born. **Heredity**, the biological passing along of traits and characteristics from your parents, is one of the three major factors in molding personality. The other two—environment and behavior—are also important.

Personality and Heredity

Heredity is the first influence on your personality. You inherit obvious physical traits such as your hair and eye color, the shape of your nose and ears, and your body type and height. You also inherit basic intellectual abilities as well as temperament, or emotional tendencies. Studies of twins separated at birth suggest that even such characteristics as preferences for foods, colors, and scents may, in fact, have inherited components. There is also increasing evidence that heredity may play a role in behaviors such as risk-taking and in talents such as the ability to draw or sing well.

hotlink

heredity For more information on heredity and its effect on the total person you are, see Chapter 20, page 461.

connections

Social Studies

When Needs Aren't Met

Elie Wiesel, an author and concentration-camp survivor, writes that while in the horrifying camp during World War II, he had "neither the time nor the strength" to think about the meaning of the universe. "The daily bread ration was the center of our concerns," he notes. "Would it be a centimeter thicker or thinner? Would they give us margarine or jam?…I remember a Dutchman who shared his bread with a comrade sicker than he was, a comrade he did not know. 'I prefer to be hungry than to feel remorse,' he said."

1. Where on Maslow's "pyramid" do you think Wiesel was forced to spend most of his time?

2. Where on Maslow's "hierarchy of needs" would you place the Dutchman when he offered his bread to his comrade?

3. What qualities or traits in human nature do you think make it possible for people to bypass or temporarily overlook their basic needs to help another human being? Do you think you could have done what the Dutchman did? Why or why not?

L2 Writing

Write the statement *Beauty is in the eye of the beholder* on the chalkboard. Ask students to write a paragraph that either supports this statement or points out its weaknesses.

L1 Class Activity

Have each student print his or her name in a vertical line on a sheet of paper. Instruct students to list adjectives that start with each letter of their name. Have each of them write a paragraph discussing how accurately their individual lists of adjectives reflect their personalities.

connections

Social Studies

When Needs Aren't Met

Ask what students already know about Elie Wiesel. Explain that when Wiesel was 15 years old, he and the rest of his family were sent to concentration camps, where both his parents and his younger sister died. Wiesel has devoted much of his adult life to reminding people of the horrors of the concentration camp experience so that it will not be repeated. He was awarded the Nobel Peace Prize in 1986. Let students read the feature to find out more about Wiesel, and guide them in discussing their responses to the questions.

CURRICULUM CONNECTIONS

LANGUAGE ARTS. Have students write a story about someone they know well and admire greatly. Have them include the qualities this person has that they find so admirable. Ask them to explain the influence this person has had on their lives and why. Ask how this person has contributed to their self-perception or self-esteem.

SOCIAL STUDIES Ask students to do a study of TV, radio, and music messages. Have them evaluate media messages aimed at teens they hear in the media for one day. Ask students to note how these messages influence teens' perception of needs. Compare these perceived needs to Maslow's Hierarchy of Needs.

CHARACTER IN ACTION

Avoiding the Blame Game

Ask students for other suggestions to avoid playing the "blame game." Discuss the importance of assuming responsibility for one's own part in problems that arise between people.

ASSESS

EVALUATING THE LESSON

Assign and discuss the Lesson 2 Review; then administer, grade, and discuss the *Lesson 26 Quiz* in the TCR. ☞

RETEACHING

- Have students outline the lesson as they read it for a second time, using the lesson heads as Roman numeral entries. Ask them to list at least three facts from the lesson under each main entry.
- Ask students to complete *Reteaching Activity 26* in the TCR. ☞

ENRICHMENT

Help students consider possible hereditary, environmental, and behavioral factors that they think have most influenced their personality development to this point. Ask them to identify any factors they could modify to enhance their mental health and further shape the personality that they desire.

CLOSE

Have students give one positive example and one negative example of the role each of the following can play in the development of personality: heredity, environment, and behavior.

CHARACTER IN ACTION

Avoiding the Blame Game

When you take responsibility for your behavior, you skip the "victim mentality" and avoid blaming others for what you have done wrong. You thereby demonstrate the value of **accountability**, taking responsibility for all that you say and do.

Character Check The next time you are wrong and you know it, admit it. Avoid blaming anyone else. Quickly say you are sorry. Finally, make amends. Do something specific to right the situation.

Personality and Environment

The second factor affecting personality is your environment begining at your birth. Your environment includes all of your surroundings, your family, your friends at school, your neighborhood, and all of the places, people, and activities you have experienced up to this point in your life. These influences can have positive or negative effects on your developing personality.

People who come from unhealthful environments may experience neglect, abuse, rejection, or other negative treatment. These experiences and actions can leave a person with emotional scars that can lead to poor mental health. People who live in healthful environments, however, feel supported, safe, loved, and valued and, therefore, often develop higher levels of mental health.

One way in which environmental "traits" are stamped on the developing personality is through modeling. **Modeling** means *copying the behaviors of those you are exposed to.* A caring adult who gives positive messages to a small child provides a positive pattern of behavior for that child to "model" or follow. That child is more likely to grow up into a trusting adult unafraid to meet life's experiences head-on.

Personality and Personal Behavior

The influence on your personality over which you have the most control is your personal behavior. How you make decisions, what decisions you make, and what actions you take can make all the difference in the world in the quality of your life and your levels of physical and mental health. In some situations, it can even mark the difference between life and death.

LESSON 2 *Review*

Reviewing Facts and Vocabulary

1. Define the word *personality*.
2. What three influences affect the development of personality?
3. Define *modeling* and give one example.

Thinking Critically

4. *Comparing and Contrasting.* Write two versions of a fictional story in which a person faces two levels of need. In one version, the person has to make a choice that meets the more basic need; in the other, she or he must make a choice that meets the higher-level need. Share your different outcomes with the class.

5. *Synthesizing.* Write a letter to an imaginary gang or cult member giving that person tips on how to get his or her needs met in more healthful ways.

Applying Health Skills

6. *In Your Home.* Go through family photo albums or interview family members to find out which relatives you act, look, sound, or behave like. Think about which of these similarities may be the result of heredity and which are the result of environment.

Lesson 2 Review

Answers to Reviewing Facts and Vocabulary

1. Your personality is a complex set of characteristics that makes you unique and sets you apart from everyone else.
2. Heredity, environment, and behavior. You have the most control over your behavior.
3. Copying the behaviors of those you are exposed to. Examples will vary.

Answers to Thinking Critically

4.–5. Answers will vary.

Understanding Your Emotions

How do you feel right now? Are you in a good mood? Are you down or bored? Your feelings, or emotions, influence everything you do. They affect your thinking, your relationships with others, your behavior, and even your success or failure at accomplishing a given task. Your emotions have an impact on your mental and physical health.

HEALTH TERMS

emotions

empathy

phobias

hostility

HEALTH CONCEPTS

- Your emotions influence your thoughts and actions.
- Emotions are neither good nor bad.
- During adolescence, hormones can greatly affect your emotions.

Understanding Your Emotions

Emotions are *signals that tell your mind and body how to react.* They are neither good nor bad. They are simply the way your body and mind respond to input from outside your body.

Emotions can greatly affect all sides of your health triangle. Consider:

- When you are in a dangerous situation, emotions such as fear can trigger the body and mind to protect you by causing you to shout or flee the scene.
- Emotions such as joy can prompt the release of brain chemicals that not only cause warm, happy feelings but also promote mental health.

LESSON 3   UNDERSTANDING YOUR EMOTIONS   **197**

◼ Lesson 3 Resources

TEACHER'S CLASSROOM RESOURCES

- 🕮 **Concept Map** Activity 27
- 🕮 **Cooperative Learning** Activity 8
- 🕮 **Lesson 27 Quiz**
- 🕮 **Lesson Plan 27**
- 🕮 **Reteaching** Activity 27

STUDENT WORKBOOK

- 🕮 **Applying Health Skills 27**
- 🕮 **Chapter Study Guide 8**
- 🕮 **Vocabulary** Activity 8

Understanding Your Emotions

FOCUS

LESSON OBJECTIVES

After studying this lesson, students should be able to

- describe how emotions influence overall health.
- explain how emotions influence thoughts and actions.

MOTIVATOR

Write the following on the chalkboard for students to work on while attendance is being taken: *Briefly describe in writing two situations where you experienced one of the following: fear, anger, love, or mixed emotions.*

INTRODUCING THE LESSON

Point to each emotion from the Motivator on the chalkboard; ask volunteers to share their situations. As the students share, place a check by the appropriate emotion. List the most common emotions recalled by students in order of frequency. Ask students how they would rank the frequency of emotions based on their own experiences.

INTRODUCING HEALTH TERMS

- Let students use the vocabulary words in three different sentences, leaving blanks where the vocabulary words would be. Collect the sentences and read some aloud, allowing students to fill in the blanks with the appropriate vocabulary words.
- Ask students to complete Vocabulary Activity 8 and Chapter Study Guide 8 in the *Student Workbook.* 🕮

TEACH

L1 Explaining

Explain how mental health can affect physical health. Tell students that the mind-body connection is so strong that people can make themselves physically ill by worrying.

L2 Discussing

Below is a list of irrational statements. Have students discuss how each statement could affect one's mental health. Bring out in the discussion that everyone may experience these thoughts to some extent, but no one should allow such thoughts to be predominant.

- I must be punctual, courteous, and reliable all the time.
- I need to be first or to win at all costs.
- I must control everything and everyone if I possibly can, including myself.
- I should not get angry, because everything can be solved by reason and intellect.
- I must be efficient at all costs.
- I must depend on intellect and logic and ignore my feelings.
- I really should not trust anyone.
- I deserve more respect.
- Being right is more important than anything else.
- I get along best with others when I can tell them things I know.
- I must be loved or approved of by everyone important to me.
- I am not worthwhile unless I am completely competent, adequate, and achieving.

(List continued on next page.)

(List continued on next page.)

Did You Know?

➤ In the middle of the brain are two amygdalas, almond-shaped organs that receive and send all kinds of emotional messages.

➤ A woman whose amygdala had been destroyed was found to be unable to read the signs of fear and unable to feel the emotion itself.

■ Strong emotions like anger can cause physical changes within your body, including a rise in heart rate, perspiration, and a tightening of the muscles of the stomach. If no emotional outlet is found for some of this tension, it builds up inside, eventually taking a toll on your physical health.

Learning constructive ways to deal with your emotions is, therefore, extremely important. A first step toward achieving this goal is learning to identify your emotions.

Identifying Emotions

Identifying emotions can be difficult, especially in situations where you have "mixed emotions," for example, being jealous of and happy for a friend at the same time. Like two colors mixed together, it may at times be difficult to name what you are feeling.

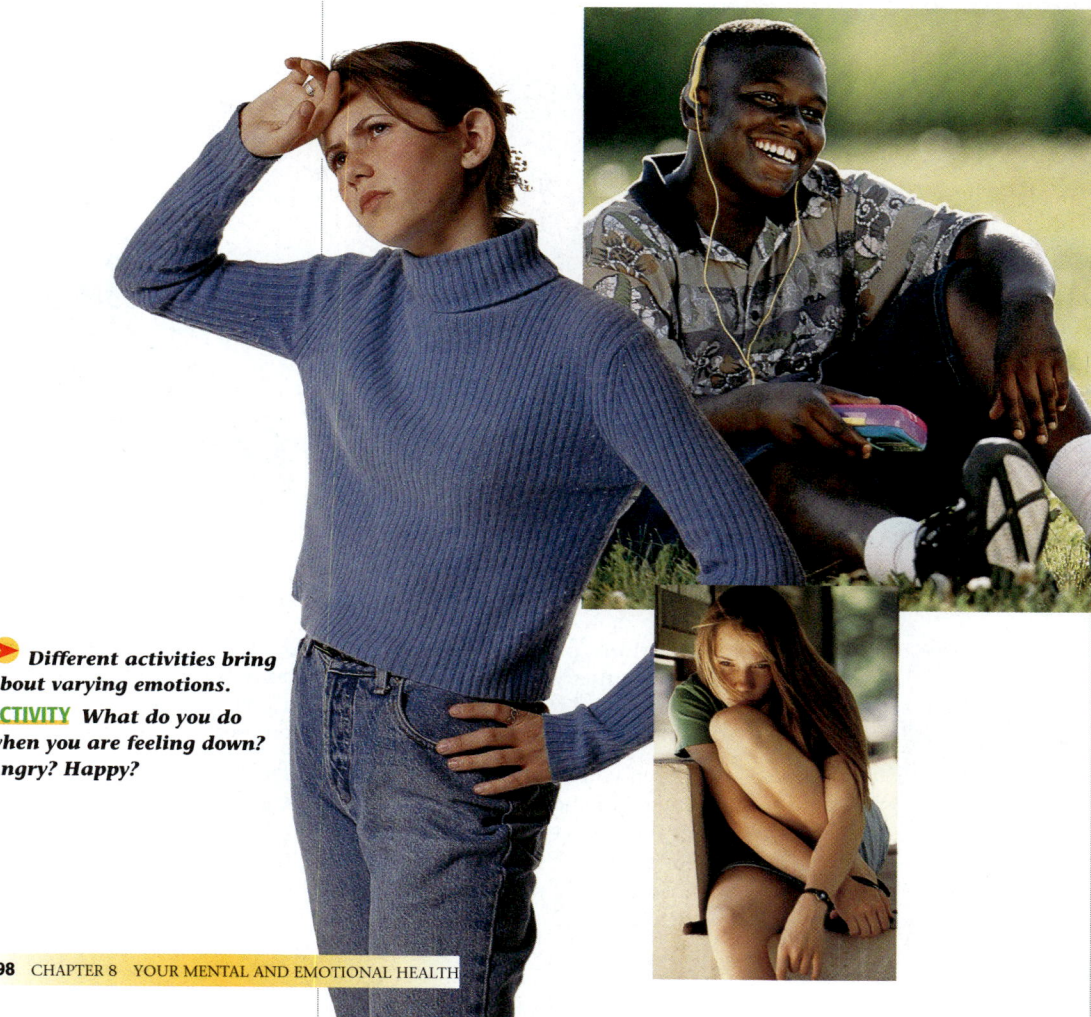

▶ *Different activities bring about varying emotions.*
ACTIVITY *What do you do when you are feeling down? Angry? Happy?*

HOME AND COMMUNITY CONNECTION

MENTAL HEALTH. Research is under way to see if mental health problems can be prevented through education programs aimed at children. The types of programs currently being assessed include family support programs, parent-infant education programs, early childhood education, school-based social competence promotion, and other social learning programs.

Some of the most important mental health problems requiring treatment in children and adolescents include autism, attention deficit disorder, hyperactivity, severe conduct disorders, depression, and alcohol and other drug abuse.

It is especially important to learn to identify unsettling emotions. Feeling worried may call for a different action than feeling terrified does. Feeling a bit down is different from feeling hopeless and may require different kinds of help. Identifying emotions correctly can help you to know how to express them more effectively the next time you experience them.

Love

All human beings need to give and receive love. This emotion involves strong affection, deep concern, and respect. It includes supporting the growth and individual needs of another person and respecting that person's boundaries and values as well as your own. Love can be expressed through words, actions, facial expressions, touch, and good deeds. It comes in many forms, including caring for family and friends, loyalty to siblings, and even a deep sense of being connected to your country or to all people. Being able to receive and give love is central to what it means to be mentally and emotionally well.

Empathy

Empathy is *the ability to imagine and understand how someone else feels.* It is being able to "walk in another's shoes." People who have empathy for others feel more connected to the world. They are better able to help others in need. They can offer insight and understanding. When you have empathy, you can reach out to others and receive their gestures of warmth and caring in return.

As with other emotions, it is important to experience this feeling with some balance. It is not healthy, for example, to be overwhelmed with concern for others' feelings at the expense of meeting all of your own needs.

Fear

Every time you hear an ambulance siren, a loud noise, or a scream, you probably feel some degree of fear. This response can be a safeguard or protection if you need to respond to a real threat.

As with other reactions, your body responds physically to the emotion, preparing itself for what it might need to do. When you experience fear, your **sympathetic nervous system** reacts by preparing your body for necessary action. Hormones cause your heart to beat faster, sending an increased supply of blood to your heart and muscles. Your breathing rate increases. Once the threatening situation has passed, your body returns to its normal state.

⬆ *Everyone needs to feel loved and be able to give love.*
ACTIVITY *Name three ways you express love to family members and close friends.*

h⊙tlink

sympathetic nervous system
For more information on the sympathetic nervous system, see Chapter 16, page 370.

- I am unable to control my own happiness.
- I am controlled by my history and by my important past experiences.
- I face disaster if I cannot find the perfect solution to my problems.
- I must always be prepared for the worst by constantly agonizing over it.
- I believe that wicked people should be blamed and punished.
- I face disaster if my life does not work out just as I plan.
- I am better off if I avoid difficulties and responsibilities rather than face them.
- I should always be very disturbed over other people's problems.

h⊙tlink

sympathetic nervous system
Tell students that the racing of the body as described in the text illustrates the "fight or flight" response. Briefly discuss the benefits and possible adverse effects of the body's reaction to perceived danger.

L1 Discussing

Have students identify a time when they were truly frightened. What happened? How did they respond? Compare this to other fears they may or may not have experienced. How do these usually develop? *(They are learned, usually from things children are told.)*

L2 Cooperative Learning

For more on childhood fears, assign *Cooperative Learning Activity 8* in the TCR. 🖛

CURRICULUM CONNECTIONS

ART. Many photographers specialize in capturing emotional moments. Ask an art teacher to talk about photography as an art form of capturing emotion and to share poignant works by famous photographers such as Margaret Bourke-White.

Divide the class into small groups. Using pictures from magazines (such as *Life*) and newspapers, as well as personal photos, have each group create a book showing the emotions of adolescence. To encourage students to study the photographs, have them write a caption for each picture. Students who enjoy doing their own photography might work together to record on film the emotions expressed by students in your school.

L2 ### Discussing

Ask students to list ten things that make them angry. Ask if they always tell the person with whom they are angry what the problem is. Explain that we sometimes don't tell others we are angry for fear of hurting their feelings or believing they would not understand or just don't care. Instead, we "bank" our anger in small deposits. After a while, the bank gets full and we cash in. We explode to vent our anger. The source of the anger may not even be relevant anymore, but it all comes out and affects everyone around us. Ask students if they can relate to this description and if they have ever released anger in this way. Discuss other, more successful ways to handle the emotions.

L2 ### Discussing

Young people often feel they are not in charge of their lives. Part of this perception is real, due to their age. Part is due to their perceptions of control. Ask students to discuss the perception of control in each of the following statements:

- I don't get a vote.
- I feel blame, shame, and regret.
- I say yes and mean no.
- Please love me.
- I fear your disapproval if I do not do what you want me to.
- I wait for someone else to handle it.
- I have a good reason for every broken agreement.
- I "try" to get things done.

A Top Ten List of Fears

Some 3,000 Americans were asked, "What do you fear most?" Here is what they answered.

1.	Speaking before a group	41%
2.	Heights	32%
3.	Insects and spiders	22%
4.	Money problems	22%
5.	Deep water	22%
6.	Sickness	19%
7.	Death	19%
8.	Flying	19%
9.	Loneliness	14%
10.	Dogs	11%

A fear of insects and spiders is quite common. As long as fear doesn't control your daily activities, it is a normal emotion to have.
ACTIVITY *List your top three fears and possible ways to overcome each one.*

Some fears—the fear of falling, for example—may be inherited. Most fears, however, are learned. The fear of fire was probably instilled in you when you were small to protect you from the potential danger of playing with matches. Such fears, which are *rational,* or reasonable, are helpful as you grow. Other fears, such as a fear of heights, are not helpful. These *irrational fears,* or **phobias,** can get in the way of leading a normal life.

Anger

Everyone feels anger at one point or another. At times it may be displayed as a simple annoyance, at other times it may rise up as boiling rage. As with other emotions, how you choose to handle that anger is one of the key factors in your mental and emotional health.

When people do not handle their anger in constructive ways, they can do great damage not only to others and to other's property but also to their own bodies and minds. **Hostility,** *the intentional use of unfriendly or nasty behavior,* can be particularly damaging. In fact, experts now think that hostile behavior is the key personality trait in predicting heart disease. People who show chronic hostile behavior are four to seven times more likely to die of heart disease and cancer than those who are not prone to anger. According to Redford Williams, a researcher at Duke University, silent "seethers" are even more likely to die earlier than those who are openly hostile.

200 CHAPTER 8 YOUR MENTAL AND EMOTIONAL HEALTH

MORE ABOUT . . . . .

FEAR. Here are some common (and uncommon) phobias: hematophobia (fear of blood); ailurophobia (fear of cats); demophobia (fear of crowds); nyctophobia (fear of the dark); thanatophobia (fear of death); mysophobia (fear of dirt); batrachophobia (fear of frogs); belonephobia (fear of needles); agoraphobia (fear of open spaces); algophobia (fear of pain); ophidiophobia (fear of snakes); arachnophobia (fear of spiders); xenophobia (fear of strangers); phobophobia (fear of phobias); and panophobia (fear of everything).

Guilt

Everyone feels guilty for their actions or thoughts some of the time. Guilt is an emotional response when you think you have done something wrong. It often results from acting against one's values or from not acting at all when direct action might have brought about a better outcome. Frequently, guilt is associated with low self-esteem. It may also act as a smokescreen, keeping you from other feelings. For example, it may seem easier to feel guilty than it is to overcome your fear of taking a particular action and perhaps failing. Though guilt can eat away at you, leaving you feeling inadequate, it can also motivate you to make positive changes. You are less likely to engage in a negative behavior if you know yourself well enough to realize that you will be left with a guilty conscience afterward.

Emotions and Adolescence

Strong emotional responses are common during your teen years. Rapid growth and other changes brought on by hormones may make you feel oversensitive on some days, insecure on others. You may overreact or suddenly feel flooded by an emotion. Such reactions are normal. Just remember, you are not alone. The other teens you know are experiencing similar kinds of emotional changes, too.

▲ *During the teen years, it is normal to experience rapid changes in emotions.*

ACTIVITY *List ways you could deal with quickly changing emotions (for example, going for a walk if you are feeling angry).*

EVALUATING THE LESSON

Assign and discuss the Lesson 3 Review; then administer, grade, and discuss the *Lesson 27 Quiz* in the TCR. 🗂

RETEACHING

- In their private Health Journals, have students write each emotion discussed in this lesson as a heading. Under each heading, have them list times when they experienced the emotion.
- Ask students to complete *Reteaching Activity 27* in the TCR. 🗂

ENRICHMENT

Direct students to use their imagination to describe how they think emotions would "look" if they had color. Ask them to write an analogy for five emotions, such as "Anger looks like the color _____ because…" Then have them paint five watercolors, one to express each of the emotions in their analogies.

CLOSE

Tell students that recognizing emotions is the first step toward handling them. The next lesson will discuss ways to handle emotions in healthful ways.

Review

Reviewing Facts and Vocabulary

1. Define the word *emotion* and give examples of three emotions.
2. Describe what happens to the body when responding to anger or fear.

Thinking Critically

3. *Analyzing.* Analyze this statement: "Emotions are neither positive nor negative, but the ways they are expressed can be either." Give examples from your own experience to support this statement.
4. *Evaluating.* Flip through your favorite magazine, identifying what emotions you think you see on the photographed faces. Find a pattern to the kinds of emotions portrayed. Which emotions seem most and least frequently featured? What effect does this have on the overall "mood" or tone created by the publication?

Applying Health Skills

5. *In Your Home.* For a week's time, practice empathy toward someone you encounter on a daily basis. Start by asking yourself, "What is it like to be that person right now? What might he or she be thinking or feeling? Why might he or she be acting in this way?" At the end of the week, record in your private Health Journal any changes in your feelings toward or understanding of that person.

LESSON 3   UNDERSTANDING YOUR EMOTIONS   **201**

Lesson 3 Review

Answers to Reviewing Facts and Vocabulary

1. Signals that tell your mind and body how to react. Examples will vary.
2. The heart rate and the breathing rate increase.

Answers to Thinking Critically

3. Answers should reflect an awareness that there are always choices available in our reaction to any situation.
4. Findings will vary.

Handling Emotions in Healthful Ways

FOCUS

LESSON OBJECTIVE

After studying this lesson, students should be able to

- give examples of positive and negative ways of handling emotions.

- discuss ways to achieve and maintain emotional health.

MOTIVATOR

Ask students if they can remember a time in their lives when something very good or very bad caused them to experience stress. How did they respond?

INTRODUCING THE LESSON

Have students share their responses to the Motivator. Ask what they think influenced their reaction to the situation most—watching others respond in a similar way, the environment they were in at the time, or past experiences. Tell students that this lesson will offer strategies for handling emotions in positive ways.

INTRODUCING HEALTH TERMS

- Have students use the vocabulary terms in a written paragraph. Ask them to read their paragraphs to the class.
- Ask students to complete Vocabulary Activity 8 and Chapter Study Guide 8 in the *Student Workbook*. ☞

Handling Emotions in Healthful Ways

As noted earlier, emotions are neither good nor bad. How you deal with your emotions, however, can strongly influence your overall level of health. Learning to recognize emotions and dealing with them in positive, healthful ways are two of the most important skills leading to good mental health.

HEALTH TERMS
defense mechanisms
resilience

HEALTH CONCEPTS
- There are positive and negative ways of dealing with emotions.
- Certain defense mechanisms are common as people face strong emotions and try to find ways to handle them.
- Your emotional health depends on your outlook on life and on protective factors.

Positive Ways of Dealing with Emotions

In growing up, you have probably learned various ways of expressing your emotions. You learn from watching others, from your environment, and from your own experiences. Suppose that as a young child you were repeatedly told that crying is a sign of weakness. Do you think that now you would be likely to express an emotion of sadness by crying? How have you learned to express joy and excitement?

Even if you learned unhealthful ways to express your emotions while growing up, it is never too late to learn new, healthful ways. There are both general strategies that can be applied to all emotions and individual strategies for coping with specific emotions, such as fear, anger, and guilt. The general strategies include the following:

Lesson 4 Resources

TEACHER'S CLASSROOM RESOURCES
☞ **Concept Map** Activity 28
☞ **Decision-Making** Activity 8
☞ **Enrichment** Activity 8
☞ **Lesson 28 Quiz**
☞ **Lesson Plan 28**
☞ **Reteaching** Activity 28

STUDENT WORKBOOK
☞ **Applying Health Skills** 28
☞ **Chapter Study Guide** 8
☞ **Vocabulary** Activity 8

MULTIMEDIA
● **ABCNews InterActive™ VHS/Videodisc,** *Violence Prevention*

- Look below the surface of your emotion. Ask yourself: What is this feeling really about? Do I have any control over what caused this feeling?
- Consider whether or not this feeling or situation will really matter so much tomorrow, next week, or next year.
- Do not take action on a strong feeling until both your head and your heart have investigated what's going on and what's at stake.
- Remind yourself that feelings are just feelings; they are not facts.
- Keep in mind that a strong feeling can be a useful signal. Listen to it. Sometimes it can even be a signal of danger.
- Use positive feelings to inspire you. Use upsetting ones to motivate you to change.
- Remember that you are not alone. All human beings have strong feelings.
- If the feeling doesn't go away, seek help from a parent, another trusted person, or a professional.

Dealing Healthfully with Emotions

Certainly the ways you express your emotions may have to do with your personality. You may be easily brought to tears or quick to fly off the handle. Many of the ways you express your feelings have been learned from observing others. Perhaps in your family, people talk about their feelings openly. Maybe they express themselves indirectly with looks or smiles or with behaviors like crying or slamming doors. Perhaps they do not talk much at all, and you learned from their example that emotions were something not to be shared. Even so, you can still learn healthful ways to express feelings. It takes practice.

There are many negative ways of dealing with feelings that do nothing to solve problems and, in fact, may create additional ones. These include exaggerating emotions for effect, acting them out instead of communicating them, pretending as if they were not there at all, or intentionally hurting another person in expressing them.

There are many positive ways to handle emotions, including playing music or creating art.

ACTIVITY *The next time you feel a strong emotion, try drawing it before you describe it with words.*

LESSON 4   HANDLING EMOTIONS IN HEALTHFUL WAYS   **203**

TEACH

L1 Discussing

Ask students if they feel it is easier for boys or girls to express their feelings and emotions: Why do they feel this way?

L2 Class Activity

Help students brainstorm a list of mental health specialists. Then guide them in creating a list of situations that might necessitate seeking help, and places students could go for appropriate help.

L2 Researching

Have students find out who helps students with mental health issues in your school. Ask them to provide each person's name and title and to write a paragraph about what each person does to help young people. The list could include the school nurse, school psychologist, school counselors, and social workers affiliated with the school. To preclude having all students visit each of these individuals in their offices to acquire information about their jobs, you may want to invite them to speak briefly to the class. Share the students' research with other classes.

L3 Community Involvement

Ask volunteers to interview clergy—ministers, priests, rabbis—about the kinds of counseling, if any, they provide to the people they serve. Have them find out what kinds of mental health problems are addressed. Request that students share their findings with the class.

HOME AND COMMUNITY
CONNECTION

COUNSELING. Students will seek support and counseling from their peers as their first step in getting help with problems. Often, teens don't know when to provide real support and when to get their friend to a trained adult. Young people may feel that it isn't serious enough to bother someone or that adults would not understand.

It's important to empower students with knowledge about mental illness and to know the difference between just feeling "blue" and being seriously depressed. Let students know who is available to talk with in the school counseling department and in the community. Don't forget to include the students' parents.

LD Writing

Let students rewrite, in their own words, the strategies for coping with emotions. Ask them to provide their own examples for each.

L2 Demonstrating

Assign students to demonstrate the use of rationalization to justify one's actions. Follow up with a discussion of why rationalization is not an effective way of managing emotions.

L1 Discussing

Have students give examples in which regression could lead to disastrous consequences. Discuss how regression can actually heighten emotions rather than reduce them.

L1 Discussing

Lead students in a discussion of ways in which a person may attempt to "escape" a situation as a means of coping. (Examples include refusing to talk about a difficult situation, daydreaming, etc.)

L2 Discussing

Guide students in brainstorming various ways that people compensate to make up for something they do not have or did not receive. Ask them to explain how compensation is often used to cope.

L2 Class Activity

Have students find examples of projection in cartoons, TV programs, or movies. Ask them to discuss their examples with the class. Talk about ways to avoid projecting one's feelings or actions on others as a means of reducing tension.

VIOLENCE PREVENTION (Side 1)

Chapter 3: What Makes You Angry?

Frames 2856-8378

---

keeping Fit

What's Your Hostility I.Q.?

Do you spend too much of your life in the "anger zone"? Your answers to the following questions will help you determine your "hostility I.Q."

➤ Have you ever been so angry at someone that you've thrown things or slammed a door?

➤ Do you tend to remember irritating incidents and get mad all over again?

➤ Do you find yourself getting annoyed at little things family and friends do that get under your skin?

➤ If someone doesn't show up on time, do you find yourself thinking about the angry words you're going to say to that person?

Common Defense Mechanisms

Repression   Involuntary, unconscious pushing of unpleasant feelings below the surface and out of conscious thought.

Suppression   Conscious, intentional pushing of unpleasantness from one's mind.

Rationalization   Making excuses to try to explain a situation or behavior rather than directly taking responsibility for it.

Regression   Reverting, or turning back, to behaviors more characteristic of an earlier stage of development rather than dealing with the conflict in a more mature manner.

Denial   Unconscious, involuntary lack of acknowledgment of something in one's environment that is obvious to others.

Compensation   Wanting to cover up weaknesses and mistakes by making up for them through gift-giving, hard work, or other extreme efforts.

Projection   Being unaware of attributing one's own feelings or faults to another person or group even when these attributes do not apply.

Idealization   Seeing someone else as perfect or more ideal, or worthy, than everyone else.

Defense Mechanisms

Defense mechanisms are *strategies used to deal with strong or stressful emotions and situations.* Everyone uses them. Sometimes these strategies occur unconsciously and may be helpful over the short term in protecting you from feeling too much pain. In the long run, however, defense mechanisms can keep you from facing and dealing with what is really troubling you.

Handling Fear

In dealing with fear, it is important to identify what your fears are and to confide in someone you trust who may give you a fresh perspective or outlook. This person may help you find a constructive way of lessening your fear or suggest a resource to which you can turn.

Managing Anger

Think of ways in which you have seen anger expressed. Perhaps you have seen a child throw a temper tantrum or seen someone kick a wall or take a swing at someone else. Some people let their anger build up without saying or doing anything, until they explode and strike out at anyone who happens to be around.

How can you express your anger in a constructive way? You must first recognize your feelings and, if possible, identify the source of those feelings. Sometimes there is nothing you can do about what is causing the anger, but you can find ways to cope with the anger so that it does not build up. Diffusing your anger can help you reduce the risk that you might act on impulse and be sorry later. Here are some suggestions:

- Rechannel your anger in positive, productive ways. Try painting, drawing, or sewing. If you need something more physical, try hammering, cleaning your room, or going on a vigorous walk or run.

- Get away by yourself, or have a good cry. Sadness or hurt is often the emotion you're really feeling.

- Pick up the phone. Call a close friend and talk it out.

- Write down exactly what you are feeling and why. Express yourself freely. No one needs to see what you write.

- Punch a pillow, or count to ten.

Learn to channel your anger in safe ways. Acting irrationally could prove dangerous to your health or someone else's health. Getting angry with someone is normal and likely if you spend

---

Myths & Realities

MYTH. All defense mechanisms are psychologically unhealthy.
FACT. There are times when defense mechanisms can contribute to emotional health by giving people relief from stress and helping them cope with problems. Difficulties occur when people depend on defense mechanisms to help them avoid facing daily problems.

MYTH. You can't do two things at once.
FACT. "Dovetailing," or overlapping activities, can frequently be done with some tasks and activities. For example, you can do exercises and watch TV at the same time, or you can sew a button on your shirt while talking on the phone. Dovetailing is an important concept in time management.

much time with that person. You can clear the air by expressing the emotion. If you bury or ignore it, you will carry it around with you. Then it will begin to affect how you feel about the other person, which can be unhealthful for you and the relationship.

◀ *Ride your emotions the way you would ride a wave, knowing there will be ups and downs but that no emotion can necessarily "wipe you out."* **ACTIVITY** *What other simile or metaphor could you use to describe the "up and down" nature of emotions?*

Making Responsible Decisions

When You're Angry with a Friend

Jennifer and Pia have been friends since junior high. A mainstay of their friendship has been sharing feelings and keeping confidences. That is why today, in the locker room, Jennifer turned red with anger when she overheard Pia casually blurt out something very personal that Jennifer had shared with her. Jennifer's first reaction was to slam her locker door and storm out, expecting that Pia would follow and apologize. Pia did not, however, and now Jennifer believes that if she tells Pia how angry she feels, it might ruin their friendship. What should she do?

What Would You Do?

Apply the six steps of the decision-making process to Jennifer's problem.

1. **State the situation.**
2. **List the options.**
3. **Weigh the possible outcomes.**
4. **Consider your values.**
5. **Make a decision and act.**
6. **Evaluate the decision.**

 SCHOOL-TO-CAREER

EMOTIONS ON THE JOB. Have students work in groups. Tell them to choose a specific occupation, such as a server in a restaurant, a computer programmer, a store manager, or a nurse. Have them brainstorm situations that would provoke an emotional response in such a worker, then role-play positive and negative ways to handle the situation and the emotion. Invite groups to choose one situation and emotion to role-play for the class. Follow with a class discussion about how handling of emotions affects job performance and the experience of customers and coworkers.

L3 Class Activity

Assign volunteers to choreograph short dances to represent instances of displacement and regression. Have them present their dances to the class. Afterward, ask the class to define and explain the two concepts. Next, ask the dancers to describe the situations depicted in their dance.

L2 Class Activity

As a way to better understand defense mechanisms, divide the class into groups of three or four students. Assign a defense mechanism to each group and have them make up and perform a skit portraying it. Have the class guess which defense mechanism is being used.

Making Responsible Decisions

1. Jennifer feels very angry with her close friend Pia, who has betrayed her confidence.
2. Jennifer might (a) try to ignore her own anger and not discuss her feelings with Pia, (b) avoid Pia until she asks Jennifer what is wrong, (c) tell Pia about her feelings and their cause.
3. Jennifer is likely to (a) continue to feel angry with Pia and perhaps feel less close to her friend, (b) become increasingly angry that Pia doesn't ask about her feelings, (c) risk feeling uncomfortable telling Pia about her anger but relieve her anger by expressing it.
4. Jennifer values her friendship with Pia. She also values keeping confidences shared between friends.
5. Responses will vary.
6. Guide students in considering both short- and long-term consequences of their decisions.

L2 Decision Making

For further study on making responsible decisions, assign *Decision-Making Activity 8* in the TCR. ☞

update
▶*Our Changing World*

Handling Emotions

Ask students: What are some common emotions that people might experience during a local or national tragedy? How might these emotions change over time? Why is there such a wide range of emotions experienced? What might be some positive ways of dealing with these emotions? Then have students read the feature to learn about handling emotions during tragedies. Finally, have students meet in discussion groups to share and compare their responses to the questions.

L2 Class Activity

Help students recognize their assets and faults so they might better evaluate their mental health status. Have students draw two circles, one with ten spokes, labeled "assets," and the other with five spokes, labeled "faults." Ask them to fill in their personal attributes accordingly between the spokes of each circle. After they have finished, tell them that during times of emotional distress, they should draw from their strengths or assets while consciously not allowing their faults to come into play. This is not a simple task, but with increased awareness of personal attributes and behavior patterns, we can learn to manage our feelings appropriately, even when we feel a bit out of control.

update
▶*Our Changing World*

Handling Emotions During Tragedies

It's difficult to read the newspaper or watch television without hearing bad news. Sometimes the news might be a local tragedy that occurred in your community or across the nation. In response to a tragedy, you may feel many strong emotions, including sadness, anger, fear, and guilt. All of these reactions are normal. Here are some tips for handling emotions during these times:

- **Maintain your daily routine.** Doing so will help you feel a sense of control. Plan a special activity each day so that you have something to look forward to.

- **Share your feelings.** Remember that friends and family members are probably experiencing similar emotions. If you're not ready to talk, try writing down your thoughts and feelings in a journal.

- **Turn off the news.** It's easy to become overwhelmed with nonstop media coverage of tragedies. Take a break by going for a walk, listening to a favorite CD, or watching a funny movie.

- **Channel your energy into a worthwhile cause.** Volunteer to help raise money for relief efforts, participate in a local memorial service, or create a memory book.

Dealing with Guilt

Guilt can be one of the most destructive emotions. When you feel guilty about something, it is important to get at the underlying source and address that issue. The sooner you take action, the better. Many people use their guilt as an excuse for inaction, letting the emotion paralyze them. When this happens, the guilt feeds on itself, causing the problem—and the emotion—to snowball.

One way of avoiding this vicious circle is by resisting doing something you know is wrong in the first place. Saying no to unhealthy demands or requests should never make you feel guilty. In the event you have done something wrong, admit it. If you have hurt another person in the process, try to make amends and resolve to do the right thing next time.

Qualities that Can Foster Emotional Health

You can free yourself of strong emotions for short periods of time, but sooner or later you will have to deal with them again. Two qualities can help ease your emotional load. One of these is your overall outlook on life. The other is your ability to adapt and recover from disappointment.

206 CHAPTER 8 YOUR MENTAL AND EMOTIONAL HEALTH

COOPERATIVE ▶ LEARNING

ADVICE COLUMN. Assign students to partners. Have them work individually to write letters to an advice columnist about a real or imagined situation involving strong emotions such as jealousy, fear, guilt, anger, or love. The emotions can be their own or those of a close friend, family member, employer, coworker, teammate, or teacher (real names should not be used). They should describe difficulty or uncertainty with handling these emotions in themselves or the other person. Tell partners to exchange letters, assume the role of advice columnist, and answer the partner's letter.

Your Outlook on Life

Do you think of yourself as a pessimist or an optimist? Your answer to this question—your outlook on life—can mean the difference between good and poor emotional health. While pessimists tend to view negative events as permanent and far-reaching, optimists see them as more temporary and specific.

The good news for pessimists is that strategies exist for changing their outlook. You can develop a more positive outlook by reminding yourself daily that no matter what happens to you, there is always hope. When something does go wrong, make a plan to address or solve the problem. If your behavior is causing the trouble, change it. Get support. Instead of seeing a stressful situation as a crisis, try to see it as a challenge.

Resiliency

Do you recall learning in Chapter 1 about protective factors that influence your health? One additional factor related to your outlook is **resilience.** This is *the ability to adapt effectively and recover from disappointment, difficulty, or crisis.* People with resilience are able to bounce back quickly, even in the face of great hardships and tragedies. Resilient people show an ability to survive and thrive. People who are resilient do not get overwhelmed when the going gets tough. Instead, they view what has gone wrong as a challenge to be faced head-on and then set out to find specific ways to meet that challenge.

LESSON 4 *Review*

Reviewing Facts and Vocabulary

1. Define the term *defense mechanism* and give examples of three different types.
2. Name three negative and three positive ways of handling anger.
3. Define *resilience* and name three characteristics of resilient people.

Thinking Critically

4. *Evaluating.* Discuss this saying: "The shortest way around a problem is directly through it." Relate the statement to the subject of emotional health.
5. *Synthesizing.* Talk about the following Swedish proverb. "Shared joy is double joy, and shared sorrow is half-sorrow."

Applying Health Skills

6. *In Your Home.* Keep an "anger log." For one week, record every instance of anger you feel. Rate the anger from 1 to 10. List the trigger for the anger, how it registers in your body, what you feel like doing at the time, and how you actually handle the emotion. Give yourself a healthful reward every time you handle the anger in a mature and positive way.

LESSON 4   HANDLING EMOTIONS IN HEALTHFUL WAYS   **207**

ASSESS

EVALUATING THE LESSON

Assign and discuss the Lesson 4 Review; then administer, grade, and discuss *the Lesson 28 Quiz* in the TCR. ☞

RETEACHING

- Have students list and explain each of the common defense mechanisms. Ask that they provide examples of each.
- Ask students to complete *Reteaching Activity 28* in the TCR. ☞

ENRICHMENT

- Divide the class into three groups with the following assignments. *Group One:* List five ways to get out of a relationship with someone who has been your friend but now does not meet your standards of behavior. *Group Two:* List five ways to deal with the fact that your friends can stay out all night on prom night and your parents won't let you. *Group Three:* List five ways to deal with the fact that you didn't get a job you wanted, which means you won't have money for a trip. Have group representatives share the responses. Ask students to identify the positive and negative responses. Which will promote good mental health best?
- Give students stress management tools and have them complete *Enrichment Activity 8,* "The Mind-Body Connection," in the TCR. ☞

CLOSE

Divide the class into small groups. Ask each group to develop a radio announcement that focuses public attention on positive ways of dealing with emotions.

Lesson 4 Review

Answers to Reviewing Facts and Vocabulary

1. See Glossary for definition. Examples can be found on page 204.
2. Negative: tantrums, kicking, hitting. Positive: rechanneling, getting away, crying, talking it out, writing it down, punching a pillow.
3. See Glossary for definition. Characteristics will vary.

Answers to Thinking Critically

4. Discussion should include many of the same steps as the decision-making process: identifying the problem, weighing consequences, selecting options—as opposed to using defense mechanisms.
5. Having a support system of friends and family is important in good times and bad.

Health **Skills** Activities

Activity 1 — Pyramid of Human Needs

Psychologist Abraham Maslow presented the concept of human needs in a pyramid form. Needs at the bottom of the pyramid must be satisfied before those higher up can be met. How are your needs addressed within the community?

Directions

1. With a small group, create a schoolwide "pyramid of needs." Begin by cutting a pyramid shape from a large sheet of cardboard.
2. Take or find photos of people within your school community fulfilling needs at each level. Alternatively, you may create art that shows this. Write a caption for each image.
3. Display your pyramid in a public place.
4. Discuss where you as a class are on Maslow's Pyramid. Create a step-by-step plan describing how you will maintain this level or attain a higher level on the pyramid.

Time
50 minutes

Materials
large sheet of cardboard, markers, photos or art, manila pocket folder

Self-Assessment

✓ Identified at least three human needs being met by people in your community.

✓ Listed the names or titles of the people that met each need and explained how they fulfilled this need.

✓ Included a plan to maintain or enhance your health.

Activity 2 — Greeting Cards for Health

Have you ever sent or received a greeting card that gave you an emotional lift? Cards are a good way of communicating positive messages. Design a greeting card that sends a positive, meaningful message to someone in your life.

Directions

1. Fold a sheet of colored paper in half lengthwise. Turn the paper with the crease to the left. You are now looking at the front of the card.
2. Decorate this front panel with a picture, symbol, or a brief introductory message.
3. Open the card, and create a positive, meaningful message for the inside. The message may address a specific event in the person's life, or it can serve to provide encouragement.
4. Send the card, or save it for a time when it will do the most good.

Time
40 minutes

Materials
8-x-11-inch colored paper, felt-tip pens of different colors

Self-Assessment

✓ Created an uplifting and encouraging message through words and images.

✓ Successfully developed a message promoting mental health.

ACTIVITY 1
HEALTH SKILLS

Comprehending Health Concepts, Analyzing Influences

➤ **National Standards**
This activity meets these National Health Standards: 1.4; 4.2.

Teach

- If students take photographs make sure they understand the importance of respecting the privacy of others. Explain that they are responsible for explaining to the person the purpose of the photograph and for sharing a copy of the image if it is so requested. Have them ask the individual to sign a "release" indicating permission to use his or her image. You might also provide students with magazines that contain photos they may use.
- Review Maslow's hierarchy in Lesson 2.
- Elicit from students specific strategies they can follow, including setting up an action plan for reaching the next level of their pyramids.

ACTIVITY 2
HEALTH SKILLS

Self Management—Building Self-esteem, Communication, Health Advocacy

➤ **National Standards**
This activity meets these National Health Standards: 3.4; 5.1; 7.4.

Teach

- Demonstrate the basic instructions for folding and creating the card.
- Ask students to brainstorm text messages and visual images that would capture a positive feeling or emotion. You may want to have one student serve as a recorder to list some of these expressions and ideas on the chalkboard.

ASSESSMENT SCORING

Using a four-level rubric, the student has achieved a 4 if:

ACTIVITY 1

✔ Student identified at least three human needs being met by people in their school.

✔ Student prepared a pyramid that was visually interesting and easy to follow.

✔ Student identified strategies for meeting their needs and the needs of others.

✔ Student took an active role in the discussion of ways the class can fulfill needs.

ACTIVITY 2

✔ Student identified features of a greeting card that would provide an emotional lift.

✔ The tone of the completed card was upbeat and promotes mental health.

✔ Student participated in an open discussion of how encouragement can be expressed.

✔ Student completed a greeting card meeting the specifications in the assignment.

Overcoming Flying Fears

At least one of seven people has some fear of going up in an airplane. For those who refuse to get on board, that phobia can be paralyzing.

People don't have to live with flying fears. Experts suggest that therapy, workshops, self-help programs, or even a few basic tips can go a long way toward getting them off the ground. Tony Martinez, a United Airlines mechanic who serves on the board of the Fear of Flying Clinic says knowledge is the key to overcoming flying anxiety.

"We're not saying you have to like to fly, but at least you have to have the tools to fly, and of course, practice makes perfect. Over time and repeated flights, your anxiety and phobias diminish dramatically," he says. The clinic features instruction by a pilot, mechanic, and air traffic controller. They explain the basics of aerodynamics and flight safety procedures and take clients on a tour of the control tower and maintenance area. A licensed therapist also works with participants to help them determine the basis of their phobia or fear.

Each clinic ends with a short orientation flight. Every one of these flights brings people closer to overcoming their fears.

Read This

Coping with Flying Fears

These expert tips help many people deal with anxiety about flying.
- Learn relaxation techniques, including deep-breathing exercises.
- Check Web sites devoted to flying fears. They may have message boards where you can swap information with other travelers.
- Learn more about aeronautics and meteorology.
- Don't be frightened by turbulence. It's a routine part of flying.
- Inform flight crewmembers that you're nervous about flying. They may be able to assist you.
- Enroll in a seminar, buy a self-help tape, or consider private therapy.

Think About It

1. How do fear of flying clinics help people control their emotional health?
2. Does this article suggest that it is possible to overcome all fears? Why or why not?

MORE ABOUT . . . . .

ASK THE EXPERTS. The "expert" who can best understand a phobia might be someone who has suffered from the same phobia. People who have overcome a phobia have direct, personal insight into the problems facing sufferers.

Barbara MacLeod would not fly for 13 years, paralyzed by her fear of flying. "It was such a shameful and exhausting experience that I vowed I was going to put this thing front and center in my life and beat it," MacLeod says. After working with a therapist, she overcame her fears and even became a pilot herself. Her story can help inspire other people to overcome their phobias.

CHECKING COMPREHENSION

- Assign and discuss the chapter review.
- Use the MindJogger Videoquiz to review the chapter. 🔴

CHAPTER 8 REVIEW ANSWERS

Using Health Terms

1. feedback
2. mental health
3. self-actualization
4. aesthetic
5. personality
6. hierarchy of needs
7. modeling
8. empathy
9. phobias
10. emotions
11. hostility
12. resilience
13. defense mechanisms

Recalling the Facts

1. People with good mental health are realistic about their strengths and weaknesses; are responsible for their behavior; avoid high-risk behaviors; are flexible; are able to relax and enjoy themselves; respect the needs of themselves and others; respect everyone's value as a human being; express their emotions in nonharmful ways.
2. Give yourself credit for what you can do; don't criticize yourself when you make a mistake—instead, focus on what you can learn from it; accept the fact that no one's perfect—including you; when someone criticizes you, stop to consider where that person's negativity comes from.
3. Family, friends, teachers, the media
4. Answers will vary.
5. Although everyone has needs, some are more basic than others.
6. Depression, boredom, mental illness, physical illness.

CHAPTER 8 · *Review*

Using Health Terms

On a separate sheet of paper, write the term that best matches each definition below.

LESSON 1

1. The messages you receive from others that indicate who they think you are or what they think you are like.
2. Generally having a positive outlook, being comfortable with self and others, and being able to meet life's challenges.

LESSON 2

3. The striving to become the best that you can be.
4. Artistic.
5. A complex set of characteristics that makes you unique and sets you apart from everyone else.
6. A ranked list of those needs essential to human growth and development presented in ascending order from basic to most fulfilling or satisfying.
7. Copying the behaviors of those you are exposed to.

LESSON 3

8. The ability to imagine and understand how someone else feels.
9. Irrational fears.
10. Signals that tell your mind and body how to react.
11. The intentional use of unfriendly or nasty behavior

LESSON 4

12. The ability to adapt and recover from disappointment, difficulty, or crisis.
13. Strategies used to deal with strong or stressful emotions and situations.

Recalling the Facts

Using complete sentences, answer the following questions.

LESSON 1

1. What are five signs of good mental health?
2. What are some of the ways a person can improve his or her self-esteem?
3. List three sources of feedback that can influence a person's feelings of self-worth.
4. Give two examples of negative feedback and two examples of positive feedback.

LESSON 2

5. What is the theory underlying Maslow's hierarchy of needs?
6. What are some of the effects of not fulfilling the need for self-actualization?
7. What are the three main influences on the development of personality?

8. Over which personality influences do you have most control?

LESSON 3

9. Describe three physical reactions that occur in the body when you feel anger.
10. Name eight basic emotions.
11. What is a phobia, and what role does it play in a person's life?
12. What are three effects hormones can have on teens' emotional well-being?

LESSON 4

13. List five defense mechanisms and give an example of each.
14. Name five strategies for handling anger in healthful ways.
15. Describe three traits of optimistic, resilient people.

7. Heredity, environment, behavior.
8. Behavior.
9. Rise in heart rate, perspiration, tightening of the stomach muscles.
10. Love, empathy, fear, anger, guilt, jealousy, happiness, sadness.
11. A phobia is an irrational fear that can interfere with leading a normal life.
12. Any three: Hormones can make you feel oversensitive, highly emotional, insecure, and can cause you to overreact.
13. Defense mechanisms include repression, suppression, rationalization, regression, denial, compensation, projection, idealization. Examples will vary.
14. Rechanneling, talking it out, writing it down, having a good cry, punching a pillow.

Thinking Critically

LESSON 1

1. ***Evaluating.*** List ten events that took place during your day and analyze how each affected your self-esteem.

LESSON 2

2. ***Synthesizing.*** Think of a question that might come from a teen whose emotional needs have not been met. Then offer suggestions on how to meet needs healthfully.

3. ***Analyzing.*** Recall a situation where your personal behavior did not include healthful choices, and analyze the factors that caused you to choose this behavior.

LESSON 3

4. ***Evaluating.*** Watch the first ten minutes of a nightly news program. List the number of stories that cause you to feel fear or anger and the number that elicit positive emotions. How does the news seem to be "weighted" emotionally?

LESSON 4

5. ***Synthesizing.*** Using the material in this chapter, write a pamphlet offering tips on how to manage anger in healthful ways.

Making the Connection

1. ***Social Studies.*** Choose a famous person from history whom you believe achieved self-actualization. The subject should have had to overcome physical, psychological, social, or other obstacles. Include details about the time in which the person lived, and investigate the kinds of resilient behaviors the person exhibited in meeting challenges. Present your findings in the form of an oral report.

2. ***Language Arts.*** A simile compares two seemingly dissimilar items using a comparing word such as *like* or *as*. For example, *Anger is like hot coals on the back of your neck*. Write five similes, one for each of the emotions covered in this chapter.

BEYOND THE CLASSROOM

PARENTAL INVOLVEMENT Present to your family what you have learned in this chapter about expressing anger in healthful ways. Ask members of your household to observe for several days when they become angry, what triggers the anger, how that anger is expressed or handled, and how others in the household react. Afterward, have a discussion in which each person is given a chance to present his or her findings. As a group, come up with a plan to help one another express anger in healthful ways.

COMMUNITY INVOLVEMENT To help those in your community who may not have their basic food needs met, work with classmates to organize a canned food drive.

SCHOOL-TO-CAREER
Exploring Careers. There are many kinds of careers relating to mental and emotional health, including school counselor, psychologist, and art therapist. Invite one of these professionals to your class to talk about his or her work and what kind of training is required.

Thinking Critically

1.–5. Answers will vary.

Making the Connection

1. Reports will vary.
2. Similes will vary.

Evaluate

- Use the reproducible *Chapter 8 Test* in the TCR or construct your own using the Testmaker software. 📁 💾
- Use *Performance Assessment Activity 8* in the TCR. 📁

Enrichment

- Have students complete *Cross-Curriculum Activity 8* in the TCR. 📁

Beyond the Classroom

Keep students involved in the community, and encourage parent participation by assigning the activities on this page for students to work on outside of class.

---

15. They bounce back quickly from setbacks, they show an ability to survive and thrive despite hardship, and they view problems as challenges to be overcome.

Managing Stress in Your Life

	FEATURES	CLASSROOM RESOURCES

LESSON 1

What Is Stress?
pages 214–218

- Concept Map Activity 29
- Cooperative Learning Activity 9
- Lesson 29 Quiz
- Lesson Plan 29
- Reteaching Activity 29
- Transparencies 20, 21

LESSON 2

Stress in Your Life
pages 219–223

Making Responsible Decisions
"Problem-Solving and Perfectionism," *page 222*

- Concept Map Activity 30
- Decision-Making Activity 9
- Health Lab 9
- Lesson 30 Quiz
- Lesson Plan 30
- Reteaching Activity 30

LESSON 3

Managing Stress
pages 224–227

Building Health Skills
"Taking Control of Your Day," *page 225*

- Concept Map Activity 31
- Enrichment Activity 9
- Lesson 31 Quiz
- Lesson Plan 31
- Reteaching Activity 31
- Transparency 36

LESSON 4

Coping with Loss
pages 228–231

Teens Making a Difference
"Helping Others Cope," *page 230*

- Concept Map Activity 32
- Lesson 32 Quiz
- Lesson Plan 32
- Reteaching Activity 32

Chapter Resources

ACTIVITIES

- Cross-Curriculum Activity 9
- Health Lab 9
- Health Skills Activities 9
- Parent Letter and Activities 9

ASSESSMENT

- Chapter 9 Test
- Performance Assessment Activity 9
- Testmaker Software

STUDENT ACTIVITIES WORKBOOK

- Applying Health Skills 29–32
- Study Guide 9
- Vocabulary Activity 9

STUDENT DIVERSITY STRATEGIES

- Audiocassette Program (English)
- Audiocassette Program (Spanish)
- Spanish Parent Letters and Activities
- Spanish Summaries, Quizzes, and Activities

MULTIMEDIA COMPONENTS

- English Audiocassette Program
- Spanish Audiocassette Program
- MindJogger Videodisc and VHS program
- ABCNews InterActive™ VHS/Videodisc Series

National Health Education Standards

One of the main goals of the National Health Education Standards is to move students toward "health literacy." Health literacy is the capacity of individuals to obtain, interpret, and understand basic health information and services and the competence to use such information and services in ways which promote health. The health standards were developed by applying the characteristics of a well-educated, literate person within the context of health. The health literate person is:

- a critical thinker and problem solver
- a self-directed learner
- a responsible, productive citizen
- an effective communicator

Listed below are the Health Education Standards Performance Indicators addressed in each lesson of this chapter.

Lesson	Health Standards Performance Indicators
1	1.2, 1.3, 3.2, 3.7
2	1.2, 3.2, 3.7, 6.1
3	1.2, 3.1, 3.2, 3.7
4	2.6, 4.3, 3.7, 5.4

ONLINE RESOURCES

For a fresh approach to health topics and an in-depth look at health issues, use these online resources found under Teacher Resources at **health.glencoe.com**.

- **BLOCK SCHEDULE LESSON PLANS** Reinforce health concepts with outside readings selected especially for students. Each reading is accompanied by a lesson plan and activities to enhance
  - Reading Skills
  - Cross Curriculum
  - Media Literacy

- **TECHNOLOGY PROJECTS** Instructions and suggestions on how to use computer, Internet, and software with health lessons.

- **HEALTH UPDATES** Timely topics in health news, including late-breaking medical advances and updates on teen risk behaviors.

Out of Time?

If time does not permit teaching this chapter, you may use these features: Making Responsible Decisions on page 222 and Building Health Skills on page 225.

BLOCK SCHEDULING

Block scheduling provides extended time for hands-on projects and activities. Use the following activity to engage students, provide further depth, and vary your instructional techniques:
- Teens Making a Difference (30 minutes) **pg. 230**
- Health Skills Activity (60–90 minutes) **pg. 232**

Managing Stress in Your Life

CHAPTER OVERVIEW

Chapter 9 introduces the body's response to stress and factors that influence how much stress the body can tolerate. It also emphasizes the need for individuals to understand stress and learn to manage it in their daily lives if they are to lessen its harmful effects.

LESSON 1 Stress is the body's general response to any situation. Some stress is vital. It can even improve the way you function. Other stress has negative consequences. The body's response to stress is involuntary, activated by the autonomic nervous system.

LESSON 2 Stress is unavoidable. However, people differ in the amount of stress their bodies can tolerate. Personality type is a factor in the way people cope with stress. The mind-body connection becomes apparent since stress is shown to be a contributing factor in many illnesses.

LESSON 3 In its responses, the body cannot distinguish between positive and negative sources of stress. As a result, your body depends on you to identify and manage stress in your life.

LESSON 4 Any loss can cause a stress response. People who suffer a major loss go through a five-stage process of coping. Recognizing feelings and bringing closure are a necessary part of grieving and moving on with life. Professional help or counseling is sometimes needed in this process.

Managing Stress in Your Life

HEALTH *Online*

STRESS MANAGEMENT

Take a time-out to flex your mind and relieve some mental stress. Challenge yourself to some brain exercises and puzzles at **health.glencoe.com**. Look for "Think of it! A Mental Health Barometer" under Interactive Projects.

Hands-On Health

TEACHING STRATEGY

Identifying Stressors Help students recognize their own stressors and the stress-reducing methods that can be most effective for them. See Activity 4, "Personal Stress Busters," in the *Hands-On Health: Creative Teaching Strategies* booklet. 📖

Time Needed

20 minutes, plus individual conference time

Supplies

- "Stress Test" student worksheet
- pens or pencils

Personal Health Inventory

Self-Inventory Write the numbers 1–10 on a sheet of paper. Read each statement below and respond by writing *yes*, *no*, or *sometimes* for each item. Write a *yes* only for items that you practice regularly. Save your responses.

1	I'm aware of when I'm feeling tense.
2	I can identify many of the situations that cause me to feel tense.
3	I know how to calm myself down in healthful ways after a stressful experience.
4	I use physical activity to help reduce my stress.
5	I plan for things in advance so that I am prepared for them.
6	I take time out every day to relax and enjoy myself.
7	When I'm feeling tense or upset, I share my thoughts and feelings with family members and friends.
8	I avoid using tobacco, alcohol, and other drugs.
9	I get enough sleep and make nutritious food choices.
10	When I feel things are getting to me, I try to deal with them in healthful ways before they build up and get the best of me.

Follow-up After completing the chapter, retake this self-inventory. Pick two items that you need to work on and set a goal to improve your health behaviors.

CHAPTER 9 MANAGING STRESS IN YOUR LIFE **213**

> **The process of living is the process of reacting to stress.**
>
> —DR. STANLEY J. SARNOFF
> PHYSICIAN

Quick Write Jot down one recent situation or event that has caused you stress. Think about what you can do to manage this one stressor.

INTRODUCING THE CHAPTER

Personal Health Inventory

Remind the class that we all have some stress in our lives. This Self-Inventory will help students understand how they are dealing with stress now and what they are doing to help reduce daily stress. Ask students to label a page "My Level of Stress Management" in their private Health Journals and record their responses to the Self-Inventory statements there. They will refer to these responses again when they have finished studying Chapter 9.

- Many corporations hold seminars and classes to help their employees deal with stress. Ask students why they think companies spend the time and money to do this. Then ask students if they experience stress. On the chalkboard, list all of the events students consider stressful. Tell them that as they study this chapter, they will learn more about recognizing stress, how it affects them, both positively and negatively, and how to manage stress.

- After students have completed the Quick Write, let volunteers share their own experiences of being "stressed out." What typically causes this high level of stress—a major crisis or a series of small disruptions? What can you do when you feel your stress levels rising?

- Distribute Parent Letter 9 in the *Parent Letters and Activities* booklet. ✍

TECHNOLOGY OPTIONS

ABCNEWS INTERACTIVE You may wish to use *Violence Prevention; Drugs and Substance Abuse;* and *Tobacco* with this chapter. For your convenience, use the separate *ABCNews InterActive™ Bar Code Correlation* that accompanies the *Glencoe Health* program. 🔴

MINDJOGGER
VIDEOQUIZ

To preview or review chapter content, you may wish to use the *MindJogger Videoquiz* that accompanies Chapter 9. 🔴

FOCUS

LESSON OBJECTIVES

After studying this lesson, students should be able to

- distinguish between distress and eustress.
- identify stressors in daily life.
- discuss how the body responds to stressors.
- distinguish between physical, pathological, and psychological fatigue.
- relate excessive stress to disease.

MOTIVATOR

Have students write a definition of *stress* and describe a stressful situation that they had to deal with. Ask: How was the situation handled? Was it handled positively or negatively? How might it have been handled more positively?

INTRODUCING THE LESSON

Ask volunteers to share responses to the Motivator. Lead the class in brainstorming a list of common stressors in an adolescent's life. Have them identify those that can be controlled or eliminated. Tell them that this lesson is about stress and how it affects the human body.

INTRODUCING HEALTH TERMS

- Assign students to work in pairs and write a short paper using each of the vocabulary words. Afterward, ask them to test each other's understanding of the words' definitions.
- Ask students to complete Vocabulary Activity 9 and Chapter Study Guide 9 in the *Student Workbook*. ☞

LESSON 1

What Is Stress?

Rory has to give a speech to the student body at his school. As he walks onto the auditorium stage, his face suddenly feels hot, his palms begin to sweat, and his heart starts beating like a bass drum. Physical symptoms like these are evidence that Rory is experiencing stress. Has this ever happened to you?

HEALTH TERMS

- **stress**
- **distress**
- **eustress**
- **stressor**
- **alarm**
- **adrenaline**
- **resistance**
- **fatigue**

HEALTH CONCEPTS

- Stress is a normal part of everyday life.
- The response to stress is different for each individual and may change from situation to situation.
- How you manage stress can greatly affect your mental, emotional, and physical health.

Stress and Your Well-Being

Stress is *the body's and mind's reaction to everyday demands or threats.* Whether real or imagined, these demands produce measurable changes in both the body and the brain.

Sometimes the stress in your day is minor and goes almost unnoticed. At other times it can be so strong that you may feel as if you are walking a tightrope, trying to keep everything in balance, afraid that at any moment the pressure might get to you and bring you crashing down. The fact is, stress is a part of daily life. It can be useful or harmful, energizing or exhausting. The key is to learn to handle it in healthful ways.

Kinds of Stress

Contrary to popular opinion, *stress* is not just a negative word. Stress can be either positive or negative, depending on how it is

---

Lesson 1 Resources

TEACHER'S CLASSROOM RESOURCES

- ☞ **Concept Map** Activity 29
- ☞ **Cooperative Learning** Activity 9
- ☞ **Lesson 29 Quiz**
- ☞ **Lesson Plan 29**
- ☞ **Parent Letter and Activities 9**
- ☞ **Reteaching** Activity 29

STUDENT WORKBOOK

- ☞ **Applying Health Skills 29**
- ☞ **Chapter Study Guide 9**
- ☞ **Vocabulary** Activity 9

TRANSPARENCIES

- Transparencies 20, 21

MULTIMEDIA

- 🔴 **ABCNews InterActive™**, *Violence Prevention*

perceived, managed, and put to use. **Distress**, or *negative stress*, on the one hand, can result when there is too much pressure or trauma and you don't know how to cope with it. Having too much homework or running to catch a bus when you are late are both examples of distress. **Eustress**, or *positive stress*, on the other hand, can help you achieve your goals. For example, if you are concerned about your final grade, you may study harder. Research suggests that acceptable levels of stress may even help you to focus and concentrate better.

Kinds of Stressors

Stress occurs in response to a **stressor.** This is *any stimulus that produces a stress response.* Stressors can be people, objects, places, events, or situations that cause you to react. Hearing an ambulance siren, being in a new school, or going out on a first date are all potential stressors. Psychologists have identified five general categories of stressors. These are:

- **biological stressors,** such as those that come from biochemical imbalances, mental or physical illnesses, disabilities, or injuries;
- **environmental stressors,** such as poverty, pollution, crowding, noise, or natural disasters;
- **cognitive or thinking stressors,** such as the way you perceive a situation or what you expect from it;
- **personal behavior stressors,** such as those negative reactions in the body and mind caused by using tobacco, alcohol, or other drugs, or not exercising;
- **life situations,** such as having a relative or pet die, parents who separate or divorce, or trouble in relationships with peers.

◄ *Local and national emergencies cause stress that can affect different people in different ways.*

ACTIVITY *How can individuals, families, and communities help one another through stressful situations?*

MEETING STUDENT DIVERSITY

COPING WITH CRISIS SITUATIONS

During periods of local or national crises, students will exhibit a variety of reactions depending on their level of involvement and their personal sense of loss. Emotional responses vary in intensity and students may need guidance and support from teachers, parents, and counselors to understand how to deal with these emotions. Feelings of fear, anxiety, and loss should be expected, but teachers should keep a watchful eye for expressions of severe stress and grief reactions in students. For resources to help identify students exhibiting extreme reactions who may need additional support, visit the link to the National Association of School Psychologists at **health.glencoe.com**.

TEACH

LD Explaining

Provide a simple working definition of *stress,* providing examples from everyday experience.

LEP Class Activity

Have students create cartoon strips of a teen meeting a date's parents for the first time. Post the cartoons in the class. Talk about the kinds of stress involved in the situation.

L3 Researching

Assign students to interview someone in each of the following age groups: 13–18, 19–25, 26–35, 36–45, 46–55, and 56 and older. Ask them to find out what each person's greatest stressors are and what he or she does to manage stress. Have students make a chart to share with the class, comparing the stressors. Help them draw conclusions about how stress varies with age.

L3 Family Involvement

Ask for volunteers to interview a parent, grandparent, or other adult in their lives about what it was like to be a teenager. Have them find answers to questions such as: When each adult was a teen, what were his or her feelings and concerns about appearance? physical changes? friends? dating? recreation? music? parents? school? What were his or her greatest fears? How were stressful events and situations handled? Afterward, ask students to write short reports on their interviews. Follow up with a class discussion of the experience.

L2 Cooperative Learning

Have students complete *Cooperative Learning Activity 9* and find "The Path to Stress-free Living."

L1 Parental Involvement

Ask volunteers to talk to their parents about the kinds of stress that they (or other adults) face in today's world and ways they cope with the stress.

L3 Guest Speaker

Invite the school counselor or a counselor or psychologist from the community to speak with the class about stress and distress and ways to deal with stressors. Afterward, have students write papers summarizing the presentation.

hotlink

nervous system
endocrine system
Help students realize the interdependency of the body systems and that the actions of the nervous and endocrine systems can affect total health.

L1 Discussing

Have students complete and discuss the following statements: *When I am at the doctor's s office, I feel…; During a test, I feel…; When I am with people who are arguing, I feel…; Having an argument with a friend makes me feel…*Explain that understanding things and events that can cause them to become upset can help students deal with stress.

Visual Learning

Adolescent Life-Change Event Scale

Lead students in a discussion of their reactions to the *Adolescent Life-Change Event Scale* shown on page 217. Ask them to identify the events they can control and those they cannot control. Discuss how too many stressors over a period of time can result in physical illness.

keeping Fit

Overcoming Test Anxiety

Does taking tests make you tense or put you on edge? Following these guidelines will help you to address your "test stress."

➤ Plan for tests in advance, studying a little bit each night.

➤ Learn to outline material, highlighting and numbering important points so you can spot them quickly.

➤ During the test, do some deep breathing. Get comfortable in your chair. Give yourself a quick positive message like, "You can do it!"

➤ Answer all the questions you are sure of, then go back to answer the ones that are more difficult.

➤ After getting your corrected test back, examine your mistakes and try to understand why you made them. If you don't understand them, ask for explanations.

hotlink

nervous system For more information on the nervous system and its parts and functions, see Chapter 16, page 364.

endocrine system For information on the endocrine system and its parts and functions, see Chapter 16, page 377.

The Body's Stress Response

When you perceive a situation or event to be a threat, your body begins a stress response. A series of events is put into action as your body prepares itself for "danger." For example, if a car suddenly backfires, the loud sound is a stressor. How your body and mind react is your stress response. The combination of the stressor and your stress response adds up to your stress. You may jump at the sound without thinking, or your heart may suddenly start to race. If you recognize the sound for what it is and realize that there is no real danger, your response may be minimal. If, however, you mistake the sound for a gunshot, you may have a much stronger reaction.

Two major systems of the body, the **nervous system** and the **endocrine system**, are active during the body's response to stressors. The body's response is largely involuntary, or automatic. It happens in three stages and can occur whether the stress is physical or emotional, positive or negative.

Alarm

Alarm is *the first stage in the stress response, when the body and mind go on high alert.* During this stage, the hypothalamus, a small nerve center at the base of the brain, is excited by the stressor. The autonomic nervous system, the system that controls involuntary actions, is activated, as is the pituitary gland. This gland secretes a hormone that stimulates the adrenal glands, which in turn secrete a hormone called adrenaline. **Adrenaline** is *the "emergency hormone" secreted by the adrenal glands to prepare the body to respond to a stressor.* This "fight or flight" response provides energy to get you through the actual or perceived emergency. Because of adrenaline, the heart speeds up its activity, providing more blood to the brain and muscles. Breathing becomes faster and deeper, providing more oxygen to the body. Throat muscles may contract, making swallowing difficult. Your face may become flushed, you may sweat, and your arms and legs may tighten to prepare the body for action. Your mind also goes on high alert so that you can take in information and become aware of your surroundings.

Resistance

Resistance is *the second stage in the stress response, when the body tries to repair its damage from the stressful event and return to its normal state.* Usually, if the stressor is prolonged, the stage of resistance occurs. During this stage, physical resistance to the stressor reaches its peak. This is why people in extremely high-stress situations have been known to accomplish incredible feats of strength, such as lifting an automobile to save a child trapped under it. The body functions at a higher-than-normal level. If this stage continues for too long, however, both the body and mind may show ill effects.

CURRICULUM CONNECTIONS

SCIENCE. Invite a science teacher to talk with the class about adrenaline and the role it plays in the body.

SOCIAL STUDIES. Have students research lifestyles in Japan where, in recent years, the incidence of stress-related illnesses has risen. Ask students to give reasons that explain this phenomenon.

SCIENCE. Select students to locate current information about two extremely powerful analgesics (endorphins and enkephalins) and their relationship to stress. Ask them to share what they learn with the class.

ART. Assign students to use various art media to illustrate the human body's response to stress.

ADOLESCENT LIFE-CHANGE EVENT SCALE

To get a sense of how much your life may have changed in the last year and how these changes might have affected your level of stress, add up the "life-change units" for the changes you've faced during the past year.

If your score is less than 150, your life hasn't changed very much. A score between 150 and 300 means moderate change. A score of over 300 indicates you have experienced a great deal of change and may have to pay special attention to how you handle the stress that can come with it.

LIFE-CHANGE UNITS	LIFE EVENT
101	Getting married
92	Being pregnant and single
87	Having a parent die
81	Getting a visible deformity
77	Having parents divorce
77	Becoming a single father
76	Getting involved with drugs or alcohol
75	Having a parent jailed for a year or more
69	Going through a parent's separation
68	Having a brother or sister die
67	Experiencing a change in peers' acceptance
64	Having a single pregnant teenage sister
64	Discovering that you are adopted
63	Having a parent get married again
62	Experiencing a close friend's death
62	Having a visible deformity since birth
58	Being seriously ill and requiring hospitalization
56	Moving to a new school district
56	Failing a grade in school
55	Not making a team or other extracurricular activity
55	Having a parent become seriously ill
53	Breaking up with a boyfriend or girlfriend
53	Having a parent go to jail for 30 days or less
51	Beginning to date
50	Being suspended from school
50	Getting a newborn sister or brother
47	Getting in more arguments with parents
46	Having an outstanding personal achievement
46	Seeing more arguments between parents
46	Having a parent lose his or her job
45	Having a change in parents' financial status
43	Being accepted at a college of your choice
41	Having a brother or sister become seriously ill
38	Having a parent be more absent from home due to a change in occupation
37	Having a brother or sister leave home
36	Experiencing the death of a grandparent
34	Having a third adult added to the family
31	Becoming a fully committed member of a religion
27	Experiencing a decrease in parents' arguments
26	Having a mother begin to work outside the home

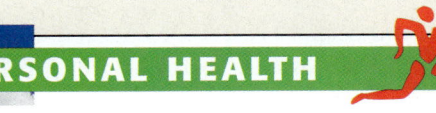

PERSONAL HEALTH

EXAM-RELATED STRESS. Many students experience stress before an exam. Indeed, by determining a grade, college or job placement, or allocation of scholarship funds, exams may alter the course of students' lives. However, stress can interfere with test performance even when the test taker is well prepared. Encourage students to make private entries in their journals detailing the symptoms of stress they experience in connection with exams, how it affects them, and what strategies might help them manage it. Emphasize that the entries are private, but that volunteers are welcome to share them if they wish.

L1 ## Personal Involvement

Have students keep journals of their daily lives, including stressors that they experience and how they respond to each of them. Let students know that they will not have to share their journal entries with anyone.

L2 ## Researching

Ask for volunteers to find examples of people experiencing stress on TV. Have them compare what they viewed on television to what they learned in this lesson.

L3 ## Guest Speaker

Invite a police officer, firefighter, or emergency medical worker to speak with the class about stress he or she experiences at work. Have the speaker talk about the effect of adrenaline on the body during stressful events.

L1 ## Discussing

Ask students why they think fatigue is a common complaint among many people. Talk about the differences between physical, pathological, and psychological fatigue.

L1 ## Discussing

Talk about why rest is the best solution to physical and pathological fatigue, but not to psychological fatigue.

VIOLENCE PREVENTION (Side 1)

Chapter 4: Managing Stress

Frames 8390–13464

ASSESS

EVALUATING THE LESSON

Assign and discuss the Lesson 1 Review; then administer, grade, and discuss the *Lesson 29 Quiz* in the TCR. ☞

RETEACHING

- Use *Transparencies 20* and *21* to review the body's response to stress and the adolescent life-change event scale. 🧴
- Ask students to complete *Reteaching Activity 29* in the TCR. ☞

ENRICHMENT

Ask students to read material by and about Dr. Hans Selye, a leading authority on stress.

CLOSE

Write the lesson's major concepts on separate, numbered slips of paper. Place the slips in a box, and let each student draw one. In numerical order, have each student summarize the concept on his or her slip of paper.

Fatigue

Fatigue is *the third stage of the stress response, resulting in a tired feeling that lowers one's level of activity.* When the body is continually exposed to stressors or a particular stressor is prolonged, the body and the mind become worn down. During this stage, there is little energy to resist the stressor.

There are many kinds of fatigue, and it is important to recognize and understand each.

- **Physical fatigue** may occur at the end of a long day or after exercise, when the body produces waste products in the form of lactic acid from the muscles and carbon dioxide from all the body's cells. A buildup of wastes in the muscles can produce soreness and, at higher levels, tiredness.

- **Pathological fatigue** is tiredness brought on by overworking the body's defenses in fighting disease. Anemia, the flu, being overweight, and having poor nutrition can all bring on pathological fatigue. So can using drugs such as alcohol or caffeine.

- **Psychological fatigue** can result from constant worry, overwork, depression, boredom, and isolation.

Prolonged or repeated periods of stress can lead to stress-related illnesses. Although these can be minor, they can also be life-threatening. It is not just the major stresses or traumas that lead to disease. Daily hassles can build up over time and have serious health consequences. It is important to try to control the amount of stress in your life.

LESSON 1 *Review*

Reviewing Facts and Vocabulary

1. Define the words *eustress* and *distress* and use them in a single paragraph.
2. Name and describe the three stages of the stress response.
3. What happens if a person is under stress too often or for too long?

Thinking Critically

4. *Analyzing.* Divide a piece of paper in half. At the top of one side, write a plus sign; at the top of the other, a minus sign. For one day, keep track of the eustress and distress that you feel and the stressors that caused each, recording each in the appropriate column.

5. *Evaluating.* Write down some major sources of stress. Then write the ways you typically handle the stressors. How well are you handling stress in your life?

Applying Health Skills

6. *In Your Home.* Survey your home, thinking about what things cause negative stress for you and other family members. For example, maybe the TV is on too much, there isn't enough privacy, or phone messages are not properly relayed. With other members of your household, discuss these stressors and how you might change or "defuse" them in healthful and creative ways.

Lesson 1 Review

Answers to Reviewing Facts and Vocabulary

1. Eustress: stress that has a positive impact. Distress: stress that has a negative impact.
2. The three stages of the stress response include: Alarm: The body and mind go on high alert; Resistance: The body tries to repair the damage from the stressful event and return to normal; Fatigue: A tired feeling that lowers one's level of activity.
3. Stress-related illness.

Answers to Thinking Critically

4.–5. Answers will vary.

Stress in Your Life

S tress is an unavoidable part of life. When it is positive, stress can make life fun, exciting, enjoyable, and challenging. When it is negative, it can severely impact your mental and physical health. Research suggests that both your brain chemistry and your personality type play a role in how you respond to stress.

HEALTH TERMS

stress tolerance
Type A personality
Type B personality
hardy personality
psychosomatic response

HEALTH CONCEPTS

- Several factors affect a person's level of stress.
- Stress can negatively impact an individual's health.
- You can learn to recognize the signs of stress in your own body and life.
- Stress can often be controlled by how you view the stressor.

Stress and the Brain

D o you thrive on challenge? Does it frighten you? Do you jump into new experiences unafraid, or does the thought of too much risk or change scare you?

Your answers to these and similar questions may be partly related to conditions in your brain that were present at birth. Scientists have determined that in some people, stress upsets a delicate balance among brain chemicals called *neurotransmitters*. This imbalance may cause sleep disturbances, panic attacks, and low enjoyment of life. The first signs of such an imbalance can include trouble falling asleep, waking up often during the night, and very vivid dreams followed by lack of energy, aches and pains, and later, depression.

Stress tolerance is *the amount of stress that you can handle before you reach a state of too much stress.* Though most people have lived

---

Lesson 2 Resources

TEACHER'S CLASSROOM RESOURCES

- ✏ **Concept Map** Activity 30
- ✏ **Decision-Making** Activity 9
- ✏ **Health Lab** 9
- ✏ **Lesson 30 Quiz**
- ✏ **Lesson Plan** 30
- ✏ **Reteaching** Activity 30

STUDENT WORKBOOK

- ✏ **Applying Health Skills** 30
- ✏ **Chapter Study Guide** 9
- ✏ **Vocabulary** Activity 9

MULTIMEDIA

- **ABCNews InterActive™ VHS/Videodiscs,** *Drugs and Substance Abuse; Tobacco*

Stress in Your Life

FOCUS

LESSON OBJECTIVES

After studying this lesson, students should be able to

- explain the roles of stress tolerance and personality in determining a person's level of stress.
- identify common stress-induced illnesses.
- describe the signs of stress.

MOTIVATOR

Write the following on the chalkboard for students to work on while attendance is being taken: *Explain the difference between a Type A and a Type B personality. Which type best describes you? What are the reasons for your choice?*

INTRODUCING THE LESSON

Ask students to share their responses to the Motivator. Discuss Type A and Type B personalities and the importance of identifying and managing stress-producing behaviors and personal responses to stress. Tell students that in this lesson they will learn more about personality types and also examine the effects of stress on the body.

INTRODUCING HEALTH TERMS

- Have students determine the meanings of the root words in the term *psychosomatic*. Then ask them what they think a psychosomatic response to stress might be.
- Ask students to complete Vocabulary Activity 9 and Chapter Study Guide 9 in the *Student Workbook.* ✏

TEACH

L1 Explaining

Help students understand and discuss just what sleep disturbances, panic attacks, and low enjoyment of life involve. Reassure them that everyone has difficulty falling or staying asleep occasionally, that fear can be normal, and that we all have "down days." However, anyone who is concerned about one or more of these persistent feelings can be encouraged to seek help from a counselor or mental health professional.

L1 Discussing

Guide students in discussing the importance of stress tolerance. Let them review some of the daily demands and activities that introduce stress into their lives. Ask: How does your ability to accept and deal with these factors affect your life? How do you think having a low stress tolerance would affect an individual's daily life?

L2 Researching

Let volunteers read more about low stress tolerance. What kinds of help are available from physical and mental health professionals?

L1 Personal Involvement

Suggest that students evaluate their own personality types. Ask: Do you consider yourself Type A or Type B? What specific habits and attitudes indicate your personality type? How do you think your personality type affects your daily life? the way you deal with stress? your relationships with others? Have students record their responses in their private Health Journals.

---

through some period of overstress, it is estimated that one in ten Americans experience low stress tolerance.

Stress and Your Personality Type

Personality is another factor in how you handle stress. Some psychologists have grouped people into Type A and Type B personalities. The **Type A personality** is described as a *competitive, high-achieving personality type most likely to develop heart disease* or other significant health problem. The **Type B personality** is seen as *a "laid back," non-competitive personality type less likely to suffer from heart disease.* Research indicates, however, that the Type A personality may actually relieve stress by working, whereas the Type B is more likely to hold on to the stress, thereby becoming more open to other stress-related disorders.

▶ *People with Type A and Type B personalities react differently to the same stressor.*

ACTIVITY *List three stressors, and tell how a Type A and Type B person would respond to each.*

The fact is that different personality types and even different individuals respond to the same stressors in different ways. Some people hold up well during certain kinds of stress while others break down more quickly. Some people seem able to remain healthy even under the most severe kinds of distress. According to psychologist Suzanne Kobasa, such people have "hardy personalities." The **hardy personality** is *a personality type that seems able to stay healthy despite major or even traumatic stressors.* In

220 CHAPTER 9 MANAGING STRESS IN YOUR LIFE

HEALTH LITERACY

STRESS-RELATED ILLNESSES. Stress plays a key role in contributing to many heart problems, ulcers, and complaints such as spastic colitis. Encourage students to conduct research about stress-caused or stress-related physical illnesses. Have them select one and research it in depth. Tell them to write up its symptoms, long-term prognosis, causative factors, and treatment. If possible, they should explain which of the effects produced by stress in the body is most responsible for causing the condition. Suggest they include any recommendations they find for managing stress to avoid the condition.

general, people with hardy personalities have a higher degree of **resilience**. Kobasa also notes that such people share three other very important characteristics:

- **Change.** The hardy personality likes and welcomes change, viewing it as an opportunity for growth.
- **Commitment.** The hardy personality has a strong sense of purpose and is committed to people, activities, and principles that bring meaning to her or his life.
- **Control.** The hardy personality has a sense of power about his or her own life and feels some influence over what happens, taking action when possible. This person also recognizes that some things cannot be controlled.

Stress During Adolescence

Certain periods of life seem to have their own characteristic stressors and stress responses. Adolescence is one of these. Learning what stressors are common among teens can help you to cope. So can sharing feelings of stress with your peers. Doing so will remind you that you're not alone, and that what you are feeling is probably perfectly normal for people your age.

Stress and the Body-Mind Connection

The body-mind connection is not entirely understood by science. Nevertheless, there is a clear connection between the health of the mind and the health of the body. Too much stress can raise blood pressure, weaken the immune system, and cause other health risks. It can even lead to premature, or early, death.

Stress and High Blood Pressure

Mental and emotional stress can cause an increase in your levels of cholesterol, the fatty substance that can block arteries. When these levels are high, high blood pressure—a condition that contributes to heart disease and stroke—can result.

Stress and Headache

It is estimated that most adults and about half of all teens get headaches. For some people, these headaches are mild and brief; for others, they can be severe and get in the way of normal functioning. Many headaches are related to tension. When stressed, the muscles in the head and neck contract.

A migraine headache can also be triggered by stress, although this more severe form of headache can also be triggered by hormone changes, food additives, fluorescent lights, changes in air pressure, and more. When the arteries leading to the brain narrow, blood flow to the brain decreases. When the arteries open up again, the nerve

hot link
resilience For more information on resilience and other protective factors that increase a person's likelihood for a healthy life, see Chapter 8, page 207.

CHARACTER IN ACTION

Honestly!

Your level of **honesty** with others can strongly impact your relationships, the kinds of stress you experience in those relationships, and, in turn, your level of mental and emotional health.

Telling lies or withholding important information that another person has the right to know adds stress to a relationship. Being insincere or manipulating others destroys trust that is essential in building healthy relationships. It also chips away at one's own energy and self-esteem.

Character Check Write a story called "Lying: The Domino Effect." In your story have a person tell one lie, and then demonstrate how it affects his or her life and the life of someone close. Tell how this causes mental and emotional stress to both parties.

L1 Discussing

Encourage students to identify and discuss characters in novels (or in movies or television programs) that represent hardy personalities. Ask them to cite specific examples of each character's resilience, attitude toward change, commitment, and sense of control.

L1 Critical Thinking

Let students share, compare, and support their responses to these questions: To what extent do you think your personality is already set, either by heredity or by your earlier experiences? Can you develop a hardy personality, even if you feel you don't have one now? If so, how? If not, why not?

L3 Class Activity

Assign selected students to locate and read current findings about the relationship of stress to physical illnesses such as heart disease, high blood pressure, asthma, ulcers, colitis, and migraine headaches. Ask them to share their findings with the class.

L2 Discussing

On the board, make a list of stress-related illnesses. Then divide the class into groups of three or four students each. Have each group pick an illness and attempt to explain how the effects of stress on the body caused the illness.

L1 Family Involvement

Suggest that students discuss the daily stressors of adolescence with their parents or other adult family members: What stressors do the students have in common with the adults? How do they cope?

L2 Health Lab

Distribute *Health Lab 9* and have students learn more about the effect of stress on blood pressure. ▰

COOPERATIVE LEARNING

ACTIVITY. Divide the class into groups of four. Have each group member in turn describe a scenario with potential to create stress for a Type A personality. For example, a ticket agent may have misplaced Sam's reservations for a concert and refuse to admit him; Regina may receive a lower grade than she believes she deserves; Mark may come in second place at the track meet; or Graciela may lose a school election. One or two other group members can role-play the incident twice, once with a Type A reaction, and then with a Type B reaction. The fourth member critiques the role-playing. Members switch roles until each has had a chance to offer a scenario, role-play, and critique.

Making Responsible Decisions

1. Jake and his best friend, who seems to outdo him at everything, are competing for a position on the school hockey team.
2. Jake could (a) devote all his time and energy to preparing for the team tryouts; (b) withdraw from the tryouts; or (c) try to reduce the pressure he feels by discussing the situation with Luke.
3. Jake might (a) do well in the tryouts and win the place on the hockey team, but also threaten his friendship with Luke by his withdrawal and competitiveness; (b) avoid the pressure and the competition, but not get to play on the hockey team; (c) risk feeling uncomfortable while discussing his feelings with Luke, but end up feeling more comfortable about the competition and more friendly with Luke.
4. Jake values winning; he also values his friendship with Luke.
5. Responses will vary.
6. Remind students to evaluate their decisions in terms of both short- and long-term consequences.

L2 Decision Making

For more on making responsible decisions, assign *Decision-Making Activity 9* in the TCR.

L2 Discussing

Talk about what physical and emotional signs of stress students sometimes see in themselves. How do these signs affect their ability to study? How do they affect friendships? What do the symptoms of stress do to family relationships?

Making Responsible Decisions

Problem-Solving and Perfectionism

Jake excels in math and is a good hockey player. Still, his best friend, Luke, always seems to outdo him at everything. Because of his desire to do as well as Luke, Jake puts undue pressure on himself. He feels anxiety before every contest, seeing everything as a "win or lose" event. Now Jake has a chance to compete with Luke for a position on the school hockey team. Jake knows he puts too much pressure on himself and that his perfectionism is a problem, but he feels like he'd love to beat Luke just once at something this important.

What Would You Do?

Apply the six steps of the decision-making process to Jake's problem.

1. **State the situation.**
2. **List the options.**
3. **Weigh the possible outcomes.**
4. **Consider your values.**
5. **Make a decision and act.**
6. **Evaluate the decision.**

---

hotlink

asthma For more information on other triggers of asthma, see Chapter 17, page 404.

Did You Know?

➤ Migraine headaches often begin with an "aura," a series of warning signs that can include seeing flickering lights, spots, or lines, ringing in the ears, strange smells, or even numbness in the limbs. These signs usually develop 10 to 30 minutes before the migraine hits, then disappear as the headache pain begins.

➤ Most migraines last 4 to 6 hours, but some have been known to last for days.

---

endings press into the artery walls, causing severe throbbing, possibly a loss of balance or coordination, and changes in mood.

Stress and Asthma

Though **asthma** may have many causes and triggers, stress can help to trigger an asthma attack. During an asthma attack, breathing becomes difficult as the bronchioles—or air-carrying tubes of the lungs—constrict. The person may cough, wheeze, or fight to get air. In some cases, if untreated, asthma can be life-threatening. If you have asthma, it is important to try to discover what triggers your attacks and to avoid those triggers. It is, therefore, important that you try to keep your stress levels low.

Stress and Immune Response

Prolonged exposure to stress can compromise your immune response. This means that your body cannot fight disease as well as it might if you had not undergone so much stress. When your immune system is not working at full capacity, you may be more prone to colds, flu, or even more severe infections or cancers. The additional stress of tobacco or alcohol use puts your immune system at a very high risk for serious problems.

Psychosomatic Response to Stress

Sometimes stress can lead to a **psychosomatic response.** This is *a physical disorder that results from stress rather than from an injury or*

 SCHOOL-TO-CAREER

JOB-RELATED STRESS. Stress is a fact of life in many professions. Reasons for the stress may vary. For example, pilots, police officers, and paramedics may experience stress because they take responsibility for people's lives. Salespeople may be under pressure to make a certain number of sales. Factory workers may be exposed to high levels of noise or toxic substances. Have students work in groups. Members may take turns suggesting occupations they consider high stress. Each time an occupation is suggested, students should suggest possible sources of stress, and strategies for managing job-related stress.

illness. Psycho- means "of the mind," and *somatic* means "of the body." These physical disorders may be minor or severe, but they are not imaginary. Some sleep disorders may be psychosomatic in origin, as are some skin disorders, stomachaches, digestive problems, and headaches.

Recognizing Signs of Stress

When stress occurs, it is important to recognize its source and then figure out how to deal with it. Train your body and mind to recognize what stressors cause distress and how your body, mind, and behaviors are affected by each. If you know that you are likely to have a large reaction to an event, consider whether or not it is worth making your body and mind "pay" in such a big way. In the next lesson, you will learn many strategies for managing stress and preventing it from getting out of hand.

Signs of Stress

- **Physical Signs:** headaches, trembling or twitching, upset stomach, migraines, sweating, rash, constipation, diarrhea, pounding heart, muscle aches and tightness, trouble sleeping, grinding teeth, dry mouth, nervous twitches or tics, dizziness, back pain, ringing in ears.

- **Emotional Signs:** frustration, nervousness, boredom, edginess, feeling powerless, being quick to anger, impatience, mood swings, worrying, loneliness, confusion, crying, low self-esteem, becoming easily upset without cause.

- **Mental Signs:** trouble reading or thinking clearly, lack of creativity, constant worry, obsessive thoughts, inability to make decisions, forgetting, losing sense of humor and perspective.

- **Behavioral Signs:** not eating, overeating, compulsive talking, verbal or physical outbursts, fidgeting, using alcohol, caffeine, or other drugs, smoking, gambling, tapping feet, drumming fingers, hurrying, forgetting one's values, withdrawing, reckless and high-risk behaviors like driving too fast.

LESSON 2 *Review*

Reviewing Facts and Vocabulary

1. Distinguish between Type A and Type B personalities, and describe how each handles stress.
2. Name three ways that stress can have negative effects on your health.

Thinking Critically

3. *Analyzing.* List the top ten stressors of your life. Rank these in order from most stressful to least stressful. Think about positive and negative effects each of these stressors has on your life.
4. *Comparing and Contrasting.* Listen to three musical numbers from each of the following categories—jazz, pop, rock, and classical. Compare and contrast your stress responses to each. Note both physical and emotional reactions.

Applying Health Skills

5. *In Your Home.* Teach your family members what you have learned about the behavioral signs of stress. For one week, have each family member keep track of those behaviors in other members that suggest they are feeling stress. In a family roundtable discussion, share these findings with one another.

DRUGS AND SUBSTANCE ABUSE (Side 2)

Chapter 13: Coping with Stress

Frames 35023-37712

TOBACCO (Side 2)

Chapter 19: Stress and Boredom

Frames 48620-51442

ASSESS

EVALUATING THE LESSON

Assign and discuss the Lesson 2 Review; then administer, grade, and discuss the *Lesson 30 Quiz* in the TCR.

RETEACHING

- Have students list the stress-induced illnesses. Next to each, tell them to identify the parts of the body affected.
- Ask students to complete *Reteaching Activity 30* in the TCR.

ENRICHMENT

Have students further investigate characteristics of the Type A personality and the Type B personality and report their findings to the class.

CLOSE

Ask students to discuss the most important concepts in this lesson.

Lesson 2 Review

Answers to Reviewing Facts and Vocabulary

1. Type A: competitive, high-achieving; may relieve stress by working. Type B: noncompetitive, "laid back"; more likely to hold on to stress.
2. Any three: Stress can raise blood pressure, weaken the immune system, cause headaches and asthma attacks, increase or decrease appetite, cause sleep disorders, and cause digestive problems.

Answers to Thinking Critically

3.–4. Answers will vary.

FOCUS

LESSON OBJECTIVES

After studying this lesson, students should be able to

- identify the two basic ways to deal with stress and provide examples of each.
- identify sources of support.
- discuss the relationship between time management and stress management.

MOTIVATOR

Begin class by quietly playing a recording, CD, or record that most individuals would find relaxing. Ask students to close their eyes and imagine they are in a beautiful place, such as a beach, the mountains, or a forest.

INTRODUCING THE LESSON

Refer to the Motivator. After a few minutes of music, talk about ways people can rechannel their energy (such as by listening to music, daydreaming, imagining a beautiful scene, etc.). Tell students that rechanneling is one way to reduce the effects of stress. Ask them what they do to reduce stress. Explain that this lesson will discuss the primary ways of managing stress.

INTRODUCING HEALTH TERMS

- Have students use the terms *time management skills* and *priorities* in a short paragraph. Ask for volunteers to read their paragraphs to the class.
- Ask students to complete Vocabulary Activity 9 and Chapter Study Guide 9 in the *Student Workbook.* 📨

LESSON 3

Managing Stress

Identifying stressors and managing stress are among the most important steps you can take in staying healthy and preventing disease. Although it is impossible to live completely free of stress, it *is* possible to learn ways to avoid certain stressors and manage your response to others.

HEALTH TERMS

rechanneling

relaxation response

support group

time management skills

priorities

HEALTH CONCEPTS

- It is important to identify major stressors in your life.
- You can learn strategies for coping with and managing stress.
- Time management is one effective way to manage stress.

Identifying the Problem

A first step in stress management is identifying the source of the stress. At times, this source may be clear-cut—anxiety over taking a major exam, for example. At other times, the stressors may be less obvious. You may have had the experience of feeling uncomfortable in a certain place or around a certain person without knowing why. Some cases of stress are caused by a combination of stressors, making identification more difficult.

Stress Management

There are two basic ways to deal with stress that is upsetting to you. The first is to eliminate the stressor or reduce your exposure to it. The second is to change the way you perceive or react to the stressor.

Lesson 3 Resources

TEACHER'S CLASSROOM RESOURCES

📨 **Concept Map** Activity 31

📨 **Enrichment** Activity 9

📨 **Lesson 31 Quiz**

📨 **Lesson Plan 31**

📨 **Reteaching** Activity 31

STUDENT WORKBOOK

📨 **Applying Health Skills 31**

📨 **Chapter Study Guide 9**

📨 **Vocabulary** Activity 9

TRANSPARENCIES

 Transparency 36

MULTIMEDIA

🔴 **ABCNews InterActive™ VHS/Videodisc,** *Violence Prevention*

Just as your natural instincts for survival tell you to jump out of the way of a vehicle that is speeding toward you, in dealing with stress, you can learn to sense the warning signs that "something is coming." You can then find ways to escape oncoming stressors. Sometimes the best strategy is simply to walk away. At other times, you may be able to "rethink," or get a new perspective on, a stressful situation, making it a learning opportunity instead of a threat.

Physical activity is one effective technique for handling stress. Other ways to manage stress include planning, rechanneling energy, relaxing, and laughing.

Planning

People who plan well tend to have less stress. When you plan, you decide in advance what you want, what you need, and what is expected of you so that you can come into situations well prepared. Planning adds to your confidence. If you are prepared for the unexpected, you are also better able to deal with changes, disappointments, frustrations, or delays when they happen, enabling you to keep your stress to a minimum.

How do you react to stressful situations? Learn how to recognize stress and manage it more effectively. At **health.glencoe.com** keep a stress diary for three days. What changes could you make to better manage stress?

Building Health Skills

Taking Control of Your Day

FOLLOW THESE SUGGESTIONS for better time management, and you'll start to feel as though you control your time instead of time controlling you.

1. **Set and prioritize goals.** Set specific goals each day. Write "A" next to any goal or task you must achieve, "B" next to any you would like to get done, and "C" for any goal or task that is not important or that can wait.

2. **Budget your time.** Set regular time slots each day for relaxation techniques, exercise, and sleep. Set deadlines for yourself. Every once in a while, go over your daily schedules for a week and make sure your "time budget" balances work and play, social time and time to yourself, time for self-improvement and time for helping others.

3. **Learn to say no.** Practice saying no to the little things, then work your way up to the bigger ones. Saying no does not mean being cruel or selfish. It means not spending your energy or time on activities that do not benefit your life or someone else's.

4. **Slow down.** Make a conscious effort to do ordinary things—talk, walk, and eat—more slowly. When you can, take a break from all schedules. Take off your watch and ignore time—at least for a little while.

CURRICULUM CONNECTIONS

PHYSICAL EDUCATION. Have students do library research and also interview physical education teachers and athletic coaches about types of lifetime sports and other types of exercise that can help teens and their families cope with daily stressors. Follow up by having students share their findings and demonstrate some of the exercises to the class.

SCIENCE. Have students compare and contrast research on biofeedback and relaxation in dealing with stress and anxiety. Also, have them interview mental health professionals in the community who teach various types of relaxation techniques. Ask students to share their research with the class.

Examine with students the phenomenon of group stress. Expand upon the activity by having students maintain a class stress diary for a prescribed period. What types of problems arose? What solutions can students recommend for reducing group stress?

TEACH

L2 Class Activity

Have students work in small groups to prepare and present a skit showing the relationship between planning and stress management.

L1 Discussing

Ask students to answer the following questions: During an average day, when do you feel the greatest need to relax? Why? What do you do to relax?

L2 Class Activity

Assign students to design posters showing a variety of relaxation techniques. Feature the posters in a display titled "Relax to the Max."

Building Health Skills

Taking Control of Your Day
Skill: Stress Management

Ask students: What are the most important things you have to do tomorrow? How much time will you devote to those activities? What will you do to relax? How much sleep will you get tomorrow night? Help students consider how knowing the answers to questions like these can make their lives both more productive and more enjoyable. Then have them work in groups to read and discuss the Building Health Skills feature.

Visual Learning

Time Management

Have students look at the photo collage on this page and identify the various activities of the teens (*studying, relaxing, socializing, completing household chores,* etc.). Ask students to think about their use of time. Ask: Are you able to efficiently manage your various tasks? In what ways could you improve your time management skills?

L1 ## Discussing

Ask students to talk about ways they can be supportive of their friends and family.

L3 ## Researching

Have volunteers research the studies done on self-help groups and how support systems have been shown to be an important factor in coping.

L1 ## Discussing

Ask students to share their responses to these questions: What kind of problem would make you want to talk to someone about your stress? To whom would you talk? Why would you choose this person?

ABCNEWS INTERACTIVE™

VIOLENCE PREVENTION (Side 1)

Chapter 4: Managing Stress

Frames 8390-13464

TIME MANAGEMENT

You can reduce stress and find time for a wide array of activities if you plan well. Time management skills, strategies to help you use time effectively and healthfully, can help. One such skill, prioritizing, simply means deciding which tasks are more important than others.

When you prioritize your tasks, you can make time for the things that bring you the most pleasure.

ACTIVITY *Think of a way to budget your time this week so that you can do one activity you love and usually don't make time for.*

Rechanneling Energy

Rechanneling means *transferring or redirecting your energies.* You can use pent-up energy in useful ways by turning negative energy into positive actions and thoughts. When you feel stressed, why not use the energy to wash the car or straighten your room? If you are unable to put physical distance between yourself and a stressful situation, find ways to take a mental break. Let your mind wander for a few minutes, listen to soothing music, or simply daydream.

Relaxing and Laughing

Perhaps nothing restores your state of mind more than relaxation. Taking the time to rest, enjoy yourself, and simply *be* rather than *do* can work wonders for the body and the mind. You can learn specific techniques, too, that offer you deeper rest. The **relaxation response** is *a state of deep rest that can be reached if one or more relaxation techniques are practiced regularly.* Among these techniques are deep breathing, thinking pleasant thoughts, repetitive exercise, and stretching.

226 CHAPTER 9 MANAGING STRESS IN YOUR LIFE

MORE ABOUT . . . . .

BENEFITS OF LAUGHTER.

- Each day in Bombay, India, in one of the largest engineering firms, executives go out to the sidewalk, sit down, and break into belly laughs.
- As they laugh, they stretch their arms upward and rock their torsos.
- This practice is being tried all over Bombay as a method of stress relief.

- The lunch-time laugh sessions are spreading, and moods are better after lunch than before.
- Some doctors are even encouraging the laughers to take especially deep breaths while laughing, not only exercising the lungs, but flooding the cells of the body with oxygen.

Laughing can instantly relieve some stress. It gets more oxygen moving through the bloodstream and works the muscles of the stomach. When you are finished laughing, your blood pressure is lower and you feel relaxed.

Seeking Support

Whatever stressors you face in life, getting support can help you to deal with them. Talking with individuals you trust is vital. Parents, teachers, coaches, siblings, close friends, clergy, neighbors, or peer helpers can prove to be helpful choices when you need support. A **support group**, *an informal or formal gathering of people who meet and share experiences, feelings, and trust,* can also be helpful.

Time Management

For many people, stress management requires time management. **Time management skills** are *specific strategies for planning and using time in effective, healthful ways*. One important time management skill is setting priorities. **Priorities** are *those goals, tasks, or activities that you judge as more important to do than others*. When you set priorities, or prioritize, you decide which things you will do in which order, ranking them from most to least important or necessary. Setting priorities can help to organize your day and reduce your stress over what must get done.

keeping Fit

Sweat Your Stress Away

The next time you're tense and don't know what to do about it, start sweating. Whack a tennis ball, run around the neighborhood, go dancing, play soccer, do anything that will keep the big muscles moving and the heart pumping. Exercise will:

➤ calm you down,

➤ wake you up,

➤ make you more alert,

➤ improve your mood,

➤ pump up your confidence,

➤ improve your appearance.

Sweat Your Stress Away

keeping Fit

Discuss ways that physical activities help reduce the effects of stress, including taking your mind off of problems, strengthening the body systems, and improving confidence and self-image.

ASSESS

EVALUATING THE LESSON

Assign and discuss the Lesson 3 Review; then administer, grade, and discuss the *Lesson 31 Quiz* in the TCR. ☞

RETEACHING

- Have students imagine they are efficiency experts. Tell them to make a list of tips for time management that they would use in advising clients.
- Ask students to complete *Reteaching Activity 31* in the TCR. ☞

ENRICHMENT

- Encourage students to investigate relaxation strategies and time management skills. Then, have them report their findings to the class.
- Discuss humor as a stress-buster. Have students complete *Enrichment Activity 9*, "Just for Laughs," in the TCR. ☞

CLOSE

Write the lesson's major concepts on numbered, separate slips of paper. Place the slips in a box, and let each student draw one. In numerical order, have students define and summarize the concept written on the slip of paper they selected.

Reviewing Facts and Vocabulary

1. What are the two basic strategies for managing stress?
2. Name and describe three relaxation techniques used for reducing stress.

Thinking Critically

3. *Synthesizing.* Make a "How to Survive" booklet or video advising teens on ways to manage the stress of one of the following life events: moving to a new school, failing a grade, not making a team, winning a major award, having an ill family member, or having a parent lose a job.
4. *Analyzing.* Consider the following saying, and explain how it is tied to

stress management: "Don't look back; something might be gaining on you."

Applying Health Skills

5. *In Your Home.* List those tasks you want or need to achieve for one day. Do not prioritize them. At the end of the day, check your list, noting which ones you accomplished, which ones you resisted and why, and which ones you forgot altogether. The next day, try the same exercise but prioritize your tasks first thing in the morning, using the "A-B-C" system.

Lesson 3 Review

Answers to Reviewing Facts and Vocabulary

1. Eliminate the stressor or reduce your exposure to it.
2. Any three: deep breathing, thinking pleasant thoughts, repetitive exercise, stretching.

Answers to Thinking Critically

3.–4. Answers will vary.

Coping with Loss

LESSON OBJECTIVES

After studying this lesson, students should be able to

- describe the stages one goes through in accepting a major loss, such as the death of a loved one.
- discuss ways to cope with a major loss.

MOTIVATOR

Have students answer the following question in writing, keeping in mind that there is no right or wrong response: *What is the first word that comes to mind when you think of loss or grieving?*

INTRODUCING THE LESSON

Refer to the Motivator. Ask volunteers to share their responses. Point out that people's perceptions of loss will vary depending on their developmental stage, life experiences, and family situations. Nonetheless, there are similarities in how people deal with loss and grief. Explain that in this lesson students will examine the stages most people go through in these processes.

INTRODUCING HEALTH TERMS

- Ask students how they think the terms *grief* and *closure* relate when considering dealing with a major loss. *(The grieving process helps bring closure or an end to the suffering of a major loss.)* Have students define and use the terms in a sentence.
- Ask students to complete Vocabulary Activity 9 and Chapter Study Guide 9 in the *Student Workbook.*

Coping with Loss

L ife is full of losses. Some losses are minor and temporary. Others are major and can disrupt your entire life. Any loss can put your body and mind into a state of stress.

Yet, no matter how severe or painful a loss is, you can learn to respond to it in ways that help you to cope. Doing so will help you to heal in time.

HEALTH TERMS

grief reaction

delayed grief response

closure

HEALTH CONCEPTS

- Any loss can cause a stress response.
- The loss of a loved one is one of the greatest stressors a person can face.
- People who suffer a major loss may go through a special five-stage process that enables them to deal with the loss.
- Grieving after a major loss is a normal and necessary step toward healing.

Different Kinds of Losses

H ave you ever lost something that could not be replaced? Maybe a pet died or ran away. Perhaps you lost an important athletic contest, such as a championship game. These are all losses. So are break-ups between girlfriends and boyfriends, rejection by a once-close friend, or the loss of a job by you or a parent. Maybe you have had to change apartments, schools, or neighborhoods, feeling the loss of whatever—or whomever—you had to leave behind.

Your reactions to each loss may vary. Any loss requires change, and that change can be stressful. Depending on its value to you, you may respond to any loss as a minor or a major stressor. Note that a loss does not have to have a dollar value to be important. Sometimes, your emotional attachment to an object, situation, pet, or person can make its loss even more painful.

Lesson 4 Resources

TEACHER'S CLASSROOM RESOURCES
- **Concept Map** Activity 32
- **Lesson 32 Quiz**
- **Lesson Plan 32**
- **Reteaching** Activity 32

STUDENT WORKBOOK
- **Applying Health Skills 32**

- **Chapter Study Guide 9**
- **Vocabulary** Activity 9

MULTIMEDIA
- ABCNews InterActive™ VHS/Videodisc, *Health: AIDS*

The Stages of Loss

When a loss occurs, it is common and natural to experience a grief reaction. A **grief reaction** is *an individual's total response to a major loss*. This reaction can take many forms and includes many stages, from feelings of emptiness or deep sadness to feelings of intense anger.

Dr. Elisabeth Kübler-Ross, a psychiatrist who has done pioneering work on the related subjects of death and dying, has identified five emotional stages that both dying and grieving people go through. These five stages, which might be experienced by anyone suffering a major loss, include:

- **Stage 1: Denial.** Denial is a person's initial reaction to any loss. At this stage, a person who has suffered a significant loss cannot believe the loss has occurred.

- **Stage 2: Anger.** A person next moves from denial to anger, or the "Why me?" stage. During this stage, the person may be critical, demanding, or uncooperative.

- **Stage 3: Bargaining.** As the reality of the loss sets in, the anger begins to subside and is replaced by bargaining. The person may pray or promise to change if only the lost person or object can be returned, even for a while.

- **Stage 4: Depression.** This stage is often marked by silence and withdrawal. Earlier feelings of disbelief, isolation, anger, and rage are replaced with a deep sense of quiet sadness.

- **Stage 5: Acceptance.** This is the last stage in dealing with a deep loss. While the depression stage may leave a person feeling helpless, this last stage can involve a sense of power, allowing the person to face reality in constructive ways and make significant and meaningful gestures surrounding the idea of the loss.

Kübler-Ross also noted that another emotion, hope, operates through all of the five stages. This hope keeps alive the thought that the lost item, situation, or person might somehow be returned.

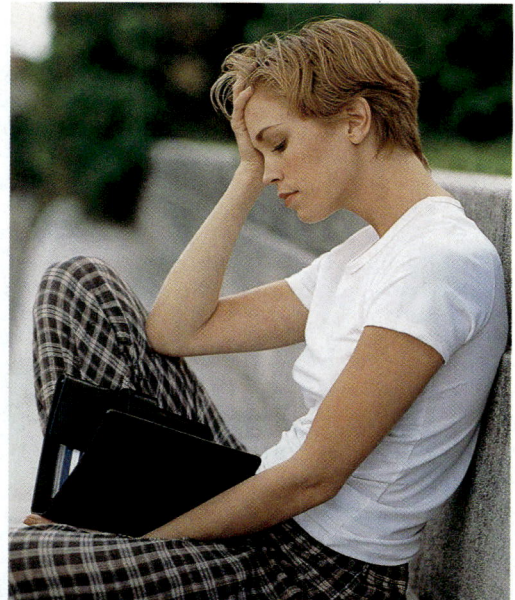

TEACH

▣ Discussing
How do the stages leading to the acceptance of death relate to other types of loss, such as the loss of a job or the breakup of a relationship?

▣ Cooperative Learning
Divide the class into five groups. Assign each group one of the stages of loss. Ask each group to identify behaviors they might see in someone at this stage. How should a supportive person act in each stage?

▣ Explaining
Explain that the stages leading to the acceptance of death vary with each individual. The stages only summarize what most people go through. Yet the description of the grieving process they provide is important—it gives people a sense of what to expect and what is normal. Most people have little experience with grief and may not understand or may feel guilty about how they are reacting to death.

HEALTH: AIDS (Side 2)
Chapter 13: What Is It Like to Face Death?

Frames 33567-38066

MORE ABOUT . . . . .

COPING WITH LOSS. Almost all societies have some cultural and ritual traditions of mourning for the dead and for dealing with grief. When the mourning period is over, a ritual of reintegrating the mourners back into the group usually takes place. This is important because death is the most socially and emotionally disruptive event the majority of us ever experience.

Often, the more important the deceased individual, the more exaggerated the mourning ritual. Worldwide, expressions of grief vary. They may include shaving the head, going unbathed, or smearing the body with clay or ashes. Mourners may tear their clothing, gash themselves, wail, or go into seclusion for varying lengths of time.

Teens Making a Difference

Helping Others Cope

Discussion. Ask students to read Danny's story and together answer the questions at its end. Add the following information about Danny: he is active in church activities and volunteer work, likes time with family and friends, and also enjoys music and sports. He wants to go to college to become a marine biologist.

Ask students to discuss the concept of loss. Have them give examples of kinds of losses other than death—for example, having to move, divorce, or natural disaster—and the kinds of stresses they cause. Ask them how a person trying to help someone deal with any major loss must exhibit the same kinds of core values, regardless of the type of loss.

Point out that the helper in a loss situation must also take care of himself or herself, sharing the following quote by Danny: When I have a problem, I go for a walk or ride my bike to relieve my stress and get away from the problem for a little while.

Read the following additional quotes by Danny and have students share their reactions, relating his words to their own lives.

- *Everyone deserves compassion and respect.*
- *I would say to other teens that community service is a good thing, and when you do it, you are not just helping others; you are helping yourself by building self-esteem. And you get great joy doing it.*

Class Activity. Ask students to share experiences they have had doing volunteer work or charitable deeds with a group.

Answers. *Danny's Story*
1. Values featured or implied include caring, compassion, kindness, initiative, hard work, perseverance, gratitude, and courage.
2. Caring and appreciation.

Responses. *Your Story* **1–2.** Answers will vary.

Teens Making a Difference
...INITIATIVE...COURAGE...CITIZENSHIP

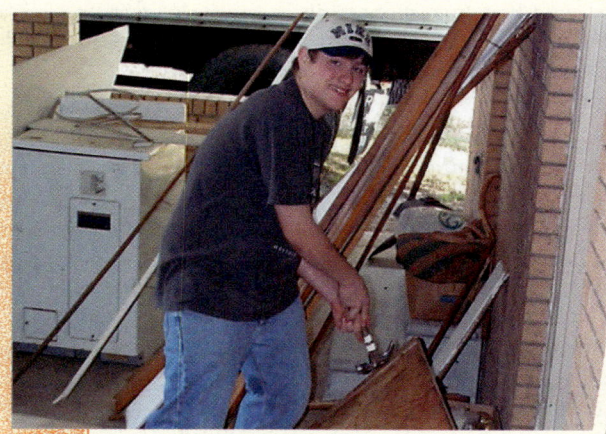

Danny is 16 and lives near the coast of North Carolina. He isn't a stranger to hurricanes, but when hurricane Floyd hit, Danny jumped in and took action to help others cope with the stress and loss caused by the storm.

ENTERING TROUBLED WATERS Danny begins, "It was one of the worst storms to hit North Carolina ever. There was terrible flooding. I was fortunate enough to get away with just a few shingles off the roof, but half an hour away from here, it got pretty bad. Through the church, we saw pictures of the flooding and got a group together and started working together rebuilding." The group formed smaller disaster recovery teams of adults and teens working together to help those who'd lost the most. "We'd go down there and work on a specific house. The damage was terrible, and the way they were living was awful. They had no electricity or running water. Some of the people were poor and elderly and had spent all of their money. We were their last hope. We'd talk to them...and they were so happy for us to be with them."

HANDS-ON HELPING
Danny not only listens with compassion to the people he helps; he offers practical help and hands-on work. "We go in there and take out floors and rotted wood and replace it. I've learned a lot about carpentry and tools, and, between doing this work and being in shop at school, I've learned a lot more than I thought I ever would. "I've been going down to help out for about a year and a half," Danny says humbly. With tools, wood, caring, and hard work, he continues, after almost two years, to give up Saturdays to help the people of North River rebuild their homes and their lives.

TOOLS FOR LIVING "I've learned not just about carpentry either," Danny continues. "I've also learned to care about what other people go through. A lot of people are really stressed out by a disaster like this, but once we could show them everything would be all right, they saw there could be a better side to it all. I've learned to appreciate that I don't have it as bad as other people. I've also learned that we all need a helping hand at some time in our lives. It's been a really good experience."

DANNY'S STORY
1. What values does Danny exhibit by helping the victims of the hurricane and flood?
2. What has he learned?

YOUR STORY
1. What steps can you take to raise your awareness about the needs of others facing different kinds of losses?
2. How can you team up with other teens to offer a "helping hand" to people in a time of stress or loss?

MORE ABOUT . . . . .

DEATH AND DYING. Across human cultures there is an almost universal belief in the continued existence of a deceased person in the form of an immortal ghost or spirit. This belief has numerous variations. Some people believe in a shadowy world where the spirits of the dead reside. It may be a heaven or a hell or just a different version of reality. Others believe in a continuous cycle of reincarnation or an ultimate absorption of the soul into some kind of cosmic spirit.

In many cultures, the spirits of the dead are thought to be evil and dangerous. In others, the spirits are believed to be protectors. In still others, they are believed to be in a sort of limbo, awaiting rebirth.

Responding to Loss

A person who has undergone a great loss needs to talk about what has happened and express feelings. In an attempt to process what has happened, this person may need to "relive" the events through talking about or thinking about them over and over again. Through such actions, over time, and with the caring of others, the survivor can come to accept the death or other loss and continue on. Though the person left behind may never forget or stop missing the beloved one, he or she can at least reach a sense of **closure**, *a coming to an end of the most intense parts of the grieving process.*

Grief Counseling

Sometimes people are so stressed by a sudden or traumatic loss that they feel paralyzed and stop coping altogether. They may have a **delayed grief response**, *a putting off of the most intense stages of grief.* They may deny the death or loss for a while until the shock wears off. They may even try to cover up their feelings by using chemicals or by assuring everyone that they are "just fine." Such strategies, however, just delay the grieving process. Seeing a counselor who specializes in grief may prove helpful. In fact, talking with a counselor can be beneficial to anyone who has suffered a major loss.

▲ *People respond to loss in different ways.*

ACTIVITY *Name three different ways that people you know have responded to losing a loved one.*

ASSESS

EVALUATING THE LESSON

Assign and discuss the Lesson 4 Review; then administer, grade, and discuss the *Lesson 32 Quiz* in the TCR. 🔖

RETEACHING

- Discuss with students the stages of grief and responses to loss when the entire community or the nation has experienced a tragedy. Allow volunteers to comment about their own observations on how sharing and supporting one another during a common experience of loss or grief helps a community cope.
- Ask students to complete *Reteaching Activity 32* in the TCR. 🔖

ENRICHMENT

Have selected students, with parental permission, visit a hospice and talk with people who are employed there and with people who stay there. Make arrangements for students to do volunteer work reading to terminally ill patients, serving meals, etc. Ask students to keep a journal of their experience and to evaluate how it has changed their views of death.

CLOSE

In this lesson, we learned that there are five stages in accepting a major loss. We saw that working through these stages with the support of loved ones is the best way of coming to terms with death and grief.

LESSON 4 *Review*

Reviewing Facts and Vocabulary

1. Name the five stages of grief and describe each one.
2. List some do's and don'ts when helping a friend through grief.
3. What is closure, and why is it so important?

Thinking Critically

4. *Analyzing.* Explain the benefits of communication in helping a person respond to the loss of a loved one.
5. *Comparing and Contrasting.* Investigate mourning rituals—the formal ways that people grieve—from at least two cultures. Present your findings to the class in the form of an oral report.

Applying Health Skills

6. *In Your Home.* Make a "loss line." Draw a line and divide it by years from birth till your present age. On the line, draw small perpendicular lines wherever you have suffered an important loss. Label each. Now step back and think about the number of losses in your lifetime, when they happened, and the effects of each.

LESSON 4   COPING WITH LOSS   **231**

Lesson 4 Review

Answers to Reviewing Facts and Vocabulary

1. See page 229 for stages and descriptions.
2. Be available to talk or just be with the person. Listen carefully. Don't suggest that something else will make up for the loss. Be patient if the person seems to reject you. Talk about the person who has died. Respect the person's way of grieving. Write a caring note.
3. A coming to the end of the most intense parts of the grieving process. This is necessary so that the grieving person can continue on with his or her life.

Answers to Thinking Critically

4.–5. Answers will vary.

Health **Skills** Activities

Health Skills Activities

ACTIVITY 1
HEALTH SKILLS

Self Management—Stress Management, Health Advocacy

➤ **National Standards**
This activity meets these National Health Standards: 3.7; 7.1.

Teach

• Introduce the activity by sharing an example, real or fictitious, of a stressful situation you recall from your own teen years. Direct the discussion away from highly personal issues in students' lives.

• After explaining the basics of the activity, set out a sign-up sheet with category heads such as those indicated in step 3 of the student activity (e.g., writing, camera operation, research, and so on). Invite students to sign up for one of the tasks based on personal interests and abilities.

• If possible, appoint volunteers to make copies of the tape to be shared with family and friends.

ACTIVITY 2
HEALTH SKILLS

Self Management—Stress Management, Communication

➤ **National Standards**
This activity meets these National Health Standards: 3.7; 5.3; 5.4.

Teach

• Remind groups that there are no correct or incorrect examples. Point out that loss is emotional and that for each individual, it is a very personal matter.

• For the discussion portion of the activity, you may wish to arrange chairs in the classroom (including one for yourself) in a circle. This emphasizes that everyone involved is an equal—that all opinions count.

Activity 1 — Reducing Stress

Businesses across the country are developing stress management programs for employees. Exercise, relaxation techniques, and stretching are all part of these efforts. What kind of program would you devise to reduce stress in a teen's life?

Directions

1. As a class, discuss typical causes of stress among teens, such as taking a test or auditioning for a school play. Brainstorm strategies for reducing the stress.
2. Make a class video that demonstrates techniques for reducing stress in such situations.
3. Include each class member in the production. Possible tasks include writing, camera operation, research, acting, set design, and editing.
4. Air the video to another class in your school. Discuss with this class whether they think the stress-reducing video will help them in the future.

Time
50 minutes
Materials
video recorder, paper, pen or pencil

Self-Assessment

✓ Identified at least three leading causes of stress in a teen's life.
✓ Described coping strategies for each stress identified.
✓ Created a clear message on the importance of managing stress.

Activity 2 — Role-Playing to Cope with Loss

A situation can have many different outcomes—some healthful, some not—depending on the strategies used to handle it. Role-playing, or acting out various scenarios, can help you "see" these different possible outcomes more vividly.

Directions

1. In a group, brainstorm various situations in which teens might experience loss, such as breaking off a relationship or failing to make tryouts for a team.
2. Role-play several strategies for dealing with the feelings of loss—for example, allowing time to deal with the loss, accepting comfort from loved ones.
3. After each scene, discuss the effectiveness of the technique used.
4. With permission, present your scenarios to members of other health classes.

Time
50 minutes
Materials
paper, pen or pencil

Self-Assessment

✓ Identified types of loss common among teens.
✓ Devised and acted out coping strategies for various types.

232 CHAPTER 9   MANAGING STRESS IN YOUR LIFE

ASSESSMENT SCORING

Using a four-level rubric, the student has achieved a 4 if:

ACTIVITY 1
✔ Student identified at least three leading causes of stress.
✔ Student participated in a discussion and identified several strategies.
✔ Student helped to create a clear message on the importance of stress management.
✔ Student completed assigned tasks according to sign-up sheets.

ACTIVITY 2
✔ Student demonstrated an understanding of the phenomenon of loss and emotions.
✔ Student identified types of teen loss.
✔ Student was instrumental in the staging of coping strategies.
✔ Student took part in identifying ways lessons learned could be shared beyond the classroom.

HEALTH NEWS ARTICLE

Bullying and Teasing in Schools

Bullying and teasing are cited as the top school troubles of students, ages 8 to 15, in a report from the Kaiser Family Foundation. With report findings indicating that most young people aren't affected or helped by sporadic talks with their parents, experts said it was crucial for parents and their children to develop an ongoing dialogue about various important issues, starting at an early age. Of these issues, students of various ages said bullying was far more common than drinking, drugs, racism or sex at their schools.

"Some kids sometimes don't know how to tell their parents, 'I have this problem. This person is bothering me, I don't know what to do,'" said Victoria Zaras, 15, who responded to the survey. "Instead, some may take matters into their own hands."

Dominic Cappello, an expert on parent-child communications, said parents often think their children will never act out on their problems.

"Parents think, 'Oh my kids are not in high school yet. I guess I will wait to talk,'" he said. "What we say is 'Oh no–when your child starts kindergarten, you have to start conversations about how you respect people.'" Tina Hoff, who oversaw the survey, says, "These issues need to get talked about on an ongoing basis."

Read This

Pressure Poll

These survey results from the Kaiser Family Foundation show some major sources of teen stress (ages 12 to 15).

Percentage of students who say the following is a big problem in school:		Percentage of students who say students experience the following:	
Teasing & Bullying	68	Get Teased or Bullied	86
Discrimination	63	Are Treated Badly Because They're Different	67
Violence	62		
Alcohol or Drugs	68	Are Threatened With Violence	60
Pressure to Have Sex	49	Smoke Cigarettes	67

Think About It

1. Explain why Dominic Cappello sees a strong connection between respect for others and bullying at school.
2. How would you have responded to the survey about sources of teen stress? Do you think your school's results would match the survey results?

MORE ABOUT . . . . .

RELIABLE SOURCES. The Kaiser Family Foundation is an independently funded research and communications organization. The goal of this foundation is to "provide timely, reliable, and non-partisan information on national health issues to policymakers, the media, and the general public." A major component of the Foundation's work is collecting, publishing, and analyzing data from public health polls. These polls provide detailed, quantified information about public health habits and opinions.

In addition to sponsoring surveys on a wide variety of health-related topics, the foundation also sponsors an Internet site devoted to providing free, up-to-date information about health news and information.

Bullying and Teasing

Objectives. After reading the article, students should be able to identify reasons why relieving stress is an important part of mental health.

Motivator. Write these two statements on the chalkboard or read them aloud:
- Bullying is a natural part of growing up and there's nothing you can do about it.
- Bullying is a serious problem that needs to be addressed.

Have students tell their beliefs about each statement. Then have them read the article to help them understand the connection between bullying, stress, and violence.

Teach
- Write the words *teasing, bullying, harassment,* and *violence* on the chalkboard. Have students discuss the definitions and connotations of each word. Discuss how some people might not view a problem such as teasing seriously because the word itself can have a light or playful connotation. Emphasize to students that they need to look beyond these connotations to understand the important health issues surrounding these problems.
- Students might anonymously respond to the survey questions in Pressure Poll. Then have them tabulate the results and compare the class's responses with those in the published survey.

Decision Making. Point out that some bullying is preventable through the use of a student or adult mediator—someone who helps two students work out a volatile relationship. Have students discuss the factors to consider when deciding whether or not to use a mediator.

Close. Reread this statement from the opening of the lesson: "Bullying is a natural part of growing up and there's nothing you can do about it." Have students explain why this statement is not accurate. Students should point out some dangerous effects of bullying, including how it can build stress that is sometimes released through violence. Students also should identify some useful strategies to stop the problem.

CHAPTER **9** *Review*

CHECKING COMPREHENSION

- Assign and discuss the chapter review.
- Use the MindJogger Videoquiz to review the chapter.

CHAPTER 9 REVIEW ANSWERS

Using Health Terms

1. distress
2. fatigue
3. stress
4. eustress
5. alarm
6. stressor
7. resistance
8. stress tolerance
9. psychosomatic response
10. hardy personality
11. support group
12. time management skills
13. rechanneling
14. closure
15. denial
16. grief reaction

RECALLING THE FACTS

1. Eustress has a positive impact. Distress has a negative impact.
2. The hypothalamus becomes excited, activating the autonomic nervous system and the pituitary gland. The pituitary gland stimulates the adrenal glands to produce adrenaline, which speeds up the heart and breathing rate. The increased flow of blood to the brain and muscles prepares you to take quick action.
3. Fatigue.
4. The hardy personality welcomes change, has a strong sense of purpose, and has a sense of power about his or her own life.
5. Physical: headaches, trembling, upset stomach, sweating, rash, digestive problems, sleep disorders, pounding

Using Health Terms

On a separate sheet of paper, write the term that best matches each definition below.

LESSON 1

1. Negative stress.
2. The third stage of the stress response, resulting in a tired feeling that lowers one's level of activity.
3. The body's and mind's reaction to everyday demands or threats.
4. Positive stress.
5. The first stage in the stress response when the body and mind go on high alert.
6. Any stimulus that produces a stress response.
7. The second stage in the stress response, when the body tries to repair its damage from the stressful event and return to its normal state.

LESSON 2

8. The amount of stress that you can handle before you reach a state of too much stress.

9. A physical disorder that results from stress rather than from an injury or illness.
10. One personality type that seems able to stay healthy despite major or even traumatic stressors.

LESSON 3

11. A formal or informal gathering of people who meet and share experiences, feelings, and trust.
12. Specific strategies for planning and using time in effective, healthful ways.
13. Transferring or redirecting your energy.

LESSON 4

14. A coming to an end of the most intense parts of the grieving process.
15. The putting off of the most intense stages of grief.
16. An individual's total response to a major loss.

Recalling the Facts

Using complete sentences, answer the following questions.

LESSON 1

1. Explain the difference between eustress and distress.
2. What occurs in your body during the alarm stage of the stress response?
3. At which of the three stages of the stress response is a person most likely to become physically ill?

LESSON 2

4. Describe the three traits of the hardy personality.

5. What are some of the physical, emotional, and behavioral signs of stress in teens?

LESSON 3

6. Name three strategies for managing stress.
7. What role does setting priorities play in stress management?

LESSON 4

8. Name and describe the five stages of loss as identified by Dr. Kübler-Ross.
9. How can friends make a difference when someone is dealing with grief?

heart, muscle aches and tightness, dry mouth, dizziness, back pain, ringing in ears.
Emotional: frustration, nervousness, boredom, edginess, feelings of powerlessness, quick temper, impatience, mood swings, worrying, loneliness, confusion, crying, low self-esteem.

Behavioral: not eating, overeating, compulsive talking, physical outbursts, fidgeting, gambling, tapping feet, drumming fingers, hurrying, forgetting one's values, withdrawing, high-risk behavior using alcohol, caffeine, or other drugs.

Thinking Critically

LESSON 1

1. *Analyzing.* What factors in modern-day society seem to make life so much more stressful than in the past?
2. *Evaluating.* Explain how stress can be a positive factor in someone's life.

LESSON 2

3. *Evaluating.* What are the limitations in trying to classify people and the way they handle stress by personality types?

LESSON 3

4. *Analyzing.* Choose a friend or family member. Analyze the person's time management skills. Describe suggestions you would offer to improve those skills.

LESSON 4

5. *Analyzing.* What factors affect the way you view loss in your family?
6. *Synthesizing.* What are some healthful ways that teens could help one another to deal with the loss of one of their favorite teachers or classmates?

Making the Connection

1. *Math.* Prepare a survey for the students at your school that asks what students believe to be the top ten stressors. Rank responses by age, grade, and gender. Using a computer, determine the top ten stressors for the school based on those responses. Then break down the information by gender, age, and grade. Make bar graphs to illustrate your findings.

2. *Language Arts.* In most short stories, the main character faces various stressors. How he or she responds to these stressors greatly affects the plot or the story line. Read a classic story, paying attention to the stressors that the main character faces and how he or she responds to each. Share your findings in a written report.

BEYOND THE CLASSROOM

PARENTAL INVOLVEMENT Observe members of your family for several days, taking note of how efficiently each seems to use time. Ask other family members to do the same. Afterward, discuss ways that each of you can better manage time. Make task charts and weekly schedules that include appointments, activities, and work and school hours. As a group, prioritize them together.

COMMUNITY INVOLVEMENT Identify three occupations represented in your community. Identify the key stressors in each, the necessary stress management techniques for being successful, and whether or not each suits your personality.

SCHOOL-TO-CAREER
Exploring Careers. Interview a grief counselor or other mental health worker who helps clients deal with loss, death, and dying. Ask what experience is needed for such a career. Find out the kinds of settings in which the counselor works, the kinds of interpersonal skills needed, and the most frequent types of losses and reactions to those losses the counselor encounters. Share your findings in an oral report.

Thinking Critically

1. Rapid rate of change, competitiveness, the fast pace of living, etc.
2. Worry about performance in an activity can cause one to spend more time preparing.
3. Each individual is affected by a limitless number of factors in determining his or her response to stress. Personality types are meant only as a general indication of how to classify behavior.
4. Answers will vary.

Making the Connection

1. Graphs should reflect survey results.
2. Reports will vary.

Evaluate

- Use the reproducible *Chapter 9 Test* in the TCR, or construct your own using the Testmaker software.
- Use *Performance Assessment Activity 9* in the TCR.

Enrichment

Ask students to complete *Cross-Curriculum Activity 9* in the TCR.

Beyond the Classroom

Keep students involved in the community, and encourage parent participation by assigning the activities on this page for students to work on outside of class.

---

6. Physical activity, planning, rechanneling energy, relaxing, laughing.
7. Setting priorities helps you decide how to organize your day so the important things get done.
8. See page 229.
9. Friends can keep the one who's grieving from feeling isolated in his or her loss.

Mental and Emotional Problems

	FEATURES	CLASSROOM RESOURCES

ACTIVITIES

- Cross-Curriculum Activity 10
- Health Lab 10
- Health Skills Activities 10
- Parent Letter and Activities 10

ASSESSMENT

- Chapter 10 Test
- Performance Assessment Activity 10
- Testmaker Software

STUDENT ACTIVITIES WORKBOOK

- Applying Health Skills 33–35
- Study Guide 10
- Vocabulary Activity 10

STUDENT DIVERSITY STRATEGIES

- Audiocassette Program (English)
- Audiocassette Program (Spanish)
- Spanish Parent Letter and Activities
- Spanish Summaries, Quizzes, and Activities

MULTIMEDIA COMPONENTS

- English Audiocassette Program
- Spanish Audiocassette Program
- MindJogger Videodisc and VHS program

MODULES

- *The Reality of Drugs,* Student Edition
- *The Reality of Drugs,* Teacher's Annotated Edition

National Health Education Standards

One of the main goals of the National Health Education Standards is to move students toward "health literacy." Health literacy is the capacity of individuals to obtain, interpret, and understand basic health information and services and the competence to use such information and services in ways which promote health. The health standards were developed by applying the characteristics of a well-educated, literate person within the context of health. The health literate person is:

- a critical thinker and problem solver
- a self-directed learner
- a responsible, productive citizen
- an effective communicator

Listed below are the Health Education Standards Performance Indicators addressed in each lesson of this chapter.

Lesson	Health Standards Performance Indicators
1	1.2, 2.6, 3.4, 5.3
2	2.6, 6.7, 7.4, 7.6
3	2.2, 2.3, 2.4, 2.6

ONLINE RESOURCES

For a fresh approach to health topics and an in-depth look at health issues, use these online resources found under Teacher Resources at **health.glencoe.com**.

- **BLOCK SCHEDULE LESSON PLANS** Reinforce health concepts with outside readings selected especially for students. Each reading is accompanied by a lesson plan and activities to enhance
  - Reading Skills
  - Cross Curriculum
  - Media Literacy

- **TECHNOLOGY PROJECTS** Instructions and suggestions on how to use computer, Internet, and software with health lessons.

- **HEALTH UPDATES** Timely topics in health news, including late-breaking medical advances and updates on teen risk behaviors.

Out of Time?

If time does not permit teaching this chapter, you may use these features: Making Responsible Decisions on page 245; Building Health Skills on page 248; and Update on page 250.

BLOCK SCHEDULING

Block scheduling provides extended time for hands-on projects and activities. Use the following activities to engage students, provide further depth, and vary your instructional techniques:

- Update (30 minutes)   **pg. 250**
- Health Skills Activity (60–90 minutes)   **pg. 252**

Mental and Emotional Problems

CHAPTER OVERVIEW

Chapter 10 describes the types of mental disorders and identifies the risk factors and warning signs of suicide. It also presents the kinds of professional help that are available.

LESSON 1 Mental illness affects the mind and prevents a person from leading a happy, healthy life. It results in an inability to cope in healthful ways with life's changes, traumatic experiences, and losses. Mental illness can be caused by a physical illness or injury that affects the brain or can be the result of psychological causes such as stress or poor coping skills. The four main categories of functional disorders are presented in this lesson.

LESSON 2 Teens who are at high risk of committing suicide generally have specific risk factors and exhibit warning signs. Individuals contemplating suicide need to seek professional help.

LESSON 3 Being aware of and recognizing early warning signs of mental illness are the keys to getting help. Intervention in the form of mental health care is sometimes necessary. Such services are provided by psychiatrists, neurologists, and clinical psychologists. A host of counselors, social workers, and therapists often assist in the intervention process. The specific mental health counselor needed depends on the nature of the illness and the type of treatment that is necessary.

HEALTH *Online*

COMMUNICATION SKILLS
Are you good at talking and listening to people about real-life issues? The role of a Mental Health Counselor plays an important part in many people's lives. Investigate the details of this profession in the Career Corner at **health.glencoe.com**.

TEACHING STRATEGY

Hands-On Health

Reinforcing and Reviewing Bring your health classroom to life with interactive teaching strategies and classroom management techniques that keep your students interested and involved. The unique *Hands-On Health: Creative Teaching Strategies* booklet that accompanies the *Glencoe Health* program offers fun, motivating activities.

The following Classroom Management Ideas can be used to reinforce chapter concepts:

- Beach Ball
- Trivia Questions
- Paper Exchange
- Mental Outburst

> *Although the world is full of suffering, it is full also of the overcoming of it.* **"**

—HELEN KELLER
AMERICAN WRITER AND LECTURER, (1880–1968)

Quick Write It is important for people to realize they do not have to go through emotional problems alone. List three people you might turn to—one peer, one family member, and one adult in your school or community—during a tough time.

Personal Health Inventory

Self-Inventory Write the numbers 1–10 on a sheet of paper. Read each statement below and respond by writing *yes*, *no*, or *sometimes* for each item. Write a *yes* only for items that you practice regularly. Save your responses.

1	I'm generally comfortable with myself and enjoy being alive.
2	There are people in my life I feel close to and comfortable with, and in whom I can confide.
3	Usually, my moods don't swing from one extreme to the other.
4	Though I sometimes feel fear, I don't generally feel flooded with panic or anxiety.
5	Though I may at times feel sad, I know how to handle my depression.
6	I don't dwell on the same thought or repeat an action over and over in a ritualistic way.
7	When I'm feeling down or upset, I don't keep my feelings to myself but talk with someone.
8	I'm not opposed to talking to a professional if times get really tough.
9	I understand that mental disorders are usually treatable.
10	I wouldn't be embarrassed to seek professional help.

Follow-up After completing the chapter, retake this self-inventory. Pick two items that you need to work on and set a goal to improve your health behaviors.

CHAPTER 10 MENTAL AND EMOTIONAL PROBLEMS **237**

TECHNOLOGY OPTIONS

MINDJOGGER

VIDEOQUIZ

To preview or review chapter content, you may wish to use the *Mindjogger Videoquiz* that accompanies Chapter 10.

INTRODUCING THE CHAPTER

Personal Health Inventory

Assure students that the Self-Inventory responses are for their own use only. Have them read and consider each inventory statement, and urge them to record their honest responses on a page labeled "My Level of Mental and Emotional Wellness." Remind students that the lessons in this chapter will help them understand the mental and emotional health issues raised in this Self-Inventory; students will review, revise, and score their responses at the end of the chapter.

- Ask students to recall a particularly sad movie they have seen that wound up with a happy ending. Ask what events in the movie elicited their sad responses. What events occurred to turn the movie around and make it end happily? Tell students that sometimes people need help in dealing with the problems they face. Intervention often speeds recovery. In this chapter, students will study some of the resources available in the mental health field.

- Have students read the quotation on this page. Ask students to think about the following questions without verbalizing their responses: Whom do you know—including yourself—who has experienced problems and has struggled to deal with them? What do you think of teens and adults who seek help from mental health professionals?

- Distribute Parent Letter 10 in the *Parent Letters and Activities* booklet in the TCR.

LESSON 1

What Are Mental Disorders?

What Are Mental Disorders?

FOCUS

LESSON OBJECTIVES

After studying this lesson, students should be able to

- define organic and functional mental disorders.
- describe the four main categories of functional mental disorders.

MOTIVATOR

Write the following on the chalkboard for students to work on while attendance is being taken: *Write as many words as you can think of when you hear the term* mental illness.

INTRODUCING THE LESSON

Collect students' responses to the Motivator. On the chalkboard, list some of the students' words. Tell students that mental illness is often misunderstood, not accepted by a community, and sometimes mistreated. Point out that mental illness can happen in any family, and for this reason, it is important to understand mental and emotional disorders.

INTRODUCING HEALTH TERMS

- Have each student create a crossword puzzle or sentence completion activity using all the vocabulary terms. Afterward, ask them to exchange their puzzle or activity with another student. Provide several minutes for them to complete each other's word challenge.
- Ask students to complete Vocabulary Activity 10 and Chapter Study Guide 10 in the *Student Workbook.*

Everyone at times feels depressed, anxious, afraid, alone, or angry. For most people, these feelings are temporary and last only a brief time. For some people, however, the feelings can be intense or endure day after day. When such feelings begin to interfere with the demands of daily life, the person may have a mental disorder.

HEALTH TERMS

mental disorder
anxiety disorder
somatoform disorder
hypochondria
affective disorder
bipolar disorder
personality disorders
schizophrenia

HEALTH CONCEPTS

- Mental disorders are rooted in emotional, psychological, physical, or biochemical problems.
- Mental disorders can interfere with an individual's normal functioning with self, others, and even society at large.
- Mental disorders can differ from person to person and episode to episode.

 HEALTH *Online*

Find more about anxiety disorders such as panic and phobias at **health.glencoe.com**.

Mental Disorders

A **mental disorder** is *an illness of the mind that can affect the thoughts, feelings, and behaviors of a person, preventing him or her from leading a happy, healthful, and productive life.* People who suffer from some form of mental disorder are often identified by their inability to cope in healthful ways with life's changes, demands, problems, or traumas.

In the past, mental disorders were misunderstood and people with such disorders were feared or shunned. Science has shed new light on these problems and their causes. Mental disorders are now widely understood not only as disturbances in the emotions but also as imbalances in the chemistry of the brain.

Lesson 1 Resources

Types of Mental Disorders

All mental disorders are classified into one of two general types: organic or functional. An *organic disorder* is one that is clearly caused by a physical illness or an injury that affects the brain. Examples of such disorders are: brain tumors, alcoholism, infections such as syphilis and meningitis, lupus, and stroke. So are some inherited chemical imbalances.

A *functional disorder* may occur as the result of psychological causes in which no clear brain damage is involved. These disorders generally include or result from such conditions as stress, emotional conflict, fear, or poor coping skills. Functional disorders may be tied to inborn causes, traumatic events in childhood, or current causes. Increasingly, research has indicated that, like organic disorders, functional disorders may be the result of chemical imbalances in the brain. Whatever their root causes, the main categories of functional disorders are *anxiety disorders, somatoform disorders, affective disorders,* and *personality disorders.*

Anxiety Disorders

Most people experience some form of anxiety from time to time, but their fears do not affect their daily lives. An **anxiety disorder** is *an illness in which real, imagined, or persistent fears prevent a person from enjoying life.* An anxiety disorder is characterized by continuous, chronic anxiety. People with anxiety disorders often arrange their lives so as to avoid the object or situation that makes them anxious or fearful. Four types of anxiety disorders are **phobias**, obsessive-compulsive disorders, panic disorders, and post-traumatic stress disorders.

PHOBIA

This is a specific fear that is so strong, a person goes to extreme measures to avoid the fear-producing object or activity. Examples of phobias include acrophobia, a fear of heights, and claustrophobia, a fear of enclosed spaces. A person with a phobia may be unable to carry out daily activities. Some mental health professionals believe that a phobia is related to some past experience that was upsetting to the individual. Although there is no longer a threat or real danger, the fear remains real.

People have phobias about all kinds of things, from snakes to speaking in public.

ACTIVITY *Think about any phobias you may have. What do they have in common?*

LESSON 1   WHAT ARE MENTAL DISORDERS?   **239**

Did You Know?

There are many phobias, including:

➤ Astraphobia, a fear of lightning.

➤ Bathophobia, a fear of depth.

➤ Dromophobia, a fear of crossing streets.

➤ Ophidiophobia, a fear of snakes.

➤ Tapephobia, a fear of being buried alive.

➤ Ailurophobia, a fear of cats.

➤ Pyrophobia, a fear of fire.

➤ Logizomechanophobia, a fear of computers and other machines.

hotlink

phobias For more on phobias, including additional examples, see Chapter 8, page 200

TEACH

LD Explaining

LD students may be able to learn the names and general symptoms of the disorders, but most will not be able to categorize them.

L1 Discussing

Ask students to describe the difference between organic and functional disorders.

L3 Guest Speaker

Invite a speaker from a local crisis center or mental health center to talk with the class about types of mental disorders that affect teens and their families in the community.

LEP Class Activity

Have students draw pictures or make collages of newspaper and/or magazine illustrations to depict individuals experiencing mental disorders. Ask them to identify the disorder they are portraying.

L1 Discussing

Have students brainstorm a list of words that stigmatize people experiencing mental illness. Discuss the impact of these words on such a person and his or her family and friends.

L1 Discussing

Students may have preconceived ideas of mental illness based on what they have seen in films and TV programs. Discuss the various characters that have been portrayed in film and on TV and compare these characters with reality.

L2 Cooperative Learning

Have students complete *Cooperative Learning Activity 10,* "Childhood Stories: What Can They Tell About You?" in the TCR. ☞

Myths & Realities

MYTH. The lives of people with mental disorders are completely different from those of most other people.

FACT. Many people with mental illnesses go to school, get married, work, have families, do laundry, shop for groceries, and so on—like everyone else.

MYTH. Today, people are more knowledgeable and accepting about the effects of a mental disorder.

FACT. Unfortunately, a stigma still exists. The National Mental Health Association conducted a nationwide survey and reported that 43 percent of those surveyed considered depression to be an emotional or personal weakness.

L1 Discussing

Have students list reasons why someone may feel embarrassed to tell friends about a family member who is suffering from mental illness. Have students respond to each listed reason.

L2 Class Activity

Help students brainstorm a list of individuals who have suffered from mental illness and are accomplished members of society. Have students list the positive contributions of these individuals.

L2 Class Activity

Have students create a play in which a character struggles with mental illness and experiences discrimination in school or on the job. Make sure they demonstrate how this individual overcomes this situation.

L2 Writing

Have the class write essays about imaginary experiences with depression. Each paper should come to some kind of conclusion regarding what was done about the depression. Have one or two volunteers share their papers with the rest of the class. Discuss each of the papers read. Talk about when help may be needed.

L1 Personal Involvement

Ask students to keep a personal journal of their daily experiences with stress, anxiety, fear, and depression. Have them write about how they dealt with their feelings. Remind them that their journals are personal and that they will not have to share them with anyone.

L2 Health Lab

Distribute *Health Lab 10* and have students investigate the various moods they have in a day. ✏

▲ Washing hands every few minutes for no particular reason may be a sign of obsessive-compulsive behavior.
ACTIVITY *In a small group, discuss how you feel about people who exhibit some form of obsessive-compulsive disorder.*

OBSESSIVE-COMPULSIVE DISORDER

A person with obsessive-compulsive disorder, or OCD, is trapped in a pattern of repeated behaviors or thoughts. *Obsessions* are persistent, recurrent, unwanted thoughts or ideas that keep people from thinking about other things. *Compulsions* are urgent, repeated, irresistable behaviors. A person with OCD might, for example, feel the urge to wash his or her hands 20 or 30 times a day. When these activities interfere with other daily functions and commitments, they are considered a problem.

PANIC DISORDER

A person with a panic disorder has a condition in which fear or anxiety prevails and gets in the way of functioning and enjoying life. The individual may feel anxious, fearful, and upset most of the time, or the feelings may arise for no apparent reason. These "panic attacks" are accompanied by severe symptoms such as trembling, a racing heartbeat, shortness of breath, dizziness, or a fear of losing control or even dying. A person can be anywhere when the attack begins, although it can usually be connected with certain "triggers"—an object, condition, or situation.

POST-TRAUMATIC STRESS DISORDER

This is a condition in which a person who has experienced or witnessed a traumatic event feels severe and long-lasting aftereffects. This disorder is common among veterans of military combat, rape survivors, and survivors of natural disasters such as floods or unnatural disasters such as plane crashes. Typical symptoms include flashbacks, nightmares, emotional numbness, dreams about the event, sleeplessness, feelings of guilt, or an extreme reaction to an image or sound that reminds the person of the event. Symptoms may appear six months or even years after the initial event.

Somatoform Disorders

A **somatoform disorder** describes *an illness in which a person complains of disease symptoms, but no physical cause can be found.* An example of this type of disorder is **hypochondria**—*a preoccupation with the body and fear of presumed diseases that are not present.* A hypochondriac constantly feels aches and pains and worries about developing cancer, heart disease, or some other serious problem. Because hypochondriacs are convinced they are suffering from some disease, they refuse to believe doctors who tell them that they are healthy.

Affective Disorders

Everyone has different moods, and these moods are always subject to change. However, some mood swings are severe, can last for long periods of time, or lead to extreme behaviors. **Affective disorder**, a mood disorder, is *an illness often with an organic cause that relates to*

240 CHAPTER 10   MENTAL AND EMOTIONAL PROBLEMS

CURRICULUM CONNECTIONS

SOCIAL STUDIES Have students collect newspaper and magazine articles about floods, earthquakes, tornadoes, hurricanes, and various natural events that might cause people to feel anxious, fearful, or upset. Discuss the articles, and ask students to share examples of situations in which they felt fear or anxiety.

HISTORY. Ask students to research mental disorders through history. In what way were mental disorders looked at differently during earlier times? What similarities still exist? Ask students to write their comparisons of mental disorders and the stigma attached to them.

emotions and may involve mood swings or mood extremes that interfere with everyday living.

CLINICAL DEPRESSION

This is an affective disorder in which feelings of sadness, hopelessness, or despair last for more than a few weeks and interfere with daily activities and interests. It can be a serious health problem that affects one's ability to concentrate, sleep, perform at school or work, or handle everyday decisions and challenges. It can also be the symptom of substance abuse or diseases such as alcoholism or drug addiction. Depression often runs in families and can be biologically based, but it can also be caused by life events and accumulated traumas or stressors.

BIPOLAR DISORDER

Bipolar disorder, often inherited and sometimes called manic depression, is *a psychological illness characterized by extreme mood swings between depression and extreme happiness, or mania.* During manic periods, those with bipolar disorder may feel extremely happy or energetic. They may be overly talkative, often going rapidly from one topic of conversation to another. They may make lots of plans and take part in all sorts of activities. They may even act impulsively or take unnecessary risks. Often this "high" period ends abruptly, and a period of deep depression sets in. Between episodes of extreme emotions, however, manic depressives may behave normally. Some people only experience the manic phase or the depressive phase.

Personality Disorders

Personality disorders include *a variety of psychological conditions that affect a person's ability to get along with others.* People with personality disorders may often be at odds with others and not see their part in the problem. Unlike anxiety disorders, personality disorders have no apparent distinct signs or symptoms. The individual continues to function, often effectively, in his or her environment but may respond in ways that offend or interfere with others' interactions. These patterns of behavior may be harmful to the person with the disorder or to those in his or her environment.

ANTISOCIAL PERSONALITY DISORDER

One common personality disorder is termed the *antisocial personality,* characterized by a person's constant conflict with society. The antisocial individual may display behavior that is cruel, uncaring, irresponsible, and impulsive. Although he or she can distinguish right from wrong, the antisocial personality

keeping Fit

The Beatable, Treatable Blues

➤ If you're going through a tough time, remember that using alcohol or illegal drugs will make it worse.

➤ Surround yourself with supportive and encouraging people.

➤ Put your feelings in a private journal, or draw, dance, or find some other creative outlet.

➤ Talk about your feelings with those you love and who love you.

➤ Eat, sleep, and get enough physical activity.

➤ Do something for someone else. Doing so takes the focus away from you and your feelings.

All human beings feel blue sometimes, but if the feelings last too long or are too intense or scary, it's a good idea to seek help.

The Beatable, Treatable Blues

 keeping Fit

Assign volunteers to investigate seasonal affective disorders, including tips for coping with the disorder, and report their findings to the class.

L1 Discussing

Have students discuss an antisocial personality. Are hermits a good example? Talk about the book *Walden* by Henry David Thoreau. Does it present a good example of an antisocial personality? Why or why not? Consider other examples in classical literature.

L1 Discussing

Ask volunteers to complete the following sentences: *I feel that mental illness is…; People with mental illness are…; Someone with a phobia is…; The hardest thing about having a mental disorder is…*

Discuss students' responses and the reasons for some of the differences among them.

L3 Community Involvement

Let volunteers develop a questionnaire surveying mental health workers in the community. Have them include questions about the types of mental disorders experienced by the population, as well as the age and sex of clientele.

PERSONAL HEALTH

Unfortunately, many people with emotional or mental disorders will not seek or accept treatment. Even with treatment, enough symptoms may remain to make family members' lives miserable. In fact, some students may be coping with a mental disorder in a family member right now. With the class, come up with a list of mental disorders. For each disorder suggested, list problems the family might face, and discuss coping strategies they might use. Encourage students to write notes in their private Health Journals about how family members might cope with various mental disorders and their symptoms.

ASSESS

EVALUATING THE LESSON

Assign and discuss the Lesson 1 Review; then administer, grade, and discuss the *Lesson 33 Quiz* in the TCR. ✍

RETEACHING

- Have students divide a sheet of paper into four sections. At the top of each section, ask them to define one of the four main categories of functional disorders. Below each definition, have them describe examples of the disorder.
- Ask students to complete *Reteaching Activity 33* in the TCR. ✍

ENRICHMENT

Tell students to imagine they have a talk show on a local radio station. A caller claims that he or she has had trouble sleeping, concentrating, and handling everyday decisions for several months. What conclusion would students draw about this caller? What would they say to the caller?

CLOSE

Write the lesson's major concepts on separate, numbered slips of paper. Place the slips in a box and let each student draw one. In numerical order, have students define and summarize the concept written on the slip of paper they have selected.

CHARACTER IN ACTION

Empathy Builders

Empathy is the ability to feel or imagine what another is feeling. It means being sensitive to another's needs and trying to become aware of what it must be like to be the other person or to be in his or her situation.

Character Check To develop empathy for people with mental disorders:

➤ Vow never to make fun of people with mental or physical challenges.

➤ Stick up for those you see being ridiculed, ignored, or talked down to by others.

➤ Remind yourself that every human being deserves dignity.

often does not care about others' needs or society's rules and therefore is often in trouble with the law.

PASSIVE-AGGRESSIVE PERSONALITY DISORDER

People with passive-aggressive personality disorder are often uncooperative with others. They resent being told what to do, yet they rely on others' direction. Angry over issues of control, they show their anger, but only indirectly. For example, a passive-aggressive person who does not want to take part in a school activity either may forget to show up or may arrive late and leave early.

SCHIZOPHRENIA

A serious mental disorder meaning "split mind," **schizophrenia** affects about one to two percent of the population and appears most frequently among people between the ages of 15 and 35. Untreated schizophrenics may behave inappropriately, exhibit abnormal emotional responses or, in some cases, show no emotional responses at all. Some schizophrenics withdraw, often losing all sense of time and space. Others hallucinate, hear voices, talk to themselves, act in an odd manner, or neglect to care for themselves. People with paranoid schizophrenia mistrust and are often suspicious of others. They may believe that they are being followed, listened to, or targeted for harm.

Much research is being carried out to better understand schizophrenia. Causes for this condition may stem from a physical disorder or may be genetic in nature. The disorder may come and go throughout a person's life. Professional help and chemical intervention are always recommended.

LESSON 1 *Review*

Reviewing Facts and Vocabulary

1. Define the term *mental disorder* and use it in a sentence that offers hope to those who suffer from one.
2. Name three possible causes of organic disorders.
3. Define the term *functional disorder* and give three examples.

Thinking Critically

4. *Analyzing.* Take an in-depth look at the reasons why a stigma about mental illness continues to exist.
5. *Synthesizing.* Make a poster summarizing the myths and facts about mental disorders.

Applying Health Skills

6. *In Your School.* With your classmates, read about the insanity defense. First, find definitions of the word *insanity,* a legal term. Next, research the topic, including recent cases in which this defense was attempted or used. Hold a debate discussing the pros and cons of the use of this defense in many trials of serious crimes.

242 CHAPTER 10 MENTAL AND EMOTIONAL PROBLEMS

Lesson 1 Review

Answers to Reviewing Facts and Vocabulary

1. A mental disorder is an illness of the mind that can affect the thoughts, feelings, and behaviors of a person, preventing him or her from leading a happy, healthful, and productive life. Sentences will vary.
2. Any three: brain tumors, alcoholism, infections, stroke, and some inherited chemical imbalances.
3. A functional disorder results from stress, emotional conflict, fear, or poor coping skills. Examples can include phobias, obsessive-compulsive disorder, panic disorder, post-traumatic stress disorder.

Answers to Thinking Critically

4. Written answers will vary.
5. Posters will vary.

Suicide Prevention

Suicide, *the taking of one's own life,* is a major health problem in the United States. Every year, some 30,000 people commit suicide. This country's rising teen suicide rate is particularly alarming and tragic, with suicide accounting for one-third of all deaths among teens. Why are these numbers so high? How can these tragic losses be stopped?

HEALTH TERMS

suicide

depression

cluster suicides

HEALTH CONCEPTS

- Adolescent suicide is a complex behavior that generally involves multiple risk factors, among them mental disorders and substance abuse.
- People considering suicide exhibit certain behaviors that may be seen as warning signs.

Depression and the Teen Years

Do you ever feel like things are pulling you down and that you just can't cope? Most people do sometimes. Life can feel overwhelming. This is especially true during the teen years when new challenges, responsibilities, and pressures can pile up and seem overpowering. For some teens, this emotional overload can lead to **depression,** *feelings of helplessness, hopelessness, and sadness.* These feelings can be further complicated by troubling life events such as the divorce or separation of parents or the loss of a loved one. Alienation—feeling isolated and separated from everyone else—can occur. When such painful feelings go unchecked over long periods, some teens may feel so filled with despair that they will try drastic, self-destructive measures to escape.

Suicide Prevention

FOCUS

LESSON OBJECTIVES

After studying this lesson, students should be able to

- identify suicide risk factors.
- describe signs of suicidal behavior.
- discuss ways to help prevent suicide.

MOTIVATOR

Lay a thin piece of cardboard between two desks to form a bridge. Gradually add weight to the center of the cardboard until it collapses.

INTRODUCING THE LESSON

Refer to the Motivator. Explain that like the cardboard, our minds and bodies are vulnerable to too much stress and can become overloaded, resulting in depression. Tell students that this lesson will focus on depression and its effects on the human psyche or mind.

INTRODUCING HEALTH TERMS

- Introduce students to the term *suicide* and discuss how it has been viewed historically by various cultures.
- Ask students to complete Vocabulary Activity 10 and Chapter Study Guide 10 in the *Student Workbook.* ☞

Lesson 2 Resources

TEACHER'S CLASSROOM RESOURCES

☞ **Concept Map** Activity 34

☞ **Decision-Making** Activity 10

☞ **Lesson 34 Quiz**

☞ **Lesson Plan 34**

☞ **Reteaching** Activity 34

STUDENT WORKBOOK

☞ **Applying Health Skills 34**

☞ **Chapter Study Guide 10**

☞ **Vocabulary** Activity 10

TEACH

L3 Guest Speaker

Invite a school counselor, psychologist, or school nurse to speak with the class about being alert to the warning signs of depression and suicide. Afterward, have students write a short paper summarizing the presentation.

L2 Discussing

Encourage students to list reasons for suicide attempts (e.g., unhappiness at home, disappointment in love, failure to achieve). Then divide them into three groups, and give each group one or two of the reasons. Have each group develop healthy ways to cope with its problem. Let them share their ideas with the class.

L1 Discussing

Ask volunteers to complete the following sentences: *If I had a friend who was thinking about suicide, I would…; When I'm feeling stressed or anxious, I…; Some of the people I would ask for help if I couldn't handle a difficult situation are…*

Discuss students' responses and the reasons for some of the differences among them.

L3 Researching

Arrange for a small group of students to interview a suicide counselor or a person who answers a crisis hotline. Have the students ask: What special training does the person have? What are the main objectives in talking with a person experiencing a crisis? What problems are most commonly heard?

Did You Know?

➤ Of the many millions of Americans who suffer from depression in any given year, 80 percent can be effectively treated, but only 30 percent seek help.

➤ In 1997, more teens died from suicide than from cancer, heart disease, AIDS, birth defects, stroke, and chronic lung disease combined.

Suicide Risk Factors

Suicide and suicidal behavior are not normal responses to the stresses experienced by most people. In general, youth at high risk are those who are depressed, isolated, and angry. Over 50 percent of suicidal adolescents are considered depressed. Other suicide risk factors include:

- Substance abuse, violence, or emotional, physical, or sexual abuse.
- Prior suicide attempts, firearms in the house, jail time, a family history of a mental disorder, and exposure to other suicides.

In some cases, suicide is accidental—the result of alcohol or drug abuse or the misuse of firearms.

Suicide's Warning Signs

Recognizing the signs of suicide in one's self or others can mean the difference between life and death. Become alert and alarmed if someone you know exhibits any of the warning signs of suicide.

Warning Signs of Suicide

VERBAL SIGNS

- Direct statements like "I want to die," "I don't want to live anymore," or "I wish I were dead."
- Indirect statements like "I (or you) won't have to put up with this much longer," "I just want to go to sleep and never wake up," "They'll be sorry when I'm gone," "Soon this pain will be over," "I can't take it anymore," "Nothing matters," "Who cares?" "I won't be a problem for you much longer," "What's the use?"
- Poems, song lyrics, or diary entries that deal with death.

NONVERBAL AND BEHAVIORAL SIGNS

- Depression and hopelessness.
- Lack of energy and zest for life.
- Withdrawal from family, friends, and social activities.
- Drop in grades or a poor student's new concern about grades, or trouble concentrating.
- Giving away possessions or otherwise settling affairs.
- Extreme sensitivity to what others say and do.
- Increased risk-taking and other aggressive activity, such as driving recklessly, or frequent accidents.
- Personality changes such as apathy or moodiness.
- A sudden upbeat mood, which can signal that the decision to attempt suicide has been made.
- Neglect of or dramatic change in appearance.
- Rebellious behavior or running away.
- Irrational or bizarre behavior.
- Drug and alcohol use.
- Violent actions.

MORE ABOUT . . . . .

TROUBLED FRIENDS. Sometimes it takes all of your time and energy to keep your own stress under control. What is your obligation to friends, sisters, or brothers? Are you responsible for their health and safety? These are questions you must answer for yourself. Everyone who is mentally and physically capable must take responsibility for his or her own behavior. Even if you help a friend, the final outcome is your friend's responsibility. Another consideration is how you feel when you need help. The golden rule to treat others as you would have them treat you still makes a lot of sense. Perhaps no one needs immediate help more than people thinking of suicide.

Making Responsible Decisions

When a Friend Seems Troubled

Anissa has been Kelly's friend and role model for as long as Kelly can remember. Lately, though, Kelly has noticed changes. Anissa has seemed down a lot, irritable the rest of the time, and very withdrawn. When Kelly tries to talk to her, Anissa gives abrupt answers. Anissa has also stopped studying, has lost weight, and has dark circles under her eyes. Kelly is worried that her friend is exhibiting warning signs of suicide but is afraid that if she approaches Anissa directly, she might push her friend "over the edge."

What Would You Do?

Apply the six steps of the decision-making process to Anissa's problem.

1. **State the situation.**
2. **List the options.**
3. **Weigh the possible outcomes.**
4. **Consider your values.**
5. **Make a decision and act.**
6. **Evaluate the decision.**

Preventing Suicide

The tragic fact is that the conditions leading to suicide are almost always treatable. Most suicide thoughts are temporary, but death is permanent. With help, people suffering from depression, extreme stress, or mental disorders can often find new levels of purpose and happiness.

Helping Others

The first thing to remember is that people who are suicidal often feel that no one cares. It is, therefore, critical to show your caring and concern. Remember, too, that the person needs professional help as soon as he or she can get it—immediately if possible. You may in fact be able to take action in time to save a life. What to do when you suspect someone you care about is a potential suicide includes the following:

- Take any and all talk of potential suicide seriously. Actively listen and show support, and be calm and understanding. Talk directly, openly, and freely. Allow the person to express his or her feelings in depth, and show **empathy** for his or her problems. Let the person know how much you and others care.
- Stress the temporary nature of the problems and feelings the person is going through, and emphasize that there is professional help available that can make things better.
- Make clear that you understand that the person wants to end his or her pain, but emphasize that suicide is not the answer. Add the

hot link

empathy For more information on empathy and its value as a positive emotion, see Chapter 8, page 199.

Making Responsible Decisions

1. Kelly is concerned that her friend Anissa is considering suicide.
2. Kelly could (a) ignore the signs she sees in her friend, (b) ask Anissa whether she is considering suicide, (c) express her concern for Anissa and ask whether there's anything Anissa wants to talk about, (d) discuss her concerns about Anissa with a parent, counselor, or other trusted adult.
3. Kelly might (a) continue to worry, and Anissa might actually commit suicide; (b) offend Anissa, but Anissa might be shocked into discussing her thoughts of suicide; (c) risk being rebuffed by Anissa, but also give her friend an opportunity to talk; (d) risk making Anissa angry, but find someone who can help her.
4. Kelly values her friendship with Anissa, and she values Anissa's mental and emotional health.
5. Responses will vary.
6. Remind students to consider both the short- and long-term consequences of their decisions.

L2 **Decision Making**

For further study on making responsible decisions, assign *Decision-Making Activity 10* in the TCR.

L3 **Writing**

Assign students to design and write a "care manual" for friends and family members of a teen who has considered suicide. Have them include in the manual warning signs of potential suicide and suggestions for dealing with an individual who shows signs of sadness and hopelessness.

COOPERATIVE LEARNING

ACTIVITY. Intervening when a person is suicidal can be a challenging task. In a crisis situation, there may be no time to plan or prepare. Students should think now about what they would say to a suicidal friend or family member. Discuss the challenges and strategies with the class. Divide the class into groups of four. Have two group members role-play a conversation between a suicidal teen and a suicide hot-line operator. The other two members may critique the operator's response and offer constructive suggestions. Have members switch roles. Suggest they continue taking turns until all members feel reasonably confident about role-playing suicide intervention.

ASSESS

EVALUATING THE LESSON

Assign and discuss the Lesson 2 Review; then administer, grade, and discuss the *Lesson 34 Quiz* in the TCR. 📁

RETEACHING

- Have students write an article for the school newspaper presenting the warning signs for a potential suicide. Ask them to include verbal and behavioral warning signs.
- Ask students to complete *Reteaching Activity 34* in the TCR. 📁

ENRICHMENT

Have the class investigate incidents of cluster suicides or suicide pacts. Ask students to write a short paper outlining ways that multiple suicides might be averted.

CLOSE

Review the signs of depression and tell students that you can best help someone who is depressed by being alert to the warning signs and by notifying trusted adults of the situation. Remember that any talk of suicide should be taken seriously.

keeping Fit

Signs of Trouble

If you or someone you know is experiencing any or many of the following symptoms, seek help.

➤ feelings of sadness or anxiety that won't go away

➤ persistent feelings of hopelessness or emptiness

➤ restlessness or irritability

➤ lack of energy or interest

➤ difficulties concentrating, remembering, or thinking

➤ trouble making decisions

➤ insomnia, early waking, or oversleeping

fact that most suicide survivors later express gratitude that they did not die.

■ Ask the person whether or not he or she has a specific plan and means to follow through with it. Be sure that no weapons or drugs are available. Do not leave the potential suicidal person alone if you feel the threat is immediate. Instead, take the person to a professional for counseling.

■ Suggest that he or she talk to a parent or other trusted adult, or a trained professional. Offer to make the contacts on his or her behalf.

■ Do not agree to "keep a secret."

Multiple Suicides

Sometimes within a teen population, there are **cluster suicides.** These are *a rash of suicides occurring within a short space of time and involving several people in the same school or community.* Some cluster suicides are the result of suicide pacts—oral or written agreements between two or more people to take part in a joint suicide. When these pacts fail, as they often do, the guilt experienced by the survivor is intolerable. If you know someone engaged in such a pact, talk with a responsible adult or to the authorities immediately. Intervention must take place quickly. Counseling must start right away for all involved in such a pact.

LESSON 2 *Review*

Reviewing Facts and Vocabulary

1. Name five warning signs of suicide.
2. What two factors seem to contribute to suicides more than any other?
3. List five suggestions for dealing with a friend or relative who is threatening suicide.

Thinking Critically

4. ***Comparing and Contrasting.*** Distinguish those traits of individuals who experience depression but seem to work through it quickly and those who seem to become overwhelmed by their feelings.
5. ***Synthesizing.*** List some of the common myths about suicide. Write them up, correcting each statement with its true counterpart.

Applying Health Skills

6. ***In Your Home.*** Make a scrapbook of pictures from newspapers, magazines, or your own photo collection called "Faces of Hope." Inside, keep pictures of people who have overcome depression, other mental disorders, suicide attempts, or other tough times and not only gotten through them but also bounced back, thriving either in spite of or even because of them. When you or someone you know is feeling really down, flip through or share this book of hope.

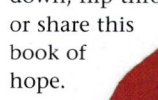

Lesson 2 Review

Answers to Reviewing Facts and Vocabulary

1. See complete list on page 244.
2. Depression and alienation.
3. See complete list on pages 245 and 246.

Answers to Thinking Critically

4. Written answers will vary.
5. Myths and correcting statements will vary.

Getting Help

A s you have seen, there are many different types of mental disorders. Within each type, the severity of the problem varies greatly. Unlike the symptoms of a cold or rash, specific symptoms of mental disorders are much more difficult to identify. There are places to go, however, to get help for these problems.

HEALTH TERMS

psychiatrist
neurologist
clinical psychologist
psychiatric social worker

HEALTH CONCEPTS

- Treatments are now available for many types of mental disorders.
- Mental disorders require the attention of a trained health professional.
- Mental health professionals can help their patients or clients to improve their perceptions of themselves, their relationships, and the outside world.

Signs of Mental Health Problems

R ecognizing early warning signs of mental disorders is one key to getting help for them. Any of the following feelings or behaviors that persist over a period of days or weeks and begin to interfere with other aspects of daily living could be a sign of a mental or emotional disorder:

- prolonged sadness for no specific reason
- hopelessness—the sense that one's life is out of control
- violent or erratic mood shifts
- inability to concentrate or to make decisions about daily life
- overwhelming fear, anxiety, or anger at the world
- severe sleep disturbances—nightmares, insomnia, fitful sleep
- compulsive behaviors such as repeated handwashing

LESSON 3   GETTING HELP   **247**

Getting Help

FOCUS

LESSON OBJECTIVES

After studying this lesson, students should be able to

- identify signs of mental health problems.
- contrast the various types of care providers for mental health.

MOTIVATOR

Write the following on the chalkboard for students to work on while attendance is being taken: *Look at the following list: sadness, hopelessness, violent or erratic mood shifts, inability to concentrate, fear and anger at the world, insomnia, and self-destructive behavior. Imagine that you or a family member is suffering from one or more of these, and write a paragraph about where you or they might go for professional help to deal with the problem.*

INTRODUCING THE LESSON

Collect students' responses to the Motivator. Ask volunteers to share reasons for their selections of help. Tell them that there are a number of mental health-care services, and that they will learn more about them as they study this lesson.

INTRODUCING HEALTH TERMS

- Have students design and write a public service brochure listing and defining the principal health care providers for mental health.
- Ask students to complete Vocabulary Activity 10 and Chapter Study Guide 10 in the *Student Workbook.* ✏

Lesson 3 Resources

TEACHER'S CLASSROOM RESOURCES

📂 **Concept Map** Activity 35
📂 **Enrichment** Activity 10
📂 **Lesson 35 Quiz**
📂 **Lesson Plan 35**
📂 **Reteaching** Activity 35

STUDENT WORKBOOK

📂 **Applying Health Skills 35**
📂 **Chapter Study Guide 10**
📂 **Vocabulary** Activity 10

TRANSPARENCIES

 Transparency 45

TEACH

[L3] Researching

Ask students to watch TV shows that deal with mental health problems and/or services. Have them prepare written synopses of the programs to share with the class. Be prepared to discuss the problems or services in detail, as well as how the problems were solved or how the services were used in the program. (If the problem was not solved, ask the students to explain why.) Ask: Does this episode of the program reinforce positive or negative thinking about mental health and mental disorders? Why?

Building Health Skills

Evaluating Sources of Self-Help
Skill: Accessing Reliable Information

Display a variety of self-help books and/or health-related magazines, and ask: What kinds of information would you expect to find in these publications? How willing are you to trust the advice and information you find there? How can you tell whether a work like this is reliable? After volunteers have shared their responses, let students read the Building Health Skills feature to learn about specific strategies that will help them evaluate sources of self-help. You may want to have students work in small groups to apply these strategies in evaluating specific publications or Web sites.

- self-destructive behaviors such as overeating, starving oneself, drinking, or other drug use
- frequent physical ailments for which no medical cause can be found

Of course, no one symptom means a person has a mental disorder. However, any one of these symptoms may be an indication that stress in your life is building. Such stresses need to be closely examined before more serious problems arise.

Building Health Skills

Evaluating Sources of Self-Help

AMONG THE RESOURCES people sometimes turn to are self-help books and Web sites for psychological services. Although these sources may offer useful hints and guidelines, you need to be a careful consumer when it comes to seeking help. Ask the following questions before proceeding:

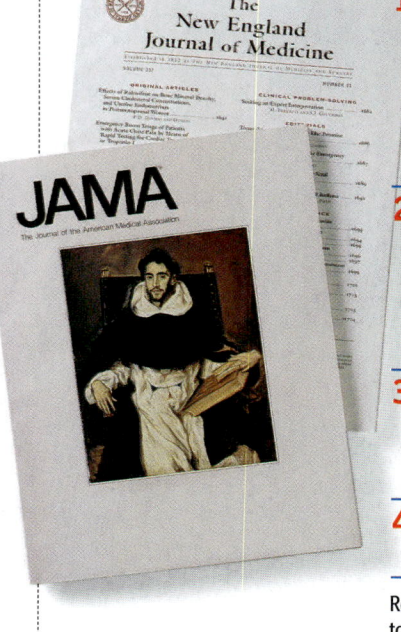

1. **What are the qualifications and background of the author or Web site administrator?** Do these people have training in the mental health area? In the case of Web sites, refuse to sign on with individuals who won't provide their names, addresses, phone numbers, and credentials. In the case of books, check the resources at the back to see if they include references to established medical journals such as *The New England Journal of Medicine* or the *Journal of the American Medical Association.*

2. **Is the book or site supported or backed by a nationally known and respected mental health organization?** Just because a self-help source is endorsed by a celebrity or listed on a best-seller list does not mean that its advice is psychologically sound. Look for backing from a reputable source such as the American Psychological Association or the National Institute of Mental Health.

3. **Are you being advised to try medication or some other remedy?** Before accepting such advice, check with your doctor, counselor, or therapist. Remedies bought "over the counter" in a drugstore can be harmful and even life threatening.

4. **Is there a cost involved?** Many resources are available at no cost. If you are asked on-line for a credit card number, use caution.

Remember, finally, that computers and telephones are not substitutes for real face-to-face encounters. You may be bypassing the healing benefits that face-to-face relationships and therapies offer. In addition, for those who have serious disorders or need medication, "diagnosis" or treatment through cyberspace may be inaccurate, insufficient, damaging, or even dangerous.

248 CHAPTER 10 MENTAL AND EMOTIONAL PROBLEMS

HEALTH LITERACY

SELF-DIRECTED LEARNER. Bipolar disorder is frequently misdiagnosed and treated inappropriately. For example, the therapist may see the patient only during an episode of depression and may believe the patient is always like this. Have students use on-line or library sources to conduct research about bipolar disorder, its organic causes, and appropriate medication. Tell them to find out, if possible, the potential consequences of mistaking bipolar disorder for another type of depression. For example, how might an antidepressant, such as Prozac or Paxil, affect a person suffering from bipolar disorder?

Myths About Seeking Help

MYTH	REALITY
Seeking help from a mental health professional means a person is weak or crazy.	Asking for needed help is a sign of strength. It shows responsibility for one's well-being.
People who set their mind to it can get better on their own.	Serious disorders, compulsions, and addictions are complex and require professional intervention.
Finding help is difficult.	Help is as close as a trusted adult, friend, family physician, clergy member, or the phone book.
Getting professional help for a mental problem is too expensive.	Some mental health care professionals have sliding pay scales. Other state and community facilities offer low-cost or no-cost help.
Sharing your deepest thoughts with a "stranger" is painful and embarrassing.	People are almost always surprised to find out that unloading their problems makes them feel better.

Kinds of Professional Help

Often it is difficult to look in the mirror and do your own mental health checkup. Sometimes others are needed to help. The principal health care providers for mental health are psychiatrists, neurologists, clinical psychologists, psychiatric social workers, and counselors of various types. These individuals may work in hospitals, clinics, or private offices.

Psychiatrist

A **psychiatrist** is *a medical doctor who specializes in diagnosing and treating mental disorders and can prescribe medications.* He or she deals with mental, emotional, and behavioral disorders of the mind.

The psychiatrist uses many therapies, or treatment techniques. Among these are:

- **psychotherapy**—an ongoing dialogue between the patient and psychiatrist designed to get to the root of the problem and find a solution.
- **psychoanalysis**—an analysis of a patient's past, particularly his or her early life, to determine the early roots of a mental problem. This is rarely used today.
- **medical psychotherapy**—the use of certain medications to treat or reduce a mental disorder or to use in conjunction with or as preparation for the above two treatments.

▲ **With time, caring, support, and proper treatment, most people with mental disorders can return to life and enjoy its simple pleasures "to the max."**

ACTIVITY *List five short-term and five long-term benefits of seeking help for a mental problem.*

L2 Cooperative Learning

Ask students to list signs of mental health problems that teens, their friends, and/or their family members might experience. Record the list on the chalkboard. Assign students to small groups, and ask each group to select one of the signs from the list on the board. Have them identify possible causes and various health care services that might be used to address the problem. Help them arrive at a consensus as to where someone might go to receive help. Ask each group to select a spokesperson to share the group's thinking with the class.

L1 Explaining

Emphasize that people seek help for many reasons, not just because they have a mental disorder. Explain to students that people seek help to strengthen family or marital relationships, to cope with sudden loss such as death of a family member, or to manage stress. Those seeking professional help can also include people who want to overcome shyness, those who need help adjusting to a new or difficult situation, or people dealing with addiction, alcohol abuse, work problems, or divorce. Tell students that therapy helps people to understand themselves better.

SCHOOL-TO-CAREER

COUNSELING AND HEALTH PLANS.
Large employers who provide health insurance offer a broad range of plans. Call on volunteers to survey several large employers. They may contact local companies, headquarters of national corporations, or government agencies. Have them find out if the health plans provided include counseling from a psychologist or psychiatrist. Ask them to explain the differences between a managed care plan and an indemnity plan. Charges have been raised that HMOs encourage psychiatrists to emphasize drugs as an inexpensive alternative to counseling. Encourage students to investigate such charges by reading magazine and newspaper articles on the subject, then report their conclusions to the class.

L2 Writing

Write the types of professionals presented in the lesson on separate slips of paper. Place the slips in a box, and let every student draw a slip. Then, have students design a brochure explaining the training received and services offered by the type of professional written on their slip of paper.

up date
▶ *Our Changing World*

Mental Health Counselors

Encourage students to share what they already know about mental health counselors. Ask: What are some types of mental health counselors? What kinds of problems do they help people with? How might counselors help in the event of a crisis or tragedy? After a brief discussion, let students read the Update feature to learn more about mental health counselors.

Before students respond to the first question, review the health skills discussed in Chapter 2. For the second activity, you might ask a school counselor to speak to the class and have students write a few paragraphs summarizing the speech.

L1 Class Activity

Let students generate a list of reasons people with mental health problems often give for refusing to seek professional help. Then have pairs of students role-play conversations between two teens—one offering excuses, and the other encouraging his or her friend to go to a mental health professional.

Neurologist

If a psychiatrist thinks a patient may have some organic problem of the brain, the patient may be referred to a neurologist. A **neurologist** is *a physician who specializes in organic disorders of the brain and nervous system.* Those who specialize in surgery are called *neurosurgeons* or *neural surgeons.* Consultation with and testing by a neurologist may be required for patients whose mental symptoms are suspected as being caused by an organic disease.

Clinical Psychologist

The **clinical psychologist** is *a psychologist who diagnoses and treats emotional and behavioral disorders but cannot prescribe medications.* State law usually determines what kinds of training is required to earn the

up date
▶ *Our Changing World*

Mental Health Counselors

In today's challenging society, the skills of mental health counselors are called upon more than ever. School counselors, social workers, psychiatrists, and psychologists can help when you're feeling overwhelmed by situations over which you feel you have no control. Their work involves helping people deal with emotional problems, relationship issues, stress management, and conflict resolution.

In a school setting, mental health counselors are often available for guidance in crisis prevention and intervention. If a crisis or tragedy does occur, counselors help students and teachers cope with grief and loss and identify victims of psychological trauma, such as post-traumatic stress disorder. They may offer counseling and group therapy sessions to assist people in dealing with their feelings about the traumatic event. Because emotions run deep in the aftermath of a crisis or tragedy, counselors must be careful to notice and try to prevent potential alcohol and drug problems as well as suicide.

1. What health skills do you think would be essential for a career as a mental health counselor? Explain your response.

2. Interview a mental health counselor. Find out about his or her daily responsibilities. Which responsibilities are most challenging, and which are most rewarding?

HOME AND COMMUNITY CONNECTION

BIAS POLL. People vary in their views toward counseling and those who receive it. Some view counseling as a healthy part of personal growth. Others distrust anyone who has consulted a therapist. Some employers have discriminated against people who were seeing counselors, regarding therapy as a sign of mental instability. Guide students in conducting a poll of attitudes in your community toward people who seek help from a psychotherapist. Have them come up with a list of questions. They can begin by surveying people at school and at home, then poll people in a public place. Encourage students to tabulate the results and post them in the classroom. Allow time to discuss the findings.

title *psychologist*. The clinical psychologist can practice psychotherapy, group therapy, and individual counseling, in addition to testing for many kinds of specific mental disorders.

Counselors

There are many kinds of counselors, including school counselors. These professionals usually have a master's degree and work with young people, helping them in personal or educational matters. Pastoral counselors, who include ministers, priests, and rabbis, often help people with mental, social, and marital problems. Addictions counselors have special certification and training requirements.

Psychiatric Social Worker

A **psychiatric social worker** is *one who has concentrated on psychiatric casework, doing fieldwork in a mental hospital, mental health clinic, or family service agency that provides guidance and treatment for clients with emotional problems.* They usually have a master's degree.

Seeking Help

More and more Americans, including many teens, are seeking professional help from mental health professionals. Though mental problems are often undiagnosed and untreated, many people are working hard to change the situation. If you or someone you know has a mental problem, you no longer have to suffer in silence. Talk to a trusted adult. Get the support and the help that you need.

ASSESS

EVALUATING THE LESSON

Assign and discuss the Lesson 3 Review; then administer, grade, and discuss the *Lesson 35 Quiz* in the TCR. 🖛

RETEACHING

- Have students use the information in the lesson to answer these questions: When should you get help with a mental health problem? Where can you go for help? Why is it important to get help?
- Ask students to complete *Reteaching Activity 35* in the TCR. 🖛
- Use *Transparency 45* to review the process and resources for getting professional help. 🖎

ENRICHMENT

- Assign students to research the use of pet therapy for persons who are experiencing sadness, hopelessness, and loneliness.
- Let students know what strategies they can expect if they seek professional counseling. Have them complete *Enrichment Activity 10,* "Therapies and How They Work," in the TCR. 🖛

CLOSE

Summarize with the class the major concepts by outlining the signs of mental health problems and listing the types of mental health professionals and the therapies or services they provide.

LESSON 3 *Review*

Reviewing Facts and Vocabulary

1. Identify five signs of mental health problems.
2. List at least five different places that a teen needing to talk with someone about mental or emotional problems or disorders might go for help.

Thinking Critically

3. *Analyzing.* What are some of the reasons a person might go to a psychiatrist instead of a psychologist or psychiatric social worker?
4. *Synthesizing.* Create a Help Wanted ad that lists the personal qualities one would need to fill a position at a mental health clinic.

Applying Health Skills

5. *In Your Home.* At a library or neighborhood bookstore, examine several books on psychology and mental health. Try to find the credentials of the authors. Now look through teen magazines that have "health" sections. Select one article about emotional or mental health and evaluate what it tells you about the author's credentials.

Lesson 3 Review

Answers to Reviewing Facts and Vocabulary

1. Any five: prolonged, unexplained sadness; hopelessness; violent or erratic mood shifts; inability to concentrate or make decisions; overwhelming fear, anxiety, or anger; severe sleep disturbances; compulsive behaviors.
2. A trusted adult, friend, family member, clergy member, physician, coach, teacher, school counselor or nurse, state or community mental health facility, hospital and/or clinic, crisis intervention center.

Answers to Thinking Critically

3. A psychiatrist has had medical training in diagnosing mental disorders and has more treatment options available.
4. Ads will vary.

Health Skills Activities

ACTIVITY 1
HEALTH SKILLS
Accessing Health Information

➤ **National Standards**
This activity meets these National Health Standards: 2.3; 2.4; 2.5; 2.6.

Teach

- Bring to class a telephone directory and pamphlets from various mental health resources in your community. As an alternative, have students provide mental health materials they can access either through the school library, the Internet, or community services.
- Review the types of mental health care providers in Lesson 3.
- Prior to distributing resource materials, ask students where they might turn for information about mental health services available in their own community.
- Have students appoint one group member to input the actual directory on the classroom computer.

ACTIVITY 2
HEALTH SKILLS
Communication, Health Advocacy

➤ **National Standards**
This activity meets these National Health Standards: 5.1; 5.4; 7.1.

Teach

- Review the various mental health disorders described and discussed in the chapter.
- Set aside class time for groups to confer with one another in devising a quiz. You may want to provide students with samples of past quizzes you have given as a model.
- Students should elect classmates known for their mathematical aptitude to tabulate the results of their inquiry.

Activity 1: Mental Health Help Directory

Many people who decide to seek help may have no idea how to go about finding that help. Having information about local mental health resources can make the process of getting help easier and less stressful.

Directions

1. In a group, research mental health resources in your community, such as general community outreach programs as well as centers for child abuse, addiction, and crisis intervention. Investigate vital information such as hours, cost, and services provided.
2. Compile all findings from the class into a Mental Health Help Directory to be printed from the classroom computer.
3. If possible, make your directory available in the school library or counselor's office.

Time
50 minutes

Materials
paper, pen or pencil, telephone directory and other community resources, computer

Self-Assessment

✓ Listed at least five sources of help for mental health problems.
✓ Provided detailed information for each source identified.

Activity 2: Building Mental Health Awareness

Despite the strides of modern research and the availability of treatment, mental problems are often a source of embarrassment to people who suffer from them. Write an editorial to explain some of the myths and misconceptions.

Directions

1. Working in a group, select one of the mental disorders covered in the chapter. Brainstorm misconceptions you know to exist or believe exist about this illness. These may be about the warning signs, behaviors, and/or symptoms.
2. Combine your misconceptions with those of other groups to create a true-false survey on mental health.
3. Administer the survey to several dozen people in the community. Tabulate the findings, and publish these as an editorial in a local newspaper.

Time
50 minutes

Materials
paper, pen

Self-Assessment

✓ Described signs, behaviors, and symptoms of the mental illness you selected.
✓ Tabulated survey results.
✓ Presented findings accurately and cohesively.

252 CHAPTER 10 MENTAL AND EMOTIONAL PROBLEMS

ASSESSMENT SCORING

Using a four-level rubric, the student has achieved a 4 if:

ACTIVITY 1
✔ Student demonstrated an awareness of the various types of mental health care providers.
✔ Student was able to extend information in text to apply to community resources.
✔ Student provided detailed information for each source identified.
✔ Student helped shape directory so that it was complete, accurate, and useful.

ACTIVITY 2
✔ Student was able to discuss various mental disorders, citing similarities and differences.
✔ Student correctly described the signs, behaviors, and symptoms of one particular mental illness.
✔ Student tabulated survey results.
✔ Student presented findings accurately and in a meaningful and cohesive manner.

VIDEO

Stolen Lives

Suicide is the eighth leading cause of death in the United States. It is the third leading cause of death among 15-24 year-olds. However, looking at statistics isn't enough. We need to find practical, working solutions.

Surgeon General David Satcher has announced a new suicide prevention plan. "Suicide has stolen lives and contributed to the disability and suffering of hundreds of thousands of Americans each year," he said. The plan focuses on reducing the feelings of shame surrounding suicide. It calls for better mental health screenings and more media programs that accurately depict suicide and mental illness.

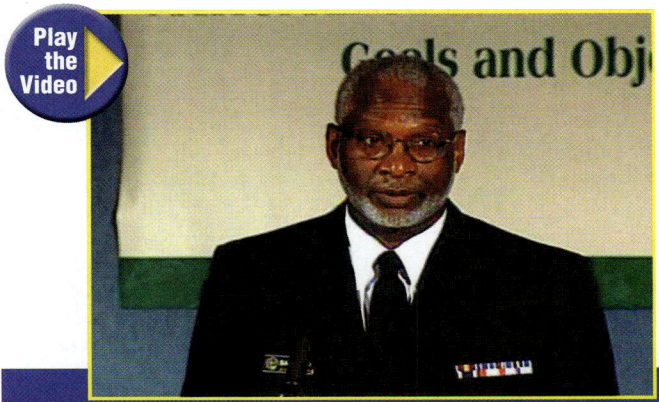

Play the Video

Goals and Obj

Think About It

- What is a stigma? How does the new suicide prevention plan try to overcome the stigma of suicide?

- Why was Maggie Ming asked to speak at the press conference announcing the plan? How does her perspective help people understand the problem of suicide?

- Why does Satcher include television and movies in his suicide prevention plan? How does the media influence people's attitudes and feelings?

MORE ABOUT . . . . .

ASK THE EXPERTS. The Surgeon General has a powerful ability to draw the public's attention to specific health problems. He or she serves as a highly visible advocate for effective disease prevention and health promotion. Many students will be familiar with the Surgeon General's warnings about dangerous products, such as tobacco and alcohol.

In addition to issuing warnings and raising public health awareness, the Surgeon General administers the U.S. Public Health Service (PHS) Commissioned Corps, which includes more than 6,100 officers trained to respond to both the current and long-term health needs of the nation.

CNN HEALTH NEWS

Stolen Lives
Video Segment 5 (Time – 1:32)

Objectives. After viewing the video, students should be able to summarize the surgeon-general's message concerning the signs, causes, and prevention of suicide.

Motivator. Remind students that Surgeon General Satcher, pictured, is a national spokesperson for health issues. Ask: "Why might the Surgeon General be concerned with suicide?" After students offer their responses, have them view Video Segment 5 to learn about a new suicide prevention plan that targets this national problem.

Teach

- Ask students to summarize the suicide statistics presented in the video. Discuss how these statistics reveal the scope of the problem, but do not suggest how to solve it. Have students offer ideas about how the Surgeon General's plan can be most effective.

- Encourage students to contribute to the Surgeon General's suicide prevention plan by writing either a storyboard or outline for a movie, a script for a classroom skit or a comic book. Student materials should present a realistic view of suicide or mental illness and depict the signs, causes and prevention of teen suicide. Allow time for groups to share their work and respond to comments from their classmates.

Investigate. Encourage students to interview therapists, counselors, or other caregivers who offer support for teens who exhibit the warning signs of suicide. Remind students to prepare for the interview by writing at least five questions about the topic. Allow students to summarize each interview and share interesting quotations from their sources.

Close. Ask students to explain why the Surgeon General has initiated a new plan to prevent suicide. Students should discuss how this issue affects national and individual health.

CHECKING COMPREHENSION

- Assign and discuss the chapter review.
- Use the MindJogger Videoquiz to review the chapter. 💿

CHAPTER 10 REVIEW ANSWERS

Using Health Terms

1. hypochondria
2. schizophrenia
3. mental disorder
4. personality disorders
5. bipolar disorder
6. anxiety disorder
7. somatoform disorder
8. affective disorder
9. cluster suicides
10. depression
11. suicide
12. psychiatric social worker
13. neurologist

Recalling the Facts

1. An organic disorder is clearly caused by a physical illness or an injury. A functional disorder occurs as the result of psychological causes.
2. Anxiety disorders: obsessive-compulsive disorder, phobia, panic disorder, post-traumatic stress disorder. Affective disorders: clinical depression, bipolar disorder.
   Personality disorders: antisocial personality disorder, passive-aggressive personality disorder, schizophrenia.
3. Their moods swing between extreme happiness and high energy to deep depression.
4. Answers will vary.
5. Any five: substance abuse; violence; emotional, physical, and sexual abuse; prior suicide attempts; firearms in the home; jail time; a family history of mental disorder; and exposure to other suicides.
6. Overdose on drugs or alcohol and misuse of firearms.

Using Health Terms

On a separate sheet of paper, write the term that best matches each definition below.

LESSON 1

1. A preoccupation with the body and fear of presumed diseases that are not present.
2. A serious mental disorder meaning "split mind."
3. An illness of the mind that can affect the thoughts, feelings, and behaviors of a person, preventing him or her from leading a happy, healthful, and productive life.
4. Psychological conditions that affect a person's ability to get along with others.
5. A psychological illness characterized by extreme mood swings between depression and extreme happiness, or mania.
6. An illness in which real, imagined, or persistent fears prevent a person from enjoying life.
7. An illness in which a person complains of disease symptoms, but no physical cause can be found.
8. A psychological illness often with an organic cause that relates to emotions and involves mood swings or mood extremes that interfere with everyday living.

LESSON 2

9. A rash of suicides occurring within a short space of time and involving several people in the same community.
10. Feelings of helplessness, hopelessness, and sadness.
11. The taking of one's own life.

LESSON 3

12. One who has concentrated on psychiatric casework, doing fieldwork in a mental hospital, mental health clinic, or family service agency.
13. A physician who specializes in organic disorders of the brain and nervous system.

Recalling the Facts

Using complete sentences, answer the following questions.

LESSON 1

1. What is the difference between organic and functional mental disorders?
2. Name two anxiety disorders, two affective disorders, and two personality disorders.
3. What happens to a person who suffers from bipolar disorder?

LESSON 2

4. What are some of the reasons teens experience depression?
5. Name five suicide risk factors.
6. What are the two most frequent ways that accidental suicides occur?

7. What are some of the things someone should *not* do or say to a person thinking of suicide?

LESSON 3

8. Name five signs of mental health disorders.
9. For what reasons would someone seek help from a psychiatrist instead of a clinical psychologist? From a clinical psychologist instead of a psychiatric social worker?
10. Name five places or people where a teen with a mental or emotional problem could turn to for help.

7. Do not treat talk of suicide casually, do not leave the person alone if the threat is immediate, do not agree to keep the person's intentions "a secret," do not avoid talking to the person, do not fail to try to find professional help for the person.
8. Any five: prolonged, unexplained sadness; hopelessness; violent mood shifts; inability to concentrate or make decisions; overwhelming fear, anxiety, or anger; severe sleep disturbances; compulsive behaviors.
9. They have different levels of experience and training, and different levels of treatment options. Which one a person might choose would depend on the seriousness of the problem.

Thinking Critically

LESSON 1

1. **Evaluating.** Evaluate the following statement: "Those with mental disorders should be kept away from the rest of society because they are a potential threat to themselves and others."

LESSON 2

2. **Synthesizing.** Summarize the key strategies used in helping to prevent teen suicide in your school.

LESSON 3

3. **Analyzing.** Look carefully at this statement: *Ignorance is at the root of myths and stereotypes about mental disorders.* How would you support this statement?

4. **Evaluating.** Research individuals who have suffered from mental disorders at some time but moved on to become accomplished members of society. Compare and contrast accomplishments, moods, and relationships when they were mentally ill and when they were healthy.

Making the Connection

1. **Science.** Find out about the new fields of medical science that may have great impact on the understanding and treatment of mental disorders in the future. Choose one area from the following: *psychobiology, chronobiology, psychoneuroimmunology, psychopharmacology, neuroscience.* Read briefly about what this branch of study covers and what kinds of basic research it is adding to the understanding of mental disorders and their treatment. Present your findings to the class in an oral report.

2. **Fine Arts.** Find a painting or piece of music that seems to capture the essence of one of the following disorders: panic disorder, bipolar disorder, or clinical depression. You may create a painting or song.

BEYOND THE CLASSROOM

PARENTAL INVOLVEMENT Parents often tell their children about the physical diseases that tend to "run in the family." With your parents, review the information provided in Lesson 1, then openly discuss people in the family who have had any of these mental disorders diagnosed and treated. Discuss the effects these disorders have had on the family, how and when the person was diagnosed, and if treated, what kinds of treatment were used with what effects. Confidentially discuss with your family how it has handled these individuals?

SCHOOL-TO-CAREER

Exploring Careers. Invite a mental health worker such as a psychiatrist, psychologist, psychiatric nurse, or suicide prevention counselor to your school. Have the person discuss the kinds of disorders people present to them, the treatments or references the worker provides, and the frustrations and rewards of the profession. Also, ask the person to talk about suicide warning signs and specific ways to help potential suicide victims.

Making the Connection

1. Reports will vary.
2. Projects will vary, but should reflect symptoms of the disorder being portrayed.

Evaluate

- Use the reproducible *Chapter 10 Test* in the TCR, or construct your own using the Testmaker software. ☞ 💾
- Use *Performance Assessment Activity 10* in the TCR. ☞

Enrichment

Ask students to complete *Cross-Curriculum Activity 10* in the TCR. ☞

Beyond the Classroom

Keep students involved in the community, and encourage parent participation by assigning the activities on this page for students to work on outside of class.

---

10. A trusted adult, friend, family member, clergy member, physician, coach, teacher, school counselor or nurse, state or community mental health facility, hospital and/or clinic, crisis intervention center.

Building Healthy Relationships

		FEATURES	**CLASSROOM RESOURCES**

"Confronting a Friend," *page 261*

- Concept Map Activity 36
- Decision-Making Activity 11
- Lesson 36 Quiz
- Lesson Plan 36
- Reteaching Activity 36
- Transparency 22

Our Changing World

"Promoting Peace Through Communications," *page 264*

Building Health Skills

"Communication: Agreeing to Disagree," *page 266*

connections
Social Studies

"Communicating Across Cultural Boundaries," *page 268*

- Concept Map Activity 37
- Cooperative Learning Activity 11
- Enrichment Activity 11
- Health Lab 11
- Lesson 37 Quiz
- Lesson Plan 37
- Reteaching Activity 37
- Transparencies 34, 39

Chapter Resources

ACTIVITIES

- Cross-Curriculum Activity 11
- Health Lab 11
- Health Skills Activities 11
- Parent Letters and Activities 11

ASSESSMENT

- Chapter 11 Test
- Performance Assessment Activity 11
- Testmaker Software

STUDENT ACTIVITIES WORKBOOK

- Applying Health Skills 36–37
- Study Guide 11
- Vocabulary Activity 11

STUDENT DIVERSITY STRATEGIES

- Audiocassette Program (English)
- Audiocassette Program (Spanish)
- Spanish Parent Letters and Activities
- Spanish Summaries, Quizzes, and Activities

MULTIMEDIA COMPONENTS

- English Audiocassette Program
- Spanish Audiocassette Program
- MindJogger Videodisc and VHS program
- ABCNews InterActive™ VHS/Videodisc Series

National Health Education Standards

One of the main goals of the National Health Education Standards is to move students toward "health literacy." Health literacy is the capacity of individuals to obtain, interpret, and understand basic health information and services and the competence to use such information and services in ways which promote health. The health standards were developed by applying the characteristics of a well-educated, literate person within the context of health. The health literate person is:

- a critical thinker and problem solver
- a self-directed learner
- a responsible, productive citizen
- an effective communicator

Listed below are the Health Education Standards Performance Indicators addressed in each lesson of this chapter.

Lesson	Health Standards Performance Indicators
1	1.4, 5.2, 5.4, 6.1
2	4.1, 4.3, 5.1, 5.3

ONLINE RESOURCES

For a fresh approach to health topics and an in-depth look at health issues, use these online resources found under Teacher Resources at **health.glencoe.com**.

- **BLOCK SCHEDULE LESSON PLANS** Reinforce health concepts with outside readings selected especially for students. Each reading is accompanied by a lesson plan and activities to enhance
  - Reading Skills
  - Cross Curriculum
  - Media Literacy

- **TECHNOLOGY PROJECTS** Instructions and suggestions on how to use computer, Internet, and software with health lessons.

- **HEALTH UPDATES** Timely topics in health news, including late-breaking medical advances and updates on teen risk behaviors.

Out of Time?

If time does not permit teaching this chapter, you may use these features: Making Responsible Decisions on page 261; Update on page 264; and Building Health Skills on page 266.

BLOCK SCHEDULING

Block scheduling provides extended time for hands-on projects and activities. Use the following activities to engage students, provide further depth, and vary your instructional techniques:

- Update (30 minutes) **pg. 264**
- Connections (30 minutes) **pg. 268**
- Health Skills Activity (60–90 minutes) **pg. 271**

Building Healthy Relationships

CHAPTER OVERVIEW

Building healthy relationships involves learning and using a variety of relationship skills, including communication skills. The types of relationships you develop depend on the traits that each party brings to the relationship and the roles each person assumes.

LESSON 1 Relationships allow us to meet our needs to be loved, safe, secure, valued, and recognized. The bond between individuals shapes more than the social aspects of health. It affects mental and physical health as well. People take on many roles in their relationships, and these roles often switch suddenly or change gradually over time. Friendships and dating provide teenagers opportunities to develop interpersonal skills and to become emotionally mature.

LESSON 2 An essential part of any relationship is the ability to communicate well. Basic communication skills include speaking, listening, and body language. These and other communication techniques can be developed and used to promote effective communication.

CHAPTER 11

Building Healthy Relationships

HEALTH *Online*

COMMUNICATION SKILLS

You live the fast-paced life of a teen, but do you take time out to nurture the relationships you have with family and friends? Computers can make written communication easier. Write a note to someone you care about using a Word Processing program or send an E-Mail Message. See Technology Projects at **health.glencoe.com** for helpful tips on these technologies.

Hands-On Health

TEACHING STRATEGY

Demonstrating Positive Feedback Build a positive classroom climate and improve self-esteem by having students share sincere, positive comments with their peers. See Activity 9, "Pat on the Back," in the *Hands-On Health: Creative Teaching Strategies* booklet. 🖿

Time Needed
30 minutes

Supplies
- "Pat on the Back" student worksheet
- pen or pencil for each student

> *You are a vital resource in and for your community. I challenge you to realize your potential, take up this cause, and reach out to other young people to make their lives better.*
>
> —GENERAL COLIN POWELL
> SECRETARY OF STATE, 2001

Quick Write Think of a teen who serves as a role model for helping others. Complete this sentence: *A person who helps others...*

Personal Health Inventory

Self-Inventory Write the numbers 1–10 on a sheet of paper. Read each statement below and respond by writing *yes*, *no*, or *sometimes* for each item. Write a *yes* only for items that you practice regularly. Save your responses.

1	I treat others with respect.
2	I am a good team player.
3	I am a trustworthy friend.
4	I often use compromise to resolve differences.
5	I am willing to work at my relationships.
6	I communicate well with others.
7	I am a good listener.
8	I ask questions if I'm not sure what is being said.
9	I use eye contact when communicating with others.
10	I am aware of my own body language.

Follow-up After completing the chapter, retake this self-inventory. Pick two items that you need to work on and set a goal to improve your health behaviors.

CHAPTER 11 BUILDING HEALTHY RELATIONSHIPS **257**

INTRODUCING THE CHAPTER

Personal Health Inventory

Let students read and discuss the Self-Inventory statements: How do the habits identified relate to building and maintaining healthy relationships? After a brief discussion, have students label the page "My Relationships" and record their inventory responses in their private Health Journals. They will refer to these journal entries again when they have finished studying the chapter lessons.

- Ask students to brainstorm and list the qualities of a friend. Have them then consider which of these characteristics they personally display on a consistent basis.
- Let volunteers describe the individuals shown in the photographs on pages 256 and 257. What kind of relationships do those depicted in each photo seem to have with the others in that scene? How do you think they developed that kind of relationship? Then, let students read the quotation on this page and encourage volunteers to list service groups or programs that teens can become involved with to reach out to others.
- Distribute Parent Letter 11 in the *Parent Letters and Activities* booklet.

TECHNOLOGY OPTIONS

 You may wish to use *Making Responsible Decisions* and *Violence Prevention* with this chapter. For your convenience, use the separate *ABCNews InterActive™ Bar Code Correlation* that accompanies the *Glencoe Health* program.

MINDJOGGER
VIDEOQUIZ

To preview or review chapter content, you may wish to use the *MindJogger Videoquiz* that accompanies Chapter 11.

LESSON 1

Getting Along with Others

Getting Along with Others

FOCUS

LESSON OBJECTIVES

After studying this lesson, students should be able to

- define the terms *relationship* and *role* and identify the needs that relationships fulfill.
- identify the traits that are present in a healthy relationship.

MOTIVATOR

Write the following on the chalkboard for students to work on while attendance is being taken: *Write the names of several people with whom you interact regularly. Include family members, people from your neighborhood, and people from school.*

INTRODUCING THE LESSON

Refer to the Motivator. Ask volunteers to share their lists. Tell students that the people they named are those with whom they have relationships—connections that satisfy basic emotional needs. Have volunteers describe their roles in the relationships they listed. Use their examples to illustrate how roles vary from one relationship to another and change within the same relationship, depending on the circumstances. Tell them that this lesson focuses on the characteristics and roles of healthy relationships.

INTRODUCING HEALTH TERMS

- Ask students to explain how the following terms are related to one another and how they differ: *relationship, friendship, role.*
- Have students complete Vocabulary Activity 11 and Chapter Study Guide 11 in the *Student Workbook.*

According to psychologist Abraham Maslow, everyone needs to be loved and to belong. Each of us also needs to feel safe, secure, valued, and recognized. By forming relationships, we are able to meet many of these basic human needs. Good relationships can affect a person's mental, social, and even physical health.

HEALTH TERMS

relationship
friendship
role
cooperation
compromise
empathy

HEALTH CONCEPTS

- Relationships affect your physical, mental, and social health.
- You play many different roles in your relationships with others.
- Cooperation and compromise are important aspects of a healthy relationship.
- Mutual trust and respect are cornerstones of a responsible relationship.
- Good relationships take time and energy.

Who Matters to You?

Think of standing in one of those photo booths where you and a friend pull a curtain, drop your coins into a slot, and get back three connected photos of the two of you. You are smiling or laughing, your faces side by side. Now imagine that you could have these three shots showing you with three different people with whom you have a significant connection—say, from your family; from your extended family, such as a grandparent or cousin; from your neighborhood; and from your school. Who would be with you in the photos?

You have many relationships in your life that affect you. A **relationship** *is a bond or connection between people.* You are part of a network of people that includes your family, extended family, neighbors, friends, as well as people from social or religious organizations, sports teams, your town or city, your nation, and the world.

Lesson 1 Resources

TEACHER'S CLASSROOM RESOURCES

- **Concept Map** Activity 36
- **Decision-Making** Activity 11
- **Lesson 36 Quiz**
- **Lesson Plan 36**
- **Parent Letter and Activities 11**
- **Reteaching** Activity 36

STUDENT WORKBOOK

- **Applying Health Skills 36**
- **Chapter Study Guide 11**
- **Vocabulary** Activity 11

TRANSPARENCIES

- **Transparency 22**

MULTIMEDIA

- **ABCNews InterActive™,** *Teenage Sexuality*

If you were suddenly plunked down on a desert island and removed from all of these relationships, you might like the peace and quiet for a short time, but chances are you would soon begin to get very lonely. Having relationships with others can, in fact, not only ward off loneliness; it can also have a direct effect on a person's total health.

Choosing Relationships

A s a small child, you had a limited circle of relationships. Now that you are older, you have a larger circle from which to choose your relationships. You may realize for the first time that there are people of all ages, races, religions, and backgrounds from which you can choose relationships. You can choose people who support and encourage your best qualities. You can change or back out of relationships that have a negative influence on your health, your safety, your self-esteem, or your values. No relationship can be healthy unless both parties feel valued and want the relationship.

Friendship

Whether you want to go to the movies or just chat, you turn to a friend. A **friendship** is *a significant relationship between two people based on caring, consideration, and trust.* A friend is someone whose companionship you enjoy and who can be a source of help when you have a problem. A friend also may be someone with whom you share confidences, interests, hobbies, or other friends. **Friendships** vary in importance and in how challenging and complicated they are. Maintaining friendships can be hard work, but it is often well worth the effort.

Family Relationships

Who do you turn to when you are sick or injured or need food, clothing, or a hug? You probably turn to someone in your family. **Family relationships** provide the strongest bonds with others. These are bonds that last a lifetime. Parents or guardians provide love and care for their children, as well as teach values and give guidance.

hotlink

friendships For more information on friendships and the qualities of a good friend, see Chapter 13, page 298.

family relationships For more information on family relationships and properties of a healthy family, see Chapter 12, page 276.

▼ *Relationships and roles are part of your everyday life.*

ACTIVITY *Name several different kinds of relationships and roles that you experience each day.*

LESSON 1 GETTING ALONG WITH OTHERS **259**

TEACH

L1 Class Activity

Divide students into several discussion groups. Have the members of each group brainstorm and record two lists: one of the benefits of spending time alone, the other of the benefits of having relationships with other people. Ask: Which list is longer? Why?

L1 Discussing

Ask: Do all your friends have to be other teens? What are some of the special benefits of having friends younger or older—perhaps much older—than you are? Encourage volunteers to share some of their experiences with friends of different ages.

hotlink

friendships
Everyone needs relationships, as they contribute to total health. Have students consider the ways that their friends contribute to their health. Ask them to jot down their thoughts in their private Health Journals.

Visual Learning

Relationships and Roles

Refer students to the photograph on this page. Ask: What roles does this teen have? (brother, friend, student) Then, have students list all the roles they play during an average week. Let a few volunteers write their lists on the chalkboard. As a class, go through the lists and discuss the behavior that is expected in each role. Encourage students to identify which roles are relatively clear-cut as guides to behavior and which are more ambiguous or situation dependent. Explain that roles help relationships go more smoothly by guiding our behavior and helping us to understand the behavior of others.

PERSONAL HEALTH

FRIENDSHIPS AND SELF-ESTEEM. Friends have a major impact on a teen's self-esteem. Often teens are eager to make new friends, only to discover that the new "friend" does not have the qualities that make a friendship valuable. Ask students to share their experiences about new friends who did not make good friends.

Did they ever have new friends who turned out to be hurtful or cruel? Ask them to explain how they felt about the situation and what they did to recover from it. Discuss general strategies for learning to trust again after being hurt by such a friend.

L1 Class Activity

Allow students to brainstorm the personal qualities they feel are important in friends. List these on the chalkboard as students call them out. Narrow down the list to about 10 qualities that the class agrees are the most important. Ask: Why do you think these particular qualities are important to have in a friend?

CHARACTER IN ACTION

Give and Take: The Golden Rule

Explain that the Golden, or "reciprocal" rule exists in cultures and beliefs around the world. Ask students to read the feature and give examples of relationships in their lives or in literature, the news, or history that seem to be truly reciprocal. Discuss the importance of core ethical values in healthful relationships.

L2 Language Arts

Suggest that students make a new friend from a different culture by getting a pen pal. Have them write to: World Pen Pals, P.O. Box 337, Saugerties, NY 12477.

CHARACTER IN ACTION

Give and Take: The Golden Rule

When a friendship is healthful, it is full of give and take. It follows one of the basic rules of ethics, sometimes called the Golden Rule. That means you treat others the way you would like to be treated, looking out for their well-being and interests as you would your own.

Character Check Think about one significant relationship in your life and whether or not the following traits of a healthful relationship apply:

➤ We value and support each other's highest values.

➤ We share feelings and thoughts.

➤ We keep each other's confidences.

➤ We help one another and neither person dominates the friendship.

➤ We each feel free to spend time with each other, alone, and with others.

➤ We leave room for personal growth and change.

Each person plays many different roles in relationships.

ACTIVITY *Name some of the relationship roles a teenager might play.*

Relationships in the Community

Your relationships extend beyond family and friends into your community. Community leaders and citizens work together for safety and to provide health services and to meet the needs of all community members. Cities and counties often sponsor classes or recreation activities at a local park. Neighbors organize block clubs. Businesses provide the community with needed products and services.

Your Many Roles

You take on many roles in your relationships with others. A **role** is *a part that you play,* especially in a relationship. You may be a sister or brother, a daughter or son; a granddaughter or grandson; a member of the orchestra; a member of the volleyball team; a Scout; a student; an employee; a member of a synagogue, church, or mosque; and even someone's boyfriend or girlfriend—all at the same time.

Sometimes the roles you play are clear-cut. You know that when you mow the neighbor's lawn or wash his or her car, you are an employee and need to act as one. Sometimes, though, roles either switch suddenly or change gradually, depending on needs and situations. For example, some days you may be the caregiver for your disabled grandfather, but at other times he is the teacher and you are the student. Perhaps your lab partner becomes the person you date. Such changes in roles can be confusing. Sometimes you may not have a clue as to what your role is in a relationship. This can make it difficult for you to know how to act.

CURRICULUM CONNECTIONS

FOREIGN LANGUAGE. Invite foreign language teachers to demonstrate and explain rules regarding the correct pronunciation of various first and last names.

DRAMA. Select students to write and perform a skit based on the following scenario: Maria, a peer mediator, is beginning a mediation session with John and Carla, who are both running for class president. Each has accused the other of destroying his or her political signs. Their adviser has suggested peer mediation. John feels positively about peer mediation because he has seen it work. Carla is unsure about the process. She fears John will get his way, and she will have to drop out of the race. After the skit, ask students to evaluate the actions of all three characters.

The Healthy Relationship

A relationship consists of not only two people but also the many ways in which they relate. For a relationship to succeed, certain traits must be present.

Cooperation

A basketball team could not win a championship without teamwork. In relationships, teamwork is called **cooperation**, *working together for the good of all*. Some activities are impossible without cooperation. Susan fixes supper each night because her parents don't get home from work until six o'clock. Because of her help, the family is able to eat supper together at night. Working together through cooperation is one good way to build strong relationships.

Compromise

Jeremy wants to see a movie, but Alexis wants to play miniature golf. Have you ever found yourself in a situation like theirs? Do you remember how you solved the problem? You probably used compromise. **Compromise** is *the result of each person's giving up something in order to reach a solution that satisfies everyone.*

The "give and take" of compromise helps a relationship run smoothly. When done effectively, compromise strengthens relationships. It is a way of letting the other person know how much you value the friendship. You can learn the skills of compromise through practice. To compromise, seek a solution that is acceptable to all persons involved. Realize that you must be willing to give up something in order to reach a solution.

Making Responsible Decisions

Confronting a Friend

Carlotta and Sondra have been close friends for several years. Lately, though, Sondra has noticed a change in Carlotta. The two friends used to meet at their lockers after school. Twice in the past week, Carlotta had told Sondra she would be there, but then hadn't shown up. The last time it happened, Sondra walked home alone. The next day, she heard from another friend that Carlotta had been telling people that Sondra was "boring." What should Sondra do?

What Would You Do?

Apply the six steps of the decision-making process to Sondra's problem.

1. **State the situation.**
2. **List the options.**
3. **Weigh the possible outcomes.**
4. **Consider your values.**
5. **Make a decision and act.**
6. **Evaluate the decision.**

PERSONAL HEALTH

FRIENDSHIP QUALITIES. Like all infants, students were once entirely self-involved and concerned with their own needs and desires. Have students list in their private Health Journals the number of times in the last 24 hours they have said or done something against their own inclinations in order to be fair, comply with a rule, keep the peace, protect someone's feelings, or maintain a friendship. Suggest they relate these compromises to the abilities, qualities, and understandings humans must develop before they can form friendships. Call on volunteers to share parts of their entries.

Making Responsible Decisions

1. Sondra is concerned that her close friend is beginning to reject her.
2. Sondra could (a) ignore Carlotta's unfriendly acts and pretend the friendship is unchanged; (b) discuss Carlotta's behavior with her; (c) reject Carlotta before Carlotta rejects her completely.
3. Sondra might (a) continue to feel hurt and find herself spending increasing amounts of time on her own; (b) discover what Carlotta's interests and concerns are, and perhaps find a way of redefining or reaffirming her friendship with Carlotta; (c) avoid being hurt by Carlotta, but lose the friendship.
4. Sondra values her friendship with Carlotta. However, she also values being treated with respect and consideration.
5. Responses will vary.
6. Encourage students to consider both the short- and long-term consequences of the decisions they make.

L2 Decision Making

For further study on making responsible decisions, assign *Decision-Making Activity 11* in the TCR.

TEENAGE SEXUALITY (Side 2)

Chapter 3: Self-Esteem and Sexuality

Frames 2008-4673

Chapter 4: Relationships: The Girl's Perspective

Frames 4675-6777

ABCNEWS INTERACTIVE™

TEENAGE SEXUALITY (Side 2)

Chapter 5: Relationships: The Boy's Perspective

Frames 6779-9045

Chapter 6: Talking to Your Parents

Frames 9047-12537

ASSESS

EVALUATING THE LESSON

Assign and discuss the Lesson 1 Review; then administer, grade, and discuss the *Lesson 36 Quiz.* 📂

RETEACHING

- Ask students to examine and write about a relationship they have with a relative or close friend. They should describe the various roles each of them plays to make the relationship work (e.g., helper, companion, adviser, etc.).
- Have the class complete *Reteaching Activity 36* in the TCR. 📂
- Use *Transparency 22* to review responsibilities associated with various roles. 🧴

ENRICHMENT

Sociology is the scientific study of human relationships or group life. Provide several books on the topic for students to browse through and expand their knowledge of relationships and social responsibility.

CLOSE

Summarize the lesson by reviewing the traits of a healthy relationship.

CHARACTER IN ACTION

Fairness in Friendship

Fairness is an important quality in a friendship. Whether you are facing a peer in a student council election or competing with a friend on the tennis court, fairness is a principle that respects the abilities, needs, and contributions of all parties. Fairness means:

➤ knowing and following the rules.

➤ participating without cheating or manipulation.

➤ taking into account the needs and rights of all parties.

➤ not showing favorites or excluding others because of your own prejudices.

Character Check Make a list of situations where you think you might have treated someone else unfairly. Now imagine how that unfair treatment may have made another person feel.

Not all disagreements can be resolved through compromise. If your friend wants you to do something that is against the law, for example, you cannot compromise. In situations like these, it is important to stand your ground. Learning when—and when *not*—to compromise is another worthwhile relationship skill.

Other Traits of a Healthy Relationship

What qualities do you look for in a friend? Most people seek the following basic traits.

- **Respect.** Mutual respect is important in friendships. Friends may not agree on all issues, such as religious views, but they can show respect for the other person's viewpoint.
- **Acceptance.** No one is perfect. Accepting others and being accepted leads to strong, healthy relationships.
- **Honesty.** Relationships are built on honesty. Lying about your actions or your feelings can tear relationships apart.
- **Trustworthiness.** Friends trust each other. If you trust someone, you know they won't do anything to hurt you.
- **Dependability.** A dependable friend is there when you need someone. You can anticipate receiving the person's help.
- **Loyalty.** A loyal friend speaks kindly of you even when you are not around.
- **Empathy.** *The ability to share another person's feelings or thoughts* is called **empathy.** If a friend feels sad because of a loss, for example, you "feel for" the person, sharing his or her sadness as well.

LESSON 1 *Review*

Reviewing Facts and Vocabulary

1. Explain some of the different roles people play in relationships.
2. Describe relationships in a community.
3. Tell why compromise is an important trait in a relationship.
4. Explain how the trait of empathy adds to a relationship.

Thinking Critically

5. *Synthesizing.* Suppose your family plans to go out to a family reunion. One member wants to see the school's final basketball playoff game. Explain a plan that would resolve this problem using compromise.

6. *Evaluating.* Emiko makes all the decisions as to what she and her friend, Kate, do when they are together. What relationship trait is missing? How could the relationship be improved?

Applying Health Skills

7. *In Your Home and School.* Analyze an important relationship in your life by making a three-column chart. In the first column, list the traits of a healthy relationship from the above list. In the second column, describe the relationship in each area. In the third column, tell what you could do to improve your relationship in that area.

262   CHAPTER 11   BUILDING HEALTHY RELATIONSHIPS

Lesson 1 Review

Answers to Reviewing Facts and Vocabulary

1. Answers may include: son/daughter, brother/sister, student, community member, employee.
2. Answers should include: citizen, leader, business, and neighbor relationships.
3. The ability to compromise is an indication that the relationship is more important than what each person wants at the moment.

4. Sharing the thoughts and feelings of the other person helps to strengthen the relationship and make it meaningful.

Answers to Thinking Critically

5. Answers will vary.
6. Compromise is the missing trait. The relationship could be improved by talking over what each person wants and making decisions together.

Communicating Effectively

To be a good athlete, you need to possess many skills. Skill development takes time and practice. In the same way, to build healthy relationships, you need to practice and master a variety of skills. Among the most important of these are skills related to the act of communication.

HEALTH TERMS

communication
"I" message
active listening
body language
constructive criticism

HEALTH CONCEPTS

- There are many ways to communicate with others.
- Effective communication means being a good listener as well as a good speaker.
- An aspect of good communication is making sure your body language and verbal communication are in sync.

Communication

Think about the messages you send to others and the messages others send to you. Think not only of messages expressed in words but also of those you deliver in the form of gestures, facial expressions, and behaviors. All of these are a part of **communication**. This is *a process through which you send messages to and receive messages from others*.

Communication is critical because it lets others know what you feel, what you want and need, and what you know. Effective communication is a two-way street. It means sending messages that are interpreted correctly, and it means correctly interpreting messages that you receive.

There are three basic skills associated with effective communication: speaking, listening, and body language. Although these skills take practice and energy, the time and effort are worth it because it helps you form healthy relationships with others.

Lesson 2 Resources

TEACHER'S CLASSROOM RESOURCES

- **Concept Map** Activity 37
- **Cooperative Learning** Activity 11
- **Enrichment** Activity 11
- **Health Lab** 11
- **Lesson 37 Quiz**
- **Lesson Plan 37**
- **Reteaching** Activity 37

STUDENT WORKBOOK

- **Applying Health Skills 37**
- **Chapter Study Guide 11**
- **Vocabulary** Activity 11

TRANSPARENCIES

 Transparencies 34, 39

MULTIMEDIA

ABCNews InterActive™, *Violence Prevention*

Communicating Effectively

FOCUS

LESSON OBJECTIVES

After studying this lesson, students should be able to

- describe characteristics of speech.
- state the techniques used by active listeners.
- give examples of nonverbal communication.
- describe barriers to effective communication.
- explain the role of constructive criticism.

MOTIVATOR

Write the following on the chalkboard for students to work on while attendance is being taken: *List ten things you communicated today and the communication methods you used.*

INTRODUCING THE LESSON

Ask several students to share their responses to the Motivator. It is likely that their lists will contain only verbal communication. From the responses, pick an example of verbal communication that probably was accompanied by a great deal of inflection and body language. Have a student role-play what was said, using actions, expressions, and inflections. Let another student simply read the line. Compare and contrast reading the line and role-playing it. Ask the class to describe the differences between the two.

INTRODUCING HEALTH TERMS

Ask students to complete Vocabulary Activity 11 and Chapter Study Guide 11 in the *Student Workbook.*

TEACH

Ask students to explore the subject of communcations skills further using the Web Links or other resources. You may wish to set aside class time for a Q & A on the topic.

L1 Discussing

Help students discuss the steps in the communication process. Ask: When you and a friend have a face-to-face conversation, which one sends messages? *(both)* Which receives messages? *(both)* What happens to the communication process if your friend stops paying attention while you are talking? *(It breaks down, because messages are no longer being received.)* How is the communication process altered when you and the same friend talk on the phone? *(Facial expressions and gestures no longer help to send the intended messages.)* What happens when you and the same friend "talk" via e-mail? *(Besides facial expressions and gestures, tone of voice is also not available to help send messages.)*

up|date
▶ *Our Changing World*

Promoting Peace through Communication

Let students read the feature title. Ask: How can promoting good speaking and listening skills help develop peaceful relationships among people? How does prejudice arise from not communicating effectively? Then let students read the feature to learn more about how effective communication can foster peace and understanding. Have students meet in groups to compare their responses to the first question. For the second activity, talking with someone of a different religion, race, or culture, have students write two paragraphs describing what they learned from the other person.

At **health.glencoe.com**, find out how to improve your speaking and listening skills to help you in effective communication.

Speaking Skills

Having good speaking skills means saying clearly what you mean. Do not assume that anyone else can read your mind or know your needs or expectations. It is your responsibility to make them clear. This is the first step to healthy communication.

The changes in your tone of voice and its pitch and loudness can also play a large role in how you communicate. Kind words delivered with a sarcastic tone, for example, may not be processed kindly. Speaking too loudly can make you sound bossy or arrogant, even if you are shy. Saying no too softly makes it seem as if you don't mean what you are saying. So it is not just *what* you say that is important to communicating but *how* you say it.

ANTAGONISTIC MESSAGE	CONSTRUCTIVE "I" MESSAGE
You idiot! What have you done with my baseball glove?	I dislike when you borrow my things and don't return them.
Why do we always have to do what you want to do?	I'll agree to go swimming today if I get to pick the activity next time we're together.
You're always late! I don't know why I even bother being your friend.	I worry about you when I expect to meet you at 6:00 and you don't show up.

An important step in the communication process, especially when the message to be delivered has a strong emotional content, is the use of "I" messages. An **"I" message** is *a statement in which a person tells how he or she feels using the pronoun "I."* Using "I" messages can help you avoid blaming, name-calling, or antagonizing the other person in other ways.

up|date
▶ *Our Changing World*

Promoting Peace through Communication

In the aftermath of a tragedy or an act of violence, a natural human reaction is to look for someone to blame. Feelings of anger and fear sometimes cause people to try to fight back in an effort to gain control or feel that they are taking an active role. Problems can arise, however, if people react with prejudice or intolerance by condemning an entire group of people based on the actions of a few.

When we accept the differences in others, we open new lines of communication and improve relationships. Using effective communication skills can keep the doors open to promote peace and understanding among all people.

1. Describe how you could be a good role model for children, promoting peace through understanding.

2. Initiate a discussion with someone of a different religion, race, or culture from you. Encourage that person to share information about special traditions, customs, or rituals practiced in his or her culture.

SCHOOL-TO-CAREER

EMPLOYMENT AD. Have students choose an occupation that demands good relationship and communication skills. If students need suggestions, provide the following list of job positions: a manager of an automobile impound yard, a store manager, a public relations manager for a corporation or government agency, a bill collector, a manager of a homeless shelter, press secretary to the president, a police officer, a real estate agent, and a receptionist in a busy office.

Ask students to write a help-wanted ad for the position they choose. In the ad, they should describe the relationship and communication skills desired.

Listening Skills

Listening is as important to effective communication as speaking, but it is the part of the communication process that is most often overlooked. Of the 80 percent of our waking hours that we spend communicating, we spend a high proportion of that time as hearers rather than as speakers. Hearing, however, is not the same as listening. Consider that the average listener correctly understands, properly evaluates, and retains only about 30 percent of what he or she hears in a 10-minute presentation. Within 48 hours, memory of what was said drops to an even lower percentage.

Skilled listeners use **active listening,** *really paying attention to what someone is saying and feeling.* Active listening involves careful attention to what the speaker is saying without making judgments or interrupting. Active listeners incorporate these listening techniques:

- **Reflective listening.** In reflective listening, you rephrase or summarize what the other person has said so that you are sure you understand what is intended.

- **Clarifying.** Clarifying is asking the person how he or she feels about the situation or asking questions to understand more fully what is being said.

- **Encouraging.** Encouraging is giving signals that you are really interested and involved. You can show your interest by quietly saying "Uh-huh" or "I understand" or "I see."

- **Empathizing.** Empathizing is actually feeling the other person's feelings as you listen. If a person is sad, an empathetic listener feels sad, too. If the person talking is angry, the listener feels angry, too.

▼ *A good friend is able to empathize with another friend's feelings.*

ACTIVITY *Name several other communication skills that are important to a good friendship.*

LESSON 2 COMMUNICATING EFFECTIVELY **265**

L1 Explaining

Frequently, students are unaware that there are several different types of listening. Introduce and compare attentive listening and selective listening. Selective listening is used to hear only enough of what is spoken to allow the listener to argue or to support a previously held point of view. Attentive listening allows students to hear not only what is spoken, but also the feelings that are being communicated.

L1 Parental Involvement

To enhance good listening skills at home, have students ask their parents about the possibility of turning the TV off during mealtime so that family communication can take place with fewer distractions.

L2 Cooperative Learning

Divide the class into groups of three: a speaker, an active listener, and an observer. Assign topics for the groups to talk about. Use time limits. Have the observer determine if good listening rules are being followed. After the speaker has spoken and the listener has paraphrased what has been said, have the observer tell them what he or she observed that was done well and where improvements could be made.

L1 Discussing

Use *Transparencies 34* and *39* to review communication strategies and listening techniques.

L2 Cooperative Learning

Have students complete *Cooperative Learning Activity 11,* "How Well Do You Listen?" in the TCR.

MORE ABOUT . . . . .

LISTENING. Jumping to conclusions is a common fault among listeners. By assuming they know what is coming next, they can seriously damage their understanding of what is actually being said at that very moment and for the rest of the conversation. Instead of continuing to listen, they lose the speaker's flow and become mired in their own thoughts.

SOUND BARRIERS. People can think much faster than most people can talk. As a result, their thoughts often race ahead of the speaker. Good listeners use the extra time to summarize the speaker's ideas, evaluate the strength and logic of the speaker's arguments, and respond nonverbally to what they hear.

Listen Up!

Use the tips in the feature and other listening skills discussed in the lesson to create a class rubric. The rubric is like an evaluation card with a scale for rating each skill. Allow groups of four to share what they would do on the perfect vacation. As one person shares his or her dream plan, a second person should rate the other two members of the group on their listening skills. As students rotate roles, have them share their scored rubrics as feedback.

L3 Researching

Have students research body language and compile the information in a written or oral report to present to the class.

Building Health Skills

Agreeing to Disagree
Skill: Communication

Let students generate a list of questions on which teens and their friends often disagree. Then ask: What do you do when you and a friend disagree about one of these questions? What can you both do to keep the disagreement friendly? Do you think it's necessary for every disagreement to end with a winner and a loser? After students have shared their ideas, let them read the Building Health Skills feature to learn more about this topic. As a follow-up activity, have pairs of volunteers plan and present skits in which teens handle a disagreement successfully.

L2 Health Lab

Distribute *Health Lab 11* and have students learn more about "body language." ✒

Listen Up!

Here are some other tips for becoming a more effective listener:

➤ Give your full attention to the person speaking.

➤ Make direct eye contact.

➤ Do not interrupt. Wait your turn.

➤ Listen for feelings and watch for gestures. These are as much or more of a clue than words are.

Nonverbal Communication

Not all communication takes place on a verbal level. People send many messages through **body language**—*nonverbal communication through gestures, facial expressions, and behaviors.* Waving your hand to say good-bye is an example of body language. So is bringing your hands up to your mouth when you are surprised.

Most nonverbal communication is subtle and often takes place on a subconscious level. A person who is feeling embarrassed or ashamed may look at the ground when speaking rather than at his or her listener. Maybe you have found yourself leaning toward a speaker who was saying something of great interest to you.

Being aware of your body language helps you make sure you are sending the messages you intend and that those messages are understood. If your words and your face or body seem to be saying two different things, the other person may be confused or unsure of what to think or believe.

Building Health Skills

Communication: Agreeing to Disagree

IT'S NOT REALISTIC to think that you and your friends will agree on everything. When you disagree, think of it as an opportunity to learn how to handle disagreements in relationships. Follow these steps:

1. **Give the person a turn to speak.** Each of you deserves the same chance to state your opinion without hostility or rebuke from the other person. Avoid shouting the person down. Keep your ears—and mind—open.

2. **Use "I" messages.** Even if your position is not accepted by the other person, you will feel better in the end if you express your beliefs and feelings in an appropriate way.

3. **Stick to the subject.** At the height of a disagreement, it is easy to lose track of what you are arguing about. Don't bring the person's character or personality into the discussion. Avoid appeals to other people's opinions as well. They are irrelevant to the situation at hand.

4. **Keep the tone friendly.** Remember, this is a friend you are dealing with—someone whose companionship you value. If your friend holds a different view from yours on a particular topic, remember that tastes vary from individual to individual. You can still enjoy your friendship on many other levels.

266 CHAPTER 11 BUILDING HEALTHY RELATIONSHIPS

HOME AND COMMUNITY CONNECTION

RELATIONSHIPS AND SOCIETY. Born entirely self-centered, humans must learn social skills before they can have true relationships. Everyone, including students, had to start at the beginning. Even learning to perceive others as people, with feelings and rights, is a long and difficult process that some people never complete. The socialization process helps humans learn to get along with others in society.

Ask students to list the cultural and relationship skills they have learned and decide whether they learned each skill from family, school, or community. Have them identify which skills children and teens are usually taught, and which ones are usually learned through observation.

Barriers to Effective Communication

A chain, it is said, is only as strong as its weakest link. The same may be said of communication. When one person in a relationship uses communication skills and another does not, the entire communication process is impeded. Other obstacles to effective communication include the following:

- **Unrealistic expectations.** If your goal is to help another person understand your feelings, you need to be prepared for the reality that he or she will not receive the message in the spirit you intended. The person may become defensive and feel attacked.

- **The need to project a tough or superior image.** During the teen years it is common to search for an **identity**—a sense of who you are and your place in the world. This search prompts some teens to develop a rough exterior or an attitude of superiority, which can make them hard to reach.

- **Prejudice.** **Prejudice** is an unfair opinion or judgment against a particular group of people. The term comes from the word *prejudge,* which means to judge without sufficient information or knowledge. Prejudice can keep one person from hearing what another is really saying and from freely communicating his or her own ideas.

When people put up communication barriers like these, there is little you can do. You simply need to accept the situation for what it is and move on. If you have made an effort yourself to follow the rules of good communication, you can at least walk away with the satisfaction of knowing you have done all you can in the interest of a healthy relationship.

h⊙t link

identity For more on the search for identity during the teen years, see Chapter 21, page 482.

prejudice For more information on prejudice and how it harms relationships, see Chapter 13, page 300.

◄ *Many statements and feelings are communicated through body language or facial expressions.*

ACTIVITY *Name the statement or emotion expressed by the gestures and facial expressions in each photo. Tell which ones the "speaker" might be doing unconsciously.*

LESSON 2   COMMUNICATING EFFECTIVELY   **267**

L2 Writing

Have students think about their responses to these questions: What identity do you try to communicate to the people around you? How does your appearance and your attitude support that identity? How do you think that identity affects your communication with your peers? with adults? Suggest that students record their responses by writing entries in their private Health Journals.

L2 Class Activity

Assign students to watch a television or movie drama or situation comedy. Have students identify and discuss specific examples of obstacles to effective communication between the characters.

VIOLENCE PREVENTION
(Side 2)

Chapter 9: Sending "I" Messages

Frames 22923-30681

Chapter 10: Active Listening

Frames 30699-35410

Chapter 11: Communication Skills and Barriers

Frames 35422-41640

COOPERATIVE ⟩ LEARNING

ADVICE COLUMN. Divide the class into groups. Have each member bring to class an advice column about a relationship problem. Tell them to separate the description of the problem from the columnist's advice. Have members take turns reading aloud the descriptions of the problems in the advice columns they contributed. Other group members should discuss the problems and agree upon the advice. If they cannot agree, they should propose advice separately. Then have the student who brought the column read the columnist's advice. Ask other members to compare their advice with that of the columnist.

L1 Class Activity

Help students generate a list of situations in which a teen is disappointed in or disapproves of another person's behavior. Record their ideas on the board. Then have students suggest constructive criticism the teen might use in each situation.

connections
Social Studies

Communicating Across Cultural Boundaries

Let volunteers share what they already know about the influence of culture on styles of communication. Students may have had experiences either within their own families or with friends, visitors, or family friends from other cultural backgrounds. After a brief introductory discussion, tell students to read the Connections feature to learn more about cultural influences on communication etiquette. Then have students work in groups to discuss each scenario and demonstrate how it would be handled in their culture. Suggest that groups develop other scenarios to be shared with the rest of the class.

L1 Discussing

Ask: Why are acknowledgments and compliments so effective in improving the health of a relationship? Why do so many people find it difficult to accept compliments? What are some appropriate responses to sincere compliments?

▼ *Accept constructive criticism positively. This is one way you can learn from others and improve yourself.*

ACTIVITY *Name an example of how a critical statement can be turned into constructive criticism.*

Constructive Criticism

No one, not even your best friend or parent, is perfect. It's not realistic to think that you won't be disappointed in a relationship at least occasionally. Perhaps your brother suddenly hogs the TV remote, insisting that you watch his show, not yours. A friend that you were to meet in front of the theater is late, causing you to miss the beginning of the movie. The dry cleaners loses or damages your favorite sweater.

Giving feedback to the person can be helpful to him or her as well as to your relationship. Make sure you use **constructive criticism,** *non-hostile comments that point out problems and have the potential to help a person change.* Using constructive criticism means that you avoid attacking the other person. It means not placing blame or resorting to name-calling. You might want to start with an "I" message. Then point out what the person is doing or has done,

connections
Social Studies

Communicating Across Cultural Boundaries

Terrell thought Enrique wasn't friendly because Enrique always looked at the ground when they talked. Then Terrell found out that, in Enrique's culture, looking someone in the eyes is considered rude. Becoming aware of various communication styles will help you communicate better with persons from different cultures. Read each scenario below. Describe how the same task or custom is handled in your culture.

1. Tanya greets her friends by kissing them on both cheeks.

2. Franklin stands about six inches away from friends as he talks.

3. Autumn makes immediate eye contact with her friends and maintains the eye contact throughout their conversation.

4. While in the audio store at the mall, Vernon nods his head toward a particular compact disc to show his friend the kind of music he likes.

268 CHAPTER 11 BUILDING HEALTHY RELATIONSHIPS

HEALTH LITERACY

COMMUNICATION SKILLS. Have students work in groups to brainstorm a list of situations that require effective listening. If they need help, suggest these examples: (1) one person wants a loan from a friend who does not like lending money, (2) two teens are dating and one wants to break up, (3) one teen wants to get ice cream with a friend who is trying to stick to healthy food choices, (4) one teen tells another about a crisis at home.

Ask students to role-play the situations twice, first using poor listening skills, then using more effective ones. Encourage other group members to offer suggestions.

and describe a better way to do it. You might say to your friend, "I really dislike missing the opening of the picture. Please try to arrive earlier next time." What might you say to the dry cleaners?

▼ *A pat on the back and praise for a job well done leads to healthful relationships.*

ACTIVITY *Describe situations in which you can encourage someone by offering compliments.*

Acknowledgments and Compliments

Have you ever received a thank-you note or a verbal pat on the back for a job well done? Have you ever given one? Complimenting another person is a way of acknowledging his or her self worth. Unlike other forms of communication, acknowledgments and compliments are not necessarily done with an eye toward receiving a response. Yet, these small, unexpected gestures can go a long way toward improving the health of a relationship and another person's opinion of you.

Some compliments are given to acknowledge a skill or to show appreciation. An example would be telling a family member how much you enjoyed a meal he or she cooked. Other compliments are purely selfless—for example, telling another person that he or she looks nice. Still others are *self-effacing.* They are kind words offered at the expense of your own pride or personal feelings. Congratulating the team that defeats yours is an example of a self-effacing compliment.

ASSESS

EVALUATING THE LESSON

Assign and discuss the Lesson 2 Review; then administer, grade, and discuss the *Lesson 37 Quiz* in the TCR. 📩

RETEACHING

- Divide the class into small groups. Hand each group a card with a situation written on it that requires an acknowledgment, a compliment, or constructive criticism. Ask students to role-play the situations to practice these communication skills. Have the groups exchange cards for more practice.
- Have students complete *Reteaching Activity 37* in the TCR. 📩

ENRICHMENT

- Ask students to watch a variety of TV programs, such as a sitcom, a documentary, or a movie. Lead a discussion of the means of communication portrayed. Have students evaluate the effectiveness of each type.
- Give students listening and other communication tools to help them build close relationships by having them complete *Enrichment Activity 11,* "You Know What I'm Saying?" in the TCR. 📩

CLOSE

Ask students to state the most important concepts learned in the lesson, and have them explain how they will use the skills when they leave the classroom.

LESSON **2** *Review*

Reviewing Facts and Vocabulary

1. Name and describe two basic communication skills.
2. In what way does sending "I" messages avoid blaming and name-calling?
3. Describe active listening.

Thinking Critically

4. *Synthesizing.* Read and respond to the following statement using reflective listening: "I don't think we should write a report. Instead, let's create a skit in which we can really show what it's like to lose a friend."
5. *Comparing and Contrasting.* Imagine that you have asked a friend to do you a favor. In your private Health Journal, create a "response grid" with four cells. Label the columns *Compliment* and *Constructive Criticism.* Label the rows *Job well done* and *Job done poorly.* Complete the grid with responses that show positive and negative communication skills.

Applying Health Skills

6. *In Your Home or School.* Think of an issue, a project, or a person you care about. How might you communicate your feelings without using words?

LESSON 2 COMMUNICATING EFFECTIVELY **269**

Lesson 2 Review

Answers to Reviewing Facts and Vocabulary

1. Speaking and listening.
2. Using "I" messages is a way to express how you feel in constructive ways.
3. Rephrasing what the other person is saying to make sure you understand; asking questions and giving signals that you are really interested; feeling what the other person feels.

Answers to Thinking Critically

4. The answer should be a rephrasing of the quotation.
5. Journal entries will vary.

Health Skills Activities

ACTIVITY 1
HEALTH SKILLS

Communication, Health Advocacy

➤ **National Standards**
This activity meets these National Health Standards: 5.1; 7.6.

Teach

- Begin by having the class make two companion lists—one of communication taboos (such as interrupting, failing to listen, raising one's voice to be heard), the other of skills that can help people avoid these pitfalls (such as active listening, "I" messages, and so on).
- Point out that since the main thrust of the activity is communication students need not focus on the problem itself. Give an example of a dialogue where you never actually find out what the problem is because communication pitfalls get in the way.

ACTIVITY 2
HEALTH SKILLS

Communication, Health Advocacy

➤ **National Standards**
This activity meets these National Health Standards: 5.1; 7.6.

Teach

- Write the word *criticism* on the chalkboard and ask students what the word means to them. After allowing time for response, which will probably focus on criticism as a negative force, write the word *constructive* before the word *criticism* on the chalkboard. Note that giving positive rather than negative criticism is just one way of contributing to the health of a relationship.
- Recommend that students choose at least one message for each pair of do's and don'ts from those brainstormed. These messages should become the focus of their positive relationships campaign.

Activity 1 — Building Communication Skills

One of the keys to building healthy relationships is effective communication with others. Think about the ways you communicate with the people in your life. Are there ways that you could improve your communication skills?

Directions

1. Working with several classmates, write a skit about a couple or family seeking help from a counselor. The skit should exhibit weak communication skills, such as interrupting, failing to listen, and so on.
2. Have the counselor identify communication as the problem and review communication skills, such as sending "I" messages, active listening, and accurate body language.
3. Conclude with a scene in which the clients try out some of their newly learned skills.

Time
30 minutes

Materials
paper, pen or pencil

Self-Assessment

✓ Correctly described at least two communication problems that can occur.
✓ Correctly described at least three communication strategies.

Activity 2 — Relationship Guidelines

Positive relationships are important to your total health. There are many do's and don'ts for having such relationships. What guidelines do you practice in your relationships?

Directions

1. Brainstorm two lists of behaviors in a friendship. One list is to be positive, the other negative.
2. Create posters, bumper stickers, and other high-visibility modes of communicating the importance of positive guidelines to follow in any relationship. Use the classroom computer or poster board and markers.
3. Distribute or display your messages to community members.

Time
40 minutes

Materials
poster board, markers, or computer with design software and color printer

Self-Assessment

✓ Described strategies for building positive relationships.
✓ Created a clear, persuasive message outlining specific communication techniques to develop healthy relationships.

ASSESSMENT SCORING

Using a four-level rubric, the student has achieved a 4 if:

ACTIVITY 1
✔ Student was able to contribute to a discussion of at least two communication problems.
✔ Student was helpful in identifying communication strategies to overcome some of these problems.
✔ Student took part in the skit development.
✔ Student showed good cooperation and communication skills within the class group.

ACTIVITY 2
✔ Student identified do's and don'ts of healthful relationships.
✔ Student described strategies for building positive relationships.
✔ Student created a clear, persuasive message outlining the importance of communication.
✔ Student showed creativity in his or her output as part of the overall project.

HEALTH NEWS ARTICLE

Two-Way Dialogue: A Crucial Step

When school violence blasts into the headlines, experts fully expect the news to trigger a flurry of emotion at schools nationwide. Young people across the country will be fearful, apprehensive, or confused.

The most important thing students must do, experts say, is talk about their feelings – with parents, educators, and one another. In the process, they gain perspective about school violence and community.

"Every kid in America is wondering, 'Can this happen at my school?'" said Jim Copple of the National Crime Prevention Council. "The foundation of all learning is creating a safe and secure environment. And we can learn from the good kids as to what is safe."

For the most part, experts insist, schools nationwide are very safe – in many cases safer than any other place in a community. Still, parents and teachers must not discard young people's concerns and fears, according to counselor Joanne McDaniel.

"What's more important is that parents and staff in schools listen to what the students have to say," she said. "It's important that they don't blow off those fears . . . They have to have a dialogue, to let them talk through what their fears are."

Read This

Warning Signs of Violence

What are the clues that someone might be on the brink of a violent act? These warning signs suggest that intervention may be needed to prevent violence before it occurs:

- abusive behavior
- frequent loss of temper
- repeated threats to hurt others
- committing vandalism or property damage
- sudden changes in demeanor or appearance
- increase in risky behaviors, including drug and alcohol use

Think About It

1. How can violent events in other schools affect stress levels in your school?
2. What strategies do experts suggest to help students work through fears of school violence?
3. How can talking about problems help relieve stress?

MORE ABOUT . . . . .

REPORTING THE STORY. Many news stories focus on problems in schools around the United States. Journalism about violence can create feelings of stress and anxiety. One constructive way to promote a full view of school life throughout the country is to write and publish articles about effective solutions in other schools.

Suggest that students write a weekly news item for their school paper or for a classroom bulletin. Each week, student reporters can describe a positive event that takes place at another school. Articles should emphasize successful programs and the obstacles overcome by students. These articles can help reassure students that schools are safe and that problems are solvable through innovative solutions.

CNN HEALTH NEWS

Two-Way Dialogue

Objectives. After reading the article, students should be able to recognize the benefits of talking about problems to relieve stress.

Motivator. Share this quotation with students by reading it or writing it on the chalkboard: "There are thousands of causes for stress, and one antidote to stress is self-expression. That's what happens to me every day. My thoughts get off my chest, down my sleeves and onto my pad." (Garson Kanin, playwright, from *Creative Quotations*) Have students identify other strategies they find useful for reducing stress. Then have them read "Two-Way Dialogue: A Crucial Step" to provide a focus for how communication with others can relieve negative stress.

Teach

- Write the words *dialogue* and *violence* on the chalkboard. Ask students to explain the relationship between these two concepts. They should point out that an effective two-way dialogue might reduce stress that can otherwise lead to violence.
- Discuss why students in one school can be affected by violence that takes place in another school that is located in a different city or state. Emphasize valid student responses to emotional incidents in the news.

Group Activity. Have student teams work together to design a format and structure for a discussion group for students. Encourage them to brainstorm ideas that will make their discussion group effective. Suggest that they carefully weigh alternatives, such as the choice to meet once a day, once a week, or once a month.

Close. Ask students to describe specific school situations that could lead to violence. Write student suggestions on the chalkboard. Then discuss how each volatile situation might be resolved through a two-way dialogue.

CHECKING COMPREHENSION

- Assign and discuss the chapter review.
- Use the MindJogger Videoquiz to review the chapter.

CHAPTER 11 REVIEW ANSWERS

Using Health Terms

1. role
2. cooperation
3. compromise
4. relationship
5. friendship
6. empathy
7. active listening
8. communication
9. "I" message
10. constructive criticism
11. body language

Recalling the Facts

1. They meet many of the basic human needs.
2. Employee.
3. Those based on respect, caring, cooperation, and trust.
4. Cooperation.
5. Compromise makes each person feel that she or he has been heard, but it also places the relationship in a place of greater importance than individual wants.
6. Respect, acceptance, honesty, trustworthiness, dependability, loyalty, empathy.
7. Backing away is a form of body language that indicates that you want to end the conversation.
8. Effective communication requires that you express your thoughts clearly.
9. Rephrasing what the other person is saying, asking questions, responding with interest, and feeling empathy.
10. When people are prejudiced, they have already made up their mind and will not listen to new information.

Using Health Terms

On a separate sheet of paper, write the term that best matches each definition below.

LESSON 1

1. A part that you play in a relationship.
2. Working together for the good of all.
3. The result of each person's giving up something in order to reach a solution that satisfies everyone.
4. A bond or connection between people.
5. A significant relationship between two people based on caring, consideration, and trust.
6. The ability to share another person's feelings or thoughts.

LESSON 2

7. Really paying attention to what someone is saying and feeling.
8. A process through which you send messages to and receive messages from others.
9. A statement in which a person tells how he or she feels using the pronoun "I."
10. Non-hostile comments that point out problems and have the potential to help a person change.
11. Nonverbal communication through gestures, facial expressions, and behaviors.

Recalling the Facts

Using complete sentences, answer the following questions.

LESSON 1

1. Why are relationships so important to your health?
2. What role are you playing when a friend comes into a fast-food restaurant where you work?
3. Which kinds of relationships are usually the strongest and last a lifetime?
4. What quality of a healthy relationship do two students working together on a poster exhibit?
5. How does compromise help to strengthen a relationship?
6. Name several traits of a healthy relationship.

LESSON 2

7. How is backing away from someone a form of communication?
8. Why are good speaking skills an important part of effective communication?
9. What are three techniques you can use for active listening?
10. How does prejudice set up a barrier to effective communication?
11. Give an example of constructive criticism.
12. How should you deal with a disagreement in a relationship?

272 CHAPTER 11 BUILDING HEALTHY RELATIONSHIPS

---

11. Answers will vary.
12. Either try to reach a compromise or accept the fact that you disagree without judging the other person.

Thinking Critically

LESSON 1

1. **Analyzing.** Explain whether or not a compromise is the right choice in this situation: Peter is Jackie's first boyfriend. Peter wants Jackie to go to a late-night party with him, but it would mean breaking her curfew. Jackie feels that she should respect her family's house rules and come home on time.

2. **Evaluating.** Ken and William recently became friends at soccer practice. Yesterday, upon learning that Ken's dog had died, William told Ken, "Cheer up. At least it wasn't a person." Do you think this relationship will survive?

LESSON 2

3. **Evaluating.** Gustavo's girlfriend, Karen, expects him to pay for everything when they go out. Gustavo resents footing the bill each time. Write an "I" message that Gustavo could tell Karen to explain his feelings.

4. **Analyzing.** Kim's father is criticizing her report card and threatening to cut off her allowance if her grades don't improve. Kim puts her head and shoulders down and shoves her hands into the pockets of her jeans. What emotion is she probably experiencing, based on her body language?

Making the Connection

1. **Math.** Pilar gets 8 hours of sleep each night. If she spends 80 percent of her waking hours communicating and 60 percent of those hours listening, how many hours a day does Pilar spend listening?

2. **Language Arts.** Write a guest editorial for the school newspaper with one of the following titles: *Traits of a Healthy Relationship, How to Compromise,* or *Resolving Differences Through Communication Skills.*

BEYOND THE CLASSROOM

PARENTAL INVOLVEMENT Ask your parents to call a family meeting on the subject of communication among family members. Allow members to give their opinions about communication in the family. Present several communication tips, including the use of "I" messages and active listening. Discuss how your family can improve its communication skills.

COMMUNITY INVOLVEMENT Research community programs in your area to help (1) a new family in the community to make new friends; (2) a senior citizen who lives alone and is lonely; (3) a teen who is looking for an opportunity to do volunteer work.

SCHOOL-TO-CAREER
Exploring Careers. Invite a school counselor to speak to your class about a career in family counseling. Ask this person to explain how counselors help individuals and families in crisis. Also, find out where counselors work, what training they need, and average salaries for counselors. Write a summary of your findings, and add the information to a classroom career booklet.

Thinking Critically

1. Peter should respect the rules Jackie lives by. Compromise is not the right choice.
2. No, because there is a lack of empathy.
3. Answers will vary.
4. Answers will vary.

Making the Connection

1. 7.68 hours.
2. Editorials will vary.

Evaluate

- Use the reproducible *Chapter 11 Test* in the TCR or construct your own using the Testmaker software.
- Use *Performance Assessment Activity 11* in the TCR.

Enrichment

Ask students to complete *Cross-Curriculum Activity 11* in the TCR.

Beyond the Classroom

Keep students involved in the community, and encourage parent participation by assigning the activities on this page for students to work on outside of class.

Healthy Family Relationships

	FEATURES	CLASSROOM RESOURCES

ACTIVITIES

- 🖝 Cross-Curriculum Activity 12
- 🖝 Health Lab 12
- 🖝 Health Skills Activities 12
- 🖝 Parent Letter and Activities 12

ASSESSMENT

- 🖝 Chapter 12 Test
- 🖝 Performance Assessment Activity 12
- 💾 Testmaker Software

STUDENT ACTIVITIES WORKBOOK

- 🖝 Applying Health Skills 38–40
- 🖝 Study Guide 12
- 🖝 Vocabulary Activity 12

STUDENT DIVERSITY STRATEGIES

- 🎧 Audiocassette Program (English)
- 🎧 Audiocassette Program (Spanish)
- 🖝 Spanish Parent Letters and Activities
- 🖝 Spanish Summaries, Quizzes, and Activities

MULTIMEDIA COMPONENTS

- 🎧 English Audiocassette Program
- 🎧 Spanish Audiocassette Program
- 🔴 MindJogger Videodisc and VHS program
- 🔴 ABCNews InterActive™ VHS/Videodisc Series

National Health Education Standards

One of the main goals of the National Health Education Standards is to move students toward "health literacy." Health literacy is the capacity of individuals to obtain, interpret, and understand basic health information and services and the competence to use such information and services in ways which promote health. The health standards were developed by applying the characteristics of a well-educated, literate person within the context of health. The health literate person is:

- a critical thinker and problem solver
- a self-directed learner
- a responsible, productive citizen
- an effective communicator

Listed below are the Health Education Standards Performance Indicators addressed in each lesson of this chapter.

Lesson	Health Standards Performance Indicators
1	1.4, 4.1, 5.1, 5.2
2	5.5, 5.6, 5.7, 5.8
3	2.4, 2.6, 3.4, 5.4

ONLINE RESOURCES

For a fresh approach to health topics and an in-depth look at health issues, use these online resources found under Teacher Resources at **health.glencoe.com**.

- **BLOCK SCHEDULE LESSON PLANS** Reinforce health concepts with outside readings selected especially for students. Each reading is accompanied by a lesson plan and activities to enhance
  - Reading Skills
  - Cross Curriculum
  - Media Literacy

- **TECHNOLOGY PROJECTS** Instructions and suggestions on how to use computer, Internet, and software with health lessons.

- **HEALTH UPDATES** Timely topics in health news, including late-breaking medical advances and updates on teen risk behaviors.

Out of Time?

If time does not permit teaching this chapter, you may use these features: Update on page 280; Making Responsible Decisions on page 285; and Building Health Skills on page 290.

BLOCK SCHEDULING

Block scheduling provides extended time for hands-on projects and activities. Use the following activities to engage students, provide further depth, and vary your instructional techniques:

- Connections (30 minutes) **pg. 279**
- Update (30 minutes) **pg. 280**
- Health Skills Activity (60–90 minutes) **pg. 292**

Healthy Family Relationships

CHAPTER OVERVIEW

Chapter 12 explores the area of family health. The chapter emphasizes the importance of strengthening relationships and seeking support during times of crisis.

LESSON 1 The family is the basic unit of society. A family exerts a strong influence on the lives and personalities of its members, just as each member affects the physical, mental, and social levels of the total family's health. The many types of families and some of the changes that families have gone through during the last 50 years are discussed in this lesson.

LESSON 2 It is important to be aware of threats to the health of families, so that steps can be taken to maintain a healthy family and thus a strong society. A family system can break down for a variety of reasons, often ending in divorce and/or restructuring. In many cases, the troubled family remains intact and, depending on the type of problem and whether or not family members seek help, the health of individual members can be threatened as a result.

LESSON 3 Both public and private agencies are available to assist members of a troubled family. Sources of help range from services that assist the entire family to individual counseling.

CHAPTER 12

Healthy Family Relationships

HEALTH Online
STRESS MANAGEMENT
Strong support systems are integral to the health of the family. What approach can you take to maintain that support when families separate? Read the Health Update on "When Parents Divorce" at **health.glencoe.com** to understand more about dealing with this type of change in family relationships.

Hands-On Health

TEACHING STRATEGY

Using "I" Messages Give students real-life examples of the effectiveness of "I" Messages and help them practice this form of communication. See Activity 8, "Sharing Concern: I Messages," in the *Hands-On Health: Creative Teaching Strategies* booklet.

Time Needed
20 minutes

Supplies
• copies of the Sharing Concern Skill card (1 per student)

> *Treasure your families...*

—JOHN PAUL II
ROMAN CATHOLIC POPE, (1920–)

Quick Write Write a quick thank-you note to someone in your family who has taught you that you matter and have an important role to play in this world. Think about how the person demonstrates this through actions and words.

Personal Health Inventory

Self-Inventory Write the numbers 1–10 on a sheet of paper. Read each statement below and respond by writing *yes, no,* or *sometimes* for each item. Write a *yes* only for items that you practice regularly. Save your responses.

1	I care about the members of my family.
2	I spend time with my family.
3	I pitch in and help family members when needed.
4	I share household responsibilities with my family.
5	I ask for help from family members when I need support.
6	I don't expect perfection in my family.
7	I am committed to healthy family relationships.
8	When a disagreement comes up, I try to see the other family members' points of view.
9	I am a loyal and trustworthy member of my family.
10	I provide positive input that helps other family members feel appreciated and supported.

Follow-up After completing the chapter, retake this self-inventory. Pick two items that you need to work on and set a goal to improve your health behaviors.

CHAPTER 12   HEALTHY FAMILY RELATIONSHIPS   **275**

INTRODUCING THE CHAPTER

Personal Health Inventory

Let students read and briefly discuss the Self-Inventory statements. Then have them record their responses to these statements in their private Health Journals and label the page "My Relationship with My Family." Remind students that they should respond honestly and openly; suggest that they keep their own set of family members in mind and avoid comparing their family groups with the families of friends and neighbors, or even those seen on TV programs.

- Tell students that members of a family affect one another economically, socially, emotionally, and in some ways, physically. As the basic unit of society, the family plays a critical role in the healthy growth and development of the individual. Remind students that this material is not intended to delve into their private lives; rather, it is meant to create an awareness of the importance of the family unit and an understanding of what constitutes a healthy family.
- Let students describe the photographs on these pages: What does each scene show or suggest about family relationships? If you were to take a photo showing your own family, what activities and emotions would you show? After a brief discussion, explain that students will learn more about families and family relationships as they read Chapter 12.
- Distribute Parent Letter 12 in the *Parent Letters and Activities* booklet. ☞

TECHNOLOGY OPTIONS

ABCNEWS INTERACTIVE™ You may wish to use *Making Responsible Decisions* with this chapter. For your convenience, use the separate *ABCNews InterActive™ Bar Code Correlation* that accompanies the *Glencoe Health* program.

MINDJOGGER
VIDEOQUIZ

To preview or review chapter content, you may wish to use the *Mindjogger Videoquiz* that accompanies Chapter 12.

Strengthening Family Relationships

Strengthening Family Relationships

FOCUS

LESSON OBJECTIVES

After studying this lesson, students should be able to

- describe the family in terms of a system.
- explain some of the major functions of the family.
- discuss responsibilities of individual members of a family.
- identify traits that healthy families have in common.

MOTIVATOR

Write the following on the chalkboard for students to work on while attendance is being taken: *Think of ten families that you know. List the people (mother, father, children, and so on) who make up each family. Please do not use names.*

INTRODUCING THE LESSON

Refer to the Motivator. Ask volunteers to share their lists of families. Discuss the differences and the similarities. Point out that the structure of the family refers to the types of people who belong to it. Ask them if any one structure is more common than others. Explain that the lesson will focus on the family as a social system.

INTRODUCING HEALTH TERMS

- Have students use the terms *sibling* and *affirmation* in a sentence. Ask them to read their sentences to the class.
- Ask students to complete Vocabulary Activity 12 and Chapter Study Guide 12 in the *Student Workbook.* ☞

From the time you were born, your family has had a strong influence on your life. Families not only provide food, clothing, and shelter but also give family members a sense of security and a feeling of belonging. It is through the family that a child receives his or her first opportunities for physical well-being, learning, and loving.

HEALTH TERMS

sibling
affirmation

HEALTH CONCEPTS

- The family is the basic social unit of society.
- Even though structures vary, the family unit performs similar functions.
- Family members have responsibilities to the health of the family.

The Family as a System

If every student in your class were to bring in a family photo, you would probably see a wide representation of family types and sizes. Some families are made up of two parents and one or more children. Others are headed by a single parent. Still others are "blended"— headed by two adults who have remarried following a divorce or the death of a spouse, plus the children of both previous marriages.

Regardless of its makeup, every family may be viewed as a system similar to the human body. All parts of the body are interconnected to compose a whole being. No part exists in isolation. As a system, each family member's level of health—physical, mental and emotional, and social—affects the health of the total family. The reverse is also true. The health of the family system directly affects the health of its individual members. In addition, because the family is

Lesson 1 Resources

TEACHER'S CLASSROOM RESOURCES
☞ **Concept Map** Activity 38
☞ **Cooperative Learning** Activity 12
☞ **Enrichment** Activity 12
☞ **Health Lab** 12
☞ **Lesson 38 Quiz**
☞ **Lesson Plan 38**

☞ **Parent Letter and Activities 12**
☞ **Reteaching** Activity 38

STUDENT WORKBOOK
☞ **Applying Health Skills 38**
☞ **Chapter Study Guide 12**
☞ **Vocabulary** Activity 12

the basic social unit of society, society's health is directly related to the family's health. If we are to survive and maintain a healthy society, then everyone must work to promote healthy families.

Functions of the Family

As a social unit, the family serves several important functions. These include:

- Constituting the primary support system to which individuals turn in order to have their basic needs met.
- Meeting the emotional needs of children and providing nurturing.
- Instilling values and religious beliefs in children.
- Passing on traditions and customs from one generation to the next.

Meeting Basic Needs

Most parents work hard to earn money so they can provide basic needs such as food, clothing, and shelter for their children. Children have other basic needs as well. Have you ever watched a parent teach a toddler not to touch a hot stove? Young children need to be taught basic knowledge about how to live safely in their environment. Families also teach their children basic social skills, such as how to get along with others in society. The family is the essential mechanism by which a child develops the capability to survive and to function independently in the world. This can happen only when the child's needs are met.

Meeting Emotional Needs

Growing up and becoming a well-adjusted person is a complex process. Children need to develop a sense of belonging. They need families that help them feel secure and loved.

▼ *Instilling values and religious beliefs is an important function of the family.*
ACTIVITY *Explain how teaching cultural heritage strengthens family ties.*

HOME AND COMMUNITY CONNECTION

FAMILIES AND ECONOMICS. In the 1990s, women with families accounted for a rapidly increasing percentage of homeless and impoverished people in the United States. Some were employed at minimum-wage jobs. Have students conduct research about homeless or poverty-stricken families. How many are single women with children? What factors account for their homelessness—lack of affordable child care? inadequate wages for women? teen pregnancy? lack of child support? Encourage students to discuss problems and solutions.

TEACH

L1 Discussing

Lead students in brainstorming a list of words they think of when they hear the word *family*. Write the words on the chalkboard. Next, discuss ways in which families are similar to body systems.

L1 Class Activity

On the chalkboard, list the names of some popular TV programs. Ask students to determine what the programs have in common. When they identify family as a common denominator, discuss the strengths portrayed in TV families. Ask questions such as these: Why are these families successful (or unsuccessful)? Are the portrayals realistic? Are there any elderly people and/or two-income couples in these families? Conclude by saying that there are many kinds of families, and each one has its strengths and weaknesses.

L1 Self-Esteem

Divide the class into two groups. One group will list ways the family can affect an individual's level of self-esteem. The other group will list ways an individual's level of self-esteem can affect the family's level of health.

L3 Writing

Ask volunteers to write a story, poem, or song about a favorite holiday or vacation with their family. Suggest that they share their completed project with at least one family member.

L2 Cooperative Learning

Have students complete *Cooperative Learning Activity 12*, "Family Council," in the TCR. 🔴

hotlink

values
Have students write in their private Health Journals the values they have learned from their family.

L2 Parental Involvement

Assign volunteers to plan and carry out a family holiday or vacation activity. Afterward, have them write a short paper about the family experience. Make sure students identify the values that were reinforced by the activities they chose.

LEP Personal Involvement

Ask students to write the name of each member of their family at the top of a sheet of paper. Then, under each name, have them list ways they could show they care for that individual.

L1 Discussing

Talk about some of the responsibilities that teens can assume to help a family function smoothly. Survey the class to see what responsibilities are currently being assumed by students.

Visual Learning

Roles and Responsibilities

Have the class refer to the picture on this page. Ask students to identify the family roles and responsibilities that this teen assumes. (*Acting as a role model for a younger sibling, listening and showing support for another family member, assuming tasks in the household, reading a book to a younger sibling, sharing time together.*) Allow students time to list roles and responsibilities they assume around the house. Ask volunteers to share their lists.

hotlink

self-esteem For more information on self-esteem and ways of improving your own self-esteem, see Chapter 8, page 188.

hotlink

values For more information on values and their importance, see Chapter 1, page 20.

▼ **When family members share responsibilities, all benefit.**
ACTIVITY *Identify at least two benefits for each family member in the activities pictured.*

When going through rough times, children need to know they can turn to family members for support. By providing emotional support, families promote **self-esteem** in their children. Self-esteem is the way people feel about themselves. Good self-esteem provides children with confidence to become successful and happy adults.

Instilling Values

Families teach children **values**, or beliefs and feelings about what is important. Developing a good value system helps children know right from wrong. It helps them make decisions that will affect their future, and turns them into good citizens who follow the laws and contribute in a positive way to society.

Instilling Culture and Traditions

Does your family have certain traditions, such as spending the Fourth of July at the lake or celebrating Kwanzaa at the end of the year? It is through traditions such as these that families pass their

SCHOOL-TO-CAREER

CHILD CARE PROVIDER. Given today's changing families, quality child care is among the services most beneficial to society. Child care providers operate in a variety of settings. They may work at preschools, day care centers, on-site child care centers in the workplace, or the homes of the children. They may be licensed to provide care in their own homes.

Have students research careers as child care providers in a variety of settings. Encourage them to list the advantages and disadvantages of a career as a child care provider. Follow the activity with a class discussion about the importance of child care workers to families, and their low pay and status relative to other workers.

- **Trust.** Families with a high level of trust know that other members will not do anything to hurt the family. Both parents and children must earn trust, and can do so by keeping promises and being honest.
- **Commitment.** Building a strong family requires commitment. Family members are willing to work together and make sacrifices for the benefit of the whole family.
- **Time Together.** It is not possible to have strong healthy family relationships without spending time together.
- **Communication.** In families, effective communication means listening to the viewpoint of others as well as being heard.
- **Respect.** Strong families have respect for each other. They accept individual tastes, talents, and opinions.
- **Solving Problems.** Healthy families try to identify problems before they become too serious and ask for outside help if needed.
- **Love.** Healthy families give and receive love. They express love to each other, physically and verbally.

LESSON 1 *Review*

Reviewing Facts and Vocabulary

1. Name three functions of the family.
2. How can family members give affirmation to one another?

Thinking Critically

3. *Comparing and Contrasting.* Tell what need the following family members are providing: (a) A teenager stops her toddler sibling from running out into the street. (b) Parents host a bar mitzvah for their son. (c) A father and son collect goods for a local food shelf. (d) A teenager hugs his grandmother.
4. *Synthesizing.* Last year, Bart told his parents he was going over to a friend's house when he was really going to a party. Now they won't let him go out at all at night. What advice would you give Bart to help him regain his parents' trust?

Applying Health Skills

5. *In Your Home.* Practice giving affirmations by finding a situation in which you can give positive input to each member in your family. If you find it difficult to give the affirmation out loud, write the affirmation as a note that you can give to the person. Explain what affirmations are to family members and ask them to join you in giving at least one affirmation to a family member each day.

Lesson 1 Review

Answers to Reviewing Facts and Vocabulary

1. Meeting basic needs, meeting emotional needs, instilling values, instilling culture and traditions.
2. By making positive statements to one another on their achievements, looks, character traits, etc.

Answers to Thinking Critically

3. (a) the need to feel safe; (b) the need to feel part of a group; (c) the need to contribute to society; (d) the need to love and be loved.
4. Advice will vary.

ASSESS

EVALUATING THE LESSON

Assign and discuss the Lesson 1 Review; then administer, grade, and discuss the *Lesson 38 Quiz* in the TCR. ☞

RETEACHING

- Ask students to describe how a family is a system, and let them explain the relationship between the health of the family and the health of the individual. Next, have students discuss their responsibility to contribute to their family's health.
- Ask students to complete *Reteaching Activity 38* in the TCR. ☞

ENRICHMENT

- Have students select two different cultures and compare and contrast their life patterns, family structure, behavior, and health practices. Ask them to write a comparative report on their findings.
- Help students analyze media representations (and misrepresentations) of family life portrayed on television by having them complete *Enrichment Activity 12,* "Families and Television," in the TCR. ☞

CLOSE

Review the traits of a healthy family with the class. Discuss how each trait is essential, like links in a chain. If any area is neglected or misapplied, the chain is broken, and the health of the family or individual members could be affected. Stress the importance of individuals assuming responsibility for one another in maintaining a strong and resilient family.

Looking at the Health of the Family

LESSON **2**

FOCUS

LESSON OBJECTIVES

After studying this lesson, students should be able to

- explain factors that may cause a family system to break down.
- describe means of coping with family stress.
- discuss the forms of domestic violence.

MOTIVATOR

Write the following on the chalkboard for students to work on while attendance is being taken: *List ways that individual stress can affect other family members.*

INTRODUCING THE LESSON

Have students share their responses to the Motivator. Tell the class that this lesson will focus on the causes and effects of stress on the family.

INTRODUCING HEALTH TERMS

- Divide the class into two groups. Assign half the vocabulary terms to one group and have each member use each term individually in a written paragraph. Assign the other half of the terms to the other group. Allow volunteers from each group to read their paragraphs to the class. Afterward, ask them to test each other's understanding of the words' definitions.
- Ask students to complete Vocabulary Activity 12 and Chapter Study Guide 12 in the *Student Workbook.* ▱

Looking at the Health of the Family

Most families experience some type of stress. When one problem leads to another, stress can become a vicious and destructive cycle. Without intervention, a family system can break down. In this lesson, you will become aware of the threats to the health of a family and learn how families can cope.

HEALTH TERMS

custody
domestic violence
spousal abuse
child abuse
emotional abuse
neglect
exploitation

HEALTH CONCEPTS

- Some families experience problems that can interfere with the normal healthy working of the family.
- Couples who cannot resolve their differences sometimes choose to separate or to end their marriages through divorce.
- Domestic violence brings fear and abuse into the family system and is the single most destructive force in American families today.
- There are techniques for coping with family problems and improving the health of the family.

Family Stress

When people live under one roof, problems are sure to arise. Maybe you have had the experience of a family member "getting under your skin." Usually, good communication and problem-solving skills can help family members successfully work out these minor problems.

Sometimes major changes occur, triggering stress in families. Sources of family stress can be sudden, such as the loss of a job, or they can occur over time, as with a chronic illness. Whatever the cause, the stress must be dealt with effectively.

Lesson 2 Resources

TEACHER'S CLASSROOM RESOURCES
▱ **Concept Map** Activity 39
▱ **Decision-Making** Activity 12
▱ **Lesson 39** Quiz
▱ **Lesson Plan** 39
▱ **Reteaching** Activity 39
STUDENT WORKBOOK
▱ **Applying Health Skills** 39

▱ **Chapter Study Guide** 12
▱ **Vocabulary** Activity 12
TRANSPARENCIES
🖐 **Transparency 36**
MULTIMEDIA
🔴 **ABCNews InterActive™ VHS/Videodisc,** *Drugs and Substance Abuse*

Changes in Family Structure

The arrival of a new baby is a cause for great joy in a family. It can also, however, be a cause for stress among young siblings who may view the newcomer as a rival. The addition of a new baby can be stressful even on older children since the baby makes demands on the parents' time and diverts their attention from the older child's needs and wants.

Other changes to a family's structure include becoming a part of a blended family or having an older relative such as a grandparent move into the household. Either of these situations may mean that space is redefined and, hence, requires an adjustment.

Moving

Whether a family moves across town or across the country, a family faces the stress of uncertainty as they adjust to a new neighborhood. Members may miss friends or loved ones they left behind. Moving from a house into an apartment can also be a stressful adjustment, if families need to adjust to new rules.

Financial Problems

Meeting all of a family's expenses in today's society is not easy. Financial problems from overdue bills or loss of a job are a major cause of stress for families. Other financial problems are caused by impulse buying or poor planning. "Credit card abuse," the situation in which one or more family members overuse a credit card to the point of spending past the approved credit limit, can be a particularly serious source of stress for the family bill payer. Resulting arguments over this habit can further fuel the stress.

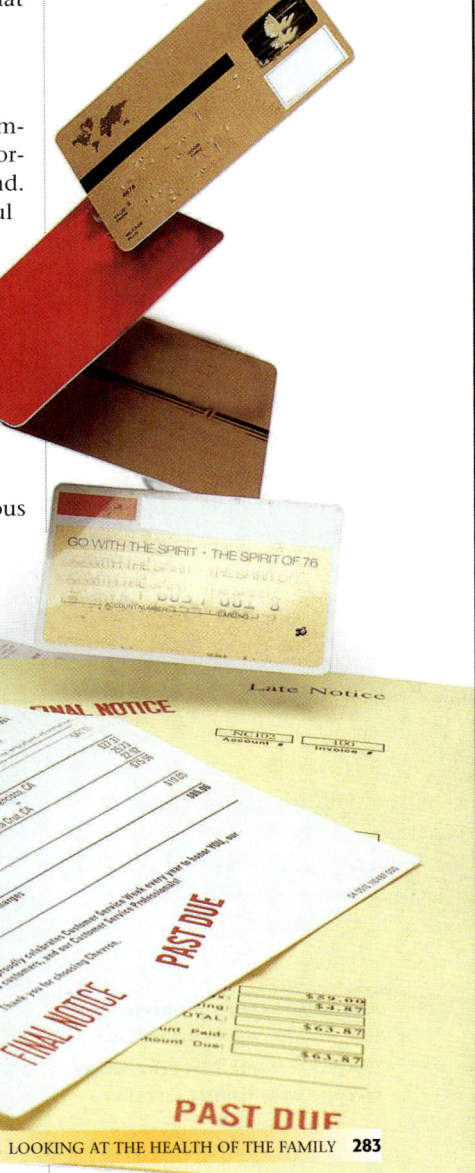

▼ *Financial problems can be a cause of family stress.*
ACTIVITY *List habits you can start now, such as a regular savings account, that will help you learn to manage your money.*

LESSON 2 LOOKING AT THE HEALTH OF THE FAMILY **283**

TEACH

L2 Class Activity

Choose students to write and present positive public service announcements about the changing family system.

L1 Discussing

Lead students in brainstorming problems children may have when living in single-parent families and in blended families. Ask them to analyze the problems and give suggestions for dealing with them.

L3 Community Involvement

Suggest that students interview adults who have adopted new roles that meet their needs, interests, and abilities. The new roles might be the result of a career change, the addition of a job to existing work requirements, or the addition of new family members due to birth, remarriage, adoption, etc.

L3 Parental Involvement

Have students interview their grandparents or an adult of their grandparents' generation. Ask them to focus on questions that reflect the older adult's type of family and its functions. For example: Who was the head of the household? Who provided child care? Encourage volunteers to share their findings. Discuss the changes in today's families and some of the reasons for the changes.

L1 Discussing

Use *Transparency 36* to discuss ways to manage stress.

CURRICULUM CONNECTIONS

LANGUAGE ARTS. Assign students to look in magazines and newspapers for stories about troubled families. Ask them to select one family. Have them write a letter they would like to send to that family, suggesting ways to keep the family together and where to get help locally. Choose several letters (and their original stories) to read to the class.

HISTORY. Arrange class time for students to visit the library to research the cultural background of their families. Then have students write several paragraphs on how this background may have influenced the families' traditions, values, and lifestyles.

L3 Community Involvement

Select students to interview representatives from the local chapter of the Alzheimer's Association. Ask students to request information about ways family members can deal with stress when caring for an Alzheimer's patient.

L1 Discussing

Of the following changes affecting the family system today, have students identify which they think is the most significant: smaller families, working wives and mothers, or single-parent heads of households. Ask them to discuss reasons for their choices.

L1 Discussing

Ask students to identify situations in which a teenager may face the danger of physical or mental abuse. List their responses on the chalkboard. Then have the class discuss how some of the situations might be avoided.

L2 Community Involvement

Select students to interview one or more single-parent heads of households. Have them ask about ways the parents deal with increased responsibilities and stress while playing multiple roles, such as mother, father, worker, housekeeper, cook, chauffeur, etc.

L2 Writing

Instruct each student to write a one-page paper titled "Maintaining a Healthy Family While Coping with a Changing World." Ask them to present ideas for positive ways that families can address the stresses of change that face them.

Illness or Disability

When a family member becomes ill with a serious health problem, the family is faced with many stresses. When Sandy learned that her mother had cancer, for example, Sandy's worry kept her awake at night, and her grades dropped. Because Sandy's mother had to quit her job while undergoing expensive treatment, the family faced financial problems as well.

A grandparent in poor health may cause stress as family members determine how best to care for him or her. If a disability affects one member of a household, the other members of the family may need to make adjustments. The family may need to work out a schedule around work, school, and recreation activities so that everyone can share the responsibility of caring for that person.

Substance Abuse

Substance abuse within the family is almost always destructive. Parents—and others in the family who are alcoholic or who use other drugs—neglect their responsibilities, become very irritable, often lose their jobs, and may even abuse other family members.

When the health of the family is threatened by drug use, all of the members need help. By asking the right people for assistance, you can be the one who starts your family on the way back to a healthy life. The people most likely to help you are members of your extended family, a member of the clergy, a school counselor or trusted teacher, your school nurse, or a youth worker. Knowing how to get help is a way of caring for your family. These people can help you understand the problem and help you get additional assistance.

▶ *Talking with a parent is one way to cope with stress.*
ACTIVITY *Name two other ways to cope with family stress.*

284 CHAPTER 12 HEALTHY FAMILY RELATIONSHIPS

PERSONAL HEALTH

LISTENING AND EMPATHY. Much family conflict and stress could be minimized if family members really listened to and empathized with one another. Encourage students to make a point of listening carefully to at least one member of the family or household each day and putting themselves in the family members' positions. Suggest that they make daily notes in their private Health Journals for at least two weeks. Does their understanding of family members change? Has their relationship with family members changed? Do they wish to increase the amount of time they spend really listening and empathizing?

Coping with Family Stress

Think of stress as water boiling in a teapot. To deal with stress, people need to find a "release valve." Depending on the nature of the problem, finding the release valve might be as easy as turning to someone within the family for help. Talking with family members about problems can help alleviate some of the stress and lead to successful problem-solving. Use these suggestions for coping with family stress:

- Talk with one or both of your parents. Find an adult who will listen to you, such as a teacher, guidance counselor, or member of the clergy. You might also talk with a brother or sister; after all, they are probably facing the same problem you are.
- Do what you can to help. If the problem is money, you could get a part-time job to pay for your own expenses. If your parents are stressed, taking on added chores or responsibilities might reduce their stress load. Regardless, helping out will make you feel better.
- Read books about people who have faced the same problem you are facing. You might also find it helpful to speak with classmates who have had similar difficulties in their families.

Separation and Divorce

Stress, as noted, is a normal part of living with other people. Most of the time, a married couple finds ways to work out their problems. When differences become too much to work out, however, a couple may go through a separation or divorce. During a separation,

CHARACTER IN ACTION

Avoiding Sibling Quibbling

One way to better sibling relationships is to exercise **self-control**. That means not overreacting. You can try to communicate in effective and caring ways that don't inflame others.

Character Check
Next time you're about to "go at it" with a brother or sister, try these tips:

➤ Talk out your differences before they escalate.

➤ When disagreeing, make an effort to stay on the subject.

➤ Use "I" messages rather than accusing with "you" messages.

➤ Learn to distinguish between the behavior and the person.

➤ Take responsibility for your part of the argument.

➤ Try saying one nice thing each day to each other.

Making Responsible Decisions

All in the Family

For the past six months Bart's dad has been ill, and the family has been under extreme stress. Bart's mother has been dividing her time between work and the hospital. Bart, who is the oldest of three brothers, has been responsible for running the house. Lately, the combined pressures of school, household chores, and looking after his younger brothers has begun to overwhelm him. Bart would like just an occasional evening or weekend afternoon to himself, but he feels it would be selfish even to ask his mother under the circumstances. What should Bart do?

What Would You Do?

Apply the six steps of the decision-making process to Bart's problem.

1. **State the situation.**
2. **List the options.**
3. **Weigh the possible outcomes.**
4. **Consider your values.**
5. **Make a decision and act.**
6. **Evaluate the decision.**

MORE ABOUT . . . . .

DIVORCE. Divorce can be a result of troubled families. About one in two marriages ends in divorce. When divorce involves children, it puts extreme emotional stress on family members. Children often are caught in a battle between parents. Many times they blame themselves. They may fear abandonment and loss of love. Children experience stages of grieving before they finally accept the finality of divorce. This may take years.

Divorce may also create a financial crisis. Without child support, it is difficult to rear children on one income. For the parent with custody, being a single parent can be both physically and emotionally exhausting, frustrating, and lonely.

Making Responsible Decisions

1. Bart feels overwhelmed by family responsibilities.
2. Bart could (a) ignore his own need for some time on his own; (b) talk with his mother about his need to have some "free" time; (c) ask an adult relative or another trusted adult for occasional help at home.
3. Bart might (a) avoid appearing selfish but risk his own physical, emotional, and social health; (b) risk making his mother feel angry or disappointed—but perhaps also arrange to have some time for himself; (c) risk making his mother angry that he has turned to others for help, but also have a chance to get a break from family pressures without letting his family members down.
4. Bart values his family and his own ability to help family members. He also values his own health.
5. Responses will vary.
6. Help students consider both short- and long-term consequences of their decisions.

L2 Decision Making

For further study on making responsible decisions, assign *Decision-Making Activity 12* in the TCR.

CHARACTER IN ACTION

Avoiding Sibling Quibbling

Have students ask themselves the following questions as they relate to siblings and other family members: How often do you try to…

- say something nice to the other person?
- say you're sorry when you make a mistake?
- treat your sibling or other family member as you wish to be treated?

CHAPTER 12 • LESSON 2

Coping with Divorce

keeping **Fit**

Ask several students to investigate local sources of support for families going through a divorce. Have them find out the kinds of services provided and how someone in need could get involved. Provide the students with a small bulletin board to share their findings.

L1 Guest Speaker

Invite an attorney to speak to the class about the issue of divorce. Ask the speaker to talk about the emotional and financial costs of divorce.

L1 Explaining

Tell students that abuse in a family is a very serious problem. Stress the availability of help for both the child and the parents. Explain that the child is not at fault in these situations and should not feel guilty.

L1 Class Activity

Have students locate newspaper and magazine articles about cases of spouse abuse, elder abuse, and child abuse. Discuss factors that apparently led up to the situation. Talk about ways the abuse might have been prevented.

L1 Guest Speaker

Invite a police officer, other community worker, or a school counselor to address the class about the problems of young runaways in today's society. Have the speaker talk about the reasons for running away, the ages of young runaways, the dangers they face on the street, where runaways can go for help, and the percentage who return to their original families.

---

keeping **Fit**

Coping with Divorce

If your parents are going through a divorce, you can use many of the coping skills for dealing with stress. Here are some additional strategies that may help ease the emotional turmoil.

➤ Remind yourself that you did not cause the problem.

➤ Ask your parents not to fight in front of you.

➤ Tell your parents that you do not wish to take sides.

➤ Freely express your feelings about the divorce when talking to your parents and others.

➤ Accept the idea that you have little or no control in a divorce situation and the changes it brings.

➤ Take care of yourself. When faced with choices, choose what's best for you, keeping your own health and future in mind.

➤ Consider joining a support group for children of divorce. Doing so will help you realize that you are not alone.

---

a couple lives apart from each other. Sometimes parents live apart for a while until they resolve their differences and can live together again. Other times, a separation leads to a divorce, a permanent separation. A separation or divorce is painful for all family members.

Meeting the Needs of Children

When parents divorce, it must be decided where the children will live. Usually, one parent is granted custody. **Custody** is *a legal decision about who has the right to make decisions that affect the children and who has the physical responsibility of caring for them.* Sometimes dual custody is awarded so that both parents share in the child-rearing. Adapting to a divorce requires a period of emotional adjustment for everyone. Children may experience the stages of grief—from shock and disbelief to anger, sorrow, and finally, acceptance.

Family Adjustments

Other changes occur in families after a separation or divorce. Children must learn to cope with the absence of a parent. They may have to adjust to a lower standard of living, as maintaining separate residences means less money to go around. Eventually, the children may need to adjust to a stepparent or a blended family.

Surviving a Breakup

Regardless of which parent gets custody of the children, it is important to remember that parents divorce each other, not their children. Although parents' feelings for each other have changed, their love for their children can stay the same. Sometimes, children feel they are the cause of the parents' separation. Divorce happens for many reasons, but the children are seldom the cause.

Domestic Violence

When stress explodes in a family and reactions are out of control, domestic violence can result. **Domestic violence** is *any acts of violence involving family members.* Domestic violence usually takes place at home but can occur anywhere. The violence may be directed by or at any family member and can be of a physical, sexual, or emotional nature. No one deserves to be a victim of abuse, and domestic violence is a criminal act that can be prosecuted by law.

Spousal Abuse

The amount of **spousal abuse**, *domestic abuse directed at a spouse,* in our society is disturbing. Each year women are the victims of more than 4.5 million violent abuse crimes in the United States. Spousal abuse occurs in all kinds of families regardless of income, level of education, or race. Fortunately, groups and agencies have formed to help victims of spousal abuse and their children. You may

---

COOPERATIVE LEARNING

ABUSE, VALUES, AND MEDIA. Spousal and child abuse was long tolerated or ignored in the United States and still is in parts of the world. People have tended to write off family abuse as parental, spousal, or cultural prerogatives. More recently, the media has raised public awareness and shifted societal attitudes. Have students work in groups, using Readers Guide or computers to research the number and types of articles about family abuse over the past 20 years. At what point does the amount and type of coverage shift? How do students see the media affecting public values on abuse? Have them examine their own values by suggesting abusive situations, such as beating a child or leaving a young child home alone, and deciding whether they would report the situation.

be familiar with programs in your community that are available to assist these families.

Child Abuse

No one knows exactly how much child abuse occurs in our country, since many cases go unreported. **Child abuse** is *domestic abuse directed at a child.* The abuse need not be physical or sexual. **Emotional abuse** is *a pattern of behavior that attacks a child's emotional development and sense of self-worth.* Emotional abuse can be just as damaging to a child as physical or sexual abuse. Child abuse also may include **neglect,** *a failure to provide a child's physical or emotional needs.* Physical needs include adequate food, clothing, shelter, and medical care. Emotional neglect may take the form of indifference or refusing to listen when the child has a problem.

RUNNING AWAY

Children who live in abusive homes may try to escape the abuse by running away. Living on the streets with no money or job skills, however, is a poor solution. Runaways often become victims of **exploitation,** *being used for someone else's benefit.* Runaways are prime targets for people dealing in pornography and prostitution. The best solution for children suffering abuse or neglect is to ask for help from reliable sources. Some of these resources are addressed in Lesson 3 of this chapter.

LESSON 2 Review

Reviewing Facts and Vocabulary

1. Name three changes that might cause stress in a family.
2. What are some options available to a teen trying to cope with family stress?
3. Why do runaways often become victims of exploitation?

Thinking Critically

4. *Analyzing.* What problems might you expect a friend to face whose sick grandfather is coming to live with the family? Tell how your friend could cope with the stress.
5. *Synthesizing.* What are the important issues for a person who is considering running away to escape an abusive situation at home?

Applying Health Skills

6. *In Your Home and School.* Think of one stress your family is currently facing and decide how you can help. Remember that one way to help is to learn to cope with stress. You might decide to read books or talk to others at school who have faced similar problems. Talk with your parents about the stress the problem is causing you. Make a list of things you can do to help.

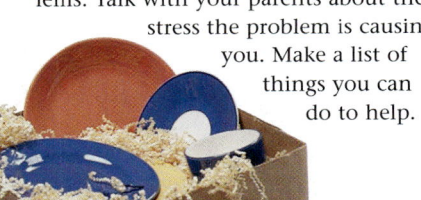

LESSON 2 LOOKING AT THE HEALTH OF THE FAMILY **287**

ASSESS

EVALUATING THE LESSON

Assign and discuss the Lesson 2 Review; then administer, grade, and discuss the *Lesson 39 Quiz* in the TCR. 📁

RETEACHING

- Encourage students to use the headings within the lesson to create graphic organizers. The organizers should illustrate important points and provide a summary of the lesson at a glance.
- Ask students to complete *Reteaching Activity 39* in the TCR. 📁

ENRICHMENT

Have students investigate the kidnapping of children by a parent. Ask them to find answers to questions such as: In what kinds of situations does this occur? How often does it happen? What effects do they think the experience might have on the children involved? What are the legal consequences for the kidnappers? Have students summarize their findings and speculations in writing.

CLOSE

Write the lesson's major concepts on numbered, separate slips of paper. Place the slips into a box, and let each student draw one. Going in numerical order, have students define and summarize the concept written on the slip of paper they selected.

Lesson 2 Review

Answers to Reviewing Facts and Vocabulary

1. Any three: arrival of a baby or grandparent, moving, loss of a job, illness or disability.
2. Talking with a parent or other adult or with siblings; doing what one can to help the family out; reading books on the subject or talking with classmates.
3. Because they have no money or skills.

Answers to Thinking Critically

4. Change in family routine, less room in the home, financial strain, less attention paid to the children, change in lines of communication among family members. Other answers will vary.
5. Where to live, how to support himself or herself, sources of emotional support, where to find help to avoid leaving home.

Support Systems for Families

FOCUS

LESSON OBJECTIVES

After studying this lesson, students should be able to

- identify sources of help for families in crisis.
- outline steps they can take to show they care and to strengthen their family.

MOTIVATOR

Write the following on the chalkboard for students to work on while attendance is being taken: *There are many threats to the health of today's families. List some specific things that you can do to help strengthen your family.*

INTRODUCING THE LESSON

Have students share their responses to the Motivator. Tell the class that this lesson is about troubled families as well as healthy family systems. Students will learn more about where families can go for help in times of crisis.

INTRODUCING HEALTH TERMS

- Have each student create a crossword puzzle or sentence completion activity using all the vocabulary terms. Afterward, ask them to exchange their puzzle or activity with another student. Provide several minutes for them to complete each other's word challenge.
- Ask students to complete Vocabulary Activity 12 and Chapter Study Guide 12 in the *Student Workbook.* ☞

Support Systems for Families

A s noted in Lesson 1, the health of a family system is dependent on the health of individual family members. When one member suffers from substance abuse or a similarly serious problem, the health of the entire family suffers. Fortunately, sources are available to which families can turn when the family system is in a state of turmoil.

HEALTH TERMS

crisis center
foster care
family counseling
mediator

HEALTH CONCEPTS

- Sources of help in the community exist for families in distress.
- A healthy family is a work in progress, requiring an ongoing effort on the part of each member.

Sources of Help

Help for families in crisis is often only a phone call away. Any family member can call a **crisis center**, *a facility equipped to handle emergencies and make referrals for persons who need help.* Many communities also provide crisis hot lines, special phone numbers people can call to receive help 24 hours a day. Persons who answer the phones at crisis centers and hot lines are caring listeners. They have had training and can advise you where to get help. They are familiar with many different kinds of problems and can guide the caller to a solution. The solution often includes a referral to a community service, a support group, or a family counselor.

Lesson 3 Resources

TEACHER'S CLASSROOM RESOURCES
- ☞ **Concept Map** Activity 40
- ☞ **Lesson 40 Quiz**
- ☞ **Lesson Plan 40**
- ☞ **Reteaching** Activity 40

STUDENT WORKBOOK
- ☞ **Applying Health Skills 40**

- ☞ **Chapter Study Guide 12**
- ☞ **Vocabulary** Activity 12

TRANSPARENCIES
- 💧 **Transparency 45**

MULTIMEDIA
- 🔴 **ABCNews InterActive™ VHS/Videodisc,** *Violence Prevention*

Community Services

Most communities have a variety of services helpful to families in distress. Both public and private agencies offer parenting and conflict resolution classes. Food, clothing, and shelter can be provided for families who are having trouble meeting their basic needs. Agencies also offer financial aid, medical care, and help in finding employment.

Parents in distress who feel they cannot safely care for their children may be able to bring them to a crisis nursery, where the children will be safe and cared for. Children in abusive situations also are sometimes removed from their families and placed in **foster care**, *under the guidance and supervision of a family headed up by parents or a parent who is not related to the child by birth.* Foster families often serve as a "port in the storm" for an abused or neglected child by providing the gentle and loving care that has been missing from the child's life. Women who are victims of spousal abuse and their children can be placed in safe houses until they are ready to start a new life free from violence.

Support Groups

Talking with others who face similar problems can be very beneficial to persons in distress. Millions of people attend **support groups**, meetings at which persons share their problems and get help from others who struggle with the same problem. Just knowing that they are not alone is helpful to many people. Hearing how others have handled the problem helps many persons cope on a day-to-day basis.

Alcoholics Anonymous (AA) is probably the best-known network of support groups in the country. Many alcoholics have found the strength to stay sober through AA. Support groups also are available for teen alcoholics as well as family members of alcoholics. Other support groups help persons who face such problems as violence and serious illness in the family.

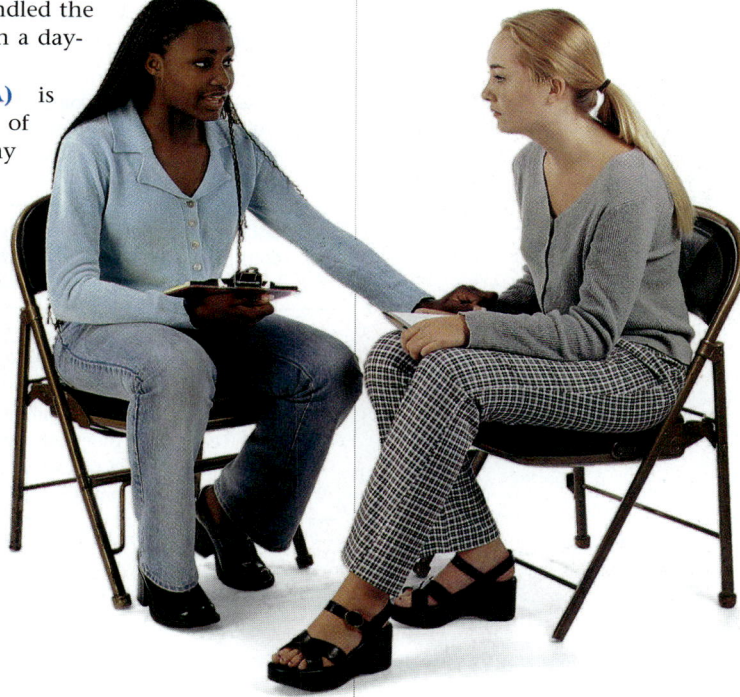

> ▶ *Support groups help teens cope with family stress.*
> **ACTIVITY** *Explain how support groups help people deal with problems.*

hotlink

support group For more information about support groups, see Chapter 9, page 227.

Alcoholics Anonymous For more on Alcoholics Anonymous (AA) and the work this organization does to help recovering alcoholics, see Chapter 25, page 565.

TEACH

L3 Guest Speaker

Invite representatives of community agencies, counseling services, and self-help groups to discuss their efforts in helping families cope with crises.

L1 Discussing

Lead students in brainstorming a list of factors that might deter families from seeking outside support or help with problems. *(Examples might include embarrassment, denial that a problem exists, fear of the unknown, lack of knowledge about what help is available, refusal to admit failure or inadequacy, cost of professional services, fear of a breach of confidentiality, etc.)*

LEP Personal Involvement

Ask students: Who could you go to if your family were in trouble? Have students use their private Health Journals to list the names of some people who could help.

L2 Class Activity

Select students to act out situations involving a friend who is a victim of abuse or neglect. Have them practice encouraging the friend to seek help. Follow up by discussing sources of help available at the local level.

PROMOTING COMPREHENSIVE SCHOOL HEALTH

ADULTS AS MODELS. You can use resources in the immediate school environment to stress the importance of lifelong responsibility for personal health. Since most school sites involve employees from a wide spectrum of age groups, students can witness how employees model good health behavior. For example, faculty and staff can be encouraged to participate in a student-teacher volleyball game. They might speak to your class about their personal evolution of maturity and intellect. Above all, everyone of all ages should be encouraged to recognize their role in making the school community function positively. For more information, consult *Promoting Comprehensive School Health* in the TCR.

Building Health Skills

Obtaining Help
Skill: Obtaining Help

Ask: What kinds of phone calls are difficult for you—or for other teens—to make? What can you do to overcome your worries and make those difficult calls? Let volunteers share their own experiences and approaches. Then explain that many people have trouble using the phone to find help with a difficult family situation. Which of the techniques described in class today might help a person make that kind of call? After a brief discussion, have students read the Building Health Skills feature to learn specific steps that teens can use to make calling for help easier.

ABCNEWS INTERACTIVE™

VIOLENCE PREVENTION
(Side 1)

Chapter 7: Getting Along at Home

Frames 22859-27023

VIOLENCE PREVENTION
(Side 2)

Chapter 10: Active Listening

Frames 30699-35410

Psychological Counseling

Some families receive help from **family counseling**, *therapy to restore healthy relationships in a family.* They meet regularly with counselors to discuss the family's issues and work on finding solutions. This counseling can provide families with the skills they need for setting boundaries and solving conflicts on their own.

Occasionally, a person may benefit from **psychotherapy**. Psychotherapists may help a person realize that she or he learned abusive family patterns in childhood. These patterns can be broken by recognizing the patterns and replacing them with healthy behaviors.

Mediation

Couples going through a divorce or trying to resolve custody issues may go into mediation. A **mediator** is *a person who helps others resolve issues to the satisfaction of both parties.* The mediator sets ground rules

hotlink

psychotherapy For more on psychotherapy and the problems it is used to treat, see Chapter 10, page 250.

Building Health Skills

Obtaining Help

MOST PEOPLE FIND it difficult to actually pick up the phone and place a call for help. "What will I say?" they wonder. "What if I can't think of anything to say at all?"

Imagine that you have a friend who wants to make a call to ask for help. You could assist your friend in preparing to call by helping him or her follow these steps.

1. **State the problem to yourself.** Write down on a piece of paper what the problem is and what you will say to the person who answers the phone. Then, if you become tongue-tied, you can simply read your statement from the piece of paper.

2. **List any questions you have.** Think about your reasons for calling, and write down all questions you might have for the counselor. Don't dismiss a topic because you think it might be trivial.

3. **Practice.** Rehearse the call with a close friend or family member who will act as the counselor on the phone. Practice until you feel confident.

4. **Make the call.** Go ahead and call the resource. Have a pencil and blank paper ready. If the counselor makes suggestions or offers the names of other personnel you might contact, write them down. Consider the suggestions that the counselor has for you.

5. **Be prepared.** Decide on the best course of action, in case the problem does not go away or comes up again. Being prepared and knowing how you will act can lessen the stress you feel. Also, knowing that help is just a phone call away can make the problem seem less severe.

HEALTH LITERACY

SELF-DIRECTED LEARNER. Invite students to use on-line and print sources to examine research suggesting that patterns of relating formed with siblings may determine adult patterns of relating with peers, coworkers, spouses, and romantic partners. Some experts believe that in many cases, siblings influence patterns of relating to peers even more than parents do. They may wish to look for specific information, such as which patterns of relating with siblings are most likely to be repeated in relationships with adult peers, which have healthy or unhealthy effects, what the articles say about only children. Have them summarize their findings in a brief written report. Suggest that students with siblings examine their patterns of relating and determine those that they would like to carry into adulthood.

and facilitates effective **communication** that allows each party to be heard. Mediators do not solve the problem, but help the two parties find a solution, usually through **compromise**. Mediation is less stressful than taking problems to court and can be used to solve any conflicts that family members cannot resolve on their own.

Doing Your Part

What can you do to help keep your family strong? What steps should you follow if your family is hurting? Here are some ways to show you care and to strengthen your family.

- Show appreciation for things done well. Saying "thank you" works at home, too.
- Encourage others, even your parents. Most people never get enough encouragement or know they are appreciated.
- Show concern when a family member has a problem. Offer to help or to get help.
- Stop criticizing. Be tactful and constructive. Avoid nagging.
- Show empathy by putting yourself in the other person's position. Try to see situations from his or her point of view.
- Listen to what other family members say. Listening is more than simply not talking. Avoid interrupting, daydreaming, jumping to conclusions, or just waiting for your turn to talk.

hotlink

communication For more information on communication and the steps involved in being an effective speaker and listener, see Chapter 11, page 263.

compromise For more information on the skill of compromise, see Chapter 11, page 261.

LESSON 3 *Review*

Reviewing Facts and Vocabulary

1. Give two reasons why a family would seek outside help for a problem.
2. What is the purpose of family counseling?
3. How does a mediator help families resolve conflicts?

Thinking Critically

4. **Evaluating.** Alicia often hears shouts and screams coming from the apartment next door. She has seen bruises on the neighbor's son. What do you think Alicia should do?
5. **Synthesizing.** Tell what kind of help each family is receiving: (a) Leon's family meets with a therapist every week to learn conflict resolution skills. (b) A person not related to the family helps the Smiths decide how to divide up their property after a divorce. (c) Dinesh meets every week with other teens whose parents have serious illnesses.

Applying Health Skills

6. ***In Your Home.*** Meet with family members to discuss ways in which your family could benefit from outside support systems or how your family could provide support for other families. Develop a plan and put the plan into action.

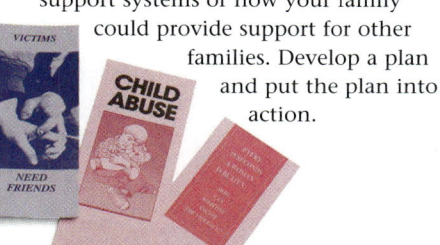

ASSESS

EVALUATING THE LESSON

Assign and discuss the Lesson 3 Review; then administer, grade, and discuss the *Lesson 40 Quiz* in the TCR.

RETEACHING

- Have students create a brochure that presents the types of services available to families in crisis.
- Ask students to complete *Reteaching Activity 40* in the TCR.
- Use *Transparency 45* to review resources for getting help.

ENRICHMENT

Have students find out what services are available in the community to assist families. Ask them to telephone one of them to learn what the most common family problems seem to be. Allow them to share their findings with the class.

CLOSE

Discuss with the class the many sources of support available for members of a family in trouble. Emphasize, however, that it is important that members recognize and seek help early, before the problem worsens. Any incident or concern should be discussed with a parent or trusted adult.

Lesson 3 Review

Answers to Reviewing Facts and Vocabulary

1. Answers may include: Intervention is necessary to stop abusive behavior, the family is too unhealthy to solve its own problems, substance abuse has created serious disruption in family communication, etc.
2. To restore healthy family relationships.
3. By setting ground rules and facilitating communication.

Answers to Thinking Critically

4. Answers will vary.
5. (a) family counseling; (b) mediation; (c) support group.

Health Skills Activities

Health Skills Activities

ACTIVITY 1
HEALTH SKILLS

Communication—Conflict Resolution

➤ **National Standards**
This activity meets these National Health Standards: 5.7; 5.8.

Teach

- Create as many brief conflict scenarios as there will be groups carrying out the activity. Each should be written on an index card to be handed out at random to groups. Vary the family composition and type of problem as much as possible.
- Suggest that group members each choose a character within the scenario and try "getting inside that person's head." In other words, how would they feel if they were that person? What would their needs and wants be?
- Remind students during the voting phase that this is intended to be a learning experience and that skits should be chosen on how effectively they teach a lesson on conflict resolution.

ACTIVITY 2
HEALTH SKILLS

Self Management

➤ **National Standards**
This activity meets this National Health Standard: 3.4.

Teach

- Suggest that each student begin by using what he or she already knows about hobbies, likes, and dislikes among members of his or her family. By making a list of such points, the student will have an easier time initiating a dialogue with family members, as well as coming up with an idea for an activity that will appeal to all members.
- Allow students to share their successes on a volunteer basis. Do not insist that all class members speak, since some may have difficulty sharing experiences.
- Encourage students to make a handbook of ideas for family traditions to be kept in a classroom resource corner.

Activity 1 — Solving Family Conflicts

Acting out problems in skits is one good way for families to practice conflict resolution. What steps do you take to solve conflicts within your family?

Directions

1. Working in a group, read the family conflict description provided by your teacher. Brainstorm a solution that would be acceptable to all family members.
2. Share and compare resolutions with the class. Vote on the best idea (which may be a composite of several or even all), and develop it into a 10-minute skit.
3. If possible, videotape the skit to share with other classes.

Time
50 minutes

Materials
paper, pen or pencil, video recorder (optional)

Self-Assessment

✓ Identified at least three strategies for resolving family conflicts.
✓ Demonstrated effective communication skills outlined in the chapter.

Activity 2 — Starting a Family Tradition

Does your family have traditions? These ritual celebrations can help bring about a feeling of belonging and help strengthen the family unit.

Directions

1. Explore with family members the types of activities each enjoys doing. Think about how the activity could be made appealing for all family members.
2. Based on this input, propose three new family traditions, such as an annual family biking day or a monthly movie night.
3. Get family members' reactions to your proposal. Refine ideas as needed.
4. Follow through with one or more events. Take snapshots, or write about the event. Share your experiences in class.

Time
50 minutes plus outside interview time

Materials
paper, pen or pencil, camera (optional)

Self-Assessment

✓ Created at least three ideas for new family traditions.
✓ Recorded the event and shared it with the class.

292 CHAPTER 12 HEALTHY FAMILY RELATIONSHIPS

ASSESSMENT SCORING

Using a four-level rubric, the student has achieved a 4 if:

ACTIVITY 1

✔ Student demonstrated an understanding of the nature of conflict.
✔ Student demonstrated an understanding of the nature of relationships within families.
✔ Student identified at least three strategies for resolving family conflicts.
✔ Student demonstrated effective communication skills outlined in the chapter.

ACTIVITY 2

✔ Student was attentive in discussion of family traditions.
✔ Student successfully completed a list of personal hobbies and pastimes in the family.
✔ Student developed at least three ideas for new family traditions.
✔ Student gave evidence of having tried to initiate new traditions in his or her family.

HEALTH NEWS VIDEO

Balancing Family Stress

Healthy family relationships are an important aspect of your overall health. Stressful situations are often a natural part of living with a family. Stress creates physical changes in your body.

Researchers say that temporary stress is healthier than stress that lasts for a long time. Stressful family relationships are more harmful because they are long term. When you reduce ongoing sources of stress, you improve all aspects of your health. Recognizing this and knowing how to handle stress can help you and your family cope.

Play the Video

STRESS
Which is the least harmful?

CNN. All Rights Reserved.

Think About It

◗ Explain the relationships between stress, ACTH, cortisol, and your immune system. Then tell how these physical changes can affect your mental well-being.

◗ Which examples are most harmful? Why are family stressors more damaging to your health?

◗ What criteria do researchers use to evaluate different kinds of stress?

◗ What advice might stress researchers give to help you build healthy family relationships?

CNN HEALTH NEWS **293**

MORE ABOUT . . . . .

TECHNOLOGY AND SCIENCE. Although too much cortisol can be dangerous, some is essential. Cortisol is a hormone released by the adrenal glands. It helps regulate blood pressure and the way the body uses of proteins, fats, and carbohydrates.

The amount of cortisol released into the body increases during physical stress (such as injury, illness, or extreme temperatures) or emotional stress. Cortisol helps the body handle stress by changing how it gets energy. Cortisol breaks down muscle proteins, releasing amino acids which are converted to glucose by the liver. This process helps to provide the brain with the energy needed to handle the stress.

CHAPTER **12** *Review*

CHECKING COMPREHENSION

- Assign and discuss the chapter review.
- Use the MindJogger Videoquiz to review the chapter. 🔴

CHAPTER 12 REVIEW ANSWERS

Using Health Terms

1. affirmation
2. sibling
3. exploitation
4. child abuse
5. custody
6. domestic violence
7. spousal abuse
8. neglect
9. emotional abuse
10. family counseling
11. crisis center
12. mediator
13. support group
14. foster care

Recalling the Facts

1. Siblings.
2. Because society's health is directly related to the family's health.
3. Physical, mental, emotional.
4. A sense of belonging, feeling secure and loved, and good self-esteem.
5. Affirmation, trust, commitment, time together, communication, respect, solving problems together, love.
6. Financial strain, less room in the house, rivalry for parents' attention, increased demands on parents, new responsibilities for siblings.
7. Loss of a job, overuse of credit cards, substance abuse, illness or disability.
8. During separation, a couple lives apart and tries to resolve their differences. Divorce is a permanent end of the marriage.
9. Answers will vary.
10. Failure to provide for a child's emotional and physical needs. Examples will vary.

Using Health Terms

On a separate sheet of paper, write the term that best matches each definition below.

LESSON 1

1. Providing positive input that helps others feel appreciated and supported.
2. Brother or sister.

LESSON 2

3. Being used for someone else's benefit.
4. Domestic abuse directed at a child.
5. A legal decision about who has the right to make decisions that affect the children and who has the physical responsibility of caring for them.
6. Any acts of violence involving family members.
7. Domestic abuse directed at a spouse.
8. A failure to provide a child's physical or emotional needs.
9. A pattern of behavior that attacks a child's emotional development and sense of self-worth.

LESSON 3

10. Therapy to restore healthy relationships in a family.
11. A facility equipped to handle emergencies and make referrals for persons who need help.
12. A person who helps others resolve issues to the satisfaction of both parties.
13. Meetings at which persons share their problems and get help from others who struggle with the same problem.
14. Under the guidance and supervision of a family headed up by parents or a parent who is not related to the child by birth.

Recalling the Facts

Using complete sentences, answer the following questions.

LESSON 1

1. What is another term for a person's brothers and sisters?
2. Why is the family called a basic unit of society?
3. Name three different kinds of basic needs of children.
4. What emotional needs do children have?
5. What are some of the traits of a healthy family?

LESSON 2

6. How might the arrival of a new baby create family stress?
7. Name three things that cause financial problems in families.

8. What is the difference between a separation and a divorce?
9. How might an illness or disability in one family member affect all family members?
10. What kinds of omissions on the part of parents can be considered neglect?

LESSON 3

11. What services do communities offer for families in distress?
12. What is a hot line?
13. In what ways might an agency protect family members in danger from abuse?
14. How might a support group help a teenager whose father is an alcoholic?

11. Crisis centers, support groups, family counseling, foster care, shelters for abused spouses and children.
12. A special phone number that people can call to receive help 24 hours a day.
13. Placement in a safe house, providing help from mental health professionals, referral to legal counsel, etc.
14. A support group can offer coping strategies and, just by allowing a teen to talk about the problem, can help him or her become better able to live with the situation and not feel alone.

Thinking Critically

LESSON 1

1. ***Analyzing.*** When both his parents work late, Carlo prepares dinner for his family. Identify two benefits Carlo might derive from this action.
2. ***Synthesizing.*** Explain how taking responsibility and sharing family tasks can strengthen family relationships and prepare you for adulthood.

LESSON 2

3. ***Synthesizing.*** Your cousin Angela's parents have recently separated. While they are trying to work out their problems, Angela is coming to live with your family. What kind of support and help will Angela need?

LESSON 3

4. ***Comparing and Contrasting.*** How could each person best be helped? (a) Dan's parents both drink heavily, and he has no one he can talk to about it. (b) Connie is a single mother who has just lost her job and doesn't have enough food to feed her three children. (c) The Huyhns are getting a divorce and cannot agree among themselves whom their son, Pat, will live with.

Making the Connection

1. ***Social Studies.*** Interview a grandparent or elderly neighbor to find out how that person's family dealt with family stress or conflict when he or she was your age. Compare these methods with the ones recommended for families today.
2. ***Math.*** Keep track of the time you spend with your family for one week. Multiply by 52 to find out how much time you spend with your family in a year. Do the same for several other categories, such as school, sports, and friends. Then determine what percentage of time per year is spent in each category. Make a pie chart to illustrate your findings.

BEYOND THE CLASSROOM

PARENTAL INVOLVEMENT Interview a family member who has experienced a loss of job or relationship or faced financial or other hardships. Find out what he or she did to cope with the stress. Write a report on your findings to share with your class.

COMMUNITY INVOLVEMENT Investigate agencies in your community to find out about resources that are available to assist families. Make a list of community resources and what services they offer. Share the list with family members and classmates.

SCHOOL-TO-CAREER

Exploring Careers. Invite a school counselor to speak to the class and discuss the types of family problems that occur among students. Have the counselor explain how he or she works with the families to find solutions to their problems. What training and qualities are needed for someone in this position?

Thinking Critically

1. Any two: a sense of worth, a sense of being able to help the family, more time spent with the family together, an opportunity to express love.
2. Answers will vary.
3. Someone to listen, encouragement in getting on with her life and activities, reassurance that she's not the cause of the problem, etc.
4. (a) support group; (b) community agency; (c) mediator.

Making the Connection

1. Findings will vary.
2. Charts will vary.

Evaluate

- Use the reproducible *Chapter 12 Test* in the TCR, or construct your own using the Testmaker software.
- Use *Performance Assessment Activity 12* in the TCR.

Enrichment

Ask students to complete *Cross-Curriculum Activity 12* in the TCR.

Beyond the Classroom

Keep students involved in the community, and encourage parent participation by assigning the activities on this page for students to work on outside of class.

Peer Relationships

	FEATURES	CLASSROOM RESOURCES

LESSON 1

Developing Responsible Relationships

pages 298–303

connections
Social Studies

"Rites of Passage," *page 301*

health lab

"Dating and Television," *page 302*

☞ Concept Map Activity 41
☞ Lesson 41 Quiz
☞ Lesson Plan 41
☞ Reteaching Activity 41

LESSON 2

Peer Pressure and Refusal Skills

pages 304–309

Building Health Skills

"Resisting Peer Pressure," *page 306*

update
▶ Our Changing World

"Dealing with School Bullies" *page 307*

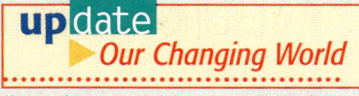

Making Responsible Decisions

"Using Refusal Skills," *page 308*

☞ Concept Map Activity 42
☞ Cooperative Learning Activity 13
☞ Decision-Making Activity 13
☞ Enrichment Activity 13
☞ Health Lab 13
☞ Lesson 42 Quiz
☞ Lesson Plan 42
☞ Reteaching Activity 42
🖐 Transparencies 43, 44

Chapter Resources

ACTIVITIES

- Cross-Curriculum Activity 13
- Health Lab 13
- Health Skills Activities 13
- Parent Letter and Activities 13

ASSESSMENT

- Chapter 13 Test
- Performance Assessment Activity 13
- Testmaker Software

STUDENT ACTIVITIES WORKBOOK

- Applying Health Skills 41, 42
- Study Guide 13
- Vocabulary Activity 13

STUDENT DIVERSITY STRATEGIES

- Audiocassette Program (English)
- Audiocassette Program (Spanish)
- Spanish Parent Letters and Activities
- Spanish Summaries, Quizzes, and Activities

MULTIMEDIA COMPONENTS

- English Audiocassette Program
- Spanish Audiocassette Program
- MindJogger Videodisc and VHS program
- ABCNews InterActive™ VHS/Videodisc Series

MODULES

- *Abstinence,* Student Edition
- *Abstinence,* Teacher's Annotated Edition

National Health Education Standards

One of the main goals of the National Health Education Standards is to move students toward "health literacy." Health literacy is the capacity of individuals to obtain, interpret, and understand basic health information and services and the competence to use such information and services in ways which promote health. The health standards were developed by applying the characteristics of a well-educated, literate person within the context of health. The health literate person is:

- a critical thinker and problem solver
- a self-directed learner
- a responsible, productive citizen
- an effective communicator

Listed below are the Health Education Standards Performance Indicators addressed in each lesson of this chapter.

Lesson	Health Standards Performance Indicators
1	1.4, 4.1, 4.2, 5.3
2	1.4, 1.7, 5.6, 6.1

ONLINE RESOURCES

For a fresh approach to health topics and an in-depth look at health issues, use these online resources found under Teacher Resources at **health.glencoe.com**.

- **BLOCK SCHEDULE LESSON PLANS** Reinforce health concepts with outside readings selected especially for students. Each reading is accompanied by a lesson plan and activities to enhance
  - Reading Skills
  - Cross Curriculum
  - Media Literacy

- **TECHNOLOGY PROJECTS** Instructions and suggestions on how to use computer, Internet, and software with health lessons.

- **HEALTH UPDATES** Timely topics in health news, including late-breaking medical advances and updates on teen risk behaviors.

Out of Time?

If time does not permit teaching this chapter, you may use these features: Building Health Skills on page 306; Update on page 307; and Making Responsible Decisions on page 308.

BLOCK SCHEDULING

Block scheduling provides extended time for hands-on projects and activities. Use the following activities to engage students, provide further depth, and vary your instructional techniques:

- Connections (30 minutes) **pg. 301**
- Health Lab (45 minutes) **pg. 302**
- Update (30 minutes) **pg. 307**
- Health Skills Activity (60–90 minutes) **pg. 310**

Peer Relationships

CHAPTER OVERVIEW

Chapter 13 discusses the types of peer relationships and the impact peer influence has on the individual. Forms of negative peer pressure are examined and refusal skills are introduced.

LESSON 1 Peer relationships can take many forms, with varying amounts of personal involvement. Close relationships fulfill some of our most basic needs. As teens experience different relationships, they learn interpersonal skills, and they also learn about themselves.

LESSON 2 Peer pressure can have a positive or negative impact on an individual. To stand up to negative peer pressure, teens must recognize the situation and apply refusal skills. The decisions they make when negatively influenced and the manner in which they enforce those decisions has an effect on their health and the health of people around them.

Peer Relationships

HEALTH Online

CONFLICT RESOLUTION

What tactics do you and your peers rely on when faced with aggression or bullying in school? "Bully-proofing Programs" in the Health Updates section of **health.glencoe.com** talks about plans in place in schools across the country to deal with this social issue.

Hands-On Health

TEACHING STRATEGY

Sharing Health Skills Encourage students to prepare and share informational presentations with younger students. See Activity 50, "Peer to Peer," in the *Hands-On Health: Creative Teaching Strategies* booklet. 📕

Time Needed

30 minutes in class additional time to present posters

Supplies

• poster board
• art supplies

> ## 66 ...the only way to have a friend is to be one. 99
>
> —RALPH WALDO EMERSON
> AMERICAN WRITER AND ESSAYIST, (1803–1882)

Quick Write

Write five sentences, each one beginning with the words *A true friend is someone who*…. Share your definitions with your classmates of what it means to be a true friend.

Personal Health Inventory

Self-Inventory Write the numbers 1–10 on a sheet of paper. Read each statement below and respond by writing *yes, no,* or *sometimes* for each item. Write a *yes* only for items that you practice regularly. Save your responses.

1	I enjoy spending time with peers.
2	I have both casual and close friendships.
3	I am comfortable having friends of the opposite gender.
4	I recognize some of the limitations of belonging to cliques or clubs that exclude other teens.
5	I expect to be treated with consideration and respect by my friends or dates.
6	I spend time with groups as well as with individuals.
7	I use good communication skills and express my wishes clearly with friends or dates.
8	I try to exert positive peer pressure on my friends to behave responsibly.
9	I am able to say no to negative peer pressure.
10	I know how to assert myself when being pressured to do something I know to be wrong.

Follow-up After completing the chapter, retake this self-inventory. Pick two items that you need to work on and set a goal to improve your health behaviors.

TECHNOLOGY OPTIONS

ABC NEWS INTERACTIVE™ You may wish to use *Making Responsible Decisions* with this chapter. For your convenience, use the separate *ABCNews InterActive™ Bar Code Correlation* that accompanies the *Glencoe Health* program. ▶

MINDJOGGER VIDEOQUIZ

To preview or review chapter content, you may wish to use the *MindJogger Videoquiz* that accompanies Chapter 13. ▶

INTRODUCING THE CHAPTER

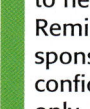

Personal Health Inventory

Have students read the Self-Inventory, and ask volunteers to explain how each statement relates to healthy relationships with peers. Remind students that their responses to these statements are confidential and for their own use only. Let them record those responses in their private Health Journals, and suggest that they head their journal entries "My Relationships with Peers."

- Review how family relationships provide the foundation for emotional health. Introduce how peer relationships increasingly take on importance and contribute to the emotional needs of the individual as the person matures. Explain that this chapter will discuss the different types of peer relationships and examine the positive and negative impact peer relationships can have on the individual.
- Let students read the quotation on this page and complete the Quick Write. Ask for volunteers to share their definitions of true friendship. Discuss with students how longtime friendships often change over the years and can become more exciting, and sometimes more confusing, as part of the process of growing into adulthood. Tell students they will learn more about different kinds of peer relationships as they study Chapter 13.
- Distribute Parent Letter 13 in the *Parent Letters and Activities* booklet in the TCR. ▶

Chapter 13   **297**

Developing Responsible Relationships

Developing Responsible Relationships

FOCUS

LESSON OBJECTIVES

After studying this lesson, students should be able to

- describe the types of peer relationships.
- discuss the negative effects of cliques.
- describe the dating relationship.

MOTIVATOR

Write the following on the chalkboard for students to work on while attendance is being taken: *Write a list of all the benefits of a close friendship.*

INTRODUCING THE LESSON

Refer to the Motivator. Ask students to share their lists of benefits. Discuss how the benefits satisfy basic emotional needs for closeness and sharing. Explain that this lesson will discuss friendship and the many forms it takes, as well as examine the role of dating and the importance of responsibility in such relationships.

INTRODUCING HEALTH TERMS

- Have students determine the meanings of the terms *clique, prejudice,* and *stereotype* and then write a paragraph using the terms. Ask volunteers to share their paragraphs.
- Ask students to complete Vocabulary Activity 13 and Chapter Study Guide 13 in the *Student Workbook.* ☞

D uring the teen years, you begin a search for a personal identity—shaped at least in part by people the same age as you who are going through the same search. During adolescence, peers take on a new and greater importance than ever.

HEALTH TERMS

platonic friendship
clique
prejudice
stereotype
infatuation

HEALTH CONCEPTS

- Friendships take on a greater importance during the teen years, during which time teens search for an identity and sense of belonging.
- A strong need to fit in often magnifies differences that can lead to stereotyping and prejudice.
- Physical attraction to another person is a normal, healthy part of growing up.

Types of Peer Relationships

A s a small child, you had a limited circle of peers. Now that you are older, you have a larger circle from which to choose your relationships. You may realize for the first time that there are people of all ages, races, religions, and backgrounds with whom you can cultivate relationships. You can choose people who support and encourage your best qualities. You can change or back out of relationships that have a negative influence on your health, your safety, your self-esteem, or your values. No relationship can be healthy unless both parties feel valued and want the relationship.

Friendships

As noted in Chapter 11, a friendship is a significant relationship between two people based on caring, respect, consideration, and

Lesson 1 Resources

TEACHER'S CLASSROOM RESOURCES

- **Concept Map** Activity 41
- **Lesson 41 Quiz**
- **Lesson Plan 41**
- **Parent Letter and Activities 13**
- **Reteaching** Activity 41

STUDENT WORKBOOK

- **Applying Health Skills 41**
- **Chapter Study Guide 13**
- **Vocabulary** Activity 13

MULTIMEDIA

- ABCNews InterActive™ VHS/Videodisc, *Teenage Sexuality*

trust. A friend is someone with whom you share confidences, interests, hobbies, or other friends. Having friends is a basic part of social health. It can help you define, understand, and reinforce your values.

There are many kinds of friendships. Friendships vary in importance and in how challenging and complicated they are. Maintaining friendships can be hard work, but they are usually worth the effort.

CASUAL FRIENDSHIPS

Casual friends are peers with whom you feel socially connected. You might choose to sit with casual friends at ball games or at lunchtime in the cafeteria. These friendships, however, do not fill some of the deeper needs humans have.

CLOSE FRIENDSHIPS

A close friend is more likely to share with you what he or she is really feeling and thinking and, in turn, make you feel comfortable doing the same. You may trust a close friend with your secrets or go to this person when you are hurting, confused, or in trouble. He or she might give you honest criticism and encourage you to apologize or be accountable for your mistakes. Because you may care deeply for this person, a real friend is also more likely to make you angry or hurt. Losing or having to share a close friend with someone else can be painful. It is important to remind yourself that no one owns anyone else—people must be free to choose with whom they want to be and when. Friends try to work through conflicts. This helps friendships stay healthy and grow.

PLATONIC FRIENDSHIPS

Not all close friendships are made up of same-gender pairs. Sometimes a male and a female can become real buddies in what is called a *platonic* relationship. A **platonic friendship** is *a relationship with a member of the opposite gender in which there is affection, but no sexual activity.* Such a relationship can be a wonderful way to grow to understand and feel comfortable with the opposite gender without feeling any of the pressures of dating. Such friends, in fact, can be a great source of advice in the area of dating problems. Above all else, having platonic friendships helps you begin to recognize that individuals of the opposite gender are human beings just like you, with the same kinds of fears, needs, and feelings.

HEALTH Online

Learn how good communication skills can improve relationships at **health.glencoe.com**.

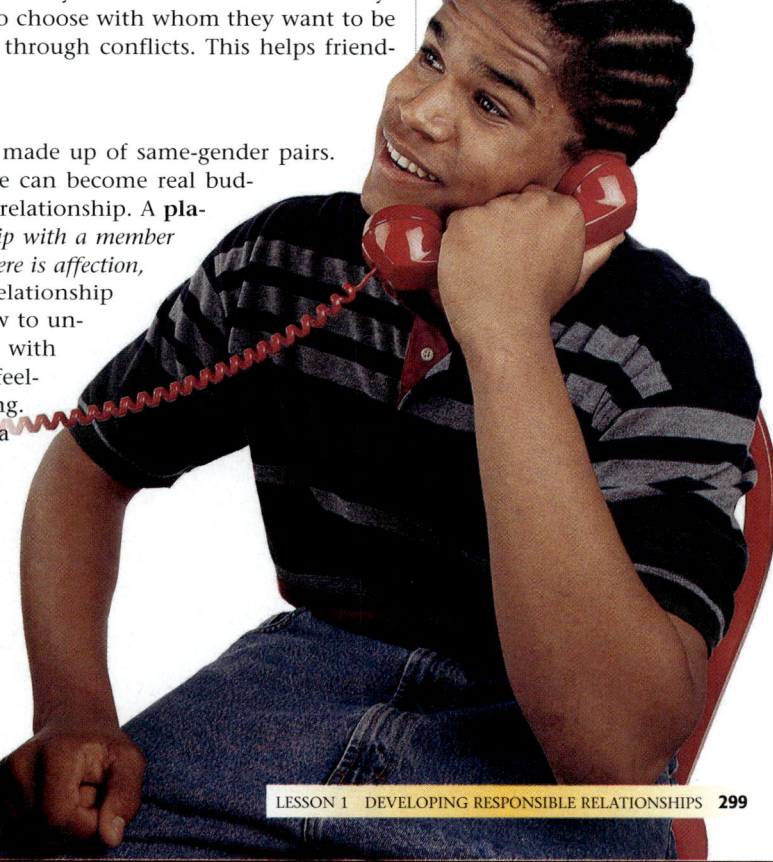

▼ *Teenagers who share the same interests often become friends.*

ACTIVITY *Name several possible interests teenagers may share with their peers.*

LESSON 1 DEVELOPING RESPONSIBLE RELATIONSHIPS **299**

TEACH

L1 Writing

Have students write private Health Journal entries recalling the small circle of peers they had as very young children. Ask: Who were your peers? How did you relate to them? Are you still friends? Why or why not?

L1 Analyzing

Ask: How are casual friendships and close friendships alike? What are the most important differences? Why is it important to have both kinds of friendships?

L1 Discussing

Pose these questions: What are some examples of platonic friendships between characters in TV programs or current movies? How can you tell those relationships are platonic friendships? What special benefits do you think this kind of friendship offers teens?

TEENAGE SEXUALITY (Side 2)

Chapter 3: Self-Esteem and Sexuality

Frames 2008-4673

Chapter 4: Relationships: The Girl's Perspective

Frames 4675-6777

Chapter 5: Relationships: The Boy's Perspective

Frames 6779-9045

COOPERATIVE ▶ LEARNING

RELATIONSHIPS IN FICTION. Group students. Tell each student to bring to class a story about a romantic or platonic relationship between a male and a female. Individual group members may watch and report on films or television programs that involve platonic or romantic relationships between males and females. Members should report on their pieces of fiction and summarize the message about the relative value of friendships and romances. Suggest they follow up with a discussion of platonic versus romantic relationships. Then have each group create a skit about both a romantic relationship and a platonic relationship between a male and a female.

L1 Parental Involvement

Suggest that students talk with their parents or other close adults about cliques. Students might ask questions such as these: What kinds of cliques existed at your school? Which—if any—did you belong to? How did you feel about cliques at school? Why?

L3 Researching

Ask students to suggest ways in which specific stereotypes might lead to prejudicial treatment.

L1 Discussing

Initiate a discussion of what is meant by dating. Ask: What do you regard as serious dating versus casual dating?

Dangers of Positive Stereotyping

keeping Fit

Discuss with students ways to respond to stereotypical comments made by a friend. Should a comment be ignored, or should you draw your friend's attention to the comment? Are there circumstances that would influence how you respond to a stereotypical comment?

Cliques

In their search for an identity, some teens form or become part of a **clique** (KLEEK)—*a small, narrow circle of friends, usually with similar backgrounds or tastes, that excludes people they view as outsiders.* A clique may be tightly or loosely knit and may have its own regular meeting place. This place can be something as simple as a table in the cafeteria that the clique has claimed as its private "turf." Clique members may treat non-members with scorn, ridicule, or indifference.

Although being part of a clique may give members a sense of belonging, it can also be damaging because members are often discouraged from thinking and acting as individuals. Being part of the popular crowd isn't fun if, in an effort to fit in, you cannot be yourself or if you feel pressure to do things that go against your values. Clique members may also be missing out on the benefits of meeting and interacting with a variety of people, which is important to an individual's social health.

One of the most negative aspects of cliques is that their beliefs and actions are prejudicial. **Prejudice** is *a negative feeling toward someone or something that is based not on experience but, rather, on stereotypes.* A **stereotype** is *an exaggerated and oversimplified belief about an entire group of people, such as an ethnic group, religious group, or a certain gender.* Prejudice is a type of ignorance. It denies each member of a particular group the right to be viewed as an individual. Openly rejecting a person based on superficial, or "surface," differences can damage the person's self-esteem. It can also damage your own in the long run.

Many teens form cliques and some may exclude others based on prejudices and stereotypes.

ACTIVITY *List two negative impacts cliques have on teens.*

HOME AND COMMUNITY CONNECTION

CLIQUES. Many children, adults, and teens are hurt when excluded from cliques. Others are indifferent. Some clique members secretly regret the compromises they make to maintain their standing. Others are delighted to be in a clique. Encourage students to find out how members of your school and community really feel about cliques. Suggest they post a list of questions such as "Do cliques determine social, economic, or political success in your school/community?" "Have you been hurt by a clique that excluded you?" "Would people be better off if cliques did not exist?" or "What do you like about your clique?" Anonymous replies may be placed in a box. Have students begin at school, then move to family members and family friends.

Responsible Relationships

At some time during adolescence, most teens go through a change in their feelings toward members of the opposite gender. For many, this change takes the form of a sudden stirring or awakening. Yesterday, the boy sitting across from you in math class was just another student. Today, like Max in the story that opened this chapter, you find it hard to stop staring at him. Yesterday, your younger sister's best friend was a pest or a bore. Today, you find yourself checking the mirror every time you know she is coming over to your house. These stirrings can lead to **infatuation**, *exaggerated feelings of passion for another person.* They will probably cause you to begin—or at least to begin thinking about—dating.

Dating Relationships

Dating is part of the process of learning interpersonal skills. Dating provides an opportunity for you to get to know yourself better—to recognize your strengths and weaknesses. It also gives you a chance to interact and feel comfortable with the opposite gender. By meeting and spending time with a variety of people, you learn what types of people you like and get along with best. Another benefit of dating is that it gives you a chance to practice your decision-making and communication skills.

Dating often leads to an ongoing relationship with one person. There are some advantages to this type of relationship. However, teenagers who date only one other person during their adolescence may be closing themselves off from meeting other people early in their social development. Although this type of relationship may

keeping Fit

Dangers of Positive Stereotyping

Sometimes, stereotypes come in a way that makes them hard to recognize as stereotypes. You may have heard, for example, that people of a certain ethnic background are good at math. Maybe you heard that members of some other group make the best lawyers or athletes. The list goes on.

What is wrong with observations such as these? All are *positive stereotypes,* which can be just as damaging as negative stereotypes. Like negative stereotypes, positive stereotypes make a generalization based on the identity of a group rather than an individual's identity. Remember, judging people on *any* basis other than individual strengths and weaknesses is a sign of narrow-minded, prejudicial, and faulty thinking.

connections

Social Studies

Rites of Passage

Many cultures publicly recognize a person's change in status. One such change is the movement from childhood to adulthood. The Mbuti people of Africa have a special rite that recognizes passage to adulthood. In the rite, boys and girls are separated from each other for the first time. Girls are joined by friends and live in a special house called an *elima.* A festival is given by the village. Each afternoon the girls sing to the boys who sit outside the house. The boys respond with their own songs, and the ritual is a type of flirtation whereby future marriage partners may be chosen.

1. How does your family or culture recognize the transition to adult status?

2. What additional recognition, if any, would you like to see incorporated into your family or culture?

MORE ABOUT . . . . .

FRIENDSHIP. Being best friends does not necessarily mean being constant companions. Many times young persons are not secure enough in their relationships to accept the fact that friendships can be maintained even though physical companionship is not possible or necessary all the time.

DATING. Students need to recognize that not all persons desire to date at the same age or desire to date at all. Care must be taken so that persons who choose not to date for whatever reason are never made to feel inferior.

L1 Discussing

Have students describe ways in which dating relationships differ from platonic relationships. Ask: Can platonic relationships turn into dating relationships, and vice versa? In their opinion, how does each type of relationship help prepare them for relationships in their adult lives?

L1 Class Activity

Have the class brainstorm the pros and cons of serious dating and going steady in high school. Ask two volunteers to record the pros and cons on the chalkboard for further discussion.

L2 Parental Involvement

Ask students to interview their parents regarding their views on dating. Share parental responses in a class discussion. What are the similarities and differences in the parental views? What might account for them?

connections

Social Studies

Rites of Passage

Let volunteers share their current understanding of the term *rite of passage,* and ask: What formal rites of passage are practiced in our community? What are some of the informal rites of passage? After a brief discussion, have students read the Connections feature to learn more about one culture's rite of passage. Then encourage students to share and discuss their responses to the feature questions.

health lab

DATING AND TELEVISION

Time Needed: A total of about one hour of class time, on two different days

Understanding Objectives:
Students will analyze the influence that TV's depictions of dating can have on their own attitudes toward dating.

Focus on the Health Lab:
Ask: What do you think influences the attitudes you and other teens have toward dating? Let volunteers share their ideas. Then explain that this Health Lab will help students explore the influence of TV on teens' dating attitudes.

Observation and Analysis:
Provide class time during which group members can plan their questionnaires and later discuss the results of their ratings.

In Conclusion Answers:
Responses will vary. Encourage students to explain and support their ideas.

Further Investigation:
Guide students in discussing other kinds of media messages (advertisements, for example) that influence teens' attitudes toward dating.

Dating Bill of Rights

Review the rights of individuals who are dating as presented in the feature. Discuss dating from the male and female perspectives. Ask: How are they alike? How are they different? Ask if there are other rights that should be added to the list.

health lab

DATING AND TELEVISION

You've probably watched several different television shows in which the characters are dating. The interaction among the characters and the scenes of these shows may influence your expectations about dating. Yet, how realistically is dating portrayed on television? This investigation will help you find out.

keeping Fit

Dating Bill of Rights

1. I deserve to be treated with consideration and respect.

2. It's my right to be liked for who I am, not by the way I dress or the car I drive.

3. I have a right to have my values recognized and respected.

4. If pressured by my date, I can say no to drugs or other high-risk activities without apologizing or offering an explanation.

5. No one has the right to force or pressure me to do anything that goes against my or my family's values.

be convenient, it may not be helpful in learning to develop healthy relationships.

It is important to remember that adolescence is a time of trying different relationships and roles. Breaking up, making up, and breaking up again can be painful, but it is part of the process of becoming emotionally mature. Staying in a relationship because you do not know how to get out of it gracefully or clinging to a relationship when the other person wants to call it off are two common but painful dating situations. In both cases, honesty and open communication are essential. So is realizing that you have control over only your own actions and emotions. You cannot control the behavior or feelings of others.

These days many teens go out as groups. Going out with a group of friends of both genders is a good way to ease into dating. In a group, you have less responsibility for keeping the conversation going. Self-conscious feelings are not as likely. Because you are less nervous, you can relax and have a good time.

Choosing Not to Date

Not all teens date. Some choose not to because of other interests or time commitments, while others simply do not feel emotionally ready. It is wise to wait until you feel comfortable about dating. Do not let anyone pressure you into doing something you are not prepared to do. It is also important to talk with parents or adults in your home about their views on dating and to learn about their values.

MEETING STUDENT DIVERSITY

LEARNING STYLES. Students with special learning needs might pair up with mainstream students to carry out similar tasks (e.g., pair researchers with those who need to improve their research skills). In assessing the performance of such pairs, use criteria that reflect the ability of the partners to work together effectively, such as cooperation and compromise.

PHYSICALLY CHALLENGED. Students with physical challenges might be called upon to participate in an exhibit on social health and friendships. The exhibit can focus on the difficulties encountered in making and maintaining friendships and on common misconceptions people have toward those with physical challenges.

What you will need

- Pencil and paper
- A weekly TV schedule
- A television or videotapes of several TV sitcoms in which dating occurs
- A VCR (if tapes are used)

What you will do

1. Work with several classmates in developing a questionnaire that probes the subject of TV's depiction of dating and the dating scene. Typical questions might include the following: How many characters in the show are shown dating? Is not dating presented as an acceptable alternative? What conflicts relating to dating are presented, and how is each resolved? Do dating partners show respect for each other? Are the relationships based on infatuation or on real feelings of love and caring for another person?

2. Each group member is to watch a different show in which dating occurs. While watching, the member is to fill out his or her copy of the questionnaire.

3. Conclude by rating each show on the following scale: *Excellent*— Shows realistic dating relationships and portrays healthy communication and decision-making skills. *Good*—For the most part realistic; communication and decision-making skills could be stronger. *Fair*—Dating relationship is unrealistic; few good skills are employed. *Poor*—Gives an unrealistic view of dating; employs poor communication and decision-making skills.

In conclusion

1. Which shows scored the highest rating? Which scored the lowest?
2. Did a show's rating correspond to how realistically dating was presented? Explain.
3. If you are dating or considering dating, what, if anything, did you learn about dating that might be of help?

Review

Reviewing Facts and Vocabulary

1. How is a casual friendship different from a close friendship?
2. What are the positive and negative aspects of being part of a clique?
3. What is infatuation?

Thinking Critically

4. **Comparing and Contrasting.** Identify advantages and disadvantages of beginning to date and of not dating.
5. **Synthesizing.** Inez has been dating Edward for six weeks. She misses seeing her other friends but doesn't want to tell Edward for fear of hurting his feelings. What are the issues for both teens?

Applying Health Skills

6. **In Your School.** Analyze the cliques at your school by writing about them in your private Health Journal. First, identify several cliques. Then determine whether or not they possess the qualities of cliques discussed in your text, such as exclusion and prejudice. Describe some of the stereotyping and prejudice present at your school as well.

ASSESS

EVALUATING THE LESSON

- Assign and discuss the Lesson 1 Review; then administer, grade, and discuss the *Lesson 41 Quiz* in the TCR.

RETEACHING

- Have students create a mobile using pictures cut from magazines to illustrate each of the types of peer relationships.
- Ask students to complete *Reteaching Activity 41* in the TCR.

ENRICHMENT

Through a series of interviews with parents, grandparents, and older friends, have students determine the changes that have taken place in dating behavior over the past several decades. Ask students to try to explain why the changes have taken place. They should share what they learn with the class through oral reports.

CLOSE

Write the lesson's major concepts on numbered, separate slips of paper. Place the slips in a box, and let each student draw one. Going in numerical order, have students define and summarize the concept written on the slip of paper they selected.

Lesson 1 Review

Answers to Reviewing Facts and Vocabulary

1. A casual friendship does not fill your deeper social needs as a close friendship does.
2. Positive: You have a sense of belonging. Negative: You may be pressured to be someone other than yourself, to compromise your values, or to avoid interacting with a variety of people.
3. Infatuation is an exaggerated feeling of passion for another person.

Answers to Thinking Critically

4. Dating provides an opportunity to get to know yourself better and to interact and feel comfortable with the opposite gender. Disadvantage: By dating only one person, you close yourself off from getting to know a variety of people. By choosing not to date, you can avoid being pressured into things you're not ready for.
5. The issues are honesty and communication.

FOCUS

LESSON OBJECTIVES

After studying this lesson, students should be able to

- give examples of both positive and negative peer pressure and manipulation.
- describe ways of responding to negative peer pressure.
- identify the three-step process of assertive refusal.

MOTIVATOR

Write the following on the chalkboard for students to work on while attendance is being taken: *Write a paragraph describing ways that you influence your friends.*

INTRODUCING THE LESSON

Refer to the Motivator. Ask volunteers to share their paragraphs. Explain that pressure may or may not be intended when a person influences a friend, but it often has that effect due to the nature of peer relationships and the need for acceptance. Tell students that this lesson will examine peer pressure and ways to deal with pressure that is potentially harmful.

INTRODUCING HEALTH TERMS

- Have students volunteer examples from their own experience of both positive and negative peer pressure and manipulation. Then have them work as a class to define *peer pressure* and *manipulation* in their own words.
- Ask students to complete Vocabulary Activity 13 and Chapter Study Guide 13 in the *Student Workbook.* ☞

304   Chapter 13

Peer Pressure and Refusal Skills

When Kendra learned that one of her friends was spending Saturdays serving food at a homeless shelter, Kendra began volunteering her time as well. After Don saw the progress teens in his neighborhood were making in cleaning debris from a vacant lot, he joined in the effort himself. Today the lot is a park where Don and his friends play softball.

HEALTH TERMS

peer pressure
manipulation
refusal skills
passive
aggressive
assertive

HEALTH CONCEPTS

- Peer pressure is the control and influence people your age can have over you.
- Peer pressure can have either a positive or negative influence on your actions and behaviors.
- Learning to resist negative peer pressure is an important skill.
- Refusal skills are ways of saying no to negative peer influence.

Peer Pressure

Your peers can have a great impact on what you think, feel, say, and do. They may exert direct or indirect **peer pressure,** *the control and influence people your age may have over you.* Peer pressure can occur in many kinds of relationships. The way you respond to peer pressure can have a great impact on the decisions you make and, in turn, your total health.

Kendra's and Don's stories in the opening each illustrate a positive response to peer pressure. Maybe

---

Lesson 2 Resources

TEACHER'S CLASSROOM RESOURCES
- ☞ **Concept Map** Activity 42
- ☞ **Cooperative Learning** Activity 13
- ☞ **Decision-Making** Activity 13
- ☞ **Enrichment** Activity 13
- ☞ **Health Lab** 13
- ☞ **Lesson 42 Quiz**
- ☞ **Lesson Plan** 42

- ☞ **Reteaching** Activity 42

STUDENT WORKBOOK
- ☞ **Applying Health Skills** 42
- ☞ **Chapter Study Guide** 13
- ☞ **Vocabulary** Activity 13

TRANSPARENCIES AND MULTIMEDIA
- 🖐 **Transparencies** 43, 44
- 🔴 **ABCNews InterActive™,** *Teenage Sexuality*

you have felt inspired by a good example set by someone your age. Maybe you have been a positive **role model** yourself. Influencing peers to take part in a positive act or worthwhile cause is a healthful way of influencing others. It can be contagious.

Positive peer pressure is not limited to following or setting good examples of what to do. It can also provide examples of *what not to do.* A teen whose friends do not use alcohol or other drugs may be positively influenced to follow their example.

Negative Peer Influence

Sometimes, peers may pressure others to accept beliefs or take part in a behavior that has a negative consequence. A teen, for example, may try to influence a date or friend to stay out past curfew. A clique or club may have an "initiation" for would-be members that includes stealing or taking part in another crime or wrongful act.

Manipulation

One way that people exert peer pressure over others is through **manipulation.** This is *a sneaky or dishonest way to control or influence others.* A person who manipulates another does so to get what he or she wants without respect for the well-being of the person being manipulated.

hotlink

role model For more on the importance of positive role models and other protective factors that influence the health of the community, see Chapter 1, page 20.

◄ *A teen may feel pressured or outnumbered when others try to exert pressure to do something that goes against his or her values.*

ACTIVITY *Name some reasons you should stand up to negative peer pressure.*

Types of Manipulation

- mocking or teasing the person in mean or hurtful ways.
- bargaining, or offering to make a deal to get what one wants.
- bribing, or promising money or favors if the person will do what another asks of him or her.
- using guilt trips to get desired results.
- making threats, or using words that show a person intends to use violence or some other negative means to get his or her way.
- using blackmail, or threatening to reveal some damaging information if the person does not conform.
- using flattery or undeserved praise to influence another person.

LESSON 2   PEER PRESSURE AND REFUSAL SKILLS   **305**

SCHOOL-TO-CAREER

RELATING AND JOBS. In some jobs, ability to relate well to peers accounts for 90 percent of performance and success. In other jobs, some disagreeable people manage to get by. Pair or group students to list a variety of workers, such as a farmer, physician, gardener, telemarketer, computer programmer, writer, teacher, hair sylist, or lab technician. For each occupation, have them list the factors affecting job performance, such as skills and knowledge, punctuality, dependability, honesty, physical strength, efficiency, etc. and to include relating well on each list. Have them rank these qualities for each job. Invite groups to share their rankings, and discuss the placement of relating well on each list.

TEACH

L1 Discussing

Allow volunteers to give examples of negative peer pressure they have observed or experienced. Then ask for examples of positive peer pressure. Point out the link between role models and positive peer pressure.

L2 Class Activity

Divide the class into groups of three. Ask each group to write a description of a case of peer pressure, either hypothetical or from the members' own experience. Have each group share its case with the rest of the class. Ask the whole class to decide if each case demonstrates peer pressure that is direct or indirect, positive or negative.

L2 Writing

Guide students in writing a short essay titled "Peer Pressure—A Positive and Negative Influence on My Life."

L3 Class Activity

Choose two or three students to write and role-play a scenario that demonstrates manipulation in a relationship. Have the rest of the class decide who is being manipulated, what means are being used (e.g., mockery, bribery, etc.), and what the manipulator hopes to gain. Ask the class to come up with other ways for the manipulative person to get what he or she wants—ways that are more direct, honest, and respectful of the other person.

L2 Health Lab

Distribute *Health Lab 13* and have students learn more about healthy peer relationships. ✍

LEP Personal Involvement

Pose this question: Who could you go to if you felt you were being pressured or manipulated by others? Have students list the names of people who might encourage them to make their own choices and decisions and not to be overly influenced by others.

L3 Researching

Select students to design and distribute a class or campus-wide questionnaire about the influence of peer pressure on teen behavior. Responses to the questionnaire are to be anonymous. Questions may include the degree of peer pressure exerted on students to shoplift, drink, smoke, take drugs, and so on. Have students summarize the results of the questionnaire in an article to submit to the school newspaper.

Building Health Skills

Resisting Peer Pressure
Skill: Refusal Skills

Let students generate a list of risk behaviors teens are often pressured to engage in; record their ideas on the board. Then let students form small discussion groups in which to read and apply the Building Health Skills information. Assign each group one of the listed risk behaviors. Let group members explain how they would use the listed questions to evaluate the pressure and formulate a healthful response. Ask each group to summarize its discussion for the rest of the class.

L2 Cooperative Learning

Have students complete *Cooperative Learning Activity 13,* "Who Are Your Role Models?" in the TCR. 🖜

Responding to Negative Peer Pressure

Throughout your life, people will make many requests and demands of you. Some of these will call for you to respond with a yes, others with a firm and unapologetic no. How you respond can directly affect your mental, social, or physical health—even your life. If you are in a group situation, submitting to peer pressure can sometimes make a conflict worse. For instance, if two people are about to fight, having others around to spur them on will probably increase the chances the fight will take place. You need to find ways to avoid becoming a part of the problem.

Peer pressure to take part in a potentially harmful or unsafe activity can be intense. If a friend is applying the pressure, you may have concerns about hurting the person's feelings or jeopardizing the relationship. If several people are exerting the pressure, you may worry that you will appear "uncool" or be talked about later. There are three ways in which you can respond to negative peer pressure.

- **The Passive Way.** Being **passive** means *giving up, giving in, or backing down without standing up for your own rights and needs.* People who are passive may think that they are making friends by going along with peer pressure. In fact, however, they may be viewed by their peers as pushovers and not worthy of much respect.

Building Health Skills

Resisting Peer Pressure

WHEN YOU FEEL pressure to take part in a behavior that goes against your values and ideals, such as experimenting with alcohol or driving fast, it is important to stand your ground. Your health, safety, and future hang in the balance. Ask yourself the following questions:

1. **What risks does this behavior carry?** This can help you identify the price you potentially stand to pay if you go along with the behavior. If you aren't aware of the risks, you have another valid reason for resisting.

2. **What personal or family values and goals would be compromised by engaging in this behavior?** Consider your plans, dreams, and ambitions, and how these might be altered. Don't forget to include such items as the risk of losing the respect of people who know or care for you.

3. **What is the source of the pressure?** Is the group one whose opinions and views you truly respect and trust? Is the pressure really coming from inside yourself? Keep in mind also that some teens boast about taking risks just to sound grown up. Maybe the simple fact is that "no one is doing it."

PROMOTING COMPREHENSIVE SCHOOL HEALTH

THE TEAM. Under the comprehensive school health program, each campus would have a site-based decision-making committee composed of teachers, business representatives, parents, community members, and campus staff. In addition to academic performance objectives, plans related to students' physical and psychological needs also must be addressed. Schools might already have a drop-out prevention committee working together with school/community drug prevention committees. These committees can also focus on the students' academic performance as related to health. For more detailed information about developing such a program, consult *Promoting a Comprehensive School Health Program* in the TCR. 🖜

Our Changing World

Dealing with School Bullies

Bullies have been around for decades—probably long before your grandparents were in school. What is the difference between bullies now and then? Bullying today has become a serious problem and sometimes escalates into violence. Some bullies carry weapons, and some of their victims feel the need to arm themselves in self-defense.

Experts estimate that one in ten teens is regularly bullied at some time during the school year. Bullying is often verbal, such as teasing or taunting, but it can also be physical. Bullies tend to pick on people who are different from them. Their victims might be taller or shorter than other classmates or heavier or thinner than average. They might wear glasses or braces. Sometimes bullies harass people from a different ethnic group or religious faith.

Bullies put down other people to boost their own self-esteem. By mocking or teasing others, they are trying to manipulate them and provoke a reaction. The best way to deal with bullies, then, is to simply ignore them. Eventually, they usually lose interest when they get no response to their taunts. If you are concerned about your health or safety, however, talk to a parent or other trusted adult. If you see someone else being harassed, resist peer pressure to laugh or join in. Think about how you would feel if you were the bully's target.

1. Why do you think bullying is a more serious problem now than it was years ago? What changes in society might have contributed to this problem?

2. Talk with a parent, grandparent, or other adult about bullies. Did they ever encounter bullies when they went to school? How did people deal with them?

■ **The Aggressive Way.** Being **aggressive** means being *overly forceful, pushy, hostile, or otherwise attacking in approach*. The aggressive approach to saying no might involve punching, yelling, shouting insults, or displaying other kinds of physical or verbal force. The aggressive way violates the rights of others. Though aggressive people may think they will get their way and perhaps be seen as powerful and popular, their approach usually backfires. In the long run, people either stay away from aggressors or jump in and fight back. Either reaction can hurt aggressive people emotionally and physically.

■ **The Assertive Way.** Being **assertive** means *standing up for your own rights, in firm but positive ways*. You state your position, acknowledge the rights of the other individual, then stand your

Our Changing World

School Bullies

Ask: How is bullying a form of peer pressure? How do bullies try to manipulate other people? In what ways has bullying changed in recent years? What are some healthy ways to deal with bullies? After students have shared their ideas, let them read the Update feature to learn more about dealing with school bullies. Then let them meet in small groups to discuss their responses to the first question. For the second activity, talking with an adult about bullies, have students write a paragraph or two about their discussion.

L2 **Writing**

Have students write a paragraph explaining a situation in which being able to say no effectively is necessary to withstand negative peer pressure. Ask them to explain how saying *no* could be handled in a passive manner, an aggressive manner, and an assertive manner. Which would be the most effective and why?

TEENAGE SEXUALITY (Side 2)

Chapter 9: Pressure from Your Peers

Frames 17241-19095

Chapter 11: Saying No

Frames 20262-22477

PERSONAL HEALTH

POEMS AND SONG LYRICS. Relationships are the topic of many song lyrics and poems. Lovers, friends, family members, and even enemies have been immortalized in verse. Encourage students to list in their journals their favorite songs or poems about relationships. Have them check any that have influenced their thoughts, feelings, or images of what love or friendship is and make notes about how they have been influenced. Is their image of an ideal partner or friend shaped by the words of a songwriter? Invite them to write songs or poems about relationships and to share them if they choose.

Avoiding Cults

Discuss the abuses of cults and how individuals are affected. Discuss (1) abuse of individuality (group mentality); (2) abuse of intimacy (relationships with friends and family are broken or hampered); (3) abuse of finances (money is donated to support the cult); "us" vs. "them" mentality (alienation from society); and abuse of free will (submission). Members of cults often experience personality changes and become paranoid. Explain that cults influence individuals in subtle ways until they are totally persuaded by the group's teachings.

Making Responsible Decisions

1. Brandy's friend wants to copy Brandy's answers on an upcoming history quiz.
2. Brandy could (a) let Anne copy her answers on the quiz; (b) agree to let Anne look over her shoulder but avoid letting her do so during the quiz; (c) tell Anne she can't help her cheat, but offer to help Anne review for the quiz during lunch or study hall.
3. Brandy might (a) help her friend, but feel guilty and risk being caught cheating; (b) make Anne angry and end up feeling uncomfortable around her friend; (c) possibly make Anne angry, but also have a chance to help Anne pass the quiz—and not feel guilty about cheating.
4. Brandy values both honesty and her friendship with Anne.
5. Responses will vary.
6. Students should consider both the short- and long-term consequences of their decisions.

L2 **Decision Making**

For further study on making responsible decisions, assign *Decision-Making Activity 13* in the TCR. 🖎

---

ground. You do not bully or back away. You directly and honestly state your case and show that you mean what you say. Assertive people often become role models for other teens. Teens respect people who have the personal power to be true to who they really are. Assertive refusal doesn't come naturally or easily for many people. Nevertheless, it is a skill worth acquiring.

Assertive Refusal

The assertive way is often the best way to deal with negative peer influence. By learning and practicing **refusal skills**, *techniques and strategies that help you say no effectively when faced with something that you do not want to do or is against your values,* you will be prepared when a high pressure situation comes along. These skills will help you now, and later in life as well. Refusal skills involve a three-step process:

1. **State your position simply but firmly.** All you need to say is "No, I don't want to." Practice saying no in front of a mirror. Make your "no" sound like you really mean it. Then, give an honest reason why you don't want to participate. This doesn't need to be more than saying, "It goes against my values." You don't need to use phony excuses or invent reasons.

2. **Suggest alternatives to the behavior being proposed.** If a friend suggests using a parent's car without permission, recommend another form of transportation, such as, "Let's go ride our skateboards in the park instead." By offering an alternative, you give your friend a chance to continue being with you in a

Making Responsible Decisions

Using Refusal Skills

Ever since Brandy moved to Elm City, Anne has been her closest friend. This morning when Brandy arrived at school, Anne was waiting for her on the steps, looking worried. "I just heard that we're having a pop quiz in history this afternoon," Anne said. "You've got to be a pal and let me look over your shoulder. History just isn't my subject." Brandy likes Anne. Yet, she knows that cheating is wrong. Besides, she could get into trouble herself if she goes along with Anne's idea and the teacher finds out. What should Brandy do?

What Would You Do?

Apply the six steps of the decision-making process to Brandy's problem.

1. **State the situation.**
2. **List the options.**
3. **Weigh the possible outcomes.**
4. **Consider your values.**
5. **Make a decision and act.**
6. **Evaluate the decision.**

HEALTH LITERACY

RESPONSIBLE, PRODUCTIVE CITIZEN.
Social activities often present challenges for teens who want a healthy lifestyle. With friends, they may spend time watching films, hanging out at the mall, cruising in cars, and partying with high-fat food, alcohol, or drugs. Encourage students to organize a social event or club built around healthy activities. It can be a weekend hike or bicycle trip, a skating or swimming event, a competitive sport, or a charity marathon for which students would train regularly. It could also be an organic gardening club, or potluck of healthy foods. Whatever the event, healthy foods should be served or carried.

comfortable way. Make sure your suggestion takes you away from the dangerous situation. For example, if a friend says it would be fun trying to take something from a store without paying for it, gently but firmly suggest another activity. Say, something like, "Let's go over to the video arcade."

3. **Back up your words with actions.** If your friend continues to try to persuade you to join in, make it clear that your no means no. Use strong body language and maintain eye contact. If that doesn't work, just leave. Simply say, "I'm going home." You will not be able to persuade every friend to stop pressuring you. In those cases, you may need to drop the friendship and seek another circle of friends. At the very least, you will need to speak with the person about how uncomfortable you felt and how such pressure in the future may jeopardize the relationship.

▲ **Being assertive doesn't always come easily.**
ACTIVITY *Name two things this girl can do to be assertive.*

ASSESS

EVALUATING THE LESSON

Assign and discuss the Lesson 2 Review; then administer, grade, and discuss the *Lesson 42 Quiz* in the TCR. 🖘

RETEACHING

- Have students write the phrase *peer pressure* at the top of a sheet of paper. Ask them to divide the sheet into two vertical columns and to label the left column *positive* and the right column *negative*. Have them define *peer pressure* and list five examples each of ways it can be positive and ways it can be negative.
- Instruct students to write a brochure for teens titled "Manipulation—Don't Let It Happen to You." In the brochure, have students identify the means of manipulation.
- Ask students to complete *Reteaching Activity 42* in the TCR. 🖘
- Use *Transparencies 43* and *44* to review refusal skills and the many sides of peer pressure. 🔖

ENRICHMENT

- Ask a police officer or youth counselor who is knowledgeable about gang violence to speak with your class. Have the speaker address the following topics: avoiding gang recruitment techniques; behavior patterns of gang members; and ways schools can deter gangs.
- Have students complete *Enrichment Activity 13*, "Self-Esteem: A Matter of Self-Control," in the TCR. 🖘

CLOSE

Summarize the lesson by reviewing the following important concepts: peer pressure and manipulation.

Review

Reviewing Facts and Vocabulary

1. Give examples of both negative and positive peer pressure.
2. What is *manipulation* and how does it relate to peer pressure?
3. How does being aggressive differ from being assertive?

Thinking Critically

4. *Analyzing.* "If you don't do the dishes for me," Gwen tells her sister, "I'll tell Mom and Dad that you weren't really at Luisa's house last night." What type of manipulation is this?

Applying Health Skills

5. *In Your Home and School.* Make a two-column chart on a page in your private Health Journal. In the first column, list any incidents of negative peer influence you have experienced, explaining how you handled the situation. In the second column, identify examples of positive influence you have experienced, explaining how the experience made you feel.

Lesson 2 Review

Answers to Reviewing Facts and Vocabulary

1. Answers will vary, but should reflect an understanding of positive and negative peer pressure.
2. Manipulation is a dishonest way to control or influence others. It can be used by your peers to exert pressure.
3. Someone who is being aggressive is pushy, hostile, or attacking in approach. Someone who is being assertive is standing up for his or her rights in firm but positive ways.

Answers to Thinking Critically

4. Blackmail.

Health Skills Activities

ACTIVITY 1
HEALTH SKILLS

Self Management; Communica-tion—Refusal Skills

➤ **National Standards**
This activity meets these National Health Standards: 3.6; 5.1; 5.6.

Teach

- Share the STOP method of refus-ing, by teaching students the meaning of each letter in the acronym (*S* is for "Say no," *T* is for "Tell why," *O* is for "Offer another idea," and *P* is for "Promptly leave if you are in danger"). You can also print this out as a vertical graphic on the classroom com-puter and make a copy available to each group.
- Challenge groups to come up with another acronym if they can by making a list of terms related to the act of refusing. The list might include the terms *REFUSE, NO WAY, NOT ME,* and *HEALTH.*

ACTIVITY 2
HEALTH SKILLS

Self Management, Communica-tion—Refusal Skills, Decision Mak-ing

➤ **National Standards**
This activity meets these National Health Standards: 3.6; 5.6; 6.1.

Teach

- Before assigning the activity, have students brainstorm situations in which one teen might feel nega-tive pressure to take part in an unhealthful activity or act that goes against his or her moral val-ues or beliefs. Have a volunteer list these ideas on the chalkboard.
- Review the key points of the dis-cussions in Lesson 2 on peer pressure and making a healthful decision. Discuss how some of the strategies outlined could apply to the situations listed.

Activity 1 — Refuse to Be Used

Having a healthy dating relationship means having control over your own actions and emotions. Have you ever felt pressure in a dating situation? Refusal skills can help you resist negative peer pressure.

Directions

1. In a group, think of a slogan or line that could be the basis of a campaign for using effective refusal skills. This might be a variation on the STOP approach explained by your teacher, or it might be a slogan you create.
2. Transfer your idea to a sheet of poster board. The poster may be illustrated with original art, photos, or symbols.
3. Share and compare your group's idea with those of other groups. Make changes as needed.
4. Complete your poster using colored markers. Posters can be displayed in the hallways of your school.

Time
45 minutes

Materials
paper, pen, poster board, colored markers

Self-Assessment

✓ Created a campaign for assertive refusal of negative peer pressure.
✓ Expressed this message in words and/or pictures.

Activity 2 — Healthful Decisions

Peer pressure can occur in many kinds of relationships. The way you respond to peer pressure can have a great impact on the decisions you make and, in turn, your total health.

Directions

1. Write a short fictional story about a teen who found him- or herself being pressured by a peer to engage in an unhealthful activity.
2. Write in the third person (*he, she, the girl, the boy*). Describe how the teen felt.
3. In your story, detail exactly what refusal techniques the teen used to resist peer pressure.
4. At the end of your story, explain how the teen benefited as a result of avoiding a high-risk situation.

Time
40 minutes

Materials
pen and paper

Self-Assessment

✓ Identified at least one effective refusal skill.
✓ Demonstrated positive outcome of teen's decision at the end of the story.

310 CHAPTER 13 PEER RELATIONSHIPS

ASSESSMENT SCORING

Using a four-level rubric, the student has achieved a 4 if:

ACTIVITY 1
✔ Student brainstormed in coming up with an acronym or slogan.
✔ Student took part in creating a campaign for assertive refusal of negative peer pressure.
✔ Student helped express group's message in words, pictures, or both.
✔ Student helped publicize the group's effort.

ACTIVITY 2
✔ Student volunteered examples of unhealthful activities involving peer pressure.
✔ Student advanced the discussion of key health concepts.
✔ Student identified at least one effective refusal skill in his or her story.
✔ Student demonstrated a positive outcome of the teen character's decision.

HEALTH NEWS VIDEO

Violence in Relationships

When you think of violence, you might think of two people who just don't like each other. However, many conflicts arise between people who think of themselves as friends or partners. Strong feelings, even strong feelings of affection and caring, can lead to violence if they are poorly managed. For example, friendly concern can turn to angry jealousy.

Domestic violence takes place in a home situation or between members of a couple. Many people are aware of the seriousness of domestic violence among adults, but the problem affects teens, too. Among high school students, approximately 1 in 10 has experienced physical violence in a dating relationship. An innovative program in San Jose, California, is helping teens recognize the warning signs and causes of domestic violence.

Play the Video ▶

Think About It

▶ What is the goal of the Next Door program? Discuss your thoughts about the program's ability to affectively achieve its goals.

▶ How does the program get its message to teen audiences?

▶ Can you think of other ways to help teens identify signs and address domestic violence?

CNN HEALTH NEWS **311**

MORE ABOUT . . . . .

RELIABLE SOURCES. Next Door is an independent organization dedicated to "providing proactive and progressive solutions to domestic violence." Serving Santa Clara County in California for 26 years, Next Door sponsors school workshops like those shown in the video as part of its education outreach.

Next Door also offers counseling and emergency shelter to individuals and their children seeking refuge from abusive relationships. Other services include a 24-hour hotline, legal assistance, and emergency interventions.

Many communities have organizations providing these essential services. Encourage students to find out about help and information available in your area.

CNN HEALTH NEWS

Violence in Relationships
Video Segment 7 (Time – 2:30)

Objectives. After viewing the video, students should be able to examine methods for helping teens identify the signs and address causes of domestic violence.

Motivator. Ask students to define the phrase *domestic violence.* Explain that this term is used to describe violence that takes place within a family or between people in a relationship. Then have students view Video Segment 7 to learn about an innovative program in which people who have suffered from domestic violence visit schools to raise students' awareness of this issue.

Teach

- Ask students to give examples of domestic violence in teen relationships. Emphasize that violence can refer to both large and small physical acts, including slapping, punching, or kicking.
- Point out that both men and women suffer from domestic violence.
- Have students summarize the importance of programs like Next Door by asking them to write letters or deliver speeches that support the use of such programs in your school.

Role Play. Have teams of students write and role-play a scene about a situation that could lead to domestic violence within a teen relationship. After the role-play, the audience should answer these questions: 1) What factors contributed to the conflict? 2) What steps could these characters take to avoid violence? 3) How could their friends help them? 4) What should the characters do if violence occurs? Encourage the scene's director to call out "Cut" to halt the scene before any violence takes place.

Close. Have students imagine they overhear someone making this statement: "Teens don't need to worry about domestic violence. We have enough problems already without worrying about something that only really affects adults." Have students tell how they would respond to this statement.

CHECKING COMPREHENSION

- Assign and discuss the chapter review.
- Use the MindJogger Videoquiz to review the chapter.

CHAPTER 13 REVIEW ANSWERS

Using Health Terms

1. stereotype
2. infatuation
3. clique
4. platonic friendship
5. prejudice
6. aggressive
7. manipulation
8. peer pressure
9. refusal skills
10. passive
11. assertive refusal

RECALLING THE FACTS

1. Peers take on a greater importance during the teen years because that is when you begin your search for identity.
2. Friendships provide us with many of the basic human social needs.
3. You are most likely to confide in a close friend.
4. Answers will vary but should reflect that stereotyping denies people the right to be judged as individuals.
5. Possible answers: a teenager might have interests that require a commitment of time and energy that makes dating difficult; a person might feel he or she is not ready emotionally to date as a couple.
6. Possible answers: a fear of being alone, not wanting to go through the pain of a breakup, convenience, fear of honestly expressing their feelings.
7. Possible answers: they haven't clearly defined their own values, they lack refusal skills, they want to feel like they belong.

Using Health Terms

On a separate sheet of paper, write the term that best matches each definition below.

LESSON 1

1. Exaggerated and oversimplified belief about an entire group of people, such as an ethnic group, religious group, or a certain gender.
2. Exaggerated feelings of passion for another person.
3. Small, narrow circle of friends, usually with similar backgrounds or tastes, that excludes people they view as outsiders.
4. Relationship with a member of the opposite gender in which there is affection, but no sexual activity.
5. Negative feeling toward someone or something that is based not on experience but, rather, on stereotypes.

LESSON 2

6. Overly forceful, pushy, hostile, or otherwise attacking in approach.
7. Sneaky or dishonest way to control or influence others.
8. Control and influence people your age may have over you.
9. Techniques and strategies that help you say no effectively when faced with something that you do not want to do or that goes against your values.
10. Giving up, giving in, or backing down without standing up for your own rights and needs.
11. Standing up for your own rights, in firm but positive ways.

Recalling the Facts

Using complete sentences, answer the following questions.

LESSON 1

1. Why do peers take on a greater importance during the teen years?
2. How do friendships add to total health?
3. Which type of friend are you most likely to confide in when you have a problem?
4. Stereotypes can lead to what kind of behavior?
5. Name two reasons why going out as a couple may not be the best choice for a teenager.
6. Explain why teens often stay in relationships even though they want to get out of the relationship.

LESSON 2

7. Why do teens sometimes have difficulty saying no to peer pressure?
8. Give three examples of manipulation.
9. Give four examples of positive peer pressure.
10. Which of the three ways of responding to negative peer pressure is most likely to result in a fight?
11. If a teen has already said no verbally and with strong body language, and a peer continues to try and persuade him or her to do something he or she doesn't want to do, what should the teen do?

8. Any three: teasing, bargaining, bribing, using guilt, making threats, blackmail, flattery.
9. Answers should reflect an understanding that positive peer pressure has beneficial results in one's life.
10. An aggressive response to negative peer pressure is the type of response most likely to result in a fight.
11. If you have exhausted all of your refusal skills and the peer pressure continues, the best response is simply to remove yourself from the situation; in other words—leave.

Thinking Critically

LESSON 1

1. ***Comparing and Contrasting.*** Jessica refers to Steven as her boyfriend, talks about him constantly, and claims to be in love with him, even though they are not actually dating. Explain to Jessica that she is experiencing an infatuation.

2. ***Analyzing.*** Ted thinks he would like to begin dating, but he is too shy to ask a girl out. Explain what he can do to become more comfortable around girls.

LESSON 2

3. ***Comparing and Contrasting.*** Darrin wants to be a friend of Sammy, but Sammy never seems to notice him. Sammy's friends spend lots of time on their computers, so Darrin begins to spend time learning how to use the Internet. Explain whether Darrin's actions are the result of direct or indirect peer pressure. Do you see this as positive or negative peer influence, and why?

Making the Connection

1. ***Science.*** The physical attraction to others that many people begin to experience during the teen years is largely the result of chemicals called *pheromones*. Learn more about pheromones and the complex ways they are used by social insects to communicate and send messages. Share your findings in a short report.

2. ***Social Studies.*** Investigate laws or efforts to create curfews in your own community. If curfews already exist, what are the terms and how effective have they been as a deterrent to teen crime? If not, what arguments were put forth by those opposed to them? Express what you have learned in a brief written report.

BEYOND THE CLASSROOM

PARENTAL INVOLVEMENT Ask a parent or adult in your home about someone with whom he or she has a long-standing relationship. Find out what the characteristics of this relationship are, and compare these with what you look for in relationships.

COMMUNITY INVOLVEMENT Interview someone in your community who lived there during the 1950s or 1960s to find out how the teen experience has changed over the years. Ask questions such as the following: What were your concerns then? Who were your role models? What kinds of problems, if any, did the neighborhood face? How has the neighborhood

changed? How have teenagers changed? What resources are available now that weren't available then? Present your findings in an oral report.

SCHOOL-TO-CAREER
Interpersonal. Speak with a law enforcement official in your community who deals with hate crimes—offenses against an individual or group that are a direct or indirect result of prejudice. Ask about interpersonal skills, such as compassion, that a person would need to pursue a career in this particular area. Share your findings with the class.

Thinking Critically

1. Answers should reflect an understanding that infatuation is an exaggerated feeling of passion that lacks the foundation of friendship.

2. Answers may include spending time in mixed-gender groups in nonthreatening social situations, joining school organizations where he will interact with many people, and cultivating platonic relationships with girls.

3. Darrin's interest in computers is a result of indirect peer pressure. Because he has learned something new that will add to his life, this is a positive influence.

Making the Connection

1. Reports will vary.
2. Reports will vary.

Evaluate

- Use the reproducible *Chapter 13 Test* in the TCR, or construct your own using the Testmaker software.
- Use *Performance Assessment Activity 13* in the TCR.

Enrichment

Ask students to complete *Cross-Curriculum Activity 13* in the TCR.

Beyond the Classroom

Keep students involved in the community, and encourage parent participation by assigning the activities on this page for students to work on outside of class.

Resolving Conflicts and Preventing Violence

		FEATURES	**CLASSROOM RESOURCES**

LESSON 1

The Nature of Conflict
pages 316–319

connections
Social Studies

"Warring Parties," *page 317*

- Concept Map Activity 43
- Health Lab 14
- Lesson 43 Quiz
- Lesson Plan 43
- Reteaching Activity 43
- Transparencies 23, 24

LESSON 2

Conflict Resolution Skills
pages 320–323

Building Health Skills

"Conflict Resolution: Steps to Take When Negotiating," *page 322*

- Concept Map Activity 44
- Cooperative Learning Activity 14
- Enrichment Activity 14
- Lesson 44 Quiz
- Lesson Plan 44
- Reteaching Activity 44
- Transparencies 40, 41

LESSON 3

Strategies for Avoiding Violence
pages 324–329

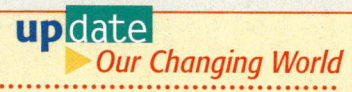

Teens *Making a* **Difference**

"Peace and Justice for All," *page 326*

update ▶ *Our Changing World*

"Violence Prevention and Intervention" *page 327*

- Concept Map Activity 45
- Lesson 45 Quiz
- Lesson Plan 45
- Reteaching Activity 45
- Transparency 49

LESSON 4

Preventing Abuse
pages 330–333

Making Responsible Decisions

"Makeup or Breakup?" *page 332*

- Concept Map Activity 46
- Decision-Making Activity 14
- Lesson 46 Quiz
- Lesson Plan 46
- Reteaching Activity 46

ACTIVITIES

- Cross-Curriculum Activity 14
- Health Lab 14
- Health Skills Activities 14
- Parent Letter and Activities 14

ASSESSMENT

- Chapter 14 Test
- Performance Assessment Activity 14
- Testmaker Software

STUDENT ACTIVITIES WORKBOOK

- Applying Health Skills 43–46
- Study Guide 14
- Vocabulary Activity 14

STUDENT DIVERSITY STRATEGIES

- Audiocassette Program (English)
- Audiocassette Program (Spanish)
- Spanish Parent Letters and Activities
- Spanish Summaries, Quizzes, and Activities

MULTIMEDIA COMPONENTS

- English Audiocassette Program
- Spanish Audiocassette Program
- MindJogger Videodisc and VHS program
- ABCNews InterActive™ VHS/Videodisc Series

National Health Education Standards

One of the main goals of the National Health Education Standards is to move students toward "health literacy." Health literacy is the capacity of individuals to obtain, interpret, and understand basic health information and services and the competence to use such information and services in ways which promote health. The health standards were developed by applying the characteristics of a well-educated, literate person within the context of health. The health literate person is:

- a critical thinker and problem solver
- a responsible, productive citizen
- a self-directed learner
- an effective communicator

Listed below are the Health Education Standards Performance Indicators addressed in each lesson of this chapter.

Lesson	Health Standards Performance Indicators
1	3.5, 3.6, 5.7, 5.8
2	5.5, 5.6, 5.7, 5.8
3	3.5, 3.6, 4.3, 6.2
4	2.6, 3.5, 5.5, 6.1

ONLINE RESOURCES

HEALTH Online

For a fresh approach to health topics and an in-depth look at health issues, use these online resources found under Teacher Resources at **health.glencoe.com**.

- **BLOCK SCHEDULE LESSON PLANS** Reinforce health concepts with outside readings selected especially for students. Each reading is accompanied by a lesson plan and activities to enhance
  - Reading Skills
  - Cross Curriculum
  - Media Literacy

- **TECHNOLOGY PROJECTS** Instructions and suggestions on how to use computer, Internet, and software with health lessons.

- **HEALTH UPDATES** Timely topics in health news, including late-breaking medical advances and updates on teen risk behaviors.

Out of Time?

If time does not permit teaching this chapter, you may use these features: Building Health Skills on page 322; Update on page 327; and Making Responsible Decisions on page 332.

BLOCK SCHEDULING

Block scheduling provides extended time for hands-on projects and activities. Use the following activities to engage students, provide further depth, and vary your instructional techniques:

- Connections (30 minutes) **pg. 317**
- Teens Making a Difference (30 minutes) **pg. 326**
- Update (30 minutes) **pg. 327**
- Health Skills Activity (60–90 minutes) **pg. 334**

Resolving Conflicts and Preventing Violence

CHAPTER OVERVIEW

Chapter 14 discusses conflict and the incidence of violence in which teens are becoming increasingly involved. Conflict resolution skills can be used to resolve differences. However, when the potential for violence is great, as in cases of abuse, the victim should get help as quickly as possible.

LESSON 1 Conflict is a normal part of life. Knowing how to recognize conflicts, how conflicts build, and knowing how to deal with them effectively are skills that impact your total health.

LESSON 2 Tolerance is key to preventing conflict. When conflict does occur, negotiation and mediation serve well as processes for conflict resolution.

LESSON 3 More teens are committing violent crimes and also are increasingly the victims of crime. Though the reasons violence has increased are complicated, many community programs are being used to successfully prevent violence.

LESSON 4 Abuse can take many forms. Of particular concern for teens is the incidence of abuse in dating relationships. Victims of abuse should seek counseling in dealing with the trauma. Counseling also benefits abusers, who in most cases were abused themselves.

CHAPTER **14**

Resolving Conflicts and Preventing Violence

HEALTH *Online*

CONFLICT RESOLUTION
School Safety Programs are spreading across the country. Check out steps being taken to prevent violence and provide safe environments for students across the country. Read the Health Update at **health.glencoe.com**.

Hands-On Health

TEACHING STRATEGY

Emphasizing Positive Behaviors Help students recognize the impact of negative words and actions, and encourage them to spend a day focused only on positive words and actions. See Activity 3, "First Aid for Avoiding Conflict," in the *Hands-On Health: Creative Teaching Strategies* booklet. 🖎

Time Needed
10 minutes
20 to 30 minutes in the next class meeting

Supplies
- 1 adhesive bandage for each student

Personal Health Inventory

Self-Inventory Write the numbers 1–10 on a sheet of paper. Read each statement below and respond by writing *yes*, *no*, or *sometimes* for each item. Write a *yes* only for items that you practice regularly. Save your responses.

1	I can recognize the signs that a conflict exists.
2	I have a good idea of how to face a conflict and when to ignore it.
3	I know several ways to keep a conflict from escalating.
4	If I see a fight building, I refuse to participate and encourage others to refuse as well.
5	When someone angers me, I know how to communicate my feelings in a way that doesn't make matters worse.
6	If I have a conflict I can't resolve on my own, I feel comfortable asking for help.
7	I know how to negotiate a conflict so that all parties feel heard and satisfied.
8	I do not use weapons to solve conflicts.
9	I do not use alcohol or drugs; I know these can cause conflicts or make them worse.
10	I do not allow others to abuse me in any way.

Follow-up After completing the chapter, retake this self-inventory. Pick two items that you need to work on and set a goal to improve your health behaviors.

CHAPTER 14 RESOLVING CONFLICTS AND PREVENTING VIOLENCE **315**

> *That message of tolerance— that message to everyone to accept and appreciate and celebrate our diversity as part of human existence— is going to be very important.*
>
> —KOFI ANNAN
> SECRETARY-GENERAL OF THE UNITED NATIONS,
> OCTOBER, 2001

Quick Write Write down three things you could do or say in a tense situation that would encourage better understanding and avoid a conflict.

Personal Health Inventory

Have students read the Self-Inventory statements and discuss their relationship to resolving conflicts and preventing violence. Then let students record their inventory responses in their private Health Journals on a paged labeled "My Level of Commitment to Peaceful Conflict Resolution and Violence Prevention." They will use these responses in a follow-up activity at the end of the chapter.

- Tell students that not all conflict is bad. At times, it can lead to positive changes, new viewpoints, and stronger commitment to one's values. However, conflict leading to violence is on the increase. For that reason, one of the major purposes of this chapter is to help students learn skills to deal with conflict in healthful ways.
- Let students read the statement made by the U.N. Secretary-General regarding relationships between diverse cultures of the world. Ask them to discuss their reactions to this quote. Then encourage volunteers to describe the conflicts that need to be resolved in their own lives. Conclude by explaining that students will learn more about conflict resolution and about the prevention of violence as they study Chapter 14.
- Distribute Parent Letter 14 in the *Parent Letters and Activities* booklet. ✎

TECHNOLOGY OPTIONS

You may wish to use *Violence Prevention* with this chapter. For your convenience, use the separate *ABCNews InterActive™ Bar Code Correlation* that accompanies the *Glencoe Health* program. 🔴

MINDJOGGER
VIDEOQUIZ

To preview or review chapter content, you may wish to use the *MindJogger Videoquiz* that accompanies Chapter 14. 🔴

The Nature of Conflict

FOCUS

LESSON OBJECTIVES

After studying this lesson, students should be able to

- define *conflict,* contrasting the two major types of conflict.
- describe how conflicts develop.
- discuss ways to recognize conflict and its source.
- discuss how to respond healthfully to conflict.

MOTIVATOR

Write the following on the board for students to complete while attendance is being taken: *List as many conflicts as you can think of that you have observed or read about in the past week. Put a check mark beside each conflict that had negative results, such as violence, suspension from school, or a lost friendship or job.*

INTRODUCING THE LESSON

Ask volunteers to give their responses to the Motivator. Have the class contrast their examples by asking: What do the conflicts have in common? How are they different? Which conflicts may have built up over time? Tell students that this lesson will focus on conflict.

INTRODUCING HEALTH TERMS

- Instruct students to use the vocabulary terms in two separate sentences, leaving blanks where the terms would be. Collect the sentences and read some aloud, allowing the class to fill in the blanks.
- Ask students to complete Vocabulary Activity 14 and Chapter Study Guide 14 in the *Student Workbook.* ☞

316 Chapter 14

The Nature of Conflict

The front-page headline of today's newspaper is about growing tensions between countries. The sports page tells of a brawl at last night's hockey game, while the "metro" section contains details of an argument between a driver and a pedestrian. Despite their differences, these stories have something in common. All are about conflict.

HEALTH TERMS

conflict

interpersonal conflicts

internal conflicts

escalate

HEALTH CONCEPTS

- Conflict is a normal part of life.
- There are common physical and emotional signs that indicate a conflict is building.
- There are times when it is wise to ignore a conflict and times when it is not.
- When conflicts are handled in a violent way, they lead to more problems.

Types of Conflict

Conflict is *any disagreement, struggle, or fight.* Conflicts are a normal part of life. Whenever your wants, needs, wishes, demands, values, or beliefs clash with someone else's, a conflict is almost certain to arise. There are two major types of conflicts—*interpersonal conflicts* and *internal conflicts.*

- **Interpersonal conflicts** are *disagreements between groups of any size, from two people to entire nations.* Conflicts of this type can start over minor issues, like the disagreement between the teens in the chapter-opening story. They can also affect the lives of entire populations, such as a dispute over whether to spend community funds to build low-income housing.

- **Internal conflicts** are *struggles within yourself.* Such conflicts, which can be common in the teen years, often involve mixed

---

Lesson 1 Resources

TEACHER'S CLASSROOM RESOURCES

- ☞ **Concept Map** Activity 43
- ☞ **Health Lab** 14
- ☞ **Lesson 43 Quiz**
- ☞ **Lesson Plan** 43
- ☞ **Parent Letter and Activities** 14
- ☞ **Reteaching** Activity 43

STUDENT WORKBOOK

- ☞ **Applying Health Skills** 43
- ☞ **Chapter Study Guide** 14
- ☞ **Vocabulary** Activity 14

TRANSPARENCIES

- 🖐 **Transparencies** 23, 24

MULTIMEDIA

- 🔴 **ABCNews InterActive™,** *Violence Prevention*

emotions. For example, a teen casting the lead role for a class play might feel "torn" between feelings of loyalty to a close friend auditioning for the part and a responsibility to select the best actor. Sometimes, internal conflicts arise over what might appear to be a good choice at the moment but what may not be best for you in the long run. In such cases, knowing how to use an effective **decision-making model** can ease you safely through the conflict with your health and self-esteem intact.

Whatever the nature of a conflict, learning to recognize conflicts when they occur, being aware of how conflicts build, and knowing how to deal with them effectively are skills that have a direct and lasting impact on your total health and well-being.

How Conflicts Build

Conflicts can begin in many ways and for many different reasons. Among these are power, property, authority, jealousy, loyalty, space, and territory. Some conflicts start innocently, such as when one person accidentally bumps another's lunch tray. Others are the result of an act or remark that provokes another person—a wet towel snapped in a locker room, for example, or a racial slur. Either way, a "fuse" is ignited.

HEALTH Online

Find facts on teens as crime victims at **health.glencoe.com** and learn ways to resolve conflicts peacefully.

hotlink

decision-making model For more information on how to make informed, healthful decisions, see Chapter 2, page 35.

connections

Social Studies

Warring Parties

Some conflicts are *chronic*, or ongoing, as when two siblings fight night after night over the TV remote control. One of the most dangerous types of chronic conflict is a *feud*, an ongoing state of hostility between people or groups that involves revenge or violent attacks. Warfare between rival gangs is one example of feuding that sometimes turns fatal. Some feuds begin over a simple misunderstanding. However, the root cause is often a need to prove something or to destroy or harm in order to feel good about oneself. For a gang member, just being in the wrong place at the wrong time is often enough to provoke a battle.

1. Using on-line or print resources, learn about the issues of feuds and gang violence in the United States. What type of injuries and fatalities have occurred from inter-gang conflicts?

2. What various steps have elected officials, law enforcement personnel, and social workers taken to help stop these senseless crimes? What recommendations can you make?

LESSON 1 THE NATURE OF CONFLICT **317**

TEACH

L2 **Class Activity**

Select students to role-play teens who are dealing with internal conflicts (e.g., whether to cheat on a test, drop out of school, and so on). Then have each student write a short letter to one of the teens, offering advice in dealing with the conflict. Choose some of the letters to share with the class.

ABCNEWS INTERACTIVE™

VIOLENCE PREVENTION (Side 1)
Chapter 3: What Makes You Angry?

Frames 2856-8378

VIOLENCE PREVENTION (Side 2)
Chapter 3: What Is Conflict?

Frames 2937-7947

Chapter 4: A Conflict "The Bump"

Frames 7962-12072

connections

Social Studies

Warring Parties

Lead students in a brief discussion of what they know about ongoing conflicts between rival gangs. Ask: What do you think causes this kind of conflict? What special dangers are associated with it? Let students read the Connections feature and respond to the feature questions.

CURRICULUM CONNECTIONS

LANGUAGE ARTS. Conflict situations can be found in many poems, novels, plays, songs, and works of nonfiction. Have students choose a poem, song, or short story and identify conflicts or tensions in the piece. Ask them to determine if the conflict was built over time or if it was dealt with at the start. In what way(s) was the conflict handled? By whom was it handled?

ART. Many artists, including photographers, capture feelings of conflict in their work. Assign students with a special interest in art to identify paintings, photographs, or sculptures that depict conflict within an individual or among others. Ask students to share some of their findings with the class.

L2 Class Activity

Choose students to design and complete a mural, display case, and/or mobile illustrating conflicts in everyday life. Afterward, lead students in a discussion of conflicts depicted in the project(s).

L1 Parental Involvement

Ask students to interview their parents about parents' physical and emotional early-warning signs of conflict. Also, have them interview other students in the school about their physical and emotional signs of conflict. Then have groups of two or three compile the signs into two lists, one experienced by parents and one by teens. Ask a representative from each group to share the lists with the rest of the class. Generate class discussion by asking whether teens experience different early-warning signs of conflict than their parents. In what ways are their warning signs the same?

L2 Health Lab

Distribute *Health Lab 14* and have students learn more about resolving conflicts. ☞

L2 Discussing

You may wish to use *Transparencies 23* and *24* to discuss sources of conflicts and the influence of gangs. 🖐

At this point, one or both parties can choose to walk away and allow the situation to drop. All too often, however, a conflict is permitted to **escalate**, or *grow into a situation that is unhealthful and even unsafe to all parties concerned.* This may result from a lack of communication, a misunderstanding, or gossip.

Learning to identify the warning signs that a conflict is brewing can help you "put out the fire" before it rages out of control. Some of the warning signs that conflict is building inside of you are physical. Others are emotional.

Recognizing Conflict

Although conflict is an unavoidable part of life, there are healthful and unhealthful ways of responding to it. The first step is to decide whether the problem is something that really deserves your time and energy. You can identify the problem and its source by asking yourself the following questions:

- What is *really* bothering me and why?
- Is this a minor, a chronic, or a major problem?

Warning Signs	
PHYSICAL	**EMOTIONAL**
a knot in the stomach	feeling concerned
faster heart rate	getting defensive
a lump in the throat	wanting to cry
cold or sweating palms	wanting to lash out
a sudden surge of energy	wanting to escape
confrontational—or "fighting"—body language, such as clenching your fists or gritting your teeth	not feeling valued

➤ *Conflicts are often over territory, space, property, and power.*

ACTIVITY *Recall one recent conflict you witnessed that involved two teens and territory, space, or property.*

PERSONAL HEALTH

CONFLICTS AND PERSONAL HEALTH. Encourage students to list in their private Health Journals all the ways conflict—and how they handle it—may affect them socially, emotionally, physically, and economically over a lifetime. Then suggest that they list their own personal barriers to conflict resolution. Do they feel compelled to humiliate an adversary? Are they ashamed to admit they were wrong? Do they need to show they are not afraid to fight? Empathy can be a tremendous asset in resolving conflict. Have students recall a recent conflict and write a dialogue. Tell them to assume the viewpoint of the other person and explain the person's feelings, view of the conflict, and the reasons for both.

- What is triggering the conflict?
- Are there hurt feelings or other unexplored emotions lurking beneath my anger?
- Have anyone's rights been violated?
- What is my part in the problem?
- Does this conflict involve my personal values or beliefs?
- What is at stake here?

Responding to Conflict

When a conflict arises, you can either face it or ignore it. In deciding on which course of action to take, the two most important points to remember are the following: (1) Your personal health and safety should be your primary concern; (2) walking away from a volatile or dangerous situation is a healthful, mature choice—not a sign of being a coward.

Sometimes teens jump into conflicts too lightly. They think that doing so may provide a thrill or prove to those around them that they are tough, cool, or unafraid. These same teens may also believe, wrongly, that getting out of a conflict is as easy as getting in. Unfortunately, once you become embroiled in a real-life conflict, you may find that there is no turning back.

CHARACTER IN ACTION

Whose Conflict *Is* This, Anyway?

One way of exercising **self-control** is to decide *not* to get involved in conflicts that are avoidable or do not really involve you.

Character Check The next time you feel the impulse to dive into someone else's conflict:

➤ Take a deep breath.
➤ Count to fifty.
➤ Walk away if you have to.
➤ Decide how you will play peacemaker instead of "fanning the fire."

LESSON 1 *Review*

Reviewing Facts and Vocabulary

1. What is a conflict?
2. Give an original example of an interpersonal conflict and another of an internal conflict.
3. Name three physical and three emotional warning signs that a conflict may be building.

Thinking Critically

4. **Synthesizing.** Think about the ways in which a conflict can be positive. Find a newspaper or magazine article that supports this concept by summarizing the beneficial results that came directly and indirectly out of a conflict.
5. **Analyzing.** Make a chart with two columns. In the first column, list a minor, a chronic, and a major conflict in your life. In the second column, write a peaceful solution for each conflict.

6. **Comparing and Contrasting.** Compare and contrast some ways you might recognize that a conflict is brewing with different ways you can respond to the conflict.

Applying Health Skills

7. **In Your Home.** Keep a Conflict Log for a week in which you "track" and record one major or chronic conflict in your life. Pay attention to the amount of time the conflict occupies your thoughts and what emotions surround each. Write down how this conflict seems to affect your health, your eating and sleeping habits, and your emotional state. As the week goes on, brainstorm ways to face and resolve this conflict, using information provided in this chapter.

CHARACTER IN ACTION

Whose Conflict Is This Anyway?

Ask students to come up with a list of one-line reminders that they might say to themselves when they feel emotions building up and want to defuse them instead of acting them out.

ASSESS

EVALUATING THE LESSON

Assign and discuss the Lesson 1 Review; then administer, grade, and discuss the *Lesson 43 Quiz* in the TCR. ✏

RETEACHING

- Have students use the information in the lesson to answer these questions: What are the two major types of conflict? What is one positive way of dealing with an internal conflict? Why is it important to recognize early warning signs of conflict?
- Ask students to complete *Reteaching Activity 43* in the TCR. ✏

ENRICHMENT

Select students to watch young children at play. Have them complete anecdotal records of conflicts observed among the children and related actions taken by the children and/or their caregivers. Ask the students to share their observations with the class.

CLOSE

Ask students to complete the following statements: *Since studying about conflict, I have learned...; Signs that conflict is building are...; Two points to remember when deciding a course of action regarding conflict are...*

Lesson 1 Review

Answers to Reviewing Facts and Vocabulary

1. Any disagreement, struggle, or fight.
2. Answers will vary.
3. Physical: a knot in the stomach, increased heart rate, a lump in the throat, clenching your fists, gritting your teeth, cold or sweating palms, a sudden surge of energy. Emotional: feeling concerned, getting defensive, not feeling valued, wanting to cry, lash out, or escape.

Answers to Thinking Critically

4. Answers will vary.
5. Charts will vary.
6. Answers will vary.

Conflict Resolution Skills

LESSON OBJECTIVES

After studying this lesson, students should be able to

- explain the process of conflict resolution and explain the role of tolerance in preventing conflict.
- explain the negotiation process.
- describe the basic steps that occur during a mediation session.

MOTIVATOR

Write the following on the board for students to complete while attendance is being taken: *Write a short description of a real or imaginary conflict between two or more people who took steps to accept and show respect for each other's differences.*

INTRODUCING THE LESSON

Refer to the Motivator. Ask volunteers to share their responses. Have them identify any cultural differences between the individuals described in their paragraphs. Then ask them to list as many similarities as possible between them. Talk about how the conflicts might have continued and escalated into violence if these differences had not been accepted and respected by each side.

INTRODUCING HEALTH TERMS

- Ask students to complete Vocabulary Activity 14 and Chapter Study Guide 14 in the *Student Workbook.* ☞

Conflict Resolution Skills

Although daily life can be full of conflicts, you don't have to think of each conflict as a battle. Instead, think of life's conflicts as opportunities to demonstrate your self-respect and integrity. During conflicts, you can practice your communication and decision-making skills.

HEALTH TERMS

conflict resolution
tolerance
negotiation
mediation
peer mediators
confidentiality

HEALTH CONCEPTS

- There are healthful and unhealthful ways to resolve conflicts.
- Good communication skills and the willingness to compromise are essential to resolving any conflict in a healthful way.
- Sometimes a conflict is so difficult that outside assistance is needed.
- People can resolve their conflicts when there is mutual respect, open-mindedness, and acceptance of other people's differences.

Conflict Resolution

When you find yourself in a conflict that is unavoidable or where you think something important is at stake, conflict resolution skills can help. **Conflict resolution** is *the process of ending a conflict by cooperating and problem solving together.* Conflict resolution involves many different interpersonal skills, several of which—communication, cooperation, and compromise—are discussed in Chapter 11. In addition to these Three C's, resolving conflict in a nonviolent way involves the following Three R's—*respect, rights,* and *responsibility.*

- **Respect.** Showing respect is an essential element in resolving conflicts in positive ways. When you show respect for others, you value each one as an individual. You also make it

---

Lesson 2 Resources

TEACHER'S CLASSROOM RESOURCES

☞ **Concept Map** Activity 44
☞ **Cooperative Learning** Activity 14
☞ **Enrichment** Activity 14
☞ **Lesson 44 Quiz**
☞ **Lesson Plan 44**
☞ **Reteaching** Activity 44

STUDENT WORKBOOK

☞ **Applying Health Skills 44**
☞ **Chapter Study Guide 14**
☞ **Vocabulary** Activity 14

TRANSPARENCIES

☞ **Transparencies 40, 41**

MULTIMEDIA

☀ **ABCNews InterActive™,** *Violence Prevention*

more likely that others will show you respect in return. People who respect others are more likely to listen with an open mind, consider the other person's views and feelings, and honor the basic values of the individual.

- **Rights.** Having respect for others also means not violating other people's basic rights. People need to remember that no one owns anyone else. No one has the right to control or harm another person or destroy another person's property. Another basic right to consider is the right to privacy. Going into other people's lockers or reading their private journals, which is a direct violation of this right, can lead to ugly, even violent, conflicts.

- **Responsibility.** With rights come responsibilities. Take responsibility for your actions. When a conflict develops, do not just blame the other person. Take a look at what your part in the conflict may be. Make responsible decisions that respect both the rights and the health of all parties. Your goal should be that any action you take is an effort to help resolve the conflict and to avoid being hurtful to you or any other human being.

Tolerance

Tolerance is important in preventing conflict and promoting peace. **Tolerance** includes *accepting others' differences and allowing them to be who they are without expressing disapproval.* People may have views and ideals that are different from your own. When people practice tolerance of different viewpoints or ideas, there are fewer conflicts.

◀ *Learning about others' cultural backgrounds can enrich your own life and make it more interesting.*
ACTIVITY *Make plans to learn about a culture different from your own from someone in your school or neighborhood.*

Did You Know?

➤ Conflict resolution has become such an important skill that dozens of universities throughout the country and world now offer programs and advanced degrees in conflict analysis and resolution.

➤ The Society for Professionals in Dispute Resolutions—an organization of conflict resolution professionals—has nearly 10,000 members.

➤ People who work in conflict resolution fields include teachers, lawyers, psychologists, and individuals from a host of other professions.

TEACH

L2 Discussing

Have students describe instances where teens show respect for one another in their daily activities. Afterward, ask how it feels when someone fails to consider their feelings or to respect them.

L1 Discussing

Have students relate how their friends deal with disagreements in peaceful ways. Discuss the need to resolve minor differences before they grow into major conflicts.

L2 Class Activity

Have students prepare lists of questions about common conflicts they have experienced or observed at school or off campus. Invite the school counselor to class. Have students ask questions from their lists and get advice from the counselor.

VIOLENCE PREVENTION (Side 2)
Chapter 5: Resolving Conflict

Frames 12074-14354

Chapter 6: Walking Away

Frames 14365-15625

Chapter 7: Fighting

Frames 15635-17614

Chapter 8: Analyzing the Conflict

Frames 17628-22900

LESSON 2 CONFLICT RESOLUTION SKILLS **321**

MORE ABOUT . . . . .

CONFLICT. Ask students to describe conflict situations they have experienced or observed that ended with a positive outcome. What role did the Three C's or Three R's play in the resolution of the conflicts? Some conflicts can have positive results, depending on how they are handled. For example, a conflict can encourage change by keeping people from getting into ruts and keeping old habits that they need to review and discard. Conflicts can make life more interesting by causing people to look more deeply into an issue, particularly from a new perspective. A conflict can even help to deepen and improve a relationship by strengthening each person's belief that the bond between the individuals is stronger than any issue causing conflict.

Building Health Skills

Steps to Take When Negotiating
Skill: Conflict Resolution

Help students discuss the importance of negotiation. Ask: What can happen when individuals or groups who disagree fail to negotiate? Why is it important to know how to negotiate? Then let students read the feature to learn more about the steps involved in effective negotiation. As a follow-up activity, have groups of students work together to apply the six steps to a specific conflict. Group members may record their ideas in a short essay, or plan and present a skit illustrating the steps.

L1 Discussing

Discuss reasons why peer mediation is increasing in popularity on school campuses.

L2 Cooperative Learning

Have students complete *Cooperative Learning Activity 14,* "Mediate a Conflict," in the TCR. ✏️

VIOLENCE PREVENTION (Side 2)

Chapter 12: Peer Mediation in Action

Frames 41662-47861

Building Health Skills

Conflict Resolution: Steps to Take When Negotiating

LIKE COMMUNICATION, decision making, and other life skills you have learned about, the skill of negotiation is one that takes practice. The steps to effective negotiation include the following:

1. **Choose a time and place conducive to working out problems.** Avoid meeting with the other person when you are feeling rushed or impatient. Choose a place that is not noisy or full of distractions.

2. **Work together at a solution.** Instead of approaching the other person as your enemy, suggest politely that you work together to brainstorm a solution.

3. **Keep an open mind.** Remember that every story has two sides. Listen carefully to what the other person has to say.

4. **Be flexible.** Be willing to bend. Meet the other person halfway.

5. **Take responsibility for your actions and role in the conflict.** There is no shame in apologizing if you see that you have unjustly hurt the other person. In fact, the ability and willingness to make amends when you are wrong is a sign that you are maturing into a responsible adult.

6. **Give the person an "out."** Your objective is to resolve your differences, not to prosecute the other person. If he or she seems embarrassed or uncomfortable about a point that is raised, suggest continuing the conversation at a later time.

Did You Know?

➤ There are over 5,000 peer mediation programs in the U.S.

➤ It is estimated that 8 out of 10 peer mediation agreements result in successful resolutions.

➤ New research reported by the American Psychological Association indicates that up to one-third of students who bully others may spend less than 30 minutes a day with adult supervision.

Negotiation

Whereas some people think that physical fighting is the best way to settle a disagreement, a better approach involves the skill of **negotiation.** This is *a process in which compromise is used to reach agreement.* Negotiation involves talking, listening, considering the other person's point of view, compromising if necessary, and coming up with a plan of working together to solve the conflict. When two parties negotiate, each does not blame the other. Instead, they talk about what is needed to solve the problem at hand. *Before* you negotiate you should:

■ Make sure that the issue is important to you.
■ Check your facts. Maybe the disagreement is based on something that isn't even true.
■ Remind yourself that your goal is to find a solution, not to fight or prove who is "in control."
■ Rehearse what you will say, even if you have to script it out in advance.

322 CHAPTER 14 RESOLVING CONFLICTS AND PREVENTING VIOLENCE

HOME AND COMMUNITY CONNECTION

MEDIATORS. Have students investigate their community to find people or agencies that act as mediators. Begin with your school. If your school has a peer mediation program, encourage students to discuss it, evaluate its effectiveness, and make suggestions for improvement. If not, ask for volunteers to try to get one started. Then have students find out what mediation resources are available in the community for families or neighbors in conflict, for businesses and their rivals or dissatisfied customers, or even for rival gangs. Have students make posters advertising these services.

Mediation

Sometimes during a conflict, the two parties reach a point where it may be time for **mediation.** This is *a process in which specially trained people help others to resolve their conflicts peacefully.*

Today, many schools are offering peer mediation programs. In these programs, **peer mediators,** *students trained to help other students in conflict find fair ways to settle their differences,* help other teens find solutions to the problem.

Peer mediation involves the use of problem-solving, communication, and negotiating skills. Schools with peer mediation programs report fewer fights, more cooperation, and less overall violence.

Effective Mediation

Mediation has well-defined ground rules. It is up to the mediator to set these rules and to describe them to both sides. The session should be held in a neutral location such as a classroom. Peer mediators must maintain strict **confidentiality**—*respecting the privacy of both parties and keeping details secret.* The mediator begins by asking each person, in turn, to describe the disagreement. The mediator next summarizes each side, asking for clarification of any points that are inaccurate. Each side is then invited to talk to the other with the mediator's supervision. The mediator may then ask the parties to sign an agreement to work out the problem within a certain time frame.

▲ *When teens work together for the common good, the rewards can be great.*

ACTIVITY *Identify three other life skills that play an essential role in conflict resolution. Give an example of how each could be used to resolve a conflict between two teens.*

LESSON 2 *Review*

Reviewing Facts and Vocabulary

1. Define the term *negotiation,* and describe how this skill is used to resolve conflicts nonviolently.
2. Explain the value of peer mediation in conflicts involving teens.
3. Summarize what takes place in a mediation session.

Thinking Critically

4. **Analyzing.** Think about some compromises that you might not be willing to make. In what kinds of situations should a compromise *not* play a part? Summarize the kinds of issues or conflicts that are not negotiable for you.

5. **Evaluating.** Read the following statement: *You must be the change you wish to see in the world.* Explain what these words mean to you and how they relate to the idea of responsibility.

Applying Health Skills

6. **In Your Home.** Keep a Relationship Conflict Journal for a week, recording conflicts that occur between you and other family members. Observe and write down what the conflicts are about, what triggers them, how they are resolved, and what factors made the conflicts better or worse. See if you can find any patterns to these conflicts and their resolutions.

LESSON 2 CONFLICT RESOLUTION SKILLS **323**

ASSESS

EVALUATING THE LESSON

Assign and discuss the Lesson 2 Review; then administer, grade, and discuss the *Lesson 44 Quiz* in the TCR.

RETEACHING

- Divide students into small groups. Assign them to write short lessons for elementary students, using the main ideas of this lesson. Have them combine groups and present their lessons to each other.
- Ask students to complete *Reteaching Activity 44* in the TCR.
- Use *Transparencies 40* and *41* to review conflict resolution skills and the peer mediation process.

ENRICHMENT

- Select students to research the availability of peer mediation programs on nearby college and university campuses. If possible, students should interview persons involved in the programs. Afterward, have students share what they learned with the class.
- Show students how peer mediation is being used in schools around the country as a win-win means of conflict resolution. Have them complete *Enrichment Activity 14,* "Can't We All Just Get Along?" in the TCR.

CLOSE

Ask students to summarize the most important concepts in this lesson. Remind them that conflicts can be resolved peacefully. Also, encourage them to use peer mediation whenever they are unable to solve differences with someone.

Lesson 2 Review

Answers to Reviewing Facts and Vocabulary

1. A process in which compromise is used to reach agreement. It resolves conflicts by having the two parties come up with a plan to work together to solve the problem.
2. The value of peer mediation for teens is that it helps them learn problem-solving, communication, and negotiating skills.

3. In a mediation session, a trained mediator listens to both sides in a neutral location and helps them to listen to and work with one another in finding resolution to the conflict.

Answers to Thinking Critically

4. Nonnegotiable issues should involve basic values and life-or-death decisions.
5. Answers will vary.

Strategies for Avoiding Violence

LESSON 3

FOCUS

LESSON OBJECTIVES

After studying this lesson, students should be able to

- identify specific types of violence common in the United States today.
- describe the increase in violence involving teens.
- explain why violence is increasing and what can be done to prevent it.

MOTIVATOR

Write the following on the chalkboard for students to work on while attendance is being taken: *Describe in a few sentences a situation you witnessed or took part in that involved violence or the potential for violence.*

INTRODUCING THE LESSON

Refer to the Motivator. Ask volunteers to share their responses. For each situation described, have students identify the victim and the perpetrator of the violence or near violence. Ask them to discuss why the situation intensified. Tell students that in this lesson they will learn why violence is on the increase in our society, particularly violence that involves teens, and what can be done to prevent it.

INTRODUCING HEALTH TERMS

- Ask students to complete Vocabulary Activity 14 and Chapter Study Guide 14 in the *Student Workbook.* 🖝

Strategies for Avoiding Violence

When conflicts are permitted to escalate or go unresolved, the risk of violence increases. **Violence** is *the use of physical force to injure or abuse another person or persons.* In addition to physical harm, acts of violence can leave victims with deep emotional scars.

HEALTH TERMS

violence
homicide
assailant
random violence
aggravated assault
carjackings

HEALTH CONCEPTS

- Teens are increasingly the people who commit violent crimes as well as the victims of these crimes.
- Crimes are more random, brutal, and remorseless today than in the past.
- New measures are being taken across the nation to stop violence in schools and communities.
- Your efforts can help to make the world a safer, healthier place.

Violence in Society

As a society, the United States is no stranger to violence. According to the Centers for Disease Control and Prevention, over 6,000 young people ages 15–24 become victims of homicide each year. This amounts to an average of 18 youth homicide victims per day in the United States. In fact, **homicide**—*the willful killing of one human being by another*—is the second leading cause of death for persons 15 to 24 years of age. For every violent death, moreover, there are at least an estimated 100 nonfatal injuries caused by violence.

Violence happens for many different reasons. Some acts of violence are unsuccessful efforts to resolve a conflict. In many such acts, the victim knows his or her assailant. An **assailant** is *a person who commits a violent act against another.* Other acts of violence are crimes of hate, stemming from **prejudice**—negative feelings toward an individual based not on experience but on misguided generalizations about race, ethnicity, or gender. Still other violent crimes arise out of

hotlink

prejudice For more information on prejudice and its dangers, see Chapter 13, page 300.

Lesson 3 Resources

TEACHER'S CLASSROOM RESOURCES
🖝 **Concept Map** Activity 45
🖝 **Lesson 45 Quiz**
🖝 **Lesson Plan 45**
🖝 **Reteaching** Activity 45

STUDENT WORKBOOK
🖝 **Applying Health Skills 45**

🖝 **Chapter Study Guide 14**
🖝 **Vocabulary** Activity 14

TRANSPARENCIES
🖝 **Transparency 49**

MULTIMEDIA
🔴 **ABCNews InterActive™ VHS/Videodisc,** *Violence Prevention*

frustration or anger over poverty or lack of opportunity. Usually, these crimes occur as robberies or thefts, though sometimes people are injured or killed in the process.

An especially distressing type of violence that has emerged in recent decades is **random violence**, *violence committed for no particular reason*. Such crimes are often committed against an innocent bystander or other person who happens to be nearby at the time. One segment of the population frequently targeted for acts of random violence is the homeless.

Violence and Teens

Teens are another group that has become involved increasingly in violent acts. Nationwide, 14.8 percent of students had been in a fight on school property one or more times in 1996. Arrest rates for rape, robbery, and **aggravated assault**—*unlawful attack with an intent to hurt or kill*—are significantly higher among young people 15 to 34 years of age than among all other age groups.

Teen violence is on the rise not only on the streets but also in schools. Every day in the United States, some 16,000 crimes take place in or near schools. There are reports of fights, attacks, shootings, and gang involvement in classrooms, restrooms, hallways, locker rooms, and on school grounds. In such stressful environments, students find it difficult to learn, and teachers find it hard to teach.

◄ *Many schools have instituted new policies, such as installing metal detectors, to protect students and make them feel safe.*

ACTIVITY *In the local newspaper, find a news story that centers on an act of violence. Identify the nature of the violence. Who was the victim? Who was the assailant?*

TEACH

L3 Discussing

Initiate a discussion of the long-lasting emotional damage caused by violence by having students imagine themselves as victims of a violent act, such as a mugging. Ask them what emotions they think they would experience both during and after the attack. How do they think their self-confidence and self-esteem would be affected over the long run by the violent act?

L1 Explaining

Explain the similarities and differences of murder, homicide, aggravated assault, battery, and rape.

L3 Researching

Have students research and write a report on the rise of random violence in our society today. They should address issues such as: the reasons for the increase in random violence; where such violence is most likely to occur and who is most likely to be involved; the specific violent acts that are most common; and what can be done to avoid being involved in random crime.

L1 Cooperative Learning

Have the class work in groups of four or five to make bulletin-board displays titled: "Teens and Violence in the U.S. Today." They should collect clippings from newspapers and magazines that describe a wide variety of violent situations involving teens both as victims and as perpetrators of violent acts. Their objective should be to increase awareness of the risk of violence faced by today's youth.

CURRICULUM CONNECTIONS

SOCIAL STUDIES. Select students to read short stories about people who suffered violence because of prejudice. Divide students into small groups to share their stories with each other.

LANGUAGE ARTS. Have students write a short story from the viewpoint of an individual who experienced violence because of an untrue rumor that was spread by one or more persons. Ask them to include information about the origin of the rumor, the persons who spread the rumor, and the effects of the rumor.

Teens Making a Difference

Peace and Justice for All

Discussion. Ask students to read the feature and discuss the questions. Indicate that Nihad has many other interests in addition to peace and justice: he plays varsity soccer, lacrosse and tennis, and he likes to rock climb, hike, and kayak. He also loves to spend time with friends.

Next, read the following additional quotes by Nihad, asking students to apply them to situations in their own lives. Ask for students to apply them also to national or global events that they have studied or read about.

- *The best way to prevent prejudice and the violence that comes from it is to become familiar with other people's cultures and differences and to acquire as much knowledge as possible about differences and similarities among people.*
- *Work hard for what your goals are in life. Set high goals and try to reach them, but try to respect other people along the way.*
- *I hope to help make people aware of the importance of learning what is happening in the world and, in the process, to promote peace.*

Class Activity. After the discussion, ask students to create a handbook called *Tips for Greater Tolerance* to be distributed through the school's student council.

Answers. *Nihad's Story*
1. He applies the values to personal relationships, in school, in community service projects, and in oversees relief work.
2. Responsibility, respect.

Responses. *Your Story* **1–3.** Answers will vary. Encourage students to consider the value of respect in their answers.

Teens Making a Difference
...TOLERANCE...RESPONSIBILITY ...COURAGE

Nihad, age 18, is committed to the values of peace, justice, and tolerance. A senior in high school, his goal is to promote nonviolence both in his own life and in the lives of other teens around the globe. These issues are particularly close to his heart because he grew up in Bosnia, in Eastern Europe, during wartime. Nihad has seen firsthand the terrible consequences of prejudice, intolerance, and violence.

"When I was ten, the war started and people started calling me names," he begins. "I felt prejudice. Living through the war and witnessing all of the massacres and slaughtering made me hate other groups. After the war, though, when I came here, I started to realize that not all people are responsible for what happened there. I saw that people could live in harmony here, and that made me realize that I should not despise and hate people just because they belong to certain groups. Every human being deserves basic respect."

RETURNING TO HIS ROOTS Last summer Nihad went back to Bosnia with an international organization for peace to do volunteer work. "The goal of the group is to get different nationalities and cultures who are at war or in conflict to find peaceful means to get along. When we got there, we organized an English-speaking school (see photo). We taught kids English as a second language. We also helped people returning to their homeland whose houses had been destroyed. The first step for us was to help to clean up all of the ruins and debris so they could rebuild."

BUILDING PEACE, BUILDING CHARACTER "I took a class in Peace and Justice at my school here," he says, "and I gave a presentation about Bosnia and told my story. We did group discussions with Bosnian students. I belong to the International Student Forum, a school club that meets to talk about cultural differences and alleviate problems. I would like to be an ambassador…I have learned a lot about peace and conflict resolution. I believe that people should never take up arms to resolve any conflict because there is always an alternative peaceful way to resolve any kind of issue. Whether personally, culturally, or internationally, you can resolve differences without violence."

NIHAD'S STORY
1. In what ways would you consider Nihad's dedication to the values of peace, justice, and tolerance balanced in all areas of his life?
2. What other values does he demonstrate through his words and actions?

YOUR STORY
1. What steps can you take to promote conflict resolution in your own family, friendships, school, and community?
2. What safe steps can you take to help others support the values of non-violence and greater tolerance for others?

326 CHAPTER 14   TEENS MAKING A DIFFERENCE

MEETING STUDENT DIVERSITY

GIFTED. Suggest to gifted students that they present a debate to the rest of the class. Each student should adopt one of the following points of view in the debate.

- Violence should be permitted at any time on television because censoring violence would be a violation of freedom of speech.

- The networks should reduce violence during prime-time hours, but it is up to parents to control their children's exposure to violence on television at other times.

- The networks should take an active role in protecting children from violence by keeping violence to a minimum in all television programming.

up|date
▶ Our Changing World

Violence Prevention and Intervention

You have probably heard or read many news stories about violence in schools and communities. Homicides, hate crimes, school shootings, and gang activities seem to make the nightly news on a regular basis. With these troubling reports, you might be worried about your own safety. In truth, though, you probably don't need to be. Statistically, schools are among the safest places in the United States. In addition, schools and communities are committing a great deal of time and resources to enhance safety and prevent violence.

Recognizing that academic failure is a risk factor for violent behavior, many schools are making changes to help students improve academic performance. For example, some schools have decreased class sizes and improved school facilities. Many schools teach conflict resolution and anger management skills, and some even offer antiviolence workshops. For increased safety, some schools not only provide metal detectors and security guards, but also offer behavioral counseling and monitoring.

Many communities also have developed strategies for preventing violence and crime. Some have neighborhood watch programs or citizen patrols, in which residents watch for and report suspicious activities. In some communities, mentoring programs provide opportunities for adult mentors to act as role models for young people. Other communities have established after-school recreation programs to teach valuable skills to at-risk students.

1. Why do you think academic failure is a risk factor for violent behavior? What might be some other risk factors?

2. Find out what violence prevention measures are being taken in your school or community.

As a reaction to this growing problem, many schools have taken preventive measures. Some have installed metal detectors to stop students from bringing guns and knives into schools. Other schools conduct physical searches or use dogs capable of sniffing out drugs and weapons.

Factors Affecting Violence

Violence, especially among teens, is a complex issue that is affected by many different factors. These include availability of weapons, territoriality, the media, and substance abuse.

AVAILABILITY OF WEAPONS

According to the CDC's 2000 *Youth Risk Behavior Survey,* nearly 7.7 percent of students have been threatened or injured with a weapon

---

CURRICULUM CONNECTIONS

LANGUAGE ARTS. After reviewing literature of past and present conflict and violence in society, have each student write a short essay on crime victims and their families. The essay should explore the personal feelings of the persons involved and the effects of the crime on their lives.

SOCIAL STUDIES. The financial costs of conflict and violence are considerable. Ask a representative from a local government agency or a community hospital to speak to the class about some of the monetary costs of violence. Discuss the impact of these expenses on society.

---

up|date
▶ Our Changing World

Violence Prevention and Intervention

Ask volunteers to share their thoughts on current violence prevention efforts. Ask: Have you noticed an increase or decrease in violence in recent years? Do you ever worry about your safety at school or in the community? Why or why not? What actions have been taken to help prevent violence? Have students read the Update feature to learn more about violence prevention and intervention. Then let them meet in small groups to discuss their responses to the first question. For the second activity, suggest that students share their findings in oral reports.

ABC NEWS INTERACTIVE™

VIOLENCE PREVENTION (Side 1)
Chapter 9: Prejudice

Frames 32608-39499

Chapter 10: Guns and Injury

Frames 39511-44733

Chapter 11: Violence and Homicide

Frames 44740-47721

Chapter 12: Substance Abuse

Frames 47736-52423

VIOLENCE PREVENTION (Side 2)
Chapter 13: Thinking About the Media

Frames 47874-52946

Parental Involvement

L1

Ask students to interview their parents about what the parents' biggest fears were when they were teens in high school. They also should interview other students in their school to find out what today's teens fear the most. Then have groups of two or three students each compile the fears into two lists—one for their parents' generation and one for their own generation. Ask a representative from each group to share their lists with the rest of the class. Generate class discussion by asking whether today's teens have more to fear than their parents did. How do they think their fears as teens will affect them when they are adults?

Reading

L1

Ask students to find at least two articles in magazines dealing with the issue of violence on TV and its effect on violent behavior in children and teens. Have them write a brief summary of each article.

Researching

L2

Have the class research and present oral reports on what happens when teens are arrested for committing violent crimes. In particular, they should investigate whether teens are tried as adults and given adult sentences. They also should address the age at which a teen is considered an adult in this context, and whether the nature of the crime plays a role.

Guest Speaker

L3

Ask a member of the school's administration to speak with the class about the level of violence in the school. Suggest that the speaker address the following: the most common types of violence that occur on school grounds; causes of the violence; and measures employed or under consideration to prevent violence in school.

▲ **Across the country, Americans are reclaiming their neighborhoods, working to make them safer.**

ACTIVITY *Name three steps that you and your classmates can take to make your school a safer place.*

on school property. In addition to conventional weapons (such as handguns, knives, and clubs), newer "state-of-the-art" weapons—including so-called assault rifles—are finding their way into the hands of teens, particularly those with gang affiliations. Some teens also report that access to information about where to get weapons is easier than ever to come by.

TERRITORIALITY

Some teens, without a true sense of personal power or control in their lives, may turn to claiming areas not their own in an attempt to look or feel important and in control. Members of gangs may stake out their "turf" or territory, often by "tagging"—spray-painting a gang's logo or a member's initials on public property that they feel belongs to the group. Such rivalries are often deadly and may center on drug deals and drug money.

THE MEDIA

By the age of 18, the average teen has seen 22,000 hours of TV and witnessed some 200,000 acts of violence, real or staged, including 16,000 murders. In addition to TV, song lyrics, videos, movies, and video games carry images of or messages about violence.

What effect does violence in the media have on young people? Some critics feel that this media exposure provides a "recipe" for violence among young people. These critics point to a rise in the number of **carjackings**—*hijacking or stealing a car by force*—after reports of this crime were first broadcast in the early 1990s. Others insist that young viewers become desensitized, or emotionally indifferent, to acts of brutality when such images are constantly displayed.

SUBSTANCE ABUSE

A rise in recent years in abuse of alcohol and other drugs has led to a corresponding increase in violent crime. Some of these crimes, as noted earlier, are related to the sale of drugs and have even added a new term—*drive-by shooting*—to the vocabulary of violence. Other crimes related to substance abuse are committed by drug users who rob or steal to pay for their habit. Drugs and alcohol also interfere with a person's ability to reason and make healthful decisions. These substances can exaggerate what a person is feeling and greatly increase the chances that emotions such as anger and jealousy will be blown out of proportion, turning a simple argument into a violent, and potentially deadly, situation.

COOPERATIVE LEARNING

MEDIA MESSAGES. Assign students to small groups. Have students discuss their usual television programs and any films or videos they have seen. Guide them in discussing the number of conflicts that are resolved without violence, and the number that lead to violence. Ask them about the images of heroes projected. Does the media encourage audiences to admire characters who avoid violence as much as those who triumphantly kill their adversaries or beat them senseless? How often does a movie audience cheer when a hero violently punishes a villain? Remind students they are consumers. They "vote" at the box office or cash register. Invite students to consider boycotting films, CDs, or videos that promote violence.

Stopping and Preventing Violence

More and more communities across the nation are working hard to prevent violence and help their young people find healthy ways to release their energy and avoid becoming either the assailants or victims of violent crimes. There are academic after-school programs, sports and camping programs, even programs in video production and the arts to keep young people off the streets and give them useful skills and meaningful activities for life. Businesses are doing their part by funding programs and providing internships for teens who are "at risk" of violence.

What You Can Do

What can you as a responsible member of your community do to help curtail the spread of violence? The following are some practical tips:

- Avoid guns and alcohol and other drugs.
- Resist becoming a member of a gang.
- Learn and practice the skills of communication and conflict resolution, both of which can help keep your **emotions** from erupting into anger.
- Work at building your self-esteem. People who feel good about themselves seldom need to lash out at others.
- Limit your exposure to media that promote and glamorize violence and prejudice.

You can also work at seeing that younger siblings and other children in your environment follow your positive example in each of these areas. Remember, we all have a stake in curbing and preventing violence.

Did You Know?

According to the Center for Media Education:

- ➤ American children watch three hours of TV a day, on average.
- ➤ By age 21, the average viewer will have seen 1 million TV commercials.
- ➤ Saturday morning children's shows average about 20 to 25 violent acts per hour.
- ➤ Prime-time shows average five acts of violence per hour.
- ➤ On average, the American TV-viewing child watches 20,000 ads per year.

hotlink

emotions For more information on emotions and strategies for handling them, see Chapter 8, page 197.

LESSON 3 *Review*

Reviewing Facts and Vocabulary

1. Define the terms *violence* and *assailant,* and use both in a paragraph.
2. What are some of the causes of violence, particularly among teens?

Thinking Critically

3. **Analysis.** Write down three goals you would like to achieve by age 25. After each goal, write how using violence could get in the way of achieving it.

4. **Evaluating.** In some communities, parents are required to pay for damage done by their children to community property. Do you think this is a useful policy? Why or why not?

Applying Health Skills

5. **In Your School.** Write a Public Service Announcement teaching teens some ways to prevent getting into fights. Ask if you can deliver this message over the school's public address system.

ASSESS

EVALUATING THE LESSON

Assign and discuss the Lesson 3 Review; then administer, grade, and discuss the *Lesson 45 Quiz* in the TCR.

RETEACHING

- Divide the class into four groups. Assign each group one of the factors affecting violence. Have each group write a public service announcement about its assigned factor. Post the announcements for others to read.
- Ask students to complete *Reteaching Activity 45* in the TCR.

ENRICHMENT

Direct students to interview a speech or drama teacher about different ways in which tone of voice can be used to avoid or reduce conflict. Have them report their findings to the class.

CLOSE

Sum up this lesson for students by reminding them that violence is on the rise in our society, and that teens are involved in much of the violence, including violence in schools. Emphasize that it is important that they know what causes violence and how to prevent it.

Lesson 3 Review

Answers to Reviewing Facts and Vocabulary

1. Violence: the use of physical force to injure or abuse another person. Assailant: a person who commits a violent act against another. Paragraphs will vary.
2. Availability of weapons, territoriality, the media, substance abuse.

Answers to Thinking Critically

3. Answers will vary.
4. Answers will vary.

FOCUS

LESSON OBJECTIVES

After studying this lesson, students should be able to

- describe the types of abuse.
- explain how to avoid abuse.
- identify help that is available for victims of abuse.

MOTIVATOR

Write the following on the chalkboard for students to work on while attendance is being taken: *Make a list of cases of abuse that you have heard or read about recently.*

INTRODUCING THE LESSON

Refer to the Motivator. Have students share some of the cases they are aware of. Discuss the prevalence of abuse in our society, citing some of the statistics provided in the lesson for physical and sexual abuse. Tell students that this lesson will narrow this topic to a discussion of abuse in dating relationships: how it happens and ways to prevent it.

INTRODUCING HEALTH TERMS

- Have students define the term *abuse* in their own words and identify the many forms of abuse.
- Ask students to complete Vocabulary Activity 14 and Chapter Study Guide 14 in the *Student Workbook.* ✒

LESSON 4

Preventing Abuse

The health of a relationship is sometimes threatened by violence between individuals in the form of abusive behaviors. It is important for you to be aware of this type of violence and to know that steps can be taken to put a stop to these behaviors.

HEALTH TERMS

abuse

rape

sexual assault

HEALTH CONCEPTS

- Many cases of abuse go unreported, partly due to fear or feelings of futility on the part of the victim.
- Many teens are in abusive relationships.
- All abuse must be stopped, and there is help available to both the abused and the abuser.

Types of Abuse

Abuse is *the intentional physical, emotional, sexual, and/or verbal maltreatment or injury of one person by another.* It can take many forms, and it happens to people from all walks of life. In fact, children, teens, adults, and senior adults are all among the victims of abuse, and it crosses all economic, racial, and ethnic lines. It also happens to both sexes. Whenever or however it occurs, the emotional scars can be devastating.

Physical Abuse

Physical abuse is intentionally inflicting bodily harm or injury on a person. It may include slapping, kicking, biting, burning, shaking, beating, and other kinds of physical violence. Physical abuse is widespread. Consider these facts:

- According to the American Medical Association, between two million and four million women in the United States are assaulted by their partners every year.

Lesson 4 Resources

TEACHER'S CLASSROOM RESOURCES

✒ **Concept Map** Activity 46

✒ **Decision-Making** Activity 14

✒ **Lesson 46 Quiz**

✒ **Lesson Plan 46**

✒ **Reteaching** Activity 46

STUDENT WORKBOOK

✒ **Applying Health Skills 46**

✒ **Chapter Study Guide 14**

✒ **Vocabulary** Activity 14

MULTIMEDIA

● ABCNews InterActive™ VHS/Videodisc, *Teenage Sexuality*

- 30 percent of American women report that they have been physically abused at some time in their lives.
- About one-third of the women abused in adulthood grew up in homes where their mothers were abused, and about 20 percent were themselves abused as children.
- According to the Family Violence Prevention Fund, 34 percent of Americans have witnessed an incidence of domestic violence.

Sexual Abuse

Sexual abuse is forcing a person to engage in sexual activities or sexual advances or contact of any kind made by an adult toward a child or teen. Known as the "silent violent epidemic," sexual abuse is a widespread problem in America. Consider these facts:

- According to the American Medical Association, over 61 percent of the victims of sexual abuse are females under the age of 18.
- Males are the victims of sexual assaults approximately 5 percent of the time.
- About 75 percent of all sexual assaults or attacks are committed by people the victim knows.
- Over 700,000 women in the United States are sexually assaulted every year.
- Child sexual abuse is reported up to 80,000 times annually in this country, and unreported cases far exceed this number.

Sexual abuse can take many forms, and it does not always involve sexual intercourse. A **sexual assault** is *any intentional sexual attack against another person.* Battery—or beating—is often used in conjunction with sexual abuse.

Abuse in Dating Relationships

There is a disturbing rise in violence in dating relationships as well as an increase in the reporting of these incidents. Counselors of teens around the country report that physical, sexual, and emotional abuse are not only widespread but are also all too accepted in many teen relationships. Some teens may mistake a boyfriend's or girlfriend's dominant treatment as an expression of caring. They may confuse jealousy with demonstrations of love, when in fact true caring involves kindness, gentleness, and respect, never control or harm.

Rape and Date Rape

Rape, *or sexual intercourse by force,* is a crime of violence. It is also one of the least reported crimes. It is estimated, in fact, that half of all rapes go unreported. Anytime two people have sexual intercourse and one does not agree to the act, it is **rape**. In instances where sexual intercourse is forced upon a spouse it is considered rape.

When a person has been raped, it is critical that the victim report the rape to authorities and go to a hospital for immediate testing and

Did You Know?

➤ In the United States, there is a new victim of sexual assault every 45 seconds.

➤ According to the American Medical Association, surveys indicate that over 87 percent of the victims of sexual assault would rather tell their physicians about the attacks than anyone else.

➤ Fewer than half of all sexual assaults are reported.

➤ Rohypnol and GHB, two illegal substances also referred to as date-rape drugs, are powerful tranquilizers used in sexual crimes. Effects can include muscle relaxation, amnesia, slowing of psychomotor responses, or death.

hotlink

rape For more information on rape and help for rape victims, see Chapter 34, page 762.

TEACH

L1 Explaining

Explain why people who do not know healthy ways to vent their anger and deal with their emotions may be prone to violent behavior.

L1 Self-Esteem

Have several groups of two or three students write and role-play scenarios in which a violent act occurs because the violent individual has low self-esteem. Ask the class to suggest alternative, nonviolent outcomes for the scenario, in which the previously violent individual shows improved self-esteem.

L3 Guest Speaker

Invite representatives from the local center for battered women, rape crisis center, and/or community mental health clinic to speak with the class about violence prevention. Ask them to discuss the role of refusal skills and assertive behavior in preventing and dealing with conflict.

L2 Class Activity

Have students name as many different types of abuse as they can. Ask a volunteer to write the list on the chalkboard. Then have the class work together to select a criterion for deciding on the seriousness of each type of abuse, such as the degree of physical or emotional damage inflicted on the victim. Ask them to rank the abuses they listed in order of seriousness. They should justify their ranking.

SCHOOL-TO-CAREER

CHILD WELFARE WORKER. When a case of child abuse or suspected child abuse is reported, county agencies need to act. Counties employ social workers to investigate reports of child abuse. When they find abuse has occurred, they report their findings and make recommendations about the appropriate course of action. If an abused child is left in the home or returned to the home after a period of parent or guardian rehabilitation, child welfare workers usually monitor the progress of the child and the family. They may also monitor the foster parents or group homes in which children might be placed after being removed from abusive parents. Have students learn about the duties of child welfare workers and the qualifications for such a position.

TEENAGE SEXUALITY (Side 2)
Chapter 12: Acquaintance Rape

Frames 22482-23377

Making Responsible Decisions

1. Sara is concerned because her steady boyfriend has begun to show an explosive temper.
2. Sara could (a) talk the situation over with Don, asking whether something is bothering him; (b) tell Don she wants to break up because she cannot accept his abusive behavior; (c) ignore Don's outbursts, accept his apologies, and hope the situation improves.
3. Sara might (a) risk making Don angry, but have an opportunity to discuss his behavior and her re-action to it; (b) spare herself any chance of further abusive behav-ior, but lose a relationship she has enjoyed; (c) maintain her relationship with Don, but ex-pose herself to the possibility of further abuse.
4. Sara values being treated with respect. She also values her relationship with Don.
5. Responses will vary.
6. Help students consider both the short- and long-term conse-quences of their decisions.

L2 Decision Making

For further study on making re-sponsible decisions, assign *Decision-Making Activity 14* in the TCR. 👉

L1 Critical Thinking

Focus students' attention on the importance of recognizing abuse. Ask: How can you respond if you recognize abuse in one of your rela-tionships? in relationships between teens you know? in relationships between adults you know?

Making Responsible Decisions

Make Up or Break Up?

Sara has been dat-ing Don for almost eight months. Lately Don has begun "blowing up" unexpectedly over little things. Last weekend, when Sara arrived ten minutes late for

their date, Don began screaming so loudly that people on the street stopped and stared. Sara was humili-ated. Later, Don called to apologize, promising it would never happen again. Don has just invited Sara to a party this coming Saturday. Sara wants to go, but she's afraid that the whole

scene might happen all over again. What should she do?

What Would You Do?

Apply the six steps of the decision-making process to Sara's problem.

1. **State the situation.**
2. **List the options.**
3. **Weigh the possible outcomes.**
4. **Consider your values.**
5. **Make a decision and act.**
6. **Evaluate the decision.**

Counseling can help family members find solutions to their problems.

evaluation. To prevent further illness or injury and to get physical ev-idence that might be used to convict the rapist, it is crucial that the rape victim act quickly.

How to Avoid Abuse

One way to lessen your chances of dating violence is to avoid using alcohol and other drugs and refuse to date people who use these substances. It is estimated that 50 percent of those who commit date violence and up to one-third of those who are its victims were using alcohol at the time of the abuse.

When it comes to preventing abuse, remember these Three R's:

■ **Recognize.** Learn to recognize abusive behavior in its many forms.

■ **Resist.** Should someone use or try to use offensive touching, sug-gestive talk, or other inappropriate behavior, resist in any way you can. Be assertive.

■ **Report.** Get away and tell someone about the incident as soon as you can.

Help for Victims of Abuse

If you become the victim of abuse or rape, remind yourself that you were the victim and that *you* did nothing wrong. The first thing to remember is that physical and sexual abuse and neglect are against

---

HEALTH LITERACY

EFFECTIVE COMMUNICATOR. Some perpetrators of date rape genuinely disbelieve a rape has occurred. Failure to communicate or interpret communications effectively can lead to date rape, unwanted sex, or physical intimacy. Have students make anonymous lists, each headed by a verbal or physical approach to greater intimacy. Suggest heads such as Kissing, Intimate Touching, Removing Clothing. Under each head, students should list verbal or physi-cal responses that mean no or yes. Instruct volunteers to make transparencies of all list heads and yes and no responses, indicating how many students listed each response. Have students discuss the responses, including how messages might be interpreted. Help students understand that no means no, regardless of other signals.

the law. The authorities can be brought in to prevent further abuse. Before anyone can help an abused person, however, someone must report the abuse. All states now have laws requiring doctors and other health professionals to report suspected cases of child abuse. In many states, anyone who suspects or knows of an abusive situation is required to report it.

Any teen who is being abused, has been abused, or knows someone who is being abused should talk to a caring, trusted, and knowledgeable adult. This might mean a parent or guardian, the police, a 911 operator, a teacher, coach, clergy member, counselor, physician, or someone at a rape crisis center, battered person's shelter, or hospital emergency room. Only when an abused teen can reach outside the abusive relationship will things start to improve in his or her life.

Counseling is available for both the child and the parents in abusive families. In fact, in all kinds of child abuse, as well as in those cases where teens have abused their parents, families should be brought in for evaluation and counseling.

Just as important as the rehabilitation of abusive parents is the long-range prevention of abuse in society as a whole. Parents and prospective parents need opportunities for learning about family life, child development, and parent-child relationships.

Help for the Abuser

Abuse is a problem not only for the victim but for the abuser, who needs help. Often, abusers were themselves victims of abuse. Such people are in need of intense counseling.

keeping Fit
Stopping Sexual Harassment

Sexual harassment at school is all too common an occurrence, and it doesn't even have to involve physical contact. It can take many forms, including sexual comments, jokes, stares, or looks. Knowing what constitutes sexual harassment may be a first step in stopping it. Sexual harassment includes any of the following criteria:

➤ making sexual comments or jokes

➤ writing sexual messages on notes or walls

➤ spreading sexual rumors

➤ spying on someone dressing or showering

➤ pulling off someone's clothes

➤ exposing body parts

➤ inappropriate touching

LESSON 4 Review

Reviewing Facts and Vocabulary

1. Define the words *abuse* and *sexual assault,* and use them in a single paragraph.
2. What steps should a teen being abused at home take to stop the abuse?

Thinking Critically

3. *Analyzing.* For what reasons do you think teens in abusive relationships too often stay in those relationships, suffering continued abuse?
4. *Evaluating.* Some say that the effects of abuse are worse in the long term than in the short term. Explain in what

way this statement might be true for many victims of abuse.

Applying Health Skills

5. *In Your School.* Invite a social worker, representative from the Department of Public Welfare, or a representative from Parents Anonymous to speak to the class about physical, mental, and sexual abuse, and where and how to get help. Formulate at least three meaningful questions to ask the visitor.

Stopping Sexual Harassment

keeping Fit

Discuss the criteria for sexual harassment. Ask students to describe the prevalence of sexual harassment at school and ways that students currently deal with the problem. Encourage them to be assertive in their actions and to report any incidents as soon as possible.

ASSESS

EVALUATING THE LESSON

Assign and discuss the Lesson 4 Review; then administer, grade, and discuss the *Lesson 46 Quiz* in the TCR. ✏

RETEACHING

- Have students prepare a detailed lesson outline using the lesson's headings.
- Ask students to complete *Reteaching Activity 46* in the TCR. ✏

ENRICHMENT

Have students research the cycle of abuse that victims become a part of, as they often become abusers themselves. Provide time for discussion of their findings.

CLOSE

Summarize the most important concepts in the lesson. Write the lesson's major concepts on separate, numbered slips of paper. Place the slips into a box, and have each student draw one. Going in numerical order, ask each student to use his or her own words to summarize the concept written on the slip of paper.

Lesson 4 Review

Answers to Reviewing Facts and Vocabulary

1. Abuse: the intentional physical, emotional, sexual, and/or verbal mistreatment or injury of one person by another. Sexual assault: any intentional sexual attack against another person. Paragraphs will vary.
2. Talk to a caring, trusted, and knowledgeable adult.

Answers to Thinking Critically

3. Answers should include guilt, low self-esteem, fear, isolation.
4. Long-term effects include the inability to trust or establish healthy relationships as well as the possibility that the abused will become the abuser.

Health Skills Activities

ACTIVITY 1
HEALTH SKILLS

Communication—Conflict Resolution

➤ **National Standards**
This activity meets these National Health Standards: 5.5; 5.6.

Teach

- Have students brainstorm situations where a conflict might arise—for example, one student pushing to get ahead in the cafeteria line or a fan at a ball game accidentally spilling a beverage on the lap of another spectator.
- Review with students negative examples of dealing with a conflict ("you" messages and accusations), as well as positive negotiating skills ("I" messages and active listening).
- Have groups choose and develop one of the ideas into a skit.

ACTIVITY 2
HEALTH SKILLS

Self Management, Communication—Refusal Skills, Health Advocacy

➤ **National Standards**
This activity meets these National Health Standards: 3.6 ; 5.6; 7.4.

Teach

- Discuss the problems of date rape and sexual abuse. Make sure students understand the nature of situations in which these problems are more likely to arise.
- Using the notes they took while examining the model brochures, students are to brainstorm features to include in their publication.
- If the brochure is to be broken into chapters or topic areas, students or pairs should each arrange to take responsibility for a different area of coverage.

Health Skills Activities

Activity 1 — Resolving Conflicts

Sometimes, role-playing conflicts and their solutions can help prepare you to handle such situations when they actually occur. What strategies do you use to manage conflicts?

Directions

1. With a group, write and role-play two versions of a scene in which two teens are involved in a conflict. One version should show positive negotiating skills ("I" messages and active listening), the other a lack of skills ("you" messages and accusations).
2. After all the groups have performed their skits, discuss as a class how good communication skills can lead to a peaceful resolution of a conflict between teens.
3. Discuss whether the process of role-playing raised consciousness about types of conflict and how to avoid them.

Time
50 minutes

Materials
paper, pen or pencil

Self-Assessment

✓ Demonstrated effective use of "I" messages and active listening skills.
✓ Noted at least two differences in communication that resulted from the use of "I" and "you" messages.

Activity 2 — Dating Do's and Don'ts

With cases of physical abuse, sexual abuse, and date rape on the rise, every teen needs to understand how to ensure personal safety when dating. What principles and behaviors can help make dating safe?

Directions

1. In groups, brainstorm and record guidelines that might be followed to prevent abuse or violence in a dating relationship (such as going out on group dates or recognizing abusive behavior).
2. Using the guidelines and what you learned in this chapter, create a brochure to inform incoming teens to your school (male and female) about safe dating behaviors.
3. You may want to organize your brochure into topic areas, such as "Communicating Personal Guidelines," "Handling Conflicts," and "Preventing Violence."

Time
50 minutes

Materials
newsprint, markers

Self-Assessment

✓ Listed at least three appropriate guidelines or behaviors for safe dating.
✓ Created a brochure that was persuasive and targeted to a teen audience.

ASSESSMENT SCORING

Using a four-level rubric, the student has achieved a 4 if:

ACTIVITY 1

✔ Student was instrumental in brainstorming conflict situations.
✔ Student showed an understanding of positive and negative ways of resolving conflict.
✔ Student demonstrated effective use of "I" messages and active listening skills.
✔ Student noted at least two differences from the use of "I" and "you" messages.

ACTIVITY 2

✔ Student identified at least three appropriate guidelines or behaviors for safe dating.
✔ Student took notes that helped prepare for the writing of his or her group's brochure.
✔ Student created a brochure that was persuasive.
✔ Student targeted his or her group's brochure at a teen audience.

HEALTH NEWS VIDEO

Teens Taking Charge

The best way to handle school violence is to stop it before it starts. Many situations that erupt into violence can be identified and addressed, but only if people are alert and communicative.

The North Carolina Center for the Prevention of School Violence has helped to develop programs to help students resolve conflicts. Student leaders participate in discussions and seminars that help pinpoint problems before they start. Students in these programs use the power of positive peer pressure to ease tensions and head off misunderstandings. Their thoughtful and caring participation can help make one of the center's slogans a reality: "School Violence. Let's Get It Out of Our System."

Play the Video ▶

CNN. All Rights Reserved.

Think About It

▶ How can student leaders help resolve conflicts that might lead to violence? Which strategies do you think are most likely to be effective?

▶ Why do you think the North Carolina program emphasizes the role of student leaders rather than adult experts?

▶ What signs indicate that a situation could turn violent?

CNN HEALTH NEWS **335**

MORE ABOUT . . . . .

RELIABLE SOURCES. The North Carolina Center for the Prevention of School Violence is a public organization founded in 1993 to help create a safe learning environment for all students. Its programs are dedicated to taking a proactive approach to both intervention and prevention.

Most of the Center's programs are focused on student participation and leadership. Its studies show that these programs are successful because they acknowledge "the important roles that students play in addressing the problems which exist in their own schools."

CNN. HEALTH NEWS

Teens Taking Charge
Video Segment 8 (Time – 2:05)

Objectives. After viewing the video, students should be able to identify positive ways teens and schools can resolve conflicts and prevent violence.

Motivator. Ask: "How can students help one another promote mental, social, and emotional health at school?" Write student suggestions on the chalkboard. Ask for specific details to elaborate on general suggestions. Then have students view Video Segment 8, "Teens Taking Charge" to show how student leaders in North Carolina are working together to identify and resolve conflicts that might lead to violence.

Teach

• Discuss the strategies to prevent violence that are used in the schools in the video. Create a chart on the chalkboard to identify important details of the program. Invite students to tell how each factor can help prevent violence.

• Encourage students to consider how the techniques of the program described could be applied in their school or community. Students should compile a list of existing programs in their school and community. Suggest that they contact one organization on the list to find out about possible peer support, counseling, or awareness groups dedicated to stopping school violence.

Role Play. Reinforce the concept of positive peer pressure by asking students to role play situations in which peer pressure has a positive effect on a situation. After each enactment, have viewers identify how peer pressure affected the player's decisions.

Close. Have students imagine that your school board or principal has asked for suggestions about how to prevent violence in schools. Have students take turns summarizing the program and its goals to show one strategy that teens can actively apply to help resolve escalating conflicts.

CHECKING COMPREHENSION

- Assign and discuss the chapter review.
- Use the MindJogger Videoquiz to review the chapter. 🔴

CHAPTER 14 REVIEW ANSWERS

Using Health Terms

1. internal conflicts
2. escalate
3. conflict
4. interpersonal conflicts
5. confidentiality
6. tolerance
7. negotiation
8. resolution
9. mediation
10. peer mediators
11. carjacking
12. homicide
13. random violence
14. assailant
15. violence
16. rape
17. sexual assault

Recalling the Facts

1. Physical: a knot in the stomach, increased heart rate, a lump in the throat, clenching your fists, gritting your teeth, cold or sweating palms, a sudden surge of energy. Emotional: feeling concerned, getting defensive, not feeling valued, wanting to cry, lash out, or escape.
2. When your health or safety is at risk.
3. Any five: power, property, authority, jealousy, loyalty, space, and territory.
4. Respect, rights, responsibility.
5. Any three: the parties must listen without blaming, respect the fact that there are differences between the parties, maintain confidentiality, and abide by the agreed-upon resolution.
6. Any two: poverty, substance abuse, the media, lack of economic opportunity.

Using Health Terms

On a separate sheet of paper, write the term that best matches each definition below.

LESSON 1

1. Struggles within yourself.
2. Grow into a situation that is unhealthful and even unsafe to all parties concerned.
3. Any disagreement, struggle, or fight.
4. Disagreements between groups of any size, from two people to entire nations.

LESSON 2

5. Respecting the privacy of both parties and keeping details secret.
6. Accepting others' differences and allowing them to be who they are without expressing disapproval.
7. A process in which compromise is used to reach agreement.
8. The process of ending a conflict by cooperating and problem solving together.

9. A process in which specially trained people help others to resolve their conflicts peacefully.
10. Students trained to help other students in conflict find fair ways to settle their differences.

LESSON 3

11. Hijacking or stealing a car by force.
12. The willful killing of one human being by another.
13. Violence committed for no particular reason.
14. A person who commits a violent act against another.
15. The use of physical force to injure or abuse another person or persons.

LESSON 4

16. Sexual intercourse by force.
17. Any intentional sexual attack.

Recalling the Facts

Using complete sentences, answer the following questions.

LESSON 1

1. What are some of the physical and emotional tip-offs that a conflict may be building?
2. In what situations is it important to avoid conflicts at all costs?
3. Name five major categories of teen conflicts—those situations over which teens are most likely to argue or fight.

LESSON 2

4. What are the Three R's of conflict resolution?
5. Name at least three ground rules for peer mediation.

LESSON 3

6. List two factors that contribute to crime in the United States.
7. If someone feels intent on fighting with you, what should you do to prevent getting into a fight?

LESSON 4

8. Name and define two different kinds of abuse.
9. What is rape, and what steps can a teen take to prevent becoming one of its victims?
10. If you know someone who is being abused, what steps should you take?

7. Walk away.
8. Physical abuse: intentionally inflicting bodily harm or injury on a person. Sexual abuse: forcing a person to engage in sexual contact.

9. Sexual intercourse by force. Avoid use of alcohol, stay in group situations, know who you're with, etc.
10. Talk to a caring, trusted, knowledgeable adult.

Thinking Critically

LESSON 1

1. **Synthesizing.** Graph one recent conflict in which you have been involved. Draw lines on graph paper indicating the conflict's start, buildup, climax, and resolution. Label each portion of your graph, telling what happened to your mind and body at each critical point in the conflict.

LESSON 2

2. **Synthesizing.** Make a picture book in which you teach elementary school students about the peer mediation process.

LESSON 3

3. **Evaluating.** Which techniques for reducing and managing school violence, including metal detectors and searches, do you think are most effective? Which are the least effective? Explain your responses.

LESSON 4

4. **Analyzing.** Why do you think many teens stay in relationships in which there is abuse?

Making the Connection

1. **Language Arts.** With several classmates, team-read Shakespeare's *Romeo and Juliet,* or view a videotape of the modern musical based on the play, *West Side Story.* Analyze the basic conflict in the story. What factors contributed to making the conflict turn violent? How might the conflict have been handled differently and nonviolently? Present your ideas in a written report.

2. **Social Studies.** Find out about current gun ownership laws in your town or city. What are these laws, and how were they passed? Research national debates on gun control and what federal laws have been passed regarding this issue.

B E Y O N D   T H E   C L A S S R O O M

PARENTAL INVOLVEMENT With your parents or guardian, discuss whether or not parents should be held responsible for their children's vandalism or other crimes. Ask how they would feel if they had to pay for damage, go to prison, or do community service because of acts of vandalism committed by one of their children. Together, come up with a pledge that family members sign, promising to work to behave in ways that promote mutual respect in words and in actions, both inside and outside the home.

COMMUNITY INVOLVEMENT Help to organize a Violence Prevention Day in your neighborhood.

Begin the day with a School and Community Breakfast in which Peace Pancakes and other foods named for nonviolence are served. Have speakers from the community, the police department, and school talk about how to prevent violence in your community.

SCHOOL-TO-CAREER

Exploring Careers. Talk with a local police officer, a crime reporter for a local newspaper or TV station, or a community organizer. Ask about years of training and experience, dangers, and rewards of the career being discussed. Brainstorm ways to help prevent violence.

Thinking Critically

1.–3. Answers will vary.
4. Answers may include: low self-esteem, a history of abuse in the family.

Making the Connection

1. Reports will vary.
2. Research results will vary.

Evaluate

- Use the reproducible *Chapter 14 Test* in the TCR, or construct your own using the Testmaker software.
- Use *Performance Assessment Activity 14* in the TCR.

Enrichment

Ask students to complete *Cross-Curriculum Activity 14* in the TCR.

Beyond the Classroom

Keep students involved in the community, and encourage parent participation by assigning the activities on this page for students to work on outside of class.

Integumentary, Skeletal, and Muscular Systems

	FEATURES	CLASSROOM RESOURCES

ACTIVITIES

- Cross-Curriculum Activity 15
- Health Lab 15
- Health Skills Activities 15
- Parent Letter and Activities 15

ASSESSMENT

- Chapter 15 Test
- Performance Assessment Activity 15
- Testmaker Software

STUDENT ACTIVITIES WORKBOOK

- Applying Health Skills 47–49
- Study Guide 15
- Vocabulary Activity 15

STUDENT DIVERSITY STRATEGIES

- Audiocassette Program (English)
- Audiocassette Program (Spanish)
- Spanish Parent Letters and Activities
- Spanish Summaries, Quizzes, and Activities

MULTIMEDIA COMPONENTS

- English Audiocassette Program
- Spanish Audiocassette Program
- MindJogger Videodisc and VHS program

National Health Education Standards

One of the main goals of the National Health Education Standards is to move students toward "health literacy." Health literacy is the capacity of individuals to obtain, interpret, and understand basic health information and services and the competence to use such information and services in ways which promote health. The health standards were developed by applying the characteristics of a well-educated, literate person within the context of health. The health literate person is:
- a critical thinker and problem solver
- a self-directed learner
- a responsible, productive citizen
- an effective communicator

Listed below are the Health Education Standards Performance Indicators addressed in each lesson of this chapter.

Lesson	Health Standards Performance Indicators
1	2.1, 2.6, 3.1, 3.4
2	1.3, 4.3, 1.6, 6.6
3	1.3, 3.1, 3.4, 6.1

ONLINE RESOURCES

For a fresh approach to health topics and an in-depth look at health issues, use these online resources found under Teacher Resources at **health.glencoe.com**.

- **BLOCK SCHEDULE LESSON PLANS** Reinforce health concepts with outside readings selected especially for students. Each reading is accompanied by a lesson plan and activities to enhance
  - Reading Skills
  - Cross Curriculum
  - Media Literacy

- **TECHNOLOGY PROJECTS** Instructions and suggestions on how to use computer, Internet, and software with health lessons.

- **HEALTH UPDATES** Timely topics in health news, including late-breaking medical advances and updates on teen risk behaviors.

Out of Time?

If time does not permit teaching this chapter, you may use these features: Building Health Skills on page 342; Update on page 351; and Making Responsible Decisions on page 356.

BLOCK SCHEDULING

Block scheduling provides extended time for hands-on projects and activities. Use the following activities to engage students, provide further depth, and vary your instructional techniques:
- Update (30 minutes) **pg. 351**
- Health Skills Activity (60–90 minutes) **pg. 358**

Integumentary, Skeletal, and Muscular Systems

CHAPTER OVERVIEW

Chapter 15 introduces students to the integumentary, skeletal, and muscular systems. The structure, function, care, and problems of each system are presented.

LESSON 1 The integumentary system includes the skin, hair, nails, and sweat glands. Skin is the primary organ of the system. It has a number of functions and affects one's overall appearance. In addition to the integumentary system's functions, its structure, potential problems, and skin care are discussed.

LESSON 2 The skeletal system is the body's framework and can be divided into two main parts: the axial skeleton, which serves to primarily protect vital organs, and the appendicular skeleton, which allows for movement. A discussion of the skeletal system's structure, problems associated with the system, and its care are presented.

LESSON 3 There are three types of muscles—smooth muscles, skeletal muscles, and cardiac muscle. The function, structure, problems associated with the muscular system, and its care are explained.

CHAPTER **15**

Integumentary, Skeletal, and Muscular Systems

HEALTH *Online*

PRACTICING HEALTHFUL BEHAVIORS

Your skin is your body's first barrier of protection, and it's up to you to protect it for a lifetime. Stay informed about the importance of protection from the sun and environmental damage by reading the Health Update "Staying Sun Smart" at **health.glencoe.com**.

Hands-On Health

TEACHING STRATEGY

Understanding the Importance of Calcium Give students an opportunity to see how a lack of calcium can affect their bones in this demonstration involving chicken bones and vinegar. See Activities 11 and 12, "Rubber Bones," and "Cup of Calcium," in the *Hands-On Health: Creative Teaching Strategies* booklet.

Time Needed

20 minutes each/2 class sessions

Supplies

- glass jar with lid
- white vinegar (2 cups)
- clean chicken bones

Personal Health Inventory

Self-Inventory Write the numbers 1–10 on a sheet of paper. Read each statement below and respond by writing *yes, no,* or *sometimes* for each item. Write a *yes* only for items that you practice regularly. Save your responses.

1	I wash my face twice daily.
2	I have a well-balanced eating style that includes an adequate source of vitamin A.
3	I include many sources of calcium and phosphorous in the foods I eat.
4	My physical activity includes weight-bearing exercises.
5	I take frequent breaks when working at a computer to prevent injury from repeated movements.
6	I wear proper equipment, including shoes, for the activities I participate in.
7	I exercise three to five times a week.
8	I warm up and stretch before beginning to exercise and cool down after exercising.
9	I practice good posture in order to strengthen my back muscles.
10	I participate in activities that increase my balance and coordination.

Follow-up After completing the chapter, retake this self-inventory. Pick two items that you need to work on and set a goal to improve your health behaviors.

> ❝ *Your bones...work with your muscles and the rest of your body to make you the marvelous living machine that you are.* ❞
>
> —Seymour Simon
> Contemporary science writer

Quick Write Write five activities you have performed today that demonstrate the importance of having healthy bones and muscles.

CHAPTER 15 INTEGUMENTARY, SKELETAL, AND MUSCULAR SYSTEMS **339**

INTRODUCING THE CHAPTER

Personal Health Inventory

Focus students' attention on the chapter title, *Integumentary, Skeletal, and Muscular Systems,* and be sure they understand each term in that title. Then ask volunteers to identify the relationship between the habits identified in the Self-Inventory statements and the health topics to be discussed in this chapter. Finally, let students record their responses to the Self-Inventory statements in their private Health Journals and label the page. "Care of My Integumentary, Skeletal, and Muscular Systems."

- Tell students that the body systems they are about to study have a great impact on their appearance, ranging from complexion to posture to physique or body build. At the same time, they are vital to life.
- Have students describe the photographs on these two pages and discuss what they already know about the body's integumentary, skeletal, and muscular systems. Then have them complete the Quick Write. Ask volunteers to share their lists of activities. Tell students that they will learn more about these systems as they read the lessons in Chapter 15.
- Distribute Parent Letter 15 in the *Parent Letters and Activities* booklet. 🔴

TECHNOLOGY OPTIONS

MINDJOGGER
VIDEOQUIZ

To preview or review chapter content, you may wish to use the *MindJogger Videoquiz* that accompanies Chapter 15.

The Integumentary System

LESSON OBJECTIVES

After studying this lesson, students should be able to

- define the structure and function of the skin.
- describe proper skin care.
- describe problems of the skin.

MOTIVATOR

Provide students with quarter sheets of white paper and ink pads. Write the following on the chalkboard for students to work on while attendance is being taken: *On the paper provided, make an imprint of the forefinger of your left hand and write your name beneath it.*

INTRODUCING THE LESSON

Refer to the Motivator. Ask students to compare the prints of all students near them and determine in what ways they are alike. How do they differ? Discuss the use of fingerprints for identification. What other area of the body has an identifiable imprint? *(Foot)* Why are babies' footprints taken immediately after birth?

INTRODUCING HEALTH TERMS

- Have students make flash cards for the vocabulary terms. On one side, have them write the word. On the other side, have them identify the body system, the definition, and a page reference.
- Ask students to complete Vocabulary Activity 15 and Chapter Study Guide 15 in the *Student Workbook.* ☞

The Integumentary System

Although it may not have occurred to you, your skin is an organ of the body, just as your heart and liver are. In fact, your skin, besides being the body's largest organ, has more functions than any other organ. Your overall appearance is affected by the condition of your skin.

HEALTH TERMS

epidermis

dermis

melanin

athlete's foot

HEALTH CONCEPTS

- The skin serves a number of vital health functions to the body.
- Problems of the skin require varying degrees of medical treatment.
- Good skin hygiene includes regular washing and bathing.

Functions of the Skin

Your skin is the primary organ of your *integumentary system.* This is the body system that includes your skin, hair, nails, sebaceous glands, and sweat glands.

The skin serves a number of vital functions that are critical to your very survival. These include:

- **Providing a protective covering for your body.** Your skin acts as the main barrier between your internal organs and the outside world. It shields them from injury, invasion by pathogens, and the sun's harmful ultraviolet (UV) rays. Your skin is waterproof. It also has a water-holding capacity that contributes to its elasticity and helps maintain the body's balance of fluid and electrolytes.

Lesson 1 Resources

TEACHER'S CLASSROOM RESOURCES

☞ **Concept Map** Activity 47

☞ **Enrichment** Activity 15

☞ **Lesson 47 Quiz**

☞ **Lesson Plan 47**

☞ **Parent Letter and Activities 15**

☞ **Reteaching** Activity 47

STUDENT WORKBOOK

☞ **Applying Health Skills 47**

☞ **Chapter Study Guide 15**

☞ **Vocabulary** Activity 15

TRANSPARENCIES

🖐 **Transparency 53**

- **Regulating body temperature.** Skin plays a role in keeping body temperature constant. When your body is hot, tiny blood vessels in the skin enlarge, permitting internal heat to escape through a process called *radiation*. The sweat glands also become active, releasing perspiration, which cools the skin as it evaporates. As your internal temperature drops, the blood vessels in the skin narrow, conserving body heat.

- **Enabling you to sense the world around you.** The skin is a major sense organ that serves as a means of communication with the outside environment. Nerve endings in your skin are responsive to touch, pain, pressure, and temperature.

Structure of the Skin

Your skin has two main layers. These are the **epidermis** (ep-uh-DUR-mihs)—*the outer, thinner layer of skin,* and the **dermis**—*the inner, thicker layer of skin.*

Epidermis

The epidermis, or outer layer, is made up of both dead and living cells. The outermost part of the epidermis is composed of dead cells that form a tough, protective coating. The epidermis contains a fatty substance called *lipids* that makes the skin waterproof.

The dead cells of the epidermis are sloughed off, or shed, when clothing rubs your skin or when you wash. As these dead cells are worn away, they are replaced by new cells. Through this shedding, your outer skin is replaced about once a month. New cells rise to the surface to replace old ones.

Some of the cells in the epidermis produce **melanin** (MEL-uh-nihn), *the pigment that gives skin, hair, and the iris of the eyes their coloring.* Skin color in humans is determined largely by the amount of melanin in the skin. The more melanin, the greater the protection from the sun and its ultraviolet rays, which have been linked to skin cancer.

THE SKIN

- Hair
- Dead epidermis
- Living epidermis
- Sweat pore
- Oil gland
- Hair follicle
- Muscle
- Duct of sweat gland
- Sweat gland
- Artery
- Vein
- Nerve
- Fat tissue

Epidermis
Dermis
Subcutaneous layer

▲ *The skin is a waterproof shield, a barrier to pathogens, a regulator of body temperature, and a sense organ.*

ACTIVITY *Name the two types of glands contained in the dermis.*

TEACH

LD Class Activity

Provide an incomplete lesson outline for students to fill in during class discussions.

L3 Class Activity

Ask: Where can you write for information about dermatology and dermatologists? What questions would you ask in letters to these associations? Select several students to write to professional associations requesting information for the class about careers in dermatology. Share the letters with the class, requesting input, before the letters are mailed. Afterward, share and discuss each of the responses with the class.

L1 Explaining

Apart from its many other functions, the skin remains one of the most reliable diagnostic tools in the treatment of hay fever and other seasonal allergies. When sensitivity to an allergen is suspected, a doctor will administer a "scratch test." The test consists of a series of surface injections of plant extracts and other possible immunosensitive culprits. Depending on the substance, a positive response will register in the form of a blotch or bump—either one is a sign that calls for immunotherapy.

MEETING STUDENT DIVERSITY

PROJECT. Have groups of students create a board game to review the body systems discussed in the chapter.

LEARNING STYLES. Students in need of special attention might have a preliminary meeting in which the goals and logistics of the project are discussed. You might arrange for them to work in pairs and small groups during the project.

PHYSICALLY CHALLENGED. Students with physical challenges may wish to serve as consultants on questions specifically geared to care of the body system affected by birth defects or an accident.

L2 Researching

Direct students to collect examples of newspaper and magazine advertising, brochures, and product inserts for items designed to aid the skin's elasticity. Have them research the effectiveness of these products.

L1 Discussing

Ask students to discuss what care should be taken by anyone who uses or plans to use makeup. Have them explain their comments. *(People who use or plan to use makeup should take care to select types that do not clog the pores or cause an allergic reaction.)*

Building Health Skills

Deodorant Claims
Skill: Assessing Health Information

Display several different deodorant ads (as from magazines or circulars), and let students discuss the appeal each ad makes. Then ask: How different do you think these deodorants really are? How can you evaluate which kind of deodorant might be most effective? After students have shared their ideas, let them read the Building Health Skills feature to learn more about evaluating the claims made by deodorant marketers. As a follow-up activity, have students work in groups to collect and compare information from the labels of various brands of deodorants.

L1 Discussing

Have the class discuss the difference between a deodorant and an antiperspirant. Appoint students to research how deodorants and antiperspirants work to mask body odors and/or reduce the amount of perspiration. Have students share their findings with the class.

hotlink

sweat glands For more information on the function of the sweat glands, see Chapter 7, page 163.

sebaceous glands For more information on the function of the sebaceous glands, see Chapter 7, page 165.

Dermis

The dermis, the inner layer of skin, is made up of connective tissue that gives the skin its elasticity, or spongy, flexible quality. Nerve endings and hair follicles extend into the dermis. So do the **sweat glands** and **sebaceous glands**. Below the dermis is tissue called the hypodermis. The hypodermis is not part of your skin, but it attaches the skin to bone and muscle.

Skin Care

Good personal hygiene and a balanced eating style promote healthy skin. Wash your face with soap and water every morning and evening. Daily washing, bathing, or showering slows the growth of bacteria that cause body odor. Vitamin A helps promote healthy skin. Good sources of this vitamin include milk, egg yolks, liver, green leafy and yellow vegetables, and yellow fruits.

Building Health Skills

Assessing Health Information: Deodorant Claims

A DEODORANT is a substance that removes or masks bad-smelling body odors. Deodorants may contain antiseptics to destroy bacteria, perfume to mask odors, and antiperspirants—chemicals that reduce sweat production. When sweat remains on the skin, it creates a moist environment in which bacteria can thrive. The bacteria break down the chemicals in the sweat, causing body odor.

Deodorant preparations can be a useful aid against body odor, but they are no substitute for good personal hygiene. If you do decide to use a deodorant, how can you choose among all the competing claims and types? Here are a few tips:

 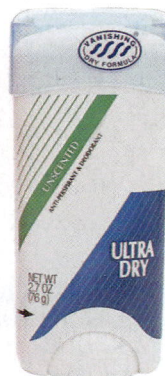

1. **Be alert to key words.** Marketers of personal hygiene products like deodorants often use key phrases such as *superior protection, unique formula,* or *extra long-lasting.* This is a typical marketing technique aimed at getting consumers to buy on impulse rather than explore the claims that are made.

2. **Read the label.** Deodorant preparations must list their ingredients on the label. Check and compare the ingredients to determine whether there is really a difference between two products that make competing claims about effectiveness. You may be surprised.

3. **Try it out.** Which is best for you: solid stick, spray, powder? Should you buy scented or unscented? Perfumes used in deodorants can cause skin irritation in sensitive people, as can antiperspirants that contain aluminum chloride. Most deodorants are available in inexpensive sample or travel sizes. Try a few until you find the one that suits you best.

COOPERATIVE ⟩ LEARNING

EXPLORING CAREERS. Teens may be learning first hand about the importance of good skin care to keep the skin healthy and blemish-free. Some may be encountering skin problems and seeing a dermatologist. Have volunteers research a career in dermatology. Tell them to include necessary qualifications, the level of education required, and specific tasks involved in the career. For more in-depth information, suggest that students interview a dermatologist in the community. Have students share their information with the class in the form of a bulletin board display or an oral presentation.

Problems of the Skin

Just as your skin has many functions, it is also a hotbed for problems, some potentially serious. One of these problems, **acne**, is common during adolescence, although it is not limited to this period. Other problems of skin include:

- **Ringworm.** Ringworm is a common fungal infection that affects various parts of the body. It gets its name from the ring-shaped, scaly, reddened, or blistery patches it forms.

- **Athlete's foot.** The same fungus that causes ringworm is also the cause of **athlete's foot**, *a fungal infection of the skin between the toes*. Athlete's foot is associated with wearing shoes and sweating. It is highly contagious. This is why it is important to wear foot coverings in locker rooms and showers.

- **Boils.** A boil is an inflamed, pus-filled area of the skin, usually an infected hair follicle. The usual cause of boils is the bacterium *Staphylococcus aureus*. Keeping skin clean helps prevent boils. Never squeeze or burst a boil; this can spread the infection. Boils can be serious and, if large, should be treated by a health care professional.

- **Warts.** Warts are contagious growths on the outer layer of the skin caused by viruses. Most warts are painless and harmless, but the virus that causes them can spread to other parts of the body and form more warts.

- **Moles.** Moles are small, usually round, slightly thickened, brown to dark brown spots on the skin. Moles are usually harmless. However, if a mole suddenly appears, grows, bleeds, or changes color, consult a physician immediately. Change in a mole may indicate a serious problem and should be checked by a doctor.

- **Psoriasis.** Psoriasis is a skin disease in which thickened patches of inflamed, red skin form, often covered by white, flaking scales. Psoriasis should be treated by a physician. The cause is not known, but this can be a lifetime skin problem if not treated.

- **Vitiligo.** Vitiligo is a disorder in which patches of skin lose their color. The affected areas of skin are extremely sensitive to sunlight and should be protected. Vitiligo is believed to be an auto-immune disorder that causes an absence of the skin cells that produce melanin. There is no cure, but in about 30 percent of cases the skin color returns naturally.

hot link

acne For more information on acne and how to treat it, see Chapter 7, page 165.

▼ *There is a wide range of skin color and skin types among the people of the world.*

ACTIVITY *Discuss the relationship between personal hygiene, a balanced eating plan, and healthy skin.*

L3 Researching

Ask volunteers to research the safety of tanning salons. Have other students determine the costs of tanning sessions and the precautions required or suggested by tanning businesses to protect their clients.

L1 Discussing

Encourage students to discuss various positive ways of dealing with severe cases of acne.

L2 Self-Esteem

Have students bring in several teen magazines containing skin care ads. Discuss the ads and whether or not they are effective in persuading teens to purchase the products advertised. Ask students to find examples of ads that emphasize emotions and peer pressure more than actual facts about acne and acne control. Ask: How might the condition of a person's skin affect his or her self-esteem?

L1 Explaining

Tell students that the most common cause of acne is the change in hormones that is a normal part of adolescence. While this can't be avoided, there are steps that can be taken to combat acne. These include washing your face two to three times daily, avoiding picking or squeezing the skin, and using over-the-counter products that contain benzoyl peroxide or resorcinol.

PERSONAL HEALTH

VITAMIN D. Vitamin D is important for bone growth and health. Direct students in conducting research to find out how much vitamin D they need and if they can obtain enough vitamin D from the sun, given year-round weather conditions. Then have them calculate the amount of exposure they would need in order to do so. Ask: Would this level of sun exposure put your health at risk? If they determine they cannot safely and feasibly obtain enough vitamin D from the sun, have them examine foods for vitamin D content. Ask: Can you obtain enough vitamin D from food, or is it advisable to take supplements? Explain that a supplement is not necessarily a pill. It can include vitamins or minerals added to milk or other processed foods.

Shedding Light on Sunscreens

keeping **Fit**

Bring to class a variety of suntan products for classroom display and discussion. Have students set up a display featuring the price of each product, the price per unit (such as per ounce), and its sun protection factor (SPF), if any. Ask students whether they use any kind of suntan product. What factors influence their decision as to whether protection is needed?

ASSESS

EVALUATING THE LESSON

Assign and discuss the Lesson 1 Review; then administer, grade, and discuss the *Lesson 47 Quiz* in the TCR. 🔖

RETEACHING

- Use *Transparency 53* to review the parts of the Integumentary System. 🧴
- Ask students to complete *Reteaching Activity 47* in the TCR. 🔖

ENRICHMENT

Alert students to the long-term dangers of tanning by having them complete *Enrichment Activity 15,* "Pale Is In and Tan Is Out," in the TCR. 🔖

CLOSE

Remind students that caring for the skin is more than a matter of cosmetic concern. The skin's many functions are essential in protecting and regulating the body, as well as enabling you to sense the world around you.

---

keeping **Fit**

Shedding Light on Sunscreens

Follow these guidelines when buying and using sunscreens:

➤ Wear a sunscreen that is water-resistant and waterproof.

➤ Apply sunscreen liberally and evenly to your skin 30 minutes before you go in the sun. Reapply at least every two hours.

➤ Wear a sunscreen with an SPF of 15 or higher. *SPF* stands for *sun protection factor.* The SPF numbers indicate the sunscreen's ability to screen out the sun's harmful UV rays.

➤ *Wearing gloves while gardening can reduce your chances of developing blisters.*

ACTIVITY *Identify techniques for reducing the risk of blisters during other physical activities.*

- **Impetigo.** A streptococcal infection in which bacteria enter a small break in the skin. This infection is highly contagious.

- **Blisters.** Blisters are raised areas filled with a watery fluid. They usually result from the skin being rubbed (your foot rubbing against the inside of your shoe, for example) or burned. A blister should be protected to keep it from breaking and left to heal on its own. A broken blister can become infected.

- **Callus.** A callus is an area of thickened skin that forms as a result of regular or continued friction or pressure. Musicians who play stringed instruments often develop calluses on their fingertips. Calluses can be reduced by rubbing them with a porous stone called pumice.

- **Corn.** A corn is a callus on a toe caused by the pressure of a tight-fitting shoe. Spongy corn pads can relieve the pressure that makes corns painful. Wearing shoes that fit properly is the main way to prevent corns.

LESSON **1** *Review*

Reviewing Facts and Vocabulary

1. What are the functions of the skin?
2. Explain the unique characteristics of the epidermis.
3. What is melanin, and what is its function?

Thinking Critically

4. *Synthesizing.* Jenna has a mole on her arm that has been growing from the time she was small. Does she need to take any action? Explain.
5. *Analyzing.* What makes cleanliness so important to skin health?

Applying Health Skills

6. *In Your Home.* Have you or has anyone in your family experienced any of the skin problems discussed in this lesson? How was the problem treated? What were the results? Discuss with family members what you have learned about the problem that you did not know before. Talk about what should be done differently—if anything—in the event the problem arises again.

Lesson 1 Review

Answers to Reviewing Facts and Vocabulary

1. See bulleted list on pages 340 and 341.
2. The outermost part of the epidermis is made of tough, protective dead cells that are shed continuously. It is waterproof.
3. Melanin is a pigment that colors the skin, hair, and eyes. In the epidermis, it provides protection from the sun and its ultraviolet (UV) rays.

Answers to Thinking Critically

4. She should consult her doctor.
5. Regular washing removes bacteria or other harmful organisms that might enter the body through the skin, thus helping the skin in its major function, which is protection.

The Skeletal System

Y ou may think of the skeleton as similar to the framework that supports a building. You will see that, unlike a building, the 206 bones that comprise the human skeleton work together with muscles to allow you to walk, run, jump, bend, lift, and carry.

HEALTH TERMS

axial skeleton

appendicular skeleton

cartilage

ossification

ligaments

tendons

repetitive motion injury

HEALTH CONCEPTS

- Bones have four primary functions.
- The skeleton gives structure and stability to the body.
- Eating well is one of the keys to maintaining the health of the skeletal system.

Functions of the Skeletal System

T he skeletal system has a number of vital functions. The skeleton plays a crucial role in movement by providing a strong, stable, and mobile framework on which muscles can act. It also supports and protects your delicate internal organs.

The bones that make up your skeleton have functions of their own. These living structures are the principal storage centers for essential body minerals, such as calcium and phosphorus. They are also the manufacturing center of the body's blood cells. Red bone marrow produces millions of blood cells each day.

Lesson 2 Resources

TEACHER'S CLASSROOM RESOURCES

- **Concept Map** Activity 48
- **Lesson 48 Quiz**
- **Lesson Plan 48**
- **Reteaching** Activity 48

STUDENT WORKBOOK

- **Applying Health Skills 48**
- **Chapter Study Guide 15**
- **Vocabulary** Activity 15

TRANSPARENCIES

- **Transparency 58**

The Skeletal System

FOCUS

LESSON OBJECTIVES

After studying this lesson, students should be able to

- define the function of the skeletal system.
- describe the structure and function of bones.
- compare the various types of joints.
- identify ways to care for the skeletal system.
- describe problems of the joints and bones.

MOTIVATOR

Write the following on the chalkboard for students to work on while attendance is being taken: *Write as many words or terms as you can that relate to the skeletal system.* Ask volunteers to share their responses.

INTRODUCING THE LESSON

Refer to the Motivator. Use a skeletal model or diagram to point out the various bones that students listed. Ask: Which bones are most often broken due to falls or other accidents? What types of padding are worn in sports to reduce the chance of breaking bones?

INTRODUCING HEALTH TERMS

- Tell students to make flash cards for the vocabulary terms. On one side, have them write the word. On the other side, have them identify the body system, the definition, and a page reference.
- Ask students to complete Vocabulary Activity 15 and Chapter Study Guide 15 in the *Student Workbook.*

TEACH

LD **Class Activity**

Provide an incomplete lesson outline for students to fill in during class discussions.

L1 **Class Activity**

Using a skeletal model, detail for the class the parts of the axial and appendicular skeleton. There are 80 bones in the axial skeleton. The appendicular skeleton consists of 126 bones. The word *appendicular* refers to a structure and its connection to the body's axial skeleton. In humans, appendages attach to the axial skeleton at the shoulder, or pectoral girdle, and the hip, or pelvic girdle. The skull has eight cranial bones, which are mostly flat, and 14 facial bones, which are irregularly shaped. There are three bones in the inner ear, and a single bone in the neck called the hyoid bone. The last is the only bone in the body that does not connect to any other bone. It serves as an attachment for the tongue muscles. The vertebral column is made up of 26 individual bones linked by cartilage and ligaments.

L1 **Class Activity**

Using models from the science department, ask students to compare the skull sizes of an infant and an adult. Ask: What is the relationship of the size of the head to the rest of the skeleton in a child and in an adult?

L2 **Class Activity**

The bones protect internal organs. Have students identify organs protected by bones. Then ask them to name the specific bones involved.

TYPES OF BONES

Long bone (femur)

Short bone (wrist)

Flat bone (rib)

Structure of the Skeleton

The skeleton provides support and protection for tissues and organs of your body. The skeletal system is divided into two main parts:

■ **Axial** (AK-see-uhl) **skeleton.** The **axial skeleton** includes *the 80 bones of the skull, spine, ribs, and sternum, or breastbone.* The vertebrae—the small bones that make up your spine—protect your spinal cord. The ribs, most of which are attached to the sternum in your chest and to the vertebrae of your spine, protect your lungs and heart.

■ **Appendicular** (ah-pen-DIHK-yoo-lar) **skeleton.** The **appendicular skeleton** includes *the 126 bones of the shoulders, arms, hands, hips, legs, and feet.* It helps you perform a wide range of movement.

Types of Bones

Bones are grouped according to their shapes. There are four basic types in the human body: long, short, flat, and irregular.

■ Strong long bones, like the femur, are found in the arms and legs. The shafts of long bones are called *diaphyses*. The ends are called *epiphyses*. The epiphyses form joints with other bones. The enlarged ends, which are composed mainly of spongy bone tissue, give stability to joints. The inner parts of the epiphyses contain red marrow, which produces all the red blood cells and most of the white blood cells and platelets in the body.

■ Short bones, like those in the wrists and ankles, are as broad as they are long. More than half of all the short bones in the body are in the hands and feet.

■ Flat bones, like the ribs and skull bones, have a thin, flat shape. These bones generally serve to protect vital organs.

■ Irregular bones, like vertebrae, have a shape that does not fit into any of the other three categories. The vertebrae on page 366 in Chapter 16 is an example of an irregular bone.

Cartilage

Your skeletal system is made up not only of bones but of **cartilage**, a *strong, flexible connective tissue*. Different types of cartilage line the surfaces of joints and enable them to move smoothly, cushion adjoining vertebrae, and support the nose and ears. A baby's skeleton is mostly cartilage. As the body grows, most cartilage cells are replaced by bone cells and minerals through **ossification** (os-suh-fuh-KAY-shun), *the process by which bone is formed, renewed, and repaired.* Bone renewal occurs as part of the body's normal process in which old cells are replaced by new cells. Bone repair fuses broken bones after a fracture.

346 CHAPTER 15 INTEGUMENTARY, SKELETAL, AND MUSCULAR SYSTEMS

HEALTH LITERACY

CRITICAL THINKER AND PROBLEM SOLVER. Humans are the only species that consumes milk past infancy. As people grow older, they may become deficient in lactase. Without lactase, humans cannot digest dairy products. Have students research lactose intolerance, finding out how prevalent it is in given age groups, which racial and ethnic groups are most affected, and symptoms of lactose intolerance. Tell them to create a meal plan for a day that provides a recommended daily intake of calcium without dairy foods. Encourage them to discuss whether calcium supplements would be advisable for lactose-intolerant individuals. If they favor supplements, suggest they find out which forms of calcium are best assimilated by the body.

THE SKELETAL SYSTEM

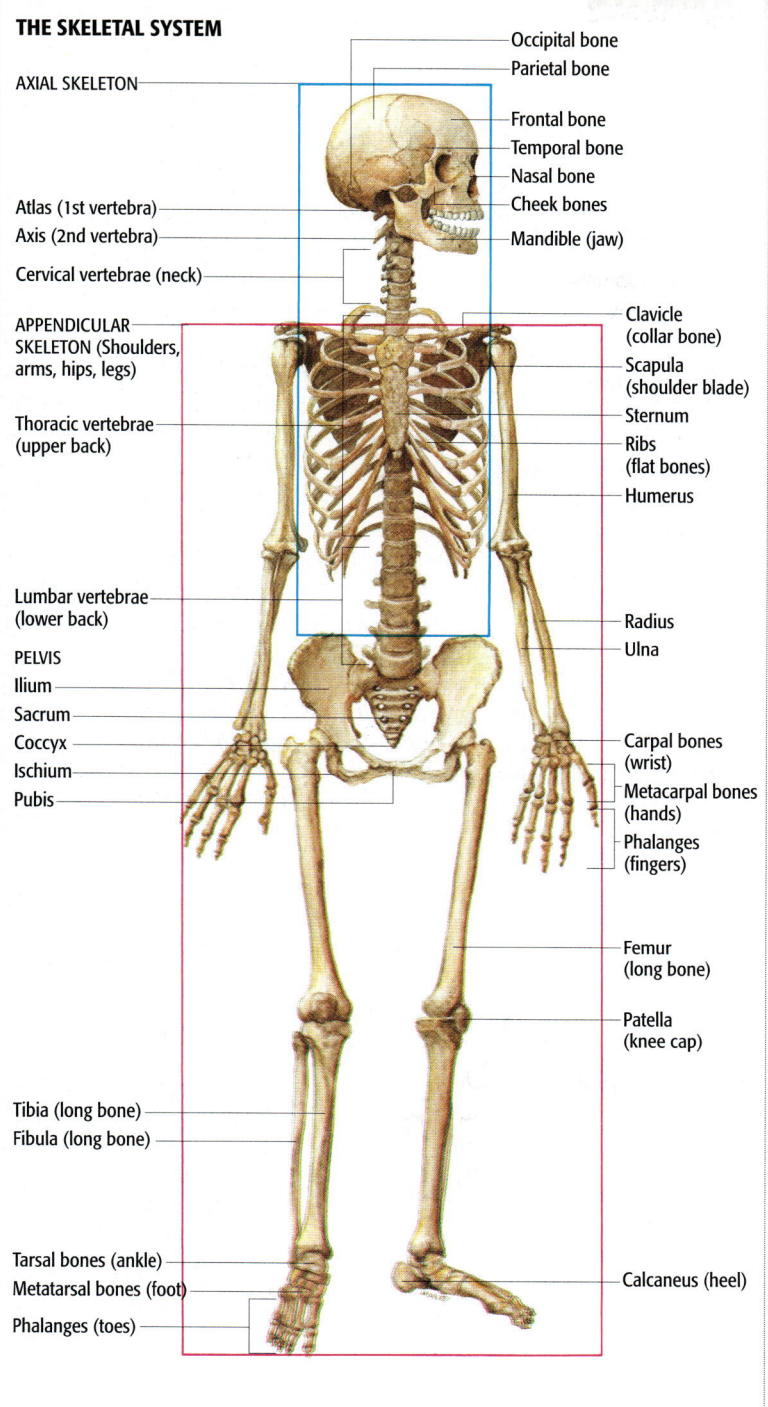

AXIAL SKELETON

Occipital bone
Parietal bone
Frontal bone
Temporal bone
Nasal bone
Cheek bones
Mandible (jaw)

Atlas (1st vertebra)
Axis (2nd vertebra)
Cervical vertebrae (neck)

APPENDICULAR SKELETON (Shoulders, arms, hips, legs)

Thoracic vertebrae (upper back)

Clavicle (collar bone)
Scapula (shoulder blade)
Sternum
Ribs (flat bones)
Humerus

Lumbar vertebrae (lower back)

PELVIS
Ilium
Sacrum
Coccyx
Ischium
Pubis

Radius
Ulna

Carpal bones (wrist)
Metacarpal bones (hands)
Phalanges (fingers)

Femur (long bone)

Patella (knee cap)

Tibia (long bone)
Fibula (long bone)

Tarsal bones (ankle)
Metatarsal bones (foot)
Phalanges (toes)

Calcaneus (heel)

◀ *The axial skeleton is shown here in blue. The appendicular skeleton is shown in pink.*

ACTIVITY *Tell how the axial and appendicular systems got their names. Consult a dictionary if necessary.*

L2 Class Activity

Skeletal injuries, especially knee, cartilage, and ligament injuries, are of interest to athletes. Instruct students to find out what happens when there is cartilage or ligament damage. They can research the newest ways of treating these injuries.

L1 Class Activity

Using the skeletal model on this page, have students identify long bones, short bones, and flat bones. Ask: Which group has the greatest number?

L1 Discussing

Calcium is an important ingredient in the diet throughout life. What measures can students employ to assure that they and their family members receive enough calcium?

L2 Class Activity

Dietary calcium additives are popular in today's advertising. Suggest that students prepare a collage of ads for these products and the varying claims. Ask: Is there scientific evidence that these products are helpful?

L2 Discussing

Ask students why the body needs phosphorus. Then ask them to list foods that are high in this mineral. *(Cereals, meats, poultry, fish, eggs, dried beans and peas, milk and milk products.)*

L1 Discussing

You may wish to use *Transparency 58* to discuss the skeletal system. 📖

CURRICULUM CONNECTIONS

SCIENCE. In a science lab, cut cross sections of the bones of a pig, cow, lamb, and chicken. Have students compare the structures for differences and similarities. The bone sections should be comparable in function, i.e., long bones of the legs.

FAMILY AND CONSUMER SCIENCES. Ask a family and consumer sciences teacher to present information on the history of rickets.

Have the teacher share how it was discovered, what the treatment was, and prevention strategies.

PHYSICAL EDUCATION. Ask a physical education teacher to discuss the problems of rapid growth and the ability to coordinate body movements. What other complications may temporarily interfere with normal growth?

LD Demonstrating

Demonstrate each type of joint. Provide a diagram if available.

L2 Discussing

Tell students that the ribs are the flat bones that protect the lungs. Ask: How does a fractured rib affect the functioning of the lungs? Is this the same as the impaired function of the brain when the skull is fractured?

L1 Class Activity

Identify with the class those areas in the body where pivot *(head and neck)*, hinge *(elbow)*, and ball-and-socket *(shoulder)* joints are found.

L1 Discussing

Lead students in a comparison of the body's hip joints with shock absorbers on a motor vehicle.

L1 Class Activity

Ask a doctor or local hospital for copies of X rays showing bone fractures. Show these to the class either by holding them up to a window or by using a projector. As you point to each X ray, ask students to identify what kind of fracture has occurred.

L1 Discussing

Encourage students to share their personal experiences, or those of their family members, with broken bones. How were the fractures treated? At what age and under what circumstances did the fracture occur?

L3 Guest Speaker

Contact an orthopedic technician at a local hospital and ask him or her to make a presentation to your class about cast application and care. Encourage students to develop a list of questions prior to the presentation.

Did You Know?

➤ Osteoporosis affects seven out of ten women over age 50. Arthritis affects one-third of women ages 45–64 and half of women over age 65.

➤ Carpal tunnel syndrome was responsible for 30 to 40 percent of worker's compensation claims in the early 1990s.

▼ *Different kinds of body movement are made possible by joints that move in several different ways.*

ACTIVITY *Name another example of a ball-and-socket joint.*

Joints

The point at which two bones meet is called a *joint*. Some joints are fixed, such as those between the bones of the skull. Some joints, such as those between the vertebrae, allow only a small amount of movement. Most joints, however, allow a wide range of movement. Imagine you did not have a joint where your arm bones meet at your elbow. What kinds of activities would you be able to perform?

There are several types of mobile joints:

- **Ball-and-socket joint.** This type of joint allows the widest range of movement: backward, forward, sideways, and in a circle. Examples are the shoulder and hip joints.

- **Pivot joint.** In a pivot joint, a bony projection allows rotation. An example is the joint between the first two vertebrae in the neck that allows your head to rotate.

- **Ellipsoidal joint.** In a joint like the one in your wrist, an oval-shaped part fits into a curved space. This allows all types of movement except pivotal.

- **Hinge joint.** A hinge joint allows bending and straightening, as in the fingers. The knee and elbow are hinge joints that also allow some degree of rotation.

At joints where movement occurs, the surfaces of the bones are coated with smooth, slippery cartilage to reduce friction during movement. **Ligaments** are *tough bands of fibrous, slightly elastic tissue that bind the bone ends at the joint.* In addition to binding the bones together, ligaments prevent excessive movement of the joint. **Tendons** are *fibrous cords that join muscle to bone or to other muscles.* Drum your fingers on your desk. The movements you see in the back of your hand are your tendons in action.

JOINTS

Skull (immovable joint)

Shoulder (ball-and-socket joint)

Elbow (hinge joint)

Head and neck (pivot joint)

348 CHAPTER 15 INTEGUMENTARY, SKELETAL, AND MUSCULAR SYSTEMS

MORE ABOUT . . . . .

FRACTURES. Broken bones may not heal as easily as we assume. Circumstances often influence how a bone heals. Younger people heal more quickly than older people. Mental stress, fatigue, and other physical problems as well as some medications may influence healing rates. Any serious disease will cause healing problems, as we know, but people who seem reasonably healthy sometimes find that a break just won't heal.

Techniques to assist the healing process include placement of pins and replacement of an entire joint or bone with synthetic bones.

Care of the Skeletal System

Your habits and decisions you make concerning nutrition and exercise can affect the health of your skeletal system now and later in life. Did you have milk or another dairy product for breakfast today? If you didn't, you should plan to tomorrow. Calcium, one of several **minerals** found in dairy products, is essential for building strong bones. It is especially important during the teen years, when the body builds most of its bone mass. Phosphorus, another vital mineral, combines with calcium to give bones their rigidity. Phosphorus can be found in milk, peas, beans, liver, cottage cheese, broccoli, and whole grains. Regular physical activity, especially weight-bearing exercise, increases bone mass. Exercise also promotes better circulation of the blood, increasing nourishment to your bones.

BONE STRUCTURE

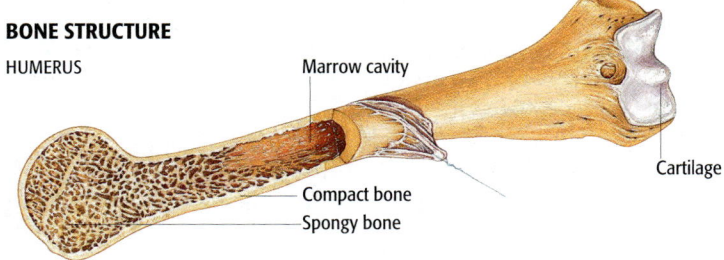

HUMERUS — Marrow cavity — Compact bone — Spongy bone — Cartilage

Problems of the Skeletal System

Skeletal system disorders and injuries to bones can be the result of many factors. These include poor nutrition, infections, sports and recreational mishaps, accidents, and poor posture. The skeletal system is also affected by degenerative disorders such as osteoporosis.

Fractures

Fractures are any type of break in a bone. Fractures are divided into two main types, simple and compound. In a simple, or "closed," fracture, the broken bone does not protrude, or stick out, through the skin. In a compound, or "open," fracture, one or both bone ends project through the skin.

Fractures may also be classified according to the shape or pattern of the break:

- **Hairline fracture.** The fracture is incomplete, and the two parts of the bones do not separate.
- **Transverse fracture.** The fracture is completely across the bone. This may result from a sharp, direct blow or stress caused, for example, by prolonged running on an already damaged bone.
- **Comminuted fracture.** The bone shatters into more than two pieces, usually from severe force as in an auto accident.

hotlink

minerals For more information on minerals and their role in bone growth and health, see Chapter 5, page 109.

◄ *A bone is made up of three types of tissue—compact bone, spongy bone, and marrow.* **ACTIVITY** *Explain how nutrition and exercise are important to healthy bones.*

L1 Discussing

Let students imagine they have broken a forearm and must wear a cast for several months. Ask them to describe the effect of the cast on the bones in the arm.

L3 Class Activity

Ask selected students to research the current first-aid treatment for joint pain and fractures. Plan a demonstration of proper splinting of long bone fractures. Include information about over-the-counter preparations for joint pain, including both pills and ointments. Is cold or heat considered the safer treatment for sprains?

L3 Discussing

Identify the word parts used to designate diseases of the skeletal system: *-itis (inflammation), osteo- (bone), -emia (lack)*. Familiarize students with the universal use of these prefixes and suffixes to identify conditions within the body.

L3 Guest Speaker

Ask a doctor of osteopathy to visit your class. Encourage him or her to describe in detail how his or her practice differs from that of a doctor of medicine.

MORE ABOUT . . . . .

FRACTURES AND OSTEOPOROSIS. Elderly people, particularly women, often fall and break their hips. It is also possible that the hip bone fractures first and causes the person to fall. As women age and go through menopause, the hormones change, making the absorption of calcium less efficient. The result is bones becoming thinner and porous, causing a condition called osteoporosis. As the bones become increasingly brittle, they break easily. A jarring movement or an effort to lift something is sometimes enough to break a fragile hip. Many women take supplemental calcium in an effort to forestall the onset of this condition. Exercise also helps maintain bone density. Estrogen therapy may be necessary for some women following menopause.

L1 Personal Involvement

Many broken bones result from accidents in the home. Suggest that students conduct a home safety check for such potential hazards as throw rugs, loose cords, blocked stairways, or toys in need of repair. Have students identify both good and poor safety practices in their homes, and then make correlations of their findings to school safety concerns.

L2 Researching

Ask students to research the causes of osteoporosis. Ask: Who is most susceptible? Why? Is the condition hereditary? What are its symptoms and how is it treated? Can it be prevented? How? Ask students to illustrate their findings in a poster.

Some older computers will not support the Java™ technology used in the animations at this site. If your classroom computer does not support Java™, you may need to download the necessary plug-in, or check with your Internet provider technical service for information on accessing the animations.

Check out drawings and overviews of body systems, discussions of organ functions, and a variety of body animations at **health.glencoe.com**.

▼ *Eating enough foods rich in calcium and phosphorus can prolong the life and health of your bones.*

ACTIVITY *Name two foods that are good sources of calcium and phosphorus.*

Osteoporosis

Loss of bone mass is a natural part of the aging process. In severe cases, osteoporosis—a condition in which bone density decreases, causing bones to become brittle and easily fractured—develops. Women are especially vulnerable to osteoporosis after menopause. Their bodies no longer produce estrogen, which helps maintain bone mass. You have the opportunity now in your teen years to prevent osteoporosis in later life. You can do this by getting ample physical activity and by eating enough foods that are sources of calcium, such as milk, cheese, and yogurt.

Scoliosis

Scoliosis is a lateral, or side-to-side, curvature of the spine. Scoliosis usually starts in childhood or adolescence and becomes more marked until the age at which growth stops. Most schools have scoliosis screening programs, usually conducted by the school nurse. Depending on the severity of the curvature, treatment may include exercise, a special brace, or surgery.

Injuries to the Joints

Common joint injuries include the following:

- **Dislocation.** A dislocation results when a bone slips from its normal position at a joint. Dislocation is usually accompanied by tearing of the joint ligaments. Never attempt to replace a dislocated bone. This condition requires the care of a physician to put the bone back in place and immobilize the joint so that the tissue can heal.

- **Torn cartilage.** Torn cartilage is a serious joint injury. It can result from a sharp blow or a severe twisting of a joint. Doctors can now repair some cartilage tears with arthroscopic surgery.

- **Bunion.** A bunion is a painful swelling of the bursa in the first joint of the big toe. Bunions are caused by wearing tight or high-heeled shoes, which cram the toes and cause them to bend in an abnormal way. To prevent this condition, it is important to wear well-fitting shoes. Large bunions may require surgery to remove the swollen tissue.

- **Bursitis.** Bursitis is a painful condition that occurs when the bursa in a joint becomes inflamed. It is common in the shoulder and knee joints. Bursitis is usually the result of pressure, friction, or slight injury to the membrane surrounding the joint.

350 CHAPTER 15 INTEGUMENTARY, SKELETAL, AND MUSCULAR SYSTEMS

COOPERATIVE ⟩ LEARNING

LIFESTYLE RISKS FOR OSTEOPOROSIS.
Students have learned that a sedentary lifestyle and inadequate calcium intake can increase the risk of osteoporosis. Have students work in groups of three to research other lifestyle factors that contribute to osteoporosis. For example, one group member might investigate the effects of dieting and weight loss on bone loss, and the consequences of recurrent weight gain followed by crash dieting. Another might research the effects of alcohol, while a third examines caffeine and its effects. After the students complete their research, have them conduct a panel discussion about risk factors and make lifestyle recommendations for preventing osteoporosis. Suggest that they comment about media messages which might tempt people to put themselves at risk for osteoporosis.

■ **Arthritis. Arthritis** is inflammation of a joint, characterized by pain, swelling, stiffness, and redness. The most common type, osteoarthritis, results from wear and tear on the joints and most commonly troubles older adults.

hotlink

arthritis For more information on arthritis and methods of treatment, see Chapter 31, page 692.

Exercise is important throughout life. Warming up before exercising can help prevent injuries to bones and joints.

ACTIVITY *Name two other ways to avoid injury to bones while exercising.*

hotlink

arthritis
Explain to students that arthritis often affects the joints in the hands. Ask them to make a list of everyday tasks, such as writing, that require strong, flexible hands. Guide students in investigating devices used by individuals with arthritis in their hands to accomplish daily tasks. Have them put their list of tasks and their research into their Health Portfolios.

L1 Researching

Have students visit a sporting goods store and examine the various types of knee, wrist, and ankle supports available. Tell them to ask a salesperson how effective the devices are and what other safeguards against injury are recommended.

update
▶ *Looking at Technology*

update
▶ *Looking at Technology*

Artificial Limbs: Skin and All

Artificial legs with a "skin-like" covering and even real-looking hair are now possible thanks to advances in the field of *prosthetics*—the making of artificial limbs and other body parts. These days, *prostheses*, or artificial limbs, are more high-tech than ever before.

Artificial limbs are nothing new. Prostheses were in use as early as 300 B.C., when crude limbs were made from wood and metal. Today, the drive to improve prostheses is in part due to increased awareness of the many great abilities of the physically challenged. David Barr, a double amputee, uses his high-tech artificial legs to walk miles a day and even ride a motorcycle!

Present-day prostheses fit better than ever. New materials have made limbs lighter and more comfortable for wearers. Even more exciting are new attempts to design prostheses that "feel." For example, two pressure sensors placed in the heel and ball of an artificial foot send signals to electrodes that touch the skin of the ends of the real, or residual, limb. These signals are carried through wires to a battery-operated device that not only signals the wearer's skin but sends messages to the brain, where they are interpreted as sensations.

Artificial Limbs: Skin and All

Ask students: What special problems do you think you would face if you were missing a hand, an arm, or a leg? What kinds of help would you expect from an artificial limb? Then have students read the Update feature to learn about the new technological developments in artificial limbs. Finally, ask interested volunteers to locate, read, and summarize magazine or journal articles about individuals who are using these modern prostheses.

LESSON 2   THE SKELETAL SYSTEM   **351**

PERSONAL HEALTH

KNEE INJURIES. Cut the risk of developing knee injuries by following these guidelines:

- Wear good athletic shoes that cushion the shock of your body's weight.
- Don't do strenuous exercises until you have stretched for at least 5 minutes.
- Don't sit cross-legged.

- If you are overweight, try to lose weight (in a sensible way) to take some of the pressure off your knees.
- Try walking instead of jogging. If you jog, be sure to give your knees some "days off."
- If you go biking, make sure your bike seat is at the right height.

ASSESS

EVALUATING THE LESSON

Assign and discuss the Lesson 2 Review; then administer, grade, and discuss the *Lesson 48 Quiz* in the TCR. 🖙

RETEACHING

- Have students define the functions of the skeletal system and name three ways to promote good health of the skeletal system.
- Ask students to complete *Reteaching Activity 48* in the TCR. 🖙

ENRICHMENT

Have students research and compare the skeletal systems of birds and humans. *(Birds' bones are hollow, thus minimizing their weight and making it easier for birds to fly.)*

CLOSE

Tell students the next lesson will present the muscular system. Ask them to relate functions of the skeletal system, particularly the joints and movable bones, to the function of skeletal muscles as they study the lesson.

▲ *The risk of repetitive motion injury can be reduced by proper placement of equipment and hand and arm positions that reduce strain.*

ACTIVITY *Describe four ways in which this teen can reduce the risk of repetitive motion injury.*

Repetitive Motion Injury

Technology has brought great things that improve our lives in many ways. Unfortunately, it has also introduced a new class of injuries to the skeletal system. Lumped together under the name **repetitive motion injury**, these result from *damage to tissues caused by prolonged, repeated movements*. Repetitive motion injury occurs when the same motions are performed for hours at a time. It is predominantly related to computer use. However, workers in industries where repetitive motions are common are affected as well.

One of the most common types of repetitive motion injury is carpal tunnel syndrome. It results from pressure on the median nerve where it passes into the hand through a gap known as the "carpal tunnel" under a ligament at the front of the wrist. Symptoms may include numbness, weakness, tingling, or burning in the fingers or hands and pain extending outward from the wrist. Treatment includes wearing a splint, resting the joint, and medication. Surgery to correct carpal tunnel syndrome has had limited success. Research is under way into how to prevent and correct this condition.

Repetitive motion injuries are turning up increasingly among students of college age. You can help prevent yourself from joining the ranks by taking steps such as these when you use a computer:

1. Keep your wrists relaxed and straight. Use only finger movements to strike the keys.
2. Press keys with the least pressure necessary. If possible, use an ergonomically designed keyboard. These specially made keyboards are designed to put less strain on the ligaments of the wrist.
3. Move your entire hand to press hard-to-reach keys.
4. Take frequent breaks, which is also good for your eyes.

LESSON 2 *Review*

Reviewing Facts and Vocabulary

1. What are the two main divisions of the skeletal system?
2. Name three functions of bones.
3. Describe two injuries or diseases of the skeletal system.

Thinking Critically

4. *Comparing and Contrasting.* How are ligaments and tendons alike? How are they different?
5. *Synthesizing.* Blanca wants to get enough phosphorus through the foods she eats, but she is allergic to milk products and dislikes beans, liver, and broccoli. What suggestions can you make that might help Blanca?

Applying Health Skills

6. *In Your Home and School.* At the grocery store, ask the butcher for soup bones. Try to get a long bone. Ask the butcher to saw it in half lengthwise so that you can look inside. With a family member at home or a partner in school, identify the periosteum, yellow marrow and epiphyses, spongy bone tissue, and red marrow. Find the hole where a blood vessel enters the bone.

Lesson 2 Review

Answers to Reviewing Facts and Vocabulary

1. Axial skeleton and appendicular skeleton.
2. Bones provide a strong, stable, and mobile framework for muscles. They support and protect the internal organs. They serve as storage centers for essential body minerals and are the manufacturing center of the body's blood cells.
3. Fractures: any type of break in a bone. Osteoporosis: loss of bone mass.

Answers to Thinking Critically

4. Ligaments and tendons are both connective tissue. Ligaments bind bones together. Tendons join muscles to bone or other muscles.
5. She can increase the amount of whole grains in her diet. She can also consult her doctor on the use of mineral supplements.

The Muscular System

T he action of a sling-shot is the result of two interdependent parts—a forked stick and a rubber band or other elastic material. The same is true of the human body. The role of the stick is taken by the skeleton. The role of the rubber band is taken by the muscular system. Muscles are elastic, stretching to allow a wide range of motions.

HEALTH TERMS

smooth muscles
skeletal muscles
flexors
extensors
cardiac muscle
muscle tone
tendinitis
hernia

HEALTH CONCEPTS

- Muscles are responsible for or involved in many body functions.
- Exercise is the main key to the health of the muscular system.
- In mass, muscle is the most abundant tissue in the body.

Functions of the Muscular System

W hen you hear the term *muscle,* does it bring to mind the image of a bodybuilder? Without muscles, nothing in your body would work. All body movements depend on muscles. Muscles pump blood throughout your body, move food through your digestive system, and control the movement of air in and out of your lungs.

LESSON **3**

The Muscular System

FOCUS

LESSON OBJECTIVES

After studying this lesson, students should be able to

- define the structure and function of muscles.
- describe what causes muscles to contract.
- identify ways to care for muscles.
- describe problems of the muscular system.

MOTIVATOR

Write the following on the chalkboard for students to work on while attendance is being taken: *Describe the actions of the biceps and triceps, muscles of the upper arm, as a weight is curled to the chest and lowered.*

INTRODUCING THE LESSON

Have students share their responses to the Motivator. Students should recall how muscles work in pairs—one contracts while the other relaxes. Ask students to recall functions other than body movement that muscles accomplish. See if students can relate movement to all muscular functions; i.e., movement of air, blood, food, and water.

INTRODUCING HEALTH TERMS

- Have students make flash cards for the vocabulary terms. On one side, have them write the word. On the other side, have them identify the body system, the definition, and a page reference.
- Ask students to complete Vocabulary Activity 15 and Chapter Study Guide 15 in the *Student Workbook.*

Lesson 3 Resources

TEACHER'S CLASSROOM RESOURCES

- **Concept Map** Activity 49
- **Cooperative Learning** Activity 15
- **Decision-Making** Activity 15
- **Health Lab** 15
- **Lesson 49 Quiz**
- **Lesson Plan 49**

- **Reteaching** Activity 49

STUDENT WORKBOOK

- **Applying Health Skills** 49
- **Chapter Study Guide** 15
- **Vocabulary** Activity 15

TRANSPARENCIES

- **Transparency 59**

TEACH

LD Class Activity

Provide an incomplete lesson outline for students to fill in during class discussions.

L2 Explaining

Introduce the term *antagonistic*. Explain that the paired muscles described in the lesson introduction were antagonistic pairs. If both were to contract equally at the same time, no movement could take place. Tell students that when a muscle relaxes, some tension is maintained to control the movement at a joint.

L1 Discussing

Using a large chart, identify for the class the major muscle groups. Ask students if the location of the muscle affects its function.

Safe Sitting

keeping Fit

Explain that back problems are common among people of all ages. Stress the importance of prevention through good posture. Tell students that keeping the head in line with the spine when standing, sitting, or lying in bed is basic in maintaining a healthy back. Explain that if they experience back pain, they should see their doctor to determine whether back pain is due to faulty posture.

L2 Cooperative Learning

Have students complete *Cooperative Learning Activity 15* in the TCR. ✏

Did You Know?

➤ Facial expressions are made by the actions of more than 40 muscles.

➤ When the hair stands up on your arms or neck, it is being raised by tiny muscles pulling on each hair follicle.

➤ Your muscles are 75 percent water.

keeping Fit

Safe Sitting

Sitting for hours at a desk every day at school can take its toll on your back. To avoid back problems, try to follow these tips for sitting fit.

➤ For mini-breaks, lean back and stretch out your arms and legs. Put your arms up in the air, spread your fingers apart, breathe deeply, and relax.

➤ Every morning and night, do the "cat arch." Get down on your hands and knees on the floor. Slowly and alternately stretch your back upward as a cat does, then downward, toward the floor.

➤ To keep blood flowing, move and flex your legs and feet during any extended period of desk work.

➤ Exercise regularly, warming up and cooling down properly. The better shape you're in, the less your chances of back pain.

Muscles work by means of two *complementary*—or opposing—actions. These are contraction, the shortening of a muscle, and extension, the stretching of a muscle. Muscle contraction is triggered by nerve impulses. At the point where a nerve enters a muscle, it breaks up into numerous nerve endings. Nerve impulses stimulate muscle fibers by means of tiny, buttonlike endings called *motor end plates*. A nerve may branch out to supply many muscle fibers.

Structure of the Muscular System

A muscle is composed of bundles of fibers. The major muscles in the body are made up of hundreds of bundles. A muscle fiber is made up of even smaller units called *myofibrils*. Each myofibril is in turn made up of microscopic filaments called *actin* and *myosin*. These are proteins that control muscle contraction.

Types of Muscles

Your body has three basic types of muscle tissue: smooth muscle, skeletal muscle, and cardiac muscle.

SMOOTH MUSCLES

Smooth muscles are *the type of muscle concerned with the movements of internal organs*. Many parts of the body, such as the intestines, the bronchi of the lungs, the bladder, and the walls of the blood vessels contain smooth muscle. Smooth muscles are also called involuntary muscles because they work without a person's conscious control.

SKELETAL MUSCLES

Skeletal muscles are *the striped, or striated, muscles attached to bones that cause body movements*. Skeletal muscles form the largest part of the body's muscular system. There are more than 600 such muscles. Skeletal muscles are voluntary. They are under conscious control.

Two or more skeletal muscles may oppose each other's actions. While one contracts, the other relaxes. Skeletal muscles are classified according to the type of action each muscle performs. *Muscles that close a joint* are called **flexors**. *Muscles that open out a joint* are called **extensors**.

CARDIAC MUSCLE

Cardiac muscle is *a special type of striated tissue that forms the walls of the heart*. Your heart is the most important muscle in your body. Its unique properties enable it to contract rhythmically about 100,000 times a day to pump blood throughout the body. Cardiac muscle is involuntary muscle.

Care of the Muscular System

Have you ever heard the expression "Use it or lose it"? It certainly holds true for muscles. An unused muscle will *atrophy,* or waste

---

MORE ABOUT . . . . .

ANAEROBIC AND AEROBIC PROCESSES. Adenosine triphosphate (ATP) is a molecule that results from the breakdown of glucose. ATP stores energy in cells. When ATP is broken down chemically, energy is released. ATP is not stored in large quantities in muscle cells. Therefore, it must be replaced. When glucose is broken down, it is stored as glycogen in the liver and in the muscles, and it provides some ATP molecules. This process does not require the presence of oxygen and, therefore, is called anaerobic. In the presence of oxygen, however, a glucose molecule is completely broken down, producing 18 to 20 times more ATP than does the anaerobic process. This aerobic process results in a higher yield of energy.

THE SKELETAL MUSCLES

Extensor muscles (dorsal surface)

FACIAL MUSCLES
Frontalis
Temporalis
Orbicularis oculi
Masseter
Orbicularis Oris

Sternocleidomastoid

Flexor muscles (inside of arm)

Biceps
Deltoid

Teres
Trapezius
Rhomboid
Triceps
Biceps (of arm)
Latissimus dorsi

External oblique (muscle of abdomen)

Gluteus maximus

Abductor muscles (pull legs away from body)
Biceps (of thigh)

Adductor muscles (pull legs toward body)

Semitendinosus

Peroneus
Gastrocnemius

Achilles tendon

Pectoralis major
Serratus anterior

External oblique

Sartorius

Adductor muscles (pull legs toward body)
Quadriceps muscles

Gastrocnemius
Soleus

Patella (kneecap)

Peroneus
Anterior tibial

away. To maintain **muscle tone**—*the natural tension in the fibers of a muscle*—you need to keep active and eat balanced, nutritious meals. This should be a lifelong goal. Activity that maintains muscle tone is especially important for older adults to prevent loss of mobility, balance, and the risk of falls.

▲ *Skeletal muscles are essential in performing physical movements.*

ACTIVITY *Identify and describe the largest muscle shown.*

LESSON 3 THE MUSCULAR SYSTEM **355**

L1 **Class Activity**
Ask students to evaluate the condition of their large muscle groups. Which groups are adequately developed? Which need additional toning?

L2 **Explaining**
Tell students that muscles and tendons contain proprioceptors controlling the stretch reflex. This reflex responds by making the muscles contract during a sudden jerking movement such as bouncing during stretching. Bouncing can cause injury if stretching is done this way. Stretching should be done in a slow, gradual motion.

L1 **Discussing**
The cardiac muscle extends to receive blood from the veins. Oxidation permits contraction of the cardiac muscle to pump blood into the arteries. Discuss other examples of this process in the body systems, such as those found in the stomach, bladder, and diaphragm.

L1 **Discussing**
Have students examine and comment on this statement: *Exercise builds more muscles.* (It is generally accepted that no additional muscle fibers develop as a result of exercise, but existing fibers enlarge. Research continues as to how exercise builds muscles.)

L2 **Health Lab**
Distribute *Health Lab 15* and have students investigate the causes of muscle fatigue. 👉

HOME AND COMMUNITY
CONNECTION

PROTECTING THE SKELETAL AND MUSCULAR SYSTEMS. Most students live with adults and, in some cases, elderly family members. The older the individual, the greater the risk of injury to or disease of the muscular and skeletal systems. Suggest that students share the information in this chapter with adults at home. If family members tend to engage in repetitive motion activities, students may research and inform them of exercises to prevent injuries. By keeping the body flexible, regular stretching can help prevent injuries to the skeletal and muscular systems. Suggest that students find out if the local recreation department offers classes in yoga or stretching. If so, they might recommend these classes to family members. If not, they might suggest that the recreation department offer classes.

L1 Community Involvement

Have students contact the local Muscular Dystrophy Association to learn more about the effects of muscular dystrophy. Does this association assist individuals with disorders other than muscular dystrophy?

Making Responsible Decisions

1. Della wants her class to organize a school dance to raise funds for a muscular dystrophy charity, but some of her classmates oppose the idea.
2. Della could (a) talk with those classmates about the importance of helping others, especially those with special needs; (b) work with teens who agree with her to organize a fund-raising dance that is not involved with the school; (c) give up her plans for organizing a fund-raising dance.
3. Della might (a) have a chance of gaining her classmates' support, although they might continue to oppose her plan; (b) succeed in raising money with a non-school dance, although the dance would probably not be as well attended; (c) avoid disagreeing with her classmates, but not have an opportunity to raise money for the charity.
4. Della values making a contribution to help those with muscular dystrophy. She also values friendly relationships with her classmates.
5. Responses will vary.
6. Remind students to consider both the short- and long-term consequences of their decisions.

L2 Decision Making

For further study on making responsible decisions, assign *Decision-Making Activity 15* in the TCR.

MUSCLE MOVEMENT

Biceps muscle contracted (flexor)

Tendons

Triceps muscle (extensor)

▲ *The biceps and triceps work together to move bones upward and downward.*

ACTIVITY *What happens when your biceps muscle contracts?*

The more you use your muscles, the more efficient and strong they will become. Remember, the heart is a muscle, too. Regular exercise strengthens the heart and makes it work more efficiently by increasing the amount of blood pumped in a single beat. As a result, the heart can pump less rapidly and has more time to rest between beats.

A program of regular exercise with stretching, warm-up, and cool down increases muscular strength and flexibility and stamina in general. Activities that promote balance and coordination can reduce the risk of falls. Practicing good posture can help strengthen back muscles. Using the proper equipment and wearing appropriate clothing can help protect muscles during exercise.

Problems of the Muscular System

How many times have your muscles ached during strenuous exercise or a tough competition? This is due to lactic acid buildup. As the lactic acid dissipates, the ache goes away. Sore muscles and bruises are a temporary condition. Some other muscular system problems, however, have a lasting impact on a person's health and lifestyle.

- **Myasthenia Gravis.** Myasthenia gravis is a disorder in which the muscles become weak and easily fatigued. The muscles most commonly affected are the eye muscles, which may result in drooping eyelids and double vision.

- **Muscular Dystrophy.** Muscular dystrophy is an inherited disorder characterized by a progressive wasting away of skeletal muscles. Early detection of muscular dystrophy is crucial because even though there is no cure, muscle weakening can be delayed by regular exercise.

Making Responsible Decisions

Who Should Benefit?

Della has had close family members who suffered from muscular dystrophy. She feels very strongly about raising funds for an upcoming muscular dystrophy telethon. She is forming a committee in her homeroom to organize a dance at her school to benefit the charity. Some of her classmates have opposed her plans, saying that any fund-raising dance should benefit the students of their school, not people they don't even know. How should Della respond to her classmates?

What Would You Do?

Apply the six steps of the decision-making process to Della's problem.

1. State the situation.
2. List the options.
3. Weigh the possible outcomes.
4. Consider your values.
5. Make a decision and act.
6. Evaluate the decision.

📖 SCHOOL-TO-CAREER

PROTECTION ON THE JOB. Invite each student to choose a job that involves risk to skin, bones, tendons, joints, or muscles. For example, gardeners are exposed to sun and must bend and pull in ways that could injure muscles or joints if they did not exercise care. Factory workers and word processors may repeat motions all day. Movers are constantly lifting heavy objects. Plumbers must perform motions in awkward positions in cramped spaces. Have each student write a page for a worker safety manual, describing potential injuries for the specific job, and listing preventive measures for the worker. Compile the pages into a book, and make it available in the classroom.

Injury-Related Muscular Problems

Even when you take care of your muscles, accidents can happen. Injury-related muscle problems can be painful, but most are temporary.

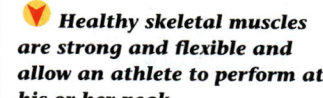
Healthy skeletal muscles are strong and flexible and allow an athlete to perform at his or her peak.

- **Muscle strain.** A strain, or a "pulled muscle," is a tearing or stretching of muscle fibers as a result of suddenly pulling them too far. Strains usually occur in large muscles and are a result of overexertion. They are most common in athletes. Treatment consists of applying an ice pack to the affected area to reduce swelling, wrapping it with a compression bandage, and resting the limb in a raised position.
- **Bruise.** A bruise is a discolored area under the skin caused by leakage of blood after an injury. Ice or a cold pack can reduce the pain and swelling of a large bruise.
- **Tendinitis.** Tendinitis is *the inflammation of a tendon,* usually caused by overuse. Symptoms include pain, tenderness, and restricted movement of the muscle attached to the affected tendon. Treatment may include anti-inflammatory medications, ultrasound, or injection of corticosteroids.
- **Hernia.** One of the more serious muscle injuries is a **hernia**, which is *protrusion of an organ or tissue through a weak area in the muscle.* In abdominal hernias, the intestine protrudes through a weak area in the abdominal wall. Abdominal hernias may appear after a person lifts a heavy object. Surgery is usually required to repair a hernia.

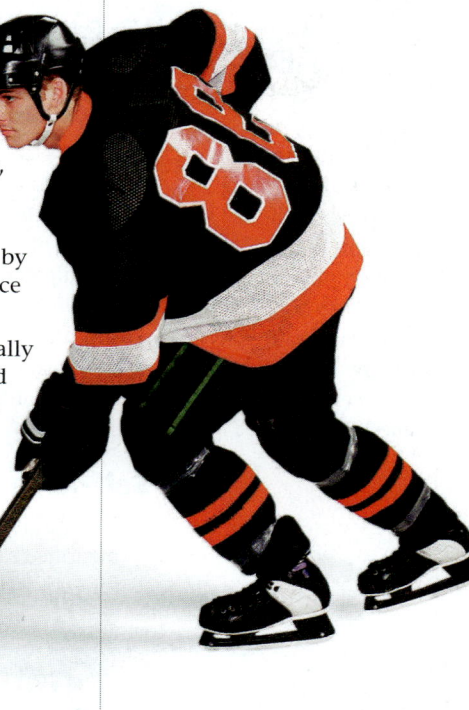

LESSON 3 *Review*

Reviewing Facts and Vocabulary
1. Name and describe the two types of muscle movement.
2. Describe two injuries or diseases related to the muscular system.

Thinking Critically
3. *Synthesizing.* What possible benefits to muscles may be derived from warming up and stretching before exercise? What about stretching after exercise?
4. *Synthesizing.* Suggest ways that a person can prevent injury to skeletal muscles.

Applying Health Skills
5. *In Your Home and School.* Interview family members and several classmates to find out what physical activities, particularly sports, they enjoy and are good at. Ask which activities they do not enjoy or find difficult. Use your findings to draw conclusions about the types of muscles that are used most often during these activities. Share your findings with the people you interviewed.

LESSON 3 THE MUSCULAR SYSTEM **357**

ASSESS

EVALUATING THE LESSON
Assign and discuss the Lesson 3 Review; then administer, grade, and discuss the *Lesson 49 Quiz* in the TCR.

RETEACHING
- Ask students to recall the three types of muscles. Have them describe similarities and differences and provide an example and location of each type.
- Ask students to complete *Reteaching Activity 49* in the TCR.
- Use *Transparency 59* to review the skeletal muscles.

ENRICHMENT
Have students investigate the anaerobic and aerobic processes of muscles. Ask them to explain how both systems operate during exercise.

CLOSE

Tell students that the muscular system is one body system that they really can enhance with effort. Reinforce that exercise and proper stretching can strengthen and build flexibility to improve function and safeguard against injury.

Lesson 3 Review

Answers to Reviewing Facts and Vocabulary
1. Extending (getting longer) and contracting (getting shorter).
2. Answers may vary. Students may select from the diseases and injuries identified on pages 356 and 357.

Answers to Thinking Critically
3. Warming up and stretching before exercise prevents tearing of the muscle cells from sudden use. Stretching after exercise prevents muscle cells from cramping from the sudden ending of muscle use.
4. A nutritious, balanced diet and regular exercise with proper warm-up and cool-down.

Health **Skills** Activities

Health Skills Activities

ACTIVITY 1
HEALTH SKILLS

Comprehending Health Concepts, Self Management

➤ **National Standards**
This activity meets these National Health Standards: 1.1; 1.3; 3.1; 3.3.

Teach

- Use the map activity as a bridge to a discussion of outdoor physical activity, such as running, yard work, partner sports, and so on.
- Discuss with students activities and exercises to which your community is most—and least—conducive, along with reasons.
- Shift the discussion to safety issues, such as the impact of extreme cold or hot on outdoor activities, hills versus flat terrain, and so on.
- Assign students to work independently, following the instructions for the activity in their books.

ACTIVITY 2
HEALTH SKILLS

Accessing Health Information, Health Advocacy

➤ **National Standards**
This activity meets these National Health Standards: 2.4; 2.6; 7.2; 7.5.

Teach

- Spend some time prescreening health Internet sites to which students might be directed for additional information. A good starting point is Glencoe's Health Web site (health.glencoe.com), which provides links to a number of government-sponsored sites featuring extensive information on diseases of the various systems and current funding for research into cures and treatments.
- Review with students diseases and disorders of the various systems mentioned.
- To avoid repetition, you may wish to assign a different system to each group, or allow groups to sign up for the system that interests them most.

Activity 1 — Training Safety Checklist

Weight-bearing exercise throughout a person's life is important both to maintain muscle tone and to keep bones strong and healthy. As with any physical activity, however, safety comes first.

Directions

1. Create a safety checklist for teens doing weight or resistance training.
2. Begin by forming groups to work on safety aspects of various topics, such as the proper use of equipment, appropriate clothing, and when and where to work out.
3. Use information from your book as well as outside sources.
4. If your classroom has a computer, input the guide and print out copies for the gymnasium and other prominent places around the school and community.

Time
40 minutes

Materials
paper, pen or pencil, computer (optional)

Self-Assessment

✓ Listed at least five tips for practicing weight training safely.
✓ Identified safe exercise procedures and proper use of exercise equipment for each weight-bearing exercise.

Activity 2 — Report to Congress

You have been asked to write and present a report to Congress on a disease affecting the integumentary, skeletal or muscular system. Your report must be informative. It must also convince Congress to fund additional research to find a cure.

Directions

1. With a group, locate a disease or disorder of the integumentary, skeletal, or muscular system that can be treated but not cured.
2. Research the disease, including symptoms, and how it affects the individual. Tell what medical treatments are currently available.
3. Each group will present an oral report to the class (Congress) on its disease. The report must convince "Congress" that additional funding is needed for further research.

Time
50 minutes plus outside research

Materials
library or Internet health resources

Self-Assessment

✓ Reported correctly on a disease, noting symptoms, effects, and treatments.
✓ Presented facts on importance of a cure in a persuasive and convincing manner.

ASSESSMENT SCORING

Using a four-level rubric, the student has achieved a 4 if:

ACTIVITY 1

✔ Student correctly identified terrain and temperature features of your community.
✔ Student showed an awareness of the importance of safety during physical activity.
✔ Student listed at least five tips for exercising safely.
✔ Student identified safe and proper use of exercise equipment.

ACTIVITY 2

✔ Student reported on a disease of the integumentary, skeletal, or muscular system.
✔ Student noted symptoms, effects, and treatments of diseases.
✔ Student report presented facts on importance of a cure in a persuasive manner.
✔ Report was written in a cohesive and grammatically sound fashion.

HEALTH NEWS VIDEO

Extreme Sports Arthritis Warning

Snowboarders fly through the air, seeming to defy gravity. Of course, sometimes they crash into icy banks of snow. Inline-skaters slide gracefully along narrow rails. But not all slides end gracefully—some end in hard falls.

Extreme athletes put stress on their skeletal and muscular systems. It's hardly surprising that they sometimes break bones. However, it might surprise you that those injuries can have lasting effects. Long after a major joint injury has healed, extreme athletes may develop painful arthritis.

Every athlete—from amateur to pro—can apply rules of caution and safety to prevent injuries today. This prevention may pay off years from now in an increased resistance to diseases like arthritis.

Play the Video

CNN. All Rights Reserved.

Think About It

- How are the skeletal and muscular systems involved during inline skating? During mountain biking?
- What precautions can athletes use to take care of their skeletal and muscular systems?

CNN HEALTH NEWS **359**

MORE ABOUT . . . . .

TECHNOLOGY AND SCIENCE. Doctors often use X rays to diagnose arthritis. After learning the patient's full history, including type of pain and description of previous injuries, the doctor may request an X ray examination.

X rays are radiation with a higher frequency than visible light. These rays can pass through matter. Some substances, such as flesh and muscle, are easily penetrated. Others, such as bone or arthritic material, are more opaque. An X ray image is produced by placing part of the body against a photographic plate and exposing it to X rays. The image will show the relative opacity of different parts of the body.

CNN HEALTH NEWS

Extreme Sports Arthritis Warning
Video Segment 9 (Time – 2:53)

Objectives. After viewing the video, students should be able to recognize some of the long-term dangers of putting stress on the skeletal and muscular system.

Motivator. Write the phrase Extreme Sports on the chalkboard. Ask students for examples, such as mountain biking, skateboarding, and skiboarding. Discuss how these sports can affect the body's muscular and skeletal system. Most student suggestions will relate to short-term effects and injuries, such as muscle strains, sprains, and broken bones. Have students view Video Segment 9, "Extreme Sports Arthritis Warning," to introduce one long-term effect of placing stress on these body systems.

Teach
- Write *Arthritis* next to the heading Extreme Sports on the chalkboard. Have students explain the relationship between these two topics.
- Compare short-term and long-term effects of extreme sports. Create a chart that lists both positive and negative effects. For example, a short-term effect might be injury or strain, but a long-term effect can be strengthening the muscle or increasing flexibility.

Making Decisions. Have students evaluate the effectiveness of the information in the video as a deterrent for students who might want to start an extreme sport. As students evaluate their decisions, emphasize that much of the danger of arthritis comes from repeated injuries. Players who use appropriate safety precautions and take fewer risks are less likely to develop arthritis.

Close. Have students imagine they are giving information to a friend who is learning new inline skating stunts. Have them explain the dangers of arthritis and describe strategies that can help protect the skater's skeletal and muscular systems.

CHECKING COMPREHENSION

- Assign and discuss the chapter review.
- Use the MindJogger Videoquiz to review the chapter. 🔴

CHAPTER 15 REVIEW ANSWERS

Using Health Terms

1. melanin
2. dermis
3. athlete's foot
4. epidermis
5. cartilage
6. ossification
7. axial skeleton
8. tendons
9. ligaments
10. appendicular skeleton
11. repetitive motion injury
12. muscle tone
13. skeletal muscles
14. tendinitis
15. extensors
16. hernia
17. smooth muscle
18. flexors

RECALLING THE FACTS

1. The skin.
2. When the body is hot, tiny blood vessels in the skin enlarge, allowing heat to escape. The sweat glands release perspiration, which cools the skin as it evaporates. When the body's internal temperature drops, the blood vessels close to conserve body heat.
3. They shed.
4. In the dermis.
5. Athlete's foot is a fungal infection. It can be avoided by proper hygiene and by protecting the foot from exposure in locker rooms and showers.
6. Long bones: in the arms and legs. Short bones: wrists, ankles, hands, and feet. Flat bones: ribs and skull bones. Irregular bones: vertebrae.

Using Health Terms

On a separate sheet of paper, write the term that best matches each definition below.

LESSON 1

1. The pigment that gives skin, hair, and the iris of the eyes their coloring.
2. The inner, thicker layer of skin.
3. A fungal infection of the skin between the toes.
4. The outer, thinner layer of skin.

LESSON 2

5. Strong, flexible connective tissue.
6. The process by which bone is formed, renewed, and repaired.
7. The 80 bones of the skull, spine, ribs, and sternum, or breastbone.
8. Fibrous cords that join muscle to bone or to other muscles.

9. Tough bands of fibrous, slightly elastic tissue that bind the bone ends at the joint.
10. The 126 bones of the shoulders, arms, hands, hips, legs, and feet.
11. Damage to tissues caused by prolonged, repeated movements.

LESSON 3

12. Natural tension in the fibers of muscle.
13. The striped, or striated, muscles attached to bones that cause body movements.
14. The inflammation of a tendon.
15. Muscles that open out a joint.
16. Protrusion of an organ or tissue through a weak area in the muscle.
17. The type of muscle concerned with the movements of internal organs.
18. Muscles that close a joint.

Recalling the Facts

Using complete sentences, answer the following questions.

LESSON 1

1. What is the largest organ in the body?
2. Explain the process by which your skin helps regulate body temperature.
3. What eventually happens to dead cells in the epidermis?
4. In what part of the skin are new cells formed?
5. What causes athlete's foot, and how can it be avoided?

LESSON 2

6. Name the four kinds of bones in the human body and give an example of each.
7. In what part of the population is osteoporosis most common?

8. What two minerals are important for your bones to grow, harden, and repair?
9. What happens during the process of ossification?

LESSON 3

10. Name the three types of muscles and describe their functions.
11. What is the most important muscle in the body?
12. What is the best way to keep your muscles strong and working efficiently?
13. What is the difference between a voluntary muscle and an involuntary muscle?

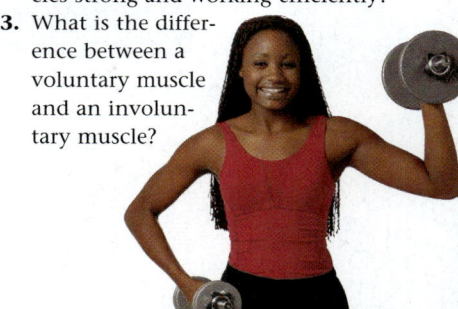

---

7. In post-menopausal women.
8. Calcium and phosphorus.
9. In ossification, bone is formed, renewed, and repaired.
10. Smooth muscles are involved in the workings of the internal organs, skeletal muscles are attached to bones and cause body movements, and cardiac muscles form the walls of the heart and make it contract.

11. The heart.
12. Eat a nutritious, balanced diet and exercise regularly.
13. Voluntary muscles are used for body movement and are under our conscious control. Involuntary muscles are used in the workings of the internal organs and are not under our conscious control.

Review

Thinking Critically

LESSON 1

1. *Analyzing.* Compare the functions of the dermis and epidermis in terms of their importance to the body.
2. *Analyzing.* Review this statement: *Sweating a lot is good for you.* Do you agree with this statement? Tell why or why not?

LESSON 2

3. *Synthesizing.* Devise and write out a plan for a person who has a deficiency in calcium and phosphorus.

4. *Synthesizing.* Which player on a baseball team is most likely to develop a repetitive motion injury and why?

LESSON 3

5. *Analyzing.* Compare the functions of flexor and extensor muscles.
6. *Comparing and Contrasting.* Compare and contrast the three basic types of muscles. Explain the function of each type.

Making the Connection

1. *Science.* Place a chicken bone from which the meat has been removed in a jar with a tight-fitting lid. Fill the jar with white vinegar to cover the bone by several inches. Then close the lid. Let the jar sit for a week. Remove the bone and observe how the removal of its calcium by the acid in the vinegar has affected it.

2. *Language Arts.* Numerous advertisements appear in the media for suntanning products that profess to protect the skin from the sun's harmful UV rays. Find television and print ads geared toward teens. Investigate the truth of claims by consulting reputable on-line sources. Share your findings in an oral report.

BEYOND THE CLASSROOM

PARENTAL INVOLVEMENT Make a list of food sources for the vitamins and minerals that promote healthy skin, bones, and muscles. Share the list with family members and discuss ways of incorporating more of these foods into family meals. Write about your experiences in improving your family's awareness of the nutritional needs of these systems.

COMMUNITY INVOLVEMENT Contact the local chapter of an organization such as the Arthritis Foundation, the National Psoriasis Foundation, the Muscular Dystrophy Association, or the Myasthenia Gravis Foundation. Find out what

the organization provides in terms of education and support, and what it is doing to help people who have the disease or disorder. Inquire about volunteer opportunities with the group.

SCHOOL-TO-CAREER

Exploring Careers. Interview several people who work in the field of sports or exercise. Examples include a physical therapist, a coach, a trainer, or an aerobics instructor. Describe the academic preparation necessary for that career and the personal characteristics that would be necessary to be successful in that field.

Thinking Critically

1. The epidermis forms a tough, protective covering for the body. The dermis regulates body temperature by means of the sweat glands and tiny blood vessels.
2. Answers will vary.
3. This person should eat more dairy products, broccoli, beans, liver, and whole grains.
4. The pitcher, because he goes through the same motion time after time when he plays and practices.
5. Extensor muscles open a joint; flexor muscles close it.
6. The smooth muscles move the internal organs. The skeletal muscles move the bones and joints. The cardiac muscles operate the heart.

Making the Connection

1. Students should observe a pitted surface, indicating a loss of calcium.
2. Findings will vary.

Evaluate

- Use the reproducible *Chapter 15 Test* in the TCR, or construct your own using the Testmaker software.
- Use *Performance Assessment Activity 15* in the TCR.

Enrichment

Ask students to complete *Cross-Curriculum Activity 15* in the TCR.

Beyond the Classroom

Keep students involved in the community, and encourage parent participation by assigning the activities on this page for students to work on outside of class.

Your Nervous and Endocrine Systems

	FEATURES	CLASSROOM RESOURCES

Chapter Resources

ACTIVITIES
- Cross-Curriculum Activity 16
- Health Lab 16
- Health Skills Activities 16
- Parent Letter and Activities 16

ASSESSMENT
- Chapter 16 Test
- Performance Assessment Activity 16
- Testmaker Software

STUDENT ACTIVITIES WORKBOOK
- Applying Health Skills 50–52
- Study Guide 16
- Vocabulary Activity 16

STUDENT DIVERSITY STRATEGIES
- Audiocassette Program (English)
- Audiocassette Program (Spanish)
- Spanish Parent Letters and Activities
- Spanish Summaries, Quizzes, and Activities

MULTIMEDIA COMPONENTS
- English Audiocassette Program
- Spanish Audiocassette Program
- MindJogger Videodisc and VHS program

MODULES
- *The Reality of Drugs,* Student Edition
- *The Reality of Drugs,* Teacher's Annotated Edition
- *HIV/AIDS and Society,* Student Edition
- *HIV/AIDS and Society,* Teacher's Annotated Edition
- *El VIH/SIDA y la Sociedad*

National Health Education Standards

One of the main goals of the National Health Education Standards is to move students toward "health literacy." Health literacy is the capacity of individuals to obtain, interpret, and understand basic health information and services and the competence to use such information and services in ways which promote health. The health standards were developed by applying the characteristics of a well-educated, literate person within the context of health. The health literate person is:
- a critical thinker and problem solver
- a self-directed learner
- a responsible, productive citizen
- an effective communicator

Listed below are the Health Education Standards Performance Indicators addressed in each lesson of this chapter.

Lesson	Health Standards Performance Indicators
1	1.2
2	1.3, 3.5, 4.3, 6.1
3	1.2, 1.6

ONLINE RESOURCES

For a fresh approach to health topics and an in-depth look at health issues, use these online resources found under Teacher Resources at **health.glencoe.com**.

- **BLOCK SCHEDULE LESSON PLANS** Reinforce health concepts with outside readings selected especially for students. Each reading is accompanied by a lesson plan and activities to enhance
  - Reading Skills
  - Cross Curriculum
  - Media Literacy

- **TECHNOLOGY PROJECTS** Instructions and suggestions on how to use computer, Internet, and software with health lessons.

- **HEALTH UPDATES** Timely topics in health news, including late-breaking medical advances and updates on teen risk behaviors.

Out of Time?

If time does not permit teaching this chapter, you may use these features: Making Responsible Decisions on page 373; Building Health Skills on page 374; and Update on page 375.

BLOCK SCHEDULING

Block scheduling provides extended time for hands-on projects and activities. Use the following activities to engage students, provide further depth, and vary your instructional techniques:
- Update (30 minutes) **pg. 375**
- Health Skills Activity (60–90 minutes) **pg. 382**

Your Nervous and Endocrine Systems

CHAPTER OVERVIEW

Chapter 16 introduces students to the nervous and endocrine systems. The structure, function, care, and problems of each system are presented.

LESSON 1 The nervous system is the body's communication network and control center. It has two main divisions—the central and the peripheral nervous systems. The structure and function of these divisions are presented in this lesson.

LESSON 2 Normal functioning of the nervous system can be impaired by infectious diseases, accidents, or the use of illegal drugs, particularly alcohol. Genetic disorders can also affect this system. Daily exercise, proper nutrition, and adequate sleep will keep this system functioning well.

LESSON 3 The endocrine system is made up of glands that secrete hormones. These hormones affect the autonomic nervous system and hypothalamus. Most disorders are related to the glands producing too much or too little of a hormone. Good health habits can help maintain this system.

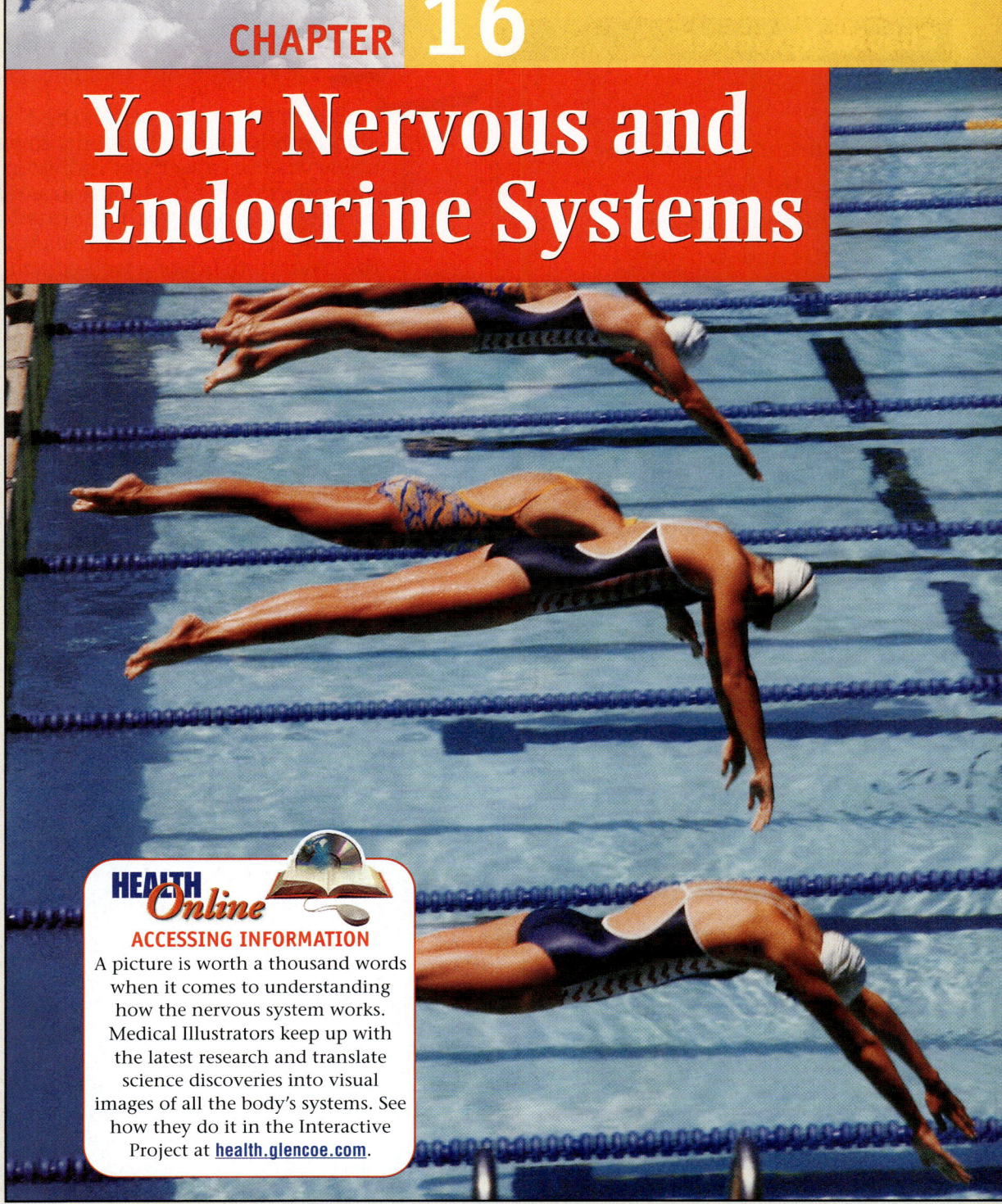

CHAPTER **16**

Your Nervous and Endocrine Systems

HEALTH *Online*

ACCESSING INFORMATION

A picture is worth a thousand words when it comes to understanding how the nervous system works. Medical Illustrators keep up with the latest research and translate science discoveries into visual images of all the body's systems. See how they do it in the Interactive Project at **health.glencoe.com**.

TEACHING STRATEGY

Hands-On Health

Reinforcing and Reviewing Bring your health classroom to life with interactive teaching strategies and classroom management techniques that keep your students interested and involved. The unique *Hands-On Health: Creative Teaching Strategies* booklet that accompanies the *Glencoe Health* program offers fun, motivating activities. 📖

The following Classroom Management Ideas can be used to reinforce chapter concepts:

- Beach Ball
- Trivia Questions
- Paper Exchange
- Mental Outburst

> **The brain's task is to make sense of the world....**
>
> —NICHOLAS WADE
> CONTEMPORARY WRITER

Quick Write How much do you really know about the workings of your brain? List three facts about its structure and three about its functions. Share this knowledge with your classmates.

Personal Health Inventory

Self-Inventory Write the numbers 1–10 on a sheet of paper. Read each statement below and respond by writing *yes*, *no*, or *sometimes* for each item. Write a *yes* only for items that you practice regularly. Save your responses.

1	I wear a seat belt when traveling by car.
2	I wear a helmet when riding a bicycle, a skateboard, or a motorcycle, and when skating.
3	I wear protective headgear whenever I participate in a contact sport.
4	I get at least eight hours of sleep each night.
5	I exercise regularly.
6	I avoid alcohol and other drugs.
7	I determine the depth of water in a pool or lake before diving in.
8	I wear safety goggles when required for class or sports.
9	I avoid injuries to the spinal cord by lifting and carrying objects properly.
10	I include sources of iodine as part of my eating pattern.

Follow-up After completing the chapter, retake this self-inventory. Pick two items that you need to work on and set a goal to improve your health behaviors.

TECHNOLOGY OPTIONS

MINDJOGGER
VIDEOQUIZ

To preview or review chapter content, you may wish to use the *MindJogger Videoquiz* that accompanies Chapter 16.

INTRODUCING THE CHAPTER

Personal Health Inventory

Let students meet in small groups to discuss the Self-Inventory statements. Ask: What health and safety habits do these statements highlight? Why is it so important to develop and maintain those habits? Then have students work independently to record their own responses to these statements in their private Health Journals, labeling the page "My Nervous System." Remind students that they will be using their responses at the end of Chapter 16.

- Students are probably familiar with the analogy that likens the brain to a computer. It receives, processes, stores, and finds information and transmits messages to all parts of the body. The nervous system, in fact, co-ordinates and regulates all of the body's functions. Tell students that the endocrine system works closely with the nervous system in regulating certain activities in the body and that these two body systems will be studied in this chapter.

- Let students read and discuss the quotation and complete the Quick Write on this page. Ask: Why do you think teens sometimes neglect familiar health and safety habits? After a brief discussion, explain that the lessons in Chapter 16 include information about behaviors teens can follow to protect the health of their nervous and endocrine systems.

- Distribute Parent Letter 16 from the *Parent Letters and Activities* booklet in the TCR. ☞

LESSON 1

The Nervous System

LESSON OBJECTIVES

After studying this lesson, students should be able to

- explain the functions and characteristics of neurons.
- describe the central nervous system.
- discuss the functions of the parts of the brain.
- define the peripheral nervous system.
- explain the reflex action.

MOTIVATOR

Write the following on the chalkboard for students to work on while attendance is being taken: *Make a list of the things you do that do not involve the use of the nervous system.*

INTRODUCING THE LESSON

Refer to the Motivator. Ask volunteers to share their responses. Ask students to think about many actions taking place inside their bodies right now *(breathing, seeing, heartbeat, etc.).* Tell students that this lesson will explain how the nervous system controls body activities.

INTRODUCING HEALTH TERMS

- Have students make flash cards for the vocabulary terms. On one side, have them write the word. On the other side, have them identify the body system, the definition, and a page reference.
- Ask students to complete Vocabulary Activity 16 and Chapter Study Guide 16 in the *Student Workbook.*

C omputers are remarkable machines, capable of performing complex calculations in seconds. Yet even the fastest, most sophisticated computer is unable to compose a symphony or write a play. Only the human brain is capable of such achievements. In fact, if not for the human brain, there would be no computers.

HEALTH TERMS

- **neurons**
- **cerebrum**
- **cerebellum**
- **brain stem**
- **reflex**

HEALTH CONCEPTS

- The nervous system is the body's communications network and control center.
- Your brain is a complex, computer-like organ at the core of your nervous system that continuously receives, processes, and gives information.
- The brain plays a key role in the development of speech and language, two distinctly human characteristics.

Functions of the Nervous System

Y our brain is just one part, but an important part, of your nervous system—your body's communication network and control center. Your nervous system controls all of your body's actions and functions. It senses changes not only within your body but also outside of it in your environment and enables you to respond within fractions of a second.

Structure of the Nervous System

T here are two main divisions of the nervous system, the *central nervous system* (CNS) and the *peripheral nervous system* (PNS). The PNS gathers information from inside and outside your body. The CNS receives and analyzes this information and initiates responses. The

Lesson 1 Resources

TEACHER'S CLASSROOM RESOURCES

- **Concept Map** Activity 50
- **Health Lab** 16
- **Lesson 50 Quiz**
- **Lesson Plan** 50
- **Parent Letter and Activities** 16
- **Reteaching** Activity 50

STUDENT WORKBOOK

- **Applying Health Skills** 50
- **Chapter Study Guide** 16
- **Vocabulary** Activity 16

TRANSPARENCIES

- **Transparencies 60, 61**

PNS then picks up and carries the response signals. This information is transmitted throughout your body by means of electrical charges—or *impulses*—that travel at speeds of up to 248 miles per hour (399 kmph). The messengers and receivers of these transmissions are **neurons**, or *nerve cells*.

Functions of Neurons

Neurons are classified according to their functions. There are three main types of neurons: sensory neurons, motor neurons, and interneurons. Sensory neurons carry signals from sense receptors into the CNS. Motor neurons carry signals from the CNS to muscles or glands. Interneurons form all the electrical connections within the CNS itself.

Unlike other cells, neurons cannot replace themselves. If the cell body of a neuron is damaged or degenerates, the cell dies. Each neuron is made up of three basic parts:

- **Cell body.** The cell body consists of a nucleus—the control center of the cell—in a sack of fluid contained within an outer skin called the *cell membrane*. The nucleus receives and sends nerve impulses. It also regulates the amount and types of proteins made in the cell.

- **Dendrites.** Dendrites are branching projections of the cell body. They receive and carry impulses toward the cell body.

- **Axons.** Every neuron has one threadlike extension called an *axon* that carries impulses away from the cell body. An axon branches at its end to form terminals through which signals are sent to target cells, such as the dendrites of other neurons, muscle cells, or glands. Axons vary in length from a fraction of an inch (a few mm) to several feet (more than 1 m). Most axons have a coating or sheath of fatty material called *myelin*. The myelin sheath insulates the nerve fiber and speeds the transmission of impulses.

 A nerve impulse travels from the receptors of a sensory neuron, across an interneuron to a motor neuron, then to muscle fibers.

ACTIVITY *Describe the nerve actions that take place when you accidentally touch something that is very sharp.*

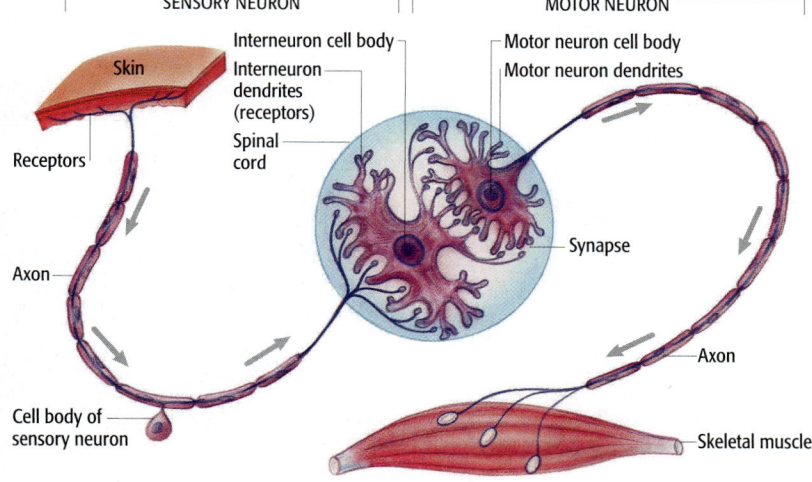

SENSORY NEURON   MOTOR NEURON   **THE NERVE IMPULSE**

Skin
Interneuron cell body
Interneuron dendrites (receptors)
Spinal cord
Receptors
Motor neuron cell body
Motor neuron dendrites
Synapse
Axon
Axon
Cell body of sensory neuron
Skeletal muscle

TEACH

L2 Class Activity

Emphasize the importance of the sensory neurons in protecting people from environmental hazards such as burns, frostbite, indigestion, and muscle strains. Ask students to write about their own experiences in hazardous situations: Did your nervous system function effectively?

LD Explaining

Try to narrow down the information you expect LD students to learn. Provide easy-to-follow diagrams of the components of the nervous system.

L2 Explaining

Explain to students that sensory receptors receive messages about digestion, hunger, illness, etc. that make us feel hungry, sick, etc. All of these receptors send messages toward the brain or spinal cord.

L2 Discussing

Have students describe the spectrum of sensations that produce pleasure or pain from the receptor of sensory neurons. *(Examples: music and shrill sirens, a caress and a pinch, the aroma of fresh bread and the smell of a skunk.)*

L3 Class Activity

Present the following scenario. Explain to students that they are attending a concert. At the conclusion, they are so excited that they stand and applaud the entertainers. Ask the students to write down all of the processes involved in the nervous system that are related to this type of reaction.

L2 Health Lab

Distribute *Health Lab 16* and have students investigate another function of the nervous system.

MORE ABOUT . . . . .

SENSORY NEURONS. Sensory neurons in the cerebrum allow a sensation—seeing, hearing, feeling, smelling, or tasting—to trigger the re-creation of a past experience.

Sensory neurons located in muscles are triggering mechanisms for the stretch reflex. The body reacts to overstretching with muscle contractions and pain.

Sensory neurons in the walls of the stomach send us "hunger pangs" when the stomach is empty and ready to be filled.

Sensory neurons in the esophagus and pharynx signal the gag reflex when contacted, causing the stomach to contract and possibly regurgitate its contents.

L2 Demonstrating

Using a skeletal model, have students locate cervical *(neck)*, thoracic *(chest)*, and lumbar *(lower back)* vertebrae that are the origin of nerves. Compare the sizes of these bones. Ask: Are larger nerves associated with larger vertebrae?

L2 Class Activity

Divide the class into three sections, and have each section take the role of a certain kind of neuron. Describe routine tasks that involve one or more neuron types, and ask the section representing that type to stand. Say, for example, "I see my toothbrush." *(The sensory neurons should rise.)* "I reach for my toothbrush." *(The motor neurons should rise.)*

L3 Class Activity

Explain to students how a flow chart works. Then instruct them to create flow charts showing how the message would be received and acted on by the nervous system if a person saw and reached for a pencil.

L2 Demonstrating

Ask an instructor in the school auto shop to demonstrate electric arcing to the students. Then have each student write a paragraph comparing the electrical phenomenon to a synapse of the nervous system.

The Central Nervous System

In one way or another, every body function involves the CNS. The CNS is made up of two main parts, the spinal cord and the brain.

The Spinal Cord

The spinal cord is a cylinder of nerve tissue about 18 inches (45.7 cm) long and about as thick as your index finger. It is a downward extension of the brain. The spinal cord runs down the central canal in the spine and is protected by the vertebrae, the bones that make up your spine. It is also protected by cerebro-spinal fluid that acts like a shock absorber and by three layers of connective membranes called the *spinal meninges.*

At the center of the spinal cord is a region called the *gray matter.* It contains the cell bodies of neurons along with supporting cells. Some of the neurons are interneurons. Others are motor neurons whose axons pass out of the spinal cord in bundles and extend to muscles and glands. The axons of sensory neurons enter the gray matter and connect with the motor neurons and interneurons. The gray matter is surrounded with areas of white matter that consist of nerve cell axons running lengthwise through the spinal cord.

NERVOUS SYSTEM

- 12 pairs of cranial nerves
- Cerebrum
- Cerebellum
- 8 pairs of cervical nerves
- Spinal cord
- Vertebra
- 12 pairs of thoracic nerves
- 5 pairs of lumbar nerves
- 5 pairs of sacral nerves
- 1 pair of coccygeal nerves

> ► *The CNS consists of the brain and spinal cord. The PNS is made up of the cranial and spinal nerves that branch from the brain and spinal cord.*
>
> **ACTIVITY** *Use the illustration to locate cervical (neck), thoracic (chest), and lumbar (lower back) vertebrae which are the origin of nerves.*

CROSS SECTION OF SPINAL CORD

- White matter
- Spinal cord
- Gray matter
- SPINAL MENINGES
- Pia mater
- Arachnoid
- Dura mater
- Spinal nerve
- Vertebra (bone)

366   CHAPTER 16   YOUR NERVOUS AND ENDOCRINE SYSTEMS

PERSONAL HEALTH

LEGAL DRUGS. The body does not know whether a drug acting on the nervous or endocrine system is in the body legally or illegally. Many street drugs have medical uses and are sold with prescription. However, a prescription does not cancel the adverse effects. Encourage students to use a reference book such as the *Physician's Desk Reference.* Have them research how drugs such as amphetamines, barbiturates, and antidepressants act on the nervous and endocrine systems, and note their side effects. Over-the-counter drugs affect the nervous and endocrine systems, too. Ask students to investigate the effects on the nervous and endocrine systems of medications such as cold remedies and preparations to induce sleep or to stay awake.

The Brain

Your brain is the largest, most complex part of your nervous system. Your brain helps you receive and process messages—to think, remember, and reason—and coordinates your muscular movement. Your brain is involved in your emotions and everything you sense.

The brain weighs about three pounds (1.4 kg) and contains almost 100 billion neurons. At birth, the brain weighs about one pound (0.5 kg). In humans, it reaches full size by age six. Although the brain makes up only about 2 percent of your total body weight, it uses more than 20 percent of the oxygen you inhale. Without oxygen, the brain can last for only four to five minutes before suffering serious and irreversible damage.

The brain is protected by eight cranial bones that form the skull and three layers of membranes called *cranial meninges*. Cerebrospinal fluid between the meninges cushions the brain from injury.

The function of the brain is similar, on the one hand, to that of a computer and, on the other hand, to that of a chemical plant. Brain cells produce electrical signals and send them along pathways called *circuits*. These circuits receive, process, store, and retrieve information much as a computer does. Unlike a computer, however, the brain creates its electrical signals by chemical means. The proper functioning of the brain depends on the many complicated chemical substances that brain cells produce.

The brain has three main divisions: the cerebrum, the cerebellum, and the brain stem.

THE CEREBRUM

The largest, most complex part of the brain is the **cerebrum.** The cerebrum is the site of most conscious and intelligent activities. Its outer layer, or cortex, is where conscious thought takes place.

The cerebrum is divided into two halves called the *cerebral hemispheres*. These hemispheres are connected to the rest of the CNS in a crossed-over fashion. The right hemisphere controls the muscular activity of and receives sensory input from the left half of the body. The left hemisphere does the same for the right half of the body.

In the brains of animals, the cerebral hemispheres are essentially alike in function. In the brains of humans, however, they have developed different functions. The left hemisphere is mainly responsible for language, logic, arithmetic calculation, analysis, and critical thinking. The right hemisphere is concerned with imagination and

THE BRAIN

- Cerebrum
- Midbrain
- Pons
- Medulla oblongata
- Cerebellum
- Spinal cord

▲ *Your brain is an incredibly complex, responsive, and powerful structure.*

ACTIVITY *Describe the functions of each part of the brain shown in the diagram.*

L2 Class Activity

Organize students into pairs. Ask each pair to write a paragraph explaining the relationship of the nervous system to posture. Then have the pairs examine each other's posture when standing and sitting.

L2 Discussing

The cartilage in the spinal column gets squashed when we are upright and expands when we lie down. In the morning, you are about ¼ inch taller than the night before. Discuss how cartilage gets squashed or expands.

L2 Discussing

Discuss the implications of an accident where a person dives into a pool that is too shallow. Ask: What would probably happen to the person diving? What could you do as an observer? What do you think the long-range prognosis is for the accident victim? What would be the best and worst-case scenario? Can damaged nerves replace or heal themselves?

L2 Demonstrating

Use an anatomical model of the brain to show the actual size of its parts and the location of each.

L2 Class Activity

Thought and memory are functions of the nervous system. Ask students to describe the importance of these impulses that enable us to function as human beings. Instruct them to write paragraphs about the importance of thought and memory to them.

PROMOTING COMPREHENSIVE SCHOOL HEALTH

COMMUNITY SUPPORT. Tapping into local resources is a key to effectively working a comprehensive school health plan. It is important to involve local health agencies, parents, churches, youth groups, and other organizations. By enlisting local groups and individuals, the committee establishes grassroots support. Community involvement provides the resources and support needed to reduce fragmentation of efforts or duplication of programs. Ongoing collaboration and cooperation between the team and other community members prevents unwarranted controversy. For information about community support, consult *Promoting a Comprehensive School Health Program* in the TCR.

L1 Class Activity

Have students compare the function of a telephone network to the nervous system. *(Both carry messages and have control centers.)*

L2 Class Activity

Ask students to describe how an EEG is analogous to an EKG. *(An EEG shows activity in the brain, whereas an EKG shows activity in the heart.)*

L2 Discussing

Guide students in discussing how an understanding of the nervous system relates to decision making.

LD Class Activity

Have students trace the drawing of the brain. Then have them use colored pencils or crayons to shade the cerebrum blue, the cerebellum red, and the brain stem yellow.

L1 Class Activity

Direct students to write paragraphs or poems describing what life might be like if they lost one of the five senses.

L2 Discussing

Ask students to give examples of how a person with poor vision can compensate with other sense organs.

L2 Class Activity

Have the class determine what happens when the sense of smell is impaired. Ask students to pinch their noses, then give each student something to eat or taste. Tell students to share with the class a description of what it is like to eat something, yet not be able to smell it.

▼ *Each hemisphere of the brain is responsible for a different range of mental activities.*

ACTIVITY *Explain why playing music requires left hemisphere activity and why painting uses the right hemisphere.*

BRAIN LOBES

Sensory information
Voluntary movements
Parietal lobe
Frontal lobe
Hearing and smell
Temporal lobe
Occipital lobe
Vision
Brain stem
Cerebellum

visual thinking—spatial relationships, form, artistic activities, and emotional responses such as color appreciation.

Each hemisphere has four lobes. Each lobe is named after the bone in the skull that protects it:

- The frontal lobe controls voluntary movements and also has a role in the use of language. The prefrontal areas of this lobe are believed to be involved with intellect and personality.
- The parietal lobe is involved with a wide variety of sensory information—heat, cold, pain, touch, and body position in space.
- The occipital lobe contains the sense of vision.
- The temporal lobe contains the senses of hearing and smell as well as memory, thought, and judgment.

THE CEREBELLUM

The **cerebellum** is *the second largest part of the brain.* It is a rounded structure located beneath the occipital lobes of the cerebrum. Like the cerebrum, the cerebellum is divided into two hemispheres.

The cerebellum is concerned mainly with maintaining posture and balance and coordinating skeletal muscle movement. It receives impulses from the balance organs of the inner ear and from muscles. After receiving this information, the cerebellum refines the orders

CURRICULUM CONNECTIONS

PSYCHOLOGY. Ask a psychology teacher in your school to help students research the right-brain and left-brain theory. Have students make a notebook about the theory. Include articles from newspapers or magazines relating to the theory.

Ask each student to determine whether he or she is right-brain or left-brain dominant. Have students provide an assessment from their research to determine right- or left-brain dominance.

Ask students to include information relating to the theory that "we can all draw." What would it imply for those who can't draw? *(They have not developed that part of the brain.)*

sent to muscles from the motor cortex in the cerebrum to ensure smooth, coordinated movements and balance. It also maintains equilibrium during movements as it receives information from the sensory organs.

THE BRAIN STEM

The **brain stem** is *a 3-inch-long (7.6-cm-long) stalk of nerve cells and fibers that connects the spinal cord to the rest of the brain*. It acts partly as a pathway for messages traveling between other parts of the brain and the spinal cord. The brain stem also connects with 10 of the 12 pairs of cranial nerves and controls basic functions such as breathing, heartbeat, and eye reflexes. The activities of the brain stem are not under conscious control.

The brain stem consists of three main parts—the medulla oblongata, pons, and midbrain.

- **Medulla oblongata.** The medulla oblongata is the lowest part of the brain stem. It contains vital control centers that regulate heartbeat, breathing, blood pressure, and digestion as well as control centers for swallowing, vomiting, sneezing, and coughing. The medulla also receives and relays taste sensations from the tongue and is involved in speech and in tongue movements.

- **Pons.** Just above the medulla, the brain stem enlarges to form the pons. The pons serves mainly as a pathway for nerve impulses passing to and from the cerebrum. The pons also contains the nuclei for four pairs of cranial nerves. It relays sensory information from the ear, face, and teeth as well as the signals that move the jaw and adjust facial expressions.

- **Midbrain.** The shortest part of the brain stem is the midbrain, which lies just above the pons. It contains the nuclei of the two pairs of cranial nerves that control eye movements and the size and reactions of the pupils. Closely associated with the brain stem are the thalamus and hypothalamus.

- **Thalamus.** Located above the midbrain are the two egg-shaped lobes of the thalamus. Each lobe is about the size of a walnut. The thalamus is an important relay center for incoming sensory impulses. Different clusters of nerve cells within the thalamus receive information from different sense organs such as the eyes and ears. Through the spine, the thalamus also receives information from touch and pressure receptors in the skin.

- **Hypothalamus.** Behind the eyes and under the thalamus is a tiny region of the brain called the *hypothalamus*. The hypothalamus has nerve centers that control various body processes and keep body conditions balanced. For example, different groups of nerve cells regulate body temperature, stimulate appetite for food and drink, and regulate sleep. The hypothalamus also controls secretions from the pituitary gland that control many processes such as metabolism and sexual development and emotional responses.

Explore illustrations of the brain, spinal cord, and central nervous system at **health.glencoe.com**.

▲ *Pediatric neurosurgeon Dr. Ben Carson is world-renowned for his achievements in medicine. As a student he was motivated to earn scholarships to attend medical school. He encourages all young people to develop their potential and reach their goals.*

ACTIVITY *Find out what classes you should take now to prepare for a career in the medical profession.*

L2 Explaining

Much interesting research has been done on right- and left-brain thinking. The two frontal hemispheres of the cortex function in separate, almost opposite, ways. The right hemisphere is described as playful, spontaneous, flexible, creative, intuitive, irrational, illogical. The left side is characterized as logical, rational, knowledge-seeking, factual, serious, and is associated with rules and order. We all function using both hemispheres, but scientists believe we each have a dominant side.

L2 Discussing

Direct students to the photo of Dr. Carson and explain that he works as chief pediatric neurosurgeon at Johns Hopkins Children's Center in Baltimore. He struggled as a young student to overcome difficult odds and become successful in his field. He focuses now on developing opportunities for young people to achieve academic excellence. With his wife he has created a scholarship fund. He travels, lectures, and has written two books telling about his own experiences, inspiring others to use their talents to make a difference. Have interested students find out more about the work of Dr. Carson.

You may want to build on this activity by having students locate more information on the health of the spinal cord. Some Internet sites provide downloadable booklets on skateboard and inline skating safety and the importance of helmets in reducing the risk of brain or spinal cord injury. Students could print out and distribute copies of such booklets as the basis of a schoolwide Brain Injury Prevention Week.

SCHOOL-TO-CAREER

HELP FOR DAMAGED NERVOUS SYSTEMS. Suggest that students conduct research about the function that crawling and opposite arm and leg movements play in the development of infants' and children's nervous systems. They may wish to relate this research to modern rehabilitation techniques. Have students research the difference between a physical therapist and an occupational therapist and the qualifications for each. Encourage them to find out about what such therapists can do, in partnership with neurologists, to help victims of brain or nerve damage recover part or all of their functions. Ask them to identify the types of damage for which such rehabilitation is possible.

L1 Writing

Assign each student a body part, such as heart, lungs, or intestines. Then ask each student to write a paragraph describing the functions of the sympathetic and parasympathetic nervous systems on this organ. Ask: What are the physical signs that show the effects of the nervous system response?

L1 Discussing

Encourage students to discuss how reflexes or involuntary responses can protect you from injury.

L1 Researching

Have student volunteers research what a neurologist and a neurosurgeon do in their respective practices of medicine.

L2 Researching

Divide the class into groups. Assign each group a type of drug, such as alcohol, codeine, caffeine, or tobacco, that affects the nervous system. Ask students to research how each drug affects the nervous system. Have each group make a chart or poster and share it with the class.

L3 Researching

Let volunteers research medicines that can reduce or eliminate pain. Ask them to explain how these medicines affect the release of cholinesterase in the transmission of the signal of pain to the central nervous system.

hotlink

"fight or flight" response For more information on the "fight or flight" response and its role in stress, see Chapter 9, page 216.

The Peripheral Nervous System

Peripheral means "located away from the center." The peripheral nervous system (PNS) consists of nerves that fan out from the central nervous system to the muscles, skin, internal organs, and glands. The PNS carries messages between the CNS and the rest of the body. The PNS consists of 12 pairs of cranial nerves that branch from the brain and 31 pairs of spinal nerves that branch from the spinal cord.

The PNS is composed of two subdivisions: the autonomic nervous system and the somatic nervous system.

The Autonomic Nervous System

The autonomic nervous system (ANS) is responsible for controlling the involuntary functions of the body, such as sweating, digestion, and heart rate. The ANS consists of a network of nerves divided into two parts: the sympathetic nervous system and the parasympathetic nervous system. These two systems have opposing effects on the same organs. They act in conjunction and normally balance each other. The balance of activity between the sympathetic and parasympathetic systems is controlled by the CNS.

THE SYMPATHETIC NERVOUS SYSTEM

The sympathetic nervous system responds to the body's needs during increased activity and in emergencies. It prepares the body for a **"fight or flight" response**—the readiness to stand your ground and "fight" a stressor or "take flight" and escape. During such reactions, the heartbeat and breathing rate quicken as blood flow to the muscles increases. Nerves from the sympathetic system lead to all of the body's vital organs and glands, including the liver, heart, kidneys, pancreas, stomach, and salivary, sweat, and adrenal glands.

THE PARASYMPATHETIC NERVOUS SYSTEM

The parasympathetic system opposes the actions of the sympathetic system by slowing body functions. It slows down the heartbeat, opens blood vessels, and lowers blood pressure.

370 CHAPTER 16 YOUR NERVOUS AND ENDOCRINE SYSTEMS

COOPERATIVE) LEARNING

MEDIA INFLUENCES. When making decisions, people may be influenced by propaganda and subtle hidden persuasion techniques. Advertisers want their audience to connect or transfer desirable images and attributes to their product. Let students examine a number of printed ads featuring alcohol products. Ask: How is the alcoholic beverage photographed and in what surroundings? What types of activities are featured in the ads? What images does each ad project of the people drinking the beverage? Suggest they find examples of ads that associate an alcoholic beverage with romance, sex, success, sophistication, fun, or friendship. Have them cut out several such ads, and make posters. The ad should be at the top of each poster and a list of the actual effects of alcohol on the nervous system should be at the bottom.

The Somatic Nervous System

The somatic nervous system includes cranial and spinal nerves that transmit impulses from the CNS to skeletal muscles. This involves voluntary responses—responses that are under your control.

Reflex Action

A **reflex** is *a spontaneous response of the body to a stimulus.* It occurs automatically, without conscious thought or effort. In simple reflexes such as the sudden jerk that occurs when the doctor taps the ligament below the knee, a sensory and motor neuron interact. The doctor's tap initiates the nerve impulse, which travels along sensory neurons to the spinal cord, then on to a motor neuron. The impulse travels back to the leg muscles, causing them to contract and the knee to jerk.

In other reflexes, when a receptor is stimulated—for example, when your hand touches a hot stove—the axon of the sensory neuron makes contact with a connecting neuron in the spinal cord. This neuron, in turn, contacts a motor neuron that sends an impulse down its axon to the muscles. The muscles respond by pulling the hand away from the stove. All of this happens in a split second, before the pain is even felt.

The nervous system plays an important part in coordination and reflexes during sports activities.

ACTIVITY *Tell which part of the PNS works to transmit messages to the muscles when you want to swing a tennis racquet to return a serve.*

LESSON 1 *Review*

Reviewing Facts and Vocabulary

1. Describe the three types of neurons.
2. Name the two main parts of the central nervous system.
3. What is the difference between the sympathetic and parasympathetic divisions of the autonomic nervous system?

Thinking Critically

4. **Comparing and Contrasting.** How does the central nervous system compare with the peripheral nervous system?

Applying Health Skills

5. **In Your School.** Ask your teacher to obtain an MRI or CT scan from a teaching hospital. In a small group, examine the image. Attempt to identify the different parts of the brain. Discuss your observations and findings with other groups.

ASSESS

EVALUATING THE LESSON

Assign and discuss the Lesson 1 Review; then administer, grade, and discuss the *Lesson 50 Quiz* in the TCR. ☞

RETEACHING

- Ask students to find facts in this lesson that support the following generalization: *The nervous system is the body's communication network and control center.* Tell them to write lists of the facts they find.
- Ask students to complete *Reteaching Activity 50* in the TCR. ☞
- Use *Transparencies 60* and *61* to review the parts of the nervous system and the brain. 🖐

ENRICHMENT

Have students research phantom limbs or phantom pain. What is it? How do scientists explain this unusual sensory phenomenon? Ask students to summarize their findings in written reports.

CLOSE

Ask students to state the most important concepts learned in this lesson. Discuss with students why a computer can never replace the human brain.

Care and Problems of the Nervous System

LESSON 2

Care and Problems of the Nervous System

FOCUS

LESSON OBJECTIVES

After studying this lesson, students should be able to

- discuss care of the nervous system.
- identify symptoms, causes, and treatment of various injuries, diseases, and disorders of the nervous system.

MOTIVATOR

Write the following on the chalkboard for students to work on while attendance is being taken: *Write an explanation of the differences in these terms:* degenerative, infectious, genetic. (*Degenerative* refers to a breakdown or deterioration of the structure of an organ or tissue; *infectious* involves pathogens, or germs; and *genetic* involves inherited characteristics passed on through genes.)

INTRODUCING THE LESSON

Refer to the Motivator. Ask volunteers to share their responses. Correct any misconceptions.

INTRODUCING HEALTH TERMS

- Have students make flash cards for the vocabulary terms. On one side, have them write the word. On the other side, have them identify the body system, the definition, and a page reference.
- Ask students to complete Vocabulary Activity 16 and Chapter Study Guide 16 in the *Student Workbook.*

When your computer crashes, you can just start it up again. When your nervous system goes "down," however, the solution is not so simple. Damage to the nervous system is far-reaching and often permanent. Proper care and preventive behaviors can help maintain the health of your body's control center.

HEALTH TERMS

epilepsy
cerebral palsy

HEALTH CONCEPTS

- By following rules of safety, you will prevent many head and spinal injuries.
- The nervous system can be damaged by degenerative diseases, infectious diseases, and genetic disorders.

Care of the Nervous System

To keep your nervous system functioning well, you need regular exercise, proper nutrition, and adequate rest and sleep. Avoid using alcohol and other drugs, which can cause permanent damage to the nervous system.

Many head and spinal cord injuries can be prevented by following basic safety rules. Wearing a seat belt in a car gives you added protection in case of an accident. Before diving into a pool or lake, you should always check the depth of the water and for the presence of underwater

Lesson 2 Resources

TEACHER'S CLASSROOM RESOURCES
- Concept Map Activity 51
- Decision-Making Activity 16
- Enrichment Activity 16
- Lesson 51 Quiz
- Lesson Plan 51
- Reteaching Activity 51

STUDENT WORKBOOK
- Applying Health Skills 51
- Chapter Study Guide 16
- Vocabulary Activity 16

obstacles, such as rocks. You can protect your head from injuries by wearing a helmet whenever you ride a bike, motorcycle, or other vehicle; use in-line skates; or play contact sports.

Problems of the Nervous System

The normal functioning of the nervous system can be disturbed in a number of ways. Accidents can damage or destroy nerve tissue. Degenerative diseases, such as Parkinson's disease, can destroy nerve tissue in the brain or spinal column. Illegal drug use and alcohol abuse can destroy brain cells and lead to nervous system disorders.

Head and Spinal Cord Injuries

Each year more than a half million Americans are hospitalized with brain or spinal cord injuries resulting from motor vehicle accidents, falls, sports, and physical abuse. Some 20 percent suffer lifelong mental or physical impairment.

Head Injuries

Although the brain is protected by the skull bones and the fluid that surrounds it, any direct blow to the head can lead to possible brain injury. Concussion, a temporary disturbance of the brain's ability to function, is the most common and mildest kind of brain injury. A more serious injury to the brain is a contusion. A contusion of the brain is a bruise, which may cause swelling of the brain. A severe contusion can result in a coma, a state of unconsciousness.

Making Responsible Decisions

Use Your Head

Nick is caught in a downpour on the way home from school one afternoon. Just then, his friend Greg drives by on his motorcycle. When Greg sees Nick, he stops and offers him a ride. The only problem is that Greg is not carrying a spare helmet on his cycle, and riding without a helmet in the state the teens live in is against the law. Nick is getting soaked. He would love to get home quickly. However, accepting a ride could get him and his friend in trouble or, worse, lead to a serious injury. What should Nick do?

What Would You Do?

Apply the six steps of the decision-making process to Nick's problem.

1. **State the situation.**
2. **List the options.**
3. **Weigh the possible outcomes.**
4. **Consider your values.**
5. **Make a decision and act.**
6. **Evaluate the decision.**

HEALTH LITERACY

SELF-DIRECTED LEARNER. Students may not be aware of all of the serious problems facing many people with paraplegia and quadriplegia. For example, many cannot urinate without the use of a catheter and have difficulty moving their bowels. It is also quite normal to lose all sexual function. Encourage students to conduct research about the effects on the internal organs of spinal injury and other forms of brain or nerve damage. Have them compile the information into a brochure. Suggest they include a message reinforcing the importance of precautions to protect the brain and spine from injury. You may suggest that some students submit their information in the form of an article for the school paper.

TEACH

L1 Researching

Explain to students that the spinal cord is protected by the vertebral column, and the brain is protected by the skull. Ask students to investigate what type of extra protection is used in various sports to protect the nervous system.

L2 Class Activity

Have students list three ways to avoid injuries to the nervous system. (Explain how the use of alcohol and other drugs can affect the nervous system.)

Making Responsible Decisions

1. During a rainstorm, Nick's friend has offered him a motorcycle ride home, but there is no helmet for Nick to wear.
2. Nick can refuse the ride and walk home, or he can ride with his friend without a helmet.
3. If Nick refuses the ride, he may feel awkward or embarrassed. He will also have to walk all the way home in the rain. However, he will also not risk arrest, injury, or death. If Nick accepts the ride, he might get home more quickly, although he will still get wet. In addition, he could be arrested for riding without a helmet. Nick also could be involved in a motorcycle accident (the rain increases the risk of an accident) and might be injured or even killed.
4. Nick values his own safety and his own comfort.
5. Responses will vary.
6. Guide students in discussing both the short- and long-term consequences of their decisions.

L2 Decision Making

For further study on making responsible decisions, assign *Decision-Making Activity 16* in the TCR.

Building Health Skills

Getting the Rest You Need
Skill: Setting Goals

Let students respond to these questions with a show of hands: How many of you feel tired right now? How many of you feel tired at the end of the day? at the end of the school day? when you wake up in the morning? Then ask: What is your body telling you? What do you think you could do to help yourself feel better? After a short discussion, have students read the Building Health Skills feature to learn about steps they can take to get the rest they need. Then ask students to evaluate each suggested step: How do you think this could help you? Why is it sometimes hard to take this step? How could you make this step easier for yourself?

L2 Explaining

Stress that cranial symptoms (dizziness, headache, double vision) are indicators of problems in the central nervous system. These symptoms should be reported promptly to a doctor.

L2 Discussing

Cartilage cushions the space between bones. When it is injured, bone rubs against bone, causing pain. Have students discuss ways in which spinal cord alignment can be protected and preserved. Be sure to emphasize good posture.

L2 Researching

Have students research the effects of spinal cord damage on body functions. Find out what body parts are affected by damage at various sections of the spinal cord. Students may know someone with a spinal cord injury whom they can interview.

Spinal Cord Injuries

The spinal cord is surrounded by protective membranes, shock-absorbing fluid, and the vertebrae of the spine. These defenses protect it from the bumps and falls common in everyday life. However, they often are not enough to protect the spinal cord from more serious accidents. Injury anywhere on the spinal cord can cause paralysis.

In general, injury to the upper part of the cord causes more extensive damage. An injury at the neck level, for example, may result in *quadriplegia*—paralysis in both the arms and the legs. Injury at the chest level or lower affects the legs and lower body. Paralysis of the lower body is called *paraplegia*.

Degenerative Diseases

Degenerative means causing a breakdown or deterioration of function or structure. Three common degenerative diseases of the nervous system are:

- **Parkinson's disease.** This is a progressive disorder, meaning that it gradually involves more and more nerves. Parkinson's disease is caused by degeneration of the nerve cells within the brain that modify nerve impulses transmitted from the motor areas of the brain. The result is uncoordinated muscular movement.

Building Health Skills

Setting Goals: Getting the Rest You Need

ARE YOU GIVING your body the rest it needs? If not, there are steps you can take to improve your sleep habits. These include the following:

1. **Maintain a regular schedule seven days a week.** People who follow routines find it easier to fall—and stay—asleep.

2. **Go to bed when you feel sleepy.** Don't force yourself to stay up. Tiredness is your body's way of letting you know it's time to turn in.

3. **Avoid caffeine in the evening.** Coffee, chocolate, and some soft-drinks contain this stimulant drug.

4. **Avoid vigorous physical activity just before bedtime.** Contrary to what some people think, exercising before bed will not tire you out. Rather, it stimulates areas of the brain that keep you awake.

5. **Avoid noise at bedtime.** Listening to music can relax you as long as you keep the volume on the radio, TV, or stereo player down. Turn down the energy in your body as you would turn down the volume on your radio.

MORE ABOUT . . . . .

INJURIES TO THE CNS. Concussion occurs when the brain absorbs external forces and collides with the cranium, causing the brain to bruise. The bruise usually occurs on the side opposite the initial impact. Symptoms usually appear within 24 hours of the injury and include loss of memory, disorientation, loss of balance, blurred vision, and minor to extreme levels of unconsciousness.

Sciatica (low back pain) is caused when the sciatic nerve is obstructed or pressured, causing pain to radiate down one or both legs. The upper sections of the spine (cervical, thoracic, and lumbar) have freedom of movement, while the lower sacral and coccygeal sections have little or no movement abilities.

■ **Multiple sclerosis.** Multiple sclerosis (MS) is a progressive disease of the CNS. It involves the destruction of the myelin sheath that surrounds nerve fibers in the brain and spinal cord. MS is thought to be an autoimmune disease in which the body's defense system begins to treat the myelin as a foreign invader and attacks it. Scar tissue replaces the destroyed myelin. The underlying nerve fibers are damaged, and voluntary control of muscles gradually decreases.

■ **Alzheimer's disease.** Alzheimer's disease causes general mental deterioration. Patients gradually lose their memory and powers of judgment. Speech and body coordination may also be affected. Although there is no cure, researchers continue to search for the causes of the disease and ways of preventing it. It is the fourth leading cause of death in adults.

◀ *Specially designed wheelchairs enable persons with spinal cord injuries to lead full, active lives.*

ACTIVITY *Explain why being able to participate in sports is important to the well-being of persons with spinal cord injuries.*

L2 **Discussing**

Ask students to identify differences and similarities between multiple sclerosis and cerebral palsy. *(Both are characterized by a lack of muscle control. In multiple sclerosis, symptoms may progress to paralysis. Cerebral palsy is caused by disease, injury, or lack of oxygen to the brain at birth. The cause of multiple sclerosis is unknown.)*

update
▶*Looking at Technology*

How a CT Scan Works

Give students an opportunity to share what they already know about CT scans by asking: What tools do medical professionals have for assessing a brain in which they suspect a possible stroke or unusual bleeding? When and how can those tools be used? After a brief discussion, have students read the Update feature to learn more about CT scans. Then encourage students to discuss the usefulness and effectiveness of a CT scan. Finally, you may want to have volunteers research and report on the similarities and differences between a CT scan and an MRI.

update
▶*Looking at Technology*

How a CT Scan Works

Computerized tomography, or CT, scanning is a technique that can produce clear pictures of the brain. X rays are passed through the brain at different angles. Computer screens then display cross-sectional slices of the brain viewed from any desired angle.

Before the scan is carried out, the patient may be injected with a dye to make blood vessels or abnormalities show up more clearly. To perform a CT scan, the patient lies on a table that can be moved to allow accurate positioning within the machine. The machine itself can be tilted to allow precise areas to be X-rayed. Numbers of X-ray beams are passed through the brain at different angles as the scanner rotates around the patient. These beams are of very low dosages and last only a fraction of a second. Detectors in the scanner record the amount of X rays absorbed by different tissues. A computer then transforms this information into a detailed image. CT scans are a valuable tool in diagnosing brain abnormalities. They have proved even more invaluable in determining which parts of the brain do what.

MEETING SPECIAL NEEDS

EPILEPSY. During an epileptic seizure in the classroom:

- Move all items that may cause injury to the individual and loosen all restrictive clothing.
- Try to keep the individual on his or her side.
- Do not try to retrieve tongue if it lodges in the throat.
- Send for medical help.

Afterward:

- When the attack is over, reassure the student that everything is okay.
- Contact parents and medical personnel.
- Talk to the class about seizure-prone individuals and how to deal with the situation. Stress that the individual needs support.

CHARACTER IN ACTION

You Be the Judge

Ask students to think about popular sporting equipment, such as in-line skates or bicycles, and the injuries that are caused when people do not take proper safety precautions. Now discuss examples of good decision-making when proper use of this equipment prevented or minimized injuries.

ASSESS

EVALUATING THE LESSON

Assign and discuss the Lesson 2 Review; then administer, grade, and discuss the *Lesson 51 Quiz* in the TCR. 🗂

RETEACHING

- Have students prepare an outline on problems of the nervous system. Ask them to provide supporting facts for each of these categories, relying on the text for the information.
- Ask students to complete *Reteaching Activity 51* in the TCR. 🗂

ENRICHMENT

Have students investigate the use of acupuncture to calm nerves and ease pain without the unhealthy side-effects of illegal drugs. Have them complete *Enrichment Activity 16* in the TCR. 🗂

CLOSE

Ask students to state the most important concepts learned in this lesson. Have each student list two short-term and two long-term advantages of making choices that promote the health of the nervous system.

CHARACTER IN ACTION

You Be the Judge

When it comes to physical activity of any sort, you can demonstrate responsibility and prevent injury to yourself and others by using **good judgment**. That means planning carefully and considering the consequences of your actions *before* you head out the door.

Character Check Before you begin any physical activity, consider the following carefully:

➤ proper equipment

➤ proper use of equipment

➤ safety precautions

➤ equipment maintenance

➤ weather and temperature

➤ visibility

➤ hydration and ventilation

Other Disorders and Problems

Although many disorders of the nervous system have known causes, some may have many possible causes. In some cases, the cause is unknown.

- **Epilepsy.** The term *epilepsy* comes from a Greek word meaning "seizure." **Epilepsy** is *a disorder of the nervous system that is characterized by recurrent seizures—sudden episodes of uncontrolled electrical activity in the brain*. Epilepsy is not a disease but, rather, a symptom of an underlying problem. Seizures may result from chemical imbalance in the brain, head injury, tumor, injury to the brain before or during birth, brain infection, stroke, or withdrawal from drugs or alcohol, among other possible causes. Different types of seizures can affect people with epilepsy. A physician can identify the seizure type and prescribe proper medication to control the seizures and help the person lead a normal, healthy life.

- **Cerebral Palsy.** Cerebral palsy refers to *a group of nonprogressive neurological disorders that are the result of damage to the brain before birth, during birth, in the newborn period, or in early childhood*. It was once thought that lack of oxygen during birth was the primary cause of cerebral palsy. In truth, only a minority of cases result from oxygen deficiency. Accidental injury, radiation, certain drugs, and diseases such as encephalitis and meningitis are among the causes. In the majority of cases, the cause is unknown. Physical therapy programs, braces, and walking aids all help cerebral palsy patients to lead full, active lives.

LESSON 2 *Review*

Reviewing Facts and Vocabulary

1. Describe injuries that might result from a sharp blow to the head.
2. What is the effect of multiple sclerosis on the body?

Thinking Critically

3. *Evaluating.* Some states have enacted laws requiring that children under certain ages be restrained by seat belts or, for very young children, car seats. Do you think parents should be required by law to use such devices? Why or why not?

Applying Health Skills

4. *In Your Home and School.* Fold a sheet of paper lengthwise to form two columns. Label the first column *Risks* and the second, *Prevention*. In the first column, write risks of possible head or spinal cord injury that exist in your home (for example, stairway with no handrail). In the second column, identify preventive measures your family has taken or might take to diminish each risk (for example, installed grab bars in shower stall). Do a second risk survey for your school.

Lesson 2 Review

Answers to Reviewing Facts and Vocabulary

1. Concussion or contusion.
2. Loss of voluntary control of the body.

Answer to Thinking Critically

3. Answers will vary.

The Endocrine System

You already know that the nervous system coordinates and regulates the functions of the body. It is aided in these tasks by the endocrine system. Unlike the nervous system, which sends messages in the form of electrical impulses, the endocrine system uses chemical messengers called hormones.

HEALTH TERMS

endocrine glands
hormones
pituitary gland
gonads
thyroid gland
parathyroid glands
adrenal glands
pancreas

HEALTH CONCEPTS

- The endocrine system works with the nervous system to coordinate and regulate body functions.
- Endocrine glands send messages to organs and systems of the body via chemical messengers called *hormones.*

Insulin medication

Structure of the Endocrine System

The principal structures of the endocrine system are the **endocrine glands.** These are *ductless, or tubeless, structures that secrete hormones.* **Hormones** are *chemical substances produced by ductless glands that regulate the activities of different body cells.* They are secreted by the endocrine glands and carried to their destinations in the body via the bloodstream. This distinguishes endocrine glands from exocrine glands, which secrete substances into ducts, or tubes, to be carried to a specific area of the body.

Endocrine glands are scattered throughout the body. They work independently of one another, but they interact in well-defined ways. Major glands of the endocrine system include the pituitary, the thyroid, the parathyroid, the adrenals, the pancreas, and the gonads.

Lesson 3 Resources

TEACHER'S CLASSROOM RESOURCES
- **Concept Map** Activity 52
- **Cooperative Learning** Activity 16
- **Lesson 52 Quiz**
- **Lesson Plan 52**
- **Reteaching** Activity 52

STUDENT WORKBOOK
- **Applying Health Skills 52**
- **Chapter Study Guide 16**
- **Vocabulary** Activity 16

TRANSPARENCIES
- **Transparency 62**

The Endocrine System

FOCUS

LESSON OBJECTIVES

After studying this lesson, students should be able to

- explain the function of hormones.
- name the glands of the endocrine system.
- describe the effects of specific hormones on the body.
- explain conditions resulting from improper functioning of certain glands.

MOTIVATOR

Write the following on the chalkboard for students to work on while attendance is being taken: *Use the following information to develop a definition for endocrine glands. Endo means "inside" and crine means "separate."*

INTRODUCING THE LESSON

Refer to the Motivator. Ask volunteers to share their responses. When the definitions are adequately shared, ask students what glands they have already studied. Tell them they will learn more about the endocrine glands and the endocrine system in this lesson.

INTRODUCING HEALTH TERMS

- Have students make flash cards for the vocabulary terms. On one side, have them write the word. On the other side, have them identify the body system, the definition, and a page reference.
- Ask students to complete Vocabulary Activity 16 and Chapter Study Guide 16 in the *Student Workbook.*

TEACH

LD Class Activity

Provide LD students with short, easy-to-understand explanations of major concepts.

L2 Discussing

Because hormones "set things in motion," ask students to describe in their own words which of the endocrine glands they feel is most vital and which is least vital. Ask them to explain their choices.

L2 Discussing

Help students discuss the relationship of hormones to the nervous system.

L2 Class Activity

Ask students to recall emergency situations in which they found themselves. Following this reflection, ask each person to make a written identification of her or his autonomic responses to hormone stimulation.

L1 Explaining

There is much new research available on the varying levels of hormones in the body, especially during adolescence. Hormonal activity related to puberty and sexual development is very low to nonexistent in children. It is higher, but level, in adults (except during pregnancy). During puberty and adolescent years, it might be at a child's level one minute and, 20 minutes later, soar to an adult level. These "ups and downs" help explain the mood swings and extreme "highs and lows" experienced during these years.

▼ *The glands of the endocrine system are situated at different locations throughout the body.*

ACTIVITY *Identify the glands that are different in males and females.*

THE ENDOCRINE SYSTEM

Pineal body
Pituitary gland

Thyroid gland
Parathyroid glands

Thymus gland

Adrenal glands
Pancreas

Ovaries (in female)

Testes (in male)

The Pituitary Gland

The **pituitary gland** *regulates and controls the activities of all other endocrine glands.* It is known, therefore, as the "master gland." This pea-sized gland is located at the midpoint of the skull, roughly behind the eyes. It has three sections, or lobes—anterior, intermediate, and posterior.

ANTERIOR LOBE

Anterior means "front." The hormones produced by this lobe control a range of body functions. They regulate metabolic activities of cells and stimulate other endocrine glands. The anterior lobe produces six hormones. These are as follows:

- Somatotropic, or growth, hormone stimulates normal body growth and development by altering chemical activity in body cells. It especially influences growth of the skeleton and skeletal muscles.
- Thyroid-stimulating hormone (TSH) stimulates hormone production by the thyroid gland.
    - Adrenocorticotropic hormone (ACTH) stimulates hormone production by the adrenal glands.
    - Two gonadotropic hormones—follicle-stimulating hormone (FSH) and luteinizing hormone (LH)—control the growth, development, and functions of the **gonads**, which is another name for *the ovaries* and *testes*. In females, FSH triggers the development of egg cells, or ova, in the ovary and stimulates cells in the ovary to produce estrogen, a female sex hormone. In males, FSH stimulates the testes to produce sperm cells. In females, LH is responsible for ovulation, or the release of a mature ovum from the ovary, and stimulates cells in the ovaries to produce progesterone, a female sex hormone. In males, LH stimulates cells in the testes to produce testosterone, a male sex hormone.
    - Prolactin stimulates the production of milk in females who have given birth.

INTERMEDIATE LOBE

This lobe secretes melanocyte-stimulating hormone (MSH). MSH controls the darkening of the skin by stimulating pigment cells in the skin.

POSTERIOR LOBE

The posterior lobe secretes two hormones, antidiuretic hormone (ADH) and oxytocin. ADH's principal function is to regulate the balance of water in the body. It stimulates the kidneys to return water to the blood, which decreases water loss in the urine. Oxytocin stimulates the smooth muscles in the uterus of a pregnant female, causing contractions during the birth of a baby.

MORE ABOUT . . . . .

HORMONES. When hormones such as cortisone are taken in amounts larger than that produced by the body, they can act as drugs. They may reduce swelling, but they might also suppress the immune system. Short-term use can be beneficial in a variety of conditions, but long-term use may lead to lowered immunities, weakening of the bones, and high blood pressure. Doctors have recently discovered that serious side effects can be avoided by prescribing low doses or giving higher doses on alternate days.

The Thyroid Gland

The **thyroid gland** *produces hormones that regulate metabolism—the use of nutrients by the body's cells—body heat production, and bone growth.* One of the largest glands of the endocrine system, the thyroid gland is located in the front of the neck, just below the larynx. It consists of two lobes, one on either side of the trachea, or windpipe.

The principal hormone produced by the thyroid gland is thyroxine, which regulates the way cells release energy from nutrients or use energy to create other substances, such as proteins. Overproduction of thyroxine causes symptoms that include tiredness, anxiety, weight loss, diarrhea, and inability to tolerate heat. Low thyroxine production causes symptoms that include tiredness, dry skin, hair loss, weight gain, constipation, and sensitivity to cold.

The Parathyroid Glands

The **parathyroid glands** are *structures that produce parathyroid hormone, which regulates the body's calcium and phosphorus balance.* They are the smallest glands of the endocrine system and are situated on the lobes of the thyroid gland.

The Adrenal Glands

The **adrenal glands** are *two glands located on the top of the kidneys.* The adrenal glands consist of two parts—an outer region called the adrenal cortex and a smaller inner region called the adrenal medulla.

THE ADRENAL CORTEX

The adrenal cortex, which is absolutely essential for life, secretes a mixture of hormones that affect numerous body functions. It is made up of three distinct zones.

The outermost zone produces the hormone aldosterone. Its function is to inhibit the amount of sodium excreted in the urine. This serves to maintain blood volume and blood pressure.

Together, the inner and middle zones produce the hormones hydrocortisone and corticosterone as well as small amounts of androgen hormones. Hydrocortisone affects the metabolism of fats, proteins, and carbohydrates. It also helps the body recover from stress. The rate of hydrocortisone secretion is controlled by the release of ACTH by the pituitary gland. Both hydrocortisone and corticosterone play a role in stopping inflammation.

▲ *The demands of school, family, and extra-curricular activities require you to maintain energy throughout the day.*

ACTIVITY *Explain why the thyroid gland is important in regulating your energy level.*

L2 Class Activity

On the chalkboard, draw a schematic of the lobes of the pituitary gland. Have students name the hormones produced by each lobe by writing the hormone's name and drawing an arrow pointing to the producing lobe.

L1 Class Activity

Draw the endocrine system on the chalkboard. Have students label the parts and describe their functions to the class.

L2 Class Activity

Direct students to write paragraphs explaining why the pituitary is called "the master gland." Do they agree with this designation? Why or why not?

L2 Discussing

Abnormal physical growth is a condition that can be treated through hormone replacement in some cases. Prompt medical attention and adherence to a medical regime are recommended. What other kinds of diseases or disorders can the class recall that require long treatment periods? *(Diabetes, epilepsy, paralysis, etc.)*

L2 Explaining

The parathyroids, although very small, are essential to life. The two parts act as two separate glands, controlling separate activities.

L2 Cooperative Learning

Have students complete *Cooperative Learning Activity 16* in the TCR. ☞

PROMOTING COMPREHENSIVE SCHOOL HEALTH

INFLUENCING FACTORS. Although the school may have a great deal of influence on students during the time they are there, many other factors influence and shape student behavior and lifestyle. Factors inside the school may include the following: curriculum, effectiveness of teachers and staff members, instructional arrangements and methodology, instructional materials, and school support services. Factors outside the school may include the following: cultural practices, families, religious beliefs and customs, social environment, peer influence, economics, general government services, and health agencies. For more detailed information about addressing those influences, consult *Promoting a Comprehensive School Health Program* in the TCR. ☞

Growth Opportunity

keeping **Fit**

Explore with students the area of individual differences in growth and development. Discuss how personality and character best identify the uniqueness of individuals and how these qualities, unlike physical attributes, withstand time. Ask students to develop a list of things that promote individual worth and self-esteem.

L2 Class Activity

Ask students to differentiate between diabetes and hypoglycemia in a one-page report.

L2 Cooperative Learning

Divide the class into eight groups and assign each a different gland. Allow each group to develop a 5- to 8-minute presentation to teach a lesson regarding its assigned endocrine gland. Presentations should include illustrations, problems with the gland, new research, and interesting facts.

L2 Class Activity

Steroids are used by some athletes to improve strength and endurance. The consequence for these athletes can be dismissal from the team or even the banning of future participation in the sport. Tell students to relate steroids to the endocrine system. Have students describe the potential dangers of these drugs to the body. Ask: What are some beneficial uses for steroids under the supervision of a doctor?

L3 Reading

Ask students to read an article or book that describes an endocrine disorder found in another country. Ask: How is the condition treated there? Is the United States helping this country deal with this medical problem? If so, how?

keeping **Fit**

Growth Opportunity

Human beings come in a wide range of heights. Some of your classmates are probably taller than you, and some are probably shorter. Height differences are most obvious during the teenage years when the body is still growing and changing.

There is a great difference in the rates at which teens develop and grow. Some teens experience early growth spurts that make them taller than peers the same age. Other teens grow more slowly and take longer to achieve their full height.

Whatever a person's height, it is important to recognize and accept the uniqueness of individuals. A person's true value is not related to his or her size.

hotlink

reproduction For more information on the role of the gonads in the process of reproduction, see Chapter 19, page 434.

THE ADRENAL MEDULLA

The adrenal medulla is highly dependent on the hypothalamus and the autonomic nervous system for regulation. It secretes the hormones epinephrine (more commonly called adrenaline) and norepinephrine. Epinephrine increases heart action, raises blood pressure, increases respiration, and suppresses the digestive process. This hormone is also known as the emergency hormone because it is released into the blood in greater amounts during highly emotional states, such as when a person experiences fear or anger.

The Pancreas

The **pancreas** is *a gland that serves two systems—the digestive and the endocrine*. This elongated, tapered gland lies behind the stomach, attached to the first section of the small intestine by a duct that transports its digestive juice to the intestine. It is the largest gland in the endocrine system.

Most of the pancreas consists of exocrine tissue, which secretes digestive enzymes into a network of ducts that meet to form the main pancreatic duct. Scattered throughout the pancreas are small clusters of endocrine cells. These are called the islets of Langerhans, named after Paul Langerhans, a German scientist who first noticed them in 1869. The endocrine cells in the islets of Langerhans secrete two hormones—glucagon and insulin—that regulate the level of glucose (blood sugar) in the blood.

One hormone, glucagon, helps maintain the sugar level in the blood by stimulating the liver to convert glycogen to glucose, thus raising the blood sugar level. Glycogen is a storage form of glucose, found mainly in the liver and muscle cells. The other hormone, insulin, tends to decrease blood sugar levels. Insulin stimulates the liver to form glycogen from glucose.

The Gonads

Of all the endocrine glands, only the gonads are different in males and females. The ovaries in the female and the testes in the male are part of the reproductive system. The ovaries produce and release ova, and the testes produce and release sperm.

Hormones secreted by these glands are responsible for the development and maintenance of the secondary sex characteristics that begin to appear during adolescence, such as breasts in females and facial hair in males. Gonads also play a key role in the process of **reproduction**. This will be discussed at greater length in Chapter 19.

Endocrine System Problems

Most disorders of the endocrine system are related to the production of too much or too little of a hormone. Following is a description of some problems associated with endocrine glands.

HOME AND COMMUNITY CONNECTION

PRESERVING FUNCTION. Researchers are constantly finding new ways to protect and preserve brain and nervous system function as people age. Have students review research in this area. Suggest that they examine research about needed nutrients or replacing hormones such as dehydro-3-epiandrosterone (DHEA) as people age. Some physical and mental exercises help keep the brain and nervous system functioning. Suggest that students investigate disciplines such as yoga and acupressure, as well as medical technology. Have students share the information in this chapter with adults at home and offer information brochures to community senior centers.

- **Diabetes Mellitus.** Diabetes mellitus is a disorder in which the pancreas produces too little or no insulin. As a result, the glucose level in the blood becomes very high. Symptoms include excessive urination, constant thirst, weight loss, and fatigue.
- **Graves' Disease.** Graves' disease, or hyperthyroidism, is an autoimmune disorder in which the thyroid gland becomes overactive and enlarged, producing excessive amounts of thyroid hormones.
- **Cushing's Disease.** Overproduction of adrenal hormones can result in Cushing's disease. People with Cushing's disease develop round faces, humped upper backs, weak limbs, thin and easily bruised skin, and fragile bones. Treatment depends on whether the cause is overuse of corticosteroid drugs, a tumor or overgrowth of an adrenal gland, or a tumor on the pituitary gland.
- **Goiter.** A goiter is an enlargement of the thyroid gland. It can be seen as a swelling on the neck. In many parts of the world, the main cause of a goiter is lack of iodine in the diet. The condition has virtually disappeared in the United States since the introduction of iodized salt.

Growth Disorders

If, during the growing years, the anterior lobe of the pituitary gland does not produce enough of the growth hormone, a person does not grow. The person's stature is short because of delayed bone growth. The bones are usually normal in shape, however. If this condition is diagnosed early, proper treatment can be prescribed. With early treatment, a child may reach full height.

Did You Know?
➤ The tallest person on record, Robert Pershing Wadlow, was 8 feet 11 inches (2.7 m) tall.
➤ The shortest person on record, Gul Mohammad of Delhi, India, is 22½ inches (57 cm) tall.

LESSON 3 *Review*

Reviewing Facts and Vocabulary

1. Why is the pituitary gland called the master gland?
2. Make a chart showing the hormones produced by the pituitary gland. Include what they do.

Thinking Critically

3. **Synthesizing.** For each of the following conditions, identify the endocrine gland that probably is not functioning properly: (a) impaired growth, causing a person to be abnormally small for his or her age; (b) lowered metabolic rate accompanied by mental and physical sluggishness; (c) loss of salt through the kidneys and a drop in blood pressure. What general statement can be made about all three conditions that would characterize them?

Applying Health Skills

4. ***In Your Home and School.*** Does anyone in your family or among your classmates have diabetes? Ask the person to explain what symptoms were first experienced, how the disease was diagnosed, and what treatment was prescribed. Encourage the person to evaluate the results of the treatment.

LESSON 3   THE ENDOCRINE SYSTEM   **381**

ASSESS

EVALUATING THE LESSON

Assign and discuss the Lesson 3 Review; then administer, grade, and discuss the *Lesson 52 Quiz* in the TCR. ▱

RETEACHING

- Have students write paragraphs explaining the role of the endocrine system and make a chart with the name of each endocrine gland in the left column and its function in the right column. Ask students to describe the effects of too much or too little hormone production in the endocrine glands. Encourage them to use the text and an encyclopedia.
- Ask students to complete *Reteaching Activity 52* in the TCR. ▱
- Use *Transparency 62* to review the parts of the endocrine system. 🎨

ENRICHMENT

Ask each student to select one gland in the endocrine system. Encourage them to find out what happens if it malfunctions, whether a person can live without it, how malfunctions can be treated, and whether there are side effects from this treatment. Have each student summarize his or her findings in a written report.

CLOSE

Ask students to state the most important concepts learned in this lesson.

Lesson 3 Review

Answers to Reviewing Facts and Vocabulary

1. Because it regulates and controls the activities of all the other glands.
2. The chart should include the information listed on page 378.

Answer to Thinking Critically

3. (a) pituitary gland; (b) thyroid gland; (c) adrenal gland. In all three, there is a lack of activity.

Health Skills Activities

ACTIVITY 1
HEALTH SKILLS
Accessing Health Information, Health Advocacy

➤ **National Standards**
This activity meets these National Health Standards: 2.2; 7.2.

Teach
- Brainstorm with students to identify diseases, disorders, and injuries of the type described in step 1 of the student activity.
- Divide the class into groups. If possible, attempt to have groups cover at least five of the many disorders that affect the nervous system.

ACTIVITY 2
HEALTH SKILLS
Comprehending Health Concepts, Accessing Health Information, Health Advocacy

➤ **National Standards**
This activity meets these National Health Standards: 1.1; 1.6; 2.1; 2.3; 7.2.

Teach
- Urge students to choose a sport relatively high on the popularity scale that requires some safety precautions—either the wearing of special equipment or observing climate or other conditions. Possibilities include inline skating, skateboarding, and surfing.
- Urge students and groups to be as complete as possible when gathering information.

Health Skills Activities

Activity 1 — Understanding Problems of the Nervous System

Millions of Americans are affected by diseases and disorders of the nervous system. Create an informational pamphlet to help the general public be more understanding of persons afflicted with such diseases.

Directions
1. In a group, locate a disease or disorder of the nervous system and/or brain. Create a pamphlet that describes the disease, how a person develops it, and its effect on the individual (e.g., loss of muscular control).
2. In a separate section, discuss current medical treatments for this disease and how to help a person who has this disease.
3. Make your pamphlet available to students in your school.

Time
two 50-minute periods plus outside research

Materials
library or Internet health resources

Self-Assessment
✓ Selected a disease or disorder of the nervous system.
✓ Included all the information requested.
✓ Produced an eye-catching pamphlet.

Activity 2 — Injury Prevention

Although skating and similar activities can be fun, they can also pose a risk of injuries to the head and spine. Find out how you can increase sports safety?

Directions
1. Choose a sport that is popular among teens.
2. Using library, Internet, or other resources, research this sport. Determine what safety measures need to be taken (such as equipment, avoiding "hot-dogging") and the types of head and spine injuries that arise when safety measures are not followed.
3. If possible, download pictures of appropriate sports equipment from the Internet (or people safely practicing the sport) and, using a color computer printer, print these pictures.
4. Present your sports safety information to the class.

Time
50 minutes plus outside research

Materials
library or Internet health resources, poster board, colored markers, paper, pen or pencil, word processor with printer (optional)

Self-Assessment
✓ Presented safety information that was both clear and complete.
✓ Included visual images of appropriate sports equipment.

382 CHAPTER 16 YOUR NERVOUS AND ENDOCRINE SYSTEMS

ASSESSMENT SCORING

Using a four-level rubric, the student has achieved a 4 if:

ACTIVITY 1
✔ Student aided group in selecting a disease or disorder of the nervous system.
✔ Student demonstrated a thorough understanding of the nervous system.
✔ Student included all information requested in the assignment.
✔ Student helped produce an eye-catching and informative pamphlet.

ACTIVITY 2
✔ Student queried at least five peers on the sport or recreational activity they most enjoyed doing.
✔ Student presented the information called for.
✔ Safety information presented was both clear and complete.
✔ Student included visual images of appropriate sports equipment.

HEALTH NEWS VIDEO

Heads Up!

Use your head usually means "think about it." In some sports, however, the meaning is much more literal. Players really do use their heads—and sometimes they get hurt. Football tops the list of sports that lead to head injuries, but the list doesn't stop there. Soccer players might score an important goal by hitting the ball with their heads. They could also injure their brains with these repeated blows to the head.

Researchers are studying the effects of sports head injuries on players' ability to think. Even a mild concussion can lead to slower or confused thought processes for up to five days. They also discovered that returning to a sport before an injury is fully healed could lead to critical new injuries.

Play the Video

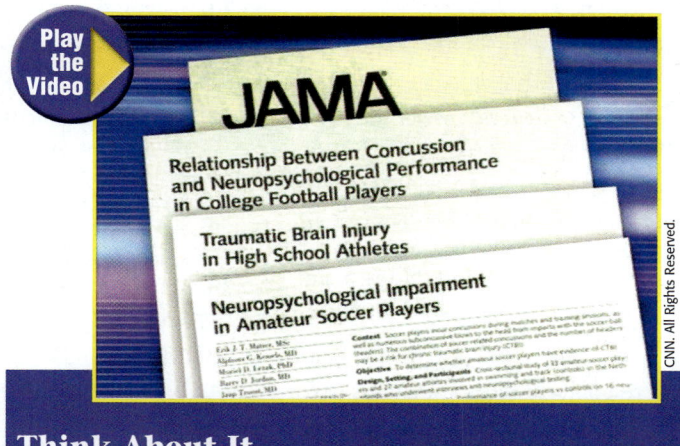

Think About It

- Why do you think head injuries are more common during games than in practice?
- How can head injuries affect a player's ability to make decisions?
- What safety precautions will help protect the nervous system? Why aren't these precautions always effective?

CNN HEALTH NEWS

Heads Up!
Video Segment 10 (Time – 1:52)

Objectives. After viewing the video, students should understand the possibility of dangerous injury to the brain and nervous system when participating in contact sports and recognize ways to protect themselves.

Motivator. Have students imagine how fragile the brain must be even though it is protected by the bones of the skeletal system. Explain that the safety gear used in many sports protects the brain and nervous system from injury. Have students view Video Segment 10, "Heads Up!" which summarizes current findings about head injuries in contact sports.

Teach

- Ask students to describe how the skeletal system serves as protection for the brain and other parts of the nervous system. Then discuss why additional protection is necessary when playing some contact sports.
- Extend discussion to include the limitations of protective safety gear. Emphasize that gear such as a helmet can protect against injury, but is not a guarantee of safety. Have students suggest strategies that can be used in conjunction with safety gear to help players avoid head injuries.

Role Play. Suggest that students role play two- or three-person interactions between coaches, players and doctors. For example, a football player gets a concussion during practice, two days before a big game. He says he feels fine and wants to play in the game. Encourage students to perform each situation twice, looking for different or additional solutions each time.

Close. Ask students to explain why journalists chose to report this story. Have them review the goals of the report, including its target audience and the information the creators hoped the audience would learn and apply.

MORE ABOUT . . . . .

ASK THE EXPERTS. There are many careers in sports medicine, including team physician, physical therapist, athletic trainer, massage therapist, dietitian, and sports psychologist. The researchers studying head injuries could be considered biomechanists.

A biomechanist studies the mechanics of the living body. A biomechanical engineer combines this knowledge with an understanding of engineering to design medical implants and devices, such as the braces that can be used to stabilize a head injury. Most biomechanical engineers acquire a graduate engineering degree. Students who want to treat patients through the application of biomechanical engineers can obtain an combined Ph.D./M.D. degree.

CHECKING COMPREHENSION

- Assign and discuss the chapter review.
- Use the MindJogger Videoquiz to review the chapter. 🔴

CHAPTER 16 REVIEW ANSWERS

Using Health Terms

1. cerebellum
2. neurons
3. reflex
4. brain stem
5. cerebrum
6. cerebral palsy
7. epilepsy
8. thyroid gland
9. pancreas
10. hormones
11. adrenal glands
12. pituitary gland
13. gonads

RECALLING THE FACTS

1. The peripheral nervous system consists of nerves that fan out from the central nervous system to the muscles, skin, internal organs, and glands.
2. Cerebrum, cerebellum, brain stem.
3. The autonomic nervous system controls the involuntary functions of the body.
4. The sympathetic nervous system.
5. The sympathetic system increases heart rate; the parasympathetic slows it. The sympathetic system increases breathing rate; the parasympathetic slows it.
6. Parkinson's disease: uncoordinated muscular movement. Multiple sclerosis: gradual decrease of voluntary control of muscles. Alzheimer's disease: loss of memory, powers of judgment, speech and body coordination.

Using Health Terms

On a separate sheet of paper, write the term that best matches each definition below.

LESSON 1

1. The second largest part of the brain.
2. Nerve cells.
3. A spontaneous response of the body to a stimulus.
4. A 3-inch-long (7.6-cm-long) stalk of nerve cells and fibers that connects the spinal cord to the rest of the brain.
5. The largest, most complex part of the brain.

LESSON 2

6. A group of nonprogressive neurological disorders that are the result of damage to the brain before birth, during birth, in the newborn period, or in early childhood.

7. A disorder of the nervous system that is characterized by recurrent seizures—sudden episodes of uncontrolled electrical activity in the brain.

LESSON 3

8. Produces hormones that regulate metabolism, body heat production, and bone growth.
9. A gland that serves two systems—the digestive and the endocrine.
10. Chemical substances produced by ductless glands that regulate the activities of different body cells.
11. Two glands located on the top of the kidneys.
12. Regulates and controls the activities of all other endocrine glands.
13. The ovaries and testes.

Recalling the Facts

Using complete sentences, answer the following questions.

LESSON 1

1. What does the peripheral nervous system consist of?
2. List the three main divisions of the brain.
3. What is the function of the autonomic nervous system?
4. What division of the autonomic nervous system responds to the body's needs during increased activities?
5. Give two examples of the opposing actions of the sympathetic and parasympathetic divisions of the autonomic nervous system.

LESSON 2

6. Name two degenerative diseases of the nervous system and describe the symptoms of each.

7. Tell what a concussion is and what the results of a concussion might be.
8. Tell what a contusion is and what the results of a contusion might be.
9. Name three ways of preventing head and spinal cord injuries.
10. What is a possible effect of injury to the spinal cord at the level of the neck?

LESSON 3

11. What are hormones and what is their function?
12. What is the difference between endocrine glands and exocrine glands?
13. Describe why the ovaries and testes are regarded as endocrine glands.
14. What does the principle hormone produced by the thyroid do?
15. What is the largest gland in the endocrine system, and what does it do?

384 CHAPTER 16 YOUR NERVOUS AND ENDOCRINE SYSTEMS

7. A concussion is the mildest and most common type of head injury. It can lead to temporary disturbance of the brain's ability to function.
8. A contusion is a more serious head injury that could cause swelling of the brain and possibly coma.
9. Wearing seat belts, wearing a good-fitting helmet when bike riding or skateboarding, using caution when diving or jumping into water, etc.
10. Quadriplegia—paralysis in both arms and legs.
11. Hormones are chemical substances produced by ductless glands that regulate the activities of different body cells.

Thinking Critically

LESSON 1

1. **Synthesizing.** Suppose that your frontal lobe was injured and you began to suffer from mood swings. How do you think your life might change?

2. **Synthesizing.** How might a person's ability to speak be affected by a stroke that damages the left hemisphere of the brain?

LESSON 2

3. **Synthesizing.** Summarize reasons for the stigma that has historically been attached to epilepsy.

4. **Analyzing.** Think of the different tasks you perform in a day. Which tasks do you think a paraplegic could perform? Which tasks would require retraining?

5. **Evaluating.** If you were to have an impairment on one side of the brain, which side would be hardest for you to live without? Why?

LESSON 3

6. **Comparing and Contrasting.** Compare the functions of the gonadotropic hormones FSH and LH in males and females.

Making the Connection

1. **Science.** Research scientific discoveries about how the left brain and right brain work. Of special interest are "split brain" studies—research done with individuals who underwent surgery that involved severing the connections between the two cerebral hemispheres.

2. **Social Studies.** Sometimes, a disease is named for a famous person who has been affected by it. Other times, a disease is named for the person who first describes its effects. Choose one of the diseases discussed in this chapter and find out the facts behind how it got its name.

BEYOND THE CLASSROOM

PARENTAL INVOLVEMENT Ask your parents whether any family members or close relatives—present and past—have ever suffered from disorders of the endocrine glands. With them, draw a family tree that includes all persons with any such disorders. Try to determine whether there seems to be a genetic component to the disorder(s).

COMMUNITY INVOLVEMENT With a small group of classmates, find out whether there is a helmet law and/or a seat belt law in your state. If there is, find out how the number of head injuries has changed since the law was enacted. If there is no law, find out what steps might be taken to enact such a law and how you can help.

SCHOOL-TO-CAREER

Technology. There are many exciting new medical and technological advances that offer new hope and improved quality of life for people with brain and spinal cord diseases and injuries. These range from experiments with repairing damaged spinal cords, to surgical implants that restore control to paralyzed limbs, to vastly improved wheelchairs. Find out about the latest technology in this field. Report your findings to the class.

Thinking Critically

1.–6. Answers will vary.

Making the Connection

1. Research findings will vary.
2. Findings will vary.

Evaluate

- Use the reproducible *Chapter 16 Test* in the TCR, or construct your own using the Testmaker software.
- Use *Performance Assessment Activity 16* in the TCR.

Enrichment

Ask students to complete *Cross-Curriculum Activity 16* in the TCR.

Beyond the Classroom

Keep students involved in the community, and encourage parent participation by assigning the activities on this page for students to work on outside of class.

12. Endocrine glands are ductless structures that secrete hormones. Exocrine glands have ducts to transport hormones to specific areas of the body.

13. Because they are ductless structures that secrete hormones that regulate other body cells.

14. It regulates the way cells release energy from nutrients or use energy to create other substances.

15. The pancreas is the largest gland in the endocrine system. It secretes digestive enzymes and regulates the level of sugar in the blood.

Your Circulatory and Respiratory Systems

	FEATURES	CLASSROOM RESOURCES

ACTIVITIES

- Cross-Curriculum Activity 17
- Health Lab 17
- Health Skills Activities 17
- Parent Letter and Activities 17

ASSESSMENT

- Chapter 17 Test
- Performance Assessment Activity 17
- Testmaker Software

STUDENT ACTIVITIES WORKBOOK

- Applying Health Skills 53–55
- Study Guide 17
- Vocabulary Activity 17

STUDENT DIVERSITY STRATEGIES

- Audiocassette Program (English)
- Audiocassette Program (Spanish)
- Spanish Parent Letters and Activities
- Spanish Summaries, Quizzes, and Activities

MULTIMEDIA COMPONENTS

- English Audiocassette Program
- Spanish Audiocassette Program
- MindJogger Videodisc and VHS program

National Health Education Standards

One of the main goals of the National Health Education Standards is to move students toward "health literacy." Health literacy is the capacity of individuals to obtain, interpret, and understand basic health information and services and the competence to use such information and services in ways which promote health. The health standards were developed by applying the characteristics of a well-educated, literate person within the context of health. The health literate person is:

- a critical thinker and problem solver
- a self-directed learner
- a responsible, productive citizen
- an effective communicator

Listed below are the Health Education Standards Performance Indicators addressed in each lesson of this chapter.

Lesson	Health Standards Performance Indicators
1	2.1, 2.2
2	2.6, 3.1, 3.4, 4.3
3	1.3, 1.6, 2.6, 6.1

ONLINE RESOURCES

For a fresh approach to health topics and an in-depth look at health issues, use these online resources found under Teacher Resources at **health.glencoe.com**.

- **BLOCK SCHEDULE LESSON PLANS** Reinforce health concepts with outside readings selected especially for students. Each reading is accompanied by a lesson plan and activities to enhance
  - Reading Skills
  - Cross Curriculum
  - Media Literacy

- **TECHNOLOGY PROJECTS** Instructions and suggestions on how to use computer, Internet, and software with health lessons.

- **HEALTH UPDATES** Timely topics in health news, including late-breaking medical advances and updates on teen risk behaviors.

Out of Time?

If time does not permit teaching this chapter, you may use these features: Building Health Skills on 391; Update on page 397; and Making Responsible Decisions on page 404.

BLOCK SCHEDULING

Block scheduling provides extended time for hands-on projects and activities. Use the following activities to engage students, provide further depth, and vary your instructional techniques:

- Update (30 minutes)   **pg. 397**
- Health Skills Activity (60–90 minutes)   **pg. 406**

Your Circulatory and Respiratory Systems

CHAPTER OVERVIEW

Chapter 17 introduces students to the circulatory and respiratory systems. The structure, function, care, and problems of each system are presented.

LESSON 1 The cardiovascular system moves blood throughout the body. It includes the heart, blood vessels, and blood. The action of the heart is critical to cardiovascular function, as it pumps blood through two major pathways, allowing for pulmonary and systemic circulation.

LESSON 2 Many problems of the cardiovascular system exist. Lifestyle choices and behaviors affect the health of the system.

LESSON 3 The respiratory system functions externally to take in air and give off carbon dioxide. Internally, it exchanges gases between the blood and body cells, releasing oxygen and taking in carbon dioxide.

Your Circulatory and Respiratory Systems

HEALTH Online

ADVOCACY

What better way to promote the health of others than to become an advocate for healthy lungs? A career in the medical field as a Respiratory Therapist offers the chance to work with infants with breathing difficulties or adults fighting respiratory disease. Visit health.glencoe.com and check the Career Corner.

Hands-On Health

TEACHING STRATEGY

Appreciating the Importance of Healthy Lungs Help students experience the effects of reduced lung capacity associated with emphysema, and encourage them to take good care of their own lung health. See Activity 21, "Straws and Emphysema," in the *Hands-On Health: Creative Teaching Strategies* booklet.

Time Needed
20 to 30 minutes

Supplies
- 1 small straw for each student

Scan of heart

> **Many a man who would not dream of putting too much pressure in his automobile tires lays a constant overstrain on his heart and arteries.**
>
> —Bruce Barton
> Contemporary writer, (1886–1967)

Quick Write Fold a paper in half. Write on one half words associated with the health of the circulatory system, on the other half words you associate with the respiratory system. Do any words fit both categories?

Personal Health Inventory

Self-Inventory Write the numbers 1–10 on a sheet of paper. Read each statement below and respond by writing *yes*, *no*, or *sometimes* for each item. Write a *yes* only for items that you practice regularly. Save your responses.

1	I try to maintain the appropriate weight for my height.
2	I avoid foods that are high in fat, cholesterol, and salt.
3	I eat foods that are rich in iron (leafy green vegetables, dried fruits, enriched cereals) daily.
4	I get at least 20 minutes of aerobic exercise at least three times a week.
5	I sleep at least seven to eight hours every night.
6	I have a regular physical checkup that includes checking my blood pressure.
7	I do not smoke.
8	I avoid breathing other people's smoke.
9	I study, work, or exercise in a well-ventilated area.
10	I avoid breathing polluted air or car fumes.

Follow-up After completing the chapter, retake this self-inventory. Pick two items that you need to work on and set a goal to improve your health behaviors.

INTRODUCING THE CHAPTER

Personal Health Inventory

Let students read the Self-Inventory statements, and ask: How do these habits affect your health? Which of these habits are completely in your control? Over which do you have only partial control? Why? Remind students that this inventory will be most useful if they are completely honest; then have them record their responses in their private Health Journals on a page labeled "My Circulatory and Respiratory Systems."

- Tell students that the circulatory system is the primary transportation system of the body, delivering needed nutrients and carrying away waste products from the body's cells. Explain that the circulatory system works closely with the respiratory system, which supplies oxygen to cells and removes carbon dioxide as waste, and the lymphatic system, which drains fluid from body tissue and helps fight infection. Explain that this chapter will examine more closely these processes.
- Have a volunteer read the quote on this page aloud to the class. Ask: What does this statement suggest about how to care for your circulatory system? Why is it so important to take good care of your circulatory and respiratory systems? Tell students that as they study Chapter 17 they will learn more about the parts, the functioning, and the care of these systems.
- Distribute Parent Letter 17 in the *Parent Letters and Activities* booklet.

T E C H N O L O G Y   O P T I O N S

MINDJOGGER
VIDEOQUIZ

To preview or review chapter content, you may wish to use the *MindJogger Videoquiz* that accompanies Chapter 17.

The Circulatory System

LESSON 1

FOCUS

LESSON OBJECTIVES

After studying this lesson, students should be able to

- describe the pathways of pulmonary and systemic circulation.
- explain the purposes of arteries, capillaries, and veins.
- explain the function of the lymphatic system.
- describe how the two main types of lymphocytes help your body fight pathogens.

MOTIVATOR

Write the following on the chalkboard for students to work on while attendance is being taken: *Write a definition of the term* cardiovascular system. (*Cardiovascular* refers to the entire circulatory system, including the heart, the blood vessels, and the blood.)

INTRODUCING THE LESSON

Tell students that without a healthy circulatory system the body could not function. Refer to the Motivator and have volunteers define the term *cardiovascular system.* Tell students that in this lesson they will learn about the heart and what influences its action.

INTRODUCING HEALTH TERMS

- Have students make flash cards for the vocabulary terms. On one side, have them write the word. On the other side, have them identify the body system, the definition, and a page reference.
- Ask students to complete Vocabulary Activity 17 and Chapter Study Guide 17 in the *Student Workbook.*

The Circulatory System

When you examine a road map of a city, you see an intricate, interconnecting network of roads over which goods are transported to and from a central hub. Without this network, the city could not function and thrive.

The same may be said of the circulatory system. It is the main transportation system for blood and other essential body fluids.

HEALTH TERMS

plasma
hemoglobin
platelets
arteries
capillaries
veins
lymph
lymphocytes

HEALTH CONCEPTS

- The heart is a pump that moves the body's blood supply through two major networks of pathways.
- Never resting, the heart continuously pumps blood throughout the body by means of the circulatory system.
- The lymphatic system works with the circulatory system to help the body maintain its fluid balance and helps the body fight infection.

Climbing equipment

Functions of the Circulatory System

Your circulatory system maintains an internal environment in which all the cells of your body are nourished. As your heart pumps blood, blood vessels carry oxygen and nutrients to body cells. At the same time, another gas, carbon dioxide, is carried along with waste matter from your cells and delivered to your lungs and **kidneys** for removal from the body.

Structure of the Circulatory System

The main parts of the circulatory system are your heart, blood, and a network of branching vessels—arteries, veins, and capillaries—that carry fluids throughout your body.

hotlink

kidneys For more information on waste removal by the kidneys, see Chapter 18, page 425.

Lesson 1 Resources

TEACHER'S CLASSROOM RESOURCES

- **Concept Map** Activity 53
- **Lesson 53 Quiz**
- **Lesson Plan 53**
- **Parent Letter and Activities 17**
- **Reteaching** Activity 53

STUDENT WORKBOOK

- **Applying Health Skills 53**
- **Chapter Study Guide 17**
- **Vocabulary** Activity 17

TRANSPARENCIES

 Transparency 63

The Heart

Along with your brain, your heart is the most important part of your body's vital organs. It never rests, even when you do. This muscular pump beats continuously to send blood to the lungs and the rest of the body.

Much of the heart consists of a special type of muscle called *myocardium*. Given sufficient oxygen and nutrients, the myocardium contracts rhythmically and automatically.

CHAMBERS OF THE HEART

A thick central muscular wall called the *septum* divides the interior of the heart into right and left halves. Each half has two chambers—an upper chamber called an *atrium* and a larger lower chamber called a *ventricle*. One-way valves at the exits from each heart chamber guarantee that blood can flow in only one direction.

A small area of the right atrium serves as a natural pacemaker, controlling the rate at which the heart beats. In response to impulses from the brain, this area sends an electrical impulse through the heart that causes both atria to contract. The contraction forces blood forward into the ventricles. Within milliseconds, this electric "charge" reaches a second piece of specialized tissue made of slow-conducting muscle cells. This tissue relays the charge to the muscles of the ventricles. The ventricles contract, increasing the pressure of blood in the heart. The increased pressure causes the valves to close, preventing backflow. The natural sound of the heart is related to the movements of these muscles and valves.

CIRCULATION IN THE HEART

Blood that has been depleted of oxygen but contains carbon dioxide and waste matter is carried to the heart by two large blood vessels called the *vena cava*. This blood enters the right atrium, is transferred to the right ventricle, and is then pumped to the lungs. In the lungs, the blood picks up oxygen from inhaled air and releases carbon dioxide. The newly oxygenated blood is returned to the heart. It enters the left atrium, is transferred to the left ventricle, and is then pumped to all the tissues of the body.

Blood

Blood is the fluid that transports all of the substances that your body needs to sustain life. Blood delivers oxygen, hormones, and nutrients to the cells and carries away wastes that the cells produce.

▼ *Rock climbing, backpacking, and other physical activities will keep your heart in good condition.*
ACTIVITY *What physical activities do you enjoy?*

TEACH

L1 Discussing

Using a model of the heart, clarify for students the direction of blood flow through the heart. Ask: Which chamber has the thickest wall for pumping blood to the body? *(Left ventricle.)* Explain that heart valves permit blood to flow only in one direction: atrium to ventricle, ventricle to vessels.

L1 Class Activity

Instruct each student to draw a picture of the heart and to label the aorta, the ventricles, and the layers of heart muscle.

L2 Class Activity

Have each student take his or her pulse for one minute. Using that pulse reading, have each student determine how many times his or her heart beats per day, week, month, and year. Then tell the class the heart pumps an average of 5.3 quarts of blood every minute. Have students determine how many quarts of blood their hearts pump in a day, a week, and a month.

L1 Explaining

Tell students that in a single day a human heart beats about 100,000 times. Have students guess and then calculate their approximate number of heartbeats since they were born. *(In one year, the heart beats approximately 36,500,000 times. In one month, the heart beats approximately 3,000,000 times.)*

MORE ABOUT . . . . .

THE HEART. The heart is a muscle that responds to an increase in anaerobic and aerobic activity. An increase in aerobic activity makes the muscle stronger and more efficient.

The ventricles are made up of the stronger muscles of the heart. They force blood out of the heart to all parts of the body.

Because the heart is a muscle, it requires nutrients, oxygen, and removal of wastes. It has its own system of veins and arteries to do the job efficiently.

The heart responds to hormones by accelerating or decelerating its beating. Control of the beating mechanism is within the medulla of the brain. Drug overdose can disrupt this connection and cause death.

Encourage students with home computers to share this informative self-test with family members. Encourage students to follow up with a round-table discussion about lifestyle changes that may benefit the family as a whole.

LD Class Activity

Provide a labeled diagram of the heart, and have LD students write notes under each label.

L1 Class Activity

Students can simulate the work a heart does by squeezing a tennis ball 70 times in one minute. The force needed to squeeze the tennis ball is about the same as the force needed to squeeze blood from the heart, which the heart does about 70 times a minute.

L1 Discussing

Ask: What role does blood play in the body? *(It transports all the substances that the body needs to sustain life.)*

L1 Discussing

Pose these questions: Have you ever noticed your own blood clotting? When? *(Whenever your blood forms a scab.)* Ask students to describe what happens when blood clots.

L1 Class Activity

Introduce the class to the four blood types, classified by type of red cells, by writing (*A, B, AB,* and *O*) on the chalkboard. Then write *Rh-negative* and *Rh-positive* on the board, explaining that these are antibodies of blood. Have students list all the possible blood-type combinations. (A+, A–, etc.)

Do you know why your heart beats faster during physical activity? Take the Healthy Heart I.Q. Test online to check your knowledge in Web Links at **health.glencoe.com**.

▼ *Blood flows into the right and left atria of the heart and leaves the heart via the right and left ventricles.*

ACTIVITY *Identify the blood vessels that carry blood from the lungs to the heart and the vessels that carry blood from the heart to the lungs.*

Blood also plays an important role in your body's defense against infection.

About 55 percent of the total volume of blood is made up of **plasma,** *the fluid in which the other parts of blood are suspended.* Plasma, which is about 92 percent water, contains many important nutrients, salts, proteins, other chemicals, and blood cells. Blood cells include red blood cells, which make up about 40 percent of normal blood, and white blood cells and platelets, which together make up less than 5 percent of your blood's volume.

RED BLOOD CELLS

Red blood cells carry oxygen from the lungs to the body tissues, where the oxygen is exchanged for carbon dioxide. Each red blood cell contains **hemoglobin,** *the oxygen-carrying part of blood.* Hemoglobin is a protein compound that is rich in iron. It binds with oxygen in the lungs and releases the oxygen in the tissues. Hemoglobin is the pigment that gives blood its red color.

WHITE BLOOD CELLS

The principal role of white blood cells is to protect the body against infection and to fight infection when it occurs. White blood cells are larger than red blood cells, but there are far fewer of them. Production of these cells increases when there is infection in the body. Some types of white blood cells surround invading pathogens and ingest them. Others form the antibodies that make you immune to second attacks of diseases such as measles.

PULMONARY CIRCULATION

Right lung — Left lung
Pulmonary artery — Pulmonary artery
Capillaries
Pulmonary veins — Left atrium
Right atrium — Left ventricle
Right ventricle

MORE ABOUT . . . . .

THE BLOOD. Variation in ABO and Rhesus blood types is studied through immunological reactions, which can best be understood by considering a specific example.

If someone has type A blood, the red blood cells bear the A antigen and the serum contains anti-B antibodies. Someone with type B blood has the B antigen and anti-A antibodies.

When red blood cells with A antigen (from the type A individual) are mixed with serum containing anti-A antibodies (from the person with type B blood), an antigen-antibody reaction occurs. Pairs of antibodies and antigens each fit together like a key in a lock, leading to agglutination, or clumping, of the red blood cells.

Building Health Skills

Becoming Health Literate: Evaluating Sources

EVERY DAY you are subjected to a barrage of health information from various sources. Lately there has been much publicity about *psychoimmunology*—"thinking yourself well." "CANCER CURED BY THOUGHTS," shrieks a tabloid headline. "RESEARCHERS EVALUATE RELATIONSHIP BETWEEN EMOTIONS AND IMMUNE RESPONSE," a newspaper headline announces. In order for you to decide how valid the information provided by a news medium is, it is important to consider the source.

1. **Primary sources.** A primary source, such as a research report published in a scholarly journal, presents the findings of a scientific investigation reported by the researchers themselves.

2. **Newspaper articles.** These and articles in newsmagazines are secondhand reports written by reporters who have either interviewed researchers and/or patients. They may have also picked up information from another source, such as a wire service. News items generally identify the source of the information, give the credentials of people quoted, and provide background information.

3. **Television programs.** Whether specials or daily news shows, these may include interviews with researchers or with people claiming to have had personal experience on a subject.

4. **Tabloid articles.** These are usually sensationalistic. Sources may not be identified and generally cannot be checked or verified.

PLATELETS

Blood **platelets**, the smallest type of blood cell, are *the cells that prevent the body's loss of blood.* (Their name means "little plates.") Platelets initiate a chain reaction that causes blood to clot. When platelets come in contact with damaged blood vessel walls, they become sticky and clump at the site of the injury. Chemicals released by the platelets cause the blood to produce small fibers, called *fibrin*. The fibrin filaments trap the platelets along with red and white blood cells. The mass of fibrin, platelets, and red and white blood cells plug the injury and form a solid clot. The scab you see on a healing cut is evidence that a clot has formed.

Blood Vessels

Blood is distributed throughout the body through a network of vessels. There are more than 60,000 miles (96,540 km) of blood vessels in your body. They are divided mainly into three types.

SCHOOL-TO-CAREER

MEDICAL ASSISTANT. In an information-based, technologically advanced society, the tests doctors and hospitals run are ever more extensive, and the paperwork required by health care agencies is ever more complicated. More and more, medical assistants are needed to perform these tasks and free doctors and nurses to do the work only they are qualified to do. Medical assistants find career opportunities in hospitals, clinics, emergency centers, and private practice. There they may help physicians examine and treat patients, take blood pressure, check vital signs, and conduct laboratory tests. They may also apply bandages, administer EKG or X rays, answer phones, schedule appointments, keep records, and process insurance forms.

L1 Explaining

Explain that a person who has type O blood can donate blood to anyone, and a person with AB blood can receive anyone's blood—otherwise, it's important that individuals receive their own blood type during an emergency. Likewise, a person with Rh-negative should not be given Rh-positive blood. Describe the life-threatening consequences of receiving an incompatible blood transfusion due to rejection or clotting.

L2 Guest Speaker

Arrange for a representative from the local blood bank to speak to the class about the current available blood supply. Is it sufficient? insufficient? overabundant? Approximately how many people donate blood in a week? Are certain times of the year more likely to bring donations? Are certain times more likely to result in insufficient supplies? Ask students to summarize the presentation in writing.

L1 Discussing

Check with a school nurse regarding immunizations required for school attendance. Begin the discussion of the lymphatic system by asking students what immunization or booster shots they can remember having so that they could attend school. As each immunization is mentioned, ask what some of the basic symptoms of the disease are. It may become necessary for you to add information. Lead a discussion that helps students differentiate between natural and artificially acquired immunities.

THE CIRCULATORY SYSTEM

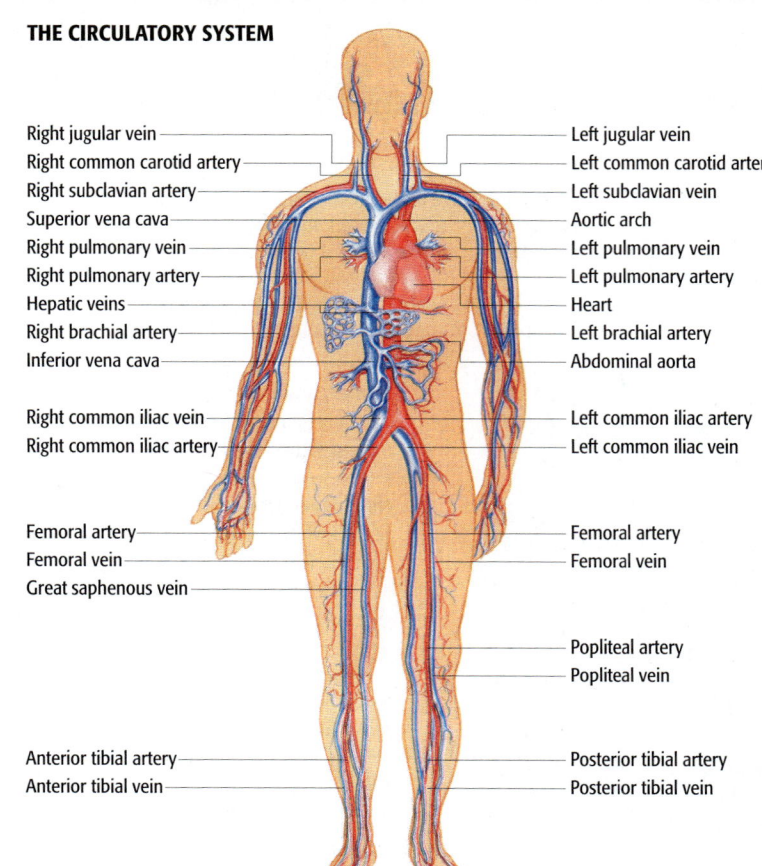

Right jugular vein
Right common carotid artery
Right subclavian artery
Superior vena cava
Right pulmonary vein
Right pulmonary artery
Hepatic veins
Right brachial artery
Inferior vena cava

Right common iliac vein
Right common iliac artery

Femoral artery
Femoral vein
Great saphenous vein

Anterior tibial artery
Anterior tibial vein

Left jugular vein
Left common carotid artery
Left subclavian vein
Aortic arch
Left pulmonary vein
Left pulmonary artery
Heart
Left brachial artery
Abdominal aorta

Left common iliac artery
Left common iliac vein

Femoral artery
Femoral vein

Popliteal artery
Popliteal vein

Posterior tibial artery
Posterior tibial vein

▶ *The circulatory system pumps blood from the heart to the body's cells to provide oxygen and nutrients and to remove waste products.*
ACTIVITY *Explain the functions of arteries, capillaries, and veins.*

ARTERIES

The largest blood vessels, the **arteries**, are *the vessels that carry blood away from the heart.* Pulmonary arteries carry blood from the right ventricle of the heart to the lungs. Systemic arteries carry blood from the left ventricle of the heart through the aorta (the largest artery in the body) to all parts of the body except the lungs.

Arteries are flexible tubes with a smooth inner lining, a thick, muscular middle layer, and a tough, fibrous outer covering. An artery's thick walls enable it to withstand the high blood pressure it is subjected to every time the heart beats.

Smaller vessels called *arterioles* branch directly off an artery. The arterioles connect to even smaller blood vessels called capillaries.

CAPILLARIES

The smallest blood vessels, the **capillaries** (KAP-uh-lair-eez), are *the vessels that carry blood between arterioles and small vessels called*

CURRICULUM CONNECTIONS

HISTORY. Claudius Galenus, known to the world of science as Galen, is often called the father of experimental physiology. Born in the second century A.D. in a city that is now in Turkey, Galen became a physician to the gladiators, and, eventually, to the Roman emperor Marcus Aurelius. Since Roman laws prevented him from dissecting humans, Galen used the bodies of monkeys and apes to learn about body systems and functions. One discovery was that arteries carry blood, not air as had been previously thought. Though many of Galen's observations were later disproved, his theories were believed and accepted for nearly 1,200 years.

venules. They form a fine network throughout the body's organs and tissues. Some capillaries are 50 times thinner than a strand of hair. It is through the thin capillary walls that nutrients and oxygen pass from the blood to body cells, and waste products move from the cells into the blood.

Capillaries are not always open to blood flow. They open and close in response to the body's need for oxygen and nutrients. The opening and closing of capillaries in the skin plays an important role in regulating the body's **temperature**.

VEINS

The system of capillaries leads into tiny vessels called *venules.* The venules join to form **veins,** *the vessels that return deoxygenated blood toward the heart from the body's organs and tissues.* There are two main exceptions to this definition: The pulmonary veins in the chest carry oxygenated blood from the lungs to the left side of the heart, and the portal vein carries nutrient-rich blood from the intestines to the liver.

Like arteries, veins have a smooth inner lining, a muscular middle layer, and a fibrous outer covering. However, blood pressure in veins is much lower than it is in arteries. The walls of veins are thinner, less flexible, less muscular, and weaker than the walls of arteries. The inner lining of many veins forms valves that help direct the flow of blood. These valves prevent blood from flowing back into the capillaries. Blood is helped on its way by pressure on the vessel walls from the contraction of surrounding muscles.

The Lymphatic System

Your body's circulatory system is supported by a second network known as the *lymphatic system.* This system serves two functions. It drains tissue fluid back into the bloodstream, and it fights **infection**. All body tissues are bathed in a watery fluid that comes from the blood. Much of this fluid returns to the blood through the walls of the capillaries. The remainder is carried to the heart through the lymphatic system. In a sense, the lymphatic system is your body's *second* circulatory system. It does not, however, have a central pump like the heart. Lymphatic fluid is circulated by movement of the body's muscles.

Lymph

The fluid that the lymphatic system transports is **lymph,** *a clear yellow fluid that fills the spaces around body cells.* Lymph is made up of proteins, fats, and **lymphocytes,** *white blood cells*

hotlink

temperature For more information on the role of the skin in regulating temperature, see Chapter 15, page 341.

infection For more information on the process by which the body fights infection, see Chapter 28, page 621.

THE LYMPHATIC SYSTEM

Tonsils

Thymus gland
Lymphatic duct

Lymphatic vessel
Spleen

Lymph node

Lymphatic vessel

⚠ *Two separate systems transport fluids throughout your body.*

ACTIVITY *Name two similarities and two differences between the circulatory and lymphatic systems.*

L2 ## Discussing

Discuss the following: What are lymphocytes? What is their relationship to the body's immune system? What are lymph nodes?

L2 ## Discussing

Ask students what the difference is between the actions of lymphocytes and antibodies in fighting infections (bacterial and viral).

L3 ## Class Activity

Select students to give an illustrated report contrasting the body's primary means of transporting oxygen, nutrients, and cell wastes with the lymphatic system—its secondary circulatory network.

L2 ## Community Involvement

Have students find out what immunization programs are sponsored by the health department in their community. What is the cost to those being immunized? How does this compare with the cost for those same immunizations at a doctor's office?

L2 ## Reading

Have students review current magazines for information about ways to strengthen the body's immune system. Ask: Why is this important? Are there ways you can incorporate this information into your own lives?

L1 ## Personal Involvement

Have students develop a system to use in keeping personal medical records.

MORE ABOUT . . . . .

LYMPHATIC SYSTEM CARE. Doctors have routinely checked around the neck, in the groin, and under the arms for lumps, but patients often didn't know why. Now patients are assuming an increasing role toward maintaining their health. They are asking for instructions on how to check for lumps in lymph nodes. Once detected, they know to return to their doctor to see if treatment is needed.

Doctors may not be able to determine if a lump in a lymph node is an indicator of a more serious problem such as cancer. They may need to take a biopsy of the tissue. Though the prospect of even outpatient surgery is very frightening, doctors would rather the patient not neglect any lump. Early diagnosis could save a patient's life.

ASSESS

EVALUATING THE LESSON

Assign and discuss the Lesson 1 Review; then administer, grade, and discuss the *Lesson 53 Quiz* in the TCR. 👈

RETEACHING

- Ask students to write questions about the lesson's key points. Compile the questions and use these as a basis for discussion.
- Ask students to complete *Reteaching Activity 53* in the TCR. 👈
- Use *Transparency 63* to review the cardiovascular system. 🧪

ENRICHMENT

Ask students to investigate how blood type affects a potential organ recipient's chances of acquiring an organ for transplantation. Is any one blood type more common than others? What are the advantages of being one blood type over another for potential organ recipients?

CLOSE

Write the lesson's major concepts on numbered, separate slips of paper. Place the slips into a box, and let each student draw one. Going in numerical order, have students define and summarize the concept written on the slip of paper they selected.

---

that protect the body against pathogens—disease-carrying agents. There are two main types of lymphocytes, B cells and T cells.

B CELLS

About 10 percent of lymphocytes are B cells. When B cells encounter pathogens, they are stimulated to enlarge and multiply. The B cells turn into cells called *plasma cells*. Plasma cells produce antibodies that destroy or neutralize invading pathogens.

T CELLS

There are two main groups of T cells, killer cells and helper cells. Killer T cells are stimulated to multiply when abnormal body cells are present. They attach to these cells and release toxins that help destroy the abnormal cells. **Helper T cells** aid the activity of the B cells and killer T cells and control other aspects of the body's immune system.

Structure of the Lymphatic System

Lymphatic vessels are distributed throughout the body much the same as blood vessels are. They form a network that carries lymph to two lymph ducts, one in the neck area and the other in the chest area. These ducts empty into veins. At certain places along the lymphatic vessels, lymph passes through lymph nodes. These are masses of tissue that filter lymph before it returns to the blood. The nodes act as a barrier to the spread of infection, destroying or filtering out bacteria before they can pass into the blood.

h⊙t link

helper T cells For more information on the relationship between helper T cells and HIV infection, see Chapter 30, page 658.

LESSON 1 *Review*

Reviewing Facts and Vocabulary

1. What are the chambers of the human heart, and how do they function?
2. What is the function of blood?
3. What substances are carried through the body in plasma?
4. Describe the functions of lymphocytes.

Thinking Critically

5. *Analyzing.* Why do you think the body has more red blood cells than white blood cells?
6. *Comparing and Contrasting.* Compare the functions of the circulatory system with those of the lymphatic system.

Applying Health Skills

7. *In Your School.* With several classmates, purchase a beef, calf, or lamb heart and a chicken heart from a local butcher or supermarket meat department. Looking down from the top, try to identify the main blood vessels. Carefully cut the beef heart in half lengthwise. See whether you can find the four chambers, the valves, and the main arteries and veins. Do the same with the chicken heart. What is the main difference between the two hearts? Share your findings with classmates.

Lesson 1 Review

Answers to Reviewing Facts and Vocabulary

1. Left atrium, left ventricle, right atrium, and right ventricle: They regulate the flow and pressure of blood in the heart.
2. Blood transports oxygen, hormones, and nutrients, carries away wastes, and carries white cells that protect the body from infection.
3. Plasma carries nutrients, salts, proteins, other chemicals, and blood cells.
4. Lymphocytes protect the body against pathogens.

Answers to Thinking Critically

5. Answers should mention the differing functions of the red and white blood cells.
6. The circulatory system carries nutrients, hormones, gases, and the waste products of cells. The lymphatic system returns tissue fluid to the bloodstream and fights infection.

Care and Problems of the Circulatory System

Some highway problems, such as rush-hour congestion, are unavoidable. Measures such as carpooling can be taken to reduce or control these situations. In the case of your circulatory system, some problems may be inherited. Most problems of the circulatory system however, can be controlled through behavior.

HEALTH TERM

congenital

HEALTH CONCEPTS

- Eating right, exercising regularly, and getting adequate rest are steps you can take to care for your circulatory and lymphatic systems.
- Taking good care of your circulatory system can help reduce risk factors related to environment and heredity.

Blood pressure cuff

hotlink

smoking For more information on the dangers of smoking and other forms of tobacco use, see Chapter 24, page 533.

weight For more information on managing your weight, see Chapter 6, page 133.

Care of the Circulatory and Lymphatic Systems

Most of the risk factors related to problems with your circulatory system are within your control. Your health choices and behaviors affect its health. You probably know that **smoking** puts added stress on your circulatory system. Nicotine in cigarettes increases blood pressure and heart rate by narrowing the arteries. Not smoking—as well as avoiding secondhand smoke from smokers—is a healthy choice for you. It is also important for you to maintain an appropriate **weight**. Being overweight is linked to high blood pressure and coronary heart disease.

LESSON 2   CARE AND PROBLEMS OF THE CIRCULATORY SYSTEM   **395**

Care and Problems of the Circulatory System

FOCUS

LESSON OBJECTIVES

After studying this lesson, students should be able to

- identify risk factors related to the circulatory system.
- describe problems that affect the cardiovascular system.
- describe problems that affect the lymphatic system.

MOTIVATOR

Write the following on the chalkboard for students to work on while attendance is being taken: *List as many diseases and disorders of the cardiovascular system as you can.*

INTRODUCING THE LESSON

Refer to the Motivator. Have students share their lists. Tell them that many of the diseases and disorders of the cardiovascular system have very serious consequences. Sickle-cell anemia, leukemia, and hemophilia are blood diseases. Heart murmur, varicose veins, and thrombosis affect the heart and blood vessels. Anemia is a blood disorder. Tell students that this lesson allows them to take a more detailed look at these diseases and disorders.

INTRODUCING HEALTH TERMS

- Introduce the term *congenital* as meaning occurring at birth. Explain that this lesson will also discuss heart diseases that people are born with.
- Ask students to complete Vocabulary Activity 17 and Chapter Study Guide 17 in the *Student Workbook.*

Chapter 17   **395**

TEACH

L1 Discussing

Encourage students to share all the ideas they have for preventing heart disease. Record their ideas on the chalkboard. Ask if these are things they are doing now so they will not have heart problems later in life. If not, why not?

L2 Class Activity

Use American Heart Association materials to assess students' risk of heart disease in the future.

L3 Class Activity

Ask students to bring in a selection of their favorite family recipes. Convert these recipes into ones that promote heart health by lowering or changing the amount or form of fat, sugar, and salt. Have students try out the revised recipes and share the results with the class.

L2 Discussing

Ask students why blood pressure is higher in the arteries. (*Blood must be pumped through the arteries to all parts of the body, which requires force. However, this pressure must be greatly reduced by the time blood reaches the capillaries because they could not withstand the pressure. As blood returns to larger veins, muscular activity is necessary to maintain blood flow.*) It is important that students be able to explain this relationship between the muscular system and the circulatory system. They should also be able to draw conclusions as to why larger arteries are thicker than capillaries.

hotlink

aerobic exercise For more information on aerobic exercise and its contribution to total fitness, see Chapter 3, page 57.

▼ *Aerobic exercise increases your heart rate and promotes the health of your heart and blood vessels.*

ACTIVITY *Make a list of aerobic activities you enjoy that increase your pulse rate.*

Care is the same for both the circulatory and lymphatic systems. This means making sure that you care for your total health by exercising regularly, eating healthfully, and getting enough sleep—at least seven to eight hours a night during the teen years. A program of regular exercise—especially **aerobic exercise** for at least 20 minutes three times a week—will strengthen your heart, making it work more efficiently, and improve your circulation. Limiting your intake of fried foods and other foods high in fat, cholesterol, and salt will protect your heart and blood vessels. Finally, having regular medical checkups enables your physician to monitor the health of your circulatory system, keep you up to date on your immunizations, and encourage healthy behaviors.

Blood Pressure

Blood pressure is the force of the blood in the main arteries. It rises and falls as the heart and muscles of your body cope with varying demands, including stress, exercise, and sleep.

Each time the ventricles contract, blood surges through the arteries with so much force that the artery walls bulge. At this point, arterial pressure is at its greatest and is called *systolic pressure*. As the ventricles relax and refill with blood, arterial pressure is at its lowest and is called *diastolic pressure*.

As part of a regular checkup for people over age 50, an electrocardiogram (ECG or EKG) may be taken to detect signs of heart disease. During the teen years, one way that a health care professional can monitor the health of your heart is to check your blood pressure.

To measure blood pressure, a health care professional wraps a soft cuff around your upper arm and inflates it until it is tight enough to stop the flow of blood. As air is slowly released from the cuff, the health professional uses a stethoscope to listen for the sound of blood as it moves through the main artery again. This is recorded as the systolic pressure. It is the upper number of the fraction representing your blood pressure and is usually between 110 and 140. He or she then deflates the cuff further and listens until the beat disappears and the blood flows steadily through the now open artery. This is the diastolic pressure. It is the lower number of the fraction and is usually between 70 and 90.

COOPERATIVE LEARNING

VITAMIN E. Direct students to examine reports on the role of vitamin E in reducing heart disease. Have students work in pairs to conduct research and determine the amount of vitamin E that has been correlated with lower incidence of heart disease. Then assign one partner to use a nutrition chart to plan a day's meals that supply the recommended dietary intake of vitamin E without exceeding the recommended dietary guidelines for fat. The other partner is to attempt to plan a day's meals that supply as much vitamin E as has been shown to reduce heart disease without exceeding dietary fat guidelines. Partners should then discuss whether a vitamin E supplement is advisable. Have partners discuss whether they would rather take a dietary supplement.

Circulatory System Problems

With proper care, some problems of the heart and circulatory system can be avoided. Some of these avoidable conditions are covered in Chapter 31. Other problems are explained below.

Congenital Heart Disease

Before birth, the heart begins as a single tube. It enlarges and divides into chambers as the fetus grows. This process involves a progression of developmental steps. A disruption in the process can result in a defect in the heart. Such a defect is called **congenital**, which means *occurring at birth*.

Congenital heart disease covers a wide range of conditions. There may be a hole between two chambers of the heart. The valves may not function properly, or there may be a blockage of the blood flow. The defect may be in the blood vessels leading into or away from the heart. Most cases can be treated with surgery.

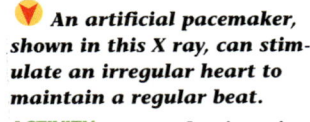

▼ *An artificial pacemaker, shown in this X ray, can stimulate an irregular heart to maintain a regular beat.*
ACTIVITY *Locate the tiny wire leading from the pacemaker to the heart.*

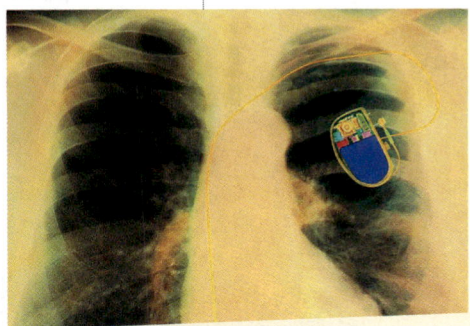

up|date
▶*Looking at Technology*

Internal Cardiac Defibrillator and Pacemaker Module

When the heart's natural pacemaker is faulty, a surgeon can implant an artificial pacemaker that supplies electrical impulses to the heart to maintain a regular heartbeat. The device may be implanted below the collarbone or into a pocket created under the skin of the abdomen. A wire from the pacemaker goes down through the vena cava into the part of the heart muscle to be stimulated. Alternatively, an electrode may be attached to the outer surface of the part of the heart muscle to be stimulated. Modern microelectronic circuits require little power, and the lithium batteries that power them have a long life. Battery replacement, when required, involves a minor operation.

Disruption of the nerve impulses through the muscle wall of a heart chamber can cause fibrillation of the heart—rapid contractions of individual muscle fibers. As a result, the chamber no longer contracts as a single unit and produces a rapid, irregular rhythm. An implanted defibrillator sends bursts of electricity through the heart to convert fibrillation back into a normal, regular heartbeat.

Combined into a single unit, defibrillator-pacemaker modules can enable a person with life-threatening heart rhythm disturbances to lead a normal life.

MORE ABOUT . . . . .

HEART DISEASE. Radiating pain that becomes gradually stronger, focusing on the left side of the body, is a sure sign of a heart attack. If the pain fades and recurs, it is probably angina, not a heart attack.

Angina is the body's way of signaling that something is happening to the heart. It is a warning that a heart attack may be next. During angina, the heart muscle cells are being deprived of oxygen-carrying blood. Years of overeating or eating high-fat foods may be the cause for many angina attacks. Such diets cause plaque and cholesterol to line the interior of the coronary arteries.

L2 Class Activity

Ask a cardiologist for a tape of the sounds of a heart that is not functioning correctly. Play the tape for the class and have students compare these sounds to healthy heart sounds. Ask students what a doctor can tell from listening to heart sounds through the stethoscope. Ask: What are the limitations of checking your own heart sounds?

L2 Discussing

Ask students if they know of anyone who is likely to develop varicose veins. Encourage them to explain their answers.

L1 Explaining

Describe the effects of iron deficiency anemia. Ask if a person can self-diagnose anemia based on his or her well-being.

L2 Guest Speaker

Invite a representative from the Leukemia Society to visit the classroom and talk about the disease, its causes, treatment, and current research.

L1 Explaining

The gene for hemophilia is on the X chromosome. For females to have the disease, they must inherit two copies of the gene, which is unlikely because it is rare. Males need to inherit only one copy of the gene, so hemophilia is much more common in males than in females.

Heart Murmur

Have you ever used a stethoscope to listen to your heart? Blood passing through a healthy heart makes a strong, clear *lub-dub* sound. A heart murmur is an abnormal sound. The major cause is a defective valve that is too narrow causing blood to be pushed through the restricted opening with more force than normal. A valve that does not close properly allows blood to leak back through it. Both situations cause the sound labeled a "murmur." Most murmurs are slight and do not need correction. Others may require surgical treatment.

Varicose Veins

Varicose veins are swollen and enlarged veins, especially in the legs. They develop when the valves in the veins are weakened and cannot close tightly to prevent the backflow of blood. Blood then collects in the veins. This condition may affect men and women of all ages. Exercise is a means of both preventing and treating varicose veins. In severe cases, surgical removal of the veins may be necessary.

Anemia

Anemia is a condition in which the concentration of hemoglobin in the blood is below normal levels. With a low level of hemoglobin, body cells do not receive a sufficient amount of oxygen. The most common cause of anemia is a deficiency of iron in the diet. This can be corrected by eating foods that are rich in iron, such as leafy green vegetables, dried fruits, or enriched cereals, or by taking iron supplements.

▲ *Green, leafy vegetables such as spinach, cabbage, and kale are rich in iron.*
ACTIVITY *What other iron-rich foods can you eat to avoid getting anemia?*

Leukemia

Leukemia is any of several types of cancer resulting from abnormal production of white blood cells in the bone marrow. The abnormal cells may spill into the blood, enter other organs, and interfere with their function. Far worse, the abnormal cells prevent the bone marrow from producing red blood cells, platelets, and normal white blood cells. There is a risk of death from overwhelming infection or blood loss. Bone marrow transplants have been successful in treating some types of leukemia. Chemotherapy and radiation are also used to slow down the disease process.

Hemophilia

Hemophilia is an inherited bleeding disorder caused by a deficiency of a blood protein (called *factor VIII*) that is essential to the process of blood clotting. This causes the blood to clot very slowly or not at all. Persons with hemophilia suffer recurrent bleeding, most often into their joints. Bleeding may occur after injury or spontaneously with no apparent cause.

398 CHAPTER 17 YOUR CIRCULATORY AND RESPIRATORY SYSTEMS

HEALTH LITERACY

CRITICAL THINKER AND PROBLEM SOLVER. Provide information about the antigens and antibodies in type A and type B blood, and how blood is tested for type using antigen-antibody reactions. After they learn about antigens and antibodies in type A and type B blood, have them explain why type O individuals are universal donors, and type AB are universal recipients, given compatible RH factors. Encourage them to research the risks of receiving donated blood. Have them examine strategies people use when they are anticipating an operation that will require transfusions. For example, some people plan long in advance, donating pints of their own blood. Others have friends and family, of compatible blood types and known lifestyles, donate blood for their use during the operation.

Lymphatic System Problems

Several problems can affect the lymphatic system. Some can usually be cured. Others have no cure.

Immune Deficiency

Normally, your body protects itself against anything that might enter it and cause it harm. Sometimes, however, the immune system's defenses fail to fight infection. Such an immune deficiency disorder may be the result of a congenital or inherited defect. Often it is the result of an acquired disease that damages the immune system's function. For example, HIV, the virus that causes AIDS, destroys the T cells that fight pathogens. The result of an immune deficiency disorder is infections that recur and are hard to treat.

Hodgkin's Disease

Hodgkin's disease, also known as Hodgkin's lymphoma, is cancer of lymph tissue, which is found mainly in the lymph nodes and spleen. The cancer cells spread quickly throughout the lymphatic system. Radiation therapy can usually successfully treat early stages.

Tonsillitis

The function of your tonsils is to help protect the upper respiratory tract against infection. However, sometimes the tonsils themselves become infected by the organisms they are fighting. Tonsillitis occurs mainly in childhood but sometimes affects teens. The tonsils become inflamed and tender, and symptoms include a sore throat and fever. Tonsillitis may be treated with antibiotics. Once common, surgical removal of the tonsils is rarely done today.

Did You Know?

➤ Many infections associated with the common cold are caused by a large group of viruses called rhinoviruses.

➤ The incubation period of the common cold is usually 18 to 48 hours. Colds often last between 4 and 10 days.

➤ A study at the University of Virginia suggests that colds are more likely spread by skin-to-skin contact (fingers and hands) than through sneezes or coughs. Hand washing might be the best preventive measure to protect yourself from cold viruses.

LESSON 2 Review

Reviewing Facts and Vocabulary

1. Name and define two problems of the circulatory system.
2. Explain how a defective valve in the heart could affect blood flow.
3. What makes an immune deficiency disorder so dangerous?

Thinking Critically

4. *Analyzing.* How might a heart or circulatory disorder affect your life?
5. *Evaluating.* Categorize the following food items as being generally healthy or unhealthy for your heart: potato chips, broccoli, cheeseburgers, donuts, coffee, fish, carrots, butter.

Applying Health Skills

6. *In Your School.* Have your blood pressure checked in class by the school nurse. What is the average blood pressure for the class? How does the blood pressure of students who exercise regularly differ from that of students who do not?

Lesson 2 Review

Answers to Reviewing Facts and Vocabulary

1. Any two: Congenital heart disease, heart murmur, varicose veins, anemia, leukemia, and hemophilia. For definitions, see pages 397–398.
2. A disruption in the function of a valve disrupts the efficient movement of blood through the heart.
3. The body becomes susceptible to disease-causing pathogens that are present everywhere in the environment.

Answers to Thinking Critically

4. Any disruption of the efficient, healthy flow of blood and fluids in the body undermines body systems and can cause weakness and illness.
5. Healthful: broccoli, fish, carrots. Unhealthful: potato chips, cheeseburgers, donuts, coffee, butter.

ASSESS

EVALUATING THE LESSON

Assign and discuss the Lesson 2 Review; then administer, grade, and discuss the *Lesson 54 Quiz* in the TCR. 🖝

RETEACHING

- Write or call your local chapter of the American Heart Association and ask for free pamphlets about cardiovascular diseases and caring for the cardiovascular system. Ask each student to select one pamphlet and rewrite it in his or her own words. Ask students to display both the original and their rewrite.
- Ask students to complete *Reteaching Activity 54* in the TCR. 🖝

ENRICHMENT

- Ask students to research bone marrow transplants. Why are they needed? What does bone marrow do? Is the surgery usually successful? Who can donate bone marrow? Instruct students to summarize their findings in writing.
- Give students background on the evolution of bio-parts replacement as a means of extending life by having them complete *Enrichment Activity 17*, "A Look at Organ Transplants," in the TCR. 🖝

CLOSE

Tell students they have studied the cardiovascular and lymphatic systems. Explain that a third system, the respiratory system, is also associated with these systems. The combined systems are sometimes referred to as the cardiorespiratory system. Inform them they will study the respiratory system in the next lesson.

The Respiratory System

LESSON 3

FOCUS

LESSON OBJECTIVES

After studying this lesson, students should be able to

- explain the function of respiration.
- describe the exchange of oxygen and carbon dioxide.
- identify ways to care for the respiratory system.
- describe problems of the respiratory system.

MOTIVATOR

Write the following on the chalkboard for students to work on while attendance is being taken: *What is the difference between breathing and respiration?*

INTRODUCING THE LESSON

Discuss student responses to the Motivator. Point out that respiration encompasses breathing and involves the overall exchange of gases by the body. Explain that breathing properly is critical to respiration.

INTRODUCING HEALTH TERMS

- Have students make flash cards for the vocabulary terms. On one side, have them write the word. On the other side, have them identify the body system, the definition, and a page reference.
- Ask students to complete Vocabulary Activity 17 and Chapter Study Guide 17 in the *Student Workbook.* ☞

The Respiratory System

While reading this paragraph, you will inhale and exhale four or five times. This will happen without your even thinking about it. Your body's respiratory system, whose principal organ is the lungs, takes care of this for you. Understanding how the lungs function will help you to keep your respiratory system healthy.

HEALTH TERMS

respiration
diaphragm
pharynx
trachea
bronchi
larynx
pleurisy
asthma

HEALTH CONCEPTS

- Respiration—the exchange of gases between your body and your environment—is essential to life.
- Regular exercise and avoidance of pollutants, especially the smoke from tobacco products, help keep the respiratory system healthy.

Functions of the Respiratory System

As its name implies, the main function of the respiratory system is **respiration**—*the exchange of gases between your body and your environment.* There are two major parts to respiration, external and internal. External respiration is the exchange of oxygen and carbon dioxide between the blood and the air in the lungs. As you breathe, you inhale air that contains oxygen into your lungs. Oxygen moves from your lungs to your blood, and carbon dioxide moves from your blood to your lungs. Internal respiration is the exchange of gases between the blood and the cells of the body. Oxygen moves from your blood to your cells, and carbon dioxide moves from your cells to your blood. Without oxygen you could live only a few minutes.

Lesson 3 Resources

TEACHER'S CLASSROOM RESOURCES

☞ **Concept Map** Activity 55
☞ **Decision-Making** Activity 17
☞ **Health Lab** 17
☞ **Lesson 55 Quiz**
☞ **Lesson Plan 55**
☞ **Reteaching** Activity 55

STUDENT WORKBOOK

☞ **Applying Health Skills** 55
☞ **Chapter Study Guide** 17
☞ **Vocabulary** Activity 17

TRANSPARENCIES

🖎 **Transparency 65**

Structure of the Respiratory System

The main structures within the respiratory system are the lungs and structures within the nose and mouth. These are supported by the **diaphragm**, *a muscle that separates the chest and abdominal cavities.* Without the diaphragm, respiration would be impossible.

The Lungs

The principal organ of your respiratory system is your lungs. They take in oxygen from the air you inhale and return carbon dioxide to the air when you exhale. Every day your lungs take in enough air to fill a fairly large room.

In a real sense, your lungs are like the bellows used to fan the flames of fires in days of old. Like a bellows, lungs rely on external muscle power to do their job. Whereas arm muscles provided the muscle power for bellows, lungs get their power from the diaphragm.

THE BREATHING PROCESS

When you inhale, your rib muscles and diaphragm contract. The diaphragm moves downward, and the ribs are pulled upward and outward. This action enlarges the chest cavity, creating lower pressure in the lungs. Air rushes into the lungs to equalize the pressure between the lungs and the outside environment. The reverse happens when you exhale. The diaphragm relaxes, moving upward, and the ribs move inward, increasing the pressure within the lungs. Air moves from the higher pressure in the lungs to the lower pressure of the outside environment.

STRUCTURE OF THE LUNGS

Each lung is divided into sections called *lobes.* There are three lobes in the right lung and two lobes in the left lung. The airways that lead into the lungs divide and subdivide to form a network of tubes called *bronchioles.* At the end of each bronchiole is a cluster of thin-walled air sacs called *alveoli,* covered with a vast network of capillaries. Thin capillary walls and equally thin alveolar walls allow the exchange of air and carbon dioxide to take place.

▼ *The alveoli in the lungs are surrounded by a network of capillaries. External respiration takes place in the alveoli.*

ACTIVITY *Make a flowchart showing the movement of air into and out of the lungs.*

THE LUNGS

- Branch of pulmonary artery
- Branch of pulmonary vein
- Bronchiole
- Capillary
- Alveolus
- Bronchus

TEACH

L2 Discussing

Help the class compare the organs of the respiratory system to a tree. Ask: What are the similarities? differences?

L1 Discussing

Ask students to list conditions and situations that can affect the proper functioning of the respiratory system. What can cause problems with the functioning of the respiratory system? *(Examples of conditions and situations are smog, pollution, infections, allergies, smoking, heredity, genetic defects, drug abuse—particularly cocaine.)*

L1 Class Activity

Have students trace the path of air from outside the body to the alveoli, describing what happens along the way. Then, using what was learned in the discussion on blood, have them continue to trace the path of oxygen to a body cell.

L1 Discussing

Ask students to describe the shape of the lobes of the lungs. Emphasize that there are three lobes on the right (upper, middle, and lower), but only two on the left (upper and lower) due to the placement of the heart. Allow students to identify how the lungs are protected by the body. *(Rib cage.)*

L2 Health Lab

Distribute *Health Lab 17* and have students investigate pulse and respiration rates. ☞

Posture and Breathing

keeping Fit

Talk students through the breathing process so that they can feel what is taking place. Have students sit erect with their backs straight and heads up. Ask them to take slow, deep breaths. Provide the following description: Feel the air entering the body through the nasal cavity. As you inhale, the diaphragm is lowered and the ribs are pulled upward and outward, enlarging the chest cavity. As you exhale, the diaphragm rises and the ribs move inward, forcing air out of the mouth and nose.

L1 Lab

Have students compare their lung capacities by taking in as much air as they can and exhaling into balloons. Compare sizes of the balloons.

L1 Class Activity

Help students record their voices into a tape recorder by saying their names. Listen to the replay and discuss why the voices sound different from one another.

L1 Discussing

Discuss the disorders of the respiratory system, emphasizing connections with smoking, especially in regard to chronic bronchitis and pulmonary emphysema.

L1 Demonstrating

Using a cranial model, detail for the class the location of the respiratory organs in the head. Clarify the size and shape of the sinus cavities.

L1 Community Involvement

Encourage students to promote the annual "Great American Smokeout" within the school and the community. Call the American Lung Association for details.

UPPER RESPIRATORY SYSTEM

▶ *The air you breathe is cleaned, moistened, and warmed as it moves through the upper respiratory system.*
ACTIVITY *Create a drawing that shows, without using words, what makes the upper respiratory system so vulnerable to infection.*

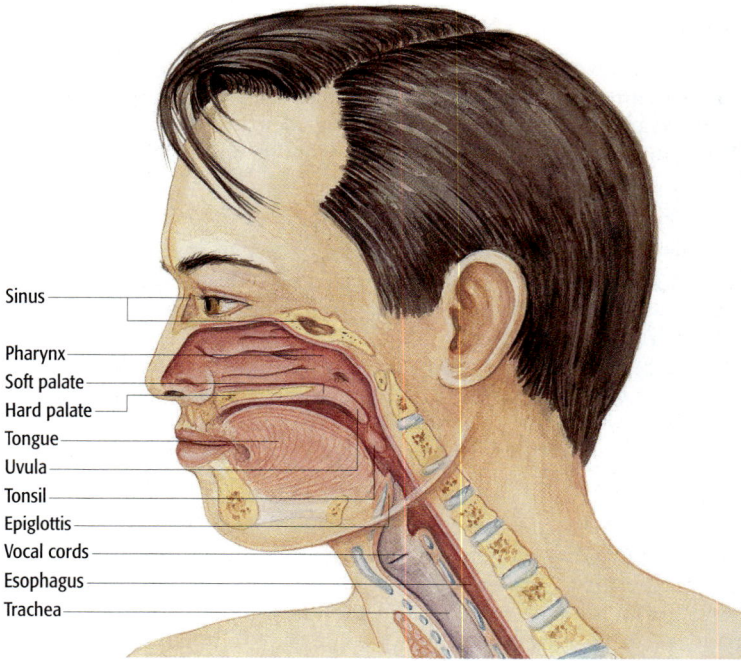

Sinus
Pharynx
Soft palate
Hard palate
Tongue
Uvula
Tonsil
Epiglottis
Vocal cords
Esophagus
Trachea

keeping Fit

Posture and Breathing

"Stand up straight! Don't slouch!" You may have felt annoyed if you were ever told this, yet it is good advice when it comes to breathing. When you stand erect, sit erect, or walk erect, you give the breathing mechanisms in your body the best opportunity to do their work. In order to work properly, your lungs need room to expand. This means that your ribs must be free to move upward and outward and your diaphragm downward as you inhale. By slouching, you hinder effective breathing.

Practice sitting with your back straight in a chair that supports your head and back. Stand with your head up, neck straight, shoulders down and back, and stomach and buttocks in, but hold yourself naturally, not stiffly. Do you notice how much more air you can take in than when you slouch?

Other Respiratory Structures

Air needs a way to get into your lungs in the first place. Two points of entry are your nose and your mouth. From a biological standpoint, the nose is better suited to this purpose. Whereas air entering the mouth goes directly to the lungs, air that enters through the nose is filtered and cleaned by mucous membranes and tiny hairs called cilia.

From your nose, air moves through the **pharynx** (FAIR-inks), or *throat,* and into the **trachea** (TRAY-kee-uh), or *windpipe.* Like the nose, the trachea is also lined with a mucous membrane and cilia. These form a second line of defense to trap foreign particles and keep them from entering the lungs. Air completes its journey to the lungs through the **bronchi** (BRAHN-kye), *the airways that connect the trachea to the lungs.*

The Larynx and the Epiglottis

On its journey to your lungs, air passes over two structures that are not directly related to inspiration—the part of respiration in which oxygen is taken in—but that are nonetheless important. One of these is the **larynx** (LAIR-inks), or *voice box.* The larynx contains two fibrous sheets of tissue known as the vocal cords. As air passes over these cords, the cords vibrate and produce sound. Without them, speech is not possible.

PERSONAL HEALTH

DEEP BREATHING AND ITS BENEFITS. Professionals such as voice teachers, yoga practitioners, many exercise coaches, and people who teach stress management say most people breathe too shallowly. They believe in the value of slow, deep breathing from the diaphragm or abdomen. Suggest that students study a system of breathing techniques and exercises taken from a class or book on yoga, speech therapy, voice training, or stress management. Have them examine the physical, mental, and emotional benefits of systematic diaphragm or abdominal breathing, as well as each breathing technique they learn. Encourage them to choose a few breathing exercises to practice each day.

Air also passes over the epiglottis, a flap of cartilage in front of the entrance to the larynx. At rest, the epiglottis is open to allow air to pass into the lungs. When you swallow, it closes to prevent food and liquid from being inhaled. Have you ever swallowed something that "went down the wrong pipe"? That is exactly what it did! Your epiglottis failed to close properly, allowing food or drink to enter your trachea.

Care of the Respiratory System

The respiratory system is highly susceptible to infection from both bacteria and viruses. Your hands are a carrier of disease organisms. To reduce the risk of infection—such as from the common cold—avoid putting your hands up to your nose and mouth, something people often do without thinking. It is vital to develop an awareness of this habit and to do it less. Remember also that washing your hands often is important.

The respiratory system is sensitive to pollutants such as tobacco smoke. Avoiding polluted air—as well as never smoking yourself—helps promote the health of your respiratory system.

A regular program of exercise helps keep the lungs working efficiently. Exercise strengthens the lungs and helps keep the other parts of the respiratory system clear.

▲ Bicycling in fresh air is a good way to strengthen the lungs.

ACTIVITY Name two other steps you can take to care for your respiratory system.

Respiratory System Problems

As you have learned, the respiratory system is a common site of infection. Pathogens have easy access into the body through the mouth and nose. Colds and sore throats are common problems with the upper respiratory tract. More serious respiratory infections are those that affect the lower respiratory tract, such as those described below.

Bronchitis

Bronchitis is an inflammation of the bronchi. The main symptoms are wheezing, shortness of breath, and coughing. Bronchitis can be either acute or chronic. Both types are more common in smokers and in areas with high pollution.

Acute bronchitis comes on suddenly and usually clears up within a short time. It is usually a complication of a viral infection such as a cold or the flu.

Chronic bronchitis is a longer-lasting, recurring disease that can get progressively worse. Most important in the treatment of chronic

L3 ## Researching

Suggest students investigate the possible environmental causes of asthma. Ask: What are the latest theories? Who is most vulnerable to this disease? What are some of the public health approaches being tested to address these environmental causes?

L1 ## Discussing

Skin testing for tuberculosis is routinely done in many communities. Ask: What are the implications of a positive test? How is the current treatment for tuberculosis different from the treatment 30 years ago?

L2 ## Guest Speaker

Invite a representative from the American Lung Association to talk with the class about emphysema. In addition to smoking, ask her or him to describe other causes of the disease.

L2 ## Class Activity

Have each student make a series of flash cards of diseases and disorders of the respiratory system. On one side of each card, students should write the name of the ailment. On the other side, they should write, in their own words, a description of that ailment.

L2 ## Researching

Ask students to trace the development of antibiotics from 1945 to the present: Why does there continue to be a market for new antibiotics? (A local pharmacist can be a good resource.)

HOME AND COMMUNITY CONNECTION

ANTIBIOTICS IN OUR FOOD. By breeding new and resistant strains of pathogens, heavy use of antibiotics has created an immune system challenge of crisis proportions. Some of the exposure to antibiotics results from use of antibiotics in the feed of meat and dairy animals. Students may wish to check the labels on meat and dairy products at the store to see if they contain antibiotics. How difficult is it to find meat and dairy products that are antibiotic free?

Making Responsible Decisions

1. Leah is concerned that her boyfriend is taking serious health risks by smoking.
2. Leah could (a) ignore her boyfriend's shortness of breath and her own dislike of the smell of cigarette smoke; (b) break up with her boyfriend unless he stops smoking; (c) discuss the importance of protecting his own health by quitting; (d) explain that he could help protect her health by quitting.
3. Leah might (a) keep her relationship with her boyfriend, but continue to feel worried and irritated about his smoking; (b) no longer be worried and irritated by his smoking, but lose her relationship with her boyfriend—and not help him protect his own health; (c and d) perhaps make him angry, but perhaps also help him at least consider quitting.
4. Leah values her relationship with her boyfriend. She also values his health and her own health.
5. Responses will vary.
6. Remind students to consider both the short-term and long-term consequences of their decisions.

L2 Decision Making

For further study on making responsible decisions, assign *Decision-Making Activity 17* in the TCR. ☞

L1 Discussing

Have students describe the symptoms of asthma. Make a list of agents known to aggravate the disorder. Ask: How do people with asthma treat it? *(inhalers, medication, respiratory therapy)*

Making Responsible Decisions

Whose Lungs Are They?

Leah's boyfriend smokes. She dislikes the fact that his clothes, his hair, and his breath smell of cigarette smoke. She has noticed that he coughs a lot and seems to be short of breath. He's even stopped playing softball on weekends because he can't run bases fast enough anymore. Leah had an uncle who died of emphysema, and she remembers that his symptoms began with shortness of breath and coughing. Leah worries about the health risks to both her and her boyfriend, but she is afraid that he will break up with her if she tries to get him to quit. When she brought the issue up before, he said to her, "They're my lungs." What should Leah do?

What Would You Do?

Apply the six steps of the decision-making process to Leah's problem.

1. **State the situation.**
2. **List the options.**
3. **Weigh the possible outcomes.**
4. **Consider your values.**
5. **Make a decision and act.**
6. **Evaluate the decision.**

A bronchiodilator from an inhaler helps relax the muscles that have tightened around the airways during an asthma attack.

ACTIVITY *Name situations that can trigger an asthma attack.*

bronchitis is avoiding respiratory irritants such as cigarette smoke, dust, fumes, or other air pollutants.

Asthma

Asthma (AZ-muh) is *an inflammatory condition in which the small airways in the lungs called bronchioles become narrowed, causing difficulty in breathing.* The mucous lining swells and secretions build up, making breathing even more difficult. The condition may be triggered by any number of causes, such as exertion, emotion, infection, allergens, even changes in the weather. About 1 in 20 people—1 in 10 children—are asthmatic.

Asthma attacks are treated with bronchodilators—medications that relax and widen the airways. Most people with asthma administer the medications themselves with a hand-held inhaler. Prophylactic (preventive) medications, taken several times daily through an inhaler, have been successful in preventing attacks.

Pneumonia

Pneumonia is an inflammation of the lungs. Pneumonia is not a single disease but the name for several types of lung inflammation caused by infectious organisms, such as bacteria and viruses. The two main types of pneumonia are lobar pneumonia and bronchial pneumonia. In lobar pneumonia, one lobe of one lung is affected at first. In bronchial pneumonia, inflammation starts in the bronchi and then spreads to tissue in one or both lungs. Symptoms of pneumonia

---

MORE ABOUT . . . . .

COLDS. Researchers have found that hundreds of viruses cause colds, not one virus, as once thought. The rhinovirus family is predominant in the winter but is active all year. Occurrence is more frequent when school starts and children gather in closed spaces. Research on prevention has included covering the nose with masks to keep the viruses from entering the main receptor. Use of antiviral drugs in nasal sprays and blocking proteins that may produce cold symptoms have opened new possibilities. Because the spread of rhinovirus is through air particles, some research is being done to develop an air-filtering system that interrupts the spread of the viruses.

include fever, chills, shortness of breath, and a severe cough. Chest pain that is worse when breathing in may occur because of **pleurisy** (PLUR-uh-see), *an inflammation of the membrane lining the lungs and chest cavity.*

Tuberculosis

Tuberculosis is an infectious bacterial disease of the lungs. Symptoms include fever and sweating, weakness, poor appetite, shortness of breath, and severe coughing. Tuberculosis is now rare in developed nations because of the use of modern antibiotic medicines. However, resistant forms of the disease have become more prevalent recently.

Emphysema

Emphysema is a disease in which the alveoli in the lungs burst and blend to form fewer, larger sacs with less surface area. The normal exchange of carbon dioxide and oxygen in the alveoli is disrupted. Symptoms include difficulty in breathing and a chronic cough. Emphysema is caused by breathing in foreign matter such as smoke and other air pollutants over a long period of time. In almost all cases, emphysema is caused by cigarette smoking. The condition cannot be reversed.

Sinusitis

Sinusitis is an inflammation of the membrane lining the facial sinuses, the air-filled cavities in the bones that surround the nose. Most sinusitis is caused by infection that spreads to the sinuses from the nose. Symptoms include fever, a stuffy nose, and a throbbing ache in the affected area. Antibiotic medications, decongestant drops or spray, and steam inhalation are used to treat sinusitis.

keeping Fit

Asthma Affects Anyone

A common misconception is that asthma is a disease of sickly people or weaklings. The truth is that asthma can affect anyone. Among other world-class athletes, major league fastballer Bob Gibson was an asthma sufferer. So is three-time Olympic gold medalist Jackie Joyner-Kersee.

Teens who suffer from asthma may feel self-conscious about using an inhaler in public because this singles them out. It is important to remember that quick response to an asthma attack is critical to restoring normal breathing. The longer you delay treatment, the longer the attack will last.

LESSON 3 *Review*

Reviewing Facts and Vocabulary

1. Why is it better to breathe through your nose than through your mouth?
2. What is the difference between chronic and acute bronchitis?
3. Describe how emphysema affects the alveoli.

Thinking Critically

4. ***Comparing and Contrasting.*** Compare external and internal respiration.

5. ***Analyzing.*** Explain the relationship between oxygen and carbon dioxide in the body.

Applying Health Skills

6. ***In Your Home and School.*** Interview three smokers and three nonsmokers. Ask them how often they experience respiratory infections, sore throats, and colds. Draw conclusions from your findings and share them with the class.

LESSON 3   THE RESPIRATORY SYSTEM   **405**

ASSESS

EVALUATING THE LESSON

Assign and discuss the Lesson 3 Review; then administer, grade, and discuss the *Lesson 55 Quiz* in the TCR.

RETEACHING

- Organize students into small groups. Have each group use clear plastic pages and markers to make a series of transparencies that show the major parts of the respiratory system. Ask them to draw one major system part on each sheet and organize the transparencies so that when they are placed on top of one another, they look like a diagram. Ask them to make a final transparency showing a respirator hooked up to the respiratory system. Have each group show the transparencies to the class and explain the respirator and its uses.
- Ask students to complete *Reteaching Activity 55* in the TCR.
- Use *Transparency 65* to review the parts of the respiratory system.

ENRICHMENT

Have students research how respiration is affected by high altitudes, space travel, and being underwater. What adaptations are required in each situation? Have them report their findings to the class.

CLOSE

Ask students to describe the interdependence of the cardiovascular and respiratory systems studied in this chapter.

Lesson 3 Review

Answers to Reviewing Facts and Vocabulary

1. Air is cleaned and filtered by mucous membranes and tiny hairs in the nose called cilia.
2. Acute bronchitis comes on suddenly as a complication of a viral infection. Chronic bronchitis is longer-lasting and recurring, often getting worse.
3. Alveoli burst and blend to form fewer, larger sacs with less surface area.

Answers to Thinking Critically

4. External respiration is the exchange of gases between the body and its environment. Internal respiration is the exchange of gases within the body.
5. Oxygen is necessary for the chemical reactions in cells that keep the body functioning. Carbon dioxide is a waste product of those reactions.

Health Skills Activities

ACTIVITY 1
HEALTH SKILLS
Comprehending Health Concepts, Accessing Health Information

➤ **National Standards**
This activity meets these National Health Standards: 1.1; 2..

Teach

- Prior to class, write the systems you will be assigning on the chalkboard, and have students sign up to investigate the one that most interests them.
- Have students refer to the book or to other health resources as necessary. One possibility would be the interactive body systems link at Glencoe's Health Web site (health.glencoe.com).
- Strive for as complete a list of lifestyle factors as possible, including posture (slumping back in one's chair vs. sitting up straight), eating plan, and amount and nature of physical activity.
- Allow time for a discussion of group findings.

ACTIVITY 2
HEALTH SKILLS
Self Management

➤ **National Standards**
This activity meets these National Health Standards: 3.2; 3.4.

Teach

- Prior to assigning this activity, prepare and send home a questionnaire regarding the health of the student and his or her ability to take part in this activity. The questionnaire should be completed and signed by a parent or guardian.
- Review with students the procedure for computing heart rate. Make sure all understand the procedure.
- Set aside time during a class in the week following to check back with students so that they may share and compare progress.

Activity 1: Keeping Body Systems Healthy

How much do you know about your circulatory, respiratory, muscular, or skeletal system? You and a group of classmates are about to become an expert on one of these systems.

Directions

1. Find a drawing or photo of a person and, using a grid for accurate proportions, transfer a full-length outline drawing of the person onto a large sheet of bulletin board paper. All group members are then to fill in and label the body system organs designated by your teacher. Use your textbook as a guide.
2. Around the border of your poster, identify lifestyle factors (for example, physical activity, low-fat diet) that promotes the health of the system.
3. Display your diagram along with those of other groups.

Time
50 minutes

Materials
6-x-8-foot sections of bulletin board paper, colored markers, index cards, scissors, masking tape, colored sheets of paper

Self-Assessment

✓ Labeled all structures of the body system accurately.
✓ Identified lifestyle-related factors for the body system.

Activity 2: Health Is a Heartbeat Away

Any physical activity that raises your heart rate to between 60 and 85 percent of its maximum rate and keeps it there for 15 to 20 minutes is good for your heart. Do you get enough of this type of activity?

Directions

1. Name an exercise or vigorous physical activity that you enjoy—or might enjoy—doing.
2. Create a chart listing these benefits as well as disadvantages (such as the stress that jogging places on the joints). You may need to do some research.
3. With a partner, perform your activity twice in the following week. Time your sessions to make sure you are active between 15 to 20 minutes. Your partner should record your heart rate before and after the activity.
4. What changes if any did you notice? Did the activity offer aerobic benefits?

Time
50 minutes plus outside research and exercise time

Materials
paper, pen or pencil, watch with a second hand

Self-Assessment

✓ Organized chart clearly and with all information requested.
✓ Recorded heart rate for an exercise or activity tried during the week.

406 CHAPTER 17 YOUR CIRCULATORY AND RESPIRATORY SYSTEMS

ASSESSMENT SCORING

Using a four-level rubric, the student has achieved a 4 if:

ACTIVITY 1

✔ Student was complete and thorough in researching the system under scrutiny.
✔ Student labeled all structures of the body system accurately.
✔ Student identified lifestyle-related factors for the body system.
✔ Student actively participated in any follow-up discussion.

ACTIVITY 2

✔ Student organized chart clearly and with all information requested.
✔ Student demonstrated an understanding of the method for computing heart rate.
✔ Student followed through with an exercise during the week.
✔ Student worked with a partner and recorded the heart rate.

HEALTH NEWS VIDEO

Nothing to Sneeze At

A beautiful spring brings fresh new flowers and bright green leaves. For people who suffer from pollen allergies, this beauty can be hard to see. They're too busy sneezing and wiping their watery eyes.

Every spring, plants create pollen, a spore that helps plants reproduce. Since plants can't move, they release pollen into the air. Some of it lands on other plants, but people inhale a lot of pollen, too.

When pollen enters your respiratory system, your immune system identifies it as a foreign object. To get rid of these spores, your body begins to sneeze and your eyes begin to water.

You can avoid the problems of pollen by staying inside. Medicines and treatments can help you enjoy the beauty of spring without tears.

Play the Video

CNN. All Rights Reserved.

Think About It

▶ What happens when people inhale pollen? Why do some people respond more dramatically to pollen than others?

▶ What parts of your respiratory system are involved in pollen allergies?

▶ What can you do to avoid the effects of pollen?

CNN HEALTH NEWS **407**

MORE ABOUT . . . . .

TECHNOLOGY AND SCIENCE. The scientific name for hay fever is allergic rhinitis. Experts estimate that more than 26 million people in the United States experience some hay fever symptoms each spring.

The allergy to pollen is usually inherited. This means that children of parents with spring allergies are likely to experience similar reactions. For many people, hay fever is an annoyance. For some people with severe allergies, the condition can lead to serious medical conditions, including chronic sinusitis, nasal polyps, and asthma.

Many allergies occur during other seasons. Ragweed, the plant associated with the greatest number of allergic reactions, produces allergens in the late fall.

Objectives. After viewing the video, students should understand the causes and effects of airborne allergens and how to deal with them.

Motivator. Pretend to sneeze. Ask students to suggest some triggers that can cause sneezing, such as pollen, animal dander, and smoke. Explain that sneezing is one of the body's immune responses—the sneeze ejects foreign substances from the body. Then have students view Video Segment 11, "Nothing to Sneeze At," which illustrates the regular cycle that creates spring allergens.

Teach

• Write the terms allergen and pollen on the chalkboard. Have students offer definitions for each word. (An allergen is a substance that induces an allergic reaction. Pollen is the spore in a seed plant.)

• Explain that spring allergies are often called hay fever because they are associated with the pollen created by hays and other grasses during the springtime. Emphasize that many plants in addition to hay produce pollen and can lead to allergic reactions.

• Review strategies for avoiding or treating allergies. Emphasize that the best way to handle an allergy is to avoid the allergen. However, in many cases, such as in the springtime, this is not possible or healthy.

Group Activity. Direct students to create a series of diagrams showing how pollen enters the air and how it affects the respiratory and immune systems. Suggest that students create a classroom flow chart to illustrate this process. Each student will produce a single step in the process by which the production of pollen in the spring contributes to hay fever.

Close. Have students explain why hay fever occurs at about the same time each year. Make sure they understand the connections between the natural growth cycle, the production of pollen, and the body's allergic response.

CHECKING COMPREHENSION

- Assign and discuss the chapter review.
- Use the MindJogger Videoquiz to review the chapter.

CHAPTER 17 REVIEW ANSWERS

Using Health Terms

1. veins
2. hemoglobin
3. lymph
4. plasma
5. lymphocyte
6. platelets
7. capillaries
8. arteries
9. congenital
10. pleurisy
11. trachea
12. bronchi
13. asthma
14. respiration
15. pharynx
16. diaphragm
17. larynx

Recalling the Facts

1. Plasma is the fluid in which all the other parts of the blood are suspended.
2. The blood carries oxygen, hormones, and nutrients throughout the body to all the cells and removes waste products from the cells.
3. Platelets are cells in the blood that cause clotting at the site of an injury to stop the bleeding.
4. The lymphatic system drains tissue fluid into the bloodstream and fights infection.
5. The lymph nodes act as a barrier to the spread of infection by destroying or filtering out bacteria before they can pass into the blood.
6. Any two: faulty valve, heart murmur, hole in heart chamber, blockage of flow, defect in vessels leading to or from the heart.

Using Health Terms

On a separate sheet of paper, write the term that best matches each definition below.

LESSON 1

1. The vessels that return deoxygenated blood toward the heart from the body's organs and tissues.
2. The oxygen-carrying part of blood.
3. A clear yellow fluid that fills the spaces around body cells.
4. The fluid in which the other parts of blood are suspended.
5. A type of white blood cell that protects the body against pathogens.
6. The cells that prevent the body's loss of blood.
7. The vessels that carry blood between arterioles and small vessels called venules.
8. The vessels that carry blood away from the heart.

LESSON 2

9. Occurring at birth.

LESSON 3

10. An inflammation of the membrane lining the lungs and chest cavity.
11. Windpipe.
12. The airways that connect the trachea to the lungs.
13. An inflammatory condition in which the small airways in the lungs called bronchioles become narrowed, causing difficulty in breathing.
14. The exchange of gases between your body and your environment.
15. Throat.
16. A muscle that separates the chest and abdominal cavities.
17. Voice box.

Recalling the Facts

Using complete sentences, answer the following questions.

LESSON 1

1. What is plasma?
2. What are the functions of the blood?
3. Why are platelets important to your health?
4. Explain the functions of the lymphatic system.
5. What is the function of the lymph nodes?

LESSON 2

6. Describe two conditions that are examples of congenital heart disease.
7. What causes varicose veins?
8. What is anemia and what is its main cause?

9. Name and briefly describe three problems of the lymphatic system.
10. How can you care for your lymphatic system?

LESSON 3

11. What are the main parts of the respiratory system?
12. What are the functions of the mucous membranes and cilia in the nose?
13. Name and briefly describe three serious respiratory diseases.
14. What regulates the movement of air in and out of the lungs?
15. Explain why food and drink do not usually get into the trachea.

7. Varicose veins are caused by a weakening of the blood vessels, often caused by lack of exercise.
8. A condition in which there is too little hemoglobin in the blood to carry sufficient oxygen. The most common cause is too little iron in the diet.
9. Immune deficiency: the body's defenses against infection are damaged and cannot fight infection. Hodgkin's disease: cancer of lymph tissue. Tonsillitis: the tonsils become infected by the organisms they are fighting.
10. Eating a nutritious diet, getting at least eight hours of sleep each night, and exercising regularly keep the lymphatic system healthy.
11. Lungs, nose, mouth, pharynx, trachea, bronchi.

Thinking Critically

LESSON 1

1. ***Analyzing.*** Discuss ways in which the circulatory and lymphatic systems are mutually supportive.
2. ***Comparing and Contrasting.*** Discuss ways in which the circulatory and lymphatic systems are alike and different.

LESSON 2

3. ***Analyzing.*** How do nutrition and exercise contribute to the health of your circulatory and lymphatic systems?

4. ***Synthesizing.*** Summarize the major contributions of the lymphatic system to your health.

LESSON 3

5. ***Evaluating.*** Some workplaces are smoke-free. What are some advantages and disadvantages of this policy? Judge the appropriateness of such a policy.
6. ***Synthesizing.*** How might suffering from asthma affect your life?

Making the Connection

1. ***Math.*** Compare the survival rates for people with cardiovascular diseases 40 years ago and today. Prepare a bar graph or a line graph that shows your findings. Interpret these statistics and suggest reasons for the changes.
2. ***Science.*** Vitamin E is being credited with many health benefits including lowering heart disease, warding off cancer, preventing infection, even preserving youth. Investigate the claims made for this vitamin. Determine what evidence supports the claims, how vitamin E works, and how much of the vitamin is needed. Prepare a written report of your findings.

BEYOND THE CLASSROOM

PARENTAL INVOLVEMENT Ask your parents to tell you about any problems with the circulatory or respiratory system they have experienced. Find out what their symptoms were, what actions they took to correct the problem, and how they evaluated the effectiveness of their actions.

COMMUNITY INVOLVEMENT Just about all communities today have laws and ordinances identifying certain areas and types of retail establishments as smoke-free. Some communities, in fact, are entirely smoke-free. Unfortunately, not all individuals or retailers uphold these laws. Learn about the rulings in your own community and about the penalties for violating them. Share your findings in the form of a public service announcement, if possible, to be broadcast over a public access cable station in your locality.

SCHOOL-TO-CAREER
Technology. With multiplying advances in technology, health care professionals in the field of cardiology are able to diagnose and treat heart problems in ways they were not capable of just a few years ago. Learn more about technological advances in this important area of medicine.

12. The mucous membranes and cilia clean and filter the air.
13. Bronchitis: an inflammation of the bronchi. Asthma: an inflammatory condition in which the small airways in the lungs become narrowed, causing difficulty in breathing. Pneumonia: an inflammation of the lungs. Tuberculosis: an infectious bacterial disease of the lungs. Emphysema: a disease in which the alveoli burst and blend. Sinusitis: an inflammation of the membrane lining the facial sinuses.
14. The diaphragm regulates the movement of air in and out of the lungs.
15. Food and drink do not usually get into the trachea because muscles close it off when you swallow.

Thinking Critically

1. The circulatory system produces the white cells that function in the lymph system to fight infection. The circulatory system picks up the wastes produced as a result of the lymphocytes' bacteria-fighting activity.
2. Both transport fluid, both support the functions of body cells. The circulatory system provides nutrients, oxygen, and hormones to the cells; it also transports wastes from the cells. The lymphatic system drains fluids from the cells into the bloodstream and it fights infection.
3. Good nutrition provides the raw materials needed for the operation of both systems. Exercise keeps the body moving, which helps keep the fluids flowing efficiently.
4. The lymphatic system fights infection.
5. Answers will vary.
6. Asthma may require daily medication as well as limit your activities.

Making the Connection

1.–2. Answers will vary.

Evaluate

- Use the reproducible *Chapter 17 Test* in the TCR, or construct your own using the Testmaker software.
- Use *Performance Assessment Activity 17* in the TCR.

Enrichment

- Ask students to complete *Cross-Curriculum Activity 17* in the TCR.

Beyond the Classroom

Keep students involved in the community, and encourage parent participation by assigning the activities on this page for students to work on outside of class.

Your Digestive and Urinary Systems

	FEATURES	**CLASSROOM RESOURCES**

LESSON 1

The Digestive System

pages 412–416

- Concept Map Activity 56
- Enrichment Activity 18
- Health Lab 18
- Lesson 56 Quiz
- Lesson Plan 56
- Reteaching Activity 56
- Transparency 66

LESSON 2

Care and Problems of the Digestive System

pages 417–423

Building Health Skills

"Adding Sources of Fiber,"
page 419

health lab

"Comparing Antacids,"
page 420

Making Responsible Decisions

"A Milk Dilemma," *page 422*

- Concept Map Activity 57
- Decision-Making Activity 18
- Lesson 57 Quiz
- Lesson Plan 57
- Reteaching Activity 57

LESSON 3

The Urinary System

pages 424–429

Teens Making a **Difference**

"The Gift of Life," *page 427*

- Concept Map Activity 58
- Cooperative Learning Activity 18
- Lesson 58 Quiz
- Lesson Plan 58
- Reteaching Activity 58
- Transparency 67

Chapter Resources

ACTIVITIES

- Cross-Curriculum Activity 18
- Health Lab 18
- Health Skills Activities 18
- Parent Letter and Activities 18

ASSESSMENT

- Chapter 18 Test
- Performance Assessment Activity 18
- Testmaker Software

STUDENT ACTIVITIES WORKBOOK

- Applying Health Skills 56–58
- Study Guide 18
- Vocabulary Activity 18

STUDENT DIVERSITY STRATEGIES

- Audiocassette Program (English)
- Audiocassette Program (Spanish)
- Spanish Parent Letters and Activities
- Spanish Summaries, Quizzes, and Activities

MULTIMEDIA COMPONENTS

- English Audiocassette Program
- Spanish Audiocassette Program
- MindJogger Videodisc and VHS program

National Health Education Standards

One of the main goals of the National Health Education Standards is to move students toward "health literacy." Health literacy is the capacity of individuals to obtain, interpret, and understand basic health information and services and the competence to use such information and services in ways which promote health. The health standards were developed by applying the characteristics of a well-educated, literate person within the context of health. The health literate person is:

- a critical thinker and problem solver
- a responsible, productive citizen
- a self-directed learner
- an effective communicator

Listed below are the Health Education Standards Performance Indicators addressed in each lesson of this chapter.

Lesson	Health Standards Performance Indicators
1	7.2, 7.6
2	2.1, 3.4, 6.1, 6.6
3	2.6, 3.1, 3.4, 4.3

ONLINE RESOURCES

For a fresh approach to health topics and an in-depth look at health issues, use these online resources found under Teacher Resources at **health.glencoe.com**.

- **BLOCK SCHEDULE LESSON PLANS** Reinforce health concepts with outside readings selected especially for students. Each reading is accompanied by a lesson plan and activities to enhance
  - Reading Skills
  - Cross Curriculum
  - Media Literacy

- **TECHNOLOGY PROJECTS** Instructions and suggestions on how to use computer, Internet, and software with health lessons.

- **HEALTH UPDATES** Timely topics in health news, including late-breaking medical advances and updates on teen risk behaviors.

Out of Time?

If time does not permit teaching this chapter, you may use these features: Building Health Skills on page 419 and Making Responsible Decisions on page 422.

BLOCK SCHEDULING

Block scheduling provides extended time for hands-on projects and activities. Use the following activities to engage students, provide further depth, and vary your instructional techniques:

- Health Lab (45 minutes) **pg. 420**
- Teens Making a Difference (30 minutes) **pg. 427**
- Health Skills Activity (60–90 minutes) **pg. 430**

Your Digestive and Urinary Systems

CHAPTER OVERVIEW

Chapter 18 introduces students to the digestive and urinary systems. The structure, function, care, and problems of each system are presented.

LESSON 1 The digestive system breaks down food into microscopic molecules to be carried in the blood to the body's cells. This is achieved through mechanical and chemical processes. Digestion, absorption, and elimination are discussed in this lesson.

LESSON 2 The complicated digestive system normally functions as it should, though a variety of problems are associated with it. This lesson focuses on common digestive problems, digestive disorders and diseases, and ways to care for the digestive system.

LESSON 3 The urinary system, consisting of two kidneys, two ureters, a bladder, and the urethra, removes water-soluble waste from the blood, tissues, and cells. The system's structure, function, problems, and care are presented in this lesson.

CHAPTER 18

Your Digestive and Urinary Systems

HEALTH Online
DECISION MAKING
You're hungry, and you head to your favorite restaurant for a quick bite to satisfy that hunger. Will your meal also satisfy the nutritional needs to keep your digestive and urinary systems healthy? Check out the "Fast-Food Dining Guide" in the Interactive Projects at **health.glencoe.com** to see whether your meal meets the Dietary Guidelines for Americans.

Hands-On Health

TEACHING STRATEGY

Reinforcing and Reviewing Bring your health classroom to life with interactive teaching strategies and classroom management techniques that keep your students interested and involved. The unique *Hands-On Health: Creative Teaching Strategies* booklet that accompanies the *Glencoe Health* program offers fun, motivating activities.

The following Classroom Management Ideas can be used to reinforce chapter concepts:

- Beach Ball
- Trivia Questions
- Paper Exchange
- Mental Outburst

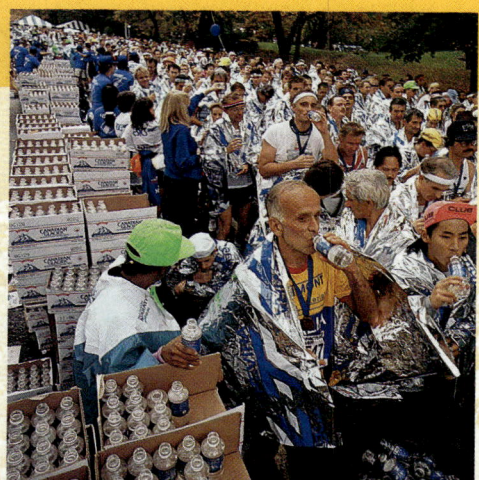

Now good digestion wait on appetite, And health on both!

—WILLIAM SHAKESPEARE
ENGLISH PLAYWRIGHT AND POET, (1564–1616)

Quick Write Create a short paragraph in which you tie together the key words in the quote above: *digestion*, *appetite*, and *health*.

Personal Health Inventory

Self-Inventory Write the numbers 1–10 on a sheet of paper. Read each statement below and respond by writing *yes*, *no*, or *sometimes* for each item. Write a *yes* only for items that you practice regularly. Save your responses.

1	I eat a variety of healthful foods that are high in fiber every day.
2	I eat salty snacks and fried foods in moderation.
3	I chew each bite of food throughly before swallowing.
4	I do not eat as a way of coping with stress or when I am emotionally upset.
5	I drink at least six to eight glasses of water a day.
6	I brush my teeth after every meal and floss my teeth daily.
7	I use laxatives only when recommended by a health care professional.
8	I have regular bowel movements.
9	I seek medical attention when diarrhea persists for more than 48 hours.
10	I discuss any changes in urine color, odor, or frequency with a health care professional.

Follow-up After completing the chapter, retake this self-inventory. Pick two items that you need to work on and set a goal to improve your health behaviors.

CHAPTER 18   YOUR DIGESTIVE AND URINARY SYSTMES   **411**

INTRODUCING THE CHAPTER

Personal Health Inventory

Remind students that the Self-Inventory is for their own use; they will find it most helpful if they respond honestly to each statement. Ask students to record their responses to the inventory in their private Health Journals on a page labeled "My Digestive and Urinary Systems." They will use these responses in the Self-Inventory Follow-up activity at the end of Chapter 18.

- Ask students to recall how they, as very young children, viewed the process of digestion. Most likely they once thought that the food they ate retained its form as it was used to supply the body with energy. Tell them that as young adults they learned the process is much more complex, and that in this chapter they will study the process and the body's way of ridding waste products in more detail.
- Have volunteers describe the photographs on these two pages. Ask: What does each picture suggest about taking good care of your digestive and urinary systems? Why is it so important to establish healthy habits related to these systems now, while you are young? Let students read and discuss the Shakespeare quotation on this page. Explain that the lessons in Chapter 18 will help students learn more about the function and care of their digestive and urinary systems.
- Distribute Parent Letter 18 from the *Parent Letters and Activities* booklet in the TCR.

The Digestive System

FOCUS

LESSON OBJECTIVES

After studying this lesson, students should be able to

- describe digestion.
- identify and explain the function of each organ of the digestive system.

MOTIVATOR

Write the following on the chalkboard for students to work on while attendance is being taken: *Describe in your own words the purpose of the digestive system.*

INTRODUCING THE LESSON

Have students share their responses to the Motivator. Emphasize that digestion allows the nutrients of food to be used by the body. Introduce this lesson by stating that digestion takes place mainly in the stomach and the small intestine, but that other organs make this effort successful. Tell students that this lesson will explain the function and processes of each organ involved in digestion and elimination.

INTRODUCING HEALTH TERMS

- Have students make flash cards for the vocabulary terms. On one side, have them write the word. On the other side, have them identify the body system, the definition, and a page reference.
- Ask students to complete Vocabulary Activity 18 and Chapter Study Guide 18 in the *Student Workbook.* ☞

The Digestive System

Digestion is the breaking down of food into simpler substances to be carried in the blood to body cells. This process is both mechanical and chemical. The mechanical portion involves chewing, mashing, and breaking food into smaller pieces. The chemical portion involves changing food into simpler substances.

HEALTH TERMS

digestion
absorption
elimination
ingestion
mastication
peristalsis
gastric juices
chyme
bile

HEALTH CONCEPTS

- Food is the body's fuel.
- Digestion is both a mechanical and a chemical process.
- Digestion begins with ingestion, the taking in of food, and ends with the elimination of wastes.
- Each organ of the gastrointestinal tract has a specific function.

Functions of the Digestive System

The digestive system performs three different functions that are essential to provide nutrition:

- **Digestion**—*the mechanical and chemical breakdown of foods for use by the body's cells.*
- **Absorption**—*the passage of digested food from the digestive tract into the circulatory system.*
- **Elimination**—*the expulsion of undigested food or body wastes.*

Once food is broken down, nutrients from it are absorbed through the small intestine. The nutrients are then passed along to the circulatory system. Any food that is not broken down in this process is eliminated in the form of wastes.

Lesson 1 Resources

TEACHER'S CLASSROOM RESOURCES

☞ **Concept Map** Activity 56
☞ **Enrichment** Activity 18
☞ **Health Lab** 18
☞ **Lesson 56 Quiz**
☞ **Lesson Plan 56**
☞ **Parent Letters and Activities** 18

☞ **Reteaching** Activity 56

STUDENT WORKBOOK

☞ **Applying Health Skills** 56
☞ **Chapter Study Guide** 18
☞ **Vocabulary** Activity 18

TRANSPARENCIES

🖋 **Transparency 66**

Structure of the Digestive System

You might assume that the process of digestion begins in your stomach or intestines. In truth, it begins before you take a bite of food when the aroma of food activates the salivary glands.

The Mouth and Teeth

A number of different structures are involved in **ingestion**, *the taking of food into the body,* which is the earliest stage of digestion. These structures include the teeth, the salivary glands, and the tongue.

THE TEETH

The primary function of your teeth is to break the food you eat into smaller pieces. **Mastication** (MAS-tuh-KAY-shuhn)—*the process of chewing*—prepares the food to be swallowed.

THE SALIVARY GLANDS

As food moves through your digestive system, various secretions are added to it. This process starts in your mouth, where three pairs of salivary glands secrete saliva. Saliva is a watery solution containing an enzyme that starts the digestion of carbohydrates by converting them to a soluble form of sugar. It also lubricates your food, making it easier to swallow.

THE TONGUE

Your tongue forms food into a ball to prepare for swallowing. As you begin to swallow, a wave of muscular contractions passes over your tongue, forcing food into the pharynx. At the same time, the uvula, a small, muscular flap of tissue suspended at the back of your mouth, closes over the opening to the nasal passages. The epiglottis, the flap of tissue covering the trachea, closes to keep food from entering the respiratory system. If you talk or laugh while swallowing, the epiglottis will open and food may enter the windpipe. A reflex response causes you to cough to force food out of the windpipe.

DIGESTIVE SYSTEM

- Mouth
- Salivary glands
- Pharynx
- Esophagus
- Diaphragm
- Liver
- Stomach
- Gallbladder
- Pancreas
- Large intestine
- Small intestine
- Appendix
- Rectum

⚠ *The organs of the digestive system form a continuous passageway for the movement of food through your body.*

ACTIVITY *Locate the stomach and tell whether it is where you expected to find it.*

TEACH

🔲 Explaining

LD students may have difficulty with this chapter due to the complex subject matter and high-level vocabulary. You may need to provide a very basic summary of each lesson and test them only on that material.

L2 Class Activity

Give each student a soda cracker and point out the dryness of that cracker. Ask students to take a bite of the cracker and chew it thoroughly. As they are chewing, have them notice the actions of their teeth and tongue. Point out that saliva moistens and dissolves the cracker so it can be tasted. As they swallow, ask them to take note of the tongue action forcing the food into the esophagus. Explain that this is the first stage of digestion.

L1 Discussing

Using a denture model or diagram, explain the function of the 32 permanent teeth. Point out the incisors *(cut and bite)* and molars *(grind)*. Describe the difference in mastication for an infant, a young child, and a teenager.

L2 Class Activity

Following a discussion of mastication and swallowing, ask students to develop a chart of the sequential steps, identifying the other body systems that help carry out this process—nervous, circulatory, muscular, endocrine.

MORE ABOUT . . . . .

THE ROLE OF TEETH IN DIGESTION. Not only in humans, but in most other mammalian species as well, teeth are the prime agents of mechanical digestion. Unlike other animals with dentition, mammalian teeth reflect their specialization for chewing. Mammals usually have several different types of teeth, each type suited for a particular function: Incisors shear food, canines rip, and molars grind.

For most mammals, the volume of food is not reduced significantly by chewing. However, by breaking up food into small particles, chewing greatly increases the surface area of food that is exposed to digestive juices. This makes us very efficient at getting the greatest amount of energy from what we eat.

L2 Explaining

A sphincter muscle controls the entrance to the stomach. Identify for the class other sphincters or valves that regulate flow—oral, intestinal, cardiac.

L2 Explaining

Food may stay in the stomach two to six hours. Carbohydrates leave first, proteins next, and fats remain the longest.

L2 Cooperative Learning

Divide the class into groups. Provide each group with poster board. Ask the students to prepare a chart of the organs of the digestive tract, the enzymes produced in each organ, and the types of food digested in each organ. Have students list the organs in the order in which food is digested, from the oral cavity to the anal cavity. Display the posters in the classroom.

LD Class Activity

Have students diagram and label the organs of the digestive system.

L2 Lab

Working with a member of the science department, prepare a demonstration showing the action of hydrochloric acid on a protein, a fat, and a carbohydrate. Ask students to compare the time and type of digestion that takes place. Ask: Do gastric juices contain hydrochloric acid?

L2 Explaining

Tell students that food must undergo both physical and chemical changes before it can be used in the body. Have students explain the meaning of this statement.

L2 Health Lab

Distribute *Health Lab 18* and have students investigate the effect of heating enzymes. ▱

The Esophagus

When you swallow, food enters the esophagus. This is a muscular tube that extends from the pharynx to the stomach and is situated behind the trachea and the heart. It is about 10 inches (25 cm) long. A process called **peristalsis** (PER-uh-STAWL-suhs)—*a series of involuntary muscular contractions*—moves food through the esophagus. Solid food takes about nine seconds to complete this brief journey. Food moves through the entire digestive tract as the result of peristalsis.

A sphincter muscle—a circular muscle at the entrance to the stomach—allows food to move from the esophagus into the stomach. When the muscle is relaxed, it forms an opening. When it contracts, the opening closes. Sphincter muscles located along the digestive tract prevent food from backing up as it moves through the digestive process.

The Stomach

The stomach is a hollow, saclike organ enclosed in a muscular wall. This wall consists of three layers of muscles. The stomach is flexible, allowing it to expand when you eat. The main activities of the stomach are to:

▼ *The stomach's role in digestion is both physical: churning food; and chemical: producing gastric juices that begin the digestion of proteins.*
ACTIVITY *Explain why the three layers of muscles move in three different directions.*

- continue the breakdown of food.
- serve as a storage organ for food until it is ready to enter the small intestine.
- mix together food and **gastric juices**—*secretions from the stomach lining that contain pepsin and hydrochloric acid.* Pepsin is an enzyme that breaks down protein. Hydrochloric acid kills bacteria taken in with the food and creates the best environment for the pepsin to do its work. The hydrochloric acid your stomach produces is

THE STOMACH

Esophagus

MUSCLE LAYERS
Longitudinal
Circular
Oblique

Duodenum
Mucous membrane
Sphincter muscle

414 CHAPTER 18   YOUR DIGESTIVE AND URINARY SYSTEMS

MEETING STUDENT DIVERSITY

LEARNING STYLES. To help students with diverse learning styles comprehend the process of digestion, have students work in pairs. Ask each pair of students to create a chart or three-dimensional model summarizing the process of digestion and the removal of wastes from the body. Suggest that students use simple cardboard boxes or other objects to help visualize the process. Encourage each student pair to come up with their own creative, individual approach to depicting the process. When students are ready, have them take turns presenting their models or charts to the class.

strong enough to dissolve metal. In fact, if it were not for the mucus your stomach produces to form a protective lining, your stomach would digest itself!

■ control the rate at which food enters the small intestine.

As the stomach fills, the layers of muscle produce rhythmic contractions that churn the food and gastric juices together. This action produces a substance called **chyme** (kym), *a creamy, fluid mixture of food and gastric juices.* Peristalsis moves the chyme into the small intestine.

The Small Intestine

The major part of digestion and absorption occurs in the small intestine, which is 20 to 23 feet (6 to 7 m) in length and 1 inch (2.5 cm) in diameter. (The small intestine gets its name from its diameter, not its length.) It consists of three parts: the duodenum, the jejunum, and the ileum. Chyme enters the duodenum from the stomach. The ileum opens into the large intestine.

Peristalsis moves chyme through the small intestine at a relatively slow rate for approximately three to five hours. Chyme that enters the small intestine includes partially digested carbohydrates and proteins and undigested fats. Intestinal juices produced by glands in the lining of the small intestine, along with secretions from the liver and the pancreas, complete the chemical breakdown of all food. You will learn about the liver and pancreas later in this lesson.

The small intestine is lined with millions of fingerlike projections called villi (VIL-eye). Each villus has a network of capillaries. These capillaries absorb digested food particles from the small intestine. Villi, especially those in the jejunum, increase the surface area for the absorption of digested food particles about 600 times. Once food particles enter the capillaries in the villi, they are carried throughout the body by the blood. Unabsorbed material leaves the small intestine in the form of liquid and fiber, moving by peristalsis into the large intestine.

The Large Intestine

The large intestine, or colon, forms the lower part of the digestive tract. The large intestine is 5 to 6 feet (1.5 to 1.8 m) long and about 2½ inches (6 cm) in diameter. Movement of undigested food materials through the large intestine is very slow. The main functions of the large intestine are to absorb water and eliminate undigested food.

As unabsorbed material from the small intestine passes through the large intestine, water, vitamins, and mineral salts are absorbed into the bloodstream. This action is important in maintaining the water balance in your body.

Many harmless bacteria normally live in the large intestine, changing the consistency of undigested food to a semisolid waste, called feces. Feces pass from the body through the anus and is excreted as a bowel movement.

L3 **Class Activity**

Ask volunteers to work with the science department to microscopically compare available tissue samples from the various organs of the digestive tract. Ask the students to report to the class the variance in wall size and muscle structure in the organs.

L2 **Writing**

Have students select one organ involved in the digestive process and write a paper on it, including the organ's function, importance, maintenance, and relation to other body organs. Have students end the paper with an analogy about the particular organ. "The (name of organ) is like (…) because…"

MORE ABOUT . . . . .

THE DIGESTIVE SYSTEM. Smooth muscles contract to move food down the esophagus and along the rest of the digestive tract.

Stomach walls contain small pressure sensors that tell the body when the stomach is empty. These sensations are commonly called hunger pangs.

The stomach is a storehouse for food where acids break down contents into simpler components that are absorbed in the small intestine.

Alcohol doesn't need to be broken down chemically before it is absorbed into the bloodstream.

The presence of food in the stomach slows down the absorption of alcohol. Even so, food in the stomach will not keep one from being intoxicated.

ASSESS

EVALUATING THE LESSON

Assign and discuss the Lesson 1 Review; then administer, grade, and discuss the *Lesson 56 Quiz* in the TCR. 🖘

RETEACHING

- Have students make a chart of the parts of the digestive system, indicating what each part does.
- Ask students to complete *Reteaching Activity 56* in the TCR. 🖘
- Use *Transparency 66* to review the parts of the digestive system. ✋

ENRICHMENT

- Have students learn about the digestive systems of cows, chickens, and other animals. What foods do these animals eat? How are their digestive systems designed to digest those particular foods?
- Have students complete *Enrichment Activity 18,* "A Matter of Taste," in the TCR. 🖘

CLOSE

Ask students to state the most important concepts studied in the lesson.

Organs That Aid Digestion

Three other organs play key roles in digestion.

- **The Liver.** The second-largest organ in your body (your skin is the largest), your liver functions as your body's chemical factory and regulates the levels of most of the main chemicals in your blood.

  The liver acts to clear the blood of drugs and poisonous substances. The liver absorbs the substances, changes their chemical structure, and makes them water soluble. It then excretes them in the **bile**, *a yellowish-green, bitter fluid important in the breakdown of fats.* Bile flows through the hepatic duct to the gallbladder, where it is stored.

- **The Gallbladder.** The gallbladder is a small, pear-shaped sac 3 to 4 inches (7 to 10 cm) long and located underneath the liver. The neck of the gallbladder forms a duct leading to the duodenum, the first section of the small intestine. The gallbladder stores bile until food moves into the duodenum from the stomach. A hormone produced in the small intestine stimulates the release of bile through the bile duct into the duodenum, where the bile breaks down fats contained in the food.

- **The Pancreas.** The pancreas, as part of the endocrine system, produces the hormone insulin. As part of the digestive system, the pancreas produces three digestive enzymes: trypsin, which digests proteins; amylase, which digests carbohydrates; and lipase, which digests fats.

LESSON 1 *Review*

Reviewing Facts and Vocabulary

1. Trace the path a bite of pizza follows until it is absorbed into the bloodstream.
2. Describe the three different functions of the digestive system.
3. Define the following terms and use each in a sentence: *mastication, peristalsis, saliva, bile.*

Thinking Critically

4. ***Analyzing.*** Support the following statement: *The real work of the digestive system is done in the small intestine.*
5. ***Synthesizing.*** Explain in what way chewing food well contributes to the health of the digestive system.

6. ***Synthesizing.*** Based on their actions, change the names of the different parts of the digestive system to parts of machines. Draw a diagram of the digestive system and label it with the new names.

Applying Health Skills

7. ***In Your Home and School.*** Prepare a chart that shows what happens to food once it leaves the stomach. Describe the function of each organ involved in the digestive process. Share the chart with classmates and with your family.

Lesson 1 Review

Answers to Reviewing Facts and Vocabulary

1. Answers should reflect an understanding of the digestive process.
2. Digestion—food is broken down for use by the body. Absorption—nutrients from digested food are transported into the circulatory system for distribution to the rest of the body. Elimination—undigested food and/or body wastes are expelled from the body.
3. See pages 413–416 for definitions. Sentences will vary.

Answers to Thinking Critically

4. Answers should mention that nutrients are absorbed into the bloodstream through the walls of the small intestine.
5. By breaking down food into small pieces and beginning the process of carbohydrate digestion.
6. Answers will vary.

Care and Problems of the Digestive System

There are many parts to your digestive system, all vital to the process of digestion. Some parts of this system, such as your teeth and tongue, are essential to a second process—speech production. It is, therefore, critical to take care of your digestive system.

HEALTH TERMS

indigestion

hiatal hernia

appendicitis

peptic ulcer

HEALTH CONCEPTS

- The health of the digestive system depends in large part on healthful eating habits.
- The more you chew your food, the easier it is on your digestive system.

Fiber-rich foods: kale, bran, fruits, oatmeal

Care of the Digestive System

Good eating habits are the best way to avoid or minimize digestive system problems. The reward for maintaining good eating habits may well be a lifetime free of the kinds of problems that lead drugstores to stock their shelves with antacids, laxatives, and other such products. Make the following suggestions part of your lifestyle habits:

- Eat a variety of foods.
- Avoid an overabundance of fried foods. Choose foods that are low in fat and high in **fiber**.
- Do not hurry through your meals—eat slowly while sitting down. Relax and enjoy your meal!
- Do not wash food down with liquid. Wait until you are finished chewing—swallow, and then take a sip of liquid.
- Drink plenty of water. Your digestive system needs a lot of water to do its job properly.

hotlink

fiber For more information on the importance of fiber, see Chapter 5, page 103.

Lesson 2 Resources

TEACHER'S CLASSROOM RESOURCES

- **Concept Map** Activity 57
- **Decision-Making** Activity 18
- **Lesson 57 Quiz**
- **Lesson Plan 57**
- **Reteaching** Activity 57

STUDENT WORKBOOK

- **Applying Health Skills 57**
- **Chapter Study Guide 18**
- **Vocabulary** Activity 18

Care and Problems of the Digestive System

FOCUS

LESSON OBJECTIVES

After studying this lesson, students should be able to

- explain the preventive measures for digestive disorders.
- describe problems associated with the digestive system.

MOTIVATOR

Write the following on the chalkboard for students to work on while attendance is being taken: *List as many minor disorders of the digestive system as you can.* (Halitosis, indigestion, heartburn, flatulence, nausea, diarrhea, dehydration, constipation.)

INTRODUCING THE LESSON

Refer to the Motivator. Ask volunteers to share their responses. Tell students they will learn more about digestive disorders and diseases as well as how to prevent them as they study this lesson.

INTRODUCING HEALTH TERMS

- Have students make flash cards for the vocabulary terms. On one side, have them write the word. On the other side, have them identify the body system, the definition, and a page reference.
- Ask students to complete Vocabulary Activity 18 and Chapter Study Guide 18 in the *Student Workbook.*

TEACH

L1 Discussing

Review the habits for care of the digestive system listed on pages 417 and 418.

L2 Self-Esteem

Ask students to think of situations at school that could contribute to a digestive disorder. Have students list the situations. *(Exam, breakup in a relationship, grades.)* Discuss with students how emotions can affect the digestive system. Encourage them to describe some healthful and unhealthful ways to deal with these situations. Ask: What effect would a person's level of self-esteem have on his or her ability to cope with disorders of the digestive system?

L2 Class Activity

The suffix *-itis* means inflammation. Ask students to recall and write down five *-itis* diseases they have studied. What organ is inflamed? What are the symptoms of the inflammation?

Improving Digestion

Review the guidelines provided in the feature. Are there other tips of which your students may be aware? Discuss with students aspects of their lifestyles that sometimes hinder them from following the guidelines to help the digestive process. Ask the class to develop a list of things that can be done to promote the development of healthful eating habits.

---

hotlink

stress For more information on managing stress in your life, see Chapter 9, page 214.

Improving Digestion

Americans spend millions of dollars a year on medications to aid in the digestive process. Much of this money is wasted. Promoting healthy digestion is a simple matter when you:

➤ Chew your food thoroughly.

➤ Eat slowly.

➤ Eat a balanced assortment of foods.

➤ Try to swallow your food without drinking liquids.

➤ Drink six to eight glasses of water daily.

➤ Limit your intake of carbonated, acidic beverages.

➤ Avoid eating fried foods or other greasy foods.

➤ Avoid eating as a way of dealing with problems, or when under extreme stress.

➤ By choosing a variety of foods that are high in fiber, you will promote the health of your digestive system.

ACTIVITY *Name foods other than fruits and vegetables that are good sources of fiber.*

■ Do not eat when you are under **stress**. Avoid using food as a way of coping with stress.

Problems of the Digestive System

Your complex digestive system usually functions normally, digesting and absorbing food and eliminating undigested material. However, problems can occur, some of them functional and some of them structural.

Functional Digestive System Problems

Even with care, on occasion problems with the digestive system arise for most people. These include indigestion, heartburn, gas, nausea, diarrhea, and constipation.

■ **Indigestion. Indigestion** refers to *a burning discomfort in the upper abdomen.* It may be accompanied by a buildup of gas and nausea. Indigestion can result from eating too much, eating too quickly, eating certain foods, stomach disorders, or stress. To prevent food-related indigestion, avoid eating foods that in the past have caused you discomfort, eat slowly, and avoid eating when under stress.

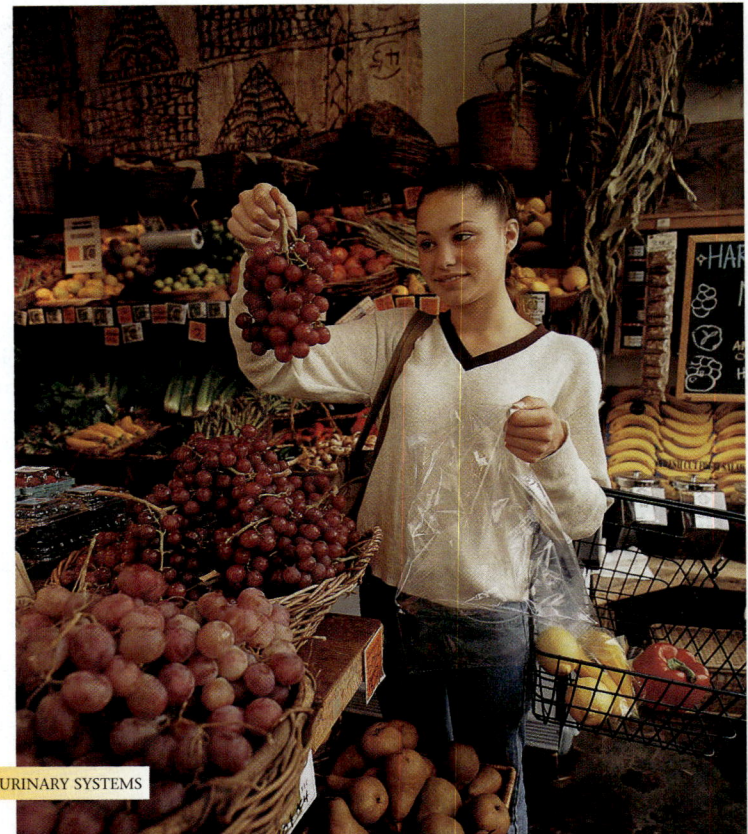

Myths & Realities

MYTH. An individual cannot live without all of the parts of the digestive system.

FACT. An individual can live a healthy life if some part has to be removed surgically. For example, a person can digest food even if the stomach has been removed, because most of the digestive process occurs after food leaves the stomach area. Individuals can live with up to two-thirds of their small intestine removed.

Following an operation in which a section of the colon is removed, solid wastes are eliminated into a bag attached to the individual in the lower abdominal area. The gallbladder's removal usually causes no health complications. Individuals in each of these cases usually have to make adjustments in their eating habits, but they can live healthy lives.

- **Heartburn.** Heartburn is a burning pain in the center of the chest that may travel from the tip of the breastbone to the throat. This condition has nothing to do with your heart. It is caused by *acid reflux*—a backflow of stomach acid into the esophagus. Acid reflux can occur if the sphincter muscle between the esophagus and stomach does not close tightly. The irritating stomach acids are responsible for the burning sensation of heartburn and can cause inflammation of the esophagus.

  Heartburn may also be a symptom of a **hiatal hernia,** *a condition in which part of the stomach pushes through an opening in the diaphragm.* If heartburn continues or recurs, it is important to consult a health care professional.

- **Gas.** A certain amount of gas in the stomach or the intestines is normal. An excess amount of gas, however, can cause a great deal of discomfort. Certain foods, including cooked onions and heavily spiced dishes, seem to be gas-producing for some people.

- **Nausea.** Nausea is a feeling of distress, fullness, and weakness and often precedes vomiting. It can be caused by motion (such as that on a boat or in a car), pathogens, medicines, drugs, or other substances in the stomach. Vomiting is a reflex response that provides a kind of built-in protection if you swallow a foreign substance. Vomiting is the result of reverse peristalsis, or waves of muscular contractions, in the stomach and esophagus.

HEALTH Online

Adding fiber to your diet helps decrease the risk of some cancers that affect the digestive system. Learn how cancers could be prevented by better health and eating habits at **health.glencoe.com**.

HEALTH Online

Invite students to expand upon the activity by investigating the fiber content of foods eaten in the home. If necessary, work with students to locate the fiber content line on the standard Nutrition Facts label (under carbohydrates) found on the majority of packaged food products. Have students share their findings and discuss strategies for making any necessary changes in their families' eating plans.

FONTBONNE CURRICULUM LIBRARY

Building Health Skills

Adding Sources of Fiber

ADDING FIBER to your daily intake of food during your teenage years can provide benefits that will last throughout your lifetime. There are two forms of fiber, soluble and insoluble. Soluble fiber, which dissolves in water, may lower cholesterol. Insoluble fiber, which does not dissolve in water, may help protect you against colon cancer and other bowel problems. To get more fiber from the foods you eat:

1. **Start the day with a good breakfast.** If you don't eat breakfast already, now is the time to start. Breakfast cereals made with oats or bran are excellent sources of soluble fiber. So are whole-grain muffins.

2. **Eat meatless meals several times a week.** Try a bean burrito with cheese at lunch or dinner. The legumes in it will give you a fiber boost, and the cheese will convert the beans—an incomplete protein by themselves—into a complete protein.

3. **Choose high-fiber snacks.** It's easy. Popcorn is a great source of fiber, and so are nuts. Reach for a piece of fruit, especially the kind with edible skin, such as apples and pears.

Building Health Skills

Adding Sources of Fiber
Skill: Nutrition

Show students these foods (or pictures of these foods): popcorn, an apple, oatmeal, pinto beans, lentils, a potato, and a carrot. Ask: What do all these foods have in common? *(Students may be able to identify them as good sources of dietary fiber.)* Then have students read the Building Health Skills feature to learn more about the benefits of fiber and about adding fiber to their diets. After they have read and discussed the feature, ask students to write entries in their private Health Journals, discussing their own goals for including fiber in their daily diets.

MORE ABOUT . . . . .

DIET AND DENTITION. The relationship between diet and dentition is a complex one—but it is evident that your teeth are affected by what you eat.

Paleontologists study wear patterns on teeth to get an idea of the type of food extinct species ate regularly. They compare microscopic scratches and signs of wear on fossilized teeth with those on the teeth of living animals whose diets are known.

Diets are also reflected by orthodontic problems. In populations like ours that eat relatively soft foods, the mechanical force of chewing is often insufficient to keep teeth aligned. In people who eat a coarser, tougher diet, fewer problems of alignment are found.

health lab

COMPARING ANTACIDS

Time Needed: about 45 minutes

Understanding Objectives:
Students will observe antacid products neutralizing an acid (vinegar) and will compare the effectiveness of different antacid products.

Focus on the Health Lab:
Show students the packages of the antacids to be used in the Health Lab, and ask: Which of these products do you have at home? How do you, or other members of your household, select a specific antacid to buy and use? Then explain that students will perform an experiment to observe and compare the effectiveness of these antacids.

Observation and Analysis:
Have students form small groups to conduct the experiment.

In Conclusion Answers:
Responses will vary. Let students continue in their same groups to discuss the results and their ideas about those results.

Further Investigation:
Have students plan and conduct a survey of consumers' antacid choices. How do the results of the survey compare with the results of the lab experiment?

L2 Parental Involvement

Explain that diarrhea can be serious if it is not treated properly. Have students ask their parents what steps were taken when, as infants or small children, they had diarrhea. Why is diarrhea more serious in an infant than in an adult?

health lab

COMPARING ANTACIDS

Magazine ads and TV commercials for over-the-counter medicines, which relieve the discomfort of indigestion and heartburn, share claims to be "better" or to "go to work faster." Are these claims true? A simple test can help you find out.

■ **Diarrhea.** Diarrhea is a condition in which the feces are watery and are expelled frequently. If food residue passes too quickly through the large intestine, it cannot absorb enough water, and diarrhea results. Numerous conditions can cause diarrhea, including a change in eating style, food poisoning, overeating, emotional turmoil, and nutritional deficiencies. Diarrhea can also be caused by viral and bacterial infections.

To avoid dehydration, it is important to replace the water and electrolytes lost during an attack of diarrhea by drinking plenty of liquids, especially water. Diarrhea usually clears up when the cause is eliminated. Medical help may be necessary.

■ **Constipation.** Constipation is a condition in which feces become dry and hard, and bowel movements are difficult. Feces that stay in the large intestine too long will have too much water absorbed from them. Constipation can be caused by a lack of fiber, erratic eating habits, drinking too little water, or lack of exercise. Healthful eating—especially of foods high in fiber—drinking plenty of water, and exercising regularly are the best ways to avoid constipation. It is rare for teenagers to suffer from chronic constipation.

When recommended by a health care professional, laxative drugs may be useful in clearing up constipation. However, continued use of laxatives should be avoided. Laxatives can cause diarrhea, abdominal cramps, gas, and a chemical imbalance in the blood. Some types may coat the intestine and prevent vitamin absorption. The body may also become dependent on laxatives and fail to function normally on its own.

420 CHAPTER 18 YOUR DIGESTIVE AND URINARY SYSTEMS

SCHOOL-TO-CAREER

DIETITIAN AND DIET TECHNICIAN. A registered dietitian is a professional trained in food and nutrition. Dietitians may work for hospitals, health maintenance organizations, weight-reduction centers, food service companies, or company cafeterias. Some work in private practice with medical or other health care professionals. They develop diets to meet special needs and counsel groups or individuals in making food choices. Dietitians need bachelor's degrees in food and nutrition, followed by one-year internships at approved institutions. They must pass a registered examination for dietitians. Students who do not wish to complete a four-year program may investigate two-year programs for diet technicians, who assist dietitians.

What you will need

- 8-ounce cups (250 ml) of water
- Self-stick labels
- Marking pen
- Samples of several commercial over-the-counter antacid remedies
- Stopwatch or watch with second hand
- Vinegar
- Eye dropper
- Litmus paper

What you will do

1. Label each cup of water with the name of the antacid remedy to be tested. Then dissolve a standard dose of the product in each cup.

2. Test one product at a time. Set the stopwatch or make note of the time in seconds. Add vinegar to the container, an eye-dropperful at a time. After each addition, test the acidity of the solution with litmus paper. Keep track of how much vinegar you add. Stop when the solution tests acidic. You will know this because the litmus paper will turn red.

3. For each container, note how much vinegar it took to make the solution acidic and how long it took.

In conclusion

1. Did one antacid neutralize the acid more quickly than the others?

2. Did one antacid neutralize more acid than the others?

3. Which antacid, if any, seemed to be the most effective?

4. What ingredient or ingredients listed on the product's label do you think contributed to the antacid's effectiveness?

5. What conclusions, if any, can you draw about the advertising of health products as a whole? about the comparative costs of the products?

Structural Digestive System Problems

Structural problems of the digestive system vary in seriousness. Most problems are temporary and not serious. However, if any problem persists for a long period of time or is accompanied by fever or other symptoms of illness, a health care professional should be consulted.

GALLSTONES

Gallstones are small crystals that form in the gallbladder when an upset occurs in the chemical composition of the bile. They may block the bile duct between the gallbladder and the duodenum, causing pain. Stones that do not cause symptoms may be left alone. Gallstones can be treated with medicines that dissolve them, or they can be shattered by ultrasound-guided shock waves. When symptoms are severe, the gallbladder may be surgically removed.

APPENDICITIS

Appendicitis is *the inflammation of the appendix,* which is a 3- to 4-inch (8- to 10-cm) extension at one end of the large intestine. When bacteria or other foreign matter lodges in the appendix, the closed end beyond the blockage becomes swollen and fills with pus. If the appendix ruptures, the infection spreads into the abdomen, which is an extremely serious condition. The symptoms of appendicitis include pain and cramps in the lower right portion of the abdomen, fever, loss of appetite, nausea, and vomiting. Medical care is essential. The usual treatment is surgical removal of the appendix.

LESSON 2   CARE AND PROBLEMS OF THE DIGESTIVE SYSTEM   **421**

L3 Researching

Ask a volunteer to prepare a report describing the differences in color and structure of kidney stones and gallstones. Ask the student to share the information with the class. Pictures or actual stones would enhance the report.

L3 Community Involvement

Have a student contact the local health department to acquire information about techniques to prevent transmission of hepatitis. Tell the student to share the information with the class.

L2 Researching

Introduce students to the problem of hepatitis, a serious inflammation of the liver that is most often caused by a viral infection. The severity of the disease depends upon the type of virus involved. Direct students to investigate the types of hepatitis and how it is transmitted. Ask that they share their findings with the class.

L3 Researching

Barium is used in diagnosing certain problems of the gastrointestinal tract. Have students find out what barium does and how it is used and then summarize their findings for the class.

L2 Discussing

Ask if any students have had appendectomies. What were their symptoms? What tests were done to determine their condition? Review with the class the role of white blood cells in fighting infections.

MEETING STUDENT DIVERSITY

DIABETICS. Individuals with diabetes have special needs in order for their digestive systems to function properly. They may need to take daily doses of insulin, usually by injection, to lead healthy lives. Modern technology has now produced an "artificial pancreas" in the form of an insulin pump for these individuals. The pump supplies insulin to their bodies continuously, eliminating the need for daily injections. The insulin pump is a small device that is embedded beneath the skin. A tube connects the pump to a large vein, where the insulin is injected into the bloodstream. Every two weeks the patient returns to the hospital to have the pump refilled with insulin.

L2 Discussing

Almost everyone experiences disorders of the digestive system. Ask students to list some of the digestive disorders they have experienced and answer the following questions: What caused the disorder? How did you treat the disorder? Did you have to use medicine for the disorder? Discuss responses with the class.

Making Responsible Decisions

1. Rashid, who is lactose intolerant, must decide whether to drink milk at his friend's house.
2. Rashid could (a) accept a glass of cold milk; (b) ask for a glass of water; (c) not have anything to drink.
3. Rashid might (a) satisfy his thirst but later suffer a painful reaction to the milk; (b) satisfy his thirst but possibly have to explain his refusal of the milk; (c) continue to feel thirsty but not have to deal with his reaction to lactose.
4. Rashid values his own health and comfort. He also values fitting in with his friends.
5. Responses will vary.
6. Students should explore both the short- and long-term consequences of their decisions.

L2 Decision Making

For further study on making responsible decisions, assign *Decision-Making Activity 18* in the TCR.

GASTRITIS

One of the most common disorders of the digestive system is gastritis, an inflammation of the mucous membrane that lines the stomach. Gastritis can be caused by irritation of the stomach lining from foods, aspirin, tobacco smoke, or alcohol or by bacterial infection. Symptoms include pain in the upper abdomen, nausea, and vomiting. A person with gastritis should avoid irritating substances. Antibiotics can cure the condition if bacteria are the cause. A health professional may also prescribe or recommend an acid controller or medication that "coats" the stomach lining.

LACTOSE INTOLERANCE

Lactose is one of the sugars present in milk. For the body to digest lactose, it must be broken down by lactase, an enzyme released by the lining of the small intestine. Some people have a deficiency of lactase, resulting in lactose **intolerance**—the inability to digest lactose. Undigested lactose ferments in the intestine and causes severe abdominal cramps, bloating, gas, and diarrhea. People with lactose intolerance should drink only lactase-reduced milk or use enzyme replacements that help break down lactose. Fermented milk products such as yogurt can be eaten without a problem.

PEPTIC ULCER

A **peptic ulcer** is *a sore in the lining of the digestive tract*. A peptic ulcer may occur in the esophagus, stomach (gastric ulcer), or duodenum. The lining of the stomach is constantly at risk from acid produced by the stomach wall. Gastric ulcers develop when something damages the protective lining and allows stomach acid to eat away at

hotlink

intolerance For more information on other food intolerances and food allergies, see Chapter 6, page 155.

Making Responsible Decisions

A Milk Dilemma

Rashid is over at his friend Curt's house. The teens have just returned from a softball game in the park and are feeling hot and thirsty. Upon examining the contents of the refrigerator, Curt announces that the only cold beverage is milk. This poses a problem for Rashid, who is lactose intolerant. Even though Rashid recalls how ill he felt the last time he consumed a dairy product, right now the thought of an ice-cold glass of milk is tempting. Besides, he knows the importance of restoring body fluids after vigorous physical activity. What should Rashid do?

What Would You Do?

Apply the six steps of the decision-making process to Rashid's problem.

1. **State the situation.**
2. **List the options.**
3. **Weigh the possible outcomes.**
4. **Consider your values.**
5. **Make a decision and act.**
6. **Evaluate the decision.**

PERSONAL HEALTH

MEDICATIONS FOR THE DIGESTIVE SYSTEM. Encourage students to gather information about a variety of products sold over the counter or by prescription as remedies for digestive problems such as ulcers, indigestion, constipation, heartburn, and diarrhea. Have them investigate side effects and long-term effects of prolonged use. They can gather such information from the *Physicians' Desk Reference*, literature on labels or in package inserts, the manufacturer upon request, or pharmacists and health care professionals. Have students choose five such products and list the side effects and consequences of overuse or misuse. They may end with a paragraph explaining why maintaining digestive health and preventing disorders is a better strategy than using remedies when the disorders occur.

it. Factors that increase the risk of ulcers include regular use of aspirin, ibuprofen, and other anti-inflammatory drugs, smoking, and infection with the bacterium *Helicobacter pylori (H. pylori)*.

The typical symptom of a gastric ulcer is a gnawing pain in the abdomen when the stomach is empty. Ulcers can cause bleeding in the stomach. Without treatment, ulcers may perforate, or break through, the stomach wall. Ulcers may be treated with medicines that neutralize or reduce stomach acids or with antibiotics.

COLITIS

Colitis is inflammation of the colon. It may be caused by a virus, an amoeba, a bacterium such as the one that causes peptic ulcers, or stress. Symptoms include diarrhea (usually with blood and mucus), abdominal pain, and sometimes fever. The cause of ulcerative colitis is unknown. In most cases, medical treatment controls the disease.

HEMORRHOIDS

Hemorrhoids are swollen veins in the lower rectum and anus and are the result of increased pressure in the veins of the anus. They are most common in people with constipation or who sit a lot, in pregnant women, and following childbirth. Itching, pain, and bleeding are signs of hemorrhoids. Regular exercise and eating fiber-rich foods can help reduce your risk of developing hemorrhoids.

TOOTH DECAY

It may surprise you to find **tooth decay** listed as a digestive system problem. Your teeth are part of your digestive system. Tooth decay weakens a tooth and affects the way a person bites and chews food. This is one more reason to care for your teeth.

hotlink

tooth decay For more information on tooth decay and strategies for maintaining healthy teeth, see Chapter 7, page 167.

LESSON 2 *Review*

Reviewing Facts and Vocabulary

1. Why is fiber so important to the health of your digestive system?
2. What are some of the causes of indigestion?
3. What makes tooth decay a problem of the digestive system?

Thinking Critically

4. *Analyzing.* How do nutrition and exercise contribute to the prevention of many common digestive system disorders?
5. *Synthesizing.* Review the digestive disorders detailed in the chapter.

Summarize what you have learned by stating one or two concepts that apply to digestive disorders in general.

Applying Health Skills

6. *In Your Home and School.* Visit a drugstore or the health care aisle of a supermarket. Make a list of over-the-counter medicines for common digestive disorders that are available. Make notes on what each product can be used for. Then suggest a behavior that might eliminate the problem without the need for medicine. Share your list with your family and classmates.

LESSON 2 CARE AND PROBLEMS OF THE DIGESTIVE SYSTEM **423**

CHAPTER 18 • LESSON 2

ASSESS

EVALUATING THE LESSON

Assign and discuss the Lesson 2 Review; then administer, grade, and discuss the *Lesson 57 Quiz* in the TCR. ☞

RETEACHING

- Ask students to list the types of digestive disorders discussed in this lesson. Have them describe how these disorders can be avoided or eliminated.
- Have students complete *Reteaching Activity 57* in the TCR. ☞

ENRICHMENT

Ask students to further investigate digestive disorders. Suggest that they ask the school dietitian about disorders that are caused by food contamination.

CLOSE

Guide students in discussing the most important concepts studied in this lesson. Have them write a plan of action on behaviors they will change to prevent digestive disorders.

Lesson 2 Review

Answers to Reviewing Facts and Vocabulary

1. Fiber helps food move through the intestines.
2. Indigestion can result from eating too much, eating too quickly, eating certain foods, stomach disorders, or stress.
3. The teeth are part of the digestive system. If they don't function properly, they affect the rest of the system, making digestion more difficult.

Answers to Thinking Critically

4.–5. Answers will vary.

The Urinary System

J ust as your city or community has a fleet of sanitation trucks that systematically remove waste and prevent its accumulation, so your body has its own waste removal systems. One of these systems, the digestive system, was covered in Lesson 1. Another such system is the urinary system.

HEALTH TERMS
urine
nephrons
ureters
bladder
urethra
cystitis
urethritis
incontinence
hemodialysis

HEALTH CONCEPTS
- Filtering waste from the circulatory system is essential to maintaining life.
- The urinary system regulates the concentration and volume of blood by removing and restoring selected amounts of water and chemicals.
- Any change in the normal functioning of the urinary system represents a health threat and should be reported to a health care professional.

Functions of the Urinary System

T he chief function of the urinary system is removal of water-soluble waste products that result from chemical changes to cells. This *liquid waste material*—**urine**—contains nitrogen and, therefore, would become toxic if allowed to remain in your body. Urination, the process whereby this waste is removed, is thus essential to life.

Structure of the Urinary System

T he urinary system consists of several organs that are linked together, forming the urinary tract. These include the kidneys, the ureters, the bladder, and the urethra.

FOCUS

LESSON OBJECTIVES

After studying this lesson, students should be able to

- explain the function of each organ of the urinary system.
- describe problems of the urinary system.

MOTIVATOR

Write the following on the chalkboard for students to work on while attendance is being taken: *Why is it important to drink an adequate amount of water every day?*

INTRODUCING THE LESSON

Introduce the lesson by explaining that the kidneys are responsible for removing waste products that can be dissolved in water from the body. Refer to the Motivator. Ask students to share their responses with the class. Inform students that there are other reasons why drinking water is important for the body to function effectively. Explain that this lesson will focus on the importance of the urinary system in excreting wastes from the body.

INTRODUCING HEALTH TERMS

- Have students make flash cards for the vocabulary terms. On one side, have them write the word. On the other side, have them identify the body system, the definition, and a page reference.
- Ask students to complete Vocabulary Activity 18 and Chapter Study Guide 18 in the *Student Workbook.*

Lesson 3 Resources

◄ *Drinking six to eight glasses of water a day will help keep your urinary system functioning efficiently.*

ACTIVITY *Explain why other liquids, such as coffee or cola drinks, should not be counted as part of the six to eight glasses of water.*

The Kidneys

Your kidneys are your body's master chemists. Shaped like beans and each about the size of a fist, the kidneys lie on either side of the spine in the small of the back. They are embedded in a protective mass of fatty tissue. Within each kidney are as many as one million highly specialized, microscopic units called **nephrons** (NEH-frahnz), *the functional units of the kidneys*. Each nephron consists of a tubule and a cluster of capillaries, called a glomerulus, that functions as a filtering funnel. Your kidneys filter about 50 gallons (189.2 l) of blood each day.

Your kidneys filter waste products from your blood and modify the amount of salts and water excreted in the urine according to your body's needs. Your kidneys are miraculous organs, monitoring and maintaining your body's acid-base and water balances automatically. When your blood and body fluids become too acid or too alkaline, your kidneys alter the acidity of the urine to restore the balance. When your body is dehydrated, your kidneys release a hormone that signals your brain. In turn, your brain sends a message you recognize as "I'm thirsty," and you are stimulated to take a drink.

The urine that your kidneys excrete is carried along to the next step in its journey by **ureters**—*tubes that connect the kidneys with the bladder*.

TEACH

L1 Discussing

Ask students to describe how the kidneys act as a filter to remove waste from the body. Have students list other filters used to clean, such as air conditioner filters, filters used in automobiles, etc. How do these filters work compared to the kidneys?

L3 Guest Speaker

If possible, invite as a speaker someone who is a candidate for or a recipient of a kidney, liver, or pancreatic transplant. Ask the speaker to answer questions such as these: What advantages do you see in the transplant? disadvantages? Why are (or were) you a candidate for this treatment? What are the emotional costs of this treatment?

L2 Class Activity

Using a torso model or chart, trace the flow of fluid wastes from the kidneys. Ask the class to identify areas in which stones might get lodged. Why can infections easily travel to the kidney from the bladder? Does the size of the urethra vary with age or sex? How are kidney stones treated? (Surgery, diet, exercise, lasers?)

L2 Class Activity

Using a pictorial model, show students the structure of a nephron. Ask students to make a drawing of the nephron and label its parts.

COOPERATIVE LEARNING

WEIGHT-REDUCTION AIDS: WHAT IS BEING LOST? Many weight-loss aids contain such substances as caffeine, diuretics, laxatives, and nervous system stimulants such as ephedra-containing herbs. Group students. Assign each group member a different weight-loss formula to evaluate. Have students list the ingredients in the products and look up each substance in reference sources. Which herbs, for example, contain caffeine, stimulate the nervous system, and/or have diuretic or laxative effects? Have each group discuss the benefits and risks of using each product, discussing such questions as how a product containing laxatives and diuretics appears to promote weight loss. Would such a loss be stable? Have them recommend, discourage, or give a qualified recommendation for each product.

L2 ## Class Activity

Using a body systems model, ask students to compare the size of the bile duct with the size of the aorta and the size of the urethra. How are these vessels similar?

L2 ## Discussing

Kidneys can sustain damage both before birth and after birth. Discuss with the class some of the causes of kidney problems. (*Examples: diet, drugs, hypertension, diabetes, heredity, genetic disorders.*) What can students do to protect the function of their kidneys?

L2 ## Explaining

Explain that urinalysis is an important part of a physical examination. Analysis of the urine can help a doctor diagnose certain diseases.

L3 ## Researching

Allow a volunteer to calculate the cost of kidney dialysis for an individual for one year. A hospital billing office or insurance agency can assist by providing current figures. Ask the volunteer to share his or her findings with the class.

L2 ## Researching

Instruct a volunteer to determine when in prenatal development the kidneys are developed. (*First trimester.*) What prudent measures should be taken by a pregnant woman to assure proper development of the kidneys? Have the student report back to the class.

L2 ## Cooperative Learning

Have students complete *Cooperative Learning Activity 18,* "Jigsaw the Digestive and Urinary Systems," in the TCR.

The Bladder and the Urethra

Your **bladder** is *a hollow, muscular organ that acts as a reservoir for urine.* It is like a holding tank, but it has walls that can expand. The bladder in males is somewhat larger than the bladder in females. The average bladder may hold as much as a pint (500–600 ml) of urine. The need to urinate is stimulated as the bladder becomes full. Sphincter muscles under your voluntary control relax and allow urine to flow through the **urethra**, *the tube that leads from the bladder to the outside of the body.* The urethra is different, both structurally and functionally, for males and females. The male urethra is much longer than the female urethra: 9 inches (23 cm) versus 1½ inches (4 cm). Whereas the female urethra has the sole function of emptying waste products from the body, the male urethra has a second function—the release of semen, a fluid necessary for the process of reproduction. More information about this process can be found in Chapter 19.

Care of the Urinary System

Waste products that are not removed from your body can be toxic to your body's organs and tissues. Care of your urinary system can assure the regular movement of these wastes out of your body and keep you healthy.

The main way to care for your urinary system is to drink plenty of fluids—at least six to eight glasses of water every day and more in hot weather. A well-balanced eating style also plays a part in the care of the urinary system. Practicing good personal health care will help prevent the risk of bacterial infection to the organs of your urinary system. Regular physical checkups are necessary to detect changes in urine content.

Your urinary system removes waste products and excess water or chemical substances from your body.

ACTIVITY *Describe the process by which your urinary system removes body wastes.*

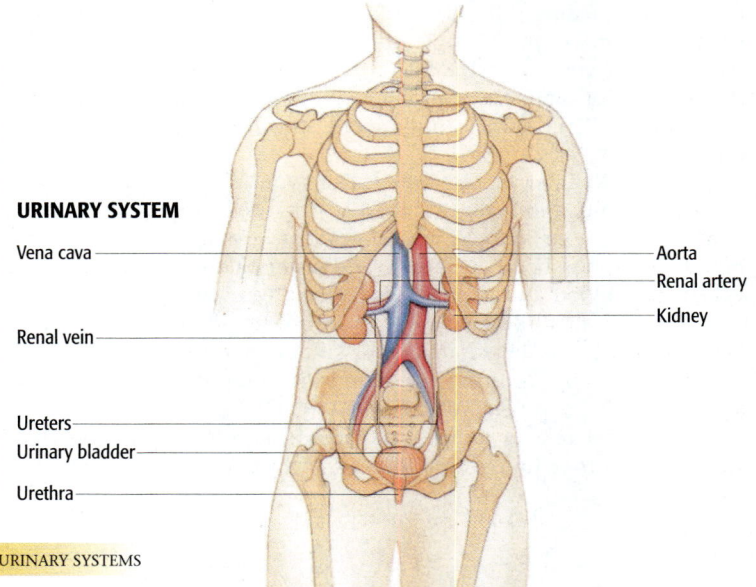

URINARY SYSTEM

Vena cava
Renal vein
Ureters
Urinary bladder
Urethra
Aorta
Renal artery
Kidney

Teens Making a Difference

...COMPASSION...CARING...EMPATHY

Will, 17, likes to play lacrosse and basketball, listen to music, and hang out with friends. He doesn't take any of these activities for granted because, as a kidney transplant recipient, he knows how lucky he is to simply be alive. In turn, he feels a responsibility to help others receive the gift of life as well, and he has made organ donation one of his causes.

RECEIVING THE GIFT "I was born with a kidney disorder called Post Urethral Valve Syndrome," he begins. "That pretty much means my kidneys didn't work right. I was sick from the time I was born. I had to be fed by a tube for a while, and I couldn't run or be as active as other kids. I was on the waiting list for the kidney for a long time," he says. Will speaks of the organ donor to whom he owes so much. "I know that the donor was a young teacher who died in a car accident. We met her parents last year for the first time. I told them how much it meant for me to meet them. They had to give their okay for the donation, so they played a part in saving my life, too.

EDUCATING OTHERS I try to do things for Gift of Life, an organ transplant organization, and for St. Christopher's Hospital for Children, where I had my transplant. The Phillies had an Organ Donation Day, and I got involved. They had organ donor cards at the baseball stadium, and I talked to people from the radio station about it and taped a message. I even got to throw out the first pitch," he adds. "That was really fun. Last year I gave a talk at my high school about the importance of organ donation. I talk to kids at the hospital who are going through transplantation. I take part in the Transplant Olympics, an event where organ recipients from all over come together to compete in athletic contests. I've also done interviews for articles because education about organ donation is so important."

WHAT YOU CAN DO "I think it's incredible to be an organ donor. One person donating organs can save not just one life but many lives. The waiting lists are huge. People die waiting. You never know who is going to need a transplant," Will concludes. "It could be you or someone you love."

WILL'S STORY
1. How does Will's story demonstrate the importance of both giving and receiving?
2. What work does he do to educate others?

YOUR STORY
1. What values will you be demonstrating by signing an organ donor card or discussing willingness to be an organ donor with your parents?
2. How can you educate others about the importance of organ donation? What might the benefit be to yourself and others?

MORE ABOUT . . . . .

THE KIDNEYS. Kidney stones range in size from very tiny (and passable) to an inch (2.5 centimeters) or more in diameter. Pain is caused when a large stone gets caught in the bladder, ureter, or renal pelvis.

Kidney stones can sometimes be dissolved by a machine that uses shock waves to break large stones into smaller, sand-sized particles.

An adult's kidney weighs about 5 ounces. In an adult, the two kidneys filter about 425 gallons of blood each day.

Teens Making a Difference

Giving and Receiving the Gift of Life

Discussing. Ask students to read the feature and answer the questions at its end. Point out that Will is in every way a typical teen and that his interest in helping others is not confined to the subject of organ donation. Read the following quotes by Will and ask students for reactions to what he says:

- *I do [church] service, making meals for the hungry, and I'm going to help Habitat for Humanity. I write for the school paper and the local paper, too. I'm going to be writing about organ donation, but mostly right now, for the local paper, I cover sports.*
- *Signing an organ donor card shows your generosity and your gratitude toward humanity in general.*
- *You never know who is going to need a transplant...It could be you or someone you love.*

Class Activity. Ask students to do one or more of the following:
- Invite the recipient of a donated organ to speak to the class about his or her experience and how he or she benefited from someone else's generosity.
- Have a speaker from a national donor program come to class to tell about the importance of organ donation and how people can become organ donors.

Answers. *Will's Story*
1. Will received a kidney then reached out to help others going through transplantation; he thanked the donor's family.
2. He used his experience to speak and write about the importance of becoming an organ donor.

Responses. *Your Story* **1–2.** Sign an organ donation card; have organ donor designated on your driver's license; discuss with family about organ donation and have your wishes put in writing; generosity, kindness, caring, compassion, etc; by speaking out, educating others.

L2 Researching

Explain to students that a lithotripter is a device that crumbles kidney stones so that an individual is not required to undergo surgery to remove kidney stones. Ask students to research a lithotripter and write a report on this modern procedure to remove kidney stones.

L3 Researching

Let volunteers investigate the complications of transplants and dialysis and prepare a table comparing these treatments. Are there side effects to both therapies? Are costs comparable?

L2 Class Activity

Ask students to write paragraphs explaining why a person can survive with a single functioning kidney.

L1 Explaining

Point out to students that 30 years ago, organ transplants were experimental. Explain that technological advances have made these procedures safer than ever before. However, there are many more people in need of new organs than there are organs being donated. In the United States, for example, more than 25,000 patients are awaiting kidney transplants. Discuss with students how continued progress in the development of artificial organs can reduce the need for donors.

CHARACTER IN ACTION

Sensitivity in Times of Illness

Think back to a time when you felt really sick and needed special understanding or attention. You can put yourself in other people's shoes to develop understanding and **sensitivity** to the needs of others when they are ill or not feeling well.

Character Check The next time you have the opportunity to help someone who is ill, practice being sensitive in the following ways:

➤ Imagine what it might be like to feel the way he or she is feeling.

➤ Do not make the person feel guilty or weak for having his or her condition or illness.

➤ Learn about the condition or illness.

➤ Offer to do specific tasks to help make the person comfortable or speed his or her recovery efforts.

Problems of the Urinary System

Because of the shortness of the urethra in females, it is prone to allowing infectious bacteria to reach the bladder. Urinary tract infections are therefore more common in females than in males. Any changes in urine color, odor, or frequency should be discussed with a health care professional; so should any discomfort or pain during urination. These symptoms might signal one of the following conditions:

- **Cystitis** is *a bacterial infection of the bladder* that occurs most frequently in females. Symptoms include a burning sensation and a high frequency of urination. Fever may be present as well as blood in the urine. If left untreated, the infection can move to the ureter and kidneys.

- **Urethritis** is *an inflammation of the urethra*. It is usually caused by an infection. The passage of urine becomes painful and difficult.

Another urinary system problem is urinary **incontinence**, *the inability of the body to control the bladder and the elimination of waste*. Urinary incontinence may occur if the sphincter muscle that closes the urethra is weak or damaged. This condition is more common in older adults.

Kidney Problems

Because the function of the kidneys is so essential to maintaining the balance of fluids in the body, any disruption of their function is potentially serious. However, only one normal kidney is needed for good health. Kidney problems are rarely life-threatening unless both kidneys are affected. Some problems include the following:

NEPHRITIS

Nephritis is an inflammation of the nephrons in the kidneys. Symptoms may include high blood pressure, weakness, fatigue, and swelling of body tissues.

KIDNEY STONES

Kidney stones are small, hard crystals formed from substances in the urine. Small stones may pass out of the body in the urine. With larger stones, or if an infection is present or the urinary tract is blocked, medical treatment is necessary.

In the past, surgery was necessary to remove a kidney stone. Now, however, a procedure called lithotripsy has largely replaced surgery. High-intensity sound waves are focused on the area where the stones are located. The sound waves pass through the body and literally disintegrate the stones. The process is painless, and the resulting fragments pass out of the body in urine.

UREMIA

When the kidneys are unable to rid wastes from the body, poisonous substances build up. The presence of excess urea and other

HOME AND COMMUNITY CONNECTION

ANTIBIOTICS AND THE GOOD GUYS. Students have learned that microorganisms in the body provide health benefits. Encourage students to conduct research to find out how the use of antibiotics affects beneficial microorganisms. What problems do people develop in the urinary tract subsequent to a course of antibiotics? Have them find out what doctors and other health care professionals recommend to protect urinary tract health after a course of antibiotics has killed the beneficial organisms along with the disease-causing pathogens. Ask students to find out how they can encourage the growth of beneficial microorganisms in their systems, while discouraging the growth of fungi and other organisms that can cause health problems.

chemical waste products in the blood is called uremia. Uremia develops as a result of kidney failure.

KIDNEY FAILURE

Kidney failure can be acute, meaning of sudden onset, or chronic, meaning it develops gradually. It may be caused by blockage of urine, a serious case of nephritis, loss of blood, or any disease that causes damage to the kidneys. Treatment of acute kidney failure varies depending on the cause. Three techniques are in use today to help people who suffer from chronic kidney failure.

- **Hemodialysis** (HEE-moh-dy-AL-uh-suhs) is *a technique in which an artificial kidney machine removes waste products from the blood.* A needle connected to plastic tubing passes blood from the patient to the kidney machine and the cleansed blood back to the patient. The process takes two to six hours and is usually carried out three times a week. This kind of dialysis usually takes place in a hospital or clinic setting, although it may also be carried out in the patient's home.
- Peritoneal dialysis involves insertion of a catheter—a tube that provides a passageway for fluids—through an abdominal incision into the peritoneal cavity. It uses the peritoneum, a thin membrane that surrounds the digestive organs, to filter the blood and remove waste products. Peritoneal dialysis allows the patient to be treated at home.
- In the third technique, kidney transplant, the diseased kidney is surgically replaced with a healthy kidney from a donor. Kidney transplants are successful in more than 80 percent of cases when the donor is not related to the patient and 90 percent if the donor is a close blood relative.

▼ *Medical technology has made it possible to treat kidney failure by filtering blood artificially.*

ACTIVITY *List the steps you should take to maintain the health of your urinary system.*

LESSON 3

Review

Reviewing Facts and Vocabulary

1. Describe the function of the kidneys.
2. Define the terms *urine, nephrons,* and *hemodialysis.*

Thinking Critically

3. **Analyzing.** How does drinking plenty of water each day promote a healthy urinary system?
4. **Analyzing.** How might kidney dialysis affect a person's lifestyle?

Applying Health Skills

5. ***In Your Home and School.*** Ask the butcher for lambs' kidneys, which are similar in size and shape to your own. Split the kidney in half lengthwise (you may want to ask the butcher to do this for you) and make a crosscut to see the inside. Use a magnifying glass to locate the tiny, threadlike nephrons. Find the tubes that collect liquid from the nephrons and drain it from the kidney through the ureter. Share your findings with your family and classmates.

LESSON 3   THE URINARY SYSTEM   **429**

ASSESS

EVALUATING THE LESSON

Assign and discuss the Lesson 3 Review; then administer, grade, and discuss the *Lesson 58 Quiz* in the TCR. ▱

RETEACHING

- Encourage students to explain the function of the urinary system in eliminating waste from the body. Have them describe the process, beginning with the function of the kidneys.
- Ask students to complete *Reteaching Activity 58* in the TCR. ▱
- Use *Transparency 67* to review the parts of the urinary system. 🖐

ENRICHMENT

Have students research a kidney dialysis machine. Have them use the following questions to guide their research: How does it work, and why do people need it? What problems are associated with it? Is there an adequate number of machines in your community? What is CAPD or continuous ambulatory peritoneal dialysis? Why do some people choose it over kidney dialysis machines?

CLOSE

Ask students to discuss the most important concepts studied in this lesson.

Lesson 3 Review

Answers to Reviewing Facts and Vocabulary

1. The kidneys filter waste products from your blood and modify the amount of salts and water excreted in the urine.
2. Urine: liquid body waste. Nephrons: the functional units of the kidneys. Hemodialysis: a technique in which an artificial kidney machine removes waste from the blood.

Answers to Thinking Critically

3. It helps the kidneys cleanse the blood by keeping up a continuous flow of waste-carrying fluid out of the body.
4. Kidney dialysis would make travel difficult. Also, a person would have to plan his or her activities around being on the dialysis machine. It would certainly restrict a person's freedom of movement and activity.

Health Skills Activities

Health Skills Activities

ACTIVITY 1
HEALTH SKILLS
Comprehending Health Concepts, Health Advocacy

➤ **National Standards**
This activity meets these National Health Standards: 1.1; 1.6; 7.4.

Teach
• Review with students the organs of the digestive system. Include such parts as the teeth and tongue.
• Arrange group composition and size to ensure that all organs are given some coverage. Due to the number of organs in the digestive tract, you may wish to assign regions of the tract (e.g., oral cavity, intestine) to groups, making each group responsible for the organs of its region.

ACTIVITY 2
HEALTH SKILLS
Goal Setting, Health Advocacy

➤ **National Standards**
This activity meets these National Health Standards: 6.4; 7.2; 7.4.

Teach
• Begin with a review of the Food Guide Pyramid and Dietary Guidelines, both discussed in Chapter 5. Underscore the daily requirement for water.
• You may also refer to Glencoe's Health Web site (health.glencoe.com) for links to sites with this type of information.
• Recommend that students make copies of their pamphlet to circulate among family members and others in the community who could benefit from this knowledge.

Activity 1 — Digestive System—What's Your Function?

The digestive system is composed of many different organs that work together. Do you know all these organs and how to maintain the health of each? As a class, you will write an informational booklet about digestion.

Directions
1. With a group, select an organ of the digestive system.
2. Using information from the chapter, determine the functions of the organ you have selected. Describe the best ways to maintain the health of this organ and what problems when care is not taken in choosing foods, rate of speed in eating, and so on.
3. Include photos, illustrations, or other visual aids if possible.
4. Combine your findings with those of other groups. Arrange your booklet in the order in which digestion (mouth first, then esophagus, and so on.).

Time
50 minutes
Materials
colored markers, paper, pen or pencil

Self-Assessment
✓ Correctly described the functions of the organ selected and identified ways to maintain its health.
✓ Listed at least two problems that can occur when care is not taken.

Activity 2 — Water, Water Everywhere

You have learned that one of the keys to a healthy urinary system is drinking plenty of fluids. Many people find it difficult, however, to drink 8 glasses of water in a day. Is there an alternative?

Directions
1. With a group, think about and list fruits, vegetables, and other foods you would describe as juicy (for example, oranges, tomatoes, and watermelon).
2. Compare your list with that of other groups. Investigate the actual water content of these and other foods by speaking with a family and consumer science teacher in the school or visiting the Web site your teacher recommended.
3. Use the information to create a pamphlet explaining how people can meet their daily water requirement through "solid" foods.

Time
50 minutes (20 minutes for discussion, 30 minutes for research)
Materials
paper and pencil, computer hooked up to the Internet

Self-Assessment
✓ Identified at least three foods with high water content.
✓ Created a persuasive and eye-catching health pamphlet.

ASSESSMENT SCORING

Using a four-level rubric, the student has achieved a 4 if:

ACTIVITY 1
✔ Student correctly described the functions of the organ or region selected
✔ Student identified ways to maintain the health of the organ selected.
✔ Student identified problems that can occur when care is not taken in food choices or manner in which food is eaten.
✔ Student developed booklet with group.

ACTIVITY 2
✔ Student recognized of the importance of water as a nutrient and key to urinary health.
✔ Student demonstrated a retention of key concepts from other areas of health.
✔ Student identified foods with high water content.
✔ Student took part in creating a persuasive and informative pamphlet.

Camera in a Capsule

Soon doctors might prescribe a pill to view the inside of their patients' intestines.

In the past, doctors diagnosed digestive problems by using X rays or endoscopy, which involves sedating a person and guiding a tube with a camera attached down the throat into the stomach and intestinal tract.

Now physicians are developing a less invasive device. Called pill endoscopy, the device uses a dime-size capsule that contains a miniature camera. A patient swallows the capsule. As the tablet moves through the digestive system, it transmits signals that are downloaded as images on a computer.

On his 1998 trip into outer space, former U.S. Sen. John Glenn swallowed a device similar to a pill endoscopy capsule to measure his core body temperature. The device offers several advantages over endoscopy.

"It's relatively painless," said Dr. Paul Swain. Second, the pill's camera would provide images of the intestine that before now have been too difficult to reach with an endoscope camera.

But there also are drawbacks. Physicians can use endoscopies to perform biopsies, which means collecting tissue samples, to test for cancer. They also can use the endoscopy device to stop bleeding.

The biggest disadvantage of the pill is the inability to direct the device. Physicians performing traditional endoscopy can aim the camera at areas to examine more closely. But the free-floating nature of the pill makes that impossible.

Think About It

1. How is a pill endoscopy different from a traditional endoscopy?
2. What are the advantages of this new technology? What are the drawbacks?
3. How do you think promising new devices and techniques become accepted medical practice?

CNN HEALTH NEWS **431**

MORE ABOUT . . . . .

TECHNOLOGY AND SCIENCE. The capsule used in pill endoscopy contains a miniature video camera, a light source, batteries, and a transmitter. The camera lens is designed with a fixed focal length and can transmit video data for up to six hours.

The signals from the camera are received by an antenna array. The antennas, similar to the readers on an EKG test, are taped to the patient. Image data is passed from the antennas to a recorder worn on the patient's waist.

Finally, the recorder sends the data to a computer, which translates the data into images and produces a 20-minute video segment.

CHAPTER 18 Review

CHECKING COMPREHENSION

- Assign and discuss the chapter review.
- Use the MindJogger Videoquiz to review the chapter.

CHAPTER 18 REVIEW ANSWERS

Using Health Terms

1. gastric acid
2. bile
3. ingestion
4. chyme
5. peristalsis
6. digestion
7. mastication
8. absorption
9. elimination
10. indigestion
11. hiatal hernia
12. appendicitis
13. peptic ulcer
14. urethra
15. hemodialysis
16. bladder
17. urethritis
18. urine
19. nephrons
20. ureters

RECALLING THE FACTS

1. Biting, chewing, swallowing, peristalsis, absorption, and elimination are the mechanical processes that take place during digestion.
2. The chemical processes that take place during digestion are the breaking down of carbohydrates in saliva, the mixing of food with gastric acids in the stomach, and secretions from the liver, pancreas, and gallbladder.
3. The sphincter muscles prevent chyme from backing up.
4. Most of the chemical breakdown of food takes place in the small intestine.
5. The main functions of the large intestine are to absorb water and eliminate food.

Using Health Terms

On a separate sheet of paper, write the term that best matches each definition below.

LESSON 1

1. Secretions from the stomach lining that contain pepsin and hydrochloric acid.
2. A yellowish-green, bitter fluid important in the breakdown of fats.
3. The taking of food into the body.
4. A creamy, fluid mixture of food and gastric juices.
5. A series of involuntary muscular contractions.
6. The mechanical and chemical breakdown of foods for use by the body's cells.
7. The process of chewing.
8. The passage of digested food from the digestive tract into the circulatory system.
9. The expulsion of undigested food or body wastes.

LESSON 2

10. A burning discomfort in the upper abdomen.
11. A condition in which part of the stomach pushes through an opening in the diaphragm.
12. The inflammation of the appendix.
13. A sore in the lining of the digestive tract.

LESSON 3

14. The tube that leads from the bladder to the outside of the body.
15. Use of artificial kidney machine to remove waste products from the blood.
16. A hollow, muscular organ that acts as a reservoir for urine.
17. An inflammation of the urethra.
18. Liquid waste material.
19. The functional units of the kidneys.
20. Tubes that connect the kidneys with the bladder.

Recalling the Facts

Using complete sentences, answer the following questions.

LESSON 1

1. What are the mechanical processes that take place during digestion?
2. What are the chemical processes that take place during digestion?
3. What is the role of the sphincter muscles located along the digestive tract?
4. In what part of the digestive system does most of the chemical breakdown of food take place?
5. What are the two main functions of the large intestine?

LESSON 2

6. What causes heartburn?
7. What is a hiatal hernia?
8. List three symptoms that may be present in a person suffering from appendicitis.
9. What is lactose intolerance?
10. List three ways to prevent tooth decay.

LESSON 3

11. Name the four parts of the urinary system.
12. In what body organ is urine stored?
13. Why are the kidneys important?
14. Name and define four problems that may be associated with the urinary system.
15. Describe the process of hemodialysis.

6. Acid reflux, or the backflow of gastric acid, causes heartburn.
7. Hiatal hernia is a condition in which part of the stomach pushes through an opening in the diaphragm.
8. The symptoms of appendicitis are pain and cramps in the lower right portion of the abdomen, fever, loss of appetite, nausea, and vomiting.
9. Lactose intolerance is the inability to digest the sugar, lactose, in milk as a result of a missing digestive enzyme, lactase.
10. Brushing at least twice daily, flossing daily, eating a nutritious diet rich in calcium, avoiding sugary foods.
11. The four parts of the urinary system are the kidneys, the ureters, the bladder, and the urethra.

Thinking Critically

LESSON 1

1. **Synthesizing.** Explain why the teeth should be included in any discussion of the digestive system.
2. **Analyzing.** Summarize the work of gastric juices.
3. **Analyzing.** What makes the liver, gallbladder, and pancreas important to the digestive system even though they are not part of it?

LESSON 2

4. **Analyzing.** In what ways are smoking, stress, and digestive problems related?

5. **Synthesizing.** Develop a plan that would help young people prevent gastrointestinal problems.

LESSON 3

6. **Synthesizing.** Make a diagram or chart of the urinary system of the human body to show how this system works. Name and label the parts of the system and tell how each part functions.
7. **Evaluating.** Think of some ways in which you could determine whether your urinary system is healthy.

Making the Connection

1. **Science.** Research one of the digestive problems described in Lesson 2. Write a short paper on its causes, symptoms, and cures.
2. **Math.** Calculate the cost to an individual of kidney dialysis for one year based on average costs of treatment in your local area. A hospital billing office or a medical insurer can assist by providing current figures. Share your findings with the class.

BEYOND THE CLASSROOM

PARENTAL INVOLVEMENT Ask your parents to share with you any problems they have experienced with their digestive or urinary systems. Ask them to describe their symptoms, to tell what actions they took to correct the problem, and to evaluate the effectiveness of the treatment. Work together at devising a plan that reduces the risk of future problems of the digestive or urinary system.

COMMUNITY INVOLVEMENT Find out what support groups are available in your community for people suffering from digestive and urinary system problems. There may, for example, be groups for people with colitis or irritable bowel syndrome. Prepare a pamphlet listing the name of each group, its contact person and telephone number, meeting location, and when the group meets. In addition, indicate the types of medical specialists who treat these problems. Make the pamphlet available through your school health office.

SCHOOL-TO-CAREER
Technology. Find out what is involved in kidney transplants. How do physicians match a donor and a recipient? How long is the average wait for a donor organ? What advancements have been made in the procedure? What is the success rate for this type of surgery?

Thinking Critically

1. The teeth should be included because they begin the process of digesting by biting and chewing food.
2. Gastric juices break food down chemically in the stomach.
3. The liver, gallbladder, and pancreas secrete chemicals that are vital to the body's use of the nutrients made available in the process of digestion.
4.–7. Answers will vary.

Making the Connection

1.–2. Research findings will vary.

Evaluate

- Use the reproducible *Chapter 18 Test* in the TCR, or construct your own using the Testmaker software. ☞ 💾
- Use *Performance Assessment Activity 18* in the TCR. ☞

Enrichment

Ask students to complete *Cross-Curriculum Activity 18* in the TCR. ☞

Beyond the Classroom

Keep students involved in the community, and encourage parent participation by assigning the activities on this page for students to work on outside of class.

12. Urine is stored in the bladder.
13. The kidneys are important because they filter waste products from the blood and modify the amount of salts and water excreted in the urine according to your body's needs.
14. Cystitis: a bacterial infection of the bladder. Urethritis: an inflammation of the urethra. Nephritis: an inflammation of the nephrons. Kidney stones: small, hard crystals formed from substances in the urine. Uremia: the presence of excess urea and other chemical waste products in the blood. Kidney failure: the inability of the kidney(s) to function.
15. In hemodialysis, the blood passes through a tube into an artificial kidney machine for cleaning, and then is returned to the body.

Your Body's Reproductive System

	FEATURES	CLASSROOM RESOURCES

LESSON 1

The Male Reproductive System

pages 436–441

Making Responsible Decisions

"The Voice of Reason,"
page 438

- Concept Map Activity 59
- Decision-Making Activity 19
- Enrichment Activity 19
- Lesson 59 Quiz
- Lesson Plan 59
- Reteaching Activity 59
- Transparency 68

LESSON 2

The Female Reproductive System

pages 442–447

Building Health Skills

"Expressing Concerns About Sexual Maturity," *page 446*

- Concept Map Activity 60
- Cooperative Learning Activity 19
- Health Lab 19
- Lesson 60 Quiz
- Lesson Plan 60
- Reteaching Activity 60
- Transparency 69

ACTIVITIES

- Cross-Curriculum Activity 19
- Health Lab 19
- Health Skills Activities 19
- Parent Letter and Activities 19

ASSESSMENT

- Chapter 19 Test
- Performance Assessment Activity 19
- Testmaker Software

STUDENT ACTIVITIES WORKBOOK

- Applying Health Skills 59, 60
- Study Guide 19
- Vocabulary Activity 19

STUDENT DIVERSITY STRATEGIES

- Audiocassette Program (English)
- Audiocassette Program (Spanish)
- Spanish Parent Letters and Activities
- Spanish Summaries, Quizzes, and Activities

MULTIMEDIA COMPONENTS

- English Audiocassette Program
- Spanish Audiocassette Program
- MindJogger Videodisc and VHS program
- ABCNews InterActive™ VHS/Videodisc Series

MODULES

- *Abstinence,* Student Edition
- *Abstinence,* Teacher's Annotated Edition
- *Education in Sexuality,* Student Edition
- *Education in Sexuality,* Teacher's Annotated Edition

National Health Education Standards

One of the main goals of the National Health Education Standards is to move students toward "health literacy." Health literacy is the capacity of individuals to obtain, interpret, and understand basic health information and services and the competence to use such information and services in ways which promote health. The health standards were developed by applying the characteristics of a well-educated, literate person within the context of health. The health literate person is:

- a critical thinker and problem solver
- a self-directed learner
- a responsible, productive citizen
- an effective communicator

Listed below are the Health Education Standards Performance Indicators addressed in each lesson of this chapter.

Lesson	Health Standards Performance Indicators
1	3.1, 3.4, 6.1, 6.6
2	1.2, 6.6, 7.1, 7.3

ONLINE RESOURCES

For a fresh approach to health topics and an in-depth look at health issues, use these online resources found under Teacher Resources at **health.glencoe.com**.

- **BLOCK SCHEDULE LESSON PLANS** Reinforce health concepts with outside readings selected especially for students. Each reading is accompanied by a lesson plan and activities to enhance
  - Reading Skills
  - Cross Curriculum
  - Media Literacy

- **TECHNOLOGY PROJECTS** Instructions and suggestions on how to use computer, Internet, and software with health lessons.

- **HEALTH UPDATES** Timely topics in health news, including late-breaking medical advances and updates on teen risk behaviors.

Out of Time?

If time does not permit teaching this chapter, you may use these features: Making Responsible Decisions on page 438 and Building Health Skills on page 446.

BLOCK SCHEDULING

Block scheduling provides extended time for hands-on projects and activities. Use the following activities to engage students, provide further depth, and vary your instructional techniques:

- Health Skills Activity (60–90 minutes) **pg. 448**

Your Body's Reproductive System

CHAPTER OVERVIEW

Chapter 19 introduces students to the reproductive system. The structure, function, care, and problems of the male and female systems are presented.

LESSON 1 When a male reaches puberty, hormones stimulate the production of testosterone, initiating sperm production and the development of secondary sex characteristics. This lesson discusses the structure, function, and ways to care for the male reproductive system, as well as problems associated with the system.

LESSON 2 When a female reaches puberty, hormones stimulate the production of estrogen and progesterone. Secondary sex characteristics result. During the reproductive years, one ovum a month matures, allowing an opportunity for fertilization. The structure, function, ways to care for the female reproductive system, and problems associated with the system are presented.

CHAPTER 19

Your Body's Reproductive System

HEALTH Online

ACCESSING INFORMATION
This chapter will give you an understanding of important reproductive system terms. Tackle these terms and definitions with a plan to learn the correct meanings and spellings. Find out how to use a Word Processing program to make study notes and flash cards. See health.glencoe.com, *Technology Projects.

Hands-On Health

TEACHING STRATEGY

Reviewing Reproductive Systems Terms
Help students review the names and functions of organs in the male and female reproductive systems. See Activity 32, "Who's Who?" in the *Hands-On Health: Creative Teaching Strategies* booklet.

Time Needed
30 minutes

Supplies
• envelopes
• cards with names of reproductive organs written on them

Gamma scans of male and female

> **Pay attention to the most important thing of all, the care of your health.**

—CATO THE ELDER
ROMAN STATESMAN, (234–149 B.C.)

Quick Write Write five different sentences in which the phrase *reproductive system* and the words *responsibility* and *health* all appear. Share these sentences with your classmates.

Personal Health Inventory

Self-Inventory Write the numbers 1–10 on a sheet of paper. Read each statement below and respond by writing *yes, no,* or *sometimes* for each item. Write a *yes* only for items that you practice regularly. Save your responses.

1	I eat a well-balanced diet.
2	I exercise regularly.
3	I manage the stress in my life.
4	I practice daily health care.
5	I avoid situations that might put me at risk of contracting an STD or HIV/AIDS.
6	I have regular physical checkups.
7	For males only: I do a monthly testicular self-exam.
8	For males only: I wear a protector or supporter if I am participating in strenuous activity.
9	For females only: I do a monthly breast self-exam.
10	For females only: I avoid using feminine hygiene products, such as sprays or douches.

Follow-up After completing the chapter, retake this self-inventory. Pick two items that you need to work on and set a goal to improve your health behaviors.

INTRODUCING THE CHAPTER

Personal Health Inventory

Have students read the Self-Inventory statements. Then ask: How do you think the habits identified in the first four statements relate to protecting the health of your reproductive system? Be sure students recognize that two of the statements are for males only, and two others are for females only; each student will write only eight responses. Have students record their responses in their private Health Journals on a page labeled "The Reproductive System."

- Provide on the chalkboard a typical "life plan" on a time line. Include time spent as a student, single worker, married person, parent, grandparent, retiree, etc. Relate one's personal health to each time period. Highlight possible childbearing years. Discuss the importance of maintaining the health of one's reproductive system.
- Ask students to describe and briefly discuss the photographs on these two pages. Ask: What does each show or suggest about the body's reproductive system? Point out to students that the hip bone in males is narrower than in females. Ask: What probably accounts for the difference between male and female hip bones? Tell students that in Chapter 19 they will explore the body system in which the most differences are evident between males and females—the reproductive system.
- Distribute Parent Letter 19 from the *Parent Letters and Activities* booklet in the TCR.

TECHNOLOGY OPTIONS

ABCNEWS INTERACTIVE™ You may wish to use *Teenage Sexuality* with this chapter. For your convenience, use the separate *ABCNews InterActive™ Bar Code Correlation* that accompanies the *Glencoe Health* program.

MINDJOGGER
VIDEOQUIZ

To preview or review chapter content, you may wish to use the *MindJogger Videoquiz* that accompanies Chapter 19.

LESSON 1

The Male Reproductive System

FOCUS

LESSON OBJECTIVES

After studying this lesson, students should be able to

- describe the structure and function of the male reproductive system.
- describe ways to care for the male reproductive system.
- identify some disorders of the male reproductive system.

MOTIVATOR

Write the following on the chalkboard for students to work on while attendance is being taken: *List three traits that you share with someone in your family and two traits that you do not have in common with anyone in your family.*

INTRODUCING THE LESSON

Have students share their responses to the Motivator. Explain that the reproductive system produces offspring and that students' characteristics were passed to them through their parents' reproductive systems. Tell the class that Lesson 1 details how to protect this system.

INTRODUCING HEALTH TERMS

- Have students make flash cards for the vocabulary terms. On one side, have them write the word. On the other side, have them identify the body system, the definition, and a page reference.
- Ask students to complete Vocabulary Activity 19 and Chapter Study Guide 19 in the *Student Workbook.* ☞

436 Chapter 19

The Male Reproductive System

Reproduction is one of the essential functions of living organisms. It is as necessary for the preservation of the species as getting food is for the preservation of the individual. In humans, as in many other animal species, reproduction occurs by means of a system of organs known as the *reproductive system.*

HEALTH TERMS

testosterone

sperm

testes

penis

semen

fertilization

circumcision

sterility

HEALTH CONCEPTS

- The male reproductive system produces sperm, male reproductive cells.
- Regular hygiene and self-examinations are important components of male reproductive system care.

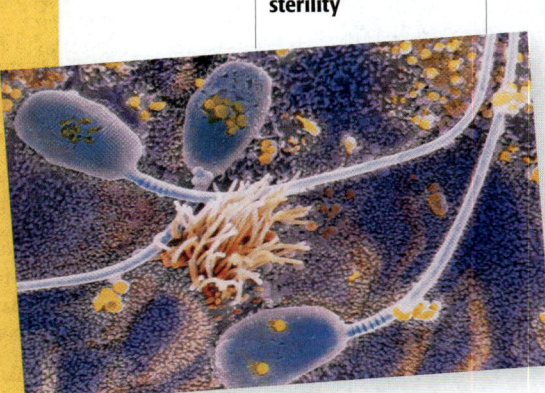

Sperm cells magnified

Functions and Structure of the Male Reproductive System

During the early teen years, the male reproductive system reaches maturity. Hormones released by the pituitary gland stimulate the testes to begin producing the *male sex hormone* **testosterone.** Testosterone initiates physical changes, including broadening of the shoulders, development of muscles, facial and other body hair, and deepening of the voice.

Testosterone also causes the production of **sperm**, *male reproductive cells.* Once a male is physically mature, he is capable of manufacturing sperm for the rest of his life. The production of sperm and the transfer of it to the female's body during sexual intercourse are the two main biological functions of the male reproductive system.

Lesson 1 Resources

TEACHER'S CLASSROOM RESOURCES

☞ **Concept Map** Activity 59

☞ **Decision-Making** Activity 19

☞ **Enrichment** Activity 19

☞ **Lesson 59 Quiz**

☞ **Lesson Plan 59**

☞ **Parent Letter and Activities 19**

☞ **Reteaching** Activity 59

STUDENT WORKBOOK

☞ **Applying Health Skills 59**

☞ **Chapter Study Guide 19**

☞ **Vocabulary** Activity 19

TRANSPARENCIES

🔦 **Transparency 68**

MULTIMEDIA

🔴 **ABCNews InterActive™,** *Teenage Sexuality*

External Male Reproductive Organs

Some of the organs involved in the process of reproduction are internal to the male's body; others are external. The main external organs are the testes and penis.

Also known as the *testicles,* the **testes** are *two small glands that produce sperm* at the rate of 100 million per day. The sperm resemble tadpoles and are so tiny that 500 of them lined up would measure only an inch.

The testes hang outside the body in a sac called the *scrotum.* This sac protects sperm by keeping the testes at a temperature slightly below the normal body temperature of 98.6°F (37°C). If body temperature rises, the muscles of the scrotum relax, lowering the testes away from the body. If body temperature drops, the muscles contract, pulling the testes closer to the body. Any clothing or other restraint that holds the testicles too close to the body can interfere with sperm production. Even wearing pants that are too tight is believed to interfere with the natural cooling of the testicles.

The **penis** is *a tube-shaped organ attached to the trunk of the body just above the testes.* The penis is composed of spongy tissue that contains many blood vessels. As a result of increased blood flow, the penis becomes enlarged and erect. Males of every age experience erections, and these can occur for no reason at all. Sometimes an erection results from friction of the clothing a male is wearing.

THE MALE REPRODUCTIVE SYSTEM

Urinary bladder
Seminal vesicle
Vas deferens
Prostate gland

Cowper's gland

Urethra
Penis
Epididymis

Testis

Scrotum

Did You Know?

➤ One spoonful of semen contains between 100 million and 500 million sperm.

➤ There are 300 million to 400 million sperm in each ejaculation, but only one can fertilize an ovum.

▼ *The male reproductive system produces sperm in the testes.*

ACTIVITY *Name the other main function of the male reproductive system.*

TEACH

LD Explaining

LD students may rely on class discussions for comprehension of the lesson's content due to high-level vocabulary. Assignment of independent reading is not recommended.

LEP Class Activity

Use charts or models to review the names and locations of the male reproductive system. Provide students with a drawing of the male reproductive anatomy, and have students fill in the names of each of the parts as you describe them.

L2 Discussing

Bring out in discussion that many adults may be uncomfortable talking about sexuality in realistic terms and that they try to talk at the child's level. Also mention that society has not always looked favorably upon open discussion of sexuality, and many adults still consider it to be entirely private.

TEENAGE SEXUALITY (Side 1)
Chapter 3: Changing Bodies

Frames 2368-4987

Chapter 5: The Male Body

Frames 7325-9628

MORE ABOUT . . . . .

PRENATAL SEX DIFFERENTIATION. It appears that the female is the "basic" sex into which embryos develop if not stimulated to do otherwise. When the gonads first appear in a developing embryo, they look the same in both sexes; but by eight weeks after fertilization, they become recognizable as testes in male embryos, presumably due to genes in the Y chromosome.

For female embryos, the gonads develop into ovaries by week nine without any stimulation.

Shortly after the male embryo's testes develop, they start secreting testosterone, which causes the previously undifferentiated external genitalia to form the penis and scrotum. In the absence of testosterone, the external genitalia develop into those of the female.

Making Responsible Decisions

1. Claude wants to compete in an important debate, but he feels very self-conscious because his voice is changing.
2. Claude can (a) withdraw from the debate; (b) participate in the debate and hope his voice doesn't "crack"; (c) ask the debate coach or a voice teacher for help, and then participate in the debate.
3. Claude will probably (a) feel safe from embarrassment, but miss being part of the debate and feel he has let the team down; (b) feel worried and self-conscious during the debate and probably not do his best; (c) participate in the debate with improved confidence.
4. Claude values his ability to debate well and to contribute to the debate team. He also values fitting in and not feeling embarrassed.
5. Responses will vary.
6. Remind students to consider both short- and long-term consequences.

L2 Decision Making

For further study on making responsible decisions, assign *Decision-Making Activity 19* in the TCR.

Steps to Performing a Testicular Exam

keeping Fit

Review with students the steps of a testicular self-exam. Follow up with a discussion regarding why many males do not regularly examine themselves for testicular abnormalities, such as nodules or lumps.

Making Responsible Decisions

The Voice of Reason

Claude is the star of his school's debating team. The problem is that his voice is changing, causing it to "crack." Although no one has said anything to him, Claude is very self-conscious—almost to the point of being afraid to speak.

A big debate is coming up, and Claude doesn't know what to do. One thing he *does* know is that his team is counting on him!

What Would You Do?

Apply the six steps of the decision-making process to Claude's problem.

1. **State the situation.**
2. **List the options.**
3. **Weigh the possible outcomes.**
4. **Consider your values.**
5. **Make a decision and act.**
6. **Evaluate the decision.**

keeping Fit

Steps to Performing a Testicular Exam

Once a month, males should examine themselves for testicular cancer. Although the majority of testicular lumps do not signify cancer, it is wise to seek a doctor's advice if you do find a lump.

➤ Examine the testicles after a warm bath or shower, and lying down.

➤ Cup the scrotum in the palms of both hands. Note any changes from the last examination.

➤ With thumb and fingers, gently roll each testicle around.

➤ Squeeze the testicles gently to note the firm, not hard, consistency.

➤ Examine the epididymis. It feels softer than the testicles and it may be spongy and a little tender.

➤ A hard, painless pea-sized nodule and any swelling on the testicle should be reported to a doctor.

Erections also occur as the result of becoming sexually aroused. At the height of sexual arousal, a series of muscular contractions known as *ejaculation* may occur. During ejaculation, **semen**—*a thick fluid containing sperm and other secretions from the male reproductive organs*—is propelled from the penis. If this happens during sexual intercourse, fertilization may be initiated. **Fertilization** is *the union of a reproductive cell from a male and one from a female.*

When a male begins to produce sperm, he may experience a nocturnal emission, or "wet dream," in which he becomes erect and ejaculates during sleep. This is a normal occurrence.

At birth, the tip of the penis is covered with a fold of skin called *foreskin*. Some parents choose **circumcision**—*surgical removal of the foreskin of the penis*—for their male child. It is important to remember that a male child is normal whether he is circumcised or not.

Internal Male Reproductive Organs

The internal structures of the male reproductive system play a role in the delivery of sperm. These include the epididymis, the vas deferens, the seminal vesicles, the prostate gland, the Cowper's glands, and the urethra. The urethra is also involved in the removal of liquid wastes from the body.

The tubes in each testis join a larger coiled tube, which is called the *epididymis*. Located at the outer surface of the testes, the epididymis is a temporary storage facility for sperm. Sperm mature in the epididymis.

The vas deferens are a pair of connecting tubes, each about 18 inches (46 cm) long, that lead up into the male's body toward two other internal organs, the seminal vesicles and the prostate gland. The thick muscle walls of the vas deferens propel the sperm forward in powerful spurts just before ejaculation.

PERSONAL HEALTH

Suggest that students investigate environmental factors which can affect their reproductive systems. For example, pesticides called endocrine disruptors alter sexual characteristics such as sperm counts and breast development in animals. Scientists have investigated proliferation of endocrine-disrupting chemicals as a possible cause of declining human sperm counts, as well as rising incidence of cancers and developmental problems in human prostates, breasts, and testicles. The 1996 publication of *Stolen Future*, by Colburn et al., increased public interest. Studies are available from the EPA and the National Coalition Against the Misuse of Pesticides. Have students consider how to protect reproductive systems from environmental damage.

As sperm move through the vas deferens, they are combined with a fluid produced by the seminal vesicles. These are glands that are about 2 inches (5 cm) long and attached to the vas deferens near the base of the bladder. The fluid contains nutrients and mixes with sperm to make them more mobile and to provide nourishment. The seminal vesicles and vas deferens meet to form the ejaculatory duct.

As sperm continue on their journey through the ejaculatory duct, they are next mixed with fluids secreted from the prostate gland—a small gland that surrounds the urethra—and from Cowper's glands, which are located below the prostate gland. Semen, or seminal fluid, is now fully formed. The secretion from the Cowper's glands also neutralizes the acid content before semen is ejaculated.

The urethra is the passageway through which both semen and urine leave the body. Semen and urine do not pass through the body at the same time. A muscle near the bladder contracts, preventing urine from entering the urethra when semen is present.

▼ *The groin area should be protected from possible injury when playing sports.*
ACTIVITY *List sports that you play and name the protective equipment you wear during these sports.*

Care of the Male Reproductive System

Caring for the male reproductive system involves cleanliness, protection, and self-examination. To stay healthy, males should shower daily, completely cleansing the penis and scrotum. A male who is uncircumcised must practice extra hygiene, taking care to wash underneath the foreskin.

Another aspect of male reproductive care is avoiding clothing that is too tight and wearing a protector or supporter during strenuous activity to help shield the groin area and the external reproductive organs.

In addition, once a male is physically mature, he should perform a monthly self-examination of his testes for signs of cancer. Any lumps, thickenings, or change in texture or size of the testes should be reported to a doctor, even though such signs do not always mean cancer has developed. If cancer is present, however, early detection usually leads to successful treatment.

L2 Discussing

Key male reproductive sex organs are on the exterior of the body. Ask: What means of protection for these organs should be considered when participating in sports? What could happen to a male if he received a hit in the groin area? Why is a kick to the groin suggested as a means of self-defense against an attack by a male?

L2 Discussing

Lead a class discussion on male characteristics. What is masculinity? How do males learn to be masculine? Are male babies treated differently than female babies?

L3 Class Activity

Ask students to write a story for young boys ages 8 to 10 about growing into a man. The story should provide facts that are important for boys to know to assist them in understanding their bodily functions and what to expect as changes occur at puberty.

L3 Writing

Have students read about circumcision, looking for information that answers the following questions: What is circumcision? When is it usually performed? How is it done? What cultural, physical, health-related, social, and psychological reasons are given in defending the procedure? What arguments are used against it? Ask students to summarize their findings in well-developed paragraphs.

PROMOTING COMPREHENSIVE SCHOOL HEALTH

CREATING A TEAM. Sometimes school health policies respond to state mandates or programs and services of the past, regardless of their appropriateness, adequacy, or effectiveness. To develop or clarify the vision for school health, the entire system of public school education must be considered. School health committees should consist of representatives of the following: parents, community members, and business representatives; teachers, counselors, nurses, and other school staff; religious groups; state, county, or local health agency representatives; human services representatives; and volunteer health organizations. For more information about the school health team, consult *Promoting a Comprehensive School Health Program* in the TCR.

Explaining

Prostate cancer may be treated by hormones, radiation, or surgery. Explain that prostate cancer is usually not termed an aggressive cancer and that many older men who develop prostate cancer do not die from it.

Researching

Have students research the treatment for testicular cancer. What are the implications for a young man who is found to have this condition? Can he father children?

Researching

Assign students to learn more about the incidence of undescended testicles. When do the testicles normally descend into the scrotum? What happens if one testicle does not descend? Why may surgery be advisable? If it does not descend, will it impede normal sexual functioning?

Discussing

Ask students to think of all the problems that could cause sterility in males. What could cause temporary sterility? *(Tight clothing, extreme cold, illness.)* What could cause permanent sterility? *(Chemical exposure, having mumps as an older child.)* Explain that a sterile male can function sexually; however, he is not able to impregnate a female.

Steps to Becoming a Responsible Young Male

Review the points regarding male responsibility that are provided in the feature. Discuss how peer pressure can influence male sexual behavior. What behaviors are promoted by a male's peers? What behaviors are not acceptable? How do male and female perspectives differ in regard to sexual behavior?

➤ *Talk to a school nurse, doctor, or other health professional to get accurate health information.*
ACTIVITY *List questions you may have that can be answered by a health professional.*

hotlink

sexually transmitted diseases (STDs) For more information on sexually transmitted diseases (STDs) and ways to avoid them, see Chapter 29, page 640.

Steps to Becoming a Responsible Young Male

The ability to produce sperm is a major responsibility. Yet, in truth, it has nothing to do with becoming a responsible man. Here are some ways to show you are responsible:

➤ Respect yourself and other people.

➤ Control your sexual feelings and never impose them on others.

➤ Distinguish between sexual information that is designed to excite and "sell" and sexual information that is designed to inform.

Problems of the Male Reproductive System

The organs of the male reproductive system can be affected by both functional and structural problems. The effect of **sexually transmitted diseases (STDs)** on these organs will be discussed in Chapter 29.

Hernia

A hernia occurs when part of an organ pushes through an opening of a membrane or muscle that usually contains the organ. Hernias occur in various parts of the body. A common hernia of the male reproductive system is an inguinal hernia. This is a weak spot in the abdominal wall in the lowest lateral regions of the abdomen near the top of the scrotum. Sometimes straining the abdominal muscles can cause a tear in this spot. A part of the intestine can then push through into the abdominal area. Surgery is usually necessary to correct such a hernia.

Sterility

Sterility is *a condition in which a person is unable to reproduce.* In a male, this can be the result of producing too few sperm—less than 20 million sperm per milliliter (ml) of seminal fluid—or sperm of poor quality. Environmental hazards that damage the sperm-making process include exposure to X rays, radiation, and lead from motor exhaust. Sterility can arise as a result of temperature change, exposure to certain chemicals, smoking, contracting mumps as an adult,

---

SCHOOL-TO-CAREER

MEDICAL TECHNICIANS. Many diagnostic procedures for detecting problems with the reproductive system are performed by people other than physicians and nurses. Technicians may have special training in administering X rays, ultrasound, and mammograms. Most technical assistant positions require special training; however, some require a four-year college degree, and others do not require any college credits. Suggest that students call doctors' offices or clinics and find out who performs various tests of reproductive systems. Encourage each student to choose a technical position of potential interest, and then conduct research into the duties, qualifications, and training for each.

complications of an STD, or malfunction of one of the internal male reproductive organs.

Enlarged Prostate Gland

The prostate gland can enlarge for reasons such as infection, a tumor, or old age. When the gland enlarges, it tends to squeeze the urethra, resulting in frequent or difficult urination. Treatments for enlarged prostate include special exercises to improve bladder control, medications that shrink an enlarged prostate or relax the prostatic muscle, and surgery to remove excess tissue.

Cancer of the Prostate Gland

Cancer is an uncontrolled growth of cells. The prostate gland is often a cancer site in older males. Prostate cancer is the second highest incidence of cancer in males. Only a doctor can diagnose prostate cancer. Early detection is important because prostate cancer can be treated if it is localized in the gland. Surgical removal of the prostate or radiation therapy and hormone therapy are current treatments.

Cancer of the Testes

Cancer of the testes occurs most frequently in males between the ages of 15 and 35 in the United States. The first sign of testicular cancer is usually a slight enlargement of one of the testes. The male may not experience any pain at all, or he might have a dull ache in the lower abdomen and groin. Hard lumps, or nodules, on the testes may be a sign of cancer. Testicular cancer can be cured in 90 percent of cases if it is caught early.

hotlink

cancer For more information on cancers and their treatment, see Chapter 31, page 683.

LESSON **1** *Review*

Reviewing Facts and Vocabulary

1. Trace the path that sperm follow from the testes to the urethra.
2. Name two problems that can affect the male reproductive system and describe them.

Thinking Critically

3. *Analyzing.* Why would it be important for a male to get a medical checkup if he experienced difficulty urinating?
4. *Synthesizing.* Contact the American Cancer Society for information about testicular and prostate cancers. Make a list that shows how a male can increase his chances of surviving both cancers.

Applying Health Skills

5. *In Your Home.* Increasing evidence suggests that toxic chemicals are responsible for decreased sperm counts in men. Find out what chemicals may be at fault. Research if any of these chemicals exist in your neighborhood. Write letters to your local government to ask what can be done to limit or remove any such harmful substances uncovered in your investigation.

Lesson 1 Review

Answers to Reviewing Facts and Vocabulary

1. From the testes, the sperm go to the epididymis to mature. They then pass through the vas deferens and the urethra on the way out of the body.
2. See pages 440 and 441 for problems of the male reproductive system.

Answers to Thinking Critically

3. It could be a symptom of one of a number of problems, including an enlarged prostate gland.
4. Lists may vary.

ASSESS

EVALUATING THE LESSON

Assign and discuss the Lesson 1 Review; then administer, grade, and discuss the *Lesson 59 Quiz* in the TCR. ☞

RETEACHING

- Ask each student to develop a summary outline for teaching a short course on male reproduction. Have them outline the topics, vocabulary terms, definitions, and major facts that they would cover in teaching such a course.
- Let students complete *Reteaching Activity 59* in the TCR. ☞
- Use *Transparency 68* to review the parts of the male reproductive system. ♨

ENRICHMENT

- Have students explore the relationship between tobacco, alcohol, drugs, and the reproductive system. How do these substances affect the male reproductive system? Encourage students to use the text plus additional resources.
- Introduce students to the on-line resource provided by the National Library of Medicine, which includes a three-dimensional imaging of human anatomy. Have them complete *Enrichment Activity 19,* "The Body Visible," in the TCR. ☞

CLOSE

Ask students to state the most important concepts studied in the lesson.

LESSON OBJECTIVES

After studying this lesson, students should be able to

- describe the structure and function of the female reproductive system.
- describe ways to care for the female reproductive system.
- identify some disorders of the female reproductive system.

MOTIVATOR

Write the following on the chalkboard for students to work on while attendance is being taken: *Complete the following statement: Becoming a woman means…*

INTRODUCING THE LESSON

Refer to the Motivator. Write some of the student responses on the chalkboard. If there are differences between male and female responses, discuss why these occurred. Ask: Is being a woman a matter of physical body parts?

INTRODUCING HEALTH TERMS

- Have students make flash cards for the vocabulary terms. On one side, have them write the word. On the other side, have them identify the body system, the definition, and a page reference.
- Ask students to complete Vocabulary Activity 19 and Chapter Study Guide 19 in the *Student Workbook.*

The Female Reproductive System

Like the male reproductive system, the female reproductive system matures during the early teen years. Like the male body, the female body goes through a number of changes. These include the development of breasts and widening of the hips. Other changes that occur are treated in the paragraphs that follow.

HEALTH TERMS

ova

vagina

ovaries

ovulation

fallopian tubes

zygote

uterus

cervix

menstrual cycle

infertility

HEALTH CONCEPTS

- The female reproductive system produces ova, or egg cells.
- The menstrual flow rids the body of tissue when fertilization does not take place.
- In order to keep the female reproductive system in good health, it is important to practice regular hygiene and breast self-examination.
- Females should have a Pap test done by age 18 to help prevent cervical cancer.

Magnified ovum

Functions and Structure of the Female Reproductive System

As with the male, the primary biological functions of the female reproductive system are related to the process of reproduction. The female reproductive system stores *female reproductive cells,* or **ova.** It also nourishes and protects each fertilized ovum from the beginning of pregnancy through birth. Sperm from the male enter the female reproductive system through the **vagina,** *a muscular, elastic passageway that extends from the uterus to the outside of the body.*

Lesson 2 Resources

TEACHER'S CLASSROOM RESOURCES

- **Concept Map** Activity 60
- **Cooperative Learning** Activity 19
- **Health Lab** 19
- **Lesson 60 Quiz**
- **Lesson Plan 60**
- **Reteaching** Activity 60

STUDENT WORKBOOK

- **Applying Health Skills** 60
- **Chapter Study Guide** 19
- **Vocabulary** Activity 19

TRANSPARENCIES

- **Transparency 69**

MULTIMEDIA

- **ABCNews InterActive™,** *Teenage Sexuality*

Female Reproductive Organs

Ova are stored in the **ovaries,** *the female sex glands that house the ova and produce female sex hormones.* The two ovaries are almond-shaped and located on each side of the body in the lower abdominal area. At birth, a female has over 400,000 immature ova in her ovaries.

During the early teen years, hormones cause the immature ova to mature. The ovaries begin *the process of releasing one mature ovum each month.* This process is called **ovulation.** Usually, one ovary releases a mature ovum one month, and the other ovary releases a mature ovum the next month.

When a mature ovum is released from an ovary, it moves into one of the **fallopian tubes.** These are *a pair of tubes with fingerlike projections that draw the ovum in.* Each fallopian tube is about 4 inches (10 cm) long and about ⅓ inch (0.8 cm) in diameter. Tiny hairlike structures and muscular contractions move the ovum along.

If a sperm cell introduced during intercourse is present in the fallopian tubes, it may unite with an ovum and fertilization occurs. *The cell that results from the union of sperm and ovum* is a **zygote.**

The **uterus** is *a small, muscular, pear-shaped organ, about the size of a fist.* Once a zygote has been formed, it leaves the fallopian tube, travels to the uterus, and attaches itself to the uterine wall.

▼ **The female reproductive system produces ova to unite with sperm in the process of reproduction.**

ACTIVITY *Name another function of the female reproductive system.*

THE FEMALE REPRODUCTIVE SYSTEM

- Fallopian tube
- Maturing ovum
- Mature ovum
- Ovary
- Uterus
- Endometrium
- Cervix
- Urinary bladder
- Vagina
- Urethra
- Labia minora
- Labia majora

TEACH

LD Explaining

LD students may rely on class discussion for comprehension of the lesson's content due to high-level vocabulary. Assignment of independent reading is not recommended.

L1 Explaining

Use a model or chart to show students where the female body parts are located, naming them correctly as they are identified. Provide students with a diagram of the female body genitalia, and have them write in the names of the female reproductive body parts.

L2 Health Lab

Distribute *Health Lab 19* and have students investigate the differences between ova and sperm. 👉

L2 Demonstrating

The uterus is a most amazing organ. It is normally the size of a fist but stretches to accommodate a full-grown baby—some weighing over 10 pounds. Draw ovals on the chalkboard illustrating the ability of the uterus to stretch to meet the baby's needs and then shrink to normal size within 3 to 6 weeks.

MORE ABOUT . . . . .

CONCEPTION. Despite all the unplanned pregnancies, conception is still a matter of odds. A married couple can go through the rest of their lives without ever having a baby.

Fertilization of the ovum can occur only during a two- to three-day time period, when the cervical mucus forms small channels that allow sperm cells to enter the uterus. Once in the mucus, the sperm can live up to 48 hours. So, fertilization could theoretically occur two days after sexual intercourse. Females of fertile couples in their 20s have a 20 percent chance each month of conceiving. Females of couples in their late 30s have about an eight percent chance per month of getting pregnant.

L3 Discussing

Ask students how hormone treatment can be used to control menstrual flow. Why are hormones used to control the cramping or discomfort of menstruation? Why would hormone therapy cause nausea in some patients?

L2 Cooperative Learning

Have students complete *Cooperative Learning Activity 19,* "The Case of the Frozen Embryos," in the TCR. ☞

L2 Guest Speaker

Breast self-examination (BSE) is not a difficult procedure and can alert women to potential problems in the early stages. Invite a representative from the American Cancer Society to give a demonstration of BSE and teach your female students how to do this on their own on a monthly basis. Questions to ask the speaker include: Why would some women choose not to do BSE? How can reluctant women be encouraged to adopt this practice?

THE MENSTRUAL CYCLE

On average, the menstrual cycle is 28 days.

ACTIVITY *Name the days during which the ovum is most likely to be fertilized.*

Menstruation

If the ovum does not become fertilized, the lining of the uterus breaks down into blood, tissue, and fluids which pass through the **cervix**, or *neck of the uterus,* and out of the vagina. This process of shedding the lining of the uterus is called *menstruation,* from the Latin word *mensis,* meaning "month."

The menstrual flow usually lasts about three to five days. Women wear either sanitary pads or tampons to absorb the blood flow from menstruation. After the menstrual period ends, the entire cycle begins again. The lining of the uterus thickens again, preparing for the possibility of receiving a fertilized egg. Although there can be great variations, the **menstrual cycle**—*the time from the beginning of one menstrual period to the onset of the next*—is usually 28 days. The menstrual cycle is regulated by endocrine hormones.

Most females begin menstruating between the ages of 10 and 15. The menstrual cycle may be irregular at first. Although hormones control the menstrual cycle, poor nutrition, stress, and illness can influence the cycle. Irregularity of the menstrual cycle is caused not only by these factors but also by physical maturity. Growth and time usually result in more predictable onset and duration of the cycle.

Care of the Female Reproductive System

Cleanliness is an important part of keeping the reproductive system healthy. The vagina is a self-cleansing organ. Once a female matures, the cells in the lining of the vagina are constantly being shed, causing a slight vaginal discharge. This is normal. Cleanliness is especially important during the menstrual period, when menstrual flow may cause a slight odor. Sanitary napkins and tampons should be changed every few hours. Feminine hygiene products such as deodorant sprays and douches should not be necessary and may, in fact, cause irritation to the sensitive tissues around the vagina.

Breast Self-Examination

Breast self-examination (BSE) is an important habit for females to develop. It is one way that they can take charge of their bodies and maintain good health. BSE should be done once a month, about a week after the start of their menstrual period, when the breasts are usually not tender or swollen.

COOPERATIVE) LEARNING

GENDER ROLES. Group students to discuss historical and modern gender roles. Suggest they discuss their observations of male and female roles in families, the workplace, and society. Have them list their observations. Then suggest they distinguish between gender role differences that are inevitable because of physiological distinctions between males and females, and gender role differences that are not. Encourage them to discuss briefly their feelings about gender roles. Are they more comfortable with strictly defined gender roles? Would they prefer more equality? To what extent do they feel nature imposes restrictions on equality and flexibility of gender roles? Suggest that students set up a panel discussion about gender roles in our society, with different group members expressing different points of view.

There are three ways to examine the breasts: in the shower, in front of a mirror, and lying down. In all cases, a thorough BSE includes the following steps:

- Inspect both breasts for anything unusual, such as any discharge from the nipples or puckering, dimpling, or scaling of the skin. If standing in front of a mirror, clasp your hands behind your head and press your hands forward. Then, press your hands firmly on your hips and bow slightly toward the mirror as you pull your shoulders and elbows forward. Get to know the shape of your breasts and note any changes.

- Raise your left arm. Use three or four fingers of your right hand to explore your left breast firmly, carefully, and thoroughly. Beginning at the outer edge, press the flat part of your fingers in small circles, moving the circles slowly around the breast. Gradually work toward the nipple. Finally, squeeze the nipple gently. Look for any discharge.

- Pay special attention to the area between the breast and the armpit, including the armpit itself. Feel for any unusual lump or mass under the skin. Using the left hand, repeat the process for the right breast. If you find anything unusual, contact your doctor at once. Only a doctor can make a diagnosis.

Problems of the Female Reproductive System

Problems with the female reproductive system can be functional or structural. Some of the problems that can occur are related to menstruation. Others are related to **infertility**, *the inability of a woman to become pregnant.*

Problems Related to Menstruation

Problems related to menstruation can range from minor discomfort to life-threatening illness. Problems include:

- **Menstrual Cramps.** A female may experience abdominal cramps at the beginning of the menstrual period. Menstrual cramps are usually mild, lasting several hours. Light exercise can help relieve cramps. A heating pad might also help relax the muscles. If cramps are severe, the doctor may recommend an over-the-counter medication that contains antiprostaglandins, or the doctor may prescribe medication for pain relief. Severe or persistent cramping may be an indication that medical attention is necessary.

▼ *Physical activity, good nutrition, and regular check-ups can contribute to a healthy reproductive system.*

LESSON 2   THE FEMALE REPRODUCTIVE SYSTEM   **445**

L2 **Discussing**

Ask students what is required to maintain female reproductive health. The discussion should include annual physical, pelvic exam, breast exam, reporting of problems, irregularities, and pain. Menstruation records should also be kept. If a person is sexually active, health maintenance should include an annual Pap smear. Discuss how each of these helps maintain good reproductive health. What is the potential impact on having children if good reproductive health is not maintained?

L1 **Researching**

Suggest that volunteers visit a local pharmacy or other store where feminine hygiene products are sold. Students should be able to determine which products are necessary for females to use and which are marketed as necessary, but are not (*deodorants, powders, and douches*). Ask: How expensive are these items? How have feminine products changed over the years?

L3 **Researching**

Have interested class members research problems associated with a tubal pregnancy. How frequently do they occur? How does the female know there is a problem? What is the treatment? Ask the students to present their findings to the class.

TEENAGE SEXUALITY (Side 1)
Chapter 3: Changing Bodies

Frames 2368-4987

Chapter 4: The Female Body

Frames 5001-7296

HOME AND COMMUNITY
C O N N E C T I O N

AFTER MENOPAUSE. Scientific evidence suggests that nature takes better care of women who can perpetuate the species than of women who are past childbearing age. After menopause, women's risk of cancer, heart disease, and osteoporosis jumps dramatically. Encourage students to talk to older family members or members of their household who are approaching, passing through, or finished with menopause about how they experienced changes and any uncomfortable symptoms. Encourage students to research the functions of estrogen and progesterone, and the benefits and risks of replacing either or both. Invite students to search the community for low-cost access to tests, such as mammograms and bone densitometry, that provide for early detection of health problems in menopausal and postmenopausal women.

Building Health Skills

Expressing Concerns About Sexual Maturity
Skill: Obtaining Help

Ask students: What do you do when you need help with a problem? Let several volunteers respond; then, if necessary, point out that your actions should depend on the kind of problem you have. Have students read the Building Health Skills feature to learn how teens can find reliable help in dealing with their concerns about sexual maturity. After discussing the information in the feature, suggest that students write private Health Journal entries expressing their own ideas about whom and what to consult for help.

L2 Researching

Encourage students to research cervical cancer. How is it identified? What is its statistical frequency? What behaviors increase the chance of cervical cancer? Ask students to report their findings to the class.

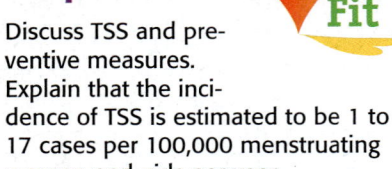

TSS and Tampons

Discuss TSS and preventive measures. Explain that the incidence of TSS is estimated to be 1 to 17 cases per 100,000 menstruating women and girls per year.

Building Health Skills

Expressing Concerns About Sexual Maturity

THE CHANGES THAT OCCUR to your body and your emotions during the teen years can be exciting. Yet, they can also be a source of concern. Fortunately, there are people who can put some of your worries to rest. In seeking help, remember:

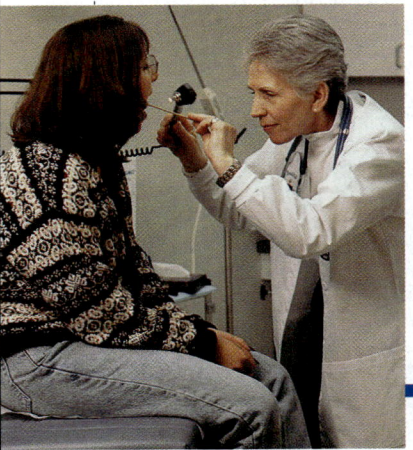

1. **Different people possess different strengths and skills.** Choose a "consultant" based on your needs. If your concerns are of a physical or medical nature, you might speak with the school nurse or your family's health care provider. For problems of a general nature, remember that parents were once teens themselves and often have good answers.

2. **Choose someone who will listen.** This can be a parent, teacher, counselor, or even a mature older brother or sister. The only qualification is that the person should have time to give you his or her undivided attention.

3. **Make sure the information you get is reliable.** Discussing your concerns with a peer might only deepen them. The same is true of "popular" print materials, such as supermarket tabloids, which often contain misinformation.

keeping Fit

TSS and Tampons

TSS risk increases with tampon absorbency. If you use tampons, it is important to use the products with the lowest absorbency that meets your needs. There is usually less need for high-absorbency tampons at the end of a menstrual period.

Also, it is important to follow the manufacturer's instructions. Remember to:

➤ Store tampons in a clean, dry place.

➤ Wash your hands with soap and water before and after inserting or removing a tampon.

➤ Seek medical attention if you have symptoms of TSS.

- **Premenstrual Syndrome (PMS).** Although many females do not experience PMS, others may have a variety of symptoms they experience several days to two weeks before the menstrual period. The symptoms of PMS include nervous tension, anxiety, irritability, bloating, weight gain, depression, mood swings, and fatigue. The causes of PMS are not completely understood. Some doctors believe that PMS is related to a hormonal imbalance.

- **Toxic Shock Syndrome (TSS).** Young women ages 15–19 are the most frequent victims of TSS, but there is a risk of TSS to all women using tampons during their menstrual period. TSS is a rare but serious disease that may be fatal. Scientists believe that TSS requires the presence of the bacterium *Staphylococcus aureus* that causes infection. Signs of TSS include aching muscles, bloodshot eyes, a sore throat, a sudden high fever, vomiting, diarrhea, dizziness, fainting, and a rash that looks like a sunburn.

Problems that Can Cause Infertility

Infertility can affect as many as 8 percent of women of childbearing age. Some of the more common causes are:

- **Blocked Fallopian Tube.** A blocked fallopian tube is the leading cause of female infertility. Some of the causes of a blocked fallopian tube include pelvic inflammatory disease (PID) or abdominal surgery.

HEALTH LITERACY

EFFECTIVE COMMUNICATOR. As a precaution, students may examine themselves regularly for cancer in their reproductive systems; however, they may not be prepared if they find something wrong. Such a situation would be terrifying to almost everyone. Turning to an individual they could confide in should be the first step they take, followed in quick order by consultation with their family doctor. If cancer were confirmed, they may be faced with choices that have long-term or even lifelong consequences. Most doctors attempt to explain the treatment options and their possible consequences and make knowledgeable recommendations, but not all that doctors say registers when life has been turned upside down. It is up to the individual to ask questions and address concerns before making a commitment to a treatment process.

- **Endometriosis.** Endometriosis is the second leading cause of infertility. In this disease, uterine tissue grows outside the uterus, often appearing on the ovaries, fallopian tubes, and in the abdominal cavity.
- **Pelvic Inflammatory Disease (PID).** Pelvic inflammatory disease is an infection of the fallopian tubes, ovaries, and surrounding areas in a woman's pelvis. It can damage the reproductive organs and is usually caused by sexually transmitted diseases.

Other Reproductive Disorders

Other reproductive disorders include ovarian cysts and cancers of the reproductive system. An ovarian cyst is a fluid-filled sac on the ovary. Small, noncancerous cysts can develop often but usually dissolve on their own. Large cysts may have to be surgically removed.

About one out of eight females develop cancer at some time. Most breast lumps are found during breast self-examination. About 80 percent of these lumps are not cancerous, but should be checked.

The cervix, uterus, and ovaries are common sites of cancer in females. Cervical cancer is detected through a Pap test, a test in which samples of cells are taken from the cervix by a doctor and viewed under a microscope. Early detection contributes to successful treatment. Early sexual activity, as well as a family history of cervical cancer and other factors, is related to an increased incidence of cervical cancer. A Pap test should be done every one or two years after a woman has reached 18 years of age or has become sexually active.

keeping Fit

Why Have a Pelvic Exam?

A pelvic exam is one in which a gynecologist checks a female's pelvic area, first with an instrument called a speculum and then by hand. The American College of Obstetricians and Gynecologists (ACOG) recommends that young females have pelvic exams by the time they are 18. The following are reasons having a pelvic exam is important:

➤ During a pelvic exam, the doctor can check the shape, size, and position of pelvic organs.

➤ The doctor can check for any tumors or cysts.

➤ If a female has unusual vaginal discharge, the doctor can check to find the possible cause.

Why Have a Pelvic Exam?

keeping Fit

Discuss the reasons for a pelvic exam. Explain that these exams should occur yearly, even if there are no problems.

ASSESS

EVALUATING THE LESSON

Assign and discuss the Lesson 2 Review; then administer, grade, and discuss the *Lesson 60 Quiz* in the TCR. ✎

RETEACHING

- Use *Transparency 69* to review the parts of the female reproductive system. ✎
- Ask students to complete *Reteaching Activity 60* in the TCR. ✎

ENRICHMENT

Encourage students to consider the options currently available to females who have breast cancer. One is to have a complete mastectomy. The second is to have a lumpectomy and radiation. Another is to have a mastectomy, but delay reconstruction until a later date. Some patients may need chemotherapy in addition to the other procedures. The lumpectomy and the mastectomy each have a 50 percent chance of survival. Ask: What considerations would a female have to think about to choose between the procedures?

CLOSE

Ask students to state the most important concepts studied in the lesson.

LESSON 2 *Review*

Reviewing Facts and Vocabulary

1. What is menstruation?
2. What is PMS?
3. Name two causes of infertility in females.
4. Name at least two ways to lessen menstrual cramps.

Thinking Critically

5. *Analyzing.* What is the relationship between ovulation, fertilization, and menstruation?
6. *Comparing and Contrasting.* Compare and contrast the male and female reproductive systems.
7. *Synthesizing.* While the causes of PMS are still being researched, some medicine companies are producing over-the-counter medications to treat PMS. From what you have learned, how effective do you think the medicines might be? What symptoms do you think the medicines might help alleviate?

Applying Health Skills

8. *In Your Home.* Make a list of some of the myths you have heard about menstruation. Discuss these myths with a parent or an adult female relative. Why do you think there is so much misinformation? Talk about some ways to clarify and correct some of these myths.

Lesson 2 Review

Answers to Reviewing Facts and Vocabulary

1. The monthly flow of blood, tissue, and fluid from the uterus when there is no fertilized egg present.
2. See page 446.
3. Any two: blocked fallopian tube, endometriosis, pelvic inflammatory disease.
4. Any two: light exercise, a heating pad, over-the-counter or prescription medication.

Answers to Thinking Critically

5. Ovulation is the release of an ovum. Fertilization occurs at the joining of sperm and ovum. If the ovum is not fertilized, menstruation occurs.
6. Male: delivers the sperm to the female reproductive system. Female: supports the growth of a fertilized ovum into a viable human being.
7. Answers will vary.

Health **Skills** Activities

ACTIVITY 1
HEALTH SKILLS

Comprehending Health Concepts, Health Advocacy

➤ **National Standards**
This activity meets these National Health Standards: 1.1; 1.6; 7.4.

Teach

- It may be beneficial to have students work in task-oriented groups. One group, for example, can be in charge of gathering and/or researching data and facts, another for gathering materials to be used for students' visual media (bumper stickers, leaflets, and so on), yet another for developing the verbal messages to be communicated.

- Arrange for groups to meet periodically and assess each other's progress. One or two students might take responsibility for ensuring that groups complete assigned tasks on time.

ACTIVITY 2
HEALTH SKILLS

Comprehending Health Concepts, Health Advocacy

➤ **National Standards**
This activity meets these National Health Standards: 1.1; 1.8; 7.3.

Teach

- Discuss with students high-profile diseases of the reproductive system, such as breast cancer (in both males and females) and ovarian cancer. Ask what students know about these diseases.

- Present the health articles you have gathered. Note that, like all news articles, these follow the five w's of journalism—the who, what, when, where, and why.

- Invite students to read and discuss features of health articles, such as the use of charts, graphs, references to researchers, etc.

- Urge students to incorporate these and other features in their articles.

Activity 1 — Cancer Awareness Day

Cancer claims numerous lives each year. As with so many other diseases, education can be the key to reducing the risks of various cancers. Plan your own Cancer Awareness Day to educate others about cancers that affect the reproductive system.

Directions

1. With a group, gather information about the reproductive cancers detailed in your book.
2. From the American Cancer Society and other health organizations, learn about lifestyle behaviors and choices that can reduce a person's risk of one of these cancers.
3. Using the information that you have gathered, create promotional and informational literature in the form of bumper stickers, badges, and leaflets to be passed out to other students on a day designated as Cancer Awareness Day.

Time
two 50-minute periods

Materials
poster board, markers, library or Internet resources with cancer information, computer with design software and color printer (optional)

Self-Assessment

✓ Described prevention strategies associated with primary health care (e.g., BSE, testicular self-exam, Pap smear, etc.).
✓ Presented a clear message promoting healthful behaviors that reduce risk of disease.

Activity 2 — Be a Health Reporter

Care of the reproductive system is important, but it is also a topic that many people are embarrassed to talk about. Be a health reporter. Write an article that will provide the public with the information they need.

Directions

1. Choose a reproductive health topic that would make a good health article (such as diseases of the reproductive system, proper care, or advancements in reproductive health).
2. Write a feature article or editorial. Include information such as how to screen for a disease or recognize a problem, how to prevent problems from occurring, and so on.
3. Share your health articles with your classmates. You may want to submit your article to the school or local newspaper.

Time
50 minutes plus outside writing time

Materials
paper, pen or pencil, or word processor with printer

Self-Assessment

✓ Selected a topic concerning reproductive health.
✓ Included adequate information about the topic selected.

ASSESSMENT SCORING

Using a four-level rubric, the student has achieved a 4 if:

ACTIVITY 1

✔ Student showed a spirit of cooperation in working with group and class members.
✔ Student completed all tasks assigned.
✔ Student described prevention strategies associated with primary health care (e.g., BSE, testicular self-exam, Pap smear, etc.).
✔ Student presented a clear message promoting healthful behaviors that reduce risk of disease.

ACTIVITY 2

✔ Student selected a topic concerning reproductive health.
✔ Student followed the five w's of journalism.
✔ Student wrote an article with features found in sample health articles.
✔ Student included adequate information about the topic.

HEALTH NEWS VIDEO

Fitness and Gender

Many people think that men are naturally stronger than women. Scientists studying athletes have discovered that's simply not true.

Men have more upper body strength, but women's lower body muscles can be as strong as a man's. These strengths may explain why men are drawn to upper-body activities like baseball and weight lifting. Women favor activities like tennis and gymnastics because they use lower body strength.

Men also experience more sports injuries, partly because they participate in more events. However, men are also less flexible than women. For both genders, the keys to avoiding injury are stretching, warming-up, and building endurance.

Play the Video ▶

CNN. All Rights Reserved.

Think About It

- ▶ What are the differences between men's and women's body strength? Name three sports that focus on each type of strength.
- ▶ What types of injuries are women more vulnerable to?
- ▶ What strategies can you use to avoid injury? Are these strategies the same for men and women? Explain.

CNN HEALTH NEWS **449**

MORE ABOUT . . . . .

REPORTING THE STORY. Have students consider why reporters decided to cover this medical research. Ask them to consider why this type of gender research is relevant and important.

Use these questions to help students focus on media depictions of gender differences.

- What makes this video newsworthy?
- Do you think the report addresses the title fairly and without bias?
- How do reporters and networks treat male and female athletes? Do you think they are both treated fairly?
- What report would you like to see broadcast about fitness for men and women?

CNN HEALTH NEWS

Fitness and Gender
Video Segment 12 (Time – :53)

Objectives. After viewing the video, students should recognize ways males and females differ in fitness concerns and identify the special considerations of each group when taking care of their body's fitness.

Motivator. Ask the question posed in the title of this video, Are men stronger than women? Allow students to offer their opinions before viewing Video Segment 12, "Fitness and Gender," which provides scientific analysis of the fitness differences between men's and women's bodies.

Teach

- Use the questions in Think About It to discuss the key points raised by the video. Have students consider the type of tests scientists used to compare the strength of men and women. Then have them summarize the results of those tests.
- Emphasize that the strengths identified in the video are comparative. Students should beware of making false inferences, such as "women have weak upper bodies" or "men experience few knee injuries." Help students explain why each of these conclusions is not supported by the video.

Investigate. Direct students to interview two students, a man and a woman, about their sports habits. They should find out about their stretching, warm-up, and practice schedules. Encourage them to combine their observations to draw accurate conclusions about the fitness of both genders. Help students make accurate generalizations by identifying words such as *all, no, none,* or *every,* which can make a generalization false.

Close. Return to the opening question about whether men are stronger than women. Ask students if their opinions have changed as a result of viewing the video. Invite them to explain why or why not.

CHECKING COMPREHENSION

- Assign and discuss the chapter review.
- Use the MindJogger Videoquiz to review the chapter. 🔴

CHAPTER 19 REVIEW ANSWERS

Using Health Terms

1. fertilization
2. sterility
3. testosterone
4. semen
5. testes
6. circumcision
7. penis
8. sperm
9. infertility
10. vagina
11. menstrual cycle
12. ova
13. fallopian tubes
14. cervix
15. ovulation
16. zygote
17. uterus
18. ovaries

Recalling the Facts

1. It initiates physical changes in the maturing male teen. Any three: broadening of the shoulders, development of muscles, facial and other body hair, deepening of the voice, and production of sperm.
2. The production of sperm and the transfer of it to the female body.
3. It holds the testes away from the body.
4. Cleanliness, protection, self-examination.
5. To check for testicular cancer. This should be done once a month.
6. It stores female reproductive cells and also nourishes and protects each fertilized ovum from the beginning of pregnancy through birth.

Using Health Terms

On a separate sheet of paper, write the term that best matches each definition below.

LESSON 1

1. The union of a reproductive cell from a male and one from a female.
2. A condition in which a person is unable to reproduce.
3. Male sex hormone.
4. A thick fluid containing sperm and other secretions from the male reproductive organs.
5. Two small glands that produce sperm.
6. Surgical removal of the foreskin of the penis.
7. A tube-shaped organ attached to the trunk of the body just above the testes.
8. Male reproductive cells.

LESSON 2

9. The inability of a woman to become pregnant.

10. A muscular, elastic passageway that extends from the uterus to the outside of the body.
11. The time from the beginning of one menstrual period to the onset of the next.
12. Female reproductive cells.
13. A pair of tubes with fingerlike projections that draw the ovum in.
14. Neck of the uterus.
15. The process of releasing one mature ovum each month.
16. The cell that results from the union of sperm and ovum.
17. A small, muscular, pear-shaped organ, about the size of a fist.
18. The female sex glands that house the ova and produce female sex hormones.

Recalling the Facts

Using complete sentences, answer the following questions.

LESSON 1

1. What is the function of testosterone? Name three physical changes initiated by testosterone in the male.
2. What are the functions of the male reproductive system?
3. Explain how the scrotum keeps the testes at a temperature that is slightly below normal body temperature.
4. Explain what is involved in caring for the male reproductive system.
5. Why is it important for a male to examine his testes regularly? How often should this be done?

LESSON 2

6. What functions does the female reproductive system serve?
7. What can relieve menstrual cramps?
8. What functions do the ovaries serve?
9. What are the internal reproductive organs in females?
10. How does a mature ovum travel through the fallopian tube?
11. What is one suspected cause of PMS?
12. What is the purpose of performing a breast self-examination (BSE)? How often should it be done? What is the best time to do it and why?
13. What is a Pap test? What does it detect?
14. What is toxic shock syndrome?

7. Light exercise, heating pad, over-the-counter or prescription medications.
8. They store the female reproductive cells, or ova, and produce female sex hormones.
9. Ovaries, fallopian tubes, uterus, vagina.
10. Tiny hair-like structures and muscular contractions move the ovum along.
11. Hormonal imbalance.

12. To check for breast cancer. This should be done once a month, about one week after the start of the menstrual period, when the breasts are usually not tender or swollen.
13. It's a test in which samples of cells are taken from the cervix by a doctor and viewed under a microscope. It is used to detect the presence of cervical cancer cells.

Thinking Critically

LESSON 1

1. **Evaluating.** Compare testicular cancer and prostate cancer.
2. **Synthesizing.** What advice might you have for individuals who say they would not go to the doctor if they found a suspicious lump after a testicular self-examination for fear that the lump might be cancer?

LESSON 2

3. **Analyzing.** What factors do you think may have prompted people to make up myths about menstruation? Suggest ways to clear up these types of myths.
4. **Synthesizing.** What information would you include in an accurate and persuasive advertisement to encourage women to have an annual mammogram and Pap test?
5. **Evaluating.** Kim, who is 13, is about to have her first appointment with a gynecologist. What questions should she prepare to ask before she sees the doctor? Explain your answer.

Making the Connection

1. **Language Arts.** Read an article about one of the following issues or problems concerning the reproductive system: the spread of STDs, multiple births, or effectiveness of feminine hygiene products. Create an outline for the article that summarizes its key and supporting points.

2. **Mathematics.** Contact the American Cancer Society for current statistics on cancers that affect people in the United States today. Compare the number of people who had breast or prostate cancer in 1980 with those in more recent years. Learn about medical breakthroughs. Present your findings in a report.

BEYOND THE CLASSROOM

PARENTAL INVOLVEMENT With your parents' help, make a family tree. Find out what diseases members of the family tree had. Discuss with your parents why it is important for you to be aware of a history of cancer and other diseases in your family.

COMMUNITY INVOLVEMENT The "Race for the Cure" is an annual foot race that benefits breast cancer research and is held in many communities. Find out if your community sponsors this race and, if so, when the next race is to be held. If possible, participate in this worthwhile event with other classmates and the community. In your private Health Journal, write a brief account of your experiences, summarizing any comments made by organizers of the race.

SCHOOL-TO-CAREER

Exploring Careers. Interview a gynecologist or a urologist. Find out how a gynecologist helps keep women in good health and how a urologist helps keep men in good health. Determine requirements for this career, including schooling and types of interpersonal skills. Learn in what settings these doctors work. Share your findings with the class in the form of a brief oral report.

Thinking Critically

1. Prostate cancer causes symptoms that are easily noticed. Testicular cancer may not create symptoms. A doctor must do an examination to detect prostate cancer. A person can examine himself for testicular cancer.
2.–5. Answers will vary.

Making the Connection

1. Outlines will vary.
2. Reports will vary.

Evaluate

- Use the reproducible *Chapter 19 Test* in the TCR, or construct your own using the Testmaker software.
- Use *Performance Assessment Activity 19* in the TCR.

Enrichment

Ask students to complete *Cross-Curriculum Activity 19* in the TCR.

Beyond the Classroom

Keep students involved in the community, and encourage parent participation by assigning the activities on this page for students to work on outside of class.

14. Toxic shock syndrome is a rare but serious disease that occurs in the presence of an infectious bacterium.

The Beginning of the Life Cycle

	FEATURES	**CLASSROOM RESOURCES**

Chapter Resources

ACTIVITIES

- Cross-Curriculum Activity 20
- Health Lab 20
- Health Skills Activities 20
- Parent Letter and Activities 20

ASSESSMENT

- Chapter 20 Test
- Performance Assessment Activity 20
- Testmaker Software

STUDENT ACTIVITIES WORKBOOK

- Applying Health Skills 61–63
- Study Guide 20
- Vocabulary Activity 20

STUDENT DIVERSITY STRATEGIES

- Audiocassette Program (English)
- Audiocassette Program (Spanish)
- Spanish Parent Letters and Activities
- Spanish Summaries, Quizzes, and Activities

MULTIMEDIA COMPONENTS

- English Audiocassette Program
- Spanish Audiocassette Program
- MindJogger Videodisc and VHS program
- ABCNews InterActive™ VHS/Videodisc Series

National Health Education Standards

One of the main goals of the National Health Education Standards is to move students toward "health literacy." Health literacy is the capacity of individuals to obtain, interpret, and understand basic health information and services and the competence to use such information and services in ways which promote health. The health standards were developed by applying the characteristics of a well-educated, literate person within the context of health. The health literate person is:

- a critical thinker and problem solver
- a responsible, productive citizen
- a self-directed learner
- an effective communicator

Listed below are the Health Education Standards Performance Indicators addressed in each lesson of this chapter.

Lesson	Health Standards Performance Indicators
1	1.4, 2.4, 3.3, 6.1
2	1.6, 1.7, 1.8, 4.3
3	1.2, 1.4, 3.4, 6.3

ONLINE RESOURCES

For a fresh approach to health topics and an in-depth look at health issues, use these online resources found under Teacher Resources at **health.glencoe.com**.

- **BLOCK SCHEDULE LESSON PLANS** Reinforce health concepts with outside readings selected especially for students. Each reading is accompanied by a lesson plan and activities to enhance
  - Reading Skills
  - Cross Curriculum
  - Media Literacy

- **TECHNOLOGY PROJECTS** Instructions and suggestions on how to use computer, Internet, and software with health lessons.

- **HEALTH UPDATES** Timely topics in health news, including late-breaking medical advances and updates on teen risk behaviors.

Out of Time?

If time does not permit teaching this chapter, you may use these features: Building Health Skills on page 456; Making Responsible Decisions on page 458; and Update on page 465.

BLOCK SCHEDULING

Block scheduling provides extended time for hands-on projects and activities. Use the following activities to engage students, provide further depth, and vary your instructional techniques:

- Teens Making a Difference (30 minutes) **pg. 463**
- Update (30 minutes) **pg. 465**
- Health Lab (30 minutes) **pg. 470**
- Health Skills Activity (60–90 minutes) **pg. 472**

The Beginning of the Life Cycle

CHAPTER OVERVIEW

Chapter 20 explores life, from its initial stage as a single cell through the developmental stages of childhood. The process of heredity is also explained.

LESSON 1 Life begins as a single microscopic cell. Over a nine-month period of time, the cell divides millions of times and develops the tissues, organs, and systems necessary for life. When an ovum is fertilized, it goes through numerous transitional stages as it is implanted in the uterus and goes through fetal development. Prenatal care is important because the female's health choices affect the health and well-being of the developing baby.

LESSON 2 Chromosomes within the nuclei of cells contain genes that control hereditary characteristics. The determination of sex is based on the father's sperm cell. In almost all other body cell development, the hereditary process involves complex chemical activity that results in dominant and recessive characteristics.

LESSON 3 Growth and development are affected by heredity, environment, and health choices. An individual's growth and development follows a predictable pattern, though the rate of these changes is unique to each individual.

CHAPTER 20
The Beginning of the Life Cycle

HEALTH Online

ADVOCACY

You can make learning fun for younger students, and share what you know about healthy behaviors. Visit **health.glencoe.com** and find the Interactive Project on how to "Create a Health Lesson Plan" for an elementary class or a younger brother or sister.

Hands-On Health

TEACHING STRATEGY

Reinforcing and Reviewing Bring your health classroom to life with interactive teaching strategies and classroom management techniques that keep your students interested and involved. The unique *Hands-On Health: Creative Teaching Strategies* booklet that accompanies the *Glencoe Health* program offers fun, motivating activities.

The following Classroom Management Ideas can be used to reinforce chapter concepts:

- Beach Ball
- Trivia Questions
- Paper Exchange
- Mental Outburst

> **You had better live your best and act your best and think your best today; for today is the sure preparation for tomorrow and all the other tomorrows that follow.**

—Harriet Martineau
English writer, (1802–1876)

Quick Write Write down one example of a healthful behavior that you can practice now to prepare for a healthful tomorrow.

Personal Health Inventory

Self-Inventory Write the numbers 1–10 on a sheet of paper. Read each statement below and respond by writing *yes*, *no*, or *sometimes* for each item. Write a *yes* only for items that you practice regularly. Save your responses.

1	A pregnant female has a responsibility to make healthy choices for her unborn child.
2	I come to children's assistance if they are in trouble.
3	I have taken care of younger brothers, sisters, cousins, or neighbors.
4	Children with special needs can experience a healthy development.
5	I treat children with respect.
6	I intervene if I see a child is being mistreated.
7	Children make a valuable contribution to society.
8	The way I treat a younger child has a positive impact on that child's self-concept.
9	I avoid picking on or teasing younger children.
10	I occasionally enjoy fun-filled, quality time with younger children.

Follow-up After completing the chapter, retake this self-inventory. Pick two items that you need to work on and set a goal to improve your health behaviors.

INTRODUCING THE CHAPTER

Personal Health Inventory

Have students read and briefly discuss the Self-Inventory statements: What do they indicate about the beginning of the life cycle? What do they say about your responsibilities toward babies and children? Ask students to record their responses to these statements in their private Health Journals on a page labeled "The Beginning of the Life Cycle." They will refer to these responses in the Self-Inventory Follow-up activity at the end of the chapter.

- Ask students to recall family reunions and some of the comments they heard from relatives they hadn't seen in a number of years. Follow their comments with the fact that physical changes are particularly obvious during early development, but that emotional, social, and intellectual growth and development are lifelong processes.
- Let students read the introductory quotation on this page, and encourage volunteers to share their reactions to this statement. Have them then complete the Quick Write. Ask: What are some of the advantages of practicing healthful behaviors now for a healthful tomorrow? After a brief discussion, explain that students will learn more about individual growth and health behaviors as they study the lessons in Chapter 20.
- Distribute Parent Letter 20 from the Parent Letters and Activities booklet in the TCR. ✐

TECHNOLOGY OPTIONS

ABCNEWS INTERACTIVE™ You may wish to use *Teenage Sexuality* with this chapter. For your convenience, use the separate *ABCNews InterActive™ Bar Code Correlation* that accompanies the *Glencoe Health* program. 💿

MINDJOGGER
VIDEOQUIZ

To preview or review chapter content, you may wish to use the *MindJogger Videoquiz* that accompanies Chapter 20. 💿

Prenatal Development and Care

LESSON 1

FOCUS

LESSON OBJECTIVES

After studying this lesson, students should be able to

- outline the major events in the first nine months of life, from fertilization through birth.
- describe prenatal care and why it is important.
- identify prenatal risks.

MOTIVATOR

Write the following on the chalkboard for students to work on while attendance is being taken: *List substances that pregnant females should avoid because they are harmful to the developing fetus.*

INTRODUCING THE LESSON

Refer to the Motivator. Ask volunteers to share their responses. Point out that in addition to alcohol, tobacco, and illegal drugs, many medications and disease organisms may also harm the fetus. Tell students that in this lesson they will learn how a fetus develops and why such substances lead to problems in fetal development.

INTRODUCING HEALTH TERMS

- Have each student create a crossword puzzle or sentence completion game using all of the vocabulary terms. Then ask students to exchange and complete each other's word challenge.
- Ask students to complete Vocabulary Activity 20 and Chapter Study Guide 20 in the *Student Workbook.*

Prenatal Development and Care

You and everyone you know began as a single microscopic cell smaller than the head of a pin. Within a nine-month period, this cell divided again and again, millions of times. Ultimately, it formed tissues, organs, and systems that made up your body, your characteristics, and the person you are today.

HEALTH TERMS

embryo
placenta
umbilical cord
fetus
Apgar test
miscarriage
stillbirth

HEALTH CONCEPTS

- Every individual starts off as a single microscopic cell.
- The health of a developing child is dependent on a number of factors, many of which are controlled by the mother-to-be.
- Eating healthfully, getting enough rest, and avoiding harmful substances, including tobacco, alcohol, and other drugs are all essential steps in sound prenatal care.

Cell division

Prenatal Development

The entire complex human body begins as one cell that is formed by the union of an egg cell, or ovum, from a female and a sperm cell from a male. These two cells are microscopic in size. The union of these cells is called *fertilization*. As soon as the ovum is fertilized, it is called a *zygote*. Once the zygote has been formed, a protective membrane around it prevents more sperm from entering the ovum. By the time the zygote reaches the uterus, it has divided many times to form a cluster of cells that has a hollow space in the center. It is now called a *blastocyst*.

Implantation

As the cells of the blastocyst divide, they begin to implant, or attach, to the lining of the uterus. This process is called *implantation*.

Lesson 1 Resources

TEACHER'S CLASSROOM RESOURCES
- **Concept Map** Activity 61
- **Decision-Making** Activity 20
- **Enrichment** Activity 20
- **Lesson 61 Quiz**
- **Lesson Plan 61**
- **Parent Letter and Activities 20**
- **Reteaching** Activity 61

STUDENT WORKBOOK
- **Applying Health Skills 61**
- **Chapter Study Guide 20**
- **Vocabulary** Activity 20

MULTIMEDIA
- **ABCNews InterActive™ VHS/Videodisc,** *Teenage Sexuality*

The lining of the uterus is made up of layers of tissue that will protect and nourish the fertilized egg throughout pregnancy. The *cluster of developing cells following implantation* is called an **embryo**. At this time, the embryo is about the size of the dot over the letter *i*.

Embryonic Development

The cells of the embryo continue to divide, forming three layers of tissue. One layer becomes the respiratory and digestive systems. Another layer develops into muscles, bones, blood vessels, and skin. The third layer becomes the nervous system, sense organs, and mouth.

At the same time, a thin membrane called the *amniotic sac* forms and surrounds the developing embryo. Fluid in this sac acts as a shock absorber that protects the embryo when it is jarred or bumped. The fluid also helps insulate the embryo from temperature changes.

A blood-rich tissue developed from an outer layer of cells from the embryo and tissue from the mother develops into the **placenta**. The embryo is connected to the placenta by the **umbilical cord**, *a tube through which nutrients and oxygen pass from the mother's blood into the embryo's blood*. The blood vessels of the umbilical cord also carry waste products from the embryo, where they diffuse into the mother's blood. These wastes are then excreted from the mother's body along with other body wastes.

Fetal Development

During the first six weeks of pregnancy, the embryo grows rapidly in length and gains weight. At the start of the third week, it is about one-half to one inch long (2 to 2.5 cm), or 10,000 times the size of the original egg cell! At eight weeks the embryo measures about 1½ inches in length (3.5 to 4 cm). *The name by which the embryo is known from the end of the eighth week until birth* is **fetus**. The skin of the fetus is clear and hairless and covered with a waxy protective coating. The fetus contains millions of cells that will arrange themselves into tissues and organs.

TWINS

In most cases of twins, a female's ovaries release two mature ova instead of one. If a separate sperm fertilizes each ovum, two embryos develop. The two embryos, called *fraternal twins*, have different genetic makeup and therefore do not look any more alike than brothers and sisters normally do. Fraternal twins can be the same gender or different gender.

In about one-third of these cases of twins, *identical twins* result. In this situation, a single ovum that has been fertilized divides and two embryos develop. These embryos have the same genetic information. These twins will be the same gender and look almost exactly the same. They are identical twins.

⬧ **Identical twins have the same genetic makeup.**

ACTIVITY *How is genetic research with twins helpful in finding health cures?*

TEACH

LD Explaining

Due to the high-level vocabulary and complex subject matter of this chapter, LD students may depend upon class discussions for comprehension. Assignment of this lesson as independent reading is not recommended.

LEP Demonstration

Using a schematic drawing, show the hierarchical relationship between cells, tissues, and organs.

LEP Class Activity

Have students locate the female reproductive organs on a chart or model. Ask volunteers to explain the role of each organ in fertilization, pregnancy, and birth.

L1 Explaining

Describe the process of fertilization. Explain why so many sperm are necessary for fertilization to occur even though only one sperm actually fertilizes the ovum.

LEP Demonstration

Show how a zygote is formed, using illustrations, transparencies, or a drawing on the chalkboard.

L1 Discussing

Guide a discussion of where fertilization usually occurs. Ask: Where does the zygote go after fertilization? What is a blastocyst? What does it look like?

L1 Discussing

Pose the following questions for discussion: What is the difference between an embryo and a fetus? What is the placenta? What does it do? Explain the difference between placenta and afterbirth.

 SCHOOL-TO-CAREER

PARENTAL LEAVE. Have students call several of the largest employers in your area. These might include government agencies and large corporations. Tell students to ask about their maternity and paternity leave policies. Is paternity leave allowed? Are maternity and paternity leave paid or unpaid? How long can parents take leave without losing a job? What benefits are provided during the leave? Encourage them to discuss whether the allowed leave is long enough for the mother to regain her strength after childbirth, for the parents to adjust to the new infant, and to allow enough time for parents to be with the newborn during important early development. Have students consider a situation in which one parent will stay home with the new baby for a time. What substantial advantages can students list for having one of the parents stay home?

L1 Discussing

Elicit from several volunteers and list on the chalkboard the names of the organs and systems that develop from each of the three layers of the embryo.

Building Health Skills

Choosing a Health Professional
Skill: Obtaining Help

Explain to students that the machine featured in the photograph is an ultrasound recorder. Ask students: How do you think most mothers-to-be choose their health care professionals? Why is this choice so important? After a brief discussion, have students read the Building Health Skills feature to learn about the questions a pregnant woman should consider. Help students discuss the suggestions. Is there one "best" health care provider for pregnant women? Why not? As a follow-up activity, let interested volunteers research the educational and licensing requirements and the career opportunities for obstetricians and for midwives.

ABCNEWS INTERACTIVE

TEENAGE SEXUALITY (Side 1)

Chapter 6: The Fertilization Process

Frames 9635-13280

Chapter 7: Fetal Development

Frames 13289-13579

Chapter 15: Prenatal Care

Frames 40712-42195

Did You Know?

The average pregnant woman gains 24 pounds, as follows:

➤ The fetus weighs 7 pounds.
➤ The amniotic fluid weighs 4 pounds.
➤ The increased weight of the uterus is 2 pounds.
➤ Enlargement of the breasts accounts for 3 pounds.
➤ Increased body fluids add an additional 3 pounds.
➤ Increase in lean body mass contributes 2 pounds.
➤ Increased fat equals 3 pounds.
➤ Total weight gain = 24 pounds.

The brain is one of the first organs to develop. The nervous system grows rapidly, and at nine weeks the head develops. All the body systems are now present.

Growth of the fetus is rapid during the fourth month, but it slows down in the fifth month. During this time, the mother can feel the fetus move. It may begin to suck its thumb. By the end of the sixth month, the fetus is about 14 inches (36 cm) long.

During the last three months of pregnancy, the weight of the fetus more than triples. The fetus moves freely within the amniotic sac. The eyes open during the seventh month. During the ninth month, the fetus usually moves into a head-down position and is ready for birth. The fetus is now 18 to 20 inches (46 to 51 cm) long and weighs about 7 to 9 pounds (3 to 4 kg).

Prenatal Care

The health of a developing baby is not totally within the control of the mother-to-be. Heredity, which will be addressed in the next lesson, is one unavoidable factor that can affect the developing baby. Yet, there is much the mother can do to improve the chances of having a healthy baby.

Building Health Skills

Obtaining Help: Choosing a Health Professional

THE HEALTH PROFESSIONAL whom the mother-to-be chooses is a partner in the health care of the baby and mother. When selecting a professional, whether it be an obstetrician or certified nurse midwife, a female should address the following considerations and questions:

1. Qualifications. What professional training has the person received? Do I know anyone who has made use of his or her services? Am I able to obtain reliable references?

2. Cost. Can I afford this professional? Is this type of service covered by my health insurance or health plan? If not, can I set up a payment schedule?

3. Interpersonal Skills. What kind of "bedside manner" does the person have? Am I comfortable talking to this professional? Am I encouraged to call if I have questions?

4. Location. Is the office located nearby? What are the office hours? Will I have to wait long? Is the professional associated with a hospital or a birthing center?

Other issues that need to be taken into account are the professional's views on natural childbirth and whether he or she is able to administer pain relief during labor, if desired.

456 CHAPTER 20 THE BEGINNING OF THE LIFE CYCLE

HOME AND COMMUNITY CONNECTION

BIRTH-FRIENDLY FACILITIES. Encourage students to survey the community for birth-friendly information and facilities. Suggest that they find out how many alternative birth centers are available. What is the cost savings over standard hospital deliveries? Are they located close to a hospital in case medical care is needed? What classes are available to teach the many birth methods? What is the cost? Are schedules convenient for working parents? What are the qualifications of the instructors? If students find abundant resources, invite them to create brochures and, with permission, leave them in places frequented by the public. If facilities are inadequate, suggest students express their concerns in a letter to a newspaper editor.

L2 Researching

Have students locate newspaper and magazine articles about the role of exercise during pregnancy. Ask them to discuss their findings with the class.

L2 Researching

Assign students to research and report to the class on how much weight is typically gained during pregnancy. How much weight gain is considered too little, and how much is too much? What are some of the negative health impacts on mother and fetus of too little and too much weight gain?

L1 Discussing

Ask the class: How is low birth weight defined? What is the increased risk of death in the first month and year of life if a baby is low in weight at birth? What factors contribute to low birth weight?

L3 Class Activity

Based on their personal knowledge and what they have gleaned from the media, ask the class to identify and discuss ways in which medical science has affected the process of reproduction, thus raising ethical and legal questions. Possible issues include surrogate motherhood, *in vitro* fertilization with donor sperm (test-tube babies), and post-menopausal pregnancy.

As soon as a female confirms her pregnancy, she should begin prenatal care. This includes having regular visits with either an obstetrician or a certified nurse midwife. An obstetrician is a doctor who specializes in the care of a female and her developing baby. A certified nurse midwife is an advanced practice nurse who, in addition to providing prenatal care, specializes in the delivery of healthy babies. Either professional will give the pregnant female a complete physical, including blood tests and a pelvic examination. Possible problems may be identified and corrected early.

Prenatal care gives the mother-to-be a chance to ask questions about pregnancy and the birth process, and it helps educate her with respect to important health behaviors. Nutrition is a special concern. The mother-to-be needs increased amounts of many micronutrients, especially calcium, vitamin E, and iron. Without sufficient iron, the fetus will draw its supply of iron from the mother, leaving her exhausted and possibly anemic. Eating foods rich in folic acid, such as whole grains and fish, reduces the chance of certain birth defects such as spina bifida, a neural tube defect that affects the baby's spine.

During prenatal care, the obstetrician or certified nurse midwife will also monitor the female's weight and discuss the importance of physical activity. An exercise program will be recommended depending on the female's health and level of fitness.

By the fourth month the fetus is 8 to 10 inches long and weighs about 6 ounces.
ACTIVITY *Compare the size of a fetus at 4 months and at 9 months.*

HEALTH Online

The March of Dimes works to reduce the rate of infant deaths due to birth defects. Visit **health.glencoe.com** and gather material to create a booklet for couples expecting their first child.

HEALTH Online

Appoint a team of volunteers to supervise print production of the booklets. One student in the group could be in charge of the art and design, another could manage research, and so on.

LESSON 1   PRENATAL DEVELOPMENT AND CARE   **457**

CURRICULUM CONNECTIONS

MATH The infant mortality rate is relatively high in the United States compared with most Western European countries. This is because many economically disadvantaged Americans do not have healthy diets or access to good prenatal care. This is especially true of members of racial and ethnic minorities. In these groups, the infant mortality rate may be as high as

that in countries that are economically disadvantaged. The infant mortality rate for middle-class U.S. whites, by contrast, is as high as that in any European country.

To reinforce basic math skills, have students demonstrate how an average rate calculated for an entire group can be influenced by a high rate in some of its component groups.

L1 Explaining

Explain the effect of alcohol on the developing fetus and the risk of fetal alcohol syndrome.

Making Responsible Decisions

1. Sheila's father-in-law insists that she have a glass of wine, even though Sheila is pregnant.
2. Sheila could (a) accept the wine but not drink it; (b) accept the wine and drink it; (c) refuse the wine and explain that she is protecting the health of her father-in-law's grandchild.
3. Sheila would probably (a) protect her baby's health and stop Tom's father from making a scene about the wine, although he might later insist that she drink it; (b) risk a negative influence on her baby's health but satisfy Tom's father; (c) protect her baby's health and perhaps help Tom's father understand why she isn't drinking alcohol, although he may still argue with her.
4. Sheila values the health of her unborn baby. She also values family harmony.
5. Responses will vary.
6. Help students discuss both short- and long-term consequences of their decisions.

L2 Decision Making

For further study on making responsible decisions, assign *Decision-Making Activity 20* in the TCR. 🖙

L1 Discussing

Discuss why the United States has a relatively high infant mortality rate and how it could be lowered.

---

hotlink

medicines For more information on medicines and procedures for using them safely and correctly, see Chapter 23, page 518.

hotlink

fetal alcohol syndrome (FAS) For more information on fetal alcohol syndrome (FAS) and its dangers to the developing child, see Chapter 25, page 561.

Medicines, Drugs, and Pregnancy

A pregnant female must be very careful about what substances she takes into her body. Any medicines, even natural supplements, should be taken only with her health professional's approval. Even prescription and over-the-counter **medicines** pose a potential danger to the fetus.

No illegal drugs should be taken. Illegal drugs present a serious threat to the mother and her baby. Babies can be born physically dependent on the drugs their mothers used while pregnant. Use of certain drugs during pregnancy can cause serious birth defects, including mental retardation.

Caffeine, which is present in coffee, tea, chocolate, and cola drinks, is another potential hazard to the fetus. A high caffeine intake has been associated with an increased risk of birth defects and other problems.

ALCOHOL AND PREGNANCY

Females who drink alcohol during pregnancy may cause permanent damage to the developing baby. Alcohol use by females during pregnancy has been associated with many defects in their children, because the alcohol passes from the mother's body into the baby's bloodstream. Consumption of alcohol is associated with a risk of **fetal alcohol syndrome (FAS)** and other neurodevelopmental effects. Fetal alcohol syndrome consists of three main features: mental retardation, slow growth before and after birth; and a wide range of physical defects ranging from cleft palate to hip dislocation.

The tragedy of FAS is that the unborn baby has no control over what enters the body. The decision to drink alcohol or not is the

Making Responsible Decisions

When Saying No Counts Double

Sheila is seven months pregnant, which has her and her husband Tom very excited. Both are also eager that their baby be healthy—a point Tom's parents don't seem to understand. Tonight, Sheila and Tom are out to dinner with Tom's parents to celebrate his mother's birthday. When Sheila declined the waiter's offer of something from the bar, Tom's father insisted. "It's a doubly joyous occasion," he said loudly and ordered Sheila a glass of wine.

What Would You Do?

Apply the six steps of the decision-making process to Sheila's problem:

1. **State the situation.**
2. **List the options.**
3. **Weigh the possible outcomes.**
4. **Consider your values.**
5. **Make a decision and act.**
6. **Evaluate the decision.**

Myths & Realities

MYTH. Many people believe that only drugs such as alcohol, nicotine, and cocaine can be harmful to a developing fetus.

FACT. The following list shows other harmful substances that can cross the "placental barrier" between mother and fetus:

- disease-causing organisms, such as the rubella virus that causes measles, HIV that causes AIDS, and the herpes virus that causes oral and genital herpes;
- food additives, such as saccharin and caffeine;
- pharmaceuticals, including aspirin and many antibiotics;
- toxins, such as carbon monoxide and lead.

A HEALTHY PREGNANCY

Here are some steps that a mother-to-be should follow to increase the chances that her baby will be born healthy:

➤ See a doctor or certified nurse midwife right away to begin prenatal care.

➤ Get plenty of rest.

➤ Eat at least three well-balanced meals rich in vitamins and minerals.

➤ Use stress-coping techniques such as relaxation or doing something enjoyable.

➤ Use safety belts while in a car.

➤ Exercise safely according to your health care professional's advice.

mother's. Because even small amounts of alcohol may be harmful, the safe decision for a pregnant woman is not to drink any alcoholic beverages. FAS is entirely preventable.

TOBACCO AND PREGNANCY

A pregnant female also must avoid using tobacco. Babies born to females who use tobacco have a greater chance of being born prematurely with low birth weights. Babies weighing 5½ pounds (2.5 kg) or less at birth often develop serious health problems early in life. Low birth weight is a leading cause of death in a baby's first year of life.

Studies have found that smoking during pregnancy may affect the growth, mental development, and behavior of children at least up to the age of 11. Children whose parents smoke have a higher incidence of respiratory problems, such as bronchitis and pneumonia, than do children whose parents do not smoke.

Stages of Birth

Babies usually are born headfirst. In the last few weeks of pregnancy, the baby's head moves to the lower part of the uterus. During the birth process, the baby is pushed out of the uterus and passes out of the mother's body. There are three stages in the birth process:

keeping
Fit

Do's and Don'ts During Pregnancy

A mother-to-be should follow the guidelines above, and to protect the health of her baby she should:

➤ Never use tobacco, alcohol, or other drugs.

➤ Never take any drugs without your health care provider's permission.

➤ Limit or avoid products that contain caffeine such as tea, coffee, and cola drinks.

MORE ABOUT . . . . .

THE DELIVERY PROCESS. A cesarean delivery is the surgical removal of the fetus through the mother's abdominal wall. The most common reason for a cesarean delivery is that the baby is too large or the pelvis too small for a safe vaginal delivery. Fetal distress, detected by the baby's heart rate, is another common reason; in this case, the baby must be delivered quickly. Sometimes the fetus is in an abnormal position, making a vaginal delivery impossible. Recovery from a cesarean delivery is somewhat longer than from a vaginal delivery, though most females can resume their normal activities within six weeks.

ASSESS

EVALUATING THE LESSON

Assign and discuss the Lesson 1 Review; then administer, grade, and discuss the *Lesson 61 Quiz* in the TCR. 🖝

RETEACHING

- Have students prepare a timeline that summarizes physical development in the uterus throughout pregnancy.
- Ask students to complete *Reteaching Activity 61* in the TCR. 🖝

ENRICHMENT

- Have students do a study of midwifery—the use of midwives in childbirth. What is it? What kind of training is required? In what kinds of settings do midwives usually practice? What might be the benefits and drawbacks of using a midwife during childbirth?
- Emphasize that what a young woman does before she knows she is pregnant can affect her baby's health. Have students complete *Enrichment Activity 20*, "Fetal Alcohol Syndrome: A Preventable Birth Defect," in the TCR. 🖝

CLOSE

Tell students that in this lesson they have seen the importance of the environment in the womb to the normal development of the fetus. If the fetus is exposed to drugs or other harmful substances, the result may be lifelong disease or disability. However, much of what characterizes an individual when he or she is born is due to the genes the parents pass on. How the individual gets these genes and how the genes affect the person are explained in the next lesson, which is about heredity.

---

1. **Dilation,** or stretching of the cervix. This results from mild contractions, which are known as *labor.*
2. **Passage of the baby through the birth canal.** This is caused by continuing contractions that shorten the uterus.
3. **Afterbirth.** Once the baby is born, contractions continue for another 10 to 15 minutes, ultimately pushing the placenta, now called the *afterbirth,* out of the mother's body.

Immediately after birth, most hospitals administer an **Apgar test.** This is *a routine diagnostic test that determines an infant's physical condition at birth.* The Apgar test measures the baby's condition in five significant areas: appearance or coloring; pulse; grimace or reflex irritability; activity; and respiration. Any significant difference from the normal response in each of these areas may require further testing and observation.

Complications During Pregnancy

Although pregnancy is not an illness, complications can occur, among these miscarriage and stillbirth. A **miscarriage** is *a spontaneous abortion,* in which the female expels the embryo or fetus. A **stillbirth** is *the birth of a dead fetus.* Females who use tobacco or drugs during pregnancy are more likely to have a miscarriage or stillbirth than those who abstain from their use. As with FAS, the problems associated with tobacco and drug use during pregnancy are completely preventable.

▲ *Both mother and baby are checked for signs of problems after the birth.*
ACTIVITY *List areas checked with the Apgar test.*

LESSON 1 *Review*

Reviewing Facts and Vocabulary

1. Use the terms *embryo* and *fetus* in a paragraph about prenatal development.
2. Identify factors over which the mother-to-be has control when she is planning for the health of her developing child.

Thinking Critically

3. *Evaluating.* Consider how the use of alcohol, tobacco, and drugs is both an irresponsible act of the mother-to-be and also harmful to the unborn child. What are the consequences to both mother and child?
4. *Synthesizing.* Contact a local hospital or clinic for educational materials for mothers-to-be. Identify the health benefits of each step in prenatal care to the developing fetus.

Applying Health Skills

5. *In Your Home.* When a female becomes pregnant, her body changes. Ask your mother or the mother of a friend about the changes she experienced while she was pregnant. Discuss how these changes helped her body to nourish a fetus until birth. Discuss the other responsibilities that a pregnant woman must consider while preparing for the birth of a child.

Lesson 1 Review

Answers to Reviewing Facts and Vocabulary

1. Paragraphs should reflect an understanding of the embryo as the cluster of developing cells following implantation, and of the fetus as the name by which the embryo is known from the end of the eighth week until birth.
2. She has control over the quality of prenatal care she receives, her nutritional intake, physical fitness, preparedness for delivery, and what substances are taken into her body while pregnant.

Answers to Thinking Critically

3.–4. Answers will vary.

From Generation to Generation

W hat color eyes do you have? What color is your hair? Would you describe yourself as tall, short, or medium compared with other people your age? These and related questions are determined by heredity, the passing on of traits from parents to offspring.

HEALTH TERMS

chromosomes
genes
amniocentesis
ultrasound
chorionic villi sampling

HEALTH CONCEPTS

- Heredity is the passing on of traits from parents to offspring.
- Some traits passed along from parents lead to the development of genetic disorders.
- Tests for the presence of genetic disorders can be performed on the mother-to-be.

Chromosome pairs, magnified

Chromosomes

H eredity is determined by **chromosomes**, *tiny structures within the nuclei of cells that carry information about hereditary traits.* Most cells in the body contain 46 chromosomes—23 pairs each.

At the foundation of chromosomes is the chemical compound *deoxyribonucleic acid,* or *DNA.* All living things are made of DNA. The DNA molecule resembles a twisted ladder, or helix, the rungs of which are made up of more chemical compounds, called *bases.* There are four kinds of bases that can be paired only in certain combinations, much like pieces of a jigsaw puzzle.

Genes

S pecific information about hereditary traits are carried within sections of chromosomes called *genes.* **Genes** are *segments of DNA molecules* and, like chromosomes, are paired. A pair of genes—one from

Lesson 2 Resources

TEACHER'S CLASSROOM RESOURCES

- **Concept Map** Activity 62
- **Health Lab** 20
- **Lesson 62 Quiz**
- **Lesson Plan** 62
- **Reteaching** Activity 62

STUDENT WORKBOOK

- **Applying Health Skills** 62
- **Chapter Study Guide** 20
- **Vocabulary** Activity 20

From Generation to Generation

From Generation to Generation

FOCUS

LESSON OBJECTIVES

After studying this lesson, students should be able to

- summarize the process of heredity.
- identify and explain genetic disorders.

MOTIVATOR

Write the following on the chalkboard for students to work on while attendance is being taken: *Sit in your seat with your hands resting on the desk in front of you, fingers intertwined. Make note of which thumb is on top. Then change the position of your hands so that the other thumb is on top. How does that feel?*

INTRODUCING THE LESSON

Ask for student responses to the Motivator. Explain that the tendency to hold the hands in one position or the other is genetically controlled; putting the hands in the other position usually feels strange and awkward. Tell students that in this lesson they will learn how traits such as this are passed from parents to their children.

INTRODUCING HEALTH TERMS

- Have students discuss the relationships implied by the following analogy: *chromosome is to gene as DNA molecule is to base.*
- Ask students to complete Vocabulary Activity 20 and Chapter Study Guide 20 in the *Student Workbook.*

TEACH

LD Explaining

Do not expect LD students to learn the specifics of chromosomes. They should be able to describe their function.

LEP Demonstration

Show the class pictures of individuals that reveal the diversity of humans with regard to a few of the obvious physical traits mentioned in the text, such as eye color, nose shape, and body size.

L1 Discussing

Ask: What traits, other than obvious physical features, are genetically influenced to some degree? *(Some examples: abilities such as artistic talent, mental disorders such as schizophrenia, destructive behaviors such as alcoholism, and personality traits such as shyness.)*

L1 Class Activity

To help students make sense of and better appreciate the extent of human diversity, work with them to create categories of traits that vary. Skin color, eye color, and hair color are all related traits of pigmentation; ABO and Rh are both blood-chemistry traits; height and weight are traits of body size and shape.

L1 Explaining

Explain that many traits controlled by one or more genes are also influenced by environmental factors (e.g., body weight and skin color).

L2 Health Lab

Distribute *Health Lab 20* and have students learn more about genetic traits. ◀▬

▲ *All living cells contain the genetic material DNA.*

ACTIVITY *Give an example of a physical trait determined by dominant genes.*

each parent—contributes to a single genetic trait such as hair color or hair straightness.

You have thousands of genes in every cell, and they each contain the same four bases. The variation among genes—which is the reason no two people are exactly alike—is a result of the arrangement of the bases along the DNA molecule. Because several hundred pairs of bases are in each gene, a countless number of arrangements is possible.

Cells make proteins when they interpret the order of these bases, or DNA code. Proteins help build and maintain body tissues. Cells make different proteins when they interpret different arrangements of bases. Different kinds of proteins will result in individual traits.

Dominant and Recessive Genes

As the chromosomes divide and separate, the two genes for a particular trait line up next to each other. Some genes will be *dominant,* while others will be *recessive.* Dominant genes are genes that generally show up in the offspring whenever they are present. Recessive genes are genes that usually show up only when dominant genes are not present. Suppose, for example, one parent has one of the genes that contributes to brown eyes (B), which is dominant, and the other parent has a gene that contributes to blue eyes (b), which is recessive. The likelihood that their child will have brown eyes is greater than that of his or her having blue eyes.

In actuality, the situation is slightly more complex than in the previous example. That is because traits that express a quantity or extent—such as height, weight, or degree of color—usually depend on many gene pairs, not just one.

Genes and Gender

Every living organism has a certain number of chromosomes. Human body cells, with the exception of sperm and ova, contain 46 chromosomes each. Ova and sperm have half that amount—23 chromosomes each. After fertilization, the zygote has 46 chromosomes (23 from each parent) that carry the hereditary traits of the mother and the father. The traits are passed on to another generation.

As you have learned, the zygote divides, eventually producing trillions of cells that make up the human body. Between each cell division, each chromosome in the cell nucleus duplicates itself. As the cell divides, the two sets of 46 chromosomes separate and each new cell contains one set of 46 chromosomes, identical to those in the first cell. This process continues throughout life.

Of the 46 chromosomes in a zygote, two are specialized sex chromosomes. In females, these two chromosomes look exactly alike and are called *X* chromosomes. In males, one chromosome is shorter and does not match the other. This shorter one is the *Y* chromosome. The longer one is the *X* chromosome.

462 CHAPTER 20 THE BEGINNING OF THE LIFE CYCLE

Myths & Realities

HEREDITY. Contrary to popular belief, most traits aren't simply controlled by one gene, but instead are influenced by many genes and the environment in a complex, interactive way. Such traits are called polygenic. The genes controlling a given polygenic trait may or may not be located on the same chromosome, and tremendous numbers of genetic and environmental combinations can be produced. The result is a bewildering degree of diversity across the species.

Good examples of polygenic traits are: skin color (controlled by some half-dozen genes and exposure to sunlight), weight and height (controlled by many genes, diet, and exercise).

Teens Making a Difference

Difference ...RESPONSIBILITY...COURAGE ...PERSEVERANCE

Nicole is 16 and has a genetic disease called Osteogenesis Imperfecta, also known as "Brittle Bone Disease." The disease causes her bones to break easily, and she has had over one hundred bone breaks. "I have pain in my bones," she says matter-of-factly. "I'm in a wheelchair. I've had major surgeries, and I have rods in my arms, three of them for support." Despite these hardships, she turns the situation around, showing compassion to other young people who are chronically ill.

REACHING OUT Nicole participates in a support group in the hospital school that she attends. "We talk about our illnesses. If the kids are having a bad time, we will talk about that." Nicole has been made an informal group co-leader. "I'm like everybody's psychiatrist," she says with a smile in her voice. "I've become a leader because they see how much pain I go through and how I'm treated in public, and yet I just keep going. I'm a role model to them, I guess. They can give me support when I need it, and I can give it to them." The support group works on

projects to help others in need. "We do things for the Salvation Army. We collected stuffed animals for young people who don't have a lot. Next, we are going to make quilts for AIDS babies. I also try to raise money for medicines or to find a cure for cancer. I want somebody to find a cure for my disease, so I want to help people with other diseases."

BECOMING AN ADVOCATE
Nicole is outspoken about her condition. Small for her age, people often mistake her for a child and say insensitive things. "I understand that they don't understand. Sometimes people even pet me on the head or treat me like a baby. I just want to be treated with respect. I tell them, too." But Nicole doesn't let this stand in her way. She is a strong advocate both for her own needs and those in her support group. "It's taken a lot of courage," she adds, speaking of her condition. "It's scary, but I know I just have to get through it. I don't depend on everyone to do everything for me. Listen," she says, "You've got to believe in yourself to reach to the level you want to reach, and there is help available. You can give it; you can get it."

NICOLE'S STORY
1. What values has Nicole put into action in facing her disease?
2. How is she reaching out to help others?

YOUR STORY
1. What strategies for facing your own difficulties can you take from Nicole's story?
2. How can you turn your difficult experiences into positive actions to help others and help you build strong character along the way?

Teens Making a Difference

Compassion from Experience

Discussion. After reading the features, ask students to discuss the questions that follow. Ask: How have Nicole's physical limitations helped her to develop character strength? What examples have motivated you to strengthen your own values? To feel compassion for others with similar difficulties? When and how have you acted as an advocate for someone else?

If there is time, read the following quotes from Nicole, asking students to react to them and see how students can apply them to their own lives:
- *I did a research project on my disease and presented it. I used the Internet and interviewed the doctors. I also told about getting surgery. I tell my story as one of the ways I reach out.*
- *I tell other kids not to worry about their looks. Looks don't matter to me. What matters is what's inside.*

Class Activity. Ask the class to list some noncommunicable diseases or conditions. Have students choose one disease or condition from the list and research organizations that raise funds or awareness in trying to prevent, educate about, or cure it. Ask students to organize a fundraiser or other project to help those suffering from the disease or to support an organization's efforts to find its cure.

Answers: *Nicole's Story*
1. Values featured and implied are caring; compassion, sensitivity or empathy; respect; responsibility; initiative; perseverance; courage.
2. She is a leader, role model, and advocate.

Responses: *Your story* **1–2.** Answers will vary. Encourage students to discuss their ideas with one another in small groups.

MORE ABOUT . . . . .

FUNCTION OF GENES. Almost everyone knows that genes control heredity, but most people are unaware that genes also control the reproduction and daily functioning of all cells. It's largely through the activity of regulatory and operator genes that cell types differ from each other in structure and function. Operator genes excite nearby genes into activity unless they are repressed by a repressor substance secreted by regulatory genes.

Scientists are learning more and more about the role of genes through the Human Genome Project, a nationally funded, multifaceted research project whose aim is to determine the function of the entire human "genome" (the total genetic makeup of the species).

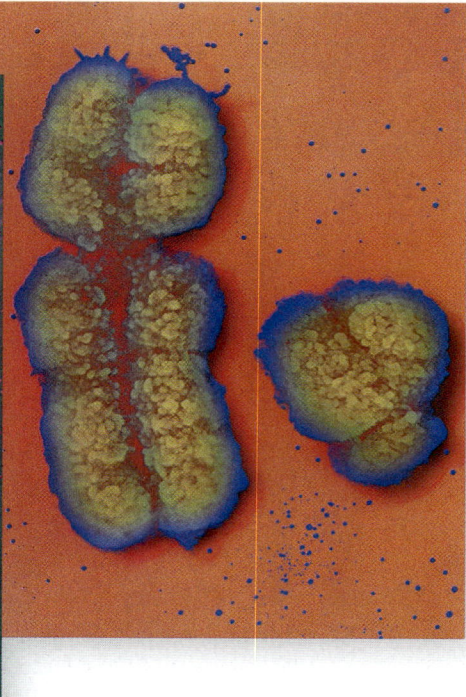

⚠ *Left: Only one sperm cell will penetrate the ovum for fertilization. Right: Human X and Y chromosomes determine gender.*

Remember that sperm and ova contain only half the number of chromosomes as other cells. This means that these cells contain only one sex chromosome, not two. Sperm may contain either an X or a Y chromosome. The ovum can have only an X chromosome. If an ovum is fertilized with a like chromosome, the combination is XX, resulting in a girl. If the sperm is carrying a Y chromosome, the pairing forms an XY combination, resulting in a boy. Thus, the determination of the gender of a child is based on which type of sperm finds the egg, an X or a Y.

Genetic Disorders

Sometimes the genes children inherit contain mutations, or abnormalities, in the genetic code. The resulting health problems and diseases, which can be severe, are known as *genetic disorders*. Some genetic disorders are observable at birth—in the form of birth defects such as cleft lip and cleft palate—whereas others tend to show up in childhood or adult life. In addition to a genetic cause, some disorders may also be affected by environmental factors, such as the lifestyle habits of one or both parents. There is an especially high rate of birth defects among children born to teenage girls, largely due to ignorance about proper prenatal care.

Types of Genetic Disorders

There are more than 4,000 hereditary disorders. A number of these disorders are recessive—caused by two defective genes, one from each parent. Others result from chromosomal abnormalities. The following are among the more common genetic disorders:

- **Sickle cell anemia.** This disease occurs when a child inherits the hemoglobin "Hbs" gene from both parents. The red blood cells develop a sickle shape and clump together, obstructing blood

Looking at the Issues

Genetic Testing, Genetic Discrimination?

In the past few years, researchers have begun to link specific genes or gene mutations with various diseases. Soon, access to even a tiny sample of a person's DNA will enable trained professionals to run a battery of genetic tests. As the number of genetic tests—and of people tested—increases, a great many legal and ethical questions are being raised. Perhaps the most troubling is the question of how these test results will be used and whether or not they may lead to certain kinds of discrimination, for example, in trying to get a job or health insurance.

ANALYZING DIFFERENT VIEWPOINTS

Viewpoint One

Those who favor genetic testing say that having the knowledge of whether a gene has been carried on can better prepare people for the future. Results of genetic tests, they add, can help decrease the risk of developing certain diseases, such as breast, ovarian, or colon cancer. Frequent screenings or even preventive surgeries can increase the potential for longer lives.

Viewpoint Two

Critics of genetic testing say that having such test results only adds to a person's fear. They point out that just because a person is genetically predisposed to a disease such as cancer doesn't mean that the person will necessarily develop it. They also point out that people who undergo genetic testing are at great risk of being discriminated against both by insurance companies, who won't insure people at risk for these diseases, and by employers, who may not want to hire those at increased risk because of large medical bills and lost productivity.

EXPLORING YOUR VIEWS

1. If there were a test that could alert you to the possibility of developing a life-threatening illness later in life, would you want to be tested? Why or why not?

2. Do you think genetic test information should be released only with a person's consent? Why or why not?

PERSONAL HEALTH

DRUGS AND UNPLANNED PREGNANCIES.
Women cannot select a baby's genes, but they can control other factors that cause defects. Much important development takes place in an embryo before a woman learns she is pregnant. Harmful substances may have been ingested before the pregnancy was discovered. Have students write in their private Health Journals about substances a sexually active woman should avoid. Drugs can inflict the same harm whether obtained illegally, by prescription, or over-the-counter. Encourage students to research drugs sold by prescription or over-the-counter that could be harmful to the embryo; then list medicines a sexually active woman should avoid.

L1 Explaining

Explain that the 46 chromosomes making up normal human cells actually consist of 23 pairs of chromosomes. (This is how ova and sperm, which have only one of each type of chromosome, can still carry a gene for each human trait.)

L1 Class Activity

Show how genes are passed from a set of parents to their children by drawing a diagram on the chalkboard. Use a capital and lowercase letter to represent dominant and recessive expressions of a single trait (e.g., *D* for dimples, *d* for no dimples). Ask student volunteers to write in all the possible combinations of the two genes in the children and how each child would appear.

update
Looking at the Issues

Genetic Testing, Genetic Discrimination?

Tell students that medical researchers have developed tests that can identify the potential an individual has to develop—or to pass on to children—a variety of serious diseases. Ask: Isn't that wonderful? Let several volunteers respond. Then, if a student has not already done so, point out that there is another, less positive aspect to genetic testing. Encourage students to discuss their ideas about this other viewpoint. Then let students work in groups to read the Update feature, to discuss the viewpoints presented there, and to share their responses to the questions.

L1 Discussing

Ask students: How is it that the father alone determines the sex of the child, even though each child receives half of his or her genes from each parent?

L1 Discussing

Lead a discussion of responses to the following question: If a person has the same genes in every cell, why do cells differ so greatly from each other (e.g., blood cells vs. skin cells)?

L3 Guest Speaker

Invite a representative from the March of Dimes to speak with the class regarding the agency's role in fighting birth defects.

L1 Discussing

What is amniocentesis? Why is it, along with some of the other methods investigating the health of the fetus, controversial to some individuals and groups? Encourage students to share their ideas.

L3 Guest Speaker

Have a genetics counselor from a local hospital speak with the class about genetic disorders and how they can be prevented through genetics counseling.

HEALTH Online

Invite a genetic counselor from a local hospital or health facility to speak to the class after students have explored the Web link on the subject. Encourage students to prepare for the visit by brainstorming thought-provoking questions.

> *Ultrasound images allow doctors to see an image of the fetus.*
> **ACTIVITY** *Identify the head and hand in this ultrasound image.*

HEALTH Online

What do genetic counselors do? What educational background do they have? Find the answers to these questions at **health.glencoe.com**. Compile information presented into a career profile for students interested in genetic counseling.

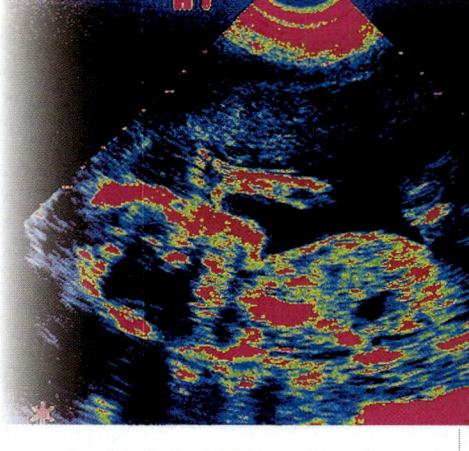

flow and oxygen to the tissues. The symptoms of sickle cell anemia are severe joint and abdominal pain, weakness, and kidney disease.

- **Phenylketonuria.** In Phenylketonuria (FEE-nuhl-kee-toh-NOOR-ee-uh)—or *PKU*—a protein called *phenylalanine* accumulates in the body, interfering with the development of brain cells and causing mental retardation. In many states, babies are screened at birth for PKU by a blood test. If results are positive, treatment can begin before mental retardation sets in. Diet can stop the retardation from happening.

- **Tay-Sachs disease.** Tay-Sachs disease affects 1 in 3,600 Americans of Eastern European Jewish ancestry. Tay-Sachs disease causes the destruction of the nervous system, blindness, paralysis, and death during early childhood. A blood test can detect carriers, and a test can diagnose the disease prenatally.

- **Cystic fibrosis.** One in every 2,000 infants is born with cystic fibrosis. The disease, which makes breathing and digestion difficult, is caused by two abnormal genes, one coming from each parent. If both parents are carriers, their offspring have a 25 percent chance of having the disease.

- **Down syndrome.** Down syndrome is primarily caused by a chromosomal abnormality known as *trisomy-21,* the presence of three copies of the twenty-first chromosome. As a result, the affected individual has an extra forty-seventh chromosome in all body cells. Down syndrome affects approximately 1 in 700 births, but the risk varies with the mother's age. By the time a woman reaches 40, the chances are about 1 in 40 that her child will be affected by Down syndrome. Children with Down syndrome share certain characteristics such as mental retardation, which can range from severe to moderate.

Identifying Genetic Disorders

There are several methods used to investigate the health of the fetus. These include the following:

- **Amniocentesis.** Amniocentesis (am-nee-oh-sen-TEE-sis) is *a procedure in which a syringe is inserted through the pregnant female's abdominal wall into the amniotic fluid surrounding the developing fetus.* The physician removes a small amount of the fluid to

---

HEALTH LITERACY

SELF-DIRECTED LEARNER. Have you ever noticed the warnings on most diet soft drinks regarding phenylalanine? Probably not, unless you or a family member has phenylketonuria (PKU). Individuals with PKU must follow a strict diet to avoid phenylalanine, because it accumulates in their blood. Accumulation can result in learning disabilities, behavior problems, and personality disorders. Children without early diagnosis of severe PKU were once destined to be mentally retarded. Since the mid-1960s, however, all states routinely test newborn infants. Those with PKU can now lead normal lives if they maintain a strict diet. Have volunteers investigate the cause and incidence of PKU. Though the condition is rare, one of every 50 people is a carrier.

examine the chromosomes, study the body chemistry, and determine the sex of the fetus. Amniocentesis is performed usually 16 to 20 weeks after fertilization.

- **Ultrasound.** Ultrasound is *a test in which sound waves are used to project light images on a screen.* The sound waves are directed at the pregnant female's abdomen and reflected onto a screen. The reflected waves act like an echo and form an image of the fetus. Ultrasound is used to determine the position of a fetus, and if there is more than one fetus in the uterus.

- **Chorionic villi sampling.** Also known as *CVS,* chorionic villi (kor-ee-ON-ik VIL-eye) **sampling** is *a test in which a small piece of membrane is removed from the chorion, a layer of tissue that develops into the placenta.* This material is examined for possible genetic defects. The procedure takes place around the eighth week of fetal development, so it is a procedure that can be done earlier than amniocentesis.

Genetic Counseling

Knowledge about genetically related diseases and about new research for diagnosing, preventing, and treating them has produced a wide variety of programs to deal with genetic disorders and birth defects. One way to help prevent genetically caused birth defects is to identify carriers. Genetic counselors can advise families about the probability of having a child with a genetically related disease. They also can guide families of children with genetic disorders about possible treatment options.

ASSESS

EVALUATING THE LESSON

Assign and discuss the Lesson 2 Review; then administer, grade, and discuss the *Lesson 62 Quiz* in the TCR.

RETEACHING

- Have students do a "chalk talk" in which they explain and diagram the process of heredity, showing how a simple trait is passed from parents to children.
- Ask students to complete *Reteaching Activity 62* in the TCR.

ENRICHMENT

Ask students to explore genetic engineering. Why is it controversial? What ethical questions come into consideration as scientists learn more about genetics? Instruct students to summarize their findings in written reports.

CLOSE

Have students list some congenital defects that are obvious at birth, and others that can be detected at birth with lab tests. This development will be presented in the next lesson.

LESSON 2 *Review*

Reviewing Facts and Vocabulary

1. Define *chromosomes* and *genes,* and identify the role each plays in heredity.
2. List two means of identifying genetic disorders, and describe the processes involved.

Thinking Critically

3. *Evaluating.* Do you think it is a good idea to know the sex of a baby before birth? Explain your answer.

Applying Health Skills

4. *In Your Community.* Visit a local garden center or greenhouse. Ask those who raise the flowers or plants how many different varieties of several particular plants there are. Read about the works of Gregor Mendel, and discuss how his work with pea plant varieties led to the science of genetics.

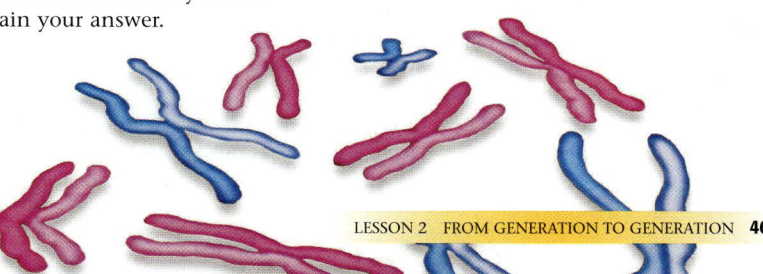

LESSON 2   FROM GENERATION TO GENERATION   **467**

Lesson 2 Review

Answers to Reviewing Facts and Vocabulary

1. Chromosomes are tiny structures within the nuclei of cells that carry information about hereditary traits. Genes are segments of DNA molecules. Each gene carries specific hereditary information within the chromosomes.

2. Two of the following: Amniocentesis— See page 466 for description of process. Ultrasound—See page 467. Chorionic villi sampling—See page 467.

Answers to Thinking Critically

3. Answers will vary.

Birth Through Late Childhood

FOCUS

LESSON OBJECTIVES

After studying this lesson, students should be able to
- describe the first four of Erikson's eight stages of development.

MOTIVATOR

Write the following on the chalkboard for students to work on while attendance is being taken: *What is the value of understanding how we grow and develop?* (We can predict the type and rate of growth to be expected in normal individuals—significant deviations may indicate that there is a problem.)

INTRODUCING THE LESSON

Refer to the Motivator. Ask volunteers to share their responses. Tell students that our physical development is well documented and very well understood, whereas our emotional and social development are not so clearly understood. Theories abound in an attempt to explain our personality development. In this lesson, students will examine one of the better-known and widely accepted theories attributed to psychologist Erik Erikson.

INTRODUCING HEALTH TERMS

- Ask students to find definitions for each of the following terms and then describe a situation that demonstrates each term: *initiative, guilt, industry,* and *inferiority.*
- Ask students to complete Vocabulary Activity 20 and Chapter Study Guide 20 in the *Student Workbook.*

Birth Through Late Childhood

Throughout life you grow and develop physically, socially, emotionally, intellectually, and culturally. Your growth and development are predictable, following certain general patterns. However, you will grow and develop at a rate that is unique to you. Your growth and development are affected by your heredity, your environment, and your health decisions.

HEALTH TERMS

developmental task

autonomy

HEALTH CONCEPTS

- The period from birth through late childhood is marked by four developmental stages.
- How well a person adapts to changes and events that occur within each stage will affect his or her growth and development.

Developmental Stages

Several noted scientists have identified certain basic stages of growth and development. For each stage, developmental tasks are identified. A **developmental task** is *something that needs to occur during a particular stage for a person to continue his or her growth toward becoming a healthy, mature adult.* Developmental tasks in adolescence, for example, include forming more mature relationships with peers and achieving emotional independence from parents.

One of the most widely accepted theories of development is that of psychologist Erik Erikson. Erikson describes stages of development from birth through old age. Our success in each stage has much to do

Lesson 3 Resources

TEACHER'S CLASSROOM RESOURCES
- **Concept Map** Activity 63
- **Cooperative Learning** Activity 20
- **Lesson 63 Quiz**
- **Lesson Plan 63**
- **Reteaching** Activity 63

STUDENT WORKBOOK
- **Applying Health Skills** 63
- **Chapter Study Guide** 20
- **Vocabulary** Activity 20

TRANSPARENCIES
- **Transparency 50**

with our experiences during that stage. Erikson believes, however, that failure at one stage can be overcome by successes in following stages.

Infancy

From birth to one and one-half years, you experienced the fastest period of growth in your life. Your weight tripled and your height doubled. The developmental tasks of an infant include learning to eat solid food, beginning to walk and explore the environment, perceiving objects and people, and learning to talk.

In the first year of life, according to Erikson, one of a child's main tasks is that of developing trust. The child of parents who play with and talk to the baby and pick him or her up when crying learns to view the world as a safe place and people as being dependable. If a child's needs are inadequately met or rejected—for example, if parents ignore or do not tend promptly or lovingly to the child's needs—he or she learns to be fearful of the world and people.

Early Childhood

Early childhood refers to the second and third years of life. During this period, children develop many new physical and mental skills. They master walking, learn to climb, and can push and pull. They increase their vocabulary and even begin talking in sentences. Among other important developmental tasks at this age is learning to control the elimination of body wastes.

Children at this age are proud of these accomplishments and try to do as many things as possible on their own. Have you ever been around a 2- or 3-year-old who insisted on putting on his or her own shoes or clothes? This behavior is very typical of a child's increasing desire for independence.

If parents accept the child's need to do whatever he or she is capable of, then the child will develop a sense of **autonomy**, *the confidence that one can control one's own body, impulses, and environment.* However, if parents insist on doing everything for the child or are critical when the child attempts something and fails, then the child will develop doubts about his or her abilities.

▲ As children go through developmental stages of infancy, early childhood, and childhood, they become more independent and capable of doing things for themselves.

TEACH

LEP Discussing

Collect newspaper and magazine pictures of children up to the age of adolescence to illustrate Erikson's first four stages of development. Discuss the developmental tasks associated with each stage.

L1 Discussing

Ask the class: What are some ways that parents help a child develop trust vs. mistrust?

L1 Discussing

How can parents help their children develop a sense of autonomy? Elicit student responses.

L1 Explaining

Explain what *initiative* means and how children may feel if the questions and activities they initiate are ignored or belittled.

L1 Community Involvement

Divide the class into four groups, and assign each group one of Erikson's first four stages of development. Ask each group to do a report on how an individual might develop healthy or unhealthy characteristics based on experiences in the stage assigned. Students should interview parents of young children to determine if they are aware of these developmental stages. Have students share the reports with the class.

L2 Cooperative Learning

Have students complete *Cooperative Learning Activity 20,* "And Baby Makes Three," in the TCR.

MORE ABOUT . . . . .

PERSONALITY DEVELOPMENT. Many anthropologists, such as John and Beatrice Whiting, question the universality of Erikson's stages of development. They believe that adult personality depends on the specific child-rearing practices found in a given society, and that these, in turn, have their roots in a society's ways of meeting the basic physical needs of its members. Autonomy, for example, may be an important trait to develop in complex societies such as our own, where self-reliance and independence help ensure social and economic success. In many other societies, particularly farming societies, such traits conflict with the need of individuals to work for the benefit of the group.

health lab

TV AND CHILD DEVELOPMENT

Time Needed: About 45 minutes of class time, divided between two days.

Understanding Objectives:
Students will observe whether and how specific TV programs encourage young children to achieve developmental tasks.

Focus on the Health Lab:
Encourage a brief discussion of the role TV plays in the lives of young children. Let volunteers identify some of the programs three- to five-year-olds watch.

Observation and Analysis:
Have students work in small groups to plan and conduct their TV viewing.

In Conclusion Answers:
Responses will vary. Have group members work together to discuss their responses and then to write a summary of their findings.

Further Investigation:
Have the members of each group identify two other shows that young children often watch—those not deemed "developmentally appropriate"—and apply the same analysis to those shows.

L1 Explaining

Describe how feelings of inferiority and self-doubt may develop if a child's sense of industry is not reinforced.

L1 Parental Involvement

Ask students to discuss with their parents and write about the stages of development that are occurring in their nuclear and extended families.

---

health lab

TV AND CHILD DEVELOPMENT

Because children of all ages spend so much time in front of the television, TV producers have begun developing shows that they claim to be "developmentally appropriate." Do these shows communicate information that will help young children master developmental tasks?

What you will need
- Annotated list of local television shows
- Several televisions
- Videocassette recorder (VCR)
- Notepads and pencils

What you will do
1. With two classmates, examine an annotated list of TV programs in your area. Find six shows that are supposedly geared toward children ages three to five. Choose three shows that are broadcast on network TV and three that are shown on public TV.

2. Each group member is to watch two programs, one network broadcast and one public TV broadcast. If the shows are aired only during school hours, use a videocassette recorder (VCR) to tape them and view them at a more convenient time.

3. As you view each show, pay close attention to its theme and content and to whether it encourages a young child to achieve or fail at a particular developmental task. Take detailed notes as you view the show. Compile your findings as a group. Use your notes to answer the questions that follow.

In conclusion
1. Did any shows encourage a young child to achieve at a particular developmental task? Which shows and which tasks? Was the task appropriate to the age?

2. Which show most surprised you? Why?

3. Do you think TV can be valuable in helping a young child achieve particular developmental tasks sooner than if the child did not watch television? Why or why not?

4. If one show did not encourage a young child to achieve a particular developmental task, what do you feel is the purpose of the show?

Childhood

During the fourth and fifth years of life, physical abilities develop. Children can initiate play activities rather than merely follow other children. They often play make-believe, imagining themselves in a variety of adult roles. They copy what they see adults doing and begin to ask many questions, a sign of intelligence.

If parents show approval of these new abilities and activities and encourage questions, children learn *initiative*, the ability to start something on their own. They also learn to be creative and explore

---

COOPERATIVE LEARNING

ACTIVITY. Ask volunteers to bring to class photographs of themselves or other babies after birth, at the age of one year, and at several stages in between. Accept photographs from publications as well as from home. Have students work in groups. Tell them to examine the photographs in their groups and discuss their observations about physical development at various ages. At what age do babies have

teeth? How much do babies grow between birth and the end of the first year? How does their appearance change within the first year? Invite each group to create a poster using the photos of babies at various ages. Beside the photos at each age, have them write summaries of what they have learned about development at the photographed stage, based on this lesson and their observations.

new ideas. If, however, the parent is impatient with all of the child's questions or makes the child think the activities are wrong, the child will likely develop a sense of guilt about self-initiated activities.

Late Childhood

Between the ages of 6 and 11, children experience a major part of their social development—school. The developmental tasks at this age reflect social, emotional, intellectual, physical, and cultural growth.

Children learn physical skills necessary for games and activities. They develop basic skills in reading, writing, and calculating. An important task during this stage is building wholesome attitudes toward themselves. Children learn to get along with peers and learn appropriate roles in society. During this stage, children develop a conscience. They learn right from wrong and develop attitudes toward social groups and institutions.

As children in this stage begin to acquire new skills, they develop a sense of industry. They begin to make things—cookies, model

planes, and the like. The child's sense of industry is reinforced if parents and teachers praise and reward these creative efforts. If, however, an adult constantly scolds a child for making a mess, getting in the way, or not following directions, the child may develop feelings of inferiority and self-doubt.

LESSON 3 *Review*

Reviewing Facts and Vocabulary

1. Define the term *developmental task,* and give two examples.
2. What are the main developmental tasks during a child's first year?

Thinking Critically

3. *Comparing and Contrasting.* Compare and contrast development during the first year of life with development from 2 to 3 years of age.

Applying Health Skills

4. *In Your Community.* Observe parents of a 3-year-old whom you know. Make a list of all the things they say or do to encourage a sense of autonomy in their child.

CHARACTER IN ACTION

Modeling Moral Behavior

Discuss how impressionable young children are. Ask students to give examples of how teens can demonstrate the highest values to younger children, including through the choices they make and behaviors they display in front of younger people.

ASSESS

EVALUATING THE LESSON

Assign and discuss the Lesson 3 Review; then administer, grade, and discuss the *Lesson 63 Quiz* in the TCR.

RETEACHING

- Have students make scrapbooks to illustrate Erikson's first four stages of development. Students should select photographs from magazines that illustrate the developmental tasks for each stage.
- Ask students to complete *Reteaching Activity 63* in the TCR.
- Use *Transparency 50* to discuss the effects of television viewing on children.

ENRICHMENT

The ages from 18 months to three years are often called the "terrible twos." Have students write an essay that discusses how Erikson's view of this age makes sense of the type of behavior attributed to the terrible twos.

CLOSE

Ask students to state the most important concepts learned in the lesson.

Lesson 3 Review

Answers to Reviewing Facts and Vocabulary

1. See page 468 or the Glossary for the definition of *developmental task*. Two examples—forming more mature relationships with peers and achieving emotional independence from parents.
2. Learning to eat solid food, beginning to walk and explore the environment, perceiving objects and people, learning to talk, and learning to trust.

Answers to Thinking Critically

3. At ages two and three, children master walking and other physical activities, increase their vocabulary and begin to talk in sentences, learn to control the elimination of body wastes, and try to establish a sense of autonomy.

Health **Skills** Activities

ACTIVITY 1
HEALTH SKILLS

Analyzing Influences, Communication

➤ **National Standards**
This activity meets these National Health Standards: 4.4 5.1.

Teach

- Follow up on the preparation phase of the activity by noting that commercials state their message within a fixed time—usually between 15 and 60 seconds.
- Emphasize that students will have exactly 60 seconds to communicate their message.
- If students are able to videotape the PSA, arrange if possible to have them share copies with pregnant women, perhaps through a social services office in the community.

ACTIVITY 2
HEALTH SKILLS

Comprehending Health Concepts, Analyzing Influences

➤ **National Standards**
This activity meets these National Health Standards: 1.4; 4.3.

Teach

- If possible, prior to assigning the activity, present a video or filmstrip that covers the stages in the development of a human fetus.
- The class might be divided into two major groups—one concerned with detailing prenatal stages, one with child development.
- Suggest that students use information from the film, if one was used, as well as from the book. Students who wish to go beyond what is presented in the book should be encouraged to log onto a Web site you have prescreened that covers this topic in a factual, yet informative way.

Activity 1 — Healthful Nutrition During Pregnancy

Following sound nutrition and exercise guide- lines benefits not only the health of a pregnant female but also of her unborn baby. Sadly, this is a reality some pregnant females do not practice.

Directions

1. In a group, review information in your book on the health needs of pregnant females and their unborn babies.
2. Compose a 60-second script on this topic for a public service announcement. As preparation, think about how best to reach the intended audience.
3. Videotape or record the announcement and share it with the class. Afterward, analyze which messages had the most influence and why.

Self-Assessment

✓ Described proper nutrition and health care for pregnant females and their unborn babies.
✓ Analyzed how media messages can influence behaviors.

Time
50 minutes

Materials
paper, pen or pencil, poster board, video or tape recorder

Activity 2 — Stages of Development

A human baby goes through a number of stages both before and after birth. Proper health care and nutrition are critical at every stage of the child's development.

Directions

1. As a class, create a detailed chart of the different stages of prenatal and child development. Begin by forming groups. Each group is to investigate a different developmental stage, determine what changes occur, the care that is needed, and any risks associated with this stage.
2. Each group is to share its findings on a sheet of poster board that has been arranged in a grid. Columns should be labeled *Growth and Development, Health Care,* and *Risks.* Rows are to correspond to stages.
3. Display your poster in the classroom.

Self-Assessment

✓ Identified factors that can influence the growth and development of a healthy baby.
✓ Described the types of growth that occurs at different stages of development.

Time
50 minutes plus outside research

Materials
poster board, colored markers, photos of the different stages of prenatal and child development, library or Internet health resources

472 CHAPTER 20 THE BEGINNING OF THE LIFE CYCLE

ASSESSMENT SCORING

Using a four-level rubric, the student has achieved a 4 if:

ACTIVITY 1

✔ Student made full and constructive use of the 60 seconds available.
✔ Student gave evidence of having researched or reviewed concepts relating to prenatal care.
✔ PSA covered key points on nutrition and health care for pregnant females and fetuses.
✔ Student demonstrated an awareness of the ways media messages can influence behaviors.

ACTIVITY 2

✔ Student played a role in identifying factors that can influence the growth and development of a healthy baby.
✔ Student documented risks that occur at that stage and ways of diminishing these risks.
✔ Student described the types of growth that occurs at this stage.
✔ Student worked effectively with others.

HEALTH NEWS
VIDEO

Fighting Cancer, One Cell at a Time

Cancers grow uncontrollably without treatment. Today, doctors use radiation, surgery, and chemotherapy to try to halt growing cancers. A promising new treatment uses genetic cancer-fighters to help cells resist cancer's invasion.

Researchers inject patients with a virus. But this virus won't make people sick. It delivers a new gene, called P-53, into the patient's cells.

P-53 acts as a cell guardian. If the cell becomes damaged by a cancer, P-53 helps the cell repair the damage. However, the gene also contains an important sensor. If the sensor discovers that too much of the cell is damaged, P-53 triggers the cell to self-destruct. Through these controls, genetic therapy may help prevent cancers from spreading.

Play the Video

Think About It

- What is gene therapy? How is it different from other types of cancer treatments?
- Describe what researchers mean by "programmed cell death"? How can this process help cancer treatment?
- What other diseases do you think might be treated with gene therapy? Name three diseases and tell why you think this type of treatment might be effective against them.

CNN HEALTH NEWS **473**

MORE ABOUT . . . . .

ASK THE EXPERTS. Medical research laboratories contain many professionals who work together to investigate promising new treatments. Although the primary investigators are doctors with Ph.Ds, most labs also employ several other types of workers.

Laboratory technicians assist doctors as they conduct their research. The training for lab technicians usually includes an undergraduate study that emphasizes the sciences, plus a clinical education in an MLT (Medical Laboratory Technician) program.

Labs also hire assistants with other specialized training, such as computer analysts, office managers, and maintenance workers. For example, many labs hire a glass cleaner who is responsible for washing test tubes and other containers to insure their sterility.

CNN HEALTH NEWS

Fighting Cancer, One Cell at a Time
Video Segment 13 (Time – 2:09)

Objectives. After viewing the video, students should be able to explain how researchers investigate ways to use gene therapy for the treatment of disease.

Motivator. Have students brainstorm a list of methods for treating disease. Students might suggest medication, radiation, physical therapy, surgery, and lifestyle changes. Have students view Video Segment 13 to introduce gene therapy, a new technique doctors are developing as a potential treatment for some genetic diseases, such as cancer.

Teach
- Have students create a flow chart on the chalkboard that shows the steps used in gene therapy for the treatment of cancer:
  1. Doctors isolate the P-53 gene.
  2. The gene is combined with a virus.
  3. The virus is injected into the patient.
  4. The P-53 gene is copied into the patient's cells.
  5. The gene helps to trigger cell repair.
  6. If too much damage is sensed, the gene triggers the cell to self-destruct.
- Ask students to predict how doctors evaluate the success of gene therapy. Point out that they probably use diagnostic techniques, including blood tests, X rays, and CAT scans, to measure the growth and spread of the patient's cancer.

Role Play. Encourage students to create a list of questions they would ask a doctor about this treatment. Students can work together to find answers in library and Internet reference sources. Then ask students to role-play the different parts in the patient-doctor discussion. Allow viewers to offer corrections or additional information after each role-play scenario.

Close. Ask students to explain how using gene therapy is different from chemotherapy, the use of drugs to treat a disease. As students offer their comparisons, point out that the treatment of cancer often combines several different therapeutic methods.

CHECKING COMPREHENSION

- Assign and discuss the chapter review.
- Use the MindJogger Videoquiz to review the chapter. 🔴

CHAPTER 20 REVIEW ANSWERS

Using Health Terms

1. umbilical cord
2. miscarriage
3. stillbirth
4. embryo
5. fetus
6. placenta
7. amniocentesis
8. genes
9. chorionic villi sampling
10. chromosomes
11. ultrasound
12. Apgar test
13. developmental task
14. autonomy

RECALLING THE FACTS

1. The umbilical cord transports nutrients and oxygen from the mother's blood to that of the embryo.
2. Whatever enters the female's body also enters the embryo's. Whatever care she receives, the embryo also receives. Whatever choices she makes for herself, she also makes for the embryo.
3. Low birth weight.
4. First: dilation, or stretching of the cervix. Second: passage of the baby through the birth canal. Third: expulsion of the placenta, or afterbirth.
5. By the contribution to the ovum of either an X or Y chromosome at fertilization.
6. Dominant genes will show up in the offspring whenever they are present. Recessive genes usually show up only when dominant genes are not present.
7. Mutations, or abnormalities, in the genetic code.

Using Health Terms

On a separate sheet of paper, write the term that best matches each definition below.

LESSON 1

1. A tube through which nutrients and oxygen pass from the mother's blood into the embryo's blood.
2. A spontaneous abortion.
3. The birth of a dead fetus.
4. Cluster of developing cells following implantation.
5. The name by which the embryo is known from the end of the eighth week until birth.
6. An outer layer of cells of the embryo with blood-rich tissue from the mother.
7. A routine diagnostic test which determines an infant's physical condition at birth.

LESSON 2

8. A procedure in which a syringe is inserted through the pregnant female's abdominal wall into the amniotic fluid surrounding the developing fetus.
9. Segments of DNA molecules.
10. A test in which a small piece of membrane is removed from the chorion, a layer of tissue that develops into the placenta.
11. Tiny structures within the nuclei of cells that carry information about hereditary traits.
12. A test in which sound waves are used to project light images on a screen.

LESSON 3

13. Something that needs to occur during a particular stage for a person to continue his or her growth toward becoming a healthy, mature adult.
14. The confidence that one can control one's own body, impulses, and his or her environment.

Recalling the Facts

Using complete sentences, answer the following questions.

LESSON 1

1. What is the function of the umbilical cord?
2. In what ways do a female's health choices affect the health of her developing baby?
3. What is the leading cause of death in an infant's first year of life in the U.S.?
4. Identify and describe each of the three stages of birth.

LESSON 2

5. How does the male determine the gender of the baby?

6. What is the relationship between dominant and recessive genes?
7. What are the causes of genetic disorders?
8. Name two tests that can be used to determine the health of a developing fetus. Explain each.

LESSON 3

9. State two developmental tasks for each of Erik Erikson's first four stages of development.
10. What causes an infant to learn mistrust?
11. What leads to autonomy in childhood?

8. Amniocentesis is a procedure in which a syringe is inserted through the pregnant female's abdominal wall into the amniotic fluid surrounding the developing fetus to examine the chromosomes, study the body chemistry, and determine the sex of the fetus. Ultrasound is a test in which sound waves are used to project light images on a screen to determine the position of a fetus and if there is more than one fetus in the uterus. Chorionic villi sampling is a test in which a small piece of membrane is removed from the chorion, a layer of tissue that develops into the placenta, to check for possible genetic defects.

9. Infancy: learning to eat solid food, beginning to walk and explore the environment, perceiving objects and people, and learning to talk and trust. Early childhood: mastery of walking;

Thinking Critically

LESSON 1

1. ***Evaluating.*** If a pregnant female goes into a bar or restaurant and orders an alcoholic beverage, how do you feel about a server who serves it to her? Support your answer.

2. ***Synthesizing.*** What advice might you give a pregnant female who says that smoking relaxes her?

LESSON 2

3. ***Synthesizing.*** Mei, who is 41, is pregnant with her first child. Mei's obstetrician has advised her to have an amniocentesis, but Mei has responded that she "wants to be surprised" about her baby's gender. What information should Mei discuss with her doctor?

LESSON 3

4. ***Synthesizing.*** For each of Erikson's first four stages of development, write two comments parents could make to their child to help him or her progress successfully through that stage.

Making the Connection

1. ***Science.*** Research in greater detail one of Erik Erikson's stages of development. Prepare a report on how an individual might develop healthy or unhealthy characteristics based on experiences in the stage you are studying. You may wish to interview parents of young children to determine if they are aware of these stages. Draw conclusions on what people do to promote healthy development.

2. ***Math.*** A Punnett square is a mathematical diagram consisting of a grid, or array, and is often used to help determine the likelihood of a child inheriting or failing to inherit a specific trait from his or her parents. Learn more about Punnett squares and their use in this regard. Then create a Punnett square that shows the chances of giving birth to a female (*XX*) or a male (*XY*) child.

BEYOND THE CLASSROOM

PARENTAL INVOLVEMENT Discuss with parents or other adult family members memories they have of you during various early developmental stages. Looking at a family photo album together may help elicit memories.

COMMUNITY INVOLVEMENT Find out what public health services your community provides for pregnant women. Share this information in the form of a pamphlet you create using computer art or desktop publishing software, if available.

SCHOOL-TO-CAREER

Exploring Careers. Interview a genetic counselor. Find out how a genetic counselor helps parents-to-be deal with the possibility of having a baby with a genetic defect. What educational background does the genetic counselor need to do this job well? Share your findings with the class in the form of a brief oral report.

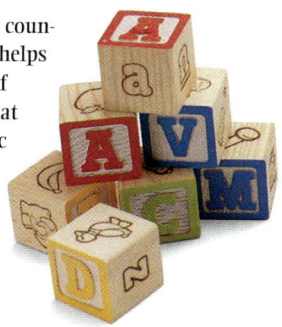

CHAPTER 20 REVIEW 475

Thinking Critically

1. Answers will vary.
2. Knowledge of the harmful effects of smoking on the fetus should give her more cause for worry.
3. Mei can ask her doctor not to tell her the baby's sex, but tell her whatever other information she should have regarding the baby's health.
4. Answers will vary.

Making the Connection

1.–2. Answers will vary.

Evaluate

- Use the reproducible *Chapter 20 Test* in the TCR, or construct your own using the Testmaker software.
- Use *Performance Assessment Activity 20* in the TCR.

Enrichment

Ask students to complete *Cross-Curriculum Activity 20* in the TCR.

Beyond the Classroom

Keep students involved in the community, and encourage parent participation by assigning the activities on this page for students to work on outside of class.

learning to climb, push, and pull; increasing vocabulary and speaking in sentences; learning to control the elimination of body wastes; establishing a sense of autonomy. Childhood: initiation of activities, developing imagination, copying the behavior of adults, asking questions, and exploring new ideas. Late childhood: learning physical skills necessary for games and activities; developing basic skills in reading, writing, and calculating; learning to get along with peers and learning appropriate roles in society; and being creative.

10. If the parents ignore or do not tend promptly or lovingly to the child's needs.

11. If parents accept the child's need to do whatever he or she is capable of, then the child will develop a sense of autonomy.

Adolescence—A Time of Change

	FEATURES	CLASSROOM RESOURCES

LESSON 1

Changes During Adolescence

pages 478–482

Making Responsible Decisions

"How Old Is Old Enough?"
page 480

Building Health Skills

"Self-Inventory: My Developmental Rate," *page 481*

- Concept Map Activity 64
- Decision-Making Activity 21
- Lesson 64 Quiz
- Lesson Plan 64
- Reteaching Activity 64

LESSON 2

Practicing Abstinence

pages 483–487

update ▶ Looking at Technology

"Hanging Out' On-Line: Is It Safe?" *page 486*

- Concept Map Activity 65
- Cooperative Learning Activity 21
- Enrichment Activity 21
- Health Lab 21
- Lesson 65 Quiz
- Lesson Plan 65
- Reteaching Activity 65

ACTIVITIES

- Cross-Curriculum Activity 21
- Health Lab 21
- Health Skills Activities 21
- Parent Letter and Activities 21

ASSESSMENT

- Chapter 21 Test
- Performance Assessment Activity 21
- Testmaker Software

STUDENT ACTIVITIES WORKBOOK

- Applying Health Skills 64, 65
- Study Guide 21
- Vocabulary Activity 21

STUDENT DIVERSITY STRATEGIES

- Audiocassette Program (English)
- Audiocassette Program (Spanish)
- Spanish Parent Letters and Activities
- Spanish Summaries, Quizzes, and Activities

MULTIMEDIA COMPONENTS

- English Audiocassette Program
- Spanish Audiocassette Program
- MindJogger Videodisc and VHS program
- ABCNews InterActive™ VHS/Videodisc Series

MODULES

- *Abstinence,* Student Edition
- *Abstinence,* Teacher's Annotated Edition
- *Education in Sexuality,* Student Edition
- *Education in Sexuality,* Teacher's Annotated Edition

National Health Education Standards

One of the main goals of the National Health Education Standards is to move students toward "health literacy." Health literacy is the capacity of individuals to obtain, interpret, and understand basic health information and services and the competence to use such information and services in ways which promote health. The health standards were developed by applying the characteristics of a well-educated, literate person within the context of health. The health literate person is:

- a critical thinker and problem solver
- a self-directed learner
- a responsible, productive citizen
- an effective communicator

Listed below are the Health Education Standards Performance Indicators addressed in each lesson of this chapter.

Lesson	Health Standards Performance Indicators
1	1.2, 1.4, 3.2, 6.1
2	3.4, 4.3, 5.6, 6.3

ONLINE RESOURCES

For a fresh approach to health topics and an in-depth look at health issues, use these online resources found under Teacher Resources at **health.glencoe.com**.

- **BLOCK SCHEDULE LESSON PLANS** Reinforce health concepts with outside readings selected especially for students. Each reading is accompanied by a lesson plan and activities to enhance
  - Reading Skills
  - Cross Curriculum
  - Media Literacy

- **TECHNOLOGY PROJECTS** Instructions and suggestions on how to use computer, Internet, and software with health lessons.

- **HEALTH UPDATES** Timely topics in health news, including late-breaking medical advances and updates on teen risk behaviors.

Out of Time?

If time does not permit teaching this chapter, you may use these features: Making Responsible Decisions on page 480; Building Health Skills on page 481; and Update on page 486.

BLOCK SCHEDULING

Block scheduling provides extended time for hands-on projects and activities. Use the following activities to engage students, provide further depth, and vary your instructional techniques:

- Update (30 minutes) **pg. 486**
- Health Skills Activity (60–90 minutes) **pg. 488**

Adolescence—A Time of Change

CHAPTER OVERVIEW

Chapter 21 presents the physical, mental, emotional, and social changes that occur during adolescence. It also discusses why abstinence from sexual activity before marriage is the best choice for teens.

LESSON 1 Adolescence, the stage between childhood and adulthood, is a period of rapid growth. During puberty, secondary sex characteristics are developed, resulting in physical, mental, emotional, and social changes. Accomplishing developmental tasks and acquiring a positive self-concept are critical during this period.

LESSON 2 Sexuality is an issue all adolescents must face. Abstinence from sexual activity before marriage is the only safe and responsible choice for adolescents. To make a decision to abstain from sexual activity, the teen must consider the consequences of sexual activity, establish priorities, and learn refusal skills to help support his or her decision.

CHAPTER 21

Adolescence— A Time of Change

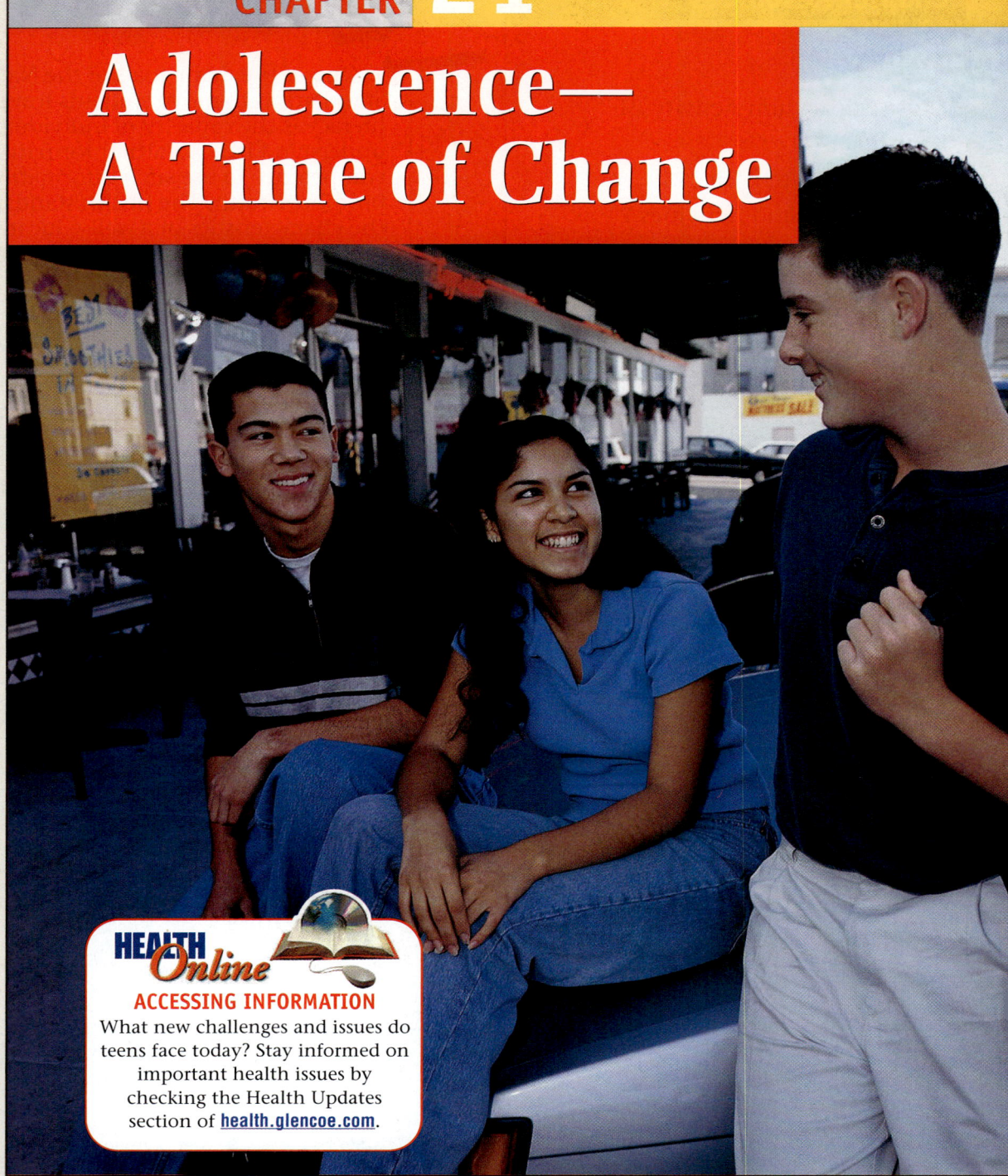

HEALTH Online

ACCESSING INFORMATION

What new challenges and issues do teens face today? Stay informed on important health issues by checking the Health Updates section of **health.glencoe.com**.

TEACHING STRATEGY

Hands-On Health

The Financial Costs of Pregnancy Help students research and calculate the costs of having a baby and raising an infant in the first year of life. See Activity 35, "How Much Does a Baby Cost?" in the *Hands-On Health: Creative Teaching Strategies* booklet.

Time Needed

30 minutes
Out-of-class research

Supplies

- student activity worksheet
- calculators (optional)

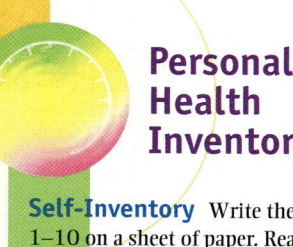

Personal Health Inventory

Self-Inventory Write the numbers 1–10 on a sheet of paper. Read each statement below and respond by writing *yes*, *no*, or *sometimes* for each item. Write a *yes* only for items that you practice regularly. Save your responses.

1	I can list the changes my body goes through during puberty.
2	I am able to think through problems and weigh possible alternative solutions.
3	I know how to handle changing emotions.
4	I am developing a strong sense of who I am.
5	I assume responsibilities in my family.
6	I take responsibility for getting my schoolwork done and for my grades.
7	I work at being a good friend by practicing listening skills and giving comfort and encouragement.
8	I can cope effectively with success and failure.
9	I follow the laws.
10	I am involved and concerned about my neighborhood and community.

Follow-up After completing the chapter, retake this self-inventory. Pick two items that you need to work on and set a goal to improve your health behaviors.

> **❝ I think what is happening to me is so wonderful, and not only what can be seen on my body, but all that is taking place inside. ❞**
>
> —ANNE FRANK
> GERMAN DIARIST, HOLOCAUST VICTIM, (1929–1945)

Quick Write Make two lists: one stating the ways adolescence is exciting to you and one stating the ways this time of life is sometimes frustrating.

INTRODUCING THE CHAPTER

Personal Health Inventory

Help students discuss the behaviors and attitudes identified in the Self-Inventory statements. Ask: How do these relate to adolescent development? Which parts of the health triangle do they involve? Then ask students to label a page with "My Journey through Adolescence" and record their Self-Inventory responses in their private Health Journals.

- To introduce this chapter, tell students that during adolescence, an individual goes through physical, mental, emotional, and social growth. Have them individually list examples of each type of growth. Write their responses on the chalkboard as students share their lists. Inform students that this chapter will explore many of the changes they mentioned, and will discuss the challenges teens face and the choices they must make as a result of these changes.
- Let students read Anne Frank's reaction to the changes she experienced as a teen. Ask: Why is change—even positive change—sometimes difficult to deal with? Encourage volunteers to identify some of the other kinds of changes adolescents go through. Then explain that students will learn more about those kinds of changes as they study Chapter 21.
- Distribute Parent Letter 21 in the *Parent Letters and Activities* booklet. 🖘

TECHNOLOGY OPTIONS

You may wish to use *Teenage Sexuality* with this chapter. For your convenience, use the separate *ABCNews InterActive™ Bar Code Correlation* that accompanies the *Glencoe Health* program. 🔴

MINDJOGGER
VIDEOQUIZ

To preview or review chapter content, you may wish to use the *MindJogger Videoquiz* that accompanies Chapter 21. 🔴

Changes During Adolescence

LESSON OBJECTIVES

After studying this lesson, students should be able to

- describe the four types of changes that occur during puberty and adolescence.
- summarize the developmental tasks of adolescence.
- discuss questions that are indicators of a well-developed personal identity.

MOTIVATOR

Write the following on the chalkboard for students to work on while attendance is being taken: *Write a paragraph describing adolescence.*

INTRODUCING THE LESSON

Refer to the Motivator. Ask a few volunteers to share their paragraphs. *(Some students may describe what it is like being an adolescent, while others may give actual definitions. Others may list particular events that occur during adolescence.)* Stress that the variations in growth and the changes in feelings are normal for this age group.

INTRODUCING HEALTH TERMS

- Have each student determine the definitions of the vocabulary terms and write sentences, leaving blanks for each term. Ask students to exchange their sentences with a partner and fill in the blanks. Allow time for discussion of some of the better sentences.
- Ask students to complete Vocabulary Activity 21 and Chapter Study Guide 21 in the *Student Workbook.* 🖙

Changes During Adolescence

During our lives, we go through two dramatic growth spurts. The first spurt occurs during the first year of life. The second spurt occurs near the beginning of **adolescence,** *the stage between childhood and adulthood.* Growth is rapid and uneven at this time—a sign of puberty and its changes.

HEALTH TERMS

adolescence
puberty
sex characteristics
gametes
cognition
personal identity

HEALTH CONCEPTS

- Adolescence is a time of physical, mental, emotional, and social changes.
- Mastering the developmental tasks of adolescence is an important step toward achieving maturity.

Puberty

Between the ages of 9 and 13, children go through puberty—the fifth of Erikson's **developmental stages.** **Puberty,** which marks the beginning of adolescence, is *the period of time when males and females become physically able to reproduce.* Puberty occurs as a result of the release of **hormones.** The male hormone, testosterone, and the female hormones, estrogen and progesterone, are responsible for the physical, emotional, and social changes that occur.

Physical Changes

Perhaps the most important of the physical changes that take place during puberty is the development of **sex characteristics,** *those traits related to one's gender.* There are two kinds of sex characteristics:

hotlink

developmental stages For more information on psychologist Erik Erikson's developmental stages of life, see Chapter 20, page 468.

hormones For more on the chemical substances called hormones and their role in growth, see Chapter 16, page 377.

Lesson 1 Resources

TEACHER'S CLASSROOM RESOURCES

🖙 **Concept Map** Activity 64
🖙 **Decision-Making** Activity 21
🖙 **Lesson 64 Quiz**
🖙 **Lesson Plan 64**
🖙 **Parent Letters and Activities 21**
🖙 **Reteaching** Activity 64

STUDENT WORKBOOK

🖙 **Applying Health Skills 64**
🖙 **Chapter Study Guide 21**
🖙 **Vocabulary** Activity 21

MULTIMEDIA

🔴 **ABCNews InterActive™ VHS/Videodisc,** *Teenage Sexuality*

- **Primary sex characteristics** are directly related to the production of **gametes**, *reproductive cells produced by the gonads*. In males, the gamete takes the form of sperm, and in females the ovum. As noted in Chapter 19, all of a female's ova are present at birth but do not mature until puberty, which is also when ovulation begins. For males, puberty marks the time when the testes begin to produce sperm.
- **Secondary sex characteristics** include body hair and the development of breasts in the female and muscle development in the male. These cover a wide range of characteristics, from broadening of the chest and deepening of the voice in males to an increase in breast size for females.

Concerns Over Physical Changes

As individuals reach puberty, and for the next four to five years that follow, there is great variation in the size and shape of people approximately the same age. This variation can be a source of concern among individual teens, who tend to compare themselves with others. Girls who are much taller than classmates, for example, may feel self-conscious about their height. An increase in the size of the larynx in males may cause the voice to "crack"—or switch abruptly from a low to high pitch—which can be a source of embarrassment. In members of either gender, the feet and hands grow and may appear large and awkward in proportion to the rest of the body.

It is important for teens to remember that changes such as these are normal. Most of these experiences are temporary and resolve themselves as time passes.

Mental Changes

During adolescence, the brain reaches its adult size and weight. **Cognition**—*the act or process of knowing, including both awareness and judgment*—and memory both increase. At this age, males and females are able to predict the outcomes of many situations. Whereas during

Acting on Acne

Acne, a condition usually accompanied by unsightly pimples or blemishes, is a common problem among adolescents. Acne is caused by androgens, male hormones that are present in both males and females. If you have acne, consider these tips:

➤ Avoid oil-based makeup and greasy lotions.

➤ Keep your face and hair clean.

➤ Change washcloths and towels often.

➤ Don't squeeze or scratch pimples.

In cases of severe acne, you may need to consult your family health care professional or a dermatologist, a doctor who specializes in problems of the skin.

Graduating from high school is one way in which teens grow into maturity.
ACTIVITY *Explain what other steps in a teen's life lead to becoming a mature adult.*

MEETING STUDENT DIVERSITY

LEARNING STYLES. Students with special learning needs might pair with mainstream students to carry out similar tasks (e.g., pairing researchers with researchers). In assessing the performance of such pairs, use criteria that reflect the ability of the partners to work together effectively, such as cooperation and compromise.

PHYSICALLY CHALLENGED. Students with physical challenges might be called upon to participate in an exhibit on social health and friendships. The exhibit can focus on the difficulties encountered in making and maintaining friendships and on common misconceptions people have toward those with physical challenges.

TEACH

L1 Explaining

Stress that the age at which puberty begins is primarily determined by heredity, although certain aspects of development are affected by the practice of good health habits, such as good nutrition and exercise.

L1 Discussing

Have students discuss this statement: *During adolescence, one of the signs of mental change is the ability to see other points of view.*

Acting on Acne
keeping Fit

Ask a volunteer to visit a dermatologist's office to collect pamphlets regarding acne and how it is treated by the health professional. Have the student share his or her findings with the class.

L2 Guest Speaker

Invite a school counselor to speak to the class about emotional changes during adolescence. Ask the counselor to discuss how changes in their bodies may affect teens' emotions.

ABCNEWS INTERACTIVE™

TEENAGE SEXUALITY (Side 1)

Chapter 3: Changing Bodies

Frames 2368-4987

Chapter 10: Evolution of American Attitudes

Frames 20363-23965

Making Responsible Decisions

1. Kelly, a freshman, wants to accept a date with a senior, but her parents say she is too young to date.
2. Kelly could (a) accept her parents' decision and tell the senior she can't go out after all; (b) try to go out with the senior and keep the date a secret from her parents; (c) discuss the situation with her parents, explaining why she feels mature and responsible enough to date.
3. Kelly might (a) avoid making her parents angry—but feel disappointed about turning down the date; (b) get to go on the date—but disappoint her parents and probably feel guilty; (c) have a chance to express her ideas and perhaps reach a compromise about dating—though she still might not get to go out with a senior.
4. Kelly values her own independence and her parents' approval.
5. Responses will vary.
6. Remind students to consider both the short- and long-term consequences of their decisions.

L2 ## Decision Making

For further study on making responsible decisions, assign *Decision-Making Activity 21* in the TCR.

L1 ## Discussing

Ask students: What is a developmental task? What are some of the major developmental tasks during adolescence? Elicit and discuss student responses.

LD ## Discussing

To demonstrate understanding, have students give examples of each developmental task.

Making Responsible Decisions

How Old Is Old Enough?

Kelly is a freshman cheerleader. After today's game, the captain of the football team—a senior—asked her to go to a party with him next Saturday. Kelly was excited, until her parents informed her she was "too young to date, and especially a senior." Kelly feels her parents are treating her like a baby. What do you think Kelly should do?

What Would You Do?

Apply the six steps of the decision-making process to Kelly's problem.

1. **State the situation.**
2. **List the options.**
3. **Weigh the possible outcomes.**
4. **Consider your values.**
5. **Make a decision and act.**
6. **Evaluate the decision.**

childhood they saw only one solution to a problem, during adolescence they begin to look at different ways of solving problems and making decisions. Adolescents' ability to think logically, or reason things out, increases. They start becoming able to solve more complicated problems.

As they begin to mature, many adolescents discover that they are able to look beyond themselves to understand someone else's point of view. Many teens will develop new interests and hobbies. Career goals begin to come into focus.

Emotional Changes

Along with spurts of physical and mental change come spurts of energy and strong emotional feelings. Many teens feel that puberty is like being on a roller coaster, with emotions and feelings that go up and down quickly. It is common for teens to feel on top of the world one day and down in the dumps the next. Friendships and the love and support of family are important, yet adolescents may feel unable to let others know what they are feeling and thinking. This difficulty in communicating is a normal part of development.

Social Changes

Social change is another important aspect of the development that occurs during puberty and the rest of adolescence. For instance, friendships and peer acceptance become very important. Peers may occasionally challenge what you stand for, what you believe, and what you think is right or wrong. Good friends, however, will not challenge you to do something that goes against what you believe. A growing ability to feel more deeply and to consider others' needs is also part of social development.

PERSONAL HEALTH

POINT OF VIEW. Students have read that one characteristic that develops during adolescence is the ability to see and feel from another's point of view. In actual fact, people tend to work on this quality, with varying degrees of success, throughout life. Provide students an opportunity to practice understanding another's point of view. Encourage them to recall a recent conflict with another person. Tell them to assume the other person's point of view and to write a letter in their private Health Journal to an advice columnist expressing the person's view and asking how to handle the conflict. Then have them write a response from the columnist giving the most unbiased advice that they can. Have students discuss their experiences during this process.

Developmental Tasks

Adolescence has been studied by psychologists and sociologists for more than 50 years. They have identified certain developmental tasks that can be considered basic to adolescence. Robert Havighurst, a well-known sociologist in the field, suggests these tasks are:

- forming more mature relationships with people your age and of both genders
- achieving a masculine or feminine social role
- accepting one's physique
- achieving emotional independence from parents and other adults
- preparing for marriage and family life and career
- acquiring a set of personal standards as a guide to behavior
- developing social intelligence, which includes becoming aware of human needs and becoming motivated to help others attain their goals

Building Health Skills

Self-Inventory: My Developmental Rate

HOW MANY OF THE DEVELOPMENTAL tasks of adolescence have you accomplished so far? This survey will help you find out. Copy the following statements into your private Health Journal. After each, write *true* or *false*. Answer the questions again every six months or so to see how far you've come—and how far you have to go.

1. I strive to be a health-literate person and to make choices that promote my overall health and well-being.

2. I have set long-term goals for myself.

3. I have more adult discussions and fewer confrontations with my parents or other adults than I used to have.

4. I am able to identify my four most important beliefs and values and act in ways that support them.

5. I am successful most of the time at maintaining relationships with friends of both genders.

6. I am aware of and able to accept my physical strengths and weaknesses.

7. I listen to other people's ideas even when they are different from mine.

8. I try to think through problems, looking at all possible solutions before arriving at a decision.

LEP Class Activity

Have students create a mobile illustrating each of the developmental tasks. Display their completed projects in the classroom.

L1 Discussing

Ask: What is involved in forming a personal identity? What are some of the most difficult questions you can ask yourself in achieving a personal identity?

L1 Class Activity

Assign students to locate newspaper and magazine features about adolescents. Ask if teens are shown positively or negatively and, based on the story, what opinions an observer would form about someone this age. Ask students what they think of those opinions.

Building Health Skills

Self-Inventory: My Developmental Rate
Skill: Goal Setting

Help students review the definition of *developmental tasks,* and ask volunteers to identify some of the developmental tasks of childhood. Then ask: What developmental tasks are part of adolescence? Let students read the feature, and guide them in briefly discussing each of the identified developmental tasks. Encourage students to consider the inventory statements as goals; no one should be discouraged by "false" responses. Remind students to return to this Self-Inventory in several months and to look for progress in their own development.

SCHOOL-TO-CAREER

EDUCATION AND CAREERS. Adolescents often make choices that will shape the rest of their lives. For example, some leave high school to work full time. Others graduate and immediately take full-time jobs, marry, and/or become parents. Others receive advanced training at a college or business school. Encourage students to read want ads and call personnel departments and placement agents. Have them survey the number and types of jobs available for teens and adults without a high school education, with a high school education, with at least a four-year college degree, and with a technical, trade, or business school education. Have them gather salary information for each type of job available. Suggest they create a graphic showing employment opportunities and earnings of workers in each of the four education categories.

EVALUATING THE LESSON

Assign and discuss the Lesson 1 Review; then administer, grade, and discuss the *Lesson 64 Quiz* in the TCR. 📖

RETEACHING

- Have each student divide a sheet of paper into three vertical columns. Ask them to label the left column *Mental Change,* and underneath, write examples of ways they have changed mentally in the past two years. In the second and third columns, labeled *Emotional Change* and *Social Change* respectively, have students list ways they have changed emotionally and socially over the past two years.
- Ask students to complete *Reteaching Activity 64* in the TCR. 📖

ENRICHMENT

Have students write at least four goals or plans that they have for the next two months. Next to each goal or plan, ask them to describe how it would change or be affected if they were (1) married, (2) pregnant or a father-to-be, or (3) a parent. Afterward, lead students in a discussion of the importance of achieving each of the developmental tasks before taking on adult responsibilities.

Ask students to state the most important concepts learned in the lesson.

- being able to cope with success and failure
- developing conceptual and problem-solving skills

Each of these tasks is important and must be achieved before reaching maturity. As you can see, there is quite a lot involved in growing up.

▼ *Volunteering to clean up your environment is one way to demonstrate social responsibility.*
ACTIVITY *Name other developmental tasks that assist adolescents in forming a personal identity.*

Personal Identity

Some researchers group a number of the developmental tasks into a general task of achieving a personal identity. A **personal identity** consists of *the factors you believe make you unique, or unlike anyone else.* Establishing your own personal identity has a great impact on all the other developmental tasks and is centered on your self-concept. Here are some questions you can ask yourself as you work toward forming your own personal identity:

- Am I carrying out my responsibilities on my own, such as getting schoolwork done on time, without needing someone to remind me of them?
- Can I make independent decisions and accept the consequences of my actions?
- Am I thinking about what I want to do after high school?
- Have I examined my beliefs about what types of behavior are appropriate for young adult males and females?
- Does my behavior reflect a personal set of values and standards by which I live?
- Do I expect to work for what I want, rather than just having things done for me or given to me?

LESSON 1 *Review*

Reviewing Facts and Vocabulary

1. What is the name of the stage of life between childhood and adulthood?
2. What are traits called that are related to one's gender?
3. Identify two physical changes, two mental changes, two emotional changes, and two social changes that occur during puberty.

Thinking Critically

4. *Analyzing.* In your private Health Journal, answer the six questions relating to personal identity. Write a short explanation of each answer, giving examples for the questions you answered *yes* and telling what changes you can make for the questions you answered *no.*

Applying Health Skills

5. *In Your Home.* Talk with parents or other adults in your home about any changes they have noticed in you since you became an adolescent. Have them list these changes in four areas—physical, mental, emotional, and social. Discuss your reactions with your family, telling how you feel about these changes.

Lesson 1 Review

Answers to Reviewing Facts and Vocabulary

1. Adolescence.
2. Sex characteristics.
3. Answers may include: any two of each *Physical:* body growth, change in voice in boys, growth of hair on body, growth of breasts in girls, etc. *Mental:* increased memory, cognition, ability to reason, ability to see the viewpoint of others. *Emotional:* broad fluctuations in emotions, difficulty in communicating thoughts and feelings. *Social:* new emphasis on friendships and peer acceptance, a growing ability to consider others' needs.

Answer to Thinking Critically

4. Allow students' entries to remain private.

Practicing Abstinence

Another aspect of the emotional changes that occur during adolescence is an awakening of feelings of sexual attraction toward others. These feelings are a normal and healthful response and are part of becoming a healthy adult.

HEALTH TERMS

abstinence

priorities

self-control

sexually transmitted disease (STD)

HEALTH CONCEPTS

■ Sexual activity before marriage carries a number of serious health risks, particularly for teens.

■ Abstinence from sexual intercourse before marriage is the only safe and responsible choice.

Decisions and Peers

The emotional awakening during adolescence is accompanied by a number of physical responses that can be a source of concern and even confusion among teens who are experiencing them for the first time. The face gets hot and flushed, the heart beats faster, the hands get clammy, and there is a fluttery feeling inside. You cannot keep these feelings from happening. They are normal and healthful. At the same time, sexual attraction is not the same as love. Sexual feelings do not have to be acted on. They can be controlled and dealt with in responsible ways.

Decisions About Sexual Activity

In our society, physical attraction and sexual activity are portrayed in movies, on television, and in advertisements. Perfume commercials describe their products as *sexy* or *alluring*. Some TV programs

LESSON 2   PRACTICING ABSTINENCE   **483**

Lesson 2 Resources

TEACHER'S CLASSROOM RESOURCES

🖙 **Concept Map** Activity 65

🖙 **Cooperative Learning** Activity 21

🖙 **Enrichment** Activity 21

🖙 **Health Lab** 21

🖙 **Lesson 65 Quiz**

🖙 **Lesson Plan** 65

🖙 **Reteaching** Activity 65

STUDENT WORKBOOK

🖙 **Applying Health Skills** 65

🖙 **Chapter Study Guide** 21

🖙 **Vocabulary** Activity 21

MULTIMEDIA

🔴 ABCNews InterActive™ VHS/Videodisc, *Teenage Sexuality*

Practicing Abstinence

FOCUS

LESSON OBJECTIVES

After studying this lesson, students should be able to

• outline the steps to follow when making the decision to practice abstinence.

• explain the role of refusal skills in maintaining abstinence.

• discuss the consequences of sexual activity before marriage.

MOTIVATOR

Write the following on the chalkboard for students to work on while attendance is being taken: *Define what is important in a loving relationship for a teenager.*

INTRODUCING THE LESSON

Have students share their responses to the Motivator. Discuss the challenge that sexuality places on teen relationships and how sexual activity can be harmful to both individuals and the relationship. Tell students that this lesson will discuss further the complexities of teen sexuality and present ways to support a decision to practice abstinence.

INTRODUCING HEALTH TERMS

• Ask students to define *priorities.* Next, have students write down some priorities that they have established. Ask them to write a sentence or phrase beside each priority describing why it is important to them.

• Ask students to complete Vocabulary Activity 21 and Chapter Study Guide 21 in the *Student Workbook.* 🖙

Chapter 21   **483**

TEACH

L1 Discussing

Talk about some of the pressures teens may experience in making decisions about having sex. *(Examples might include peers, music, movies, television, etc.)*

L1 Explaining

Stress that pressure from peers and the media are strong influences during this time in teens' lives. Remind students of the importance of being able to identify their personal values and goals when they are pressured by these outside factors. Encourage them to base decisions, especially sexual decisions, on their values rather than on peer pressure.

L1 Critical Thinking

Ask: Why do you think some young people choose not to brag about choosing abstinence? Suppose a group of teens at your school began talking proudly about their own decision to practice abstinence and began pressuring others to choose abstinence. What effect do you think this group of students would have? Why?

L1 Explaining

Emphasize to students that it is never too late to choose abstinence, even if they have already participated in sexual activity. Too often, teens who have had some sexual experience, or who have experimented with tobacco, alcohol, and other drugs, feel they cannot go back. Remind students that each instance of sexual activity—like each use of tobacco, alcohol, or other drugs—is a choice that can affect their health.

L2 Health Lab

Distribute *Health Lab 21* and have students investigate the effects of advertising on personal image. ☞

CHARACTER IN ACTION

Responsibility and Commitment

When it comes to issues of sexuality, truly responsible behavior for teens means making a **responsible commitment** to abstinence. It also means:

➤ learning to control sexual feelings or diverting them into positive activities like sports

➤ never imposing sexual impulses on others

➤ speaking up for your own highest values when others pressure you to have sexual contact

➤ taking care of reproductive organs through self-exams and doctor's exams

➤ getting and staying informed about the dangers of STDs, HIV, and teen pregnancies, keeping these real risks in mind as you continue to commit to abstinence

Character Check List all the reasons why you will make the commitment to abstinence to ensure your long-term health.

---

now carry warnings about containing "partial nudity" and "explicit sexual content." Whether out of curiosity, a desire to be an adult, or pressure by others, some teens are tempted to be sexually active. However, there are many consequences of these actions.

One of the biggest decisions any teen can make is whether or not to become sexually active. Being sexually active can have implications for life—not just for a moment. Because people do not think clearly when faced with sexual feelings, it is much easier and a lot smarter to think through a decision about sexual behavior before getting into the situation in the first place.

Abstinence Until Marriage

More teens are examining the risks of sexual behavior and deciding that the only safe and responsible choice is abstinence from sexual intercourse. **Abstinence** is *the conscious decision to avoid harmful behaviors, including sexual activity before marriage and the use of tobacco, alcohol, and other drugs.* Abstinence is the only healthful and safe choice for teenagers. By postponing sexual activity until marriage, teens avoid the many risks of sexual behavior such as unplanned pregnancy, sexually transmitted diseases, and loss of self-respect.

Making a Commitment to Abstinence

Practicing abstinence takes planning, preparation, and self-control. Here are the steps you can follow to help you practice abstinence:

■ **Establish your priorities in life. Priorities** are *those things that are first in importance.* To set priorities, give some thought to your plans for the future. Think about the goals you have set for yourself, such as going to college or pursuing a particular career. Also think about such personal values as respect, honesty, and morality. Consider the effects of an unplanned pregnancy or an STD on your life, and what it might do to your plans.

■ **Set personal limits on the ways in which you are willing to express affection.** Base these limits on your priorities for your life. Make sure you set limits in advance, not when in a situation where your sexual feelings are beginning to build.

■ **Share your feelings with your boyfriend or girlfriend.** Tell your partner about your priorities and what your limits are. Be honest about your feelings and values. If you are unable to talk openly and honestly with your partner, you are not in a mature, responsible relationship.

■ **Discuss your feelings and concerns with a trusted adult.** Talking with a parent, teacher, or other trusted adult can be a release valve for pent-up fears or frustrations you may have. Remember, your parents and other adults have lived through adolescence themselves. They may offer suggestions for demonstrating affection in safe and healthful ways.

HOME AND COMMUNITY CONNECTION

READINGS FOR TEENS. Suggest that students visit local libraries to examine the selection of fiction and nonfiction books about sex and other issues teens face. First, they should find out how their libraries classify the young adult section. Differing views of the young adult reader can create confusion. The American Library Association definition is ages 12 to 18, whereas some chain stores define the starting age as 10 or 11 years old. Assuming the library uses the ALA definition, have students survey the teen situations explored in the books that the young adult section offers. Suggest that students read recent book reviews and make a list of books they think the library should carry for adolescents. Encourage them to give the list to the librarian.

- **Steer clear of high-pressure situations.** When possible, go out on dates in a group. Avoid dark rooms and unsupervised parties. If you are in a car, avoid parking in a secluded spot. Do not use alcohol or other drugs, which can interfere with your ability to think clearly and make rational judgments.

- **If you are currently sexually active, re-evaluate.** One way of doing this is to avoid those places and situations that led to you being sexually active in the past.

Using Refusal Skills

Once you have decided to practice abstinence, you must communicate that decision clearly. This is another area where verbal and nonverbal messages may cloud the issue. One person may give a convincing no, but the nonverbal actions send a conflicting message. This confusion, added to the tension of the moment, makes communication difficult.

Before finding yourself in this situation, talk to your partner about your decisions. After stating your position simply but firmly, you may be relieved to find that your partner agrees with you. Having discussed the matter, you will find it easier to exercise **self-control,** *a person's ability to use responsibility to override emotions.* First, insist on stopping. Then back away from your partner and explain why you want to stop.

If your partner persists, you will need to become more assertive. Say no, and make sure your body language supports your verbal message.

Consequences of Sexual Activity

Sexual involvement has a number of negative consequences for which teens are not prepared—physically, mentally, emotionally, socially, and financially. These include an unplanned pregnancy, **sexually transmitted diseases**, loss of self-respect, and negative effects on social relationships.

UNPLANNED PREGNANCY

Adolescence is a full-time job. Add pregnancy—and the birth and care of an infant—and life becomes very complicated. Becoming a parent is a serious responsibility that changes a person's life. Teens are not ready for parenthood. For many teens, pregnancy is a consequence they did not plan for.

hotlink

sexually transmitted diseases (STD) For more information on avoiding sexually transmitted diseases (STD), see Chapter 29, page 642.

 Make decisions based on your own values, even if your peers disagree.

ACTIVITY *Practice some effective refusal skills both males and females can use to say no.*

LESSON 2   PRACTICING ABSTINENCE   **485**

ⓛ Discussing

Select students to debate the statement: *A real friend would not pressure you into doing something you do not want to do.*

ⓛ Analyzing

Talk about instances in which facial expressions and body language or gestures—instead of words—are used to pressure others. Have volunteers demonstrate examples of this kind of silent pressure. Ask students how they feel when they are pressured like this. How effective is this kind of pressure?

ⓛ Discussing

Elicit students' reactions to the following statements: *Once a parent, always a parent. Parenthood never ends.*

ABCNEWS INTERACTIVE™

TEENAGE SEXUALITY (Side 1)

Chapter 14: The Facts About Teenage Pregnancy

Frames 35065-40698

TEENAGE SEXUALITY (Side 2)

Chapter 14: "Sex Is Complex" Rap Song

Frames 25249-28334

HEALTH LITERACY

EFFECTIVE COMMUNICATOR. Group students in a circle to practice saying no to sexual activity. Have students go around the circle, each student in turn suggesting a line that might be used to pressure a date to engage in sexual activity. For example: "If you really loved me you would," "Everyone else does," "You can't stop now that you have me so excited. What are you, a tease?" The student to the right should role-play effective refusal skills. If students are uncomfortable with the oral group format, suggest they write the statements, exchange papers, and write private responses that will remain private unless a student volunteers to share them with the group.

L1 Class Activity

As a class, have students identify the roles of a parent. Next, ask each student to rank the roles from most important to least important. Assign students to small groups to discuss their rankings. Then, once again as a class, reach a consensus on the rankings. Discuss the preparedness of teens to adopt these roles.

L2 Cooperative Learning

Have students complete *Cooperative Learning Activity 21*, "The Ultimate Birthday Party," in the TCR. ✏️

---

update
▶ *Looking at the Issues*

"Hanging Out" On-Line: Is It Safe?

Let volunteers describe some of their own on-line social experiences, and ask: Why do you think teens enjoy meeting other people on-line? In your opinion, what are the benefits of on-line socializing? What problems might be associated with this practice? After a brief discussion, have students read the Update feature to learn more about teens' on-line social life and the two different viewpoints. Then have students meet in small groups to discuss their responses to the questions.

Eighty percent of teen pregnancies are unplanned pregnancies. Having a child at a young age risks the health of the teen mother and her child. It also limits a teen's future. Many teen parents have had to drop out of school to support a child, or give up plans for college or job training.

SEXUALLY TRANSMITTED DISEASES (STDs)

A **sexually transmitted disease** is *an infectious disease that is spread from person to person through sexual contact.* People in the 15–19 age group have the greatest risk of getting STDs. Nearly 3 million adolescents contract an STD each year. One in four sexually active adolescents will become infected before graduating from high school. STDs require medical treatment. Some STDs, such as **acquired immune deficiency syndrome (AIDS)**, which is caused by the human immunodeficiency virus (HIV), are fatal. STDs can also render a person sterile, making it impossible for her or him to ever conceive a child.

hotlink

AIDS For more information on the problems associated with the AIDS epidemic, see Chapter 30, page 656.

---

update
▶ *Looking at the Issues*

"Hanging Out" On-Line: Is It Safe?

These days, an increasing number of teens are turning to on-line connections as part of their social life. Some use their computers to meet and "hang out" with other teens in forums and chat rooms. Other teens even "date" in cyberspace. The growth of these trends has raised questions about their safety and healthfulness.

ANALYZING DIFFERENT VIEWPOINTS

▶ **Viewpoint One**
In one national teen survey, 7 out of 10 teens opposed any attempts to limit their access to the Internet. They believe that they are old enough to choose and judge responsibly whom they meet and talk to—including people they meet on-line.

▶ **Viewpoint Two**
Many teens, adults, and experts alike voice the opinion that there is no substitute for conventional in-person introductions, talking, and hanging out. They contend that you can tell more about a person by looking into his or her eyes than by the way he or she constructs a sentence. Another problem is that some people who meet and "date" on-line are not who they say they are at all.

EXPLORING YOUR VIEWS

1. What are the pros and cons of communicating with other teens in cyberspace? What safeguards can teens take when logging on?

2. What advice would you give to a peer about how to have responsible relationships?

COOPERATIVE ⟩ LEARNING

TEENS PORTRAYED IN THE MEDIA. Have students work in groups to study the power of the media to shape teens' self-images and behavior. The media may project images that teens try to emulate, but the images may or may not align with the health triangle. Instruct students to bring to class advertisements, stories, and photographs that exemplify media portrayal of teens. Guide a discussion of films and television programs featuring teens. Ask: What teens are projected as "cool"? Are these positive role models? Are the teens sexually active? Do media portrayals suggest that teens are supposed to be sexy? If so, what makes a teen sexy? Encourage each group to create a visual classifying types of images the media portrays. If possible, each type should be illustrated with a photograph, headline, or other example of media portrayal.

LOSS OF SELF-RESPECT

Engaging in sexual activity goes against many people's values and religious beliefs. A teen may find himself or herself sneaking around or lying to parents or other adult family members about his or her whereabouts. Coupled with the constant fear of being caught, such actions and feelings can lead to guilt and regret, which can be emotionally harmful to a teen. Having and following clear values leads teens to healthy feelings of self-respect. You build character and feel good about yourself when you follow your values.

NEGATIVE EFFECTS ON SOCIAL RELATIONSHIPS

Sexually active teens also risk developing a reputation among peers as someone who is "sexually easy" and may find it difficult to build new and healthy relationships in the future.

Choosing to become sexually active can even complicate the relationship with one's partner. When sexual activity is involved, expectations in relationships often change. Many teens have found that, instead of bringing them closer together, sexual activity actually tears the relationship apart.

FAMILY DISAPPROVAL

As **protective factors** in a teen's environment, most parents and guardians show their love and concern for their children by setting limits and establishing guidelines. Because parents want to protect their teens' self-respect, values, and safety, they do not want their teens to be sexually active. Going against such values can lead to feelings of parental disillusionment, disappointment, and even betrayal.

hotlink

protective factors For more information on protective factors and their effect on the risk-taking behavior of teens, see Chapter 1, page 20.

LESSON 2 *Review*

Reviewing Facts and Vocabulary

1. Name three risks of sexual activity during the teen years.
2. Why might the choice to become sexually active cause a teen to lose self-respect?
3. What is self-control?
4. Name three benefits gained from not being sexually active during the teen years.

Thinking Critically

5. **Evaluating.** In speaking of teen parenthood, adults sometimes say, "A child is raising a child." Analyze this statement.

6. **Synthesizing.** Tara's boyfriend is putting pressure on her to become sexually active. "After all," he argues, "We've been going out for a long time now." What factors will come into play in determining how Tara responds?

Applying Health Skills

7. **In Your Home.** Talk with your parents or other adults in your home about the goals and priorities they had when they were your age. Have them explain what things, if any, they would do differently if they could live their lives over again. Summarize what you can learn from your parents' experiences.

LESSON 2 PRACTICING ABSTINENCE **487**

ASSESS

EVALUATING THE LESSON

Assign and discuss the Lesson 2 Review; then administer, grade, and discuss the *Lesson 65 Quiz* in the TCR. ☞

RETEACHING

• Have students outline the steps involved in making a decision about not being sexually active and in implementing a decision to practice abstinence.
• Ask students to complete *Reteaching Activity 65* in the TCR. ☞

ENRICHMENT

• Ask a group of students to survey classmates for reasons why they would or would not want to be parents now, in five years, and in ten years. Have them assess how the responses differ between males and females as well as for the present vs. the future. Ask them to share their findings with the class.
• Increase students' awareness about the importance of setting and adhering to personal boundaries in relationships by having them complete *Enrichment Activity 21,* "Dating: A Chance to Respect Yourself," in the TCR. ☞

CLOSE

Remind students that adolescence is a time for understanding themselves and for making decisions. Talk about values and goals as the basis for decisions. Stress the need to communicate one's decisions effectively to others when faced with peer pressure.

Lesson 2 Review

Answers to Reviewing Facts and Vocabulary

1. Any three: unplanned pregnancy, STD, loss of self-respect, negative effects on social relationships.
2. It might lead to behavior such as sneaking around, lying to family members for fear of getting caught, going against one's values.
3. Self-control is a person's ability to use responsibility to override emotions.

4. Answers will vary.

Answers to Thinking Critically

5. Since the teen has not yet finished going through the developmental stages leading to adulthood, he or she is still operating as a child in many areas of his or her life.
6. Answers should include the values and religious beliefs instilled by her family, her own self-esteem, the values of her peers.

Health **Skills** Activities

Health Skills Activities

ACTIVITY 1
HEALTH SKILLS

Self Management, Communication—Refusal Skills

➤ **National Standards**
This activity meets these National Health Standards: 3.3; 3.6; 5.1; 5.6.

Teach

- Prepare several assertive comebacks that could be used to defuse a situation in which a teen was being pressured to engage in a high-risk behavior. Present these and other examples as a game, handing out two sets of index cards—one with come-on lines, the other with responses—and challenge students to match the cards.
- Review with students refusal strategies outlined in the book.
- Point out that the best way of resisting negative peer pressure is in a non-confrontational way, by being assertive, not aggressive.

ACTIVITY 2
HEALTH SKILLS

Self Management, Goal Setting

➤ **National Standards**
This activity meets these National Health Standards: 3.3; 6.4; 6.5.

Teach

- Note that just as a road map is composed of major and lesser roads, so an action plan for life goals is made up of long-term and short-term goals. To help students start their maps, you may suggest that they follow another kind of map—a word map. This might consist of a pair of word webs, one with the phrase *Short-Term Goals* at its hub, the other with the phrase *Long-Term Goals.* Help students see how the two interrelate.
- If time permits, allow volunteers to share the essays they have written.

Activity 1 Resisting Peer Pressure

For every line commonly used to persuade another person to practice a risky behavior, there is an equally powerful response. Practicing refusal skills can help you be prepared in a pressure situation.

Directions

1. In a group, list common high-pressure lines that might be used to convince someone to engage in high-risk behavior.
2. For each line, brainstorm several snappy and effective responses that can be used to defuse the situation. Your teacher will share several responses to start your thinking.
3. Share the results by creating a poster of high-pressure lines and assertive refusal responses that can be displayed in the school or community.

Time
30 minutes

Materials
paper, pen or pencil, poster board, markers or paint

Self-Assessment

✔ Listed at least three common high-pressure lines that teens may use to persuade others to practice high-risk behavior.
✔ Illustrated at least three strategies to combat each peer pressure statement.

Activity 2 Setting Life Goals

Knowing your long-term goals and values can help you make healthful decisions today that will help you achieve those goals and maintain your values. What are your goals for the future? What short-term goals will help you reach those goals?

Directions

1. Working independently, make a list of goals for your life. Include eductation, job, and career goals you would like to have.
2. List your values, those principles that you consider important and will use to guide your life.
3. Using your lists, create a "road map" for your short-term goals that will help you reach your lifetime goals.
4. In a short essay, identify what you learned from this activity. Store your essay in your private Health Journal. Reread your essay from time to time.

Time
30 minutes

Materials
paper, pen or pencil

Self-Assessment

✔ Identified at least three goals that one can work toward to achieve.
✔ Listed personal values and developed goals that are consistent with those values.

ASSESSMENT SCORING

Using a four-level rubric, the student has achieved a 4 if:

ACTIVITY 1
✔ Student took an active role in the discussion.
✔ Student identified at least three common high-pressure lines that teens may use.
✔ Student was able to differentiate between assertive and aggressive behavior.
✔ Student helped produce a poster that emphasized the importance of combating peer pressure.

ACTIVITY 2
✔ Student identified at least three goals that one can work toward to achieve.
✔ Student created a meaningful action plan for short-term goals.
✔ Student identified personal values and developed goals consistent with these.
✔ Student wrote an essay capturing the main ideas of the action plan.

Please, Get Your ZZZs

High school student Naomi Freeman is busy, like many of her peers. She juggles academic, extracurricular, and work responsibilities–and, when there's time, she sleeps.

Freeman's six hours of sleep a night is not unusual among teenagers. It's also not healthy according to experts, who say millions of young people may be risking their health and education by not making sleep a higher priority.

"Kids are too sleepy to learn well. They're too sleepy to be happy. And they're at great risk for such things as traffic accidents," said Dr. Mary Carskadon of the National Sleep Foundation.

Most adolescents need at least 8½ hours of sleep each night according to the National Sleep Foundation. But it estimates that only 15 percent of young people get that much, with 25 percent of teens getting less than seven hours.

The foundation, in what it calls a "wake-up call" to teens, parents, and educators, released a report warning of the consequences of sleep deprivation. It also suggests lifestyle changes to ensure adolescents get adequate rest.

"Teenagers don't need less sleep the older they get. They still need as much sleep as they did when they were pre-teens," Carskadon said. Her research shows that adolescents tend to fall asleep and awaken later than adults and often experience an increase in daytime sleepiness, even when they get enough rest.

The NSF recommends the creation of "sleep-smart schools" that adopt sleep education curricula and offer school starting times that adequately respond to a teen's biological need for sleep.

Think About It

1. Summarize the findings of this report on sleep and teenagers. Do observations of your peers match the report's conclusions?

2. What strategies can your school adopt to encourage healthy sleep patterns? What strategies can help at home?

CNN HEALTH NEWS **489**

MORE ABOUT . . . . .

MORE ABOUT SLEEP. Dr. Mary Carskadon explains the conflict between common teen sleep patterns and school schedules. "We, as a society, are asking [teenagers] to sleep at the wrong time."

Teens have a biological tendency to stay awake later and sleep later in the morning. "This can put their circadian rhythm, or biological clock, in conflict with the school bell," Carskadon said. "The result illustrates a critical trend: too many teens come to school too sleepy to learn. And their fatigue often leads to behavior problems that contribute to a negative overall school performance and experience."

**CHECKING
COMPREHENSION**

- Assign and discuss the chapter review.
- Use the MindJogger Videoquiz to review the chapter. 🔴

**CHAPTER 21
REVIEW ANSWERS**

Using Health Terms

1. puberty
2. gametes
3. cognition
4. adolescence
5. sex characteristics
6. personal identity
7. self-control
8. sexually transmitted disease
9. priorities
10. abstinence

Recalling the Facts

1. The primary sex characteristics are directly related to the production of gametes.
2. Body hair and breast development in females, muscle development and deepening voice in males.
3. Any three: deepening voice, muscle development, body growth, broadening of the chest.
4. Another term for the reproductive cell is *gamete*.
5. Answers will vary. Refer to pages 479–480.
6. Any three: forming more mature relationships with people your age and of both genders; achieving a masculine or feminine social role; accepting one's physique; achieving emotional independence from parents and other adults; preparing for marriage, family, and career; acquiring a set of personal standards as a guide to behavior; developing social intelligence, which includes becoming aware of human needs and becoming motivated to help others attain their goals.

7. A personal identity consists of the factors you believe make you unlike anyone else.
8. Sexual feelings come about as a result of the emotional awakening and physical responses that develop during adolescence.
9. An unplanned pregnancy can radically change or even cancel educational and career goals.
10. If sexual activity goes against the values of the family, lying begins and trust is destroyed among family members. Friends might lose respect and devalue your reputation. Dating partners might have expectations that compromise your values.
11. Setting priorities helps to put values into focus so that you can make decisions that contribute to a healthy future.

CHAPTER 21 *Review*

Using Health Terms

On a separate sheet of paper, write the term that best matches each definition below.

LESSON 1

1. The period of time when males and females become physically able to reproduce.
2. Reproductive cells produced by the gonads.
3. The act or process of knowing, including both awareness and judgment.
4. The stage between childhood and adulthood.
5. Those traits related to one's gender.
6. The factors you believe make you unique, or unlike anyone else.

LESSON 2

7. A person's ability to use responsibility to override emotions.
8. An infectious disease that is spread from person to person through sexual contact.
9. Those things that are first in importance.
10. The conscious decision to avoid harmful behaviors, including sexual activity during the teen years and the use of tobacco, alcohol, and other drugs.

Recalling the Facts

Using complete sentences, answer the following questions.

LESSON 1

1. Which sex characteristics are directly related to the production of gametes?
2. Name some secondary sex characteristics that appear at puberty.
3. Name three physical changes that occur at puberty for boys.
4. What is another term for the reproductive cell?
5. How is increased memory skill helpful to adolescents?
6. Name three developmental tasks during adolescence.
7. What is a personal identity?

LESSON 2

8. How do sexual feelings come about?
9. In what ways does an unplanned pregnancy compromise a teen's future?
10. How does becoming sexually active change relationships with family? How does it change relationships with friends and dating partners?
11. How can setting priorities help teens remain sexually abstinent?
12. How does talking about sexual feelings openly with a partner help teens use self-control?
13. What are steps you can follow to help you choose sexual abstinence before marriage?

Thinking Critically

LESSON 1

1. *Analyzing.* Although most of Candi's peers have grown several inches since reaching puberty, Candi has not. She is one of the shortest persons in her class and wonders if she will ever grow tall. Candi's mother and most of her relatives on her mother's side of the family are short. On which developmental task is Candi working on, and what can she do to complete that task?

LESSON 2

2. *Comparing and Contrasting.* Gwen likes to go with the feelings of the moment. She prefers dancing to having serious conversations. Sam brought up the issue of sexual activity as soon as he and Maddy began to see each other regularly. He explained that, even though he liked her, he had made a choice for abstinence and planned to remain abstinent until he was married. Which teen is better prepared to say no when pressured? Why?

Making the Connection

1. *Science.* Choose one of the following topics to research: acne; vocal changes in males; the sex hormones testosterone, progesterone, and estrogen. Report your findings to the class in an oral report.
2. *Social Studies.* Compare adolescence in the 1960s with adolescence today by interviewing people who were teens dating then. What were their concerns? What were their favorite songs? Who were their role models?

BEYOND THE CLASSROOM

PARENTAL INVOLVEMENT Ask your parents to share with you recollections from their adolescence. Prepare several questions you might like to ask, such as "How old were you when you reached adult height?" "What kinds of things did you worry about as a teenager?" "What responsibilities did you have?" After you finish your interview, write in your private Health Journal, telling how your experiences are similar or different from those of your parents.

COMMUNITY INVOLVEMENT Interview an employer who hires teenagers, such as the manager of a fast-food restaurant. Ask the person to describe the responsibilities of a teen employee and the responsibilities of the employer. Take notes while conducting the interview. Afterward, make two lists in your private Health Journal to describe the responsibilities of an employer and those of an employee. Tell how the responsibilities differ.

SCHOOL-TO-CAREER

Resources. Investigate a career as a sociologist. Research the educational requirements, including the time and costs of attending school. Find out the various careers a sociologist might pursue, and the responsibilities of each position.

Thinking Critically

1. She is working on accepting one's physique; answers will vary.
2. Sam. He has already thought about the consequences of sexual activity at an early age and made a decision. He won't rely on emotions to help him make a decision, since he has already thought it out.

Making the Connection

1.–2. Answers will vary.

Evaluate

- Use the reproducible *Chapter 21 Test* in the TCR, or construct your own using the Testmaker software.
- Use *Performance Assessment Activity 21* in the TCR.

Enrichment

Ask students to complete *Cross-Curriculum Activity 21* in the TCR.

Beyond the Classroom

Keep students involved in the community, and encourage parent participation by assigning the activities on this page for students to work on outside of class.

---

12. Talking about feelings makes it less likely that you will act on impulses that are out of control.
13. Discuss your feelings with an adult and with your partner, be clear about your values, avoid situations that increase the risk of sexual activity, practice your refusal skills before getting into a high-pressure situation.

The Life Cycle Continues

	FEATURES	CLASSROOM RESOURCES

ACTIVITIES

- Cross-Curriculum Activity 22
- Health Lab 22
- Health Skills Activities 22
- Parent Letter and Activities 22

ASSESSMENT

- Chapter 22 Test
- Performance Assessment Activity 22
- Testmaker Software

STUDENT ACTIVITIES WORKBOOK

- Applying Health Skills 66–68
- Study Guide 22
- Vocabulary Activity 22

STUDENT DIVERSITY STRATEGIES

- Audiocassette Program (English)
- Audiocassette Program (Spanish)
- Spanish Parent Letters and Activities
- Spanish Summaries, Quizzes, and Activities

MULTIMEDIA COMPONENTS

- English Audiocassette Program
- Spanish Audiocassette Program
- MindJogger Videodisc and VHS program
- ABCNews InterActive™ VHS/Videodisc Series

National Health Education Standards

One of the main goals of the National Health Education Standards is to move students toward "health literacy." Health literacy is the capacity of individuals to obtain, interpret, and understand basic health information and services and the competence to use such information and services in ways which promote health. The health standards were developed by applying the characteristics of a well-educated, literate person within the context of health. The health literate person is:

- a critical thinker and problem solver
- a self-directed learner
- a responsible, productive citizen
- an effective communicator

Listed below are the Health Education Standards Performance Indicators addressed in each lesson of this chapter.

Lesson	Health Standards Performance Indicators
1	1.4, 5.5, 6.1, 6.6
2	5.3, 5.7, 6.2, 6.6
3	1.2, 1.4, 3.1, 7.4

ONLINE RESOURCES

HEALTH Online

For a fresh approach to health topics and an in-depth look at health issues, use these online resources found under Teacher Resources at **health.glencoe.com**.

- **BLOCK SCHEDULE LESSON PLANS** Reinforce health concepts with outside readings selected especially for students. Each reading is accompanied by a lesson plan and activities to enhance
  - Reading Skills
  - Cross Curriculum
  - Media Literacy

- **TECHNOLOGY PROJECTS** Instructions and suggestions on how to use computer, Internet, and software with health lessons.

- **HEALTH UPDATES** Timely topics in health news, including late-breaking medical advances and updates on teen risk behaviors.

Out of Time?

If time does not permit teaching this chapter, you may use these features: Building Health Skills on page 496 and Making Responsible Decisions on page 504.

BLOCK SCHEDULING

Block scheduling provides extended time for hands-on projects and activities. Use the following activities to engage students, provide further depth, and vary your instructional techniques:

- Health Skills Activity (60–90 minutes) **pg. 506**

The Life Cycle Continues

CHAPTER OVERVIEW

Chapter 22 describes the changes and transitions that occur during adulthood. The accomplishment of developmental tasks continues to contribute to the maturity of an adult, while marriage and parenthood call upon experience and a sense of responsibility for success.

LESSON 1 The stages of infancy, childhood, and adolescence are brief compared to the entire life cycle. These stages are dramatic, but development occurs in every age group. During early adulthood, individuals are at the peak of their physical and mental abilities, though they still must adjust to the changes a career, marriage, and family may bring.

LESSON 2 Marriage is a long-term, ongoing commitment. Reasons for marriage, some of the factors that affect marital adjustment, statistics regarding teen marriage, and conflict in marriage are presented. Parenthood and the responsibilities it brings are also examined.

LESSON 3 The stages of life follow one another in a regular order, though they occur at different ages in different people. Middle adulthood often brings new insight and self-understanding with its transitions. By acting early on to prevent illness and premature death, people can also increase their quality of life.

The Life Cycle Continues

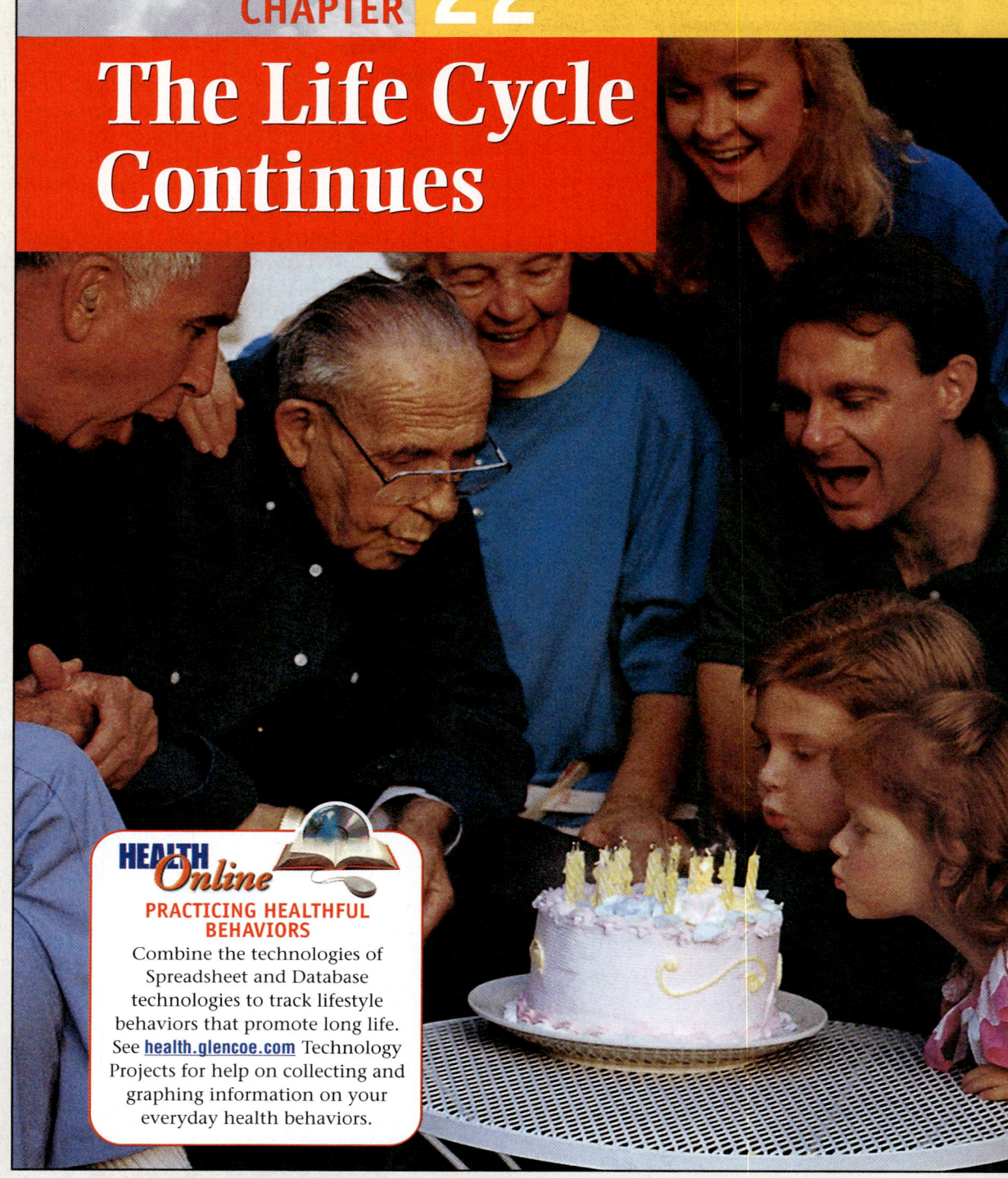

HEALTH *Online*

PRACTICING HEALTHFUL BEHAVIORS

Combine the technologies of Spreadsheet and Database technologies to track lifestyle behaviors that promote long life. See **health.glencoe.com** Technology Projects for help on collecting and graphing information on your everyday health behaviors.

Hands-On Health

TEACHING STRATEGY

Emphasizing the Importance of Abstinence Use this dramatic presentation and follow-up discussion to give students a vivid impression of the risks and costs associated with sexual activity. See Activity 34, "The $250,000 Question," in the *Hands-On Health: Creative Teaching Strategies* booklet. 🖐

Time Needed
20 minutes

Supplies
- CD player, romantic music
- scented candle and matches

> **Our todays and yesterdays are the blocks with which we build.**

—HENRY WADSWORTH LONGFELLOW
AMERICAN POET, (1807–1882)

Quick Write Imagine that you are building a structure called "Total Health." List some of the building blocks that you are using today to build a healthful tomorrow.

Personal Health Inventory

Self-Inventory Write the numbers 1–10 on a sheet of paper. Read each statement below and respond by writing *yes*, *no*, or *sometimes* for each item. Write a *yes* only for items that you practice regularly. Save your responses.

1	I have caring, loving relationships with other people.
2	I look to older adults for insights about adult life.
3	I have my own political ideas, religious views, and sense of community responsibility.
4	I have a close friend or family member with whom I can share my innermost feelings.
5	I have younger brothers or sisters, cousins, or neighbors that I have taken care of.
6	I am beginning to understand the responsibilities of caring for children.
7	I have a general understanding of the emotional and physical changes of aging.
8	I have close relationships with older adults with whom I spend time.
9	I enjoy talking to older adults.
10	I avoid making hurtful comments that stereotype the elderly.

Follow-up After completing the chapter, retake this self-inventory. Pick two items that you need to work on and set a goal to improve your health behaviors.

CHAPTER 22   THE LIFE CYCLE CONTINUES   **493**

TECHNOLOGY OPTIONS

MINDJOGGER
VIDEOQUIZ

To preview or review chapter content, you may wish to use the *MindJogger Videoquiz* that accompanies Chapter 22.

INTRODUCING THE CHAPTER

Personal Health Inventory

Have students read the ten Self-Inventory statements and briefly discuss their responses to this question: How do these attitudes and behaviors relate to the transition into adulthood? Then ask students to record their *yes, no,* or *sometimes* responses to the statements on a page titled "My Understanding of Adulthood" in their private Health Journals. Reassure students that their responses are confidential, for their personal use only.

- Tell students the old saying, "Experience is a hard teacher." Have them analyze possible meanings of this saying. Ask them to brainstorm characteristics of adulthood. Explain that growth and development continue through adulthood, as reaching one's potential is a lifelong process, and at each phase we have something new to learn and share.
- Let students describe and discuss the photographs on these two pages. Which parts of the life cycle are shown in the family photo? Which of those stages have you completed? Which parts of the life cycle lie ahead of you? What do you expect from adulthood? After a brief discussion, have students read the quote and complete the Quick Write on this page.
- Distribute Parent Letter 22 from the *Parent Letters and Activities* booklet in the TCR.

Growth for a Lifetime

LESSON OBJECTIVES

After studying this lesson, students should be able to

- describe the physical and emotional aspects of maturity.
- summarize the four developmental tasks of early adulthood.

MOTIVATOR

Write the following on the chalkboard for students to work on while attendance is being taken: *Complete the following sentence on paper: I'll know I'm really an adult when…*

INTRODUCING THE LESSON

Refer to the Motivator. Ask volunteers to share their responses. Follow up on any responses that suggest adulthood depends on gaining maturity, knowledge, or social responsibility. Tell students that the basic developmental tasks of early adulthood will be the focus of this lesson. Emphasize that attaining adulthood is not simply a matter of chronological age or the legal rights that go with it, but a matter of maturing in ways that make one a happy, productive member of society.

INTRODUCING HEALTH TERMS

- Ask students to write their own definitions of each of the following terms: *life cycle, adulthood, maturity, career, occupation, individual identity,* and *responsibility.* Let volunteers share their definitions.
- Ask students to complete Vocabulary Activity 22 and Chapter Study Guide 22 in the *Student Workbook.* ☞

Growth for a Lifetime

When compared with the entire life cycle, the stages of infancy, childhood, and adolescence last only a short time. You and your friends may feel that the years of growing up will never end, but these years are only a small part of the rest of your life. With an average life expectancy of 78 years, you truly do have a lifetime of activity ahead of you.

HEALTH TERMS

physical maturity

emotional maturity

emotional intimacy

HEALTH CONCEPTS

- During adulthood, a person's growth and development continue.
- Developmental tasks of adulthood include developing intimate relationships, establishing a career, and establishing a place in society.

Considering the Entire Life Cycle

The study of all the years of the life cycle, from birth to death, is relatively new. In the past, few scientists studied life as a whole, focusing instead on the early years, when development is so rapid. In fact, some researchers believed human development ended with childhood or early adolescence. They viewed the progression from birth to death as much like hiking up a hill to adulthood, then walking across a level plateau that finally headed downward toward the end of life's journey.

Today, it is clear that life is more dynamic than depicted in this earlier view. Human growth and development do not end at age 6 or 16. Instead, they continue through every stage of life.

Lesson 1 Resources

TEACHER'S CLASSROOM RESOURCES

☞ **Concept Map** Activity 66

☞ **Lesson 66 Quiz**

☞ **Lesson Plan 66**

☞ **Parent Letter and Activities 22**

☞ **Reteaching** Activity 66

STUDENT WORKBOOK

☞ **Applying Health Skills 66**

☞ **Chapter Study Guide 22**

☞ **Vocabulary** Activity 22

Adulthood

What does it mean to be an adult, and what steps do you take to become one? Is adulthood merely a function of age? Do you simply awake one day and find that you have become an adult?

One term often used in conjunction with adulthood is *maturity*. However, like the notion of adulthood itself, maturity can mean different things:

- **Physical maturity** is *the state at which the physical body and all its organs are fully developed.* Once your body reaches physical maturity, you will not grow any taller. By late adolescence or the early twenties, most people will have achieved maturity as it is defined in this sense.

- **Emotional maturity** is *the state at which the mental and emotional capabilities of an individual are fully developed.* Emotional maturity is a more important component of adulthood than physical maturity. It includes achieving independence but, at the same time, cultivating close relationships. Being emotionally mature means having a strong personal identity and an acceptance of self. It also means having strong values and goals. Many people reach emotional maturity after they have already matured physically— in some cases long after.

Developmental Tasks of Adulthood

Whereas physical maturity occurs automatically, emotional maturity does not. A person needs to satisfy certain well-defined developmental tasks of adulthood in order to reach this emotional plateau. The developmental tasks of adulthood focus on four major aspects of people's lives:

- occupational role
- individual identity and personal independence
- intimate relationships
- place in society

Each of these developmental tasks represents lessons that adults must learn to adjust to the world around them.

⬆ **Decisions you make now can help prepare you for a career that is satisfying.**
ACTIVITY *Name several jobs you think you might enjoy doing as a young adult.*

LESSON 1   GROWTH FOR A LIFETIME   **495**

TEACH

L1 Discussion

Ask the class: What is maturity? How can you tell if you're mature?

L1 Explaining

Explain how the developmental tasks of adulthood differ from many of those that must be achieved earlier in life. *(They take longer to achieve, and they have to do less with physical maturation than with learning and gaining insight.)*

L1 Discussing

Ask: What are the first steps most young adults take to achieve self-actualization? *(Paying expenses, leaving home, supporting themselves.)* How is the ability to maintain adult relationships established? *(Through observation and personal experience.)*

LEP Class Activity

Have students make a bulletin board that reflects the youth orientation of our culture. Ask them to bring in pictures from magazines and newspapers of young people and the elderly. How are the two age groups depicted differently?

L1 Community Involvement

Assign students to interview adults of different ages from their families or community regarding the age at which they felt they would or did complete each of the basic developmental tasks of adulthood. Were they aware of the tasks they were completing? Work with students to develop a simple list of questions to elicit this information from informants.

COOPERATIVE ⟩ LEARNING

MORAL DEVELOPMENT. Moral choices develop as children mature. Toddlers avoid behavior that brings negative consequences and choose behavior that wins approval. They begin to empathize, which lays a basis for developing a conscience. Conscience begins to develop between ages 5 and 7. Divide students into groups of four to discuss the roles of reward and punishment, group acceptance, and conscience in making and acting on moral choices. Invite groups to speculate about the relative roles in moral choices individuals make at ages 6, 10, 13, and 16. Have them make a chart showing a typical moral decision facing an individual at each of these ages, with each group member completing the example for one age. Discuss how need for approval can influence moral development in positive and negative ways.

Chapter 22   **495**

L2 Writing

Select students to write a paragraph on each of several different characters in TV programs. The characters should be either in their 20s or past retirement age. Both men and women should be included in each age group. Ask them to address how, if at all, the way in which men are depicted differs from the way in which women are depicted. What are the differences between young and elderly?

Building Health Skills

Strengthening Relationships Through TALK
Skill: Conflict Resolution

Ask students to identify some of the conflicts that arise between friends or between members of a couple; note their suggestions on the board. Then ask: What are some positive approaches to these conflicts? What are some negative approaches? After several volunteers have shared their ideas, have students read the Building Health Skills feature to learn about a specific strategy friends or couples can use to resolve such conflicts. As a follow-up activity, have students work with partners to role-play the TALK approach to the conflicts listed on the board.

Establishing an Occupational Role

During adolescence many people start to form ideas about the kind of life they want as adults. An occupation or career is usually a large part of that idea or dream of the future. As they become young adults, people begin to see themselves more clearly in an occupational role. This view of their role may occur through on-the-job training or through education beyond high school as preparation for a career. Making an occupational choice, even though it may not be the final one, is one of the major developmental tasks that must be achieved on the way to adulthood.

Establishing an Individual Identity and Personal Independence

hotlink

self-actualization For more information on self-actualization and its place in the hierarchy of human needs, see Chapter 8, page 193.

The desire for independence during adolescence is preparation for establishing an individual identity as an adult. It is also part of the continuing process of **self-actualization**, which includes developing one's capabilities to their fullest.

Leaving home or starting to work full-time are ways in which young adults can begin to achieve self-actualization. At first, they

Building Health Skills

Conflict Resolution: Strengthening Relationships Through TALK

WHETHER RELATIONSHIPS ARE intimate or merely casual, conflicts are inevitable. When conflicts or disagreements occur, relying on the TALK strategy will help both parties reach a peaceful resolution. The TALK strategy is named for the first letters of each of its four steps:

1. **T–Take time out.** Set aside at least 30 minutes, especially when tempers have flared. Go into another room, or go for a walk.

2. **A–Allow each person to express opinions uninterrupted.** Use active listening skills. Permit the other person to express his or her entire opinion on the subject.

3. **L–Let each person ask questions** as a means of clarifying any statement that was unclear.

4. **K–Keep brainstorming to find a good compromise.** Compromise, or give-and-take, is essential to every healthy relationship. Yet finding a common ground is not always easy. Invest the time searching for it. You will both be happier in the end.

496 CHAPTER 22 THE LIFE CYCLE CONTINUES

PERSONAL HEALTH

A LIFE OF DECISIONS. Over a lifetime, students will make a number of important decisions. They will select careers, places of residence, and possibly marriage partners. They will decide whether to become parents and whether to have their aging parents move in with them. As they age, they will decide when and how to retire, and whether to maintain family homes, move to retirement communities, or live with family. Have students examine available photos of themselves and older family members at several stages of life, then consider decisions that must be made at the various stages. Tell them to chart the decisions they will need to make over a lifetime. Suggest that they show a particular age span within which given decisions would be most appropriate.

may substitute the emotional support of friends for the support they once received from parents. As their development continues, however, young adults will become more self-sufficient. In so doing, they will be continuing on the developmental path that will lead to the establishment of an individual identity and personal independence.

Establishing Intimate Relationships

This developmental task involves the ability to build close relationships with people of both genders while still maintaining a sense of self. It involves developing **emotional intimacy**, *the ability to experience a caring, loving relationship with another person with whom you can share your innermost feelings*. During this time there may be several successive romantic relationships. Some people give a sense of permanence to romantic relationships through marriage. Others develop romantic relationships but prefer to remain single. Still others are occupied with establishing a career or defining their own identity, and intimate relationships come later or not at all.

Establishing a Place in Society

Another task of adulthood includes determining where and how a person fits into society. Political ideas, religious views, and a sense of community responsibility contribute to finding a place in society. They may, for example, do volunteer work, promote recycling, or join a neighborhood sports team.

LESSON 1 *Review*

Reviewing Facts and Vocabulary

1. What is the difference between emotional maturity and emotional intimacy?
2. How does forming ideas about a career help an individual meet developmental tasks as an adult?
3. Name three ways an adult determines where and how he or she fits into society.

Thinking Critically

4. *Analyzing.* James is 22 years old and married, with a child. He does not have a high school diploma or a steady job. He works odd jobs, but dreams of someday becoming a manager of a store or an artist. What task does James need to work on to reach adulthood? What can he do to complete this task?
5. *Evaluating.* Make a list of criteria based on the information in this lesson that you can use to determine when you have left adolescence and entered adulthood. Then list what tasks you need to complete to become an adult.

Applying Health Skills

6. *In Your Home and School.* Write a letter to yourself at age 30 or 35. In it, describe where you expect to be in regard to relationships, career, and place in society. Ask your parents for their input and feedback on your plans and goals for the future.

ASSESS

EVALUATING THE LESSON

Assign and discuss the Lesson 1 Review; then administer, grade, and discuss the *Lesson 66 Quiz* in the TCR.

RETEACHING

- Have students review the basic developmental tasks of adulthood by writing out one example of each.
- Ask students to complete *Reteaching Activity 66* in the TCR.

ENRICHMENT

The term *generation gap* refers to diversity in ideas and perceptions due to differences in experience and age. It is most common between teenagers and adults. Understanding and communication are key tools in bridging the generation gap. Have students work in small groups to identify specific ways in which they believe a generation gap exists between themselves and older individuals.

CLOSE

Tell students that in this lesson they have come to appreciate that growth and development are processes that don't end with adulthood, but continue on throughout life. The class identified and discussed basic developmental tasks in early adulthood. Discuss how, as these tasks are completed, the typical individual matures into a more fulfilled and productive member of society.

Lesson 1 Review

Answers to Reviewing Facts and Vocabulary

1. Emotional maturity is the state at which the mental and emotional capabilities of an individual are fully developed. Emotional intimacy is the ability to experience a caring, loving relationship with another person with whom you can share your innermost feelings.
2. Career choices play a large part in defining the life you want as an adult.
3. A person determines how he or she fits into society by means of political ideas, religious views, and a sense of community responsibility.

Answers to Thinking Critically

4.–5. Answers will vary.

Marriage and Parenthood

Marriage and Parenthood

Marriage and having children are two major components of young adulthood for many individuals. Marriage plays an important role in meeting the task of developing intimate relationships, especially the emotional intimacy you learned about in Lesson 1. Marriage and parenting bring on new experiences and additional responsibilities.

HEALTH TERMS

commitment

marital adjustment

planned pregnancy

self-directed

HEALTH CONCEPTS

- Marriage is an agreement between two people to face the realities of life as a couple.
- Teen marriages suffer a high rate of failure.
- Responsibilities of parenthood include maintaining discipline and providing love.

Marriage

Ninety-five percent of Americans who marry do so before the age of 40. Their steps down the aisle are among the most important steps they will ever take. Yet, of the millions of people who say "I do" each year, 68 percent will divorce. The primary reason for these failed marriages is that couples are not prepared to make a commitment. A **commitment** is *a promise or a pledge.* Marriage is a long-term, ongoing commitment. Getting married is deciding to spend the rest of your life with someone else.

Reasons for Marrying

Most people say they are marrying because they are "in love." Often, however, there are other motives hidden deep inside. People

Lesson 2 Resources

may decide to marry because they are lonely or they want to escape an unpleasant situation at home. They also may marry because a pregnancy is involved or because they seek financial security. Without close self-examination, couples may not even be aware of the motives driving them. If there are any doubts or questions about reasons for marrying or about the intended spouse, the best time to face them and reconsider is before the marriage.

Factors Affecting Marital Adjustment

Sociologists have conducted extensive research to develop measures of **marital adjustment**—*how well people adjust and adapt to marriage and to each other*. Researchers have concluded that a well-adjusted marriage is one in which the husband and wife

- agree on critical issues in their relationship.
- share common interests and activities.
- demonstrate affections and shared confidences.
- have few complaints about the marriage.
- do not have feelings of loneliness or irritability.
- had a close association before marriage.

Researchers have also found that some factors related to social background were also associated with successful marital adjustment. A similarity in family backgrounds and the domestic happiness of parents are positive factors.

Teen Marriages

Statistics show that teen marriage is not a good idea. Teen marriages often deteriorate as the excitement wears off and the responsibilities increase. Teens who marry, or feel forced to marry because of unplanned pregnancies, often choose their mates before they have any idea who they themselves are or what they want. The results can be disastrous. Consider:

- Females between the ages of 14 and 17 who marry are twice as likely to divorce as females who wait until they are older.
- About three-quarters of all teen couples who marry because of pregnancy divorce within six years.

Conflict in Marriage

A successful marriage requires both partners to demonstrate respect, trust, and care for one another. It also requires individuals to resolve conflicts fairly and without damaging one's own or one's partner's self-esteem. Among the issues that sometimes cause problems in marriages are:

- differences in spending and saving habits
- conflicting loyalties involving friends and families
- intimacy or sexual problems

TEACH

L1 Discussing

Ask the following: What is the single most important reason the majority of people say they want to get married? What other reasons may influence the decision to marry? How big a factor is romantic love in the decision to marry? in the success of a marriage? Discuss student responses.

L1 Class Activity

Divide the class into male and female students. Ask each group to make a list of reasons for getting married. Compare the lists. Do males and females have the same or different reasons? Discuss the differences and similarities.

L1 Class Activity

Have students rank the list of factors that affect marital adjustment from most to least important. Compare rankings and discuss the differences in opinion. Have students give reasons for their rankings.

L1 Discussing

Ask: What are some of the mutual characteristics of husbands and wives who have well-adjusted marriages?

TEENAGE SEXUALITY (Side 1)

Chapter 16: Being a Teenage Mother: Lancy

Frames 42234-43230

Chapter 17: Being a Teenage Father: Billy

Frames 43235-44207

MEETING STUDENT DIVERSITY

CULTURAL PERSPECTIVES. In some cultures, marriage and the establishment of a family are considered too important to be left to young people. Marriages are arranged for the economic, social, and political advantage of the family. Among some cultural groups, arranged marriages preserve traditional values that people fear would be lost if children married outside the group. Encourage students to research marriage traditions in various cultures and to share their findings with the class.

L1 Discussing

Pose the following questions: Why is it important to know yourself well before considering marriage? In what ways does dating give you an opportunity to get to know yourself better?

L1 Discussing

Ask: What are the primary responsibilities of parenthood? Have students create a chart outlining parent responsibilities for each of the areas of health.

L2 Cooperative Learning

Have students complete *Cooperative Learning Activity 22*, "Design a Toy," in the TCR. 🖙

L1 Discussing

Ask: What is the difference between a planned and an unplanned pregnancy? What are the advantages of planned pregnancy and the disadvantages of unplanned pregnancy?

L1 Discussing

Ask: What are the consequences of marriage and pregnancy on personal goals for teens? Discuss the problems associated with teen parenting and the risks that a pregnant teen's lifestyle could pose for her developing baby.

CHARACTER IN ACTION

Maturity and Marriage

Maturity means being ready to accept responsibility for your actions, including responsibility for your part in a long-term relationship. A successful marriage requires emotional and social maturity. Marriage partners should make a commitment to building a life of shared values that are based on ethics and their highest principles.

Character Check Consider a couple you know or have read about who seems to have a mature marriage. Ask yourself whether they demonstrate the following signs of maturity in a marriage, that each partner

➤ has the ability to give as well as receive.

➤ can compromise and accept not always getting his or her own way.

➤ accepts responsibility for his or her feelings and actions and does not blame the other.

➤ supports the growth of the partner as an individual and respects his or her partner's highest values.

🔻 *Children bring many changes and responsibilities to a couple's life.*
ACTIVITY *Name some of the responsibilities parents have when raising children.*

■ jealousy, infidelity, or lack of attention
■ housework
■ decisions about having children and child care

Developing skills in communication and resolving conflicts before they escalate, or get out of hand, are essential in dealing with the issues and conflicts in any marriage.

Parenthood

Having a child can be a wonderful experience. It can be rewarding to provide a nurturing environment for a child and watch that child grow and develop within it. However, parenting is a huge, ongoing responsibility.

The decision to have a child can be a very complex and private decision for a couple. It is often affected by religious, economic, career, emotional, cultural, and social considerations. Many couples wait until their marriage, careers, or finances are established. They may even put off having babies for years, waiting until they are in a financial and psychological position to parent. A carefully planned pregnancy between two people ready to nurture and support a child to adulthood remains the route with the best chance of success for both the parents and the child. **Planned pregnancy** is *making a decision to get pregnant before the baby is conceived.*

Responsibilities of Parenthood

Parents must provide food, clothing, shelter, education, medical care, and protection from harm for their children. They are responsible also for the emotional, social, and intellectual upbringing of their offspring. Parenting involves setting limits, providing guidance, and instilling values. Perhaps most important, it means giving unconditional love.

Setting Limits

Parents need to set limits and establish a clearly defined set of rules. When children learn limits, they become self-directed. Being **self-directed** means *making correct decisions*

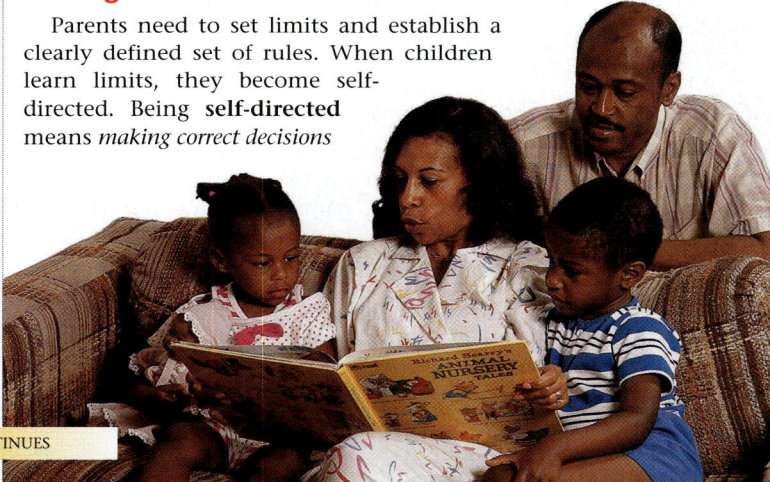

MORE ABOUT . . . . .

SOCIETAL PERCEPTIONS. Because of the baby boom, the American population has been dominated by large numbers of young people for the last several decades. This has had a tremendous influence on the way our society has perceived aging and the elderly.

As the baby-boom generation ages, society is increasingly dominated by individuals who are middle-aged and older. As a result, our attitudes toward aging and the elderly are also changing. More and more mass media, products, and advertising are slanted toward people over the age of 40, who are increasingly portrayed in a more positive way.

about behavior when adults are not there to enforce rules. Parents should follow these guidelines when disciplining their children:

- Act quickly so that children understand the link between misbehavior and consequences.
- Be consistent so that children expect that certain behaviors will result in certain consequences.
- Distinguish between the behavior (action) and the child so that children think of themselves as people who occasionally do bad things, rather than as bad children.
- Praise positive behavior.

Providing Guidance and Instilling Values

Parents can guide children by setting good examples. They can teach children skills for getting along with others and handling problems. Children need to develop a sense of pride in their studies or work and to recognize that they, more than anyone else, are responsible for their success or failure in life. One of a parent's greatest challenges is to instill **values** in his or her children.

Giving Unconditional Love

Children cannot prosper without love, attention, and guidance. Parents need to express their delight in their children and their existence whenever possible. They should praise their children for their efforts. Parents can give encouragement through words, letters, hugs, and facial expressions. They can show they care by giving their time.

hot link

values For more information on values and their function in the health of the individual and society, see Chapter 1, page 20.

ASSESS

EVALUATING THE LESSON

Assign and discuss the Lesson 2 Review; then administer, grade, and discuss the *Lesson 67 Quiz* in the TCR. ▱

RETEACHING

- Have each student interview three different married couples with children to determine what these couples believe is the key to a successful marriage. What do they think are the most common problems married couples face? How do children affect the marriage? Ask students to summarize their findings and draw conclusions about skills necessary for a successful marriage.
- Ask students to complete *Reteaching Activity 67* in the TCR. ▱

ENRICHMENT

Have students read about premarital counseling. What kinds of issues are addressed? What kinds of strategies are learned? How long does this form of counseling usually take? Have students summarize their findings in writing.

CLOSE

Tell students that marriage is a partnership in which both partners must assume a lot of responsibility, and that responsibility grows if they decide to become parents.

LESSON 2 Review

Reviewing Facts and Vocabulary

1. In what way can marriage be said to be a commitment?
2. Name three components of good marital adjustment.
3. Name several unsound reasons for having children.

Thinking Critically

4. ***Comparing and Contrasting.*** Imagine that two of your friends, Monica and Pedro, are thinking about marriage. At 18, what problems would they face that probably would not be problems if they decided to wait five years before getting married?

5. ***Analyzing.*** Explain why parenthood is one of the most serious decisions a person can make. Then list criteria people can use to determine whether they are ready to have children.

Applying Health Skills

6. ***In Your Home.*** Analyze and describe your parents' child-rearing beliefs and practices by writing about them in your private Health Journal. Have your parents review what you wrote to see whether they agree with your observations. Then tell what changes, if any, you will make if you raise children in the future.

Lesson 2 Review

Answers to Reviewing Facts and Vocabulary

1. Marriage is a commitment in the sense that it is a promise or pledge to spend the rest of your life with someone.
2. Any three: the partners agree on critical issues in their relationship, share common interests and activities, demonstrate affection and share confidences, have few complaints about the marriage, have no feelings of loneliness or irritability, and had a close association before marriage.
3. Answers will vary.

Answers to Thinking Critically

4.–5. Answers will vary.

The Aging Experience

LESSON OBJECTIVES

After studying this lesson, students should be able to

- describe the major developmental tasks and transitions of middle adulthood.
- summarize the physical changes of late adulthood.
- summarize the emotional and social changes of late adulthood.

MOTIVATOR

Write the following on the chalkboard for students to work on while attendance is being taken: *Complete the following sentences on paper: Old age starts at age...; You know you're "over the hill" when...; Never trust anyone over the age of...*

INTRODUCING THE LESSON

Refer to the Motivator. Ask volunteers to share their responses with the class. Use their responses to illustrate the point that for many teens, anyone over the age of 30 or 40 may seem old. Stress that these years are just the young to middle ages of adulthood, because most people in their 30s and 40s today can expect to live at least 40 or 50 years more.

INTRODUCING HEALTH TERMS

- Have the class arrive at a good definition for the term *transition* and then list some of the transitions that occur during middle adulthood.
- Ask students to complete Vocabulary Activity 22 and Chapter Study Guide 22 in the *Student Workbook.* ☞

The Aging Experience

For most of human history, only a tiny segment of the population has lived beyond age 40, and this is still true in many developing parts of the world today. In American society today, however, 40—the onset of middle adulthood—marks more or less a midpoint in life. This lesson will examine how people respond to the experience of aging.

HEALTH TERMS

transitions

generativity

menopause

empty-nest syndrome

integrity

HEALTH CONCEPTS

- People of every age have the same needs but different ways of meeting them.
- Aging is a normal process.
- Important changes occur during middle adulthood.
- Every person has some control over the way he or she ages.

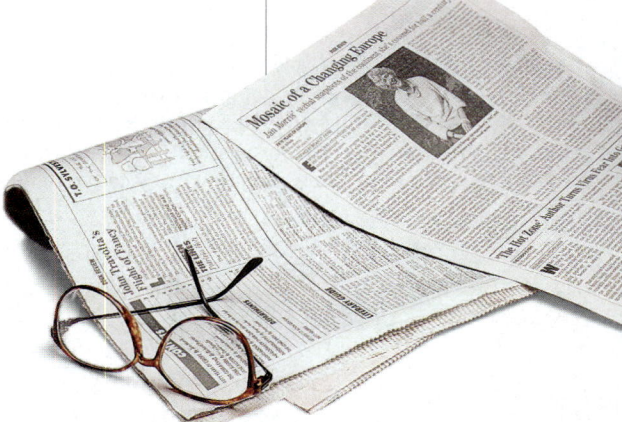

Middle Adulthood

Life is filled with transitions. **Transitions** are *critical changes that occur at all stages of life.* One important transition you will face soon, for example, is graduating from high school and going out to make your place in the world.

During middle adulthood, people go through a number of transitions, all relating to yet another of Erik Erikson's developmental tasks. This task, **generativity**, marks *a shift of attention away from oneself in the present to concerns for future generations.* Generativity includes active concern for young people and for the society in which young people will live and work as adults. Refusal to accept and deal with changes during middle adulthood can result in self-absorption, or preoccupation with meeting only one's own needs.

Lesson 3 Resources

TEACHER'S CLASSROOM RESOURCES

- ☞ **Concept Map** Activity 68
- ☞ **Decision-Making** Activity 22
- ☞ **Enrichment** Activity 22
- ☞ **Health Lab** 22
- ☞ **Lesson 68 Quiz**

- ☞ **Lesson Plan** 68
- ☞ **Reteaching** Activity 68

STUDENT WORKBOOK

- ☞ **Applying Health Skills** 68
- ☞ **Chapter Study Guide** 22
- ☞ **Vocabulary** Activity 22

Physical Transitions

As adults turn 40, their bodies begin to show signs of aging. Wrinkles and dry skin may appear, and hearing and eyesight start to decline. The hair may thin and turn gray. Adults of middle age may also experience muscle loss. It is best that adults exercise throughout life so that they can remain physically active well into late adulthood.

Around ages 45 to 55, women go through menopause. **Menopause** is *the stopping of ovulation and menstruation* that results from hormonal changes. During menopause, some women experience rapid changes in body temperature, hot flashes, and night sweats as the levels of estrogen in the body drop. After menopause, a woman cannot get pregnant.

Mental and Emotional Transitions

Middle adulthood is a time for looking both back at where you have come from and ahead to where you are going. Most people by this time have experienced many of life's greatest joys, including children, pride in their personal accomplishments as well as some disappointments, such as the death of a friend or loved one. In contrast to early adulthood, in which one's orientation tends to be focused on relationships with others, the middle years are marked by self-evaluation.

For some middle-aged adults, the emotional transitions of middle age are much like the growing pains of adolescence. People experiencing this "midlife crisis," as it is often called, may be caught up with questions and concerns about whether they have met their goals, feel loved and valued, or have made a positive difference in the lives of others.

Some middle-aged adults find it difficult to accept the passage of time and make drastic changes in their behavior and way of life. People experiencing these difficulties may imitate youthful or immature ways of living. Since these middle-aged adults have not recognized and dealt with changes within themselves, they often find they still are not happy.

Most people, however, progress through middle adulthood without serious problems. They adjust their hopes and dreams and adapt their lifestyles to their newly experienced feelings of being in touch with themselves.

▼ *Continuing to be physically active throughout life is a healthy decision.*
ACTIVITY *Name three other ways to promote overall health.*

TEACH

L1 Discussing

Discuss the following: What is a midlife crisis? Who is most likely to suffer from this difficulty?

L1 Community Involvement

Have students find a middle-aged adult in their circle of relatives and friends who will agree to be interviewed regarding midlife crisis. Do the adults feel they are in a crisis? How do they feel differently about life now than they did in young adulthood? Why? Are they more inward-looking or outward-looking? Are they optimistic or pessimistic about the rest of their lives? How much older do they think they will live to be? Does this affect how they feel and act on a day-to-day basis?

L1 Discussing

Ask: What are some of the physical changes that occur as we age? What lifestyle factors can affect these aspects of growing older?

L1 Explaining

Explain, at the cellular level, why aging occurs. (*Decrease in cell division and cell function.*)

L1 Self-Esteem

Ask students to work in small groups to identify factors they believe would help them adjust to growing older. Discuss their ideas.

L2 Health Lab

Distribute *Health Lab 22* and have students investigate the effectiveness of denture cleansers.

HEALTH LITERACY

RESPONSIBLE/PRODUCTIVE CITIZEN. Suggest that students find ways to help older adults in the community avoid isolation. Some students may wish to visit homes for older adults and volunteer to help. Students who drive can volunteer for a program that delivers meals to housebound seniors. They might also investigate opportunities to utilize the knowledge and skills seniors possess. For example, tutors may be needed at the library, charity events or citizen advisory committees may need volunteers, children may need companionship, and aides may be needed in the classroom. After students find opportunities for senior involvement, suggest that they create flyers to leave in places such as seniors' centers and housing complexes for seniors.

CHARACTER IN ACTION

Sages and Ages: Valuing Wisdom

Ask students to read the feature. Have volunteers share a rewarding experience they have had with an older person. Ask students to ask older adults to share their stories about healthful choices in their lives and the importance of core values in their decision-making.

Making Responsible Decisions

1. Krista wants to spend time with her boyfriend's family on the same weekend that she has made a commitment to visit her grandparents.
2. Krista could (a) visit her grandparents and explain her commitment to her boyfriend, saying she hopes they'll have another opportunity to spend time with his family; (b) spend time with her boyfriend and explain the situation to her grandparents, promising to visit on another weekend.
3. Krista might (a) please her grandparents but miss the time with her boyfriend's family and possibly feel resentful; (b) disappoint her grandparents and probably feel guilty, but get to spend time with her boyfriend's family.
4. Krista values family loyalty and support. She also values her relationship with her boyfriend.
5. Responses will vary.
6. Encourage students to consider both short- and long-term consequences of their decisions.

L2 **Decision Making**

For further study on making responsible decisions, assign *Decision-Making Activity 22* in the TCR. ☞

CHARACTER IN ACTION

Sages and Ages: Valuing Wisdom

Older adults often have lots of information—insights, knowledge, and good judgment based on many and varied experiences. Be **considerate** and listen to the ideas of others.

Character Check You may benefit from the wisdom of an older adult by

➤ corresponding with a grandparent or an older relative.

➤ getting to know an older adult in your neighborhood.

➤ volunteering in an organization that pairs teens with older adults.

➤ discussing the importance that ethical values have made in shaping his or her life.

Social Transitions

Social transitions during middle adulthood focus on the family. Middle-aged adults may have to adjust to the death of their parents. They also must adapt to their children's growing up and leaving home to establish independent lives. Some adults experience *feelings of despair or loneliness that accompany children's leaving home and entering adulthood.* The **empty-nest syndrome,** as this reaction is called, prompts some couples to establish a closer, more loving relationship, often similar to the one they had during their courtship. Other middle-aged adults adjust by realizing that they have more time for themselves and their interests.

Late Adulthood

Erikson's eighth and final stage of development is late adulthood. This stage is accompanied by another transition—retirement from the workforce. For the first time since early childhood, the individual is free for the most part of pressures and daily responsibilities. Retirement can occur as early as age 50 or well into one's eighties.

Physical Changes

Older adults continue to experience physical changes. As cells grow older, age pigment collects in them, prompting the appearance of so-called "liver spots." Skin loses its elasticity, the functioning of the body's organs slows, and the body's immune system becomes less

---

Making Responsible Decisions

Balancing Reponsibilities

Krista has made a commitment to visit her grandparents in another city over the weekend. She has always been the "apple of their eye" and has enjoyed doing things with them throughout the years. This time they are house-bound, because her grandmother is recovering from surgery. They hope Krista's visit will cheer them up. Today the boy Krista has been dating for a few months asked her to take part in a series of fun activities his family is planning for the weekend. This is appealing, not only for the fun, but because she has been trying to get to know his parents better. What should Krista do?

What Would You Do?

Apply the six steps of the decision-making process to Krista's problem.

1. **State the situation.**
2. **List the options.**
3. **Weigh the possible outcomes.**
4. **Consider your values.**
5. **Make a decision and act.**
6. **Evaluate the decision.**

SCHOOL-TO-CAREER

Even as the percentage of senior citizens grew during the 1990s, the media reported that some older workers faced discrimination in the workplace. Although laws prohibited age discrimination, reports indicated that some older workers were being laid off or were having difficulty finding jobs. Older job seekers often included women who were reentering the workforce after raising children, divorcing, or being widowed. They also included workers whose jobs had been cut or who had been terminated. Have students look for recent reports of age discrimination in the workplace and investigate any such reports. How widespread is age discrimination? What form does it take? What are the reasons for the discrimination? How can it occur in violation of the law? Let them summarize their findings in oral reports.

effective. When older people continue to be active, maintain good nutrition, and take good care of themselves, however, body functions remain more efficient.

Many diseases can occur in older adulthood, including cancer and heart disease. Osteoporosis occurs as the bones of older people become weak and easily breakable due to bone loss. Arthritis may cause crippling swelling and pain in joints, especially fingers. Parkinson's disease causes loss of muscle function. Alzheimer's disease is a condition that causes mental deterioration.

Although body functions decrease with older age, negative stereotypes about older people are not true. Many persons flourish in old age. Some individuals even reenter the job force through the American Association of Retired Persons (AARP) or volunteer groups.

Emotional and Social Changes

Erik Erikson's eighth and final developmental task occurs during late adulthood. This task, **integrity**, is *a feeling of wholeness and contentment.* Integrity is achieved by keeping intimate relationships and remaining committed to a cause, including family or religion. Older adults who achieve integrity can look back on life with contentment and no regrets. They are able to enjoy the time they have left and accept the approach of death.

Family and other social relationships are a very important factor in helping individuals adjust successfully to aging. In some families, grandparents not only care for young children but also do household tasks to contribute to the household.

Older adults may have social opportunities in their communities as well. Many older adults belong to groups where they enjoy such activities as playing cards, painting, or doing other hobbies such as gardening or traveling.

▲ *Many middle-aged adults find they have additional time to pursue recreational activities.*

ACTIVITY *Explain why decisions you make as a teen are important to your later years.*

---

bar

LESSON **3** *Review*

Reviewing Facts and Vocabulary

1. What transitions do middle-aged adults face?
2. Describe the developmental tasks of generativity and integrity.
3. What causes empty-nest syndrome?

Thinking Critically

4. *Comparing and Contrasting.* Make a chart in which you compare and contrast the concerns you might have in middle adulthood with those of late adulthood.

Applying Health Skills

5. *In Your Home.* Interview your parents or an aunt, uncle, or other relative in middle age to find out their plans for retirement. Ask them what steps they have taken for retirement, such as having a retirement savings account. Also find out what they want to do, including hobbies and travel, and where they want to live.

LESSON 3   THE AGING EXPERIENCE   **505**

CHAPTER 22 • LESSON 3

ASSESS

EVALUATING THE LESSON

Assign and discuss the Lesson 3 Review; then administer, grade, and discuss the *Lesson 68 Quiz* in the TCR. 📁

RETEACHING

- Have students interview at least three healthy, active adults who are in the middle or late adulthood stage. Ask students to elicit responses to this question: What are the mental, emotional, and social benefits of aging? Have students write summaries of their findings.
- Ask students to complete *Reteaching Activity 68* in the TCR. 📁

ENRICHMENT

- Encourage students to explore different perspectives on aging and the elderly by comparing their own culture with some other culture. Have them prepare a written report of their findings.
- Emphasize that many parents and grandparents may embrace life differently and more adventurously than earlier generations because of new ideas about the mind-body connection. Assign *Enrichment Activity 22*, "The Ageless Mind," in the TCR. 📁

CLOSE

Tell students that middle adulthood is a time of self-evaluation and redirection. It is a time to take pride in one's accomplishments and assess the goals one still wants to attain. As individuals age and enter the senior years, changes and transitions continue, and many still have goals and the time necessary to achieve them.

Lesson 3 Review

Answers to Reviewing Facts and Vocabulary

1. See pages 502–504 for examples of physical, mental/emotional, and social transitions.
2. Generativity is a shift of attention away from oneself in the present to concerns for future generations. Integrity is a feeling of wholeness and contentment that comes with maintaining intimate relationships and remaining committed to a cause, resulting in being able to look back on life with no regrets.
3. The cause of empty-nest syndrome is children growing up and leaving home.

Answer to Thinking Critically

4. Answers will vary.

Chapter 22   **505**

Health Skills Activities

ACTIVITY 1
HEALTH SKILLS
Goal Setting

➤ **National Standards**
This activity meets this National Health Standard: 6.3.

Teach

- Direct students' attention to a window in the classroom. Ask them to imagine they could gaze through the window and see the future. What would it look like in 5 years? In 10? In 20?
- Ask students to list life goals they have identified. If students completed the essay Health Skills activity on page 488, you may want to have them refer back to that.
- Distribute art materials. Allow students a complete class period to locate images and design their windows.

ACTIVITY 2
HEALTH SKILLS

Analyzing Influences, Communication, Health Advocacy

➤ **National Standards**
This activity meets these National Health Standards: 4.2; 5.1; 7.6.

Teach

- Help students recognize that the romanticized view of love common among traditional love songs addresses only one facet of "true love," and that is infatuation, which lasts only a brief time.
- Have students brainstorm a list of deeper feelings that replace infatuation, such as commitment, respect, and so on.

Health Skills Activities

Activity 1 — Windows of Your Life

Have you ever wondered what your life will be like 10, 20, or even 30 years from now? Create a "window" to your future, showing the different phases of your future adult life.

Directions

1. Divide a large sheet of newsprint into four equal sections. Label the sections *Early Adulthood* (25-35), *Middle Adulthood* (35-50), *Older Adulthood* (50-65), and *Late Adulthood* (65 and on).
2. Decorate each window with magazine pictures or original art showing what your life will be at that stage. Describe two goals you will have had to achieve.
3. Present your "windows of life" to the class. Identify which phase of life will be your favorite. Dress up as if you were actually in that particular phase of life.

Time
two 50-minute periods

Materials
newsprint, magazines, colored markers, masking tape, glue

Self-Assessment

✓ Listed at least two goals related to the achievements suggested.
✓ Provided meaningful reasons for the choices made.

Activity 2 — True Love Songs

The songs you hear on the radio do not always depict an accurate or positive view of love and marriage. Compose your own "true love" song describing a healthy, lifelong relationship.

Directions

1. Think about characteristics you would like in a future spouse. What words would describe the kind of marriage you hope to have?
2. Express these ideals in a "true love" song. Create at least three verses and a refrain. Use music from an existing song, or compose your own melody.
3. Read or sing your song for the class. Afterward, lead them in a discussion of the kinds of qualities you would look for in a mate. Ask whether class members feel these qualities were communicated in your song.

Time
50 minutes

Materials
paper, pen or pencil

Self-Assessment

✓ Identified characteristics and values that contribute to a healthful long-term relationship.
✓ Effectively communicated those ideals in song or verse.

ASSESSMENT SCORING

Using a four-level rubric, the student has achieved a 4 if:

ACTIVITY 1
✔ Student listed at least two goals related to future achievements.
✔ Student provided meaningful reasons for the choices made.
✔ Student created a colorful poster that captured his or her life goals.
✔ Student presented poster in a coherent manner, speaking clearly.

ACTIVITY 2
✔ Student discussed intelligently the effect of conventional love songs.
✔ Student identified characteristics and values that contribute to a healthful relationship.
✔ Student effectively communicated ideals in song or verse.
✔ Student shared or listened attentively to songs being sung by classmates.

Living Longer and Better!

"I was 16 and working summers as an orderly in a nursing home. I was seeing older adults in really bad conditions. Even at my age then, I could tell that half of them didn't even need to be there."

Still in his teens, Thomas Perls, M.D., M.P.H., was discovering what would become a career concentration. He and his research team are studying centenarians—people who live to be 100. They hope to discover the genetic reasons for their striking longevity.

Dr. Perls calls the goal of his studies the exploration of "an ideal genome." A genome is the total genetic makeup of one organism. Every person has a unique genome. Dr. Perls' study suggests that centenarians may share a genetic makeup in which most age-related illnesses are postponed or deflected.

Perls hopes that his research will "debunk the myth that the older you get, the sicker you get. Instead, the older get, the healthier you've been–that's what we're seeing with the centenarians. To live to older ages, you can't have been sick for a period of time. You have to age slowly or escape these age-related diseases.

"I'd like to think we can go on to discover some disease-resistance genes, understand how they work and find the biochemical pathways they affect. These discoveries could lead to drugs that could make people more like centenarians."

He and study co-authors Lou M. Kunkel, Ph.D. and Annibale A. Puca, M.D., believe they now can proceed to locate the precise genes responsible for such longevity—that is, for the delay or deflection of age-related diseases. The search is on.

Think About It

1. How did Dr. Perls' experiences as a teenager contribute to his profession and field of study?

2. What does Dr. Perls mean when he says, "The older you get, the healthier you've been"?

MORE ABOUT . . . . .

RELIABLE SOURCES. Dr. Perls is a geriatrician based at Beth Israel Deaconess and an assistant professor of medicine at Harvard Medical School. His New England Centenarian Study has served as a key hub of the research. Dr. Perls' book, written with Margery Hutter Silver, Ed.D., and John F. Lauerman, a writer in the Boston area – is titled: *Living to 100: Lessons in Living to Your Maximum Potential at Any Age*.

Perls' research was conducted at Beth Israel Deaconess Medical Center, Children's Hospital Boston, and other institutions.

CNN HEALTH NEWS

Living Longer and Better!

Objectives. After reading the article, students should be able to recognize the roles heredity and lifestyle choices play in leading a long and healthy life.

Motivator. Ask: What do you think all 100-year-olds have in common? Have students identify habits and traits that might help people live to be 100, such as a healthy diet, safe exercise, and effective stress management. Then have students read "Living Longer and Better!" to discover how scientists might learn from studying centenarians.

Teach

- Write the word *centenarian* on the chalkboard. Have students define the word (people who live to be 100) and identify the word part that means 100 in Latin (*cent*, as in century or one hundred *cents* in a dollar.)

- Have students discuss whether they believe that hereditary or health choices have a greater impact on aging. Emphasize that a genetic predisposition to health is not a guarantee of good health. Everyone needs to make healthy choices, even those people that might possess the "ideal genome" Dr. Perls hopes to identify.

- Have students suggest other "healthy populations" that researchers might focus on to learn more about how people stay healthy.

Role Play. Have students create a list of questions for an interview with a centenarian. Their list should include both questions that would interest an audience comprised of their classmates and questions that would intrigue a scientist like Dr. Perls. Encourage them to role-play interviews between students and centenarians. Suggest that viewers record interesting or insightful exchanges to compile fictional interviews based on these classroom improvisations.

Close. Have students explain Dr. Perls' research to someone who has not read the article. Discuss what facts and information should be mentioned.

CHECKING COMPREHENSION

- Assign and discuss the chapter review.
- Use the MindJogger Videoquiz to review the chapter. 🔴

CHAPTER 22 REVIEW ANSWERS

Using Health Terms

1. physical maturity
2. emotional maturity
3. emotional intimacy
4. self-directed
5. planned pregnancy
6. marital adjustment
7. commitment
8. integrity
9. generativity
10. empty-nest syndrome
11. transitions
12. menopause

RECALLING THE FACTS

1. Any three: defining one's occupational role, individual identity and personal independence, intimate relationships, and place in society.
2. Because it comes with experiencing relationships and situations throughout adulthood.
3. Choices regarding community involvement require a definition of oneself in relationship to the community. In making those choices, one defines one's place in society.
4. Answers may include loneliness, wanting to escape a bad situation at home, pregnancy, and financial security.
5. Because they can no longer relate to their peers in social situations in the same way they did before becoming half of a married couple.
6. Answers may include differences in spending and saving habits, conflicting loyalties involving friends and families, intimacy or sexual problems, jealousy, infidelity, lack of

Using Health Terms

On a separate sheet of paper, write the term that best matches each definition below.

LESSON 1

1. State at which the physical body and all its organs are fully developed.
2. State at which the mental and emotional capabilities of an individual are fully developed.
3. Ability to experience a caring, loving relationship with another person with whom you can share your innermost feelings.

LESSON 2

4. Making correct decisions about behavior when adults are not there to enforce rules.
5. Making a decision to get pregnant before the baby is conceived.

6. How well people adjust and adapt to marriage and to each other.
7. A promise or a pledge.

LESSON 3

8. A feeling of wholeness and contentment.
9. A shift of attention away from oneself in the present to concerns for future generations.
10. Feelings of despair or loneliness that accompany children's leaving home and entering adulthood.
11. Critical changes that occur at all stages of life.
12. The stopping of ovulation and menstruation.

Recalling the Facts

Using complete sentences, answer the following questions.

LESSON 1

1. Name three developmental tasks of adulthood.
2. Why does emotional maturity take longer to achieve than physical maturity?
3. How does becoming involved in community help adults find their place in society?

LESSON 2

4. Name several unsound reasons for getting married.
5. Why do married teens often feel like social outcasts?
6. What kinds of conflicts do married couples often face?

7. In what way is the ability to resolve conflicts necessary to establishing and maintaining a solid marriage?
8. Name several considerations a couple may make before deciding to have a child.
9. Name several guidelines for disciplining children.
10. How can parents show their children that they are loved?
11. What values should parents teach their children?

LESSON 3

12. What transitions do older adults face?
13. Why do some middle-aged adults experience a midlife crisis?
14. Describe an adult who has successfully completed the stage of integrity.

attention, housework, decisions about having children and child care.
7. Because disagreements are inevitable in any long-term relationship.
8. The stability of their relationship and finances, where they are in their careers, and their own ability to nurture a child.
9. Answers may include quick action so that children understand the link between misbehavior and

consequences, consistency so that children know that certain behaviors will bring certain consequences, distinguishing between the behavior and the child so that children think of themselves as people who sometimes do bad things rather than as bad people, and praising positive behavior.
10. By expressing delight in their children and their existence whenever

Thinking Critically

LESSON 1

1. **Comparing and Contrasting.** Make a chart in which you compare adolescence with young adulthood in the areas of relationships, jobs, and place in society.

LESSON 2

2. **Analyzing.** Is "getting out of the house" a valid reason for teens to get married? Explain your answer.

3. **Comparing and Contrasting.** At one time, marriages were arranged by the parents. Using information in this lesson, determine what might be some advantages and disadvantages of arranged marriages.

LESSON 3

4. **Evaluating.** What advice would you give someone who is suffering from empty-nest syndrome? What advice would you give someone experiencing the cluttered-nest syndrome?

5. **Analyzing.** Taking into account some of the ways your body changes as you approach old age, tell what you can be doing now to help slow down your body's aging process.

6. **Synthesizing.** Explain what needs individuals from all age groups share.

Making the Connection

1. **Social Studies.** Many famous artists, including Michelangelo, Pablo Picasso, and Georgia O'Keeffe lived to an old age. Choose an artist to research, and write an essay explaining how the person's passion for art may have led to a longer life. Then explain a passion you have or wish to develop through the years.

2. **Math.** Estimate the cost of taking care of an infant or toddler for a year. Figure out costs for food, clothing, and medical care. Include purchases of such items as a crib, car seat, and high chair. Remember to include diapers, which cost about $25 a week, and child care, which averages about $100 per week.

BEYOND THE CLASSROOM

PARENTAL INVOLVEMENT Ask your parents to draw from their own experiences to give you some advice about marriage. Ask them what they have learned about marriage over the years and what, if anything, they would do differently. Comment about their answers in your private Health Journal.

COMMUNITY INVOLVEMENT Visit a senior citizen center in your community and meet some of the older adults who use the center. Find out about the various programs they offer for older adults. If possible, become a volunteer at the center.

SCHOOL-TO-CAREER
Interpersonal. Visit a child-care center to observe the skills needed to be a child-care assistant. Also interview the workers to find out what skills they think are necessary for working with young children. Make a list in your private Health Journal of the interpersonal abilities you would need to pursue a career in this area.

Thinking Critically

1.–6. Answers will vary.

Making the Connection

1.–2. Answers will vary.

Evaluate

- Use the reproducible *Chapter 22 Test* in the TCR, or construct your own using the Testmaker software. ▱ 🖫
- Use *Performance Assessment Activity 22* in the TCR. ▱

Enrichment

Ask students to complete *Cross-Curriculum Activity 22* in the TCR. ▱

Beyond the Classroom

Keep students involved in the community, and encourage parent participation by assigning the activities on this page for students to work on outside of class.

possible, by praising them for their efforts, by giving them encouragement, and by giving their time.

11. Answers will vary.

12. The transition out of the work force as well as decreased body functions and deterioration of body structures.

13. Because they haven't recognized and dealt with the changes within themselves at this stage of their lives.

14. The adult looks back on life with contentment and no regrets, has maintained intimate relationships and commitments to causes, and can enjoy the time remaining and accept the approach of death.

Understanding Medicines

	FEATURES	CLASSROOM RESOURCES

ACTIVITIES

- Cross-Curriculum Activity 23
- Health Lab 23
- Health Skills Activities 23
- Parent Letter and Activities 23

ASSESSMENT

- Chapter 23 Test
- Performance Assessment Activity 23
- Testmaker Software

STUDENT ACTIVITIES WORKBOOK

- Applying Health Skills 69, 70
- Study Guide 23
- Vocabulary Activity 23

STUDENT DIVERSITY STRATEGIES

- Audiocassette Program (English)
- Audiocassette Program (Spanish)
- Spanish Parent Letters and Activities
- Spanish Summaries, Quizzes, and Activities

MULTIMEDIA COMPONENTS

- English Audiocassette Program
- Spanish Audiocassette Program
- MindJogger Videodisc and VHS program

MODULES

- *The Reality of Drugs,* Student Edition
- *The Reality of Drugs,* Teacher's Annotated Edition

National Health Education Standards

One of the main goals of the National Health Education Standards is to move students toward "health literacy." Health literacy is the capacity of individuals to obtain, interpret, and understand basic health information and services and the competence to use such information and services in ways which promote health. The health standards were developed by applying the characteristics of a well-educated, literate person within the context of health. The health literate person is:

- a critical thinker and problem solver
- a self-directed learner
- a responsible, productive citizen
- an effective communicator

Listed below are the Health Education Standards Performance Indicators addressed in each lesson of this chapter.

Lesson	Health Standards Performance Indicators
1	1.8, 2.6, 3.1, 3.6
2	2.6, 3.1, 3.5, 6.1

ONLINE RESOURCES

For a fresh approach to health topics and an in-depth look at health issues, use these online resources found under Teacher Resources at **health.glencoe.com**.

- **BLOCK SCHEDULE LESSON PLANS** Reinforce health concepts with outside readings selected especially for students. Each reading is accompanied by a lesson plan and activities to enhance
  - Reading Skills
  - Cross Curriculum
  - Media Literacy

- **TECHNOLOGY PROJECTS** Instructions and suggestions on how to use computer, Internet, and software with health lessons.

- **HEALTH UPDATES** Timely topics in health news, including late-breaking medical advances and updates on teen risk behaviors.

Out of Time?

If time does not permit teaching this chapter, you may use these features: Update on page 514; Building Health Skills on page 516; and Making Responsible Decisions on page 520.

BLOCK SCHEDULING

Block scheduling provides extended time for hands-on projects and activities. Use the following activities to engage students, provide further depth, and vary your instructional techniques:

- Update (30 minutes)   **pg. 514**
- Health Skills Activity (60–90 minutes)   **pg. 522**

Understanding Medicines

CHAPTER OVERVIEW

Chapter 23 details the types of medicines, explaining their appropriate usage and possible side effects. It also examines the issue of medicine safety.

LESSON 1 Medicines are generally grouped according to their effect on the body. Commonly, they are used to prevent disease, fight pathogens, relieve pain, and regulate heart function and blood pressure. The effect of medicines on the body depends upon the type of medicine and each person's body chemistry. Individual differences in body chemistry sometimes cause side effects. Medicine interaction can result in synergistic, antagonistic, or additive effects. Drug tolerance and withdrawal are two major problems associated with medicine usage.

LESSON 2 The Food and Drug Administration has established a system to protect the consumer from medicines that are ineffective or harmful. All medicines in the U.S. must meet FDA standards before being approved and made available to the public. Over-the-counter and prescription medicines should be used as directed to reduce risks associated with medicine usage. Other precautions should be taken to prevent the misuse of medicines in the home.

Understanding Medicines

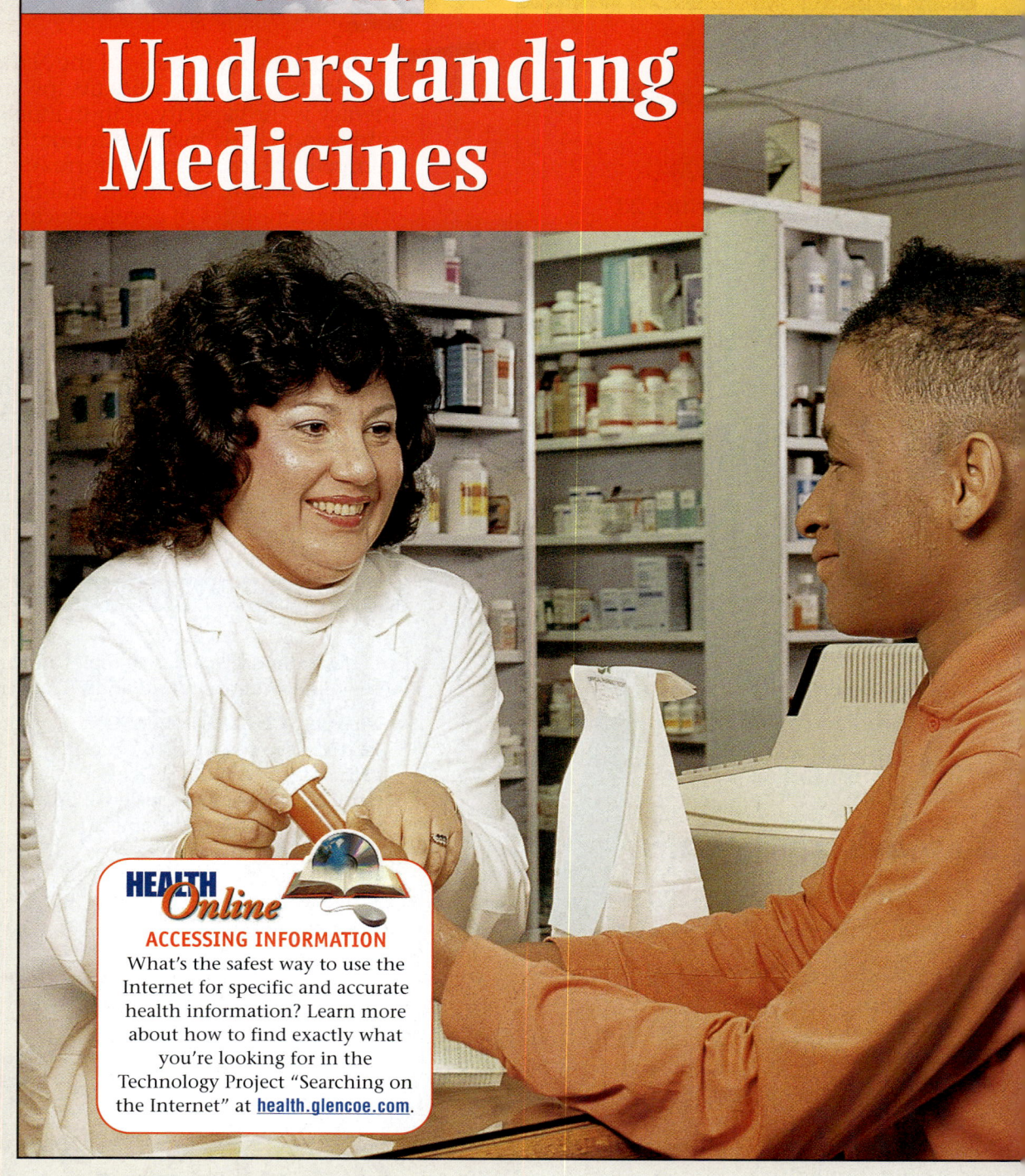

HEALTH Online

ACCESSING INFORMATION
What's the safest way to use the Internet for specific and accurate health information? Learn more about how to find exactly what you're looking for in the Technology Project "Searching on the Internet" at **health.glencoe.com**.

Hands-On Health

TEACHING STRATEGY

Reinforcing and Reviewing Bring your health classroom to life with interactive teaching strategies and classroom management techniques that keep your students interested and involved. The unique *Hands-On Health: Creative Teaching Strategies* booklet that accompanies the *Glencoe Health* program offers fun, motivating activities.

The following Classroom Management Ideas can be used to reinforce chapter concepts:

- Beach Ball
- Trivia Questions
- Paper Exchange
- Mental Outburst

Personal Health Inventory

Self-Inventory Write the numbers 1–10 on a sheet of paper. Read each statement below and respond by writing *yes*, *no*, or *sometimes* for each item. Write a *yes* only for items that you practice regularly. Save your responses.

1	I use over-the-counter medicines only when necessary.
2	I use only one kind of medicine at a time, unless otherwise instructed by my physician.
3	I take prescription medicine only with my physician's advice.
4	I ask my physician for information before using prescriptions.
5	If I am not sure about a medicine, I ask my parent, physician, or pharmacist.
6	I read all the enclosed information and follow the directions carefully when taking medicines.
7	I never take someone else's prescription medicines.
8	I keep myself informed about types of medicines, their effects on the body, and their proper use.
9	I alert my parents or physician immediately if side effects occur.
10	I do not take over-the-counter medicines for an extended period without my physician's knowledge.

Follow-up After completing the chapter, retake this self-inventory. Pick two items that you need to work on and set a goal to improve your health behaviors.

> ## " It takes a wise doctor to know when not to prescribe. "
>
> —BALTASAR GRACIÁN
> SPANISH JESUIT SCHOLAR, (1601–1658)

Quick Write Imagine talking to an elementary school student about the proper use of medicines. Write down five guidelines that you would give to the youth.

TECHNOLOGY OPTIONS

MINDJOGGER
VIDEOQUIZ

To preview or review chapter content, you may wish to use the *MindJogger Videoquiz* that accompanies Chapter 23.

INTRODUCING THE CHAPTER

Personal Health Inventory

Let students read the statements in the Self-Inventory and discuss them in general terms. How do these behaviors relate to your physical health? your social health? your mental/emotional health? Remind students of the importance of responding honestly to these statements; assure them that their inventories are confidential. Then have students write their Self-Inventory responses in their private Health Journals on a page labeled "Understanding Medicines."

- Ask students to define the term *drugs* in their own words. You should get a variety of definitions, most of which will relate to drugs as illegal substances. Explain that the term's meaning changed as a result of the problems illegal drugs have caused in our society. Tell them that in this chapter, they will study the benefits and risks of medicines that are available. The effects of illegal drugs will be discussed in Chapter 26.
- Have students read the quotation from the 1600s. Ask: In what scientific or medical context was this statement probably made? What do the photos suggest about modern medicines? Once, medicines were naturally occurring substances. Today, most medicines are produced artificially in laboratories. After a brief discussion, tell students that they will learn more about medicines as they study the lessons in Chapter 23.
- Distribute Parent Letter 23 in the *Parent Letters and Activities* booklet.

The Role of Medicines

LESSON OBJECTIVES

After studying this lesson, students should be able to

- explain how medicines are grouped.
- describe different reactions when two or more medicines are taken into the body at one time.
- explain indicators of physiological dependence.

MOTIVATOR

Write the following on the chalkboard for students to work on while attendance is being taken: *Define medicine and name three medicines with which you are familiar. Next to each, write what the medicine is used for.*

INTRODUCING THE LESSON

Make four columns on the chalkboard. Label each column with one of the following: *Prevent Disease, Fight Pathogens, Relieve Pain,* and *Treat Cardiovascular Disease.* Have volunteers read one of their responses from the Motivator. As they read what the medicine is used for, note the responses on the chalkboard in the appropriate column. Explain that this lesson will discuss the types of medicines.

INTRODUCING HEALTH TERMS

- Have students investigate common usage of the terms *medicines* and *drugs.*
- Ask students to complete Vocabulary Activity 23 and Chapter Study Guide 23 in the *Student Workbook.* ☞

The Role of Medicines

Sometimes, even the healthiest person becomes sick. A person may sustain a painful injury while playing sports or may develop a chest cold accompanied by a hacking cough. To help overcome these ailments, some people turn to medicines. **Medicines** are *substances that, when taken internally or applied to the body, help prevent or cure a disease or other medical problem.*

HEALTH TERMS

medicines
vaccine
analgesics
side effects
additive interaction
synergistic effect
antagonistic interaction
tolerance
withdrawal

HEALTH CONCEPTS

- A medicine helps prevent or cure a disease or medical problem.
- Medicines are classified according to their effect on the body.
- Safe and healthful use of medicines includes knowing how different substances behave when present in the body at the same time.

Classification of Medicines

Although there are countless medicines that treat a wide range of health problems, all may be classified into four broad categories—medicines that

- prevent disease,
- fight pathogens (microorganisms that enter the body and attack its cells and tissues),
- relieve pain,
- help the heart and regulate blood pressure.

Lesson 1 Resources

TEACHER'S CLASSROOM RESOURCES

☞ **Concept Map** Activity 69
☞ **Enrichment** Activity 23
☞ **Health Lab** 23
☞ **Lesson 69 Quiz**
☞ **Lesson Plan 69**
☞ **Parent Letter and Activities** 23
☞ **Reteaching** Activity 69

STUDENT WORKBOOK

☞ **Applying Health Skills** 69
☞ **Chapter Study Guide** 23
☞ **Vocabulary** Activity 23

Medicines That Prevent Disease

The first line of defense in modern medicine is to prevent diseases before they ever occur in an individual. There are two main types of preventive medicines:

■ **Vaccines.** Your **immunization** schedule shows a record of what shots or vaccines you were given as an infant, child, and teen. A **vaccine** is *a preparation, containing weakened or dead pathogens that cause a particular disease, given to prevent one from contracting that disease.* Vaccines stimulate your body to produce specific antibodies against those pathogens. Once the antibodies are produced, they give your body long-lasting protection against these specific pathogens, should these enter your body in the future. Current vaccine research is geared toward developing a safer, less painful vaccine against **rabies** and vaccines against hepatitis B and pneumonia-causing bacteria. A major effort, as noted in Chapter 30, is being conducted toward isolating a vaccine to combat **HIV**.

■ **Antitoxins.** Antitoxins are extracts of blood fluids that contain antibodies and act more quickly than vaccines. Antitoxins are produced by inoculating animals—such as horses, sheep, or rabbits—with specific toxins that stimulate the animal's immune system to produce antibodies against the toxins. When antitoxins are injected into a human being, they neutralize the effect of toxins, such as those that cause tetanus and diphtheria.

Medicines That Fight Pathogens

Virtually unknown before the twentieth century, antibiotics are a class of chemical agents that destroy disease-causing microorganisms while leaving the patient unharmed. The best known and earliest antibiotic—penicillin—was discovered by accident in 1928 by the British scientist Sir Alexander Fleming. Depending on the type of medicine and the dosage, antibiotics either kill harmful bacteria in the body or prevent them from reproducing. Each antibiotic has a different chemical composition and is effective against a particular range of bacteria, though none is effective against viral infections.

hotlink

immunization For more on immunization and its role in disease prevention, see Chapter 28, page 633.

rabies For more information on rabies and actions to take when someone is bitten by a suspected rabid animal, see Chapter 35, page 786.

HIV For more information on HIV and ways of reducing the risk of infection, see Chapter 30, page 656.

◀ *Immunization against once common diseases such as measles and tetanus has made instances of these diseases rare.*

ACTIVITY *Explain why it is important to adhere to the immunization schedule your physician has set for you.*

TEACH

L1 Discussing

Ask students if they have ever received medicines by injection. Ask them if they ever took prescription medicine by mouth. Discuss the reasons that some medicines are given by injection and some by mouth.

L1 Discussing

Explain to students that some medicines may have to be administered for long periods—sometimes even for the rest of the patient's life. Ask students who take insulin, medicine for asthma, or allergy medicine to volunteer to share information with the class about their therapeutic routines.

L2 Parental Involvement

Have students interview their parents and ask about any childhood diseases the parents survived or were vaccinated against that were deadly a century ago. Ask students to look at their own vaccination records to see the ages at which vaccinations were given and discuss their reactions, if any, to them. Have students write about their findings in a one-page paper.

L2 Researching

Ask students to poll three people about the first thought that comes to their minds when they hear the word *drug*. How many of the responses refer to medicines? How many refer to illegal drugs? Have students share their findings and discuss what these responses suggest about our society.

L1 Discussing

Ask students to describe the most positive aspect of medicines in our society, as compared with the most negative aspect.

SCHOOL-TO-CAREER

EMPLOYER-PROVIDED VACCINES. Some employers provide workers with free or low-cost immunizations against influenza and other diseases. Have students find out which companies in the area offer influenza immunizations free or at low cost to workers. Encourage them as well to find out what other immunizations might be provided free in the workplace. Suggest that they contact the company which contracts with employers who administer the injections, and obtain a copy of the release form workers sign when they receive a vaccine. Have them compare any warnings of adverse effects on the form with the adverse effects listed in the *Physicians' Desk Reference.* Do the warnings adequately inform the person receiving the immunization?

up|date
▶ *Our Changing World*

Medical Treatment for Biological Threats

Before students begin reading the feature, encourage them to share what they already know about bioterrorism and anthrax: What is bioterrorism? What is anthrax? Can anthrax be treated? Is a cure or vaccine available? Discuss any other contagions that pose a threat, such as smallpox. Then direct students to read the feature about medical treatment for biological threats.

Have students meet in groups to share and compare their responses to the first question. For the second activity, researching new developments, suggest that students share their findings in oral reports.

L2 Researching

Have groups of students work together to find out about the development of new antibiotics and how they are being used to fight disease.

L1 Writing

Ask students to clip newspaper articles relating to the use of medicines. Have students design their own newsletter on the use of medicines to explain how the use of these medicines relates to wellness.

In recent years, strains of bacteria have emerged that are resistant to penicillin and other commonly prescribed antibiotics. This resistance occurs when a bacterial strain undergoes a change in genetic structure as a result of overexposure to an antibiotic, making the bacterium essentially "immune" to the medicine. This development has prompted a new generation of antibiotics, including cephalosporins (sef-uh-luh-SPOHR-unz)—broad-spectrum antibiotics that kill a wide variety of bacteria, including penicillin-resistant strains.

Originally derived from molds and fungi, antibiotics today are largely made synthetically, in laboratories. This has blurred somewhat the distinction between antibiotics and a second class of antibacterial medicines that was always derived through synthetic means. This class includes the sulfa family, still used to treat some urinary tract infections, and the quinolones, still used to some extent to combat hospital-derived infections.

▼ *In one acre of rain forest there can be more than 250 species of trees and 20,000 different kinds of insects.*

ACTIVITY *Explain how this biodiversity can be important in the search for new medicines.*

up|date
▶ *Our Changing World*

Medical Treatment for Biological Threats

In recent years, the United States has been faced with increasing concern over the threat of bioterrorism. In this type of warfare, terrorists use biological agents, such as anthrax, as weapons. Anthrax is an infection caused by a type of bacteria called Bacillus anthracis. With bioterrorism, anthrax or other biological agents may be used to intentionally spread disease.

Although the potential for bioterrorism does exist, there is little cause for panic. Anthrax and other diseases can be prevented or successfully treated with common antibiotics, including penicillin and ciprofloxacin. In some cases, vaccines are available to prevent infection. Most often, however, these vaccines are given only to military personnel who may be more likely to encounter biological agents.

1. How might public panic over bioterrorism negatively affect the availability of medical treatment for bacterial infections?

2. Research new developments in the search for more effective antibiotics.

514 CHAPTER 23   UNDERSTANDING MEDICINES

COOPERATIVE ▶ LEARNING

ACTIVITY. Resistance to antibiotics has become a medical problem of crisis proportions. Have students work in groups to conduct research about the topic of antibiotic resistance. Then have them research use of antibiotics that could be reduced or eliminated. For example, tell them to investigate findings that most ear infections in children will clear up without antibiotics. Suggest that they explore questions such as these: Do patients pressure their doctors to prescribe antibiotics? Do doctors prescribe antibiotics without knowing if the condition requires them or will respond to them? Should prophylactic use of antibiotics in livestock feed be discontinued? Have students hold a panel discussion about antibiotic resistance and possible antibiotic abuse, discussing the problems and proposed solutions.

Cardiovascular Medicines

There are five main kinds of medicines that help the heart and regulate blood pressure:

- Beta blockers block the action of nerves that constrict blood vessels. This helps slow heartbeat and lower blood pressure.
- Diuretics (dy-uh-RET-iks) increase urine production to reduce the amount of water and sodium in a person's body. Removing water from the blood vessels helps reduce blood fluid volume. This is especially important after heart failure.
- Vasodilators (VAH-zo-DY-layt-uhr) dilate the veins and arteries to increase blood and oxygen flow.
- Antiarrhythmics (AN-tee-uh-RITH-miks) are used to treat arrhythmia—any disturbance in the rhythm of the heart.
- Clot-dissolving medicines lower high blood pressure and help prevent blood clots.

Medicines That Relieve Pain

"What do you take for a headache?" This advertising slogan has been answered again and again over the years as researchers look for new *pain relievers,* or **analgesics.** This class of medicines ranges from narcotics, such as the opium derivatives morphine and codeine, to comparatively mild medicines such as aspirin.

Aspirin is by far the most widely used non-prescription analgesic medicine in the United States. In common use since 1899, aspirin contains a chemical, acetylsalicylic (uh-SEE-tuh-sal-uh-SIL-ik) acid, that relieves pain and reduces fever. One of the most effective anti-inflammatory medicines, aspirin is widely used in treating arthritis. Because of its widespread use, many people do not realize that aspirin can be dangerous. Even small amounts can irritate the stomach, especially when empty. Aspirin can interfere with blood clotting, and large doses can cause dizziness and ringing in the ears. Children who take aspirin are at risk of developing Reye's syndrome, a potentially life-threatening illness of the brain and liver. Aspirin, therefore, should not be given to children when illness with fever is present and undiagnosed.

Some people who are sensitive to aspirin take acetaminophen or ibuprofen instead. Like aspirin, both these substances serve as analgesics. Ibuprofen is an anti-inflammatory agent, but acetaminophen is not.

keeping Fit

Antibiotics: Serious Medicine

If you or someone you know is taking an antibiotic to combat a bacterial infection, it is important to:

➤ *Avoid skipping a dose.* Doing so may cause antibiotic-resistant bacteria to develop.

➤ *Finish the entire supply prescribed.* Do not stop taking the medicine even if you are feeling better.

➤ *Familiarize yourself with the do's and don'ts.* The label will tell you whether to take the medicine with food or on an empty stomach, and which foods to avoid while on the medication.

⚑ *Medicines are available in a variety of forms to prevent diseases, fight pathogens, and relieve pain.*

ACTIVITY *Name two important considerations when choosing a pain relief medication.*

L1 Class Activity

Bring different brands of aspirin or an aspirin substitute to class. Show students how the brands may differ in shape and size yet have the same potency. Explain why the dosages of medicines vary for infants, adults, and the elderly. Show bottles for infants and children. Compare them with the adult doses. Have students look for other differences in the brands. Include labels from other pain relievers that contain aspirin and caffeine.

LD Explaining

LD students may have difficulty with the names and functions of specific medicines. It is recommended that they not be tested on this information.

Antibiotics: Serious Medicine

keeping Fit

Review with students the precautions for taking antibiotics. Explain that a specific dosage is prescribed based on the strain of bacteria being treated and the antibiotic chosen for treatment.

L2 Health Lab

Distribute *Health Lab 23* and have students investigate relieving headaches without medication. ☞

PERSONAL HEALTH

PERSONAL PDR. Side effects, interactions, and contraindications may not be listed on prescription bottles or on over-the-counter drugs. Pharmacists may include information sheets with side effects, physiological action, contraindications, and interactions. Doctors may not anticipate other substances and medications which patients take while on prescription medication. Patients should report the use of other substances to the doctor. Even some foods and beverages react adversely with some medicines. In most but not all cases, such foods or beverages contain alcohol or caffeine. Have students examine simplified versions of the *Physicians' Desk Reference* in the library or bookstore. Have them write reviews of at least three books and recommend one for home use.

L2 Guest Speaker

Ask a doctor or nurse to visit the class and talk about the possible side effects of medicines and medicines taken in combination. Relate the dangers of self-medicating to possible misuse of medicines. Discuss the most common mistakes individuals make in buying and using medicines.

L1 Discussing

Have students discuss why medicines affect each person differently. Ask: Which group of medicines in this lesson causes physiological (and psychological) dependence. *(Those that relieve pain.)*

Building Health Skills

Using Medicines Safely
Skill: Health Literacy

Present the following situation and ask how students would respond: You are at a classmate's house studying when you develop a painful headache. Your classmate produces an unmarked capsule—you don't see any container—and says, "We always take these for headaches. They work wonders." After students have shared their ideas, explain that there are many safety considerations to be taken into account in using medicines. Let students read the Building Health Skills feature to learn about some specific guidelines for using medicines safely.

L2 Explaining

Explain the potentially deadly effects of mixing alcohol with medicines.

Medicines and the Body

Medicines can have different effects on or cause different reactions in different people. A person's reaction to a given medicine depends on how the medicine mixes with the chemicals in his or her body. Most medicines cause some **side effects**—*reactions to medicine other than the one intended.* It is important to be aware of your reactions to medicines and report these to your physician.

When two different medicines are taken together or when a medicine is taken in combination with certain foods, the combination may produce effects different from those produced when the medicine is taken alone. In many cases, interactions are beneficial. Physicians often make use of interactions to increase the effectiveness of a treatment. Other interactions, however, are unwanted and may be harmful.

- **Additive interaction** occurs when *medicines work together in a positive way.* For example, both an anti-inflammatory and a muscle relaxant may be prescribed to treat someone with joint pain.

- **Synergistic effect** is *the interaction of two or more medicines that results in a greater effect than when the medicines are taken*

Building Health Skills

Being Health-Literate: Using Medicines Safely

CERTAIN PRECAUTIONS should be taken with all medicines. Keep in mind the following guidelines for safe use of medicines:

1. **Ask questions.** Ask your physician or pharmacist about any possible side effects or precautions to take when using a medicine. Before taking two or more medicines at the same time, ask whether they can be taken together safely. Do not take *any* medicine that contains aspirin if you are allergic to aspirin or have ulcers or a bleeding problem.

2. **Read the label.** The label on the container in which the medicine is packaged will tell you how much medicine to take and when and how to take it. Check the expiration date on medicines and discard any that have passed this date.

3. **Practice safety.** Make sure a medicine is used only by the person for whom it is prescribed. Keep medicines out of the reach of children. If anyone, particularly a child, takes a large dose, get medical help immediately.

4. **Become a partner in your health care.** As a health-literate person, it is your responsibility not to use any medicine for an extended period of time without medical supervision. If symptoms persist or unexpected symptoms develop, see your physician right away.

516 CHAPTER 23 UNDERSTANDING MEDICINES

PROMOTING COMPREHENSIVE SCHOOL HEALTH

THE COST OF PREVENTION. Many believe that a person's lifestyle cannot be influenced by schools and social agencies. Still others believe that schools cannot afford the costs of problems stemming from low self-esteem, school dropout rate, sexually transmitted diseases and teen pregnancy, health costs associated with poor prenatal care, drug abuse, ineffective parenting practices, malnutrition, and poor mental health.

Most schools recognize that it costs a great deal more to fix problems than to prevent them. Consequently, a comprehensive school health program takes into account the human costs suffered by those who do poorly academically, socially, and economically. For more information, consult *Promoting a Comprehensive School Health Program* in the TCR.

independently. It occurs when one medicine increases the strength of the other. For example, one medicine may speed the rate at which the stomach empties and thereby increase the rate at which another medicine is absorbed and takes effect.

■ **Antagonistic interaction** occurs when *the effect of a medicine is canceled or reduced when taken with another medicine.* For example, someone who receives an organ transplant must take anti-rejection medicines. If this person is diabetic and takes insulin, the effectiveness of the insulin may be decreased.

Other Problems

Sometimes people develop a dependence on a particular medicine. Physiological dependence is a chemical need for a medicine. Physiological dependence is determined when a person experiences tolerance and withdrawal.

■ **Tolerance** is *a condition in which the body becomes used to the effect of a medicine.* The body then requires increasingly larger doses of the medicine to produce the same effect. In the case of some substances and individuals' chemical makeups, a person will experience "reverse tolerance." In this condition, less of the substance is required to be effective.

■ **Withdrawal** is *the process that occurs when a person stops using a medicine or other substance to which he or she has a physiological dependence.* Withdrawal symptoms include nervousness, insomnia, severe nausea, headaches, vomiting, chills, and cramps. Symptoms gradually ease after a period of time off the medicine. Withdrawal from certain medicines may require medical attention.

LESSON 1 *Review*

Reviewing Facts and Vocabulary

1. Name two types of medicines that prevent disease, and tell how they work.
2. Define the term *antibiotic*.
3. Describe problems related to the use of aspirin.

Thinking Critically

4. **Comparing and Contrasting.** What is the difference between an additive interaction and an antagonistic interaction?
5. **Synthesizing.** Why might two people have different reactions to the same medicine?

Applying Health Skills

6. **In Your Home.** If a member of your family is taking one or more medicines for a health problem, ask the person to share information about the type of medicine, how the medicines interact if more than one is being taken, and how successful the medicine has been in treating the problem. Ask whether there have been any problems related to the medicine and, if so, how the problems were dealt with.

LESSON 1   THE ROLE OF MEDICINES   **517**

ASSESS

EVALUATING THE LESSON

Assign and discuss the Lesson 1 Review; then administer, grade, and discuss the *Lesson 69 Quiz* in the TCR.

RETEACHING

• Ask students to list the four major classifications of medicines presented in this lesson and to provide two examples of medicines in each. Have students explain the effects of medicines on the body.
• Ask students to complete *Reteaching Activity 69* in the TCR.

ENRICHMENT

Introduce students to the process of bringing new medicines from research to pharmacy by having them complete *Enrichment Activity 23,* "How Do We Get New Drugs?" in the TCR.

CLOSE

Have students list nonmedicine alternatives to treating symptoms of common physical complaints.

Lesson 1 Review

Answers to Reviewing Facts and Vocabulary

1. See page 513.
2. Antibiotics are a class of chemical agents that destroy disease-causing microorganisms while leaving the patient unharmed.
3. Aspirin can irritate the stomach, interfere with blood clotting, cause dizziness and ringing in the ears, and cause Reye's syndrome in children.

Answers to Thinking Critically

4. Additive interaction—when medicines work together in a positive way. Antagonistic interaction—when the effect of a medicine is canceled or reduced when taken with another medicine.
5. People react differently to a medication when their body chemistry is different.

LESSON OBJECTIVES

After studying this lesson, students should be able to

- describe the role of the Food and Drug Administration.
- explain the purpose of guidelines for distributors of medicines.

MOTIVATOR

Write the following on the chalkboard for students to work on while attendance is being taken: *Why is consumer protection needed in the area of medicines? List examples of consumer protection that are medicine-related.*

INTRODUCING THE LESSON

Refer to the Motivator. Ask volunteers to share their responses. Tell students they will learn more about consumer protection and medicines in this lesson.

INTRODUCING HEALTH TERMS

- Ask students to explain why a pharmacist is qualified to give us accurate information on medicine misuse. Have students list the most common ways medicine is misused.
- Ask students to complete Vocabulary Activity 23 and Chapter Study Guide 23 in the *Student Workbook.* ☞

LESSON 2

Using Medicines Wisely

Medicines can do a great deal of good. You may be familiar with some positive effects medicines can have. They can also cause harm if they are used unwisely. In this lesson, you will examine ways of getting the greatest benefit from medicines and minimizing risks in their use.

HEALTH TERMS

prescription medicines

over-the-counter (OTC) medicines

medicine misuse

HEALTH CONCEPTS

- Using medicines wisely includes learning how to read medicine labels and using medicines as prescribed or intended by the manufacturer.
- Medicine misuse is using medicine in a way other than that for which it was intended.

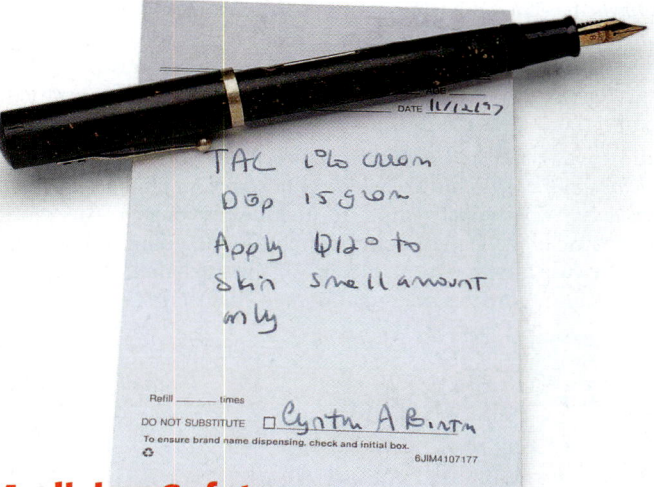

Medicine Safety

To minimize risks from medicines for the American public, the federal government has established a system for testing and approving new medicines. In the United States all medicines must meet standards set by the Food and Drug Administration (FDA) before being approved and made available to the public.

Testing and Approving New Medicines

The FDA requires a manufacturer of medicines to supply information about a medicine's chemical composition, intended use, effects, and possible side effects. Before a medicine is approved by the FDA, it undergoes a step-by-step testing process that can last from six to ten years. By federal law, a medicine must be both safe and medically

---

 Lesson 2 Resources

TEACHER'S CLASSROOM RESOURCES

☞ **Concept Map** Activity 70
☞ **Cooperative Learning** Activity 23
☞ **Decision-Making** Activity 23
☞ **Lesson 70 Quiz**
☞ **Lesson Plan 70**
☞ **Reteaching** Activity 70

STUDENT WORKBOOK

☞ **Applying Health Skills** 70
☞ **Chapter Study Guide** 23
☞ **Vocabulary** Activity 23

TRANSPARENCIES

🖐 **Transparency** 25

effective. Safety is usually established through tests. The effectiveness of a medicine is proved through tests on groups of healthy and ill patients.

Release to the Public

One function of the FDA is to determine how medicine should be released to the public. There are two ways in which this can be done:

- **Prescription medicines.** Because of their strength and potential for harm, the FDA has ruled that there are some *medicines that cannot be used safely without the written approval of a licensed physician.* These **prescription medicines** are available only by means of a doctor's written instructions to a pharmacist to give specific amounts of a certain medicine to a patient. Only a physician can prescribe such medicines, and only a licensed pharmacist can dispense them.

THE CONTROLLED SUBSTANCES ACT

The Comprehensive Drug Abuse Prevention and Control Act of 1970—commonly called the Controlled Substances Act—classifies medicines for use in the United States into five categories, or schedules, according to their use and potential for abuse.

SCHEDULE	USE OF MEDICINE
I	**Illegal and not prescribable** No current accepted medical use in United States Improper use may lead to severe physiological and psychological dependence
II	**Written prescription required** No prescription refills allowed Severe restrictions on medical use Improper use may lead to serious physiological and/or psychological dependence
III	**Written or oral prescription required** Refill up to five times in six months Has accepted medical uses Improper use may lead to moderate/low physiological and high psychological dependence
IV	**Written or oral prescription required** Refill up to five times in six months Has accepted medical uses Improper use may lead to limited physiological or psychological dependence
V	**OTC or by prescription depending on state law** Has accepted medical uses Improper use may lead to limited physiological or psychological dependence

▼ *When choosing OTC medicines, be certain to read and follow package directions.*

LESSON 2   USING MEDICINES WISELY   **519**

HOME AND COMMUNITY CONNECTION

MEDICATION OF SENIORS. During the 1990s, the media reported concerns of medical specialists that seniors tend to be overmedicated. Concerns included both the number and amounts of medicine seniors take, with different medications treating many separate conditions. Suggest that students research medication of seniors, particularly older seniors. Have them begin by asking what medications older family members take, then research on-line and library sources. Have them investigate causes for over-medication. Do seniors see different doctors for different body systems? Do their doctors fail to share information? Is the trend related to the insurance that covers most seniors? Have students summarize their findings in a pamphlet and share it with older family members or distribute them in places where seniors gather.

TEACH

L1 Discussing

Discuss tips for using medicines safely. Ask students why it is important not to share a prescription medicine. Why should medicines be destroyed after their expiration date? Why must medicines be kept away from small children?

L2 Explaining

Explain the marketing regulations of the FDA for prescription medicines.

L2 Discussing

Discuss alternatives other than taking antacids for dealing with indigestion.

L1 Discussing

Discuss reasons for the increased likelihood of heartburn during pregnancy. Why does this occur? How can it be prevented or alleviated? What must a pregnant woman consider before taking any medications?

L2 Class Activity

Have students write stories of dilemmas teens face regarding taking OTC medicines. Divide the class into groups and have them trade stories and develop ways to resolve these dilemmas. Share alternatives with the class as a group.

L2 Cooperative Learning

Assign *Cooperative Learning Activity 23*, "Over-The-Counter Cold Remedies," in the TCR.

L1 Discussing

Use *Transparency 25* to review reading medicine labels.

Chapter 23   **519**

Medicine Safety at Home

keeping Fit

Review the guide-lines in the feature. Discuss the curiosity that young children have and how these precautions could save a child's life.

L1 Parental Involvement

Ask each student to work with a parent to determine if medicines are safely located, secured, and orga-nized in their home. Have them check to see if any prescriptions have expired.

Making Responsible Decisions

1. Alicia is considering stopping her asthma medicine so she can play in an important field hockey game.
2. Alicia could (a) continue taking the medicine; (b) stop taking the medicine; (c) ask her doctor and/or coach for advice.
3. Alicia might (a) miss the game but protect her health; (b) play in the game but risk her health; (c) have responsible help in making a healthful decision.
4. Alicia values both her good phys-ical health and ability to con-tribute to the field hockey team.
5. Responses will vary.
6. Students should discuss both short- and long-term conse-quences of their decisions.

L2 Decision Making

For further study on making re-sponsible decisions, assign *Decision-Making Activity 23* in the TCR. ☞

keeping Fit

Medicine Safety at Home

All medicines can be dangerous if misused. These guidelines can help make the medicines in your home safer:

➤ Never place medicine in an un-labeled vial or other container. Keep it in the container in which it was originally packaged.

➤ Store medicines in a safe place out of the reach of children.

➤ If there is a child in the house, never disable or tamper with the child-resistant cap on a medicine container.

➤ Throw away any medicines that have passed their expiration date. Some medicines merely lose their effectiveness with age. Others can become dangerous.

■ **Over-the-counter (OTC) medicines. Over-the-counter (OTC) medicines** include a wide variety of *medicines you can buy without a doctor's prescription.* These medicines can be purchased in pharma-cies, supermarkets, and other stores that sell medicines. Although the FDA considers it safe to use these medicines without medical supervision, they still have the potential of being harmful if not used as directed.

Medicine Misuse

There are many controls—both federal and state—on medicines, but there are still risks and responsibilities when it comes to their use. **Medicine misuse** is *using a medicine in a way other than the one intended.* Examples of medicine misuse include:

■ giving your prescription medicine to someone else.
■ taking too much or too little of a medicine.
■ taking someone else's medicine.
■ discontinuing use of a medicine without informing one's doctor.
■ taking medicine for a longer period of time than was prescribed.
■ mixing medicines.

If you suspect that someone you know is guilty of medicine mis-use, urge that person to speak immediately with his or her health care professional or pharmacist. If the person refuses to seek help, discuss the situation with a responsible adult.

Making Responsible Decisions

Should I Quit This Medicine?

Alicia, who suffers with asthma, recently experienced a flare-up of the disease. Six days ago, her doctor prescribed a 10-day course of pred-nisone, a steroid medication, to reduce the inflammation in her lungs and help her breathe more easily.

The only problem is that Alicia, who plays for her school's field hockey team when healthy, knows that a big game is coming up in a few days and that her teammates are counting on her. Since her morning dose of medicine, she is feeling much better and is now thinking about not taking any more before the game. What do you think she should do?

What Would You Do?

Apply the six steps of the decision-making process to Alicia's problem.

1. **State the situation.**
2. **List the options.**
3. **Weigh the possible outcomes.**
4. **Consider your values.**
5. **Make a decision and act.**
6. **Evaluate the decision.**

520 CHAPTER 23 UNDERSTANDING MEDICINES

HEALTH LITERACY

SELF-DIRECTED LEARNER. Have students work individually or in groups to research medications that have been abused, specifically for their side effects. In particular, medications may be abused for mood-changing effects. For example, cold medication may be taken to induce sleep. Stimulants prescribed as diet pills may be used to get high or stay awake all night. Some medicines prescribed for respiratory congestion stimulate the central nervous system. For example, ephedrine, used for respiratory ailments, was added to thermogenic weight-loss formulas and herbal combinations to act as a mood elevator. Suggest that students find several types of drugs that are abused for their side effects. Have them complete a chart, showing the drugs' intended uses, the side effects leading to abuse, and the potential consequences of abuse.

Labeling

When the FDA approves a medicine, it is saying that the medicine is safe when used as directed. FDA approval also means that a medicine is effective in treating the illness or condition for which it was prescribed. The FDA requires manufacturers to include certain information on every prescription label, including the name of the prescribing doctor, patient's name, name and address of the pharmacy, date prescription was filled, prescription number, whether refills are allowed, and any special instructions. The illustration below shows basic information that must appear on every OTC medicine label.

▼ *The FDA governs the advertising and labeling of OTC medicines.*

ACTIVITY Analyze why FDA officials might feel that regulation of advertising and package labels is necessary.

Purpose of medicine

PAIN-OFF Provides temporary relief from: simple headaches; minor muscle aches; fever and discomfort due to colds and "flu."

Cautions on use

WARNING: Keep out of reach of children. As with any drugs, if you are pregnant or nursing a baby, seek the advice of a health professional before using this product. If condition persists for more than 10 days, consult a physician.

Directions for safe use

USUAL ADULT DOSE: 2 tablets four times a day as needed. For children under 12, consult a physician.

Expiration date
Control number

EXP 10/99
NO. QT 123

OVER-THE-COUNTER MEDICINE LABEL

Pain-Off

ACETAMINOPHEN ·· Ingredients

Name of product

For fast relief of minor pain

200 tablets
235 mg each ·· Exact measurement of package contents

DO NOT USE IF PROTECTIVE SEAL IS BROKEN

Medi-Labs
612 Medi-Lab Way
Mediville, NJ ·· Name and address of manufacturer

LESSON 2 Review

Reviewing Facts and Vocabulary

1. What is the role of the Food and Drug Administration in approving new medicines?

2. List actions that are examples of medicine misuse.

Thinking Critically

3. **Synthesizing.** Suggest possible reasons why a physician, not a pharmacist, is licensed to write prescriptions.

4. **Evaluating.** Do you think it is better to have a government agency or a privately owned company regulating approval of medicines? Support your answer.

Applying Health Skills

5. **In Your Home and School.** Ask your parents or guardians what questions they customarily ask a pharmacist when having a prescription filled. Interview a pharmacist to determine what questions consumers ask most often about their medicines. Draw conclusions about how active consumers are in their own health care. Share your findings with the class.

LESSON 2   USING MEDICINES WISELY   **521**

Lesson 2 Review

Answers to Reviewing Facts and Vocabulary

1. The FDA requires a manufacturer of medicines to supply information about a medicine's chemical composition, intended use, effects, and possible side effects. It also subjects new medicines to extensive testing before they are approved for use by the public.

2. See page 520 for a list of examples of medicine misuse.

Answers to Thinking Critically

3.–4. Answers will vary.

Visual Learning

Over-the-Counter Medicine Labels

Review prescription label requirements, then refer students to the pictures on this page. Ask the following questions to alert students to the information provided on OTC medicine labels: What is the purpose of the medicine? What is it made of? What is the dosage for children under 12? What precaution is given for pregnant women? Have students explain the purpose of the protective seal on medicines. *(To prevent tampering.)* Explain that the control number is useful in case of product recall.

ASSESS

EVALUATING THE LESSON

Assign and discuss the Lesson 2 Review; then administer, grade, and discuss the *Lesson 70 Quiz* in the TCR. ☞

RETEACHING

- Have students develop posters describing precautions teens should take before purchasing or taking medicine.
- Ask students to complete *Reteaching Activity 70* in the TCR. ☞

ENRICHMENT

Have students go to the library to find out about a recent medicine approved by the FDA. Tell them to summarize their findings in written reports.

CLOSE

Ask students: As consumers, what type of responsibilities do we have when using medicines?

Health **Skills** Activities

ACTIVITY 1
HEALTH SKILLS

Accessing Health Information, Self Management

➤ **National Standards**
This activity meets these National Health Standards: 1.3; 3.3.

Teach

- Gather labels from OTC medicines and remedies used to treat common ailments. Possibilities include headache, upset stomach, diarrhea, muscle ache, sunburn, rash, poison ivy, and allergy. Include price tags, and generic labels and prices wherever possible.
- Divide the class into small groups based on the number of labels you have gathered. Pass one label to a group.
- Review key concepts, such as the meaning of active ingredient, the difference between generic and brand-name medicines, and how to interpret dosages and warnings about side effects and other interactions.

ACTIVITY 2
HEALTH SKILLS

Self Management

➤ **National Standards**
This activity meets these National Health Standards: 3.3; 3.6.

Teach

- Have groups begin by reviewing information in the chapter on treatments and remedies for health conditions.
- Groups should each take a portion of the checklist and work independently at developing that portion. One useful subtopic that might be investigated is a list of local emergency numbers.
- Make sure that each class member receives a copy of the printed list. If time permits in a later class, follow up the activity by asking volunteers to report back on changes that were made at home as a result of the activity.

Activity 1 — Patient's Desk Reference

The Physician's Desk Reference—or "PDR"— is a book that lists and describes all prescription medications currently on the market. Your class will create a medical resource to help you use OTC medicines wisely.

Directions

1. Split up into groups. Each group will work with one of the OTC medicine labels handed out by the teacher.
2. For your group's medicine, note the active ingredient, the price, the price of the generic version if available, the medical problems it is used to treat, the dosages, and any warnings about side effects and other interactions. Share your findings.
3. Decide on a mode of organization for your PDR (e.g., by body system, by ailment). Publish your PDR on the classroom computer.

Time
40 minutes

Materials
labels from OTC medicines, classroom computer

Self-Assessment

✓ Included information called for with regard to each medicine.
✓ Described the best way to safely use each medicine.

Activity 2 — Medicine Cabinets That Make the Grade

Are you and your family prepared to meet the health situations that might occur in your home? Part of the answer to this question depends on how well-stocked and up-to-date your home medicine cabinet is.

Directions

1. Work in groups to develop a Medicine Cabinet Checklist.
2. One group is to brainstorm minor health problems (e.g., minor cuts, colds, and headaches) and corresponding remedies. Another will summarize useful information from the chapter.
3. Compile your findings into a checklist that includes names of essential remedies, expiration date of all medicines, etc.
4. Print out copies of the checklist to be posted on the door of home medicine cabinets. Urge family members to review the checklist periodically.

Time
30 minutes

Materials
paper, pen or pencil, computer (optional)

Self-Assessment

✓ Listed at least five common health situations that might arise.
✓ Described safe use of medicines in your checklist.

ASSESSMENT SCORING

Using a four-level rubric, the student has achieved a 4 if:

ACTIVITY 1
✔ Student worked successfully with group members at analyzing the assigned label.
✔ Student included all the information called for.
✔ Student described the best way to safely use medicines.
✔ Student worked with other groups at making entries in publication uniform.

ACTIVITY 2
✔ Student listed at least five health situations that might arise.
✔ Student identified standard at-home treatments for each of the situations and problems.
✔ Student took part in compiling a comprehensive home medicine cabinet checklist.
✔ Student described safe use of medicines.

Natural Cures for the Common Cold?

We've all felt the symptoms: sniffling, sneezing, coughing, congestion.

The average American suffers two to six colds a year, and as yet, there's no known cure. Nevertheless, stores are stocked with products claiming to be natural remedies for the common cold.

Herbal industry experts say Americans spend about $400 million yearly on cold treatments such as zinc. But natural remedies are only loosely regulated by the Food and Drug Administration and are available despite conflicting evidence about whether they work.

Devona Beard got hit with a cold. "I came down with a headache, sniffles, nasal congestion, nasal drip and sneezing," she explained. She took zinc lozenges and felt better within a few days.

Her physician, Dr. Ananda Prasad of Wayne State University, evaluated how 48 patients with colds responded to using zinc lozenges.

"Using zinc lozenges shortened the duration of the cold by almost 50 percent. The severity also decreased," Prasad said.

Prasad's study is just one of at least 10 careful studies evaluating zinc. Half the studies showed zinc shortens the duration of cold symptoms; the other half showed it did not.

Dr. Ron Turner, a noted cold remedy researcher, said his studies of zinc have found no benefit. What works for one patient may not work for another. The FDA will require strong evidence for any remedies containing drugs that they are safe and effective before they can be sold.

Think About It

1. What is the difference between a natural remedy and a drug?

2. What evidence suggests whether or not natural remedies are effective against the common cold? Are there any drawbacks to these natural remedies?

3. Why do you think similar studies have such different results?

MORE ABOUT . . . . .

THE COMMON COLD. You may wish to dispel some of the commonly held myths about common colds.

Myth: Cold weather causes colds.

Fact: Colds are caused by viruses, not weather conditions. Studies suggest that being chilly does not increase the chance of being infected with a cold virus.

Myth: Cold symptoms like sneezing and a runny nose help you recover from a cold. Therefore, you should not use medicines to eliminate symptoms.

Fact: Sneezing can help eliminate allergens, but not cold viruses. Blowing your nose can actually lead to secondary infections and can promote the spread of cold viruses. FDA-approved cold medicines can safely diminish symptoms.

Objectives. After reading the article, students should be able to analyze the benefits and drawbacks of natural remedies as treatment for the common cold.

Motivator. Ask: "What do you do when you get a cold?" Answers should include suggestions for both treating symptoms and avoiding the infection of others. Remind students that colds are most likely spread through skin-to-skin contact. Emphasize the role of hand-washing to prevent the spread of colds. Then have students read "Natural Cures for the Common Cold?" which describes scientific research into the use of natural remedies.

Teach

- Create a classroom chart to help students analyze the potential benefits and drawbacks of natural cold remedies. As students complete the chart, emphasize the contradictory results of scientific research into remedies such as zinc lozenges.

- Help students understand the reasons why two research studies might have opposite results. Point out that the brief duration of most colds can make it difficult for researchers to determine the effectiveness of a specific remedy. As researcher Ron Turner points out, "Everybody gets better from the common cold."

Group Activity. Encourage students to work together to survey classmates or community members about what types of cold remedies they use. They should classify each remedy as natural or artificial. Then they should compare the results of their poll with information in this article. Encourage students to analyze their data and create a news report summarizing their findings.

Close. Ask students if they would recommend zinc lozenges to someone who feels he or she is getting a cold. Ask them to support their advice with specific details or facts from the article.

CHECKING COMPREHENSION

- Assign and discuss the chapter review.
- Use the MindJogger Videoquiz to review the chapter. 🔴

CHAPTER 23 REVIEW ANSWERS

Using Health Terms

1. antagonistic interaction
2. withdrawal
3. analgesics
4. additive interaction
5. medicines
6. vaccine
7. synergistic effect
8. tolerance
9. side effects
10. over-the-counter
11. prescription
12. medicine misuse

Recalling the Facts

1. In recent years, strains of bacteria have emerged that are resistant to commonly prescribed antibiotics.
2. Acetylsalicylic acid is the active ingredient in aspirin. Aspirin is used to relieve pain and reduce fever.
3. The factors affecting how one's body will interact with a medicine include body weight and chemistry, what other medicines are being taken, an individual's metabolism, and what foods are eaten.
4. Additive interaction occurs when medicines work together in a positive way. Synergistic effect is the interaction of two or more medicines that results in a greater effect than when the medicines are taken independently. Antagonistic interaction occurs when the effect of a medicine is canceled or reduced when taken with another medicine.

Using Health Terms

On a separate sheet of paper, write the term that best matches each definition below.

LESSON 1

1. The effect of a medicine is canceled or reduced when taken with another medicine.
2. The process that occurs when a person stops using a medicine or other substance to which he or she has a physiological dependence.
3. Pain relievers.
4. Medicines work together in a positive way.
5. Substances that when taken internally or applied to the body help prevent or cure a disease or other medical problem.
6. A preparation, containing weakened or dead pathogens that cause a particular disease, given to prevent one from contracting that disease.
7. The interaction of two or more medicines that results in a greater effect than when the medicines are taken independently.
8. A condition in which the body becomes used to the effect of a medicine.
9. Reactions to medicine other than the one intended.

LESSON 2

10. Medicines you can buy without a doctor's prescription.
11. Medicines that cannot be used safely without the written approval of a licensed physician.
12. Using medicine in a way that is not intended.

Recalling the Facts

Using complete sentences, answer the following questions.

LESSON 1

1. What problem has arisen with the use of antibiotics?
2. What is the active ingredient in aspirin? What is aspirin used for?
3. What factors affect how one's body will interact with medicine?
4. Name and describe three types of medicine interactions.
5. Define *physiological dependence.*
6. When does withdrawal take place, and what are its symptoms?

LESSON 2

7. What information must a manufacturer of medicines provide to the FDA?

8. What does FDA approval of a medicine mean?
9. How do OTC medicines differ from prescription medicines?
10. Medicines are classified into five schedules. Describe the legal basis for categorization.
11. What information is always given on prescription medicine labels?
12. List four ways in which a medicine might be misused.

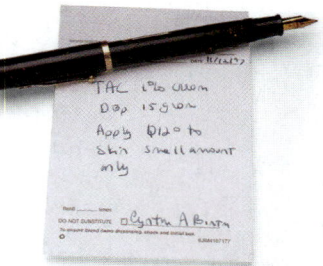

5. Physiological dependence is a chemical need for a medicine.
6. Withdrawal occurs when a person stops using a medicine or other substance to which he or she has a physiological dependence. Its symptoms include nervousness, insomnia, severe nausea, headaches, vomiting, chills, and cramps.
7. A manufacturer of medicines must supply information to the FDA about a medicine's chemical composition, intended use, effects, and possible side effects.
8. FDA approval means that a medicine is safe and medically effective.
9. Prescription medicines cannot be used safely without the written approval of a licensed physician. Over-the-counter medicines can be purchased without the approval of a doctor.

Thinking Critically

LESSON 1

1. ***Synthesizing.*** What is a person really saying when he or she says that vaccines are dangerous substances because they contain pathogens?
2. ***Evaluating.*** The FDA regulates what manufacturers can say in advertisements for both prescription and OTC medicines. Do you feel that such regulation is necessary? Support your answer.
3. ***Evaluating.*** Sometimes insurance companies will not pay for a prescription if a generic equivalent was available but not dispensed. Do you feel this practice is justified? Support your answer.

LESSON 2

4. ***Analyzing.*** In later stages of development, experimental medicines are often tested on groups of people. Where do you think these groups of people come from? What would be the possible consequences of being in such an experimental group?
5. ***Synthesizing.*** What are some appropriate questions to ask a physician before he or she writes a prescription?
6. ***Synthesizing.*** What are some questions that your physician should ask you before prescribing a drug?

Making the Connection

1. ***Math.*** Study the advertisements in a magazine. Determine what percentage of the total number of ads is for medicines. Display this information in a circle, or pie, graph.
2. ***Science.*** At your school or local library, research one of the following scientists who discovered an important medicine or a scientist of your own choosing: Sir Frederick Banting, Sir Alexander Fleming, Edward Jenner, Jonas Salk. Write a one-page paper on your findings.

BEYOND THE CLASSROOM

PARENTAL INVOLVEMENT With your parents, conduct a home safety check by determining whether all medicines at home are safely stored. Consider questions such as these: Is the cabinet difficult for small children to reach? Do medicines have childproof caps? Have out-dated medicines been discarded? Summarize your findings and recommendations in writing.

COMMUNITY INVOLVEMENT Invite a health department official to class to speak about problems connected with immunization. Write a two-page paper on what steps can be taken to remedy the situation. Work out a plan to increase community awareness of the need for immunization.

SCHOOL-TO-CAREER

Interpersonal. Invite a pharmacist to speak to the class about career possibilities and requirements in the field of pharmacy. Before the visit, prepare questions designed to elicit information about educational requirements, special training and skills, and responsibilities of the position.

Thinking Critically
1.–6. Answers will vary.

Making the Connection
1.–2. Answers will vary.

Evaluate
- Use the reproducible *Chapter 23 Test* in the TCR, or construct your own using the Testmaker software.
- Use *Performance Assessment Activity 23* in the TCR.

Enrichment
Ask students to complete *Cross-Curriculum Activity 23* in the TCR.

Beyond the Classroom
Keep students involved in the community, and encourage parent participation by assigning the activities on this page for students to work on outside of class.

10. The legal basis for categorization of medicines is their use and their potential for abuse.
11. The name of the prescribing doctor, patient name, name and address of pharmacy, date prescription was filled, prescription number, whether refills are allowed, and any special instructions.
12. Any four: giving your prescription medicine to someone else, taking too much or too little of a medicine, taking someone else's medicine, discontinuing use of a medicine without informing your doctor, taking medicine for a longer period of time than was prescribed, and mixing medicines.

Tobacco

	FEATURES	CLASSROOM RESOURCES

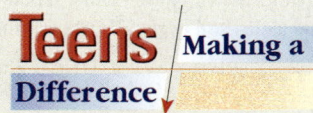

National Health Education Standards

One of the main goals of the National Health Education Standards is to move students toward "health literacy." Health literacy is the capacity of individuals to obtain, interpret, and understand basic health information and services and the competence to use such information and services in ways which promote health. The health standards were developed by applying the characteristics of a well-educated, literate person within the context of health. The health literate person is:

- a critical thinker and problem solver
- a self-directed learner
- a responsible, productive citizen
- an effective communicator

Listed below are the Health Education Standards Performance Indicators addressed in each lesson of this chapter.

Lesson	Health Standards Performance Indicators
1	1.7, 3.3, 4.2, 6.1
2	1.3, 1.4, 1.7, 6.3
3	1.7, 3.4, 6.6, 7.4

ONLINE RESOURCES

HEALTH Online

For a fresh approach to health topics and an in-depth look at health issues, use these online resources found under Teacher Resources at **health.glencoe.com**.

- **BLOCK SCHEDULE LESSON PLANS** Reinforce health concepts with outside readings selected especially for students. Each reading is accompanied by a lesson plan and activities to enhance
  - Reading Skills
  - Cross Curriculum
  - Media Literacy

- **TECHNOLOGY PROJECTS** Instructions and suggestions on how to use computer, Internet, and software with health lessons.

- **HEALTH UPDATES** Timely topics in health news, including late-breaking medical advances and updates on teen risk behaviors.

Out of Time?

If time does not permit teaching this chapter, you may use these features: Building Health Skills on page 540; Update on page 536; and Making Responsible Decisions on page 542.

BLOCK SCHEDULING

Block scheduling provides extended time for hands-on projects and activities. Use the following activities to engage students, provide further depth, and vary your instructional techniques:

- Connections (30 minutes) **pg. 531**
- Update (40 minutes) **pg. 536**
- Teens Making a Difference (30 minutes) **pg. 541**
- Health Skills Activity (60–90 minutes) **pg. 544**

Tobacco

CHAPTER OVERVIEW

Chapter 24 examines the dangers of using tobacco in any form. It also discusses the risks and rights of nonsmokers when they are around smokers. Strategies for quitting are also provided.

LESSON 1 Emphasis on quitting smoking or never starting to smoke increases every day. Major reasons teenagers begin to smoke are peer pressure, the misconception that smoking affects health only after years of smoking, and the belief that smoking is a habit that they can quit anytime they wish. Smoking cigarettes, pipes, and cigars, as well as the use of smokeless tobacco, all carry significant health risks.

LESSON 2 Smoking is associated with respiratory and cardiovascular diseases. Smokeless tobacco is also harmful, particularly to tissues in the mouth. Nonsmokers who inhale passive smoke receive the same harmful effects as the smoker.

LESSON 3 Many approaches exist to help individuals kick tobacco habits and deal with the problems and concerns associated with stopping. The benefits of quitting are both immediate and long-term.

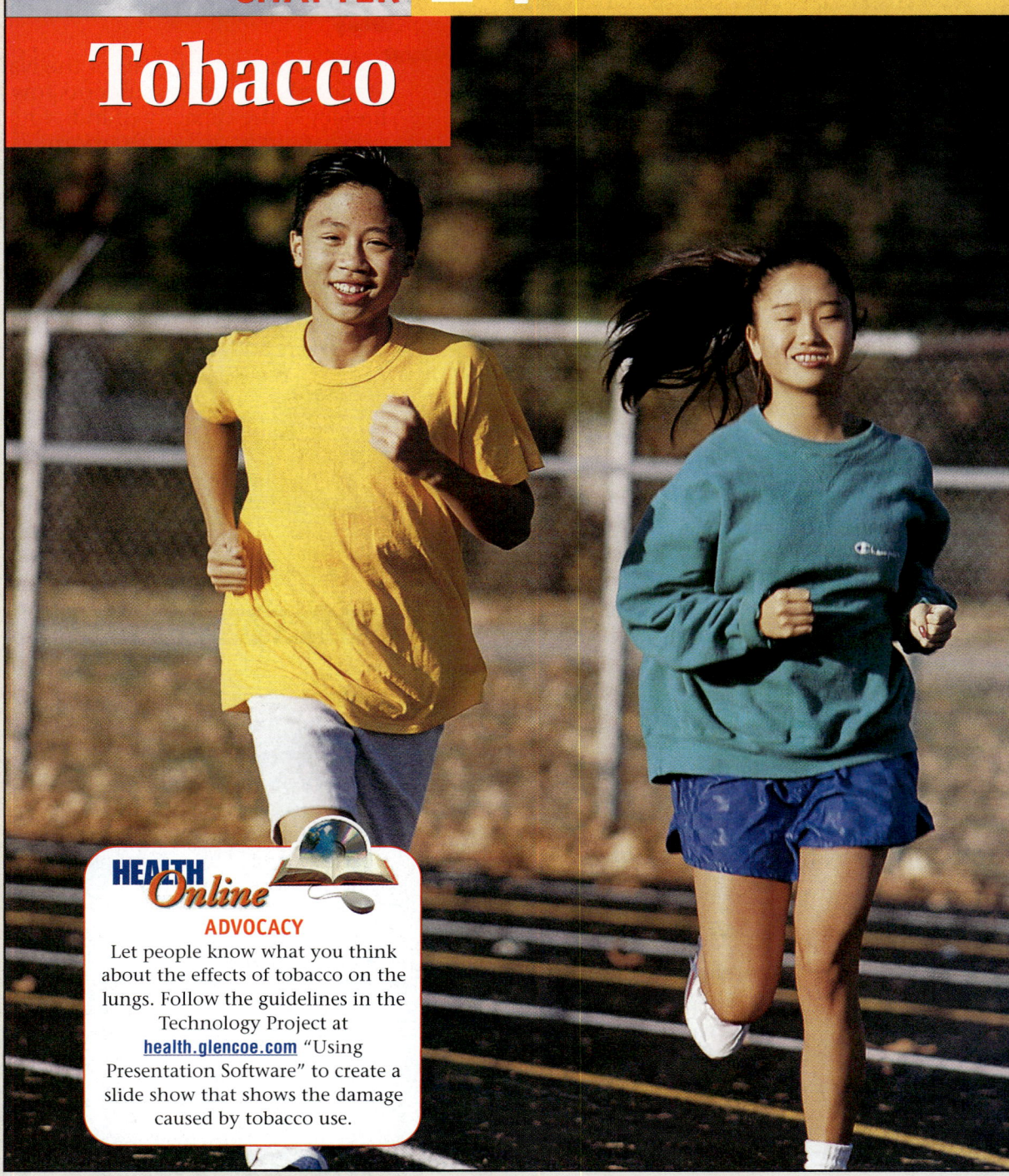

CHAPTER 24

Tobacco

HEALTH Online

ADVOCACY

Let people know what you think about the effects of tobacco on the lungs. Follow the guidelines in the Technology Project at **health.glencoe.com** "Using Presentation Software" to create a slide show that shows the damage caused by tobacco use.

Hands-On Health

TEACHING STRATEGY

Visualizing the Effects of Tar on a Smoker's Lungs Let students see how a pack-a-day cigarette habit affects a smoker's lungs. See Activity 20, "Jar of Tar," in the *Hands-On Health: Creative Teaching Strategies* booklet.

Time Needed
10 to 15 minutes

Supplies
- glass jar with lid
- 1 cup of dark syrup or dirty car oil
- packaging tape

Personal Health Inventory

> **Cigarettes cause lung cancer. It's as simple as that.**
>
> —Dr. Dan Sullivan
> Radiologist, National Cancer Institute

Quick Write Jot down some other harmful and dangerous effects you know that are caused by tobacco use.

Self-Inventory Write the numbers 1–10 on a sheet of paper. Read each statement below and respond by writing *yes*, *no*, or *sometimes* for each item. Write a *yes* only for items that you practice regularly. Save your responses.

1	I don't smoke cigarettes, cigars, or pipes.
2	I don't use smokeless tobacco.
3	I let my friends and family know that I mind when they light up around me.
4	When someone offers me a cigarette or other tobacco product, I feel comfortable refusing it.
5	I try to avoid smoke-filled places.
6	When people around me are smoking, I ask them to stop or I walk away.
7	I don't "buy into" ads that try to make smoking seem attractive or cool.
8	If I'm in a car or other enclosed space and someone is smoking, I ask him or her to stop.
9	I am knowledgeable about the dangers of tobacco use.
10	I practice stress management so that I'm not tempted to try unhealthful ways of relieving tension such as smoking.

Follow-up After completing the chapter, retake this self-inventory. Pick two items that you need to work on and set a goal to improve your health behaviors.

INTRODUCING THE CHAPTER

Personal Health Inventory

Have students read the Self-Inventory statements and explain how each relates to their physical, mental/emotional, and social health. Remind students that this Self-Inventory is for their own use only; they will benefit most by responding to the statements openly and honestly. Then have students record their responses in their private Health Journals on a page labeled "My Level of Tobacco Awareness."

- Explain to students that some of the most conclusive research in the area of health behavior and wellness deals with the impact of smoking on one's health. Have students fold a sheet of notebook paper in half lengthwise and list on the left side some of the reasons they have heard smokers give for starting or not giving up cigarettes. Ask them to look for factual responses to the excuses they have heard and note them in the second column as they read the chapter.

- Let students read the quotation and complete the Quick Write. Ask: How do you think the teens in the pictures feel about the dangers and risks associated with tobacco use? After a brief discussion, tell students that as they study the lessons in Chapter 24, they will learn more about the benefits of being smoke-free.

- Distribute Parent Letter 24 in the *Parent Letters and Activities* booklet. ▱

TECHNOLOGY OPTIONS

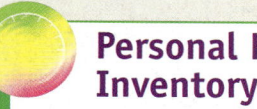

ABCNEWS INTERACTIVE™ You may wish to use *Tobacco* with this chapter. For your convenience, use the separate *ABCNews InterActive™ Bar Code Correlation* that accompanies the *Glencoe Health* program. ●

MINDJOGGER
VIDEOQUIZ

To preview or review chapter content, you may wish to use the *Mindjogger Videoquiz* that accompanies Chapter 24. ●

Tobacco Use—A High-Risk Behavior

LESSON 1

FOCUS

LESSON OBJECTIVES

After studying this lesson, students should be able to

- state reasons that some teens smoke.
- explain how tobacco use is directly linked to respiratory and circulatory diseases, as well as a variety of other health-related problems.

MOTIVATOR

Write the following on the chalkboard for students to work on while attendance is being taken: *Respond in a brief paragraph to one of the two following statements: (1) I think it is okay to smoke or use tobacco orally. (2) I do not think it is okay to smoke or use tobacco orally.*

INTRODUCING THE LESSON

Refer to the Motivator. Have students share their responses. Discuss smokers' vs. nonsmokers' rights. Ask: Who has more influence today? Why has this happened? Should we have more restrictive laws against smoking? What types of laws would reduce the use of tobacco by young teenagers?

INTRODUCING HEALTH TERMS

- Tell students to write sentences explaining each term's relationship to tobacco. Ask them to locate any other words they feel need to be clarified. Define all the identified words.
- Ask students to complete Vocabulary Activity 24 and Chapter Study Guide 24 in the *Student Workbook.* ☞

Tobacco Use—A High-Risk Behavior

Cigarette-smoking is the leading cause of avoidable death in the United States, accounting for more deaths than AIDS, car crashes, suicides, homicides, fires, and illegal drugs combined. Fifty million Americans still smoke. Even worse is that teens are the nation's fastest-growing group of smokers.

HEALTH TERMS

addiction

nicotine

stimulant

tar

carcinogens

carbon monoxide

smokeless tobacco

HEALTH CONCEPTS

- Tobacco use is a high-risk behavior that can have serious health consequences.
- A number of factors affect young people's decisions to begin using tobacco.
- The only sure way to avoid getting addicted to nicotine is to never start using any tobacco product.

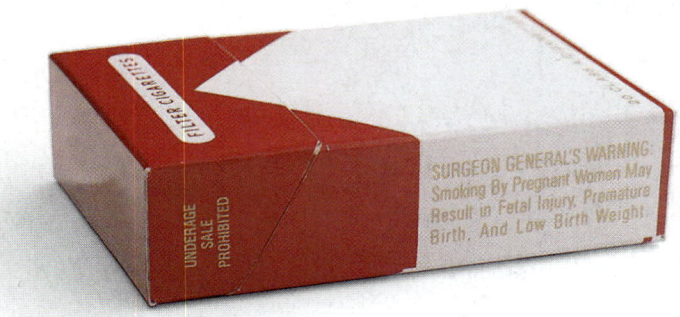

Why Young People Start Smoking

An estimated one in five American teens smokes, and about one million young people start smoking every year. Even though the message from the health community underscores the hazards of tobacco use to health, teens continue to smoke, chew, and dip tobacco in large numbers. Consider these troubling facts:

- Every day in the United States, 6,000 teens light up their first cigarette and another 3,000 teens become regular smokers.
- Approximately nine in ten adult smokers began smoking as teens and continue to smoke into adulthood, unable to stop.
- Of those who begin smoking as teens, one-third will eventually die from some smoke-related causes.
- About 2.6 million packs of cigarettes are sold illegally to minors in this country every day.

Lesson 1 Resources

TEACHER'S CLASSROOM RESOURCES

☞ **Concept Map** Activity 71

☞ **Enrichment** Activity 24

☞ **Health Lab** 24

☞ **Lesson 71 Quiz**

☞ **Lesson Plan 71**

☞ **Parent Letter and Activities** 24

☞ **Reteaching** Activity 71

STUDENT WORKBOOK

☞ **Applying Health Skills** 71

☞ **Chapter Study Guide** 24

☞ **Vocabulary** Activity 24

TRANSPARENCIES

🔥 **Transparencies 26, 27**

MULTIMEDIA

🔴 **ABCNews InterActive™,** *Tobacco*

Statistics like these might leave you wondering why teens ever start to smoke. One major reason is that many feel insecure in social situations. Before they begin smoking, some teens believe that puffing on a cigarette will somehow remove their fears or insecurities, something a cigarette simply cannot do. They may also mistakenly believe smoking will make them seem older or more sophisticated than they are.

Many teens report that they start smoking because of **peer pressure** or because advertising on billboards and in magazines has made smoking seem attractive. They may associate specific brands with good-looking models, exciting settings such as the beach, or enjoyable activities such as parties, all of which may be portrayed in these ads.

Teens may smoke because they think the bad effects of smoking on health occur only after many years of smoking. They may not realize that health risks begin from the moment the cigarette smoke from the first cigarette enters the body.

Perhaps the greatest reason young people smoke is that they believe they can drop the habit at any time. They do not realize that for many smokers, smoking is no habit. Rather, it is an **addiction**—*a physiological or psychological dependence on a substance or activity*—that is difficult to shake. Still, some teens who realize that people sometimes get addicted to cigarettes feel certain that they are the exception and can stop at any time.

In a large survey of teens who smoke, half claimed they either definitely or probably would not be smoking after five years. They viewed it as a passing habit. The problem is that after five years of smoking, many of these same teens found that they had an addiction to cigarettes. Many adult smokers who began smoking as teens are still smoking—not because they want to be but because they are addicted.

What Is in Cigarettes?

Many forms of tobacco products are on the market, but cigarettes are still the most used product. With each puff of a cigarette, the smoker comes in contact with at least 43 chemicals known to cause cancer, among these cyanide, formaldehyde, and arsenic. The chemicals in tobacco can cause ailments other than cancer. Tobacco contains **nicotine**, *the addictive drug in cigarettes.* People smoke to

hotlink

peer pressure For more information on peer pressure and ways of resisting pressure that is negative, see Chapter 13, page 304.

▼ *Even though more segments of society seem to be saying "Don't smoke," millions of Americans continue to light up.*

ACTIVITY *Discuss why you think smoking continues to be a leading cause of death.*

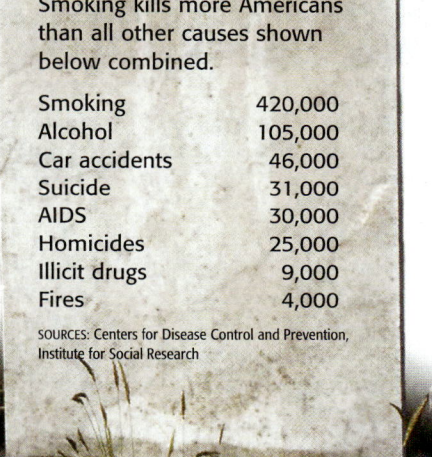

DEATHS FROM SMOKING

Smoking kills more Americans than all other causes shown below combined.

Smoking	420,000
Alcohol	105,000
Car accidents	46,000
Suicide	31,000
AIDS	30,000
Homicides	25,000
Illicit drugs	9,000
Fires	4,000

SOURCES: Centers for Disease Control and Prevention, Institute for Social Research

TEACH

L1 Discussing

Ask students: Why do you think some people continue to smoke even though they are aware of the dangers of smoking? Why do you think the number of female smokers is increasing? Discuss student responses.

L1 Discussing

Ask students how they can tell if someone smokes. List the clues on the chalkboard. Is the person who smokes aware of these clues? Why or why not?

L2 Discussing

Ask the class what products have been developed specifically for the smoking population. (*Ashtrays, tooth whiteners, breath fresheners, smoker's toothpastes, extra filters, and smoke-stopper strategies and gimmicks.*) Ask: Why has this become a lucrative industry when the number of smokers is decreasing?

ABCNEWS INTERACTIVE™

TOBACCO (Side 2)

Chapter 3: Why People Start Using Tobacco

Frames 2403-5007

Chapter 6: Advertising and the Media

Frames 10538-15621

Chapter 7: Nicotine as an Addictive Drug

Frames 15649-17640

COOPERATIVE ▶ **LEARNING**

TOBACCO AND THE LAW. Have groups of students consider what they have learned about government agencies that control substances sold in this country. Suggest that they compare the health effects of tobacco with those of other substances which the FDA has made illegal or restricted to prescription sales. Examples include tryptophan, sweeteners with cyclamates, and some food colorings. Discuss whether students would expect tobacco to be legalized if somebody tried to introduce it today. Should tobacco be permitted simply because it entered the marketplace before a federal government was created and empowered to control substances? Have students conduct a debate to resolve whether tobacco should be an illegal substance.

L2 Demonstrating

Use a smoking machine (available free from the American Cancer Society) to demonstrate tar residue left in the lungs after smoking one cigarette. If no machine is available, hold a clean white tissue or handkerchief over the smoke and let it flow through the cloth. The cloth should show a yellowish brown stain. Ask: Who is exposed to more carcinogens, the smoker or the nonsmoker who is in the room with the smoker? Why? What does the filter at the end of the cigarette look like after the cigarette has been smoked? Why do you think cigarette companies began adding filters to cigarettes?

L1 Cooperative Learning

Pass a copy of an actual "wanted poster" around the room. Your local law enforcement agency can provide copies for you. Divide the class into groups of four. Ask each group to design a wanted poster for the chemicals in cigarettes. Students can refer to chemicals' past crimes, current location, potential to be dangerous, what the reward is for their expulsion from the town or their capture, or other creative ideas students may have. Advise the groups to draw a creative diagram and design an imaginative poster that illustrates the scientific facts about the harmful chemicals in cigarettes.

L2 Health Lab

Distribute *Health Lab 24* and have students investigate whether filters in cigarettes protect smokers from the chemicals in smoke. ☞

TEEN SMOKING ON THE INCREASE

TEN REASONS TEENS START SMOKING

1. To seem more sophisticated, older, or more "cool"
2. Because of peer pressure
3. Due to the influence of advertising
4. Because teens believe they can quit at any time
5. For its short-term stimulant effect
6. To have something to handle or hold
7. For relaxation and stress relief
8. As a social crutch
9. To deal with other cravings
10. Because they see family members do it

Healthy lung

Smoke-damaged lung

▲ **There has been a steady increase in the rate of teens who smoke.**

Did You Know?

➤ Nicotine is a deadly poison that is used as an insecticide.

➤ Cigarettes contain formaldehyde, the same chemical used to preserve dead animals in biology class.

➤ Cigarettes also contain many of the same chemicals that make paint, toilet cleaner, and car antifreeze poisonous.

➤ Cigarette use has been tied to a common cause of blindness in the elderly, and a pack a day doubles that risk.

reduce the craving for nicotine, which is a poisonous stimulant. A **stimulant** is *a drug that increases the action of the central nervous system, the heart, and other organs*. Nicotine raises blood pressure and increases heart rate.

The flavor of a cigarette is due mostly to the tar in tobacco. **Tar** is *a thick, sticky, dark fluid produced when tobacco burns*. Tar penetrates the smoker's airways and lungs. Combined with the drying effect of cigarette smoke, tar paralyzes or destroys cilia, the waving hairlike projections that work to keep the respiratory tract clear. Several substances in tar are known as **carcinogens**, *cancer-causing substances*.

Low-tar, low-nicotine cigarettes, once advertised as safer than their standard counterparts, actually encourage the smoker to inhale more deeply and to smoke more cigarettes to maintain the body's accustomed nicotine levels.

Carbon monoxide is *a colorless, odorless, poisonous gas in cigarette smoke that passes through the lungs into the blood*. This is the same gas in automobile exhaust fumes that, if inhaled, could prove fatal. It unites with the hemoglobin in red blood cells, preventing them from carrying the oxygen needed for energy to the body's cells.

530 CHAPTER 24 TOBACCO

HEALTH LITERACY

RESPONSIBLE/PRODUCTIVE CITIZEN. Encourage students to conduct an anonymous poll of nonsmoking students at your school. The purpose of the poll is to find out how many students are nonsmokers and how the nonsmokers react to smokers. Encourage students to brainstorm several questions and place them on a form to be filled out anonymously. For example, they might ask whether students strongly prefer to date nonsmokers, if they object to the smell of smoke in a smoker's hair or clothes, whether it bothers them to live with a smoker, how they feel when a friend or date smokes around them. Students might enlist the help of instructors to distribute and collect the questionnaires. Have students tabulate the results and display them in the halls to raise awareness of how students really feel about smoking.

Smokeless Tobacco

Smokeless tobacco is *tobacco that is sniffed through the nose or chewed.* Over 12 million Americans are regular smokeless tobacco users, and the use of these products continues to increase, especially among teenagers, many of whom start chewing tobacco or dipping snuff between the ages of 13 and 15. Advertisements featuring famous people, especially athletes, give the false impression that smokeless products contribute to an image of being "macho" or "cool." There is nothing cool, however, about the brown-stained teeth or unsightly spitting of tobacco juice that are part of this habit. Many teens also wrongly believe that smokeless tobacco is safer than cigarettes because it does not involve taking in smoke or putting it back into the air. In truth, smokeless tobacco carries many of the same health risks as smoking cigarettes, including addiction to nicotine. Other health risks associated with chewing or dipping include mouth sores that can turn into cancer of the lip, mouth or throat; damage to teeth and gums; and damage to the digestive system.

Other Forms of Tobacco

Like smoking cigarettes, smoking pipes or cigars also presents major health risks. Although pipe and cigar smokers usually inhale less smoke, they are more likely to develop cancers of the lip, mouth, and throat because more tar and other chemicals are generated by pipes and cigars. If the pipe or cigar smoker makes it a habit to inhale the smoke, his or her chances of developing lung cancer also increase.

CHARACTER IN ACTION

Smoke-free: The Benefits for All

Being tobacco-free has positive benefits for everyone. When you decide not to smoke, you are showing **respect** for yourself and for others.

➤ You are more likely to be able to take a deep breath, taste food, and have a full sense of smell.

➤ You have endurance and energy during physical activity.

➤ You are free from addiction to nicotine, reduce the risks of heart disease, cancer, and leading respiratory diseases.

➤ You can feel good that you are not polluting the air of those around you.

Character Check Make a list similar to that above that names the benefits to those around a smoker once that smoker quits smoking.

connections

Social Studies

Tobacco, Teens, and Taxes

Recently, in many places, laws regarding the sale of tobacco to teens have become stricter. In 1997, a bill was signed increasing cigarette taxes by 10 cents per pack in the year 2000 and another 5 cents in 2002, in part to make it tougher for teens to pay for cigarettes.

1. **Research the laws regarding the sale of tobacco and tobacco products in your state or community.** Find out what the age restrictions are for buying these products, and what happens to vendors who violate the law. Write these laws up on poster board and, with permission, display them.

2. **Do research to find out about federal, state, and local tax laws regarding the sale of cigarettes.** Find out what the tax rates are and where these revenues, or tax incomes, are used by the government. Share this information with your class.

CURRICULUM CONNECTIONS

MATH. Ask students to calculate the cost of smoking one, two, or three packs of cigarettes a day beginning at age 15 through age 65. Have them base their calculations on the current price of cigarettes for the first five years, and increase it by 5 percent for each five-year period. Ask: What else could have been purchased with that amount of money? Encourage students to use the advertisements in the local paper to find costs of other articles, such as stereo equipment, a car, and even a house. Have them compare costs.

SOCIAL STUDIES. Ask a social studies teacher to discuss the history of tobacco, including the historical importance of that industry and where it stands today.

CHARACTER IN ACTION

Smoke-free: The Benefits for All

Have students discuss the benefits of being a non-smoker. Ask students what values are acted upon when a person makes the decision to be smoke-free. Also ask students to share if cigarette smoking has affected any of their relationships and how.

connections

Social Studies

Tobacco, Teens, and Taxes
Ask: How easy is it for young teens to buy cigarettes in our community? What laws do we have restricting the sale of tobacco? As far as you know, how are those laws enforced? After a brief discussion, have students read the Connections feature and then work in groups to carry out the research projects relating to restrictions and taxes. Provide time during which the groups can share their findings with the rest of the class.

L1 Cooperative Learning

Divide the class into groups of five or less. Ask each group to develop at least five laws that would prohibit or make it difficult to buy or use tobacco. The laws would have to be reasonable and possible to implement. Everyone in the group must agree with the proposed laws. Share the laws with the rest of the class. Once the laws have been proposed, ask the class to rank them by potential effectiveness. Discuss whether legislation is or is not effective in controlling behavior.

ASSESS

EVALUATING THE LESSON

Assign and discuss the Lesson 1 Review; then administer, grade, and discuss the *Lesson 71 Quiz* in the TCR. ☞

RETEACHING

- Ask students to use their texts to identify some of the by-products of tobacco use. The list should include nicotine, tar, and carbon monoxide. Have students discuss the effects of these chemicals on the body.
- Ask students to complete *Reteaching Activity 71* in the TCR. ☞
- Use *Transparencies 26* and *27* to review why teens start smoking and what substances are in cigarettes. 🖐

ENRICHMENT

- Have students research the trend of the tobacco industry to diversify its investments, companies, and products. Have students use the following questions to guide their research: Why is the industry taking this approach? What are the trends in the tobacco industry's economy? Why is the government still providing price support supplements for tobacco growers?
- Increase students' awareness of the factors influencing them to smoke by having them complete *Enrichment Activity 24*, "Cigarettes and the Media," in the TCR. ☞

CLOSE

Tell students that in this first lesson they studied the reasons some people use tobacco and the many forms tobacco can take. Explain that the next lesson will discuss the effects tobacco has on the body.

Specialty Cigarettes

Specialty cigarettes are those prepared with tobacco and other ingredients. They are often made with strong tobacco and contain spices that make them taste and smell sweet. However, the effects they can have on the body of the user are anything but sweet. Experts say that specialty cigarettes contain more cancer-causing tars than standard cigarettes. Clove cigarettes, one such specialty product, have been linked to lung problems and possible deaths and may have as much as two times the tar and nicotine as regular cigarettes.

SHEDDING LIGHT ON LIGHTING UP

The use of cigars is a growing fad and addiction among many Americans, including teens. From 1993 to 1996, the sales of larger cigars grew 45 percent to 4.5 billion. One national sample taken by the CDC showed that 27 percent of students had tried at least one cigar within the past year. However, cigars are not the safe alternative to cigarettes that many teens mistakenly assume they are. In fact, cigar smokers are 34 percent more likely to die from some form of cancer than nonsmokers and four to ten times more likely than are nonsmokers to die of cancer of the throat, mouth, or larynx. Though many states ban cigar sales to those under age, their sales to minors continue to increase.

LESSON 1 Review

Reviewing Facts and Vocabulary

1. Name at least three factors that influence teens to start smoking.
2. What is one major misconception, or mistaken idea, that many teens have about tobacco products and the health risks associated with them?

Thinking Critically

3. *Analyzing.* Bring in three print advertisements for tobacco products. Analyze the pictures that accompany them, what the ads say, and what messages concerning tobacco use these advertisements suggest. Discuss the accuracy and ethics of these sales approaches.
4. *Synthesizing.* Write a public service announcement titled "Ten Reasons for Teens Not to Smoke."

Applying Health Skills

5. *In Your Home.* Discuss with adults at home the use of tobacco among members of your immediate family as well as among aunts, uncles, grandparents, and so on. Then working as a group, compose, copy, and send a letter to all family members, sharing what you have learned about the dangers of tobacco use and the ways in which individuals and groups can become tobacco-free. Challenge the whole family to become tobacco-free. Set up a buddy system whereby those who are tobacco-free help those who are tobacco users to become tobacco-free.

Lesson 1 Review

Answers to Reviewing Facts and Vocabulary

1. They feel insecure in social situations. They think smoking will make them seem older or more sophisticated than they are. They smoke because of peer pressure or advertising. They believe they can drop the habit at any time.

2. They think the bad effects of smoking on health happen only after many years of smoking.

Answers to Thinking Critically

3.–4. Answers will vary.

What Tobacco Does to the Body

E very day in the United States over 8,000 people die from diseases caused from using tobacco. Cigarette smoking is responsible for respiratory and circulatory diseases, and this impacts a person's level of fitness, performance, and overall health.

HEALTH TERMS

leukoplakia
passive smoke
mainstream smoke
sidestream smoke

HEALTH CONCEPTS

- Smoking causes diseases of the respiratory and circulatory systems.
- Tobacco smoke can harm a fetus and lead to low birth weight and other health complications.
- Being in the presence of cigarette smoke puts a person's health in jeopardy.

Effects of Smoking on the Smoker

C igarettes impair the health of the smoker in two ways—through short-term effects that occur immediately after the smoker lights up and long-term effects that occur as the smoking continues. Over time, the tar and pollutants in tobacco smoke take their toll on several body systems. Some of the deadliest problems are those affecting the respiratory and circulatory systems.

LESSON 2   WHAT TOBACCO DOES TO THE BODY   **533**

What Tobacco Does to the Body

FOCUS

LESSON OBJECTIVES

After studying this lesson, students should be able to

- explain how tobacco use is directly linked to respiratory and circulatory diseases, as well as a variety of other health-related problems.
- describe the health hazards that nonsmokers face when in a smoke-filled environment.
- discuss the rights of a nonsmoker.

MOTIVATOR

Write the following on the chalkboard for students to work on while attendance is being taken: *List all of the possible consequences of tobacco use that you can recall.*

INTRODUCING THE LESSON

Provide three headings as categories on the chalkboard: *Physical, Mental/Emotional,* and *Social.* Have students share their responses to the Motivator. Write their responses under the appropriate category. Discuss how tobacco use can affect all areas of health. Explain that this lesson will focus on the effects of tobacco use on the body.

INTRODUCING HEALTH TERMS

- Have students differentiate *mainstream smoke* and *sidestream smoke.* How do these terms relate to *passive smoke*?
- Ask students to complete Vocabulary Activity 24 and Chapter Study Guide 24 in the *Student Workbook.*

Lesson 2 Resources

TEACHER'S CLASSROOM RESOURCES

- **Concept Map** Activity 72
- **Cooperative Learning** Activity 24
- **Lesson 72 Quiz**
- **Lesson Plan 72**
- **Reteaching** Activity 72

STUDENT WORKBOOK

- **Applying Health Skills 72**
- **Chapter Study Guide 24**
- **Vocabulary** Activity 24

MULTIMEDIA

- ABCNews InterActive™ VHS/Videodisc, *Tobacco*

TEACH

L1 Class Activity

On a diagram of the human body, follow the pathway of smoke when it is inhaled and exhaled. Have students list all the body parts that are exposed to the inhaled and exhaled smoke. Ask: If a person did not inhale, would there be less damaging potential on the tobacco user? What areas of the body would still be vulnerable?

L1 Explaining

Tell students what happens to the body when a person uses tobacco. Explain why, after about 30 minutes, the tobacco user wants more. (The constriction of the blood vessels causes a mild high. When the vessels return to normal, there is a sensation of restlessness and irritation. The smoker or oral tobacco user does not like the discomfort and will repeat the behavior that produced pleasure. This causes a cycle of use that becomes habitual. The frequent use builds up an addiction to nicotine.)

L1 Discussing

Ask: What is the purpose of cilia? Explain what can occur when they stop functioning.

L1 Discussing

Encourage students to determine as many reasons as possible why an employer would prefer to hire a person who does not smoke over one who does. If students were employers, how would they help their employees who smoke to stop?

L2 Cooperative Learning

Have students complete *Cooperative Learning Activity 24*, "Tobacco Lesson," in the TCR. ◢

hotlink

chronic bronchitis For more information on chronic bronchitis and other health measures that can help prevent you from developing this disease, see Chapter 17, page 403.

emphysema For more information on emphysema and its symptoms, see Chapter 17, page 405.

lung cancer For more on lung cancer and habits that can decrease your risks, see Chapter 31, page 686.

Diseases of the Respiratory System

Cigarette smoking is associated with the two principal diseases that make up chronic obstructive pulmonary disease, or COPD. These are chronic bronchitis and emphysema, which are ten times more likely to occur among smokers than among people who do not smoke.

Chronic bronchitis is a condition in which the bronchi are irritated. As cilia become useless, tar from cigarette smoke builds up, which results in chronic coughing and excessive mucus secretion.

Emphysema is a condition that involves the destruction of the tiny air sacs in the lungs through which oxygen is absorbed into the body. As the walls between the sacs are destroyed, they lose their elasticity and provide less total surface from which oxygen can be absorbed. More breaths are required, and instead of using 5 percent of one's energy in breathing, a person with advanced emphysema uses up to 80 percent of his or her energy just to breathe.

Lung cancer, directly linked to cigarette smoking, is the leading cause of cancer deaths among males. With the increase in female smokers, lung cancer is becoming a more significant cause of cancer

TEENS, TOBACCO, PERFORMANCE, AND HEALTH

The next time you are tempted to use tobacco, consider these hazardous effects reported in the CDC's *Facts of Youth Smoking, Health and Performance:*

- Smoking hurts your physical fitness both in endurance and performance.
- The resting heart rates of young adult smokers beat two to three beats per minute faster than the hearts of nonsmokers.
- Regular smoking in teens leads to coughing and respiratory illnesses.
- Smoking teens are twice as likely as nonsmoking teens to cough with phlegm or blood.
- They are three times more likely to report shortness of breath when exercising than nonsmoking teens.
- Teens who smoke are three times more likely as nonsmokers to drink alcohol, eight times more likely to use marijuana, and 22 times more likely to use cocaine.
- Smoking is also associated with other high-risk behaviors such as fighting.

534 CHAPTER 24 TOBACCO

MORE ABOUT . . . . .

BRONCHITIS. Acute bronchitis comes on suddenly and is usually caused by a virus entering the respiratory system and settling in the bronchial tubes. As part of the treatment for acute bronchitis, medication is administered to stop the infection. Chronic bronchitis is usually caused by smoking. A person with chronic bronchitis has a continuing heavy bark-like cough. The lungs secrete an excessive amount of sticky mucus as a means of dealing with the irritating smoke. The "smoker's cough" is a warning that the body may not be able to counteract this irritation of continual smoke, and the passageways are narrowing. The narrowing causes pressure on the alveoli, which sometimes collapse, leading to emphysema.

death among females, too. Lung cancer begins as the bronchi are irritated by cigarette smoke. Cilia are destroyed and extra mucus cannot be expelled. The smoker develops a cough. Cancerous cells can grow in these conditions, block the bronchi, and move to the lungs. In advanced stages, cancerous cells can travel to other organs through the lymphatic system. Unless caught early, lung cancer causes death.

Diseases of the Circulatory System

Nicotine makes the heart work harder and speeds up the pulse. Smoking constricts the blood vessels, which cuts down on the circulation, or blood flow, to the limbs. This can result in a tingling feeling in a smoker's hands and feet. Nicotine contributes to plaque buildup in the blood vessels. The formation of these fatty deposits in the arteries increases the chance of arteriosclerosis, or hardening of the arteries, and gradually clogs the blood vessels to the heart. This condition increases the risk of heart attack. In fact, the risk of sudden death from heart disease is three times greater for smokers than for nonsmokers. This risk increases for those who smoke more than a pack a day.

Smoking raises blood pressure and leads to increased risk of stroke. If a smoker has high blood pressure and high cholesterol, the risks of coronary heart disease are even greater. Experts estimate that if all Americans stopped smoking, deaths from heart disease could be cut by almost a third, saving more than 30,000 lives a year.

▲ *The blockage of this artery has stopped the flow of blood to surrounding tissue.*

The Dangers of Smokeless Tobacco

Although smoke does not get into the lungs when using smokeless tobacco, other health problems exist, some of which can be serious and even life-threatening. The nicotine in smokeless tobacco is as addictive as that in cigarettes. Once a person starts chewing and dipping, it can become very difficult to stop.

People who use smokeless tobacco secrete more saliva. Although the chewers usually spit this excess out, some of it is unconsciously swallowed, introducing tar and other harmful chemicals into the digestive and urinary systems. Tobacco juices also contain chemicals that may delay healing of wounds.

Tobacco and its by-products are extremely irritating to the sensitive tissues in the mouth. Irritation from direct contact with tobacco juices is responsible for **leukoplakia**, *thickened, white, leathery-appearing spots on the inside of a smokeless tobacco user's mouth that can develop into cancer of the mouth.* Oral cancer strikes about 30,000 Americans annually. Because this form of cancer is often discovered late, only 50 percent of its victims survive longer than five years.

L1 ## Discussing

Pose the following questions: What is the reason a person with heart disease is told to avoid smoke? Why does the heart have to work harder in a smoker than in a nonsmoker? What happens to the heart when it works overtime?

L2 ## Class Activity

Select a group of volunteers to develop and perform a skit about a female teen who objects to her boyfriend's use of smokeless tobacco. He chooses to dip because all his teammates do.

L1 ## Discussing

What are some of the dangers of smokeless tobacco? Elicit ideas and answers from the class.

L1 ## Discussing

Ask: Why do you think people continue to use smokeless tobacco even though they are aware of its dangers?

L1 ## Guest Speaker

Invite a representative from the American Dental Association, a school hygienist, or a local dentist to talk with the class about leukoplakia. Ask the speaker to address the following questions: What is the frequency of occurrence? How does leukoplakia look and feel? What can be done to eliminate this condition? Is it always cancerous? How fast does this condition turn into cancer? What other effects of oral tobacco use do dentists see in their practice?

MORE ABOUT . . . . .

NICOTINE AND SMOKING. It only takes five to seven seconds for nicotine to reach the brain after a person inhales tobacco smoke. In those seconds, the nicotine is absorbed into the bloodstream through the lining of the mouth and through the lungs. The smoker's blood pressure goes up; heart rate increases by up to 20 beats per minute; oxygen supply to body tissues decreases; and blood circulation to the arms, hands, legs, and feet decreases. The first "rush" of stimulation of the brain is followed by depression and fatigue, leading the smoker to seek even more nicotine—another cigarette.

ABCNEWS INTERACTIVE™

TOBACCO (Side 1)

Chapter 3: Tobacco and Nicotine

Frames 2352-5203

Chapter 4: Short-Term Consequences of Cigarette Smoking

Frames 5222-8418

Chapter 5: Long-Term Consequences of Cigarette Smoking

Frames 8426-11864

Chapter 7: Consequences of Using Smokeless Tobacco

Frames 14761-18733

up|date
▶ *Looking at the Issues*

Should All Tobacco Advertising Be Banned?

Up to $6 billion is spent annually on advertising by tobacco firms, much of it on targeting teen markets. As awareness about the dangers of smoking among teens grows, so does the commitment on the part of government and health officials to try to stop teens from smoking. One solution that has met with a mixed reaction is to ban all advertising of tobacco products.

ANALYZING DIFFERENT **VIEWPOINTS**

▶ **Viewpoint One**
Though cigarette ads have been banned from TV since 1971, print advertising remains. Those opposed to allowing tobacco ads to exist in any form point out that teens are three times as likely to be influenced by these ads as adults.

▶ **Viewpoint Two**
Other critics of tobacco-product advertising complain about tobacco companies' public image promotion and their continued aggressive marketing targeted to teen audiences.

▶ **Viewpoint Three**
Representatives of the tobacco industry counter that their ads do not target teens specifically and that the right to buy or not buy a product is the right and responsibility of each consumer. Others in this industry add that tobacco manufacturers are doing their part by investing large sums of money in anti-smoking education programs for teens.

EXPLORING YOUR **VIEWS**

1. Do you think tobacco-product advertising should be banned at all? Explain your views.

2. Do you think tobacco companies should be able to advertise indirectly but in large-scale ways by sponsoring sporting and cultural events aimed at teen audiences? Why or why not?

HEALTH *Online*

Did you know that one-third of cancer deaths are caused by cigarette smoking? At **health.glencoe.com** find healthful guidelines from the American Cancer Society.

Smokeless tobacco users also tend to show greater tooth wear than nonusers. Their gums tend to be pushed away from their teeth where the tobacco is held. The roots of the teeth become exposed and more susceptible to decay, causing early loss of teeth. Users of smokeless tobacco also develop bad breath and discolored teeth. Tobacco products decrease the user's ability to smell and taste, especially salty and sweet foods.

Effects of Smoke on the Nonsmoker

People who breathe passive smoke receive the same unhealthy effects as smokers. **Passive smoke** is *cigarette, cigar, or pipe smoke inhaled by nonsmokers as well as smoke that remains in a closed environment after the smoker is through smoking.* Passive smoke includes **mainstream smoke,** *the smoke that a smoker blows off,* as well as **sidestream smoke,** *the smoke that comes from burning tobacco.* Passive smoke

PERSONAL HEALTH

causes eye irritation, headaches, and coughing. It causes more frequent ear infections, asthma attacks and other respiratory problems and aggravates existing heart and lung diseases. It can also cause lung cancer. At least 3,000 people die annually from lung cancer because of exposure to others' smoke. Lengthy exposure to sidestream smoke can, in fact, result in the same kinds of life-threatening health problems that the smoker may experience.

A smoke-filled room may contain levels of carbon monoxide and other pollutants as high as those that occur during an air pollution emergency. A nonsmoker could inhale enough nicotine and carbon monoxide in an hour to have the same effect as having smoked a whole cigarette.

Smoking During and After Pregnancy

A 1997 study in *the Archives of Pediatrics and Adolescent Medicine* maintained that parents who smoke contribute to the deaths of at least 6,200 children in this country every year. According to the study, at least 2,800 deaths of low birth weight babies are caused by mothers who smoked while pregnant, with another 1,100 resulting from respiratory infections.

As noted in Chapter 20, cigarette smoking during pregnancy is also associated with small fetal growth, an increased chance of spontaneous abortion and prenatal death, and increased stillbirths, as well as growth and developmental problems during early childhood. Babies born to mothers who smoked during pregnancy may be adversely affected in intellectual development and behavioral characteristics.

Nicotine passes through the placenta, constricting the blood vessels of the fetus in the mother's uterus. Carbon monoxide reduces the oxygen levels in the mother's and fetus's blood. Smoking is especially harmful during the second half of pregnancy. After the baby is born, nicotine can be transferred during breast-feeding.

Most people would not give an infant or small child a cigarette, but people who smoke around children are doing the same damage to these youngsters that they would if they were helping them to light up. Children of cigarette smokers are nearly twice as likely to be in poor or fair health as those of nonsmokers. Such children are more likely to suffer from respiratory problems, including poorer lung function and more wheezing. Their risk of developing lung cancer, moreover, is double that of children of nonsmokers.

Rights of the Nonsmoker

Despite the growing awareness of the dangers of passive smoke, nearly half of all smokers light up without asking those around them

▲ *When pregnant women smoke, their unborn babies are affected, too.*
ACTIVITY *Name three negative effects on the unborn when mothers-to-be smoke.*

L1 Discussing

Ask students to explain what passive smoke is and how it affects the body of a nonsmoker who is around smoke on a regular basis.

L1 Researching

Assign students to visit local restaurants in your area. Have them ask whether each restaurant has a "no smoking" section. If so, how long has the practice been in effect? Which area—smoking or nonsmoking—attracts more customers? Are there restaurants that do not allow smoking at all? Have students graph their findings.

L3 Researching

Divide the class into four groups. Assign the following tasks to each group: (1) Investigate the cost of medical insurance for smokers vs. nonsmokers. (2) Survey students in the school to determine how many students smoke or use tobacco. Determine each tobacco user's age, how much he or she uses each week, and what type of tobacco is used. (3) Interview managers of stores in the area to determine their procedures for controlling the sale of tobacco to minors.

L1 Cooperative Learning

Divide the class into groups of two or three. Assign each group an elementary grade level from K to 6. Ask them to develop a lesson on tobacco usage for their assigned level. The lessons could include visuals, a skit, discussion questions, student activities, charts, or displays. Meet with teachers from each grade level and explain your plans. Ask permission for students to teach their lessons to the younger classes.

HOME AND COMMUNITY CONNECTION

SMOKING IN PUBLIC. Do students believe laws should protect nonsmokers by prohibiting smoking in public places? Encourage them to investigate laws and policies that prevail in their community. Do state or city laws regulate smoking in public places? Do public buildings or places of business prohibit or restrict smoking on premises? Have students list examples of local laws and policies. These may prohibit smoking altogether, or confine smoking to designated areas. Encourage interested students to write their congressional representatives proposing a uniform national law covering smoking in places where the public conducts business or recreation. The letter should be specific about what the law should require.

ASSESS

EVALUATING THE LESSON

Assign and discuss the Lesson 2 Review; then administer, grade, and discuss the *Lesson 72 Quiz* in the TCR. 📖

RETEACHING

- Have students debate this statement: *Using smokeless tobacco is less dangerous than smoking cigarettes.*
- Ask students to complete *Reteaching Activity 72* in the TCR. 📖

ENRICHMENT

Have students investigate court cases brought against tobacco companies. There have been many suits brought by "victims" of tobacco use. Have students determine what the issues of these cases are. Ask students to report their findings and share their opinions regarding these cases with the class.

CLOSE

Have the class recall the major concepts of the lesson. Ask students if they or anyone they know has tried to quit smoking and failed. Explain that Lesson 3 will focus on strategies for quitting.

🔺 *A smoke-free environment benefits your health and the health of others.*

if they mind. According to one medical report, even though at least 80 percent of nonsmokers report that they are bothered by passive smoke, only about 4 percent actually ask smokers to stop. Because of the dangers of passive smoke, that fact has to change. You can help to change it.

You have a right to express your preference that people not smoke around you. By doing so, you protect the air you breathe and the air of those around you. If you are allergic to smoke or if the smell of it makes you sick, you may be more inclined to speak up. Everyone has a right to ask that the air they breathe remain smoke-free.

If you are in a restaurant or public place that has a nonsmoking section, ask to be seated there. Choosing places that are altogether smoke-free may be the answer. Increasingly, smoke-free establishments are easier to find. Also, be sure to ask that no one smoke in your home or at public meetings or events that you attend.

It is considerate of smokers to ask others in an enclosed area if they mind their smoking. For the sake of your health, you should always say yes. Smokers should take responsibility to smoke where there are no nonsmokers around. When they do not, nonsmokers also should take responsibility for their own health by asking smokers to extinguish their cigarettes or by moving to a smoke-free space.

LESSON 2 *Review*

Reviewing Facts and Vocabulary

1. Describe the dangers of smokeless tobacco.
2. Explain in your own words the meaning of the terms *passive smoke, mainstream smoke,* and *sidestream smoke.*
3. What are some of the effects that smoking has on a fetus or newborn?

Thinking Critically

4. *Evaluating.* Health insurance companies increase premium rates for those who smoke and cut the rates of those who do not. Do you feel this a fair practice? Explain your answer.
5. *Analyzing.* Look through magazine ads aimed at teens and analyze the kinds of physical characteristics of models, expressions, emotions, activities, and settings that are used by advertisers to try to sell tobacco products. In what ways do these ads paint a false picture?

Applying Health Skills

6. *In Your School.* Have a physician from the community visit your class and discuss what percentage of his or her patients present problems related to tobacco use. Prior to the visit, brainstorm ten questions to pose to the expert. Afterward, write an entry in your private Health Journal noting how this visit has increased your awareness of the health risks of tobacco use.

Lesson 2 Review

Answers to Reviewing Facts and Vocabulary

1. See pages 535 and 536.
2. See the Glossary for definitions.
3. Smoking during pregnancy is associated with small fetal growth, increased chance of spontaneous abortion and prenatal death, and increased stillbirths, as well as growth and developmental problems during early childhood.

Answers to Thinking Critically

4.–5. Answers will vary.

Choosing to Be Tobacco-Free

More and more people are taking responsibility for their health and the health of others by giving up the use of tobacco. Quitting can be tough, but it is the way of the future. There are many ways to stop and many places that offer support and help with the process.

HEALTH TERMS

nicotine withdrawal

nicotine substitutes

HEALTH CONCEPTS

■ There are many successful approaches to stopping smoking.

■ The keys to success for a smoker are recognizing the need to quit, making the commitment, and taking the steps to do so.

■ For the addicted tobacco user, if one technique does not work, others should be tried, including medical help and short-term nicotine-replacement therapy.

Strategies for Quitting

A person who wants to quit using tobacco should be reminded that he or she will probably go through a period of **nicotine withdrawal**. This is *the process that occurs when nicotine, an addictive drug, is no longer used.* During this period the person may feel nervous or moody or have difficulty sleeping. These symptoms of withdrawal do not last long, however.

There are many techniques for quitting smoking. One involves using a series of filters over several weeks. Each filter reduces the tar and nicotine levels so that withdrawal is gradual. An increasingly popular method is the use of **nicotine substitutes.** These are *manufactured forms of nicotine that deliver small amounts of the drug into the user's system while he or she is trying to give up the tobacco habit.* Nicotine gum is one such substitute which can now be purchased as an

LESSON 3 CHOOSING TO BE TOBACCO-FREE **539**

Choosing to Be Tobacco-Free

FOCUS

LESSON OBJECTIVE

After studying this lesson, students should be able to

- recognize different approaches available to people who wish to become tobacco-free.
- discuss the challenge of quitting smoking and positive steps that can be taken by smokers who want to quit.

MOTIVATOR

Write the following on the chalkboard for students to work on while attendance is being taken: *Provide directions for someone who is trying to quit smoking.*

INTRODUCING THE LESSON

Ask students to share their responses to the Motivator. In which strategies were students most confident? How did the strategies differ between smokers and non-smokers in your class? Discuss the challenges that smokers face in deciding to quit.

INTRODUCING HEALTH TERMS

- Have students recall the effects of nicotine. Discuss the addictive aspect of nicotine and the strategies of withdrawal vs. substitutes in quitting smoking.
- Ask students to complete Vocabulary Activity 24 and Chapter Study Guide 24 in the *Student Workbook.* 🗝

TEACH

L1 Class Activity

Have students write public service announcements directed at teens about the hazards of smoking and the benefits of quitting. Ask the person who makes morning announcements at school to include one of these each day.

L2 Researching

Ask students to research the different products sold to help people stop smoking. The pharmacist in a local pharmacy may have knowledge of these products. Have students determine which are effective and why they work.

L1 Personal Involvement

Organize students who want to stop smoking into a support group that meets each morning before school. Train peers to be supporters. Have students post the number of days they have been smoke-free.

Building Health Skills

Quitting Smoking
Skill: Goal Setting

Let students share success stories about quitting smoking (either their own experiences or those of friends or family members). What attitudes and behaviors helped each person succeed? Then have students read the Building Health Skills feature to learn about specific tips that can help a tobacco user quit. After students have discussed these tips, divide them into five groups and assign one of the numbered strategies to each group. Have group members plan and present a short skit illustrating a use of their assigned strategy.

---

over-the-counter product. Another technique, the nicotine patch, requires a prescription. The patch, placed on the body, gives off decreasing amounts of nicotine.

Many people combine several of these approaches and techniques to become tobacco-free. In 1996, a prescription nicotine nasal spray was approved by the FDA, allowing nicotine to get into the bloodstream faster than gum or patches. Patients using the spray inhale it once or twice an hour, but can use it up to five times an hour. As with other nicotine substitutes, the ultimate goal is gradually to cut doses until no nicotine at all is used.

Benefits of Quitting

The benefits of quitting tobacco are both immediate and long-term. Benefits to physical health can be measured in improved cardiorespiratory endurance. Physical fitness increases as a person is able to breathe easier and has reduced chances of heart disease and stroke. Quitting not only improves a person's health physically, it also affords emotional and social benefits. Former smokers often experience a sense of freedom and a renewed vigor, as though a burden has been lifted. Constant concern over finding a place to light up or over disapproving glances from nonsmokers vanishes. The money saved from kicking an expensive habit can be spent on more healthful forms of recreation.

Building Health Skills

Goal Setting: Quitting Smoking

IF YOU ARE TRYING to give up smoking or other tobacco use, the following tips might help you to reach your goal.

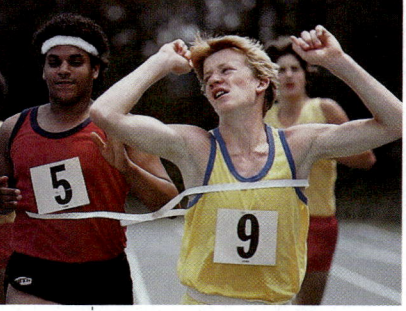

1. **Begin by deciding once and for all that you want to quit.** Although it seems obvious, many smokers never take this first step.

2. **Set a target date for quitting.** This date might be associated with a joyous event, such as the smoker's birthday.

3. **Take intermediate steps to help you reach your goal.** This might take the form of setting checkpoints at which the smoker cuts down on the number of cigarettes.

4. **Get help meeting your goal.** Many smokers find that quitting with a friend makes the experience easier. Each is there as a daily—and even hourly—source of support for the other.

5. **Plan a healthy way to reward yourself once you have kicked the habit.**

MEETING STUDENT DIVERSITY

SUPPORTERS OF EX-SMOKERS.
Encouraging someone to quit smoking and remain an ex-smoker is nearly as difficult for the supporter as for the smoker. The supporter must assume a caring, patient, nonjudgmental role. Nagging and preaching don't help. The supporter can help by giving the ex-smoker special rewards and helping the ex-smoker avoid situations where he or she would normally light up. If the ex-smoker becomes grouchy, has trouble sleeping, is dizzy, or feels tired, the supporter can reassure him or her that these symptoms are signs of chemical withdrawal and will pass. If there is a relapse, the supporter shouldn't consider it a failure—a relapse is said to be part of recovery from addiction.

Teens Making a Difference

...INITIATIVE...RESPONSIBILITY ...CIVIC DUTY

Mike (back row, center) is a tobacco-free teen. A junior at McNeil High School in Austin, Texas, he and his friends are active members of TATU, Teens Against Tobacco Use, a nationally-known peer education program sponsored by the American Lung Association. Their goal is to help themselves and others understand the dangers of tobacco and prevent its use. The group even welcomes teen smokers, and often what they learn there inspires them to quit. "In one of our groups, three smokers decided to quit," Mike says proudly.

GETTING INVOLVED "I got involved," Mike begins, "because, with TATU, you get to teach young people about smoking—a big health issue. We went to an elementary school and taught the facts, the consequences, and the statistics about people who die because of smoking. We used a metal bowl and a bunch of metal BBs to teach our lesson. Each BB represented a certain number of people who had died of a specific condition, such as AIDS, car crashes... etc. When dropped, the BBs made a pretty loud sound. But when we dropped the BBs representing the 450 thousand people a year who die of smoking related diseases—more than all the others causes combined—the kids were totally amazed! "Next, we made a cigarette out of household chemicals. We took simple household ingredients that are in cigarettes like nail polish remover, rubbing alcohol, and battery acid, and used maple syrup to represent tar, lawn grass to represent tobacco, other products to represent the rat poison and arsenic in cigarettes. We also put on a skit, teaching ways to say no when someone offers you cigarettes. Other TATU members made an anti-smoking video." TATU groups write letters to legislators and will hold a rally at the state capital.

STRENGTH IN NUMBERS "It's hard to have just one person teach a large group of people," Mike says. "With a lot of volunteers, everyone has a different approach, and those approaches are interesting and unique. You can also reach many more people." He continues, "If you care about others, you help them to choose a positive environment that will be good for them, including one in which people don't smoke."

MIKE'S STORY
1. What strategies have Mike and his group used to teach people about the dangers of tobacco use?
2. What values have they demonstrated in the process?

YOUR STORY
1. What steps can you take with your peers to make a difference on the issue of tobacco use?
2. What benefits of health and character might all of you gain in taking these actions not alone but together?

TEENS MAKING A DIFFERENCE **541**

SCHOOL-TO-CAREER

SMOKING IN THE WORKPLACE. Some states and communities have laws governing smoking in the workplace. Beyond local or state laws, many companies have no-smoking policies or designated smoking areas. Have students find out what state or local laws govern smoking in local workplaces. Suggest that students read newspaper employment columns and have them count the number of references to a nonsmoking environment. You might suggest that they read want ads for domestic help and see how many specify nonsmokers. Then have them contact several places of employment and inquire about their smoking policies. End with a class discussion about how adequately workers are protected from secondhand smoke.

Teens Making a Difference

Teaming Up Against Tobacco

Discussion. Ask students to share experiences in which working with other teens for a good and healthful cause was much easier, effective, enjoyable and/or more inspiring than working alone. After students have shared their experiences, have them read the Teens Making a Difference feature and discuss it, answering the questions at the end of the feature.

Ask students to share strategies other than those presented in the feature that teens might use in helping to teach younger students, then high school students about the dangers of tobacco products. If you have time, read the following statements by Mike Delota, the featured teen, and ask students to react to each:

- *If you are responsible, you'll try to be in an environment where people don't smoke. If you smoke, you'll try to get help to quit and won't get other people hooked.*
- *When it comes to stopping tobacco use, education is the key.*
- *You need to be a good role model to younger people.*

Class Activity. Invite in a speaker from the American Lung Association to talk about the dangers of tobacco use. If you do not have a TATU program or similar anti-tobacco group at your school, ask the speaker to help you set one up. On another day, as Mike's group did, have students collect and share magazine advertisements for tobacco products, then remake them, turning these ads into displays of the dangers of the very products being advertised.

Answers. *Mike's Story*
1. Students may mention any of the strategies mentioned in the feature.
2. Answers may include caring, responsibility, initiative, perseverance, civic duty.

Responses. *Your Story*
1. Answers will vary.
2. Answers will vary.

Making Responsible Decisions

1. Mike likes getting a ride to school with Ashley, but he dislikes her smoking.
2. Mike could (a) find another way to get to school; (b) ask Ashley not to smoke on the way to school, discussing the health risks she is taking; (c) try to ignore his own physical discomfort and his dislike of the cigarette smell.
3. Mike might (a) have to walk or get a less convenient ride to school, but avoid the risks and unpleasantness of Ashley's cigarettes; (b) risk offending Ashley, but also have a chance of convincing her not to smoke during their ride together; (c) avoid offending Ashley, but continue to risk his own health and comfort.
4. Mike values both his health and his comfort.
5. Responses will vary.
6. Encourage students to consider both the short- and long-term consequences of their decisions.

L2 Decision Making

For further study on making responsible decisions, assign *Decision-Making Activity 24* in the TCR. 🖝

TOBACCO (Side 2)

Chapter 15: Ways to Say No: "No Thanks"

Frames 42339-43157

Chapter 16: Ways to Say No: Changing the Subject

Frames 43162-44973

Making Responsible Decisions

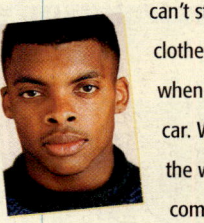

Fresh-Air Friends

Mike has been carpooling with Ashley for the past three months. Having a ride to school has made Mike's life easier, but there is a problem: Ashley smokes. After riding in her car, he feels tightness in his chest and even coughs. He also can't stand the way his clothes and hair smell when he gets out of the car. When he opens the window, Ashley complains that the wind messes up her hair. Mike doesn't want to seem ungrateful or lose his ride. He just wants to be "fresh-air friends." What should Mike do?

What Would You Do?

Apply the six steps of the decision-making process to Mike's problem.

1. **State the situation.**
2. **List the options.**
3. **Weigh the possible outcomes.**
4. **Consider your values.**
5. **Make a decision and act.**
6. **Evaluate the decision.**

---

hotlink

stress management For more information on stress and stress management, see Chapter 9, page 224.

▼ *More and more public places are becoming smoke-free.*

ACTIVITY *List those places in your community that you know are smoke-free.*

SMOKE FREE ENVIRONMENT

PACIFIC FINANCIAL COMPANIES
PROVIDE A SMOKE FREE ENVIRONMENT.
PLEASE RESPECT OUR NON SMOKING POLICY
BY REFRAINING FROM SMOKING
WITHIN THIS BUILDING AND
CENTER ATRIUM AREA.

THANK YOU.

Tips for Quitting

Although each person might approach quitting tobacco use in his or her own way, certain general tips apply. For example, those thinking about quitting might first observe how much they smoke, when and where they smoke, what triggers the desire for a cigarette, and how those needs might be addressed in other, more healthful ways. They might also begin to think of and even write down the costs of smoking, in dollars spent, health concerns, and negative reactions from family, friends, and others. They might make a list of the reasons they want to quit smoking, post the list around the house, and read it whenever the urge to smoke arises. Sometimes learning **stress management** techniques can help someone through the withdrawal process. Among the basic steps a person should take when quitting tobacco use are:

- Setting a specific date for when the person will quit and sticking to this date.
- Setting short-terms goals to reinforce one's decision.
- Deciding which approach or combination of approaches will be used to become tobacco-free.
- Getting one's environment ready for a new smoke-free life.
- Setting up a support system whereby the person is helped through the process and later helped to stay smoke-free.

PROMOTING COMPREHENSIVE SCHOOL HEALTH

DESIRED RESULTS FOR STUDENTS. As a measurement of the success of a comprehensive school health program, an exiting student should demonstrate the following: is self-directed as a learner and an individual; has high self-esteem as a learner and an individual; is able to solve problems, make decisions, and understand cause-effect relationships; accepts responsibility for his or her own physical, mental and emotional, and social well-being; has academic skills essential to being a productive member of society. For more information, consult *Promoting a Comprehensive School Health Program* in the TCR. 🖝

Toward a Smoke-Free Society

Increasingly, the American public is working toward becoming smoke-free. As people realize that the decision to smoke can affect not only their own health but also the health of loved ones, the drive to become a smoke-free society increases. Evidence of this can be seen in public places across the country.

Whole towns are now banding together to restrict smoking. Once-lax laws prohibiting the sale of tobacco products to minors are being more strictly enforced. Tobacco licenses are being revoked when stores and store chains sell cigarettes to minors. Vending machines are being moved out of unsupervised areas. Many cities are passing laws that restrict smoking in public places, such as restaurants, civic buildings, business offices, and lobbies. Airlines now prohibit smoking on commercial flights. Hotels have whole floors for nonsmokers. Laws are being proposed to ban smoking in all enclosed public spaces. Increasingly, the law is taking into consideration the rights of the nonsmoker.

Smoking is less common in private social settings, too. Meetings of all kinds are now often designated as smoke-free. Even people giving parties no longer put out ash trays, and they ask guests who smoke to do so outside. With continued commitment to health, the remaining bad news about tobacco can be turned into good news about non-use as Americans head into the future. You, too, can do your part in helping to make this society increasingly smoke-free.

keeping Fit

Weight Gain: A Common Concern

A common concern of smokers is the risk of weight gain if they quit. Although statistics vary, only approximately one-third of quitters gain weight because they substitute eating for smoking; one-third lose weight because they start a fitness program at the same time; and one-third find that their weight stays the same. If you quit smoking or using other tobacco products:

➤ Exercise vigorously and regularly.

➤ Replace the oral stimulation of using tobacco with carrot sticks or other low-calorie snacks.

➤ Don't pay attention to the scale while you're trying to stop smoking. Even if you gain a few pounds, that's much less health risk than continuing to smoke.

LESSON **3** *Review*

Reviewing Facts and Vocabulary

1. Define the word *withdrawal* and describe the process of withdrawal from nicotine.
2. Compare and contrast methods of quitting smoking, citing pros and cons of each.

Thinking Critically

3. *Analyzing.* What are some of the reasons that teens sometimes do not speak up when their peers smoke around them?
4. *Evaluating.* What positive steps have you seen taken in your home, school, community, or country in terms of becoming increasingly smoke-free?

In which of these areas does the most progress seem to have been made?

Applying Health Skills

5. *In Your School.* Take a position on your school's tobacco policies. Find out what the policies are now. Along with other class members, write individual letters to the school board about your feelings on the matter. Make suggestions where appropriate to change the policies.

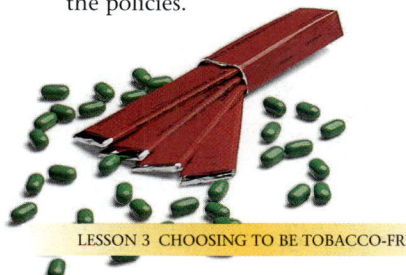

LESSON 3 CHOOSING TO BE TOBACCO-FREE **543**

Lesson 3 Review

Answers to Reviewing Facts and Vocabulary

1. Withdrawal is a process that happens when an addictive drug is no longer used. In nicotine withdrawal, a person may feel nervous or moody, or have trouble sleeping.
2. One means of quitting involves the use of a series of cigarette filters that reduces tar and nicotine levels gradually. Nicotine substitutes, such as gum, spray, or patches, deliver small amounts of the drug into the user's system while he or she is giving up the tobacco habit. Pros and cons will vary.

Answers to Thinking Critically

3.–4. Answers will vary.

Weight Gain: A Common Concern

keeping Fit

Have students read the Keeping Fit feature. Explain that weight gain is a concern for about one-third of those who quit smoking and that exercising and eating low-calorie snacks appear to be the best means of maintaining weight. Also, establishing a lifestyle involving exercise and a healthful diet proves to be motivational for many ex-smokers who strive to improve their overall health.

ASSESS

EVALUATING THE LESSON

Assign and discuss the Lesson 3 Review; then administer, grade, and discuss the *Lesson 73 Quiz* in the TCR. 🗀

RETEACHING

• Ask students to complete *Reteaching Activity 73* in the TCR. 🗀
• Use *Transparency 43* to review the process of using refusal skills. 🖌

ENRICHMENT

• Instruct students to research the impact smoking would have on a person who is diabetic. Describe the potential problems a diabetic smoker would have that a nondiabetic smoker may not experience.
• Ask students to research the connection between smoking and high cholesterol.

CLOSE

Encourage students to support each other in an effort to stay tobacco-free.

Chapter 24 **543**

Health **Skills** Activities

Health Skills Activities

ACTIVITY 1
HEALTH SKILLS

Analyzing Influences, Health Advocacy

➤ **National Standards**

This activity meets these National Health Standards: 4.2; 7.5; 7.6.

Teach

- Begin by reminding students who their audience is. Ask: What is the best way to reach people in this age group? Have them share and compare ideas.

- Suggest that students use the models you have presented as a starting point for their own anti-tobacco ads. Note that they may use humor, or a different technique that they feel will best reach their audience.

ACTIVITY 2
HEALTH SKILLS

Communication—Conflict Resolution; Health Advocacy

➤ **National Standards**

This activity meets these National Health Standards: 5.3; 7.3; 7.4.

Teach

Provide students with situations involving health risks of smoking:

A. Your best friend's parents are driving you and your friend to the mall. The father begins smoking a pipe and all the windows are closed. What would you say?

B. You and your date have been waiting for 20 minutes to be seated in a popular restaurant. A booth opens up in the smoking section and your date wants to take it. What would you say?

- Divide the class into six groups, providing Scenario A to three of the groups, Scenario B to three groups.

- Remind students of the importance of adopting a non-confrontational posture in their response. Have them review conflict resolution skills in Chapter 14.

Activity 1 — Not Allowing the Future to Go Up in Smoke

Choosing to be tobacco-free shows you care about your future. What about the future of young, impressionable children in your home and community? What steps can you take to help them avoid becoming hooked on tobacco?

Directions

1. In groups, using poster board and markers, create "anti-tobacco advertisements" that counter the claims made in typical tobacco ads.
2. Design your poster in a way that would capture the attention of elementary school-age students. One possibility would be to focus on a popular TV or video game character that appeals to students that age.
3. If possible, post the completed posters in a local elementary school.

Time
35 minutes
Materials
poster board, markers

Self-Assessment

✔ Indicated at least three reasons why young people should not start smoking.
✔ Presented a persuasive, convincing message written for a young audience.

Activity 2 — Communicating Personal Attitudes about Tobacco Use

Despite the growing awareness of the health dangers of tobacco use, there are still those who choose to smoke. What's the best way to communicate the health risks of tobacco smoke to smokers and non-smokers alike?

Directions

1. Form small groups. Read the three situations handed out by your teacher.
2. Choose one of the situations. Think about how you could effectively communicate your knowledge of the dangers of tobacco smoke to the smoker and to those in the smoker's immediate environment. Look for a non-confrontational approach.
3. Share your group's response with the class. Discuss which approaches would be most likely to encourage a smoker to put out a cigarette.

Time
30 minutes
Materials
paper, pen or pencil

Self-Assessment

✔ Included at least five negative effects of tobacco smoke on health.
✔ Used a respectful tone of voice and made use of "I" statements in your group's response.

544 CHAPTER 24 TOBACCO

ASSESSMENT SCORING

Using a four-level rubric, the student has achieved a 4 if:

ACTIVITY 1

✔ Student worked well with group at capturing and executing an idea for an anti-tobacco ad.
✔ Student provided at least three reasons why young people should not start smoking.
✔ Student's message was written for a young audience.
✔ Student's message was persuasive and convincing.

ACTIVITY 2

✔ Student helped in constructing a message that focused on at least five negative effects.
✔ Student message was written in clear and coherent fashion.
✔ Student's message did not stray from the topic.
✔ Student used a respectful tone of voice and made use of "I" statements.

HEALTH NEWS VIDEO

Targeting Teens

A recent study shows that the number of women smoking in high school is increasing. Critics of tobacco say that teens are vulnerable targets of big business.

Almost all smokers begin the deadly habit when they are teenagers. That's why tobacco companies target male and female teens with powerful ads that identify smoking with independence, rebellion, and weight loss.

Of course, the ads don't mention the conditions that are really linked with smoking: heart disease, lung cancer, reduced fertility, and premature menopause.

Although companies deny that they target teens, the statistics show that many teens are listening to tobacco ads and ignoring their health.

Play the Video

CNN. All Rights Reserved.

Think About It

▶ Do you think tobacco companies target teenagers—both males and females? Or do you believe the companies' claims that they target only older smokers?

▶ "Ad placement" refers to the specific magazines or newspapers where advertisements are printed. How can ad placement target a teen audience without using teen magazines?

CNN HEALTH NEWS **545**

MORE ABOUT . . . . .

RELIABLE SOURCES. Emphasize the importance of considering the source of funding when evaluating any medical research or report. For example, tobacco companies or other private organizations with a strong financial interest might fund a report that downplays the dangers of secondary smoke. Similarly, reporting on legal cases concerning tobacco use can be strongly biased.

Emphasize the importance of looking for reliable, impartial sources for data on any health issue. Reliable sources for up-to-date information about tobacco and smoking include private organizations such as the American Lung Association and the American Cancer Society

---

CNN HEALTH NEWS

Targeting Teens
Video Segment 14 (Time –1:54)

Objectives. After viewing the video, students should be able to identify the dangers of tobacco use and recognize how teens, both male and female, are targeted by tobacco companies.

Motivator. Draw a bull's-eye target on the chalkboard. Have students discuss what it means for an advertising campaign to be "targeted" at a specific audience. Explain that marketers use sophisticated strategies to create campaigns designed to reach very specific markets, such as women between the ages of 13 and 17. Then have students view Video Segment 14, "Targeting Teens," to extend their understanding of how advertising campaigns can target teens.

Teach

- Discuss the reasons why tobacco companies are interested in targeting teen audiences. Emphasize that these companies try to take advantage of peer pressure and common teen emotions to make an unhealthy habit seem attractive or powerful.
- Have teams work together to complete anti-smoking advertisements. Encourage teams to brainstorm ideas. Then assign specific jobs to team members who will create the final announcements. Allow teams to share or display their work. Ask viewers to identify particularly effective slogans and images.

Investigate. Have students collect examples of advertisements that make misleading or unhealthy statements. Students can create classroom or school displays that refute inaccurate claims or expose persuasive advertising techniques. Make sure advertisements are adequately analyzed and refuted before they are posted. You may wish to cover or crop any visible brand names.

Close. Point out that it is almost impossible to avoid advertisements, which are found in magazines, billboards, and newspapers, as well as those on radio, television, and the Internet. Given the persistence of advertising in most modern environments, have students discuss how they can resist the dangerous message disseminated by tobacco companies.

CHECKING COMPREHENSION

- Assign and discuss the chapter review.
- Use the MindJogger Videoquiz to review the chapter. ●

CHAPTER 24 REVIEW ANSWERS

Using Health Terms

1. stimulant
2. carcinogens
3. addiction
4. nicotine
5. carbon monoxide
6. tar
7. smokeless tobacco
8. leukoplakia
9. sidestream smoke
10. mainstream smoke
11. emphysema
12. nicotine substitute
13. nicotine withdrawal

Recalling the Facts

1. Any three: because they think it makes them look sophisticated, because of peer pressure and advertising, because they think it will make their social insecurities disappear, because they think the harmful effects of smoking occur only after years of use.
2. Nicotine is the addictive drug in tobacco. Carcinogens are substances that cause cancer. Carbon monoxide is a poisonous gas. Paragraphs will vary.
3. Oral cancers are more likely to occur in pipe and cigar smokers.
4. Specialty cigarettes are more harmful than standard cigarettes because the added ingredients generally contain more toxic substances.
5. The dangers of using smokeless tobacco include the fact that the toxins are swallowed, introducing them into the digestive and urinary systems. Irritation to mouth tissues often causes cancer of the

Using Health Terms

On a separate sheet of paper, write the term that best matches each definition below.

LESSON 1

1. A drug that increases the action of the central nervous system, the heart, and other organs.
2. Cancer-causing substances.
3. A physiological or psychological dependence on a substance or activity.
4. The addictive drug in cigarettes.
5. A colorless, odorless, poisonous gas in cigarette smoke that passes through the lungs into the blood.
6. A thick, sticky, dark fluid produced when tobacco burns.
7. Tobacco that is sniffed through the nose or chewed.

LESSON 2

8. Thickened, white, leathery-appearing spots on the inside of a smokeless tobacco user's mouth that can develop into cancer of the mouth.
9. The smoke that comes from burning tobacco.
10. The smoke that the smoker blows off.
11. Destruction of the tiny air sacs in the lungs through which oxygen is absorbed into the body.

LESSON 3

12. Manufactured forms of nicotine that deliver small amounts of the drug into the user's system while he or she is trying to give up the tobacco habit.
13. The process that occurs when nicotine, an addictive drug, is no longer used.

Recalling the Facts

Using complete sentences, answer the following questions.

LESSON 1

1. Give three reasons why teens smoke.
2. Define the words *nicotine, carcinogens,* and *carbon monoxide,* and use them in a paragraph identifying some of the dangers of smoking.
3. What kinds of cancers are more likely to occur in pipe and cigar smokers than cigarette smokers?
4. How are specialty cigarettes generally more or less harmful than standard cigarettes?
5. What are three dangers of using smokeless tobacco, and why do some teens mistakenly think it is safe to use?

LESSON 2

6. How serious is the threat of developing cancer from breathing passive cigarette smoke? The risk of heart disease?
7. List five risks associated with smoking during pregnancy.
8. What is the difference between mainstream and sidestream smoke?
9. Name three effects that cigarette smoking can have on the respiratory system.
10. List five rights of the nonsmoker.

LESSON 3

11. Describe what happens during the withdrawal process.
12. Offer five tips for quitting smoking.
13. What steps have federal, state, and local governments taken in recent years to discourage teen smoking?

mouth and tongue. It also damages the gums and teeth, causes bad breath and tooth discoloration, and decreases the ability to smell and taste. Teens often think smokeless tobacco is safe to use because you don't inhale it.

6. The risk of developing cancer and heart disease from breathing passive smoke is the same as if you were actually smoking.

7. Risks associated with smoking during pregnancy include low birth weight, increased risk of stillbirth, increased risk of death of the infant after birth, mental deficiencies, and developmental deficiencies in the child.

8. Mainstream smoke is the smoke that is blown off by a smoker. Sidestream smoke is the smoke that comes from burning tobacco.

Thinking Critically

LESSON 1

1. ***Evaluating.*** Evaluate three strategies for reducing smoking rates. Consider their effectiveness with teen groups.
2. ***Evaluating.*** How effective do you think laws forbidding the sale of cigarettes to minors are?
3. ***Synthesizing.*** What other measures might effectively decrease the use of cigarettes by teens, considering what is known about what has not worked?

LESSON 2

4. ***Evaluating.*** Should people who smoke be denied jobs because they are at greater risk for many serious illnesses? Why or why not?

LESSON 3

5. ***Comparing and Contrasting.*** Interview a former smoker. Ask him or her what his or her life and health were like while smoking and after giving it up. Ask what methods he or she used to get smoke-free.

Making the Connection

1. ***Science.*** Investigate the most common kind of tobacco plant used in tobacco products. Make a poster showing an example of this plant type. Include information about its classification, growing conditions and season, flowers, plant size, common diseases, growing regions, and standard human uses.

2. ***Social Studies.*** In your local library, look through popular magazines from the 1930s, 1940s, and 1950s. Evaluate all ads that show people smoking cigarettes. Write three paragraphs, one for each decade, summarizing what each decade's attitude about cigarette smoking seemed to be.

BEYOND THE CLASSROOM

PARENTAL INVOLVEMENT As a family, brainstorm ways that you can work together to become a smoke-free household if there are smokers in the family. Help others outside the family who smoke to learn about the dangers of tobacco use. Together, make and post no-smoking signs in your home. Create a no-tobacco-use pledge and have all family members sign it. Post this, too, within your home.

COMMUNITY INVOLVEMENT Conduct a survey of your neighborhood or local business center, recording data on the places where smoking is allowed and those where it is not. Compile this data with your observations, and write a series of articles for your local paper about what you have observed.

SCHOOL-TO-CAREER
Exploring Careers. Interview a pulmonary specialist or a respiratory therapist. Ask the person what education is needed for his or her career, what training in the field, and what kinds of practice or facility he or she is part of. In particular, ask about the effects of smoking that he or she sees in patients under his or her care.

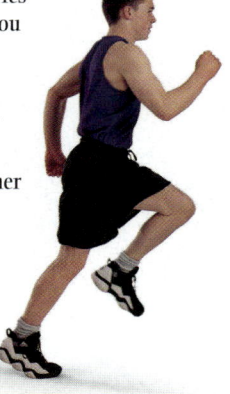

CHAPTER 24 REVIEW **547**

Thinking Critically
1.–5. Answers will vary.

Making the Connection
1. Projects will vary.
2. Reports will vary.

Evaluate
- Use the reproducible *Chapter 24 Test* in the TCR, or construct your own using the Testmaker software.
- Use *Performance Assessment Activity 24* in the TCR.

Enrichment
Have students complete *Cross-Curriculum Activity 24* in the TCR.

Beyond the Classroom
Keep students involved in the community, and encourage parent participation by assigning the activities on this page for students to work on outside of class.

---

9. It can destroy cilia in the bronchi, create conditions that allow the development of cancer, cause emphysema, irritate the bronchi, and cause bronchitis.
10. Answers will vary.
11. Withdrawal from nicotine causes moodiness, irritability, and lack of sleep.
12. Begin by making a commitment to quit. Set a target date for quitting.

Take intermediate steps to help you reach your goal. Get help meeting your goal. Plan a healthy way to reward yourself once you have quit.

13. Taxes on cigarette sales have been raised. Penalties for selling cigarettes to minors have been stiffened and enforced. Cigarette vending machines have been removed from unsupervised areas.

Alcohol

	FEATURES	CLASSROOM RESOURCES

ACTIVITIES

- ☞ Cross-Curriculum Activity 25
- ☞ Health Lab 25
- ☞ Health Skills Activities 25
- ☞ Parent Letter and Activities 25

ASSESSMENT

- ☞ Chapter 25 Test
- ☞ Performance Assessment Activity 25
- 💾 Testmaker Software

STUDENT ACTIVITIES WORKBOOK

- ☞ Applying Health Skills 74–76
- ☞ Study Guide 25
- ☞ Vocabulary Activity 25

STUDENT DIVERSITY STRATEGIES

- 🎧 Audiocassette Program (English)
- 🎧 Audiocassette Program (Spanish)
- ☞ Spanish Parent Letters and Activities
- ☞ Spanish Summaries, Quizzes, and Activities

MULTIMEDIA COMPONENTS

- 🎧 English Audiocassette Program
- 🎧 Spanish Audiocassette Program
- 🔴 MindJogger Videodisc and VHS program
- 🔴 ABCNews InterActive™ VHS/Videodisc Series

MODULES

- *The Reality of Drugs,* Student Edition
- *The Reality of Drugs,* Teacher's Annotated Edition

National Health Education Standards

One of the main goals of the National Health Education Standards is to move students toward "health literacy." Health literacy is the capacity of individuals to obtain, interpret, and understand basic health information and services and the competence to use such information and services in ways which promote health. The health standards were developed by applying the characteristics of a well-educated, literate person within the context of health. The health literate person is:

- a critical thinker and problem solver
- a self-directed learner
- a responsible, productive citizen
- an effective communicator

Listed below are the Health Education Standards Performance Indicators addressed in each lesson of this chapter.

Lesson	Health Standards Performance Indicators
1	1.4, 3.1, 3.3, 4.2
2	1.3, 1.4, 1.7, 3.3
3	2.4, 2.6, 6.1, 7.4

ONLINE RESOURCES

HEALTH Online

For a fresh approach to health topics and an in-depth look at health issues, use these online resources found under Teacher Resources at **health.glencoe.com**.

- **BLOCK SCHEDULE LESSON PLANS** Reinforce health concepts with outside readings selected especially for students. Each reading is accompanied by a lesson plan and activities to enhance
  - Reading Skills
  - Cross Curriculum
  - Media Literacy

- **TECHNOLOGY PROJECTS** Instructions and suggestions on how to use computer, Internet, and software with health lessons.

- **HEALTH UPDATES** Timely topics in health news, including late-breaking medical advances and updates on teen risk behaviors.

Out of Time?

If time does not permit teaching this chapter, you may use these features: Building Health Skills on page 558 and Making Responsible Decisions on page 564.

BLOCK SCHEDULING

Block scheduling provides extended time for hands-on projects and activities. Use the following activities to engage students, provide further depth, and vary your instructional techniques:

- Health Lab (30 minutes) **pg. 552**
- Health Skills Activity (60–90 minutes) **pg. 568**

Alcohol

CHAPTER OVERVIEW

Chapter 25 discusses the health risks of using alcohol, the process of alcoholism, and the costs of alcohol use to the family and society as a whole. It also explores influences and reasons that teens give for drinking, and concludes that abstaining from alcohol is the only healthful choice.

LESSON 1 Drinking alcohol is a high-risk behavior. Many young people will face pressures to drink. The reasons teenagers give for drinking are not very different from those reasons given by adults.

LESSON 2 Some effects of alcohol are immediate. Other effects are not seen for some time, even years. Drinking and driving has become a serious and widespread problem. Alcohol is particularly dangerous if combined with other drugs or consumed during pregnancy.

LESSON 3 For some people, alcohol becomes a serious problem that affects their lives and the lives of those around them. In some cases, it becomes life-threatening. Millions of young people are choosing not to drink.

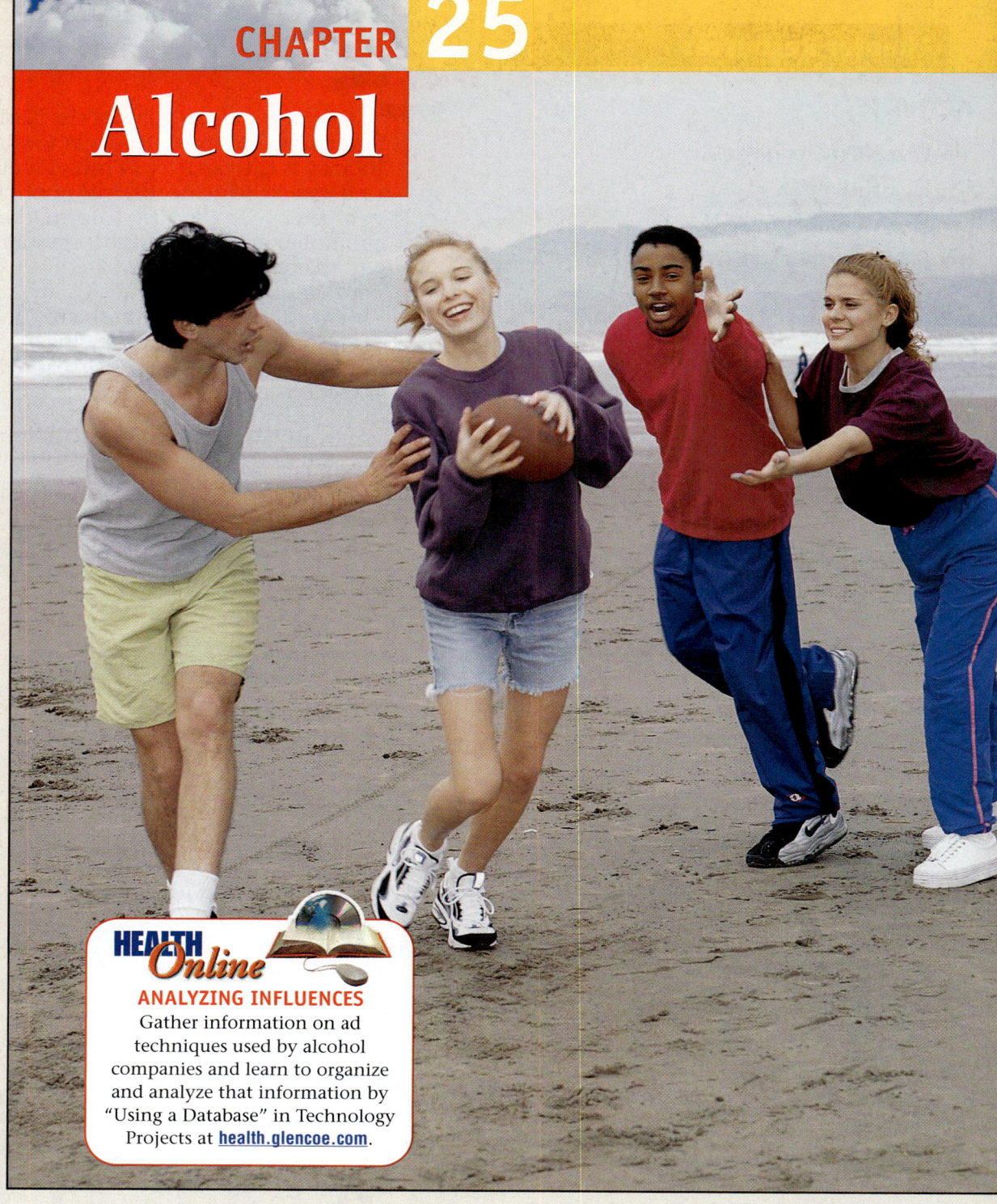

CHAPTER 25

Alcohol

HEALTH Online

ANALYZING INFLUENCES
Gather information on ad techniques used by alcohol companies and learn to organize and analyze that information by "Using a Database" in Technology Projects at **health.glencoe.com**.

Hands-On Health

TEACHING STRATEGY

Considering Alcohol-Related Risks
Guide students in considering and ranking a variety of risks teens face when they experiment with alcohol. See Activity 23, "Ranking Risk Behaviors," in the *Hands-On Health: Creative Teaching Strategies* booklet.

Time Needed
20 minutes

Supplies
• sets of teacher-prepared cards identifying 7 different risk behaviors

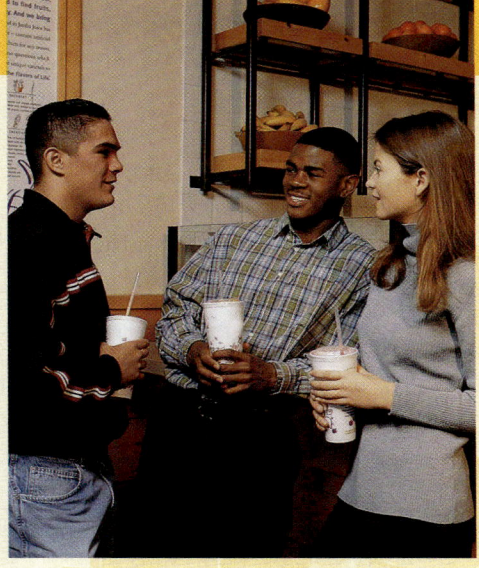

> **Drunkenness is nothing but voluntary madness.**
>
> —SENECA
> ROMAN STATESMAN AND WRITER, (C. 4 B.C.–65 A.D.)

Quick Write Use the word *responsibility* in a sentence describing some of the reasons why teens should not drink alcohol.

Personal Health Inventory

Self-Inventory Write the numbers 1–10 on a sheet of paper. Read each statement below and respond by writing *yes*, *no*, or *sometimes* for each item. Write a *yes* only for items that you practice regularly. Save your responses.

1	I have made a decision not to drink any alcohol.
2	I don't buy alcoholic beverages or ask anyone to buy them for me.
3	I don't use alcohol to escape from my problems, relieve stress, or help me to feel more comfortable with others.
4	When other teens are drinking and offer me alcohol, I say no.
5	I don't attend parties where I know there will be a lot of drinking, and I don't take part in drinking contests or dares.
6	I never drink and drive or ride in a car with a driver who has been drinking.
7	Because I don't drink, I can stay in control of my behavior.
8	I don't rescue or cover for friends who drink or get drunk.
9	I don't organize my thinking, my day, my friendships, or my social life around alcohol.
10	I know and practice stress-reducing techniques.

Follow-up After completing the chapter, retake this self-inventory. Pick two items that you need to work on and set a goal to improve your health behaviors.

INTRODUCING THE CHAPTER

Personal Health Inventory

Emphasize the importance of responding to the Self-Inventory statements openly and honestly, and remind students that this activity is strictly for their own use; they will not be asked to share or discuss any of their responses. Then provide time for students to read the Self-Inventory statements and record their responses in their private Health Journals on a page labeled "My Level of Commitment to Being Alcohol-Free."

- Explain to students that the number one drug problem in the U.S. is alcohol. Despite the fact that there are millions of alcoholics, many people do not even consider alcohol a drug. A great deal of misinformation and misunderstanding about alcohol exists. Getting the correct facts will help students know the dangers when someone asks them to take a drink. Tell students they will learn more about alcohol and its risk to their well-being as they study this chapter.
- Let students describe the photographs on these two pages. Ask: What could some of the negative effects of using alcohol be in these situations? What would some of the positive effects of avoiding alcohol be? Then have students complete the Quick Write on this page. Encourage volunteers to share their responses.
- Distribute Parent Letter 25 in the *Parent Letter and Activities* booklet in the TCR. ✏

TECHNOLOGY OPTIONS

ABCNEWS INTERACTIVE™ You may wish to use *Alcohol* with this chapter. For your convenience, use the separate *ABCNews InterActive™ Bar Code Correlation* that accompanies the *Glencoe Health* program. 🔴

MINDJOGGER
VIDEOQUIZ

To preview or review chapter content, you may wish to use the *MindJogger Videoquiz* that accompanies Chapter 25. 🔴

Alcohol Use: A High-Risk Behavior

FOCUS

LESSON OBJECTIVES

After studying this lesson, students should be able to

- list reasons young people choose to drink.
- describe some factors that affect teen alcohol use.

MOTIVATOR

Write the following on the chalkboard for students to work on while attendance is being taken: *Make two vertical columns on a sheet of paper. In the left column, list at least three reasons teens give for drinking. In the right column, list at least three reasons teens give for choosing not to drink.*

INTRODUCING THE LESSON

Ask students to share their responses to the Motivator. Reinforce the reasons given for teenagers' *not* drinking. Explain to students that alcohol is not only a physical problem, but it also affects mental, emotional, and social aspects of health, as they will learn from this lesson.

INTRODUCING HEALTH TERMS

- Have students define *intoxication* and use it in a sentence. Discuss behaviors associated with drinking alcohol.
- Ask students to complete Vocabulary Activity 25 and Chapter Study Guide 25 in the *Student Workbook.* ☞

Alcohol Use: A High-Risk Behavior

Imagine turning on your TV or opening a newspaper and seeing a large, splashy ad promoting the sale and use of a dangerous drug such as cocaine or heroin. Most people would be outraged and shocked. Yet, ads of this kind appear every day. The drug's name is *alcohol.* It can cause accidents and other serious problems.

HEALTH TERMS

ethanol

fermentation

intoxication

HEALTH CONCEPTS

- Alcohol is a drug that has great potential for abuse.
- Drinking is against the law for minors, and it can have serious legal consequences.
- Drinking alcohol can be a high-risk behavior at any age, and it can damage or even ruin one's health, one's life, and the lives of others.
- Teens who drink alcohol do so for a variety of reasons.

hotlink

depressant For more information on depressants and their effects on the body, see Chapter 26, page 582.

What Is Alcohol?

Alcohol, or more properly speaking, **ethanol**—*the type of alcohol found in alcoholic beverages*—is a powerful drug. Ethanol can be made synthetically, or it can be produced naturally by fermentation of fruits, vegetables, or grains. **Fermentation** is *the chemical action of yeast on sugars.* Water, flavoring, and minerals are added to ethanol to form one of several beverages, including beer and wine. Alcohol can also be processed to create spirits—or liquors—such as whiskey, rye, gin, and vodka. All have the potential to do serious harm.

At first, alcohol may give the drinker a certain energy and "buzz." Soon, however, its true nature as a **depressant** takes over, causing the central nervous system to slow down. At some point in the consumption of alcohol, a state of intoxication sets in. **Intoxication** is *physical and mental impairment resulting from the use of alcohol* and can

---

Lesson 1 Resources

TEACHER'S CLASSROOM RESOURCES

☞ **Concept Map** Activity 74

☞ **Lesson 74 Quiz**

☞ **Lesson Plan 74**

☞ **Parent Letter and Activities 25**

☞ **Reteaching** Activity 74

STUDENT WORKBOOK

☞ **Applying Health Skills 74**

☞ **Chapter Study Guide 25**

☞ **Vocabulary** Activity 25

MULTIMEDIA

◉ **ABCNews InterActive™ VHS/Videodisc,** *Alcohol*

range from an inability to walk to unconsciousness. Because the amount of alcohol needed for intoxication varies from person to person and because alcohol impairs judgment, driving a car or using heavy machinery when under its influence can have deadly consequences. Alcohol, moreover, robs the body of its ability to absorb key nutrients and, with long-term overuse of the drug, may lead to malnutrition.

MYTHS ABOUT ALCOHOL

MYTH

Drinking alcohol through a straw "filters out" the alcoholic content of the beverage.

FACT

The alcohol content remains the same no matter how the drug is delivered into the body.

MYTH

Someone who doesn't seem drunk can't be drunk.

FACT

Many people, particularly those with alcohol problems, can drink a lot without showing the obvious signs of drunkenness.

MYTH

Beer and wine are safer drinks than "hard" liquors like whiskey.

FACT

One standard serving of beer, wine, or spirits contains the same amount of alcohol.

MYTH

Using alcohol on weekends or only once in a while is harmless.

FACT

People can get into serious health, legal, and social situations *anytime* they use alcohol.

MYTH

When a person has a hangover, coffee, a cold shower, or fresh air will sober him or her up.

FACT

These practices do not speed up the liver's ability to break down the alcohol, so they don't help to sober a person up.

🔺 *Misconceptions about alcohol use and effects can lead you into dangerous situations.*

ACTIVITY *Investigate the truth about some myths you have heard about alcohol.*

Alcohol and Teens

In recent years, as evidence of the harm drinking can do has increased, alcohol consumption among adults has declined. Yet, among teens it has not. According to the CDC's 1998 *Youth Risk Behavior Survey,* about 80 percent of teens nationwide have had at least one alcoholic drink during their lifetime.

At any age, alcohol use can become a high-risk behavior that affects the lives and health of drinkers and of those around them. For teens in particular, alcohol can have a negative impact on schoolwork, athletic performance, friendships, family relationships, and career goals. For many, it leads to health problems and, for some, even to death. Consider these facts:

- Half of all teens who die each year die as a direct result of alcohol or other drug use, and many of these deaths happen in accidents.

CURRICULUM CONNECTIONS

FAMILY AND CONSUMER SCIENCES.
Discuss the term *empty calories*. Have students contrast the nutritional value (including number of calories) of various alcoholic and nonalcoholic beverages.

LANGUAGE ARTS. As a creative writing project, have students imagine they are an alcohol molecule entering a human body. Ask them to describe the molecule's journey through the brain, liver, bloodstream, kidneys, lung, stomach, and small intestine.

TEACH

L1 Discussing

Talk about why alcohol intake is on the rise for teens and young adults even though the average American is drinking less.

L1 Guest Speaker

Invite a guest speaker from a local alcohol rehabilitation center. Ask the speaker to address the issue of teen alcohol use. Have students take notes and write a summary of the presentation.

L1 Self-Esteem

Often someone who is drinking at a party will try to get others to drink. Ask students to share reasons why they think people do this. What can someone do to resist this pressure? How would self-esteem affect a person's ability to resist this pressure?

L1 Writing

Have students write a paragraph describing their views on drinking. Ask them to write a second paragraph describing their views on teen drinking. Request that they save these paragraphs until the end of the lesson. At that time, have students repeat the activity and compare their views, noting any changes.

ABCNEWS iNTERACTIVE

ALCOHOL (Side 1)
Chapter 3: What Is Alcohol?

Frames 2375-7204

Chapter 4: Alcohol Is a Drug

Frames 7234-11207

health lab

"SEEING THROUGH" ALCOHOL ADVERTISING

Time Needed: About two hours of class time on two or more days.

Understanding Objectives:
Students will identify some of the techniques used to promote alcohol in ads and then use those techniques to make their own ads for alcohol-free products.

Focus on the Health Lab:
Help students discuss forms of alcohol advertising they have noticed—in stores, in magazines, on billboards, and on TV, for example. Ask: To whom are these ads designed to appeal? What messages do they send? Explain that students will investigate TV advertising for alcohol in this Health Lab.

Observation and Analysis:
Suggest that students work with partners or in small groups to complete the steps of the Health Lab activity.

In Conclusion Answers:
After all the videos or posters have been presented, hold a class discussion in which students share and support their responses to these questions.

Further Investigation:
Ask students to view particular kinds of TV shows (police dramas or family comedies, for example) and analyze whether and how the use of alcohol is depicted.

health lab

"SEEING THROUGH" ALCOHOL ADVERTISING

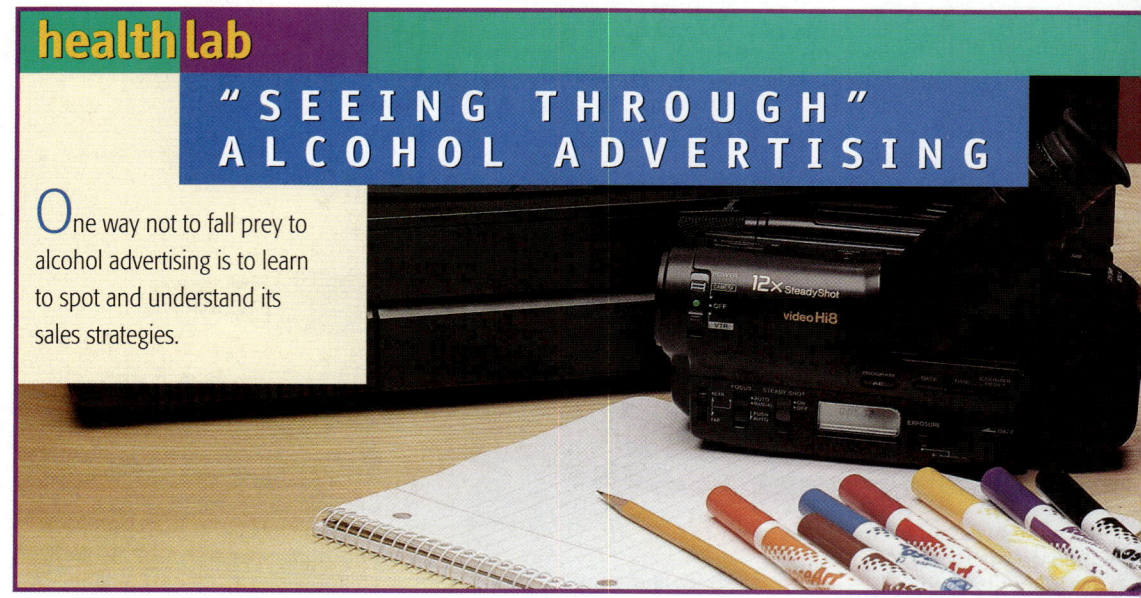

One way not to fall prey to alcohol advertising is to learn to spot and understand its sales strategies.

hot link

sexually transmitted diseases For more information on the relationship between alcohol use and sexually transmitted diseases, see Chapter 29, page 640.

dating violence For more information on alcohol as a contributing factor in dating violence, see Chapter 14, page 331.

homicides For more information on homicides and factors that trigger these violent crimes, see Chapter 14, page 324.

- Alcohol is a factor in many unplanned pregnancies as well as in cases of **sexually transmitted diseases**, **dating violence**, rapes, suicides, and **homicides**.
- Nearly 5 million problem drinkers in this country are between the ages of 14 and 17.

Consider these facts, and then consider that it is against the law for people under 21 years of age to buy, possess, or drink alcohol in the United States. Being caught drinking or drinking and driving can have serious legal consequences.

Why Young People Drink

If alcohol causes so much trouble, why do so many teens choose to drink? The reasons that teenagers give for drinking often are not very different from the reasons that adults give. Many claim that they drink

- to escape pressures or problems,
- to feel better or get over being sad or lonely,
- to deal with stress and relax,
- to feel more self-confident in social situations,
- for excitement,
- because their friends are doing it,
- to deal with boredom,
- to get away with something they are not supposed to do, and
- to fit in.

MORE ABOUT . . . . .

SAYING *NO* IN HISTORY. Early in human history, fermentation of sugar-containing mashes, such as crushed grains, was discovered; and alcoholic beverages became part of many cultures. Drinking establishments are mentioned as early as 1770 B.C. in the Code of Hammurabi of Babylonia. Choosing abstinence from alcohol has almost as long a history. Several attempts were made by the Chinese to prohibit alcohol consumption, but all met with incomplete success. Religious prohibitions have been more successful. Buddhists in India have avoided alcohol since the sixth century B.C., as do the members of the Hindu Brahmin caste. The Qu'ran, written in the seventh century, prohibits drinking alcohol for all faithful followers of Islam.

What you will need
- a notebook and pencil
- a television
- video camera (optional)
- poster board, crayons, colored pencils, or markers

What you will do

1. Divide a sheet of notebook paper into two columns. Label the first column *Images,* and the second *Messages.*

2. Tune in to one or more TV events, such as a professional sports event, in which alcohol products are likely to be advertised. Carefully watch one such commercial. In the first column, list the kinds of images used—including settings, people, and activities—as well as music. Describe the overall mood or tone of the commercial. In the second column, write down the implied messages about the use of alcohol.

3. Using techniques similar to those in the commercial, make either a short video ad or a poster showing teens in a healthful and happy recreational setting. Your ad is to "sell" healthful, alcohol-free products.

4. Present your findings and your video or poster to the class.

In conclusion

1. In what ways was the ad you examined inaccurate and deceptive?

2. Do you think alcohol products should be advertised on television? On billboards? In magazines and newspapers? Why or why not?

3. Do you understand what kind of advertising appeals to you and attracts you, and what kind doesn't? What do you think would be the most effective means of getting teens who drink to understand the dangers of drinking and to become alcohol free?

L2 Researching

Ask students to find out what the state laws are regarding the purchase, possession, and consumption of alcohol by minors and the sale or delivery of alcohol to minors.

Did You Know?

Many children with fetal alcohol syndrome and fetal alcohol effects have trouble understanding the consequences of their behavior. The average medical and institutional costs for one FAS child in a lifetime has been estimated at 1.4 million dollars. According to the Centers for Disease Control and Prevention, despite warnings, the number of drinking pregnant women in this country was four times higher in 1995 than in 1991.

ALCOHOL (Side 1)
Chapter 14: Advertising and the Media

Frames 49788-53256

Factors that Affect Teen Alcohol Use

Friends are often an important, although unconscious, influence on a teenager's choice to drink. There is pressure to drink, and it can be very difficult to say no, especially when you want to be accepted as part of the group.

The family is another major influence on a teen's attitudes and behavior with respect to drinking. If a teen sees his or her parents use alcohol when they have problems or when they want to socialize or celebrate, there is a greater likelihood the teen will do the same.

Yet another factor in the decision of many teens to drink is the portrayal of alcohol in advertisements. Advertisers spend over $1 billion a year promoting alcoholic beverages. These advertisers try to keep their product names prominent so that people remember them and are influenced when making a decision. By the time teens reach ninth grade, most will have seen more ads for wine and beer than for any other product. Many of these ads, moreover, are aimed at a teen audience and include one or more of the following:

- young people who are handsome, attractive, fit, and healthy-looking.
- a partylike atmosphere with upbeat music.
- an otherwise healthful environment, often in the beauty of the outdoors.
- problem-free drinking.
- a verbal message that really does not say anything about the risks of using the product.

Did You Know?

➤ Approximately 100 million Americans use alcohol.

➤ Ten teenagers a day die in alcohol-related crashes.

➤ About half of all fatal car crashes in this country involve alcohol.

➤ According to the National Safe Boating Council, alcohol is involved in more than 50 percent of the boating accidents in the United States.

➤ New efforts are being made to pass and enforce convictions for drunk boaters.

LESSON 1   ALCOHOL USE: A HIGH-RISK BEHAVIOR   **553**

HEALTH LITERACY

RESPONSIBLE/PRODUCTIVE CITIZEN. Tell students to monitor several popular TV shows for several weeks. Instruct them to keep track of the TV characters' alcohol use. Ask: Do the characters that the audience admires drink frequently? Do dates and celebrations always involve alcohol? Is alcohol always served in surroundings that suggest glamour, romance, prosperity, popularity, or some other trait the audience desires? Do characters head for their cars after drinking? Is drunkenness considered funny or enjoyable? Are the effects of alcohol portrayed? Have students rank the TV programs they monitored from most responsible to least responsible in portrayal of alcohol use. Suggest that they write to the producers of these programs commending their treatment of alcohol or suggesting that they send a more healthful message.

CHARACTER IN ACTION

Steering Clear of Trouble

Have students discuss the ways underage drinking or serving alcohol to teens compromises the core ethical values of caring, responsibility, trustworthiness, and civic duty. Ask students to brainstorm other values that drinking may put in jeopardy.

ASSESS

EVALUATING THE LESSON

Assign and discuss the Lesson 1 Review; then administer, grade, and discuss the *Lesson 74 Quiz* in the TCR. 📖

RETEACHING

- Divide the class into two halves. Have one half list and briefly discuss five reasons that teens give for drinking. Have the other half list and discuss 12 reasons commonly given for not drinking. Afterward, combine both groups, and close with a discussion of the negative social consequences of drinking.
- Ask students to complete *Reteaching Activity 74* in the TCR. 📖

ENRICHMENT

- Select volunteers to interview college students about the kinds of pressure to drink that they face at the college level. Have interviewers report their results to the class.

CLOSE

Ask students to state the most important concepts learned in the lesson.

CHARACTER IN ACTION

Steering Clear of Trouble

Choosing to stay alcohol-free demonstrates personal **responsibility** and helps to ensure your own and others' well-being. Consider these facts from national studies.

➤ Driving under the influence of alcohol may also diminish driving ability by as much as 20 percent.

➤ At low doses, alcohol has some of the effects of a stimulant; at higher doses, it acts as a depressant. Both impair driving ability.

➤ Even small amounts of alcohol can reduce your vision.

➤ Alcohol decreases fear, affects judgment, and increases one's likelihood of taking dangerous risks.

Character Check Create a short booklet that offers tips on why teens should not combine drinking and driving.

EFFECTS OF ADVERTISING

The hidden message advertisers are sending through these images is that alcohol is an aid to successful, romantic, and problem-free relationships, working situations, and recreational opportunities. Advertisers would not spend the large sums of money they do if these ads did not accomplish their purpose. It is rare to see a sporting event these days that is not sponsored in part by a liquor or beer company. Car races, boat races, and tennis events are just a few examples. The brand names of alcohol are in abundance on college campuses where basketball and football scoreboards are sometimes donated to a school just to make the name of the company or product visible.

One of the most effective advertising gimmicks is having the consumer buy products with the name of the company on them. T-shirts and hats are examples of this type of promotion. By wearing the product, a person actually provides free advertising for the company.

You and Your Decisions About Drinking

Everyone has the need to belong, to feel loved, and to feel important. It is possible to meet these needs in many ways. Drinking does not have to be one of them.

Using alcohol in any form has no place in your life. It is unhealthful, unsafe, and in most places illegal. As you apply your decision-making skills to the question of whether to drink, you will see that the negative consequences greatly outweigh any imagined benefits. In the remainder of this chapter, you will learn more about these consequences, and you will learn strategies for saying no to alcohol.

LESSON 1 Review

Reviewing Facts and Vocabulary

1. What is the name of the drug contained in alcoholic beverages?
2. Identify five reasons why many teens drink alcohol.
3. Name three techniques that advertisers use to get people to buy alcohol products.

Thinking Critically

4. **Evaluating.** Some teens use alcohol to deal with their emotional distress. Is this an effective approach to solving their problems? Why or why not?
5. **Synthesizing.** Summarize the reasons why so many adults use alcohol in spite of all the potential harmful consequences.
6. **Evaluating.** Why do you think older Americans usually are not featured as models or actors in ads selling alcohol products?

Applying Health Skills

7. **In Your Home.** Interview a parent and grandparent (or people from each of those generations) to find out what attitudes, practices, laws, and penalties existed regarding alcohol sale and use when they were teens.

Lesson 1 Review

Answers to Reviewing Facts and Vocabulary

1. The drug is ethanol.
2. Any five: teens drink to escape pressures or problems, to feel better or get over being sad or lonely, to deal with stress and relax, to feel more self-confident in social situations, to get away with something they're not supposed to do, and to fit in.
3. See page 553 for a list of advertising techniques for persuasion.

Answers to Thinking Critically

4.–6. Answers will vary.

What Alcohol Does to the Body

When someone has a drink, the alcohol follows the same path that food does as it travels through the digestive system. Once in the blood, alcohol affects every system in the body. Some of these effects are short-term. Others are not apparent for some time, perhaps even years. In either case, alcohol can do damage.

HEALTH TERMS

blood alcohol concentration

designated drivers

fatty liver

cirrhosis

fetal alcohol syndrome

HEALTH CONCEPTS

- Alcohol can quickly impair a person's judgment and, over time, cause permanent and serious health problems.
- Being in the presence of someone under the influence of alcohol can place a person's health and safety in jeopardy.
- Alcohol consumed by a pregnant female can damage the health of her fetus for life.
- Drinking and driving or riding with a drinking driver is taking a foolish, unnecessary, and sometimes deadly risk.

hotlink

central nervous system For more information on the central nervous system and its functions, see Chapter 16, page 364.

liver For more information on the functions of the liver and ways of caring for this vital organ, see Chapter 18, page 416.

Short-Term Effects of Drinking

The short-term effects alcohol has on the body depend on several factors. These include the amount of alcohol consumed, the person's gender and size, and whether or not there is food in the person's stomach.

- **Brain.** Alcohol reaches the brain almost as soon as it is consumed. It depresses the activity of the brain, slowing the work of the **central nervous system**. Thought processes are disorganized, and memory and concentration are dulled. Decision making can be badly affected.
- **Liver.** The **liver**, in a process called *oxidation*, changes alcohol to water, carbon dioxide, and energy. The liver can oxidize only about one-third to one-half of an ounce (10 to 15 ml) of alcohol an hour. There is no way to speed up this process. Until the liver

Lesson 2 Resources

TEACHER'S CLASSROOM RESOURCES

- **Concept Map** Activity 75
- **Cooperative Learning** Activity 25
- **Enrichment** Activity 25
- **Health Lab** 25
- **Lesson 75 Quiz**
- **Lesson Plan 75**
- **Reteaching** Activity 75

STUDENT WORKBOOK

- **Applying Health Skills** 75
- **Chapter Study Guide** 25
- **Vocabulary** Activity 25

TRANSPARENCIES AND MULTIMEDIA

- **Transparency 28**
- **ABCNews InterActive™ Videodisc,** *Alcohol*

What Alcohol Does to the Body

FOCUS

LESSON OBJECTIVES

After studying this lesson, students should be able to

- explain the effects of alcohol on the body.
- describe the consequences of drinking and driving.
- identify the consequences of DWI and efforts to reduce DWIs.
- describe problems that occur when alcohol is mixed with other drugs or used during pregnancy.

MOTIVATOR

Write the following on the chalkboard for students to work on while attendance is being taken: *List as many parts of the body as you can think of that are affected by alcohol use.*

INTRODUCING THE LESSON

Have students share their responses to the Motivator. Explain that some of the effects on the body are immediate and others are long-term. This lesson details some of the effects and dangers of alcohol.

INTRODUCING HEALTH TERMS

- Let students use each of the vocabulary terms in a short public service announcement about the effects of alcohol on the body. Select some of the announcements to be tape-recorded or videotaped for younger students.
- Ask students to complete Vocabulary Activity 25 and Chapter Study Guide 25 in the *Student Workbook.*

TEACH

Visual Learning

Short Term Effects of Alcohol

Refer students to the illustration showing the short-term effects of alcohol. Review alcohol's effect on the various organs throughout the body. Ask: Which body systems are affected? *(nervous system, cardiovascular system, respiratory system, and digestive system)* Which body change could put the drinker in immediate danger? *(changes to the brain)* Recall with students the factors that determine to what extent the body is affected by alcohol. *(amount of alcohol consumed, person's size and gender, and whether or not there is food in the stomach)*

L2 Discussing

Discuss with the class: What signs indicate that alcohol has reached the brain of someone who is drinking?

L3 Cooperative Learning

Instruct students to form small groups to write a skit about the way alcohol travels through the brain, liver, and bloodstream. Have them present their skits to the class.

SHORT-TERM EFFECTS OF ALCOHOL

BRAIN
Alcohol reaches the brain within minutes, and the brain becomes less able to control the body. Movement, speech, and vision may be affected.

LIVER
The liver changes alcohol into water and carbon dioxide. When a person drinks alcohol faster than the liver can break it down, the person becomes intoxicated.

LUNGS
The carbon dioxide is released from the body through the lungs. The water passes out of the body in the form of urine, perspiration, and breath vapor.

SMALL INTESTINE
The rest of the alcohol moves to the small intestine, where it enters the bloodstream more slowly.

MOUTH AND THROAT
Chemicals affect mucosal lining, tongue, gums, and throat.

HEART
Alcohol causes the heart to beat faster and the blood vessels to widen. The increased blood flow to the surface gradually allows body heat to escape and body temperature to drop.

STOMACH
About 20 percent of the alcohol consumed passes through the lining of the stomach and into the bloodstream. Too much alcohol in the stomach may cause vomiting.

> Alcohol has many negative effects on the drinker's body and behavior. The short-term effects are those that occur within minutes of drinking an alcoholic beverage.

has time to oxidize all the alcohol, the alcohol keeps circulating through all body parts. Contrary to popular myth, neither a cold shower nor black coffee can counter these effects and sober up a person who has been drinking.

■ **Blood Vessels.** The blood carries the alcohol to all parts of the body, including the heart, liver, and brain. When alcohol enters the blood, it causes the blood vessels to dilate, or widen. The result is an increased flow of blood, especially to the skin. This makes the skin feel flush and warm. However, it is an artificial warmth. The increase of blood flow near the surface of the skin causes the body to lose heat by radiation. Body temperature actually decreases. People who drink and then go out into cold weather are at increased risk for **hypothermia**.

■ **Heart.** Alcohol causes an increase in heart rate and an increase in blood pressure. It can lead to arrhythmias, or abnormal heartbeats.

hotlink

hypothermia For more information on the condition known as hypothermia and ways of protecting yourself against it, see Chapter 4, page 87.

CURRICULUM CONNECTIONS

SOCIAL STUDIES. The financial costs of alcohol's effects on the body are considerable. Ask a representative from a local medical facility to speak to the class about the costs of treating individuals with health problems related to alcohol. Discuss the impact of this expense on society.

MATH. Ask students to use newspaper ads to compare the costs of alcoholic beverages with those of nonalcoholic beverages.

SCIENCE. Invite a doctor or psychologist to speak to the class about the effects of alcohol on the body (and brain).

It can cause scar tissue to build up in the muscle fibers of the heart. The risk of heart attack and stroke also increases.

- **Kidneys.** Alcohol affects the pituitary gland, which, in turn, acts on the **kidneys**, causing them to produce more urine. It is for this reason that a person feels dehydrated the day after he or she has been drinking heavily.

- **Stomach.** Because the alcohol molecule is very small and water-soluble, it does not have to be digested. It can be immediately absorbed from the stomach into the blood. Having food in the stomach slows the absorption process. Even so, food will not keep a person from getting drunk if he or she drinks too much. Alcohol increases the flow of gastric juices from the stomach lining. Larger amounts of alcohol cause a larger flow of these high-acid juices, irritating the stomach lining. Repeated irritation can cause internal bleeding.

Driving Under the Influence

Among the problems related to the short-term effects of drinking, one of the deadliest and most widespread is that of driving while intoxicated (DWI), also known as *driving under the influence* (DUI). A person is said to be driving while intoxicated when his or her blood alcohol concentration exceeds the limit allowed by law in that state. **Blood alcohol concentration**, or BAC, is *the amount of alcohol in a person's blood expressed as a percentage*. Signs of being intoxicated can begin to appear at blood alcohol concentrations as low as .02. Factors that affect the amount of alcohol in a person's blood include gender, weight, **metabolism**, the amount of alcohol (not the number of drinks) consumed, whether the person ate before or while drinking, and the time that elapsed between drinks or after drinking stopped.

What effect does alcohol have on an individual's ability to operate a car or other heavy machinery? Driving experts and medical researchers have found that drinking on any level

- reduces the ability to judge distances, speeds, and turns.
- reduces the ability to judge accurately one's own capabilities and limitations.
- increases the tendency to take risks.
- slows reflexes.
- adds to forgetfulness to take precautions such as using signals when turning.
- reduces the ability to concentrate.

CONSEQUENCES OF DWI

Driving while intoxicated is the leading cause of death among teenagers. Each day in the United States, 11 teenagers are killed and over 350 are injured in alcohol-related motor vehicle crashes.

Driving under the influence is a problem not only for the drinker but also for the nondrinker, who can easily become a victim in a crash caused by an alcohol-impaired driver. Almost 50 percent of the

hotlink

kidneys For more information on the functions and problems of the kidneys, see Chapter 18, page 425.

hotlink

metabolism For more information on metabolism and its role in fitness, see Chapter 3, page 54.

Did You Know?

➤ For years, police have asked drunk drivers to perform such tests as touch their nose with their fingers or walk a straight lines, heel to toe. Now, a test called the Horizontal Gaze Nystagmus test is being used to see if further breath or blood testing is needed. This test is based on the theory that people high on alcohol or other drugs can't prevent the jerking motions of their eyes when they try to track, or follow, moving objects.

L2 Discussing

Ask students what role food plays in slowing the absorption of alcohol in the body. What kinds of food might be more successful in slowing down the absorption process?

L3 Class Activity

Choose students to report on the process of the liver's oxidation of alcohol and the common use of coffee to "sober up" a person who is drunk. Discuss why this process does not work.

L2 Demonstrating

Set up an exhibit of colored water so students can see that there is the same amount of alcohol in 12 ounces (36 ml) of beer, 5 ounces (15 ml) of wine, and 1½ ounces (4 ml) of liquor.

L1 Discussing

Talk about the reasons someone might drive after drinking despite all the information about the dangers involved. Have students suggest ways to handle a situation in which someone they know insists on driving after drinking.

ALCOHOL (Side 1)

Chapter 8:   Alcohol and Pregnancy

Frames 26106-29134

Chapter 9:   Alcohol and Women

Frames 29157-31591

Chapter 10: Alcohol and Nutrition

Frames 31608-34759

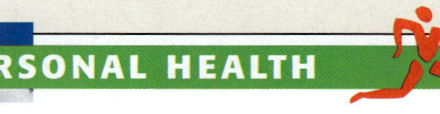

PERSONAL HEALTH

WINE AND THE HEART. Some students have probably seen or heard media reports that link daily consumption of one glass of wine with a reduction in risk of heart disease. Suggest that students critically examine several such studies. Have them look for answers to questions such as what other variables were controlled, or whether the researchers examined how one drink per day affects the liver, digestive system, and other body systems. Ask: Have researchers ruled out the possibility that in protecting the heart, people drinking a glass of wine each day are damaging other body parts? Can other substances, such as wine extracts or dietary supplements, extend similar benefits? Do students think it is wise for a nondrinker to begin drinking one alcoholic drink a day to protect the heart? Why or why not?

Building Health Skills

Ways to Turn Down a Drink

Skill: Refusal Skills

Ask students to identify occasions when teens are most susceptible to drinking. After a brief discussion, have students work in small groups to read the Building Health Skills feature and to discuss the four suggestions for refusing a drink. Allow time for group members to discuss the refusal techniques. Have each group come up with three more ways to refuse a drink. As a class, ask groups to share the refusal techniques that they came up with. Ask: Which techniques do you think will be more effective? Why?

L1 Class Activity

Drinking and driving has become a national health and social problem. Thousands of innocent people die or are injured each year because of such irresponsible behavior. Ask students to complete the sentence: *Even though I might not be a driver, I can work to reduce this tragic waste of lives by…*

L1 Guest Speaker

Invite an attorney or law student to speak with the class about current laws regarding DWI. Ask the speaker to discuss fees that might be involved in representing an individual who has been charged with driving while intoxicated.

L1 Discussing

Discuss with students what the role of a "designated driver" is.

L2 Cooperative Learning

Assign *Cooperative Learning Activity 25* for more on the effects of alcohol.

Did You Know?

➤ About 85 percent of all car crashes involving teens are linked to alcohol.

➤ In the past decade, a quarter of a million Americans have died in car crashes in this country due to the use of alcohol.

➤ Alcohol and marijuana in combination have greatly increased sedative effects. They impair manual dexterity, psychomotor skills, and the ability to process information, and they cause visual disturbances.

---

crashes in which the passenger dies occur because the drivers were legally drunk. Although traffic deaths caused by drunken driving have declined in recent years, 38 percent of all traffic deaths in 1999 were alcohol-related.

OTHER COSTS OF DWI

Even when fatal traffic accidents are averted, numerous problems exist for the individual who is stopped for driving while intoxicated. Here are some:

- immediate confiscation of driver's license
- arrest, a trip to jail, court appearance, and fine
- possible suspension of driver's license
- possible mandatory jail sentence
- cost of bail to get out of jail
- higher insurance rates
- possible lawsuits

EFFORTS TO REDUCE DWIs

Each state has determined the legal acceptable limit of alcohol in the blood. In most states, driving while intoxicated is defined as having a 0.1 percent BAC, though other states have pushed and are pushing for lower concentrations such as 0.08. In all states, driving while intoxicated is against the law. There are also laws in some

---

Building Health Skills

Using Refusal Skills: Ways to Turn Down a Drink

EVEN WHEN THE PRESSURE to use alcohol is intense, saying no becomes much easier when you're prepared. Copy the following responses into your private Health Journal. Add any other responses that work as well or better for you, and practice them in front of a mirror. Make sure your body language backs up your words.

1. Refuse politely but firmly. No, thanks. I've already got a drink (such as bottled water, juice, etc.).

2. Give a personal reason. I'm watching my weight; I'm allergic to it; I hate the taste; It gives me a headache.

3. Explain that you have more important goals. I've got a game in the morning. It affects my schoolwork. I want to be in control of my life.

4. State your values and responsibilities. I wouldn't consider it. It's against the law for people my age.

MEETING STUDENT DIVERSITY

PHYSICALLY CHALLENGED. Students who are physically challenged fall into two categories: those with orthopedic impairments (restricted use of one or more limbs) and those with other health impairments (required use of respirators or other medical equipment). To assist those students, use the following guidelines:

- Openly discuss with the student any uncertainties you have about when to offer assistance.
- Allow those students to do everything their peers do.
- Help other students and adults understand the needs of the physically challenged.

states that make it illegal to have an open alcohol container inside the car. Mandatory chemical tests for blood, breath, or urine exist in some states. Refusal to submit to a test can mean automatic suspension of the person's driver's license. In some states, anyone caught driving while intoxicated may go to jail immediately.

Organizations such as MADD, Mothers Against Drunk Driving, and SADD, Students Against Destructive Decisions, have been powerful forces in making the public and state legislators aware of the problem of drunk driving. Stricter enforcement of existing laws, tougher new laws, the banning of open containers in cars, and abolishment of drive-through liquor stores are a few of the contributions that these organizations have made in trying to reduce the problem of driving while intoxicated.

A response to the problem is also beginning to come from individual concerned citizens. Increasingly, the idea of identifying **designated drivers**—*people in social settings who choose not to drink so that they can safely drive themselves and others*—is becoming a popular trend in a drinking society. Such people recognize the importance of *never* riding with anyone who has had *any* alcohol to drink.

Long-Term Effects of Drinking

Long-term effects of alcohol on the body can include vitamin deficiencies, stomach and skin problems, and loss of appetite. Prolonged alcohol use can also do permanent damage to the liver and central nervous system.

Brain Damage

Long-term, excessive use of alcohol invariably leads to major brain damage. It may even lead to a decrease in brain size. People have been hospitalized in mental institutions for severe brain damage caused by excessive alcohol use. Even moderate drinking can destroy brain cells. There can be a loss of intellectual abilities, such as memory and problem solving. These losses can seriously interfere with everyday functions.

Chronic Liver Problems

Alcohol interferes with the liver's ability to break down fats. **Fatty liver**, *a condition in which fats build up in the liver and cannot be broken down*, develops. This increased amount of fat prevents the liver from functioning normally. It also interferes with the growth of new liver

▲ *In 1981, SADD began work to reduce alcohol-related traffic deaths. Their efforts were so successful they have since launched programs to address more issues affecting teens.*

ACTIVITY *List issues that students in your school might work on to solve through programs like SADD.*

L2 ## Discussing

Ask what the individual's responsibility is in not riding with someone who has been drinking. What can a person say or do to be assertive in this situation?

L1 ## Guest Speaker

Ask a representative from Mothers Against Drunk Driving to speak with the class about the problems of drinking and driving and the work the organization does to campaign against drunk driving.

L2 ## Community Involvement

Assign volunteers to interview a local police officer to determine what efforts have been made to crack down on DWI offenders. Have the efforts worked? What age group presents the most serious problem? What can the teenage driving population do to help fight this problem? Request that students share the findings of their interview with the rest of the class.

ALCOHOL (Side 1)

Chapter 5: Alcohol and Your Body

Frames 11223-14973

Chapter 6: Alcohol and Your Central Nervous System

Frames 15003-21095

Chapter 7: Alcohol-Related Medical Problems

Frames 21119-26069

SCHOOL-TO-CAREER

X-RAY AND ULTRASOUND TECHNOLOGISTS. Doctors who suspect liver damage or certain cancers may order various tests. Many of these tests are administered by licensed technicians. For example, they may send a patient for ultrasound, a procedure that utilizes ultrasonic waves to create a visual image of an internal organ or structure. An ultrasound technologist needs a license and special training from a trade school or medical teaching college. A student without a college degree usually takes four years to complete the program because most candidates complete training as X ray technicians first. After completing their training, candidates must take a challenging examination to qualify for the state license.

L2 Researching

Have students use class and library resources to prepare written reports on some of the withdrawal symptoms experienced by heavy drinkers who abruptly stop the intake of alcohol. Encourage them to tell the class about what they learned.

L1 Class Activity

Divide the class into small groups. Have them design mobiles showing the synergistic effect of alcohol with other drugs.

L2 Writing

Ask students to write articles to submit to the school newspaper about the multiplier effect of alcohol and other drugs.

L1 Discussing

What are some of the characteristics of infants suffering from fetal alcohol syndrome? Encourage student responses.

L1 Class Activity

Have students find the definition of *cleft palate*. Ask them to discuss the definition.

L2 Discussing

Ask students to identify the complications and risks of a pregnant woman who drinks. What responsibility does a woman have to her unborn baby?

L2 Health Lab

Distribute *Health Lab 25* and have students discover the effects of alcohol on a developing fetus.

▲ **Top: A healthy liver. Bottom: A liver damaged by alcohol use.**

ACTIVITY *Explain the function and importance of a healthy liver.*

hot link

hepatitis For more information on hepatitis and modes of treatment, see Chapter 28, page 630.

tolerance For more information on tolerance to substances, see Chapter 23, page 517.

withdrawal For more information on withdrawal from substances, see Chapter 23, page 517.

synergistic effect For more information on the synergistic effect that occurs when two or more medicines are combined, see Chapter 23, page 516.

cells. As a result, old liver cells are not replaced as quickly as they normally would be. The excess fat in the liver blocks the flow of blood in the liver cells, resulting in reduced oxygen and eventually cell death. This condition has been found in both moderate and heavy drinkers. It can be reversed when drinking stops.

Prolonged heavy alcohol use can cause **cirrhosis** (sir-ROH-sis) of the liver, *a condition in which liver tissue is destroyed and then replaced with useless scar tissue. Cirrhosis* means "scarring." There is no blood flow in the scarred area because there are no blood vessels, so the work of the liver is greatly reduced.

Alcohol abuse can also lead to **hepatitis**, an inflammation or infection of the liver that can cause weakness, jaundice, fever, and sometimes death. Also referred to as *alcoholic hepatitis*, it is caused by the toxic effects of the drug. Recovery can be slow, and liver failure sometimes results.

Tolerance and Dependence

Because alcohol is a drug, people who use it regularly may develop a **tolerance**, making it necessary to drink more and more in order to produce the same effects. As tolerance develops, a person may drink an increasing amount without appearing to be intoxicated. The person may continue to function reasonably well until some severe physical damage results or until he or she is hospitalized for some other reason. Then the individual will experience symptoms of **withdrawal** that range from jumpiness, sleeplessness, sweating, and poor appetite to severe tremors, convulsions, and hallucinations.

Some people become physiologically dependent on alcohol. The body develops a chemical need for alcohol. Physiological dependence is marked by tolerance and withdrawal. The symptoms of withdrawal are so unpleasant, a person tends to drink more alcohol in order to avoid the symptoms. As a result, the level of tolerance increases.

The Multiplier Effect

Similar to the **synergistic effect** that occurs when two or more medicines are taken simultaneously, alcohol combined with other drugs or medicines produces an interaction known as the *multiplier effect*. When alcohol is mixed with another depressant such as a tranquilizer, the effects can be particularly devastating. Impairment of both mental and physical abilities results. Many accidental deaths result from combining alcohol with other drugs or medicines. What is especially dangerous is that these effects are often not predictable.

Both over-the-counter medicines, such as aspirin and prescription medicines, can alter the way alcohol affects the body. Medicines that might cause reactions with alcohol have labels that warn against drinking any alcoholic beverages while using the medicine.

CURRICULUM CONNECTIONS

LANGUAGE ARTS. Have students write a short story from the viewpoint of a fetus experiencing alcohol use and abuse. Suggest that they include information about the physical, mental, and behavioral defects the fetus is likely to experience.

SCIENCE. Encourage students to use library resources to research current surgical procedures to correct cleft palate. Ask them to share their findings with the class.

LANGUAGE ARTS. Have groups of students write short scenarios in which members discuss the behavior of a fictional person who they suspect is an alcoholic. Descriptions should reveal the symptoms of a person at one of the three stages of alcoholism. Let groups perform their scenes before the class.

Alcohol and Pregnancy

In recent years, scientists have found that heavy drinking by pregnant females carries a risk not only to themselves but to their unborn child. **Fetal alcohol syndrome** (FAS) is *a condition in which a fetus has been adversely affected mentally and physically by its mother's heavy alcohol use during pregnancy.* FAS babies may exhibit some or all of the following problems: low birth weight, impaired speech, cleft palate, general weakness, slow body growth, facial abnormalities, poor coordination, and heart defects. Mental retardation, poor attention span, nervousness, and hyperactivity are also common in children born with FAS. FAS is, in fact, the leading cause of mental retardation in the United States.

The alcohol the pregnant female drinks moves into her blood, then across the placenta and through the umbilical cord into the blood of the unborn child. Any effects felt by the pregnant female as a result of drinking are also experienced by the unborn child. The alcohol remains in the baby's body much longer. If the pregnant female drinks three or four times a week, chances are the fetus *never* rids itself of alcohol.

The most sobering fact about FAS is that it is 100 percent preventable. It does not occur in babies of nondrinking pregnant females. Yet each year, some 5,000 FAS babies are born in this country. Many more cases go undiagnosed. The public is becoming increasingly aware of the dangers of FAS, but now every woman who is pregnant must make the choice not to drink any alcohol at all.

In 1988, the U.S. Senate passed a bill that, in part, approved a label that warned of the dangers of drinking during pregnancy. The warning reads:

> "ACCORDING TO THE SURGEON GENERAL, WOMEN SHOULD NOT DRINK ALCOHOLIC BEVERAGES DURING PREGNANCY BECAUSE OF THE RISK OF BIRTH DEFECTS."

LESSON 2 *Review*

Reviewing Facts and Vocabulary

1. List three short-term and three long-term effects of using alcohol.
2. Identify four ways that drinking impairs driving.
3. What are some of the characteristics of children suffering from fetal alcohol syndrome?

Thinking Critically

4. *Synthesizing.* In what ways can the short-term effects of alcohol sometimes become deadly?

5. *Analyzing.* Imagine that you are an alcohol molecule entering a human body. Describe your journey through the brain, liver, bloodstream, kidneys, lung, stomach, and small intestine.

Applying Health Skills

6. *In Your Home and Community.* Interview parents and other adults as to their feelings about checkpoints for drunk drivers. Summarize your findings and share them in a general class discussion.

LESSON 2   WHAT ALCOHOL DOES TO THE BODY   **561**

ASSESS

EVALUATING THE LESSON

Assign and discuss the Lesson 2 Review; then administer, grade, and discuss the *Lesson 75 Quiz* in the TCR. 📂

RETEACHING

- Help students present a mini-lesson about ways in which alcohol affects the body. Have them present their lessons to the rest of the class.
- Ask students to complete *Reteaching Activity 75* in the TCR. 📂
- Use *Transparency 28* to review the effects of alcohol. 🔖

ENRICHMENT

- Ask for volunteers to design an educational game about the long-term risks of using alcohol. Have students demonstrate their completed projects to the class.
- Have students learn how some teens are keeping others from causing drunk-driving deaths. Assign *Enrichment Activity 25*, "Students Against Driving Drunk," in the TCR. 📂

CLOSE

Outline on the chalkboard the lesson's main ideas. Ask for volunteers to come to the board, select a main idea, and summarize it for the rest of the class.

Lesson 2 Review

Answers to Reviewing Facts and Vocabulary

1. See pages 555–560.
2. Any four: alcohol reduces the ability to judge distances, speed, turns; it impairs the ability to judge accurately one's own capabilities and limitations; and it decreases the ability to concentrate. It increases the tendency to take risks, and it slows reflexes. It makes one forget to take precautions such as using turn signals.
3. See page 561 for the characteristics of fetal alcohol syndrome.

Answers to Thinking Critically

4.–5. Answers will vary.

FOCUS

LESSON OBJECTIVES

After studying this lesson, students should be able to

- relate alcohol poisoning to blood alcohol level.
- describe the three stages of alcoholism.
- discuss the costs of alcohol use to the family and society.

MOTIVATOR

Write the following on the chalkboard for students to work on while attendance is being taken: *Discuss in writing why the boisterous drunk is no longer considered to be comical.*

INTRODUCING THE LESSON

Explain to students that attitudes about alcohol have changed dramatically over the past few years. Educational efforts have helped people better understand alcoholism as a disease. Refer to the Motivator, and ask volunteers to share their written responses.

INTRODUCING HEALTH TERMS

- Instruct students to write a paragraph explaining the relationship between binge drinking and alcohol poisoning.
- Ask students to complete Vocabulary Activity 25 and Chapter Study Guide 25 in the *Student Workbook.* ☞

LESSON 3

Alcohol and Society

F or some adults, alcohol used occasionally and with moderation has pleasurable effects and few, if any, damaging ones. For others who drink, alcohol becomes a serious problem—one that negatively affects their lives and the lives of those around them. Healthy social gatherings do not include alcohol.

HEALTH TERMS

binge drinking
alcohol poisoning
alcoholism
delirium tremens (DTs)

HEALTH CONCEPTS

- You do not have to be an alcoholic to get in trouble with alcohol.
- Alcoholism is a chronic disease that can be treated with total abstinence.
- Alcoholism imposes heavy costs on the family of the alcoholic and on society.
- Not drinking is the only responsible choice.
- There are many effective ways to say no to alcohol.

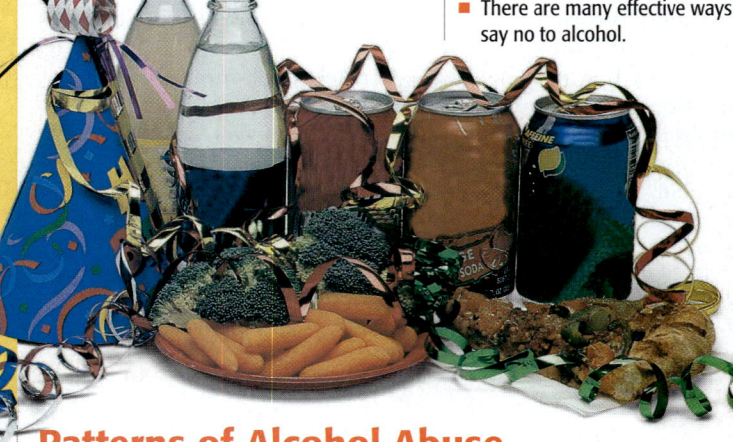

Patterns of Alcohol Abuse

Although most people equate problem drinking with the disease of alcoholism, there are other troubled patterns of alcohol use whose effects can be every bit as devastating. Some of these patterns can even be life-threatening.

Binge drinking, one such pattern, is *periodic excessive drinking*. This type of drinking, which is popular among some high school and college students, can take the form of a social event or a contest to see who can drink the most in the shortest time. Binge drinking can lead to serious difficulties. Some binge drinkers mistakenly believe that they are not really in trouble with alcohol because they do not drink every day. However, even alcoholics can go days on end without drinks until later stages of their disease.

Lesson 3 Resources

TEACHER'S CLASSROOM RESOURCES
☞ **Concept Map** Activity 76
☞ **Decision-Making** Activity 25
☞ **Lesson 76 Quiz**
☞ **Lesson Plan 76**
☞ **Reteaching** Activity 76

STUDENT WORKBOOK
☞ **Applying Health Skills 76**
☞ **Chapter Study Guide 25**
☞ **Vocabulary** Activity 25

MULTIMEDIA
● **ABCNews InterActive™ VHS/Videodisc,** *Alcohol*

A danger associated more with binge drinking than with any other pattern of alcohol abuse is **alcohol poisoning.** This is *a dangerous toxic condition that occurs when a person drinks a large amount of alcohol in a short period of time.* Generally, when a person's blood alcohol level reaches about 400 milligrams per deciliter—four times the legal limit for driving under the influence—the brain's ability to control breathing can be interrupted. Death can result.

Alcoholism

Many myths and misconceptions surround the pattern of alcohol abuse called *alcoholism.* Many people, for example, erroneously believe it is just a passing state when in fact **alcoholism**—*a physical and psychological dependence on the drug ethanol*—is a disease. Another myth is that all alcoholics are "falling down" drunk and, hence, easily recognized. Although it is true that some people reach this extreme, a great many alcoholics appear clean, orderly, and well groomed. One common denominator that does exist among alcoholics is this: They all need help.

Traits of the Alcoholic

Alcoholics are unable to stop drinking despite the toll it takes on their health and their lives. People with alcoholism may exhibit one or a combination of these behaviors or traits:

- They are preoccupied in one way or another with alcohol.
- Once they pick up the first drink, they cannot promise or predict what they will say or do or how much they will drink.
- They cannot manage tension without drinking.
- They may have personality changes or memory lapses due to drinking.

Stages of Alcoholism

There are three clearly defined stages of alcoholism that happen over a period of time. The time span can be long or short, depending on the individual and the age at which he or she started drinking. The American Medical Association states that alcoholism develops in three phases: abuse, dependence, and addiction.

STAGE ONE

Alcoholism typically begins with social drinking, often to relax or to relieve stress or depression. Gradually, this kind of drinking becomes necessary to manage stress. A physical and psychological dependency on alcohol develops. The person begins to drink and become intoxicated regularly. The drinker may have short-term memory loss and blackouts—times when he or she cannot remember with whom he or she was drinking or what was said or done after each drinking episode. Often, at this stage, the drinker makes excuses

---

Did You Know?

➤ It is estimated that there are between 10 and 16 million alcoholics in the U.S.

➤ It has been estimated that 1 in 20 Americans is addicted to alcohol.

➤ Research is beginning to show some evidence that genetics may be a contributing factor in alcoholism.

➤ A low intoxication response, or failing to show the outward signs of drunkenness as quickly as others, may be an early adulthood predictor of later alcoholism, particularly among young men whose fathers are alcoholic.

From **health.glencoe.com**, link to the M.A.D.D. home page to learn about alcohol myths and facts, the negative effects of alcohol, and advice for teens about avoiding alcohol. How can you inform people about the dangers of drinking and driving?

TEACH

L1 Discussing

Ask why it is difficult for most people who have a drinking problem to admit they have a problem.

L2 Discussing

Discuss with the class: What are the differences between problem drinking being the cause and problem drinking being the symptom of other problems?

L2 Discussing

Ask students what some of the behaviors of alcoholics are. In what way does each of the behaviors affect the others?

Encourage students to locate statistics on alcohol-related traffic fatalities for their own state and evaluate these against the figures of other states. Have students work in groups to devise a plan for reducing traffic fatalities involving alcohol abuse. Encourage them to submit their plan to state and community officials.

L1 Guest Speaker

Invite an Alcoholics Anonymous representative to speak with the class. Ask the speaker to talk about the myth of the "typical" alcoholic.

Myths & Realities

MYTHS. Using alcohol only on weekends is harmless. Drinking alcohol through a straw "filters out" the alcoholic content of a beverage.

FACT. Neither is true. People who spread false information are trying to delude themselves and others into thinking that they can avoid the hazards of alcohol.

MYTH. People suffering from alcoholism can stop drinking anytime they want to.

FACT. Alcoholics depend on alcohol to function physically and mentally; they are physically addicted.

MYTH. Only bums and street people are alcoholics.

FACT. Alcoholism affects people of all social and economic backgrounds and of all ages. In fact, many alcoholics are prominent figures in their communities.

CHARACTER IN ACTION

Signs of Trouble, Signs of Caring

Review the signs of a drinking problem in the feature. Discuss the loss of values as one of the signs of trouble. Point out that the person with the drinking problem is usually the last to recognize that there is a problem. Discuss ways to convince a friend to seek help and, in cases of denial, discuss other responsible alternatives such as intervention.

Making Responsible Decisions

1. The friend with whom Lenny has planned to ride home from a party is drinking, but Lenny feels reluctant to call home in front of the other teens at the party.
2. Lenny could (a) call home—if possible from a room away from other party guests—and ask a parent to pick him up; (b) ride home with Rod.
3. Lenny might (a) risk being embarrassed and perhaps teased by other teens at the party, but have a safe ride home with a driver who has not been drinking; (b) avoid being embarrassed, but risk being involved in an accident because Rod has been drinking.
4. Lenny values his own safety. He also values fitting in with other teens.
5. Responses will vary.
6. Guide students in considering both the short- and long-term consequences of their decisions.

L2 Decision Making

For further study on making responsible decisions, assign *Decision-Making Activity 25* in the TCR. ☞

CHARACTER IN ACTION

Signs of Trouble, Signs of Caring

One of the ways to be a **caring** friend is to notice the signs that a friend may be heading for trouble with alcohol. Look for the signs:

➤ odor on the breath
➤ trouble remembering or concentrating
➤ sudden emotional outbursts
➤ changes in choice of friends
➤ absences from school
➤ falling grades
➤ irritability
➤ poor coordination
➤ slow reflexes
➤ slurred speech

Character Check Write a fictitious "letter to a friend" showing caring ways you would encourage someone to stop drinking.

and tries to rationalize his or her drinking behavior. His or her tolerance to alcohol increases, meaning more is needed to feel the same effects. He or she may be called a problem drinker by others.

STAGE TWO

Gradually, the person reaches a point where he or she cannot stop drinking. In other words, the person is now physically dependent on the drug. He or she may drink alone and may drink every day, and the craving for a drink may occur earlier and earlier in the day. Physical and mental problems may become evident. More excuses are made for drinking, and often, others are blamed for what happens. At this stage of the disease, defensive behavior is evident. The drinker denies or tries to hide the problem. The body has developed a tolerance, and more alcohol is necessary. Drinking becomes the central event in the person's life. Performance on the job, at school, or at home decreases. Frequent absences from school, work, or other commitments occur.

STAGE THREE

In the final and worst stage of the disease, drinking is more important in the person's life than everything else. The problem can no longer be denied, and it is also uncontrolled. There may be hallucinations. Alcohol becomes a constant companion. The alcoholic becomes aggressive and is isolated from friends and family. Malnutrition results because the drinker overlooks his or her nutritional needs. The body is addicted to the drug. At this stage, the person has fallen apart physically, mentally, emotionally, and socially. He or she also now has decreased or reverse tolerance, meaning that it takes less alcohol

Making Responsible Decisions

Saying No to a Drinking Driver

Lenny, who won't be 16 for another three months, is at a party with his friend Rod and some of Rod's friends, whom he's never met before. A little while ago, when Lenny looked over at Rod, he

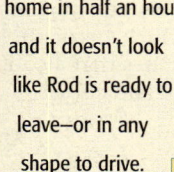

saw Rod and one of his friends drinking a beer. Lenny has to be home in half an hour, and it doesn't look like Rod is ready to leave—or in any shape to drive.

Lenny could call home for a ride, but he's afraid of how the other teens at the party might react. He's even more afraid,

however—and rightfully so—about getting into Rod's car.

What Would You Do?

Apply the six steps of the decision-making process to Lenny's problem.

1. **State the situation.**
2. **List the options.**
3. **Weigh the possible outcomes.**
4. **Consider your values.**
5. **Make a decision and act.**
6. **Evaluate the decision.**

Myths & Realities

MYTH. Alcoholics can safely drink socially if they limit their intake to no more than two drinks during a social event.

FACT. The only way to recover from alcoholism is to stop drinking. Abstinence from alcohol is the only alternative. Recovering alcoholics should avoid drinking situations whenever possible. New activities and interests may be necessary.

MYTH. Recovering alcoholics who have a relapse probably will never stop drinking.

FACT. Recovery takes time. Do not assume that once an alcoholic is committed to recovery, he or she will never have a relapse. A relapse does not mean treatment has failed. In fact, sometimes a relapse convinces the alcoholic that abstinence is the only alternative.

to cause drunkenness. If the alcoholic stopped drinking, he or she would experience the withdrawal symptoms associated with alcoholism, called **delirium tremens** (DTs), *the dramatic physical and psychological effects of alcohol withdrawal.* These consist of hot and cold flashes, severe tremors, nightmares, hallucinations, and having fear of people and animals. People with DTs need prompt medical attention.

Although alcoholism cannot be cured, it definitely can be treated. As many as two-thirds of all alcoholics recover with proper treatment. The goal of the various programs to treat alcoholism is to stop or control the intake of alcohol. Several sources are available to help people who have a drinking problem. Help is also available for the families and friends of people who have a drinking problem. These programs, such as Alcoholics Anonymous and Alateen, are discussed in Chapter 27.

Costs to the Family

It is estimated that there are more than 3 million teen alcoholics. Up to 5 million young people in this country are considered to be alcoholics or problem drinkers. In addition, alcohol use, abuse, and alcoholism are major factors in the four leading causes of accidental death: car crashes, falls, drownings, and burns caused by fire. They are also factors in 20 to 35 percent of all suicides and play a major part in **domestic violence**, spousal and child abuse, abuse of the elderly, and marital separation and divorce. Alcoholism is one of the leading stressors and factors in troubled families. People who are involved with alcoholics and whose lives are enmeshed in the alcoholic's problems are called *co-alcoholics* or *codependents* and suffer from **codependency**. By living with chronic alcoholism, they learn to ignore their own needs and center all of their energy on the alcoholic, losing trust and self-esteem, and sometimes damaging their own health in the process. Their suffering, like that of the alcoholic, is enormous.

Costs to Society

Alcohol is a major factor in the three leading causes of death for 16- to 24-year-olds. These are traffic crashes, homicides, and suicides. In all, alcohol claims about 100,000 Americans a year. Off the highway, alcohol contributes to about 6 million nonfatal and 15,000 fatal injuries per year. In the workplace, up to 40 percent of industrial fatalities and 47 percent of industrial injuries can be linked to alcohol.

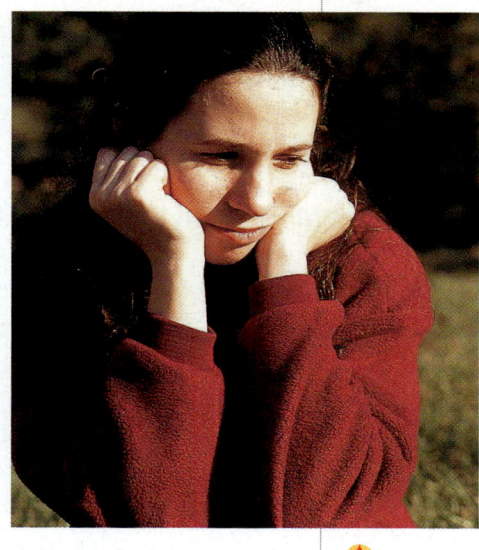

▲ *The heavy use of alcohol is often a cause of serious family problems, including child abuse, abuse of the elderly, and domestic violence.*

ACTIVITY *Name three steps that a person who lives in a family with active alcoholism might take to get help for himself or herself.*

h⭕t link

domestic violence For more information on domestic violence, including spousal abuse, child abuse, and elderly abuse, see Chapter 12, page 286.

codependency For more information on codependency and help for the codependent, see Chapter 27, page 608.

L1 Discussing

Have a volunteer look up the word *disease* in the dictionary and write the definitions on the chalkboard. Lead students in discussing the reasons alcoholism can be accurately defined as a disease. *(Alcoholism, like many diseases, can interfere with a person's normal day-to-day life.)*

L2 Community Involvement

Have students collect brochures and flyers from local groups and agencies that work with individuals and families who have difficulty with alcohol. Ask them to make a display of the materials collected.

L3 Writing

Have students write case studies showing the progression of a person from stage one to stage two and, finally, to stage three of alcoholism.

h⭕t link

domestic violence
codependency
Recall with students the basic functions of the family—providing a primary support system, meeting emotional needs, instilling values, and so on. Discuss how alcohol use by a parent can prevent normal family functioning and adversely affect a child's development. Explain that situations of abuse and the codependency that develop in families of an alcoholic affect family members for years, even after the alcoholic has recovered. Discuss counseling for the entire family as a means to treat the trauma associated with alcoholism.

COOPERATIVE ⟩ LEARNING

ACTIVITY. As children, students drank a variety of nonalcoholic drinks. Most still do. Such beverages are served at parties and other social gatherings. Unfortunately, the beverages are often unhealthy in other ways. They may contain caffeine, high levels of sugar, or artificial sweeteners. Have students work in groups to create a menu of appealing drinks that could be served at a party or recreational event. The drinks should be healthy in every possible way. Suggest that they seek recipes in cookbooks and experiment with such combinations as herbal or decaf tea and fruit juice, sparkling or filtered water with a squeeze of lemon or lime, or combinations of fruit juices with yogurt. They might find ways to serve the beverages attractively. Suggest that they create a pamphlet of recipes for healthy festive drinks.

ABCNEWS INTERACTIVE™

ALCOHOL (Side 2)

Chapter 14: Refusal Skills

Frames 48797-52877

⚠ *You have a choice in the kind of life you wish to lead.*
ACTIVITY *Think of the priorities in your life and list the choices that will allow you to fulfill your dreams.*

Did You Know?

➤ Alcohol has been linked to over 38 percent of all drownings in this country.

➤ A study by Johns Hopkins University showed that of all of the bicycle accidents in Maryland between 1987 and 1994, over one-third of those involving people over ten years old were caused by someone who had been drinking.

➤ Alcohol is linked to all of the leading causes of death among teens in the United States.

The estimated cost to society for drug abuse is up to $110 billion and for alcoholism, $167 billion. According to the National Council on Alcoholism and Drug Dependence, alcohol abuse costs employers an estimated $30 billion every year in lost revenue. In addition, about half of all hospitalizations, excluding those related to childbirth, are linked to alcohol.

However, when it comes to alcoholism, there is good news and a lot of hope. More people than ever before are joining self-help support groups to get sober, and more young people than ever before are entering treatment centers and programs for their alcohol-related problems. The best news of all is that many people, including many teens, are deciding never to drink at all. During one recent spring, almost 3 million students in 3,500 high schools across the country registered in a program to abstain from using drugs and alcohol on prom night. This is just one of many efforts across the country in which teens themselves have come forward to declare that they intend to stay alcohol free and drug free.

Choosing to Be Alcohol-Free

Despite the rise in teen drinking, many teens are deciding to remain or become alcohol-free. The most common reason given for not drinking is: "I do not need it." Some teens who choose not to drink seem to be saying, "I don't have to drink to be popular," or "I don't need to drink to be accepted, to have fun, or to act in some way that I usually wouldn't."

Saying No to Alcohol

Saying no to drinking takes a firm mental commitment from you before you go to a party or other social situation where alcohol may be served. Practicing what you are going to say in such situations can help prepare you for the event. Whatever you do to turn down a drink, keep it brief, polite, confident, and to the point. Sometimes humor or the unexpected, creative comment can do the trick.

Alcohol and Sexual Activity

Alcohol affects a person's judgment and may interfere with self-control over one's emotions, decisions, and behavior. It may cause a

Myths & Realities

MYTH. Treatment programs for alcoholics cost more than they are worth.

FACT. Successfully treating alcohol problems costs 1/10 (one-tenth) the current cost of alcohol problems to society.

MYTH. Alcoholics seldom use other drugs.

FACT. Close to half of Alcoholics Anonymous members report addiction to other drugs.

MYTH. The effects of alcohol are identical among males and females and among teens and adults.

FACT. Females become intoxicated faster and stay that way longer than males of the same size. Also, alcohol has a stronger effect on teens and older people than on young adults and middle-aged adults.

person to do or say things he or she otherwise would not normally do, including engaging in sexual activity. Some people who are shy or otherwise socially uncomfortable may use alcohol as an "ice-breaker" only to find themselves in a place or situation that they later regret. This behavior is extremely unhealthful. HIV/AIDS, sexually transmitted diseases, unplanned pregnancies, ruined reputations, date rape, and other violence can result from mixing alcohol with social relationships. Remember that making the decision to practice **abstinence** from all risk behaviors, including alcohol use, is the best way to avoid injury and illness and to maintain good health.

Which Life Do You Choose?

Picture a car being driven by a sober, careful, respectful driver. It goes at a reasonable pace, moves carefully, and makes turns only when necessary. With a destination in mind, the driver steers the car in the desired direction until it reaches its goal. Now picture a car being driven by a drunk driver. It rambles, weaves, stops and starts, and perhaps even crashes.

So it is with your life. You can choose to live an alcohol-free life in which you pursue your goals and work steadily at reaching them, or you can get sidetracked and thrown off course altogether by using alcohol. When you come right down to it, there's only one healthful choice to make: to be alcohol-free.

h⊙t link

abstinence For more information on abstinence and its importance during the teen years, see Chapter 21, page 484.

abstinence For more information on abstinence and its importance during the teen years, see Chapter 21, page 484.

ALCOHOL (Side 2)

Chapter 7: Treatment

Frames 18486-21975

Chapter 8: Drinking and the Law

Frames 21988-26279

Chapter 9: Getting Involved: Project Graduation

Frames 26297-30241

LESSON 3 *Review*

Reviewing Facts and Vocabulary

1. Define the terms *binge drinking* and *alcohol poisoning,* and use them in a single paragraph.
2. Describe the three stages of alcoholism.
3. List three of the costs of alcoholism to society at large.
4. Identify four reasons why young people choose not to drink.

Thinking Critically

5. **Synthesizing.** What makes drinking contests particularly dangerous? For what reasons do you think teens sometimes engage in them? What advice would you give to a teen about to take part in such a contest?

6. **Evaluating.** Do you think the Surgeon General and the U.S. Senate were justified in passing the bill to require a warning label on alcoholic beverages? Defend your answer.
7. **Analyzing.** Why do you think teens who have problems with alcohol might pressure others to drink?

Applying Health Skills

8. **In Your School.** Write a 30-second radio announcement about teen alcoholism and where teens in trouble with drinking can get help.

ASSESS

EVALUATING THE LESSON

Assign and discuss the Lesson 3 Review; then administer, grade, and discuss the *Lesson 76 Quiz* in the TCR. ☞

RETEACHING

- Have students describe in their own words the symptoms of the three stages of alcoholism.
- Ask students to complete *Reteaching Activity 76* in the TCR. ☞

ENRICHMENT

Encourage students to research the body's reaction to an excess of alcohol. Have them share their findings with the class.

CLOSE

Ask students to state the most important concepts learned in the lesson.

Lesson 3 Review

Answers to Reviewing Facts and Vocabulary

1. See the Glossary for definitions. Paragraphs will vary.
2. See pages 563–565.
3. Answers may include injuries and loss of life in traffic accidents, loss of productivity and accidents on the job or at school, and loss of family relationships.
4. Answers will vary.

Answers to Thinking Critically

5.–7. Answers will vary.

Health **Skills** Activities

ACTIVITY 1
HEALTH SKILLS
Health Advocacy

➤ **National Standards**
This activity meets these National Health Standards: 7.2; 7.6.

Teach
- Brainstorm with students the many costs of alcohol use, including traffic deaths, the toll it takes on family members, and loss of productivity.
- Discuss the wording of the warning labels that appear in conjunction with alcohol use during pregnancy. Ask what words students would use to warn of these other problems that can arise from use of the drug. What pictures would they use?

ACTIVITY 2
HEALTH SKILLS
Comprehending Health Concepts, Accessing Health Information

➤ **National Standards**
This activity meets these National Health Standards: 1.5; 1.6; 2.1.

Teach
- Bring consumer magazines to class. Have students thumb through the publications, looking for alcohol ads that feature pictures. Invite students to share and discuss pictures they have found. Elicit that people in the ads all seem to be having fun. Ask what general message this conveys about alcohol use.
- Note that, in addition to the short-term effects of alcohol depicted by advertisers, the drug has some negative long-term effects on the body.
- Review these effects, especially brain damage, cirrhosis of the liver, and hepatitis.
- Arrange for students to perform their documentary for other classes in the school.

Activity 1 — Redesigning Warning Labels

Warning labels on alcohol products in this country advise pregnant women to avoid drinking because of the risk of birth defects. How could a message about alcohol's other dangers be communicated to the public?

Directions
1. Think about the many health risks alcohol poses to the drinker and to those around him or her. What kinds of information would most likely influence a potential user to think twice? Think about the best visual design to communicate your message.
2. Working with a group, design a new warning label for alcohol. The label should warn the public in words and pictures.
3. Make copies of your warning label, if possible, on the classroom computer. Place these in highly visible locations in the school or community.

Time
35 minutes

Materials
computer with color printer or paper and colored markers

Self-Assessment
✓ Included at least three examples of the risks of alcohol use.
✓ Created a persuasive message that convinces others to avoid alcohol.

Activity 2 — How Alcohol Affects the Body

Many people associate fun-filled images with alcohol when, in fact, it is a lethal drug. Knowing exactly how alcohol can negatively affect the body can help you make the responsible choice to be alcohol-free.

Directions
1. Review the long-term effect of alcohol on different parts of the body, including brain damage, cirrhosis of the liver, and hepatitis.
2. As a group, investigate one effect in depth, noting how the disease or condition develops, typical effects or symptoms, and types of treatment. Combine your findings with those of other groups.
3. Present these findings, in the form of a documentary, to members of other classes in the school.

Time
two-50 minute periods

Materials
health resources found on the Internet, in the library, or in the textbook, paper, pen or pencil

Self-Assessment
✓ Included accurate and complete information.
✓ Demonstrated clarity and sound organization.

ASSESSMENT SCORING

Using a four-level rubric, the student has achieved a 4 if:

ACTIVITY 1
✔ Student helped group brainstorm costs of alcohol use.
✔ Student identified at least three categories of risk associated with alcohol use.
✔ Student created a persuasive message that convinces others to avoid alcohol.
✔ Student took care to word message in a way that was firm but not attacking.

ACTIVITY 2
✔ Student was able to read the underlying message common to alcohol advertisements.
✔ Student helped develop a documentary that presented information on the long-term damaging effects of alcohol on the body.
✔ Student included accurate information.
✔ Student demonstrated clarity and sound organization.

HEALTH NEWS VIDEO

Home Safe from the Prom

On prom night in Glen Rock, New Jersey, teens are proving that they can be safe and responsible drivers. Some teens like Rebecca Carvalho decide to wait before they get their driving license. By the time she learned to drive, she knew that she was really ready for the responsibility.

Others are taking unusual steps to alert classmates to the dangers. George Peña staged a frighteningly realistic car crash. Why? He wanted to drive home the possible consequences of drunk driving.

Teens in New Jersey, and around the country, are getting the message that drinking and driving don't mix. The number of teen drivers involved in automobile deaths has begun to decrease.

Play the Video

Think About It

◗ Do you think that staging a mock car accident would successfully draw attention to the problem of drinking and driving in your community? Why or why not?

◗ Why is prom night a particularly dangerous night for some teens? How can you make sure you will make wise choices during special events like this?

◗ Do you think students in your school respect the message that drinking and driving don't mix? Explain your response.

CNN HEALTH NEWS **569**

Home Safe from the Prom
Video Segment 15 (Time – 2:30)

Objectives. After viewing the video, students should be able to explain how choices involving alcohol can have a lifelong impact and apply this knowledge in decisions to avoid alcohol use.

Motivator. Have students explain what is meant by the slogan "Drinking and driving don't mix." Discuss how drinking dangerously impairs a person's responses, which are essential to safe driving. Then have students view Video Segment 15, "Home Safe from the Prom," which introduces a New Jersey school's program to prevent teen drinking on prom night.

Teach

• Ask students to summarize the key features of the program outlined in the video to encourage safe prom nights. Discuss the reasons why these celebratory evenings can sometimes lead teens to make poor choices about using alcohol. Remind students that special occasions, such as proms, are not an excuse to change carefully made health decisions.

• Encourage students to consider how they might apply the positive features of this program in their own school. Have students identify and evaluate specific strategies, such as having participants sign a "pact" which asserts their choice not to use alcohol. Students can write their own pacts.

Decision Making. Remind students that some health decisions, such as whether or not to use alcohol or tobacco, are best made before they are in a tempting situation. Have students explain how they can apply the steps of decision-making to these crucial health decisions. Then have them suggest strategies that can help them stick to their decisions.

Close. Invite students to explain how the New Jersey program might be adapted to help fight drinking and driving on other occasions, such as New Year's Eve.

MORE ABOUT . . . . .

RELIABLE SOURCES. As students consider strategies that can help others make smart choices about alcohol, they might consult online or printed resources provided by Students Against Destructive Decisions (SADD). Students dedicated to helping other students say "No" to drinking and driving created this organization.

Today, SADD has expanded its mission to include other dangerous behaviors. The group's goal is "to provide students with the best prevention and intervention tools possible to deal with the issues of underage drinking, drunk driving, drug abuse and other destructive decisions."

More information is available at the SADD Web site, found in Web Links at **health.glencoe.com**.

CHECKING COMPREHENSION

- Assign and discuss the chapter review.
- Use the MindJogger Videoquiz to review the chapter. ◑

CHAPTER 25 REVIEW ANSWERS

Using Health Terms

1. intoxication
2. ethanol
3. fermentation
4. cirrhosis
5. designated drivers
6. blood alcohol concentration
7. fatty liver
8. fetal alcohol syndrome
9. alcoholism
10. delirium tremens
11. alcohol poisoning

Recalling the Facts

1. Any three: alcohol can create an addiction and ruin a person's health, affect performance in school or on the job, strain relationships, lead to behavior that causes legal problems, and cause serious injury or death.
2. Dangers of being intoxicated include impairment of judgment that can lead to unwanted sexual behavior and other high-risk behavior, and decreased perception that can cause traffic or industrial accidents.
3. Advertisers depict beautiful, healthy-looking young people in happy, upbeat, even beautiful settings. They try to convey the message that "everyone who's cool is doing it." They depict problem-free drinking and never mention the risks of alcohol consumption. They promote sporting events to give the impression that drinking is a healthful activity. They promote their product on T-shirts and hats so that teens who wear them become advertisers themselves.

Using Health Terms

On a separate sheet of paper, write the term that best matches each definition below.

LESSON 1

1. Physical and mental impairment resulting from the use of alcohol.
2. The type of alcohol found in alcoholic beverages.
3. The chemical action of yeast on sugars.

LESSON 2

4. A condition in which liver tissue is destroyed and then replaced with useless scar tissue.
5. People in social settings who choose not to drink so that they can safely drive themselves and others.

6. The amount of alcohol in a person's blood expressed as a percentage.
7. A condition in which fats build up in the liver and cannot be broken down.
8. A condition in which a fetus has been adversely affected mentally and physically by its mother's heavy alcohol use during pregnancy.

LESSON 3

9. A physical and psychological dependence on the drug ethanol.
10. The dramatic physical and psychological effects of alcohol withdrawal.
11. A dangerous toxic condition that occurs when a person drinks a large amount of alcohol in a short period of time.

Recalling the Facts

Using complete sentences, answer the following questions.

LESSON 1

1. Name three ways in which alcohol can negatively affect or even destroy a teen's future.
2. What are some of the dangers of being intoxicated?
3. What are some of the techniques that advertisers use to get young adults to buy and use alcohol products?

LESSON 2

4. What is the legal definition of *driving while intoxicated,* or a DWI?
5. Name five problems that someone stopped for driving while intoxicated may face.
6. What happens when a person has cirrhosis of the liver, and what is one of its primary causes?

7. Explain the multiplier effect, also known as the synergistic effect.
8. Describe three defects or problems of children with fetal alcohol syndrome.

LESSON 3

9. What are some of the dangers of binge drinking?
10. What are the three stages of alcoholism?
11. What are some of the symptoms of withdrawal from alcohol?
12. Where can a teen alcoholic get help? Where can the teen child of an alcoholic get help?
13. What is the relationship between alcohol and self-control?
14. Write a sentence or two using the word *abstinence* in which you relate it to your personal habits.
15. For what reasons is not using alcohol the only responsible choice?

---

4. A person is driving while intoxicated when his or her blood alcohol concentration exceeds the limit allowed by the state.
5. Among the problems facing a person stopped for DWI are: confiscation of driver's license, arrest and jail time, bail to get out of jail, court appearance, fines, suspension of driver's license, higher insurance rates, and possible lawsuits.

6. Cirrhosis of the liver is a condition in which liver tissue is destroyed and then replaced with useless scar tissue, causing loss of liver function. This condition is caused by prolonged heavy alcohol use.
7. In the multiplier effect, the effects of one drug are magnified by the effects of another drug or drugs used.
8. Children with fetal alcohol syndrome may have low birth weight, impaired

Thinking Critically

LESSON 1

1. *Analyzing.* Which, in your opinion, has a greater influence on a teen's decision to drink alcohol: the influence of family, friends, or advertisements? Why?

LESSON 2

2. *Synthesizing. It is especially hazardous to use alcohol in cold climates.* Give some reasons why this statement might be accurate.

LESSON 3

3. *Analyzing.* For what reasons do you think alcoholism is considered a disease? Why do you think some people believe, mistakenly, that it is simply a matter of having little or no willpower?

4. *Evaluating.* What strategies or arguments seem to work best with teens in trying to convince them not to drink at all?

Making the Connection

1. *Social Studies.* In 1920, the Eighteenth Amendment to the Constitution was passed, prohibiting the manufacture, sale, and transportation of alcohol products. Find out what social forces led up to the signing and passing of this amendment, what its effects were, and when and why it was repealed. Share your findings with the class.

2. *Language Arts.* Interview a police officer in your community. What is being done to reduce the number of accidents caused by people who drive while intoxicated? Have the efforts worked? What age group presents the most serious problem? How can teenage drivers help fight this problem? Prepare your questions in advance, then summarize your interview.

BEYOND THE CLASSROOM

PARENTAL INVOLVEMENT With your parents or guardians, learn more about MADD. Learn when, where, and why it was founded, what its mission is, and how you and your family can get involved. Draw up a contract for all family members to sign that includes a commitment never to drink and drive and never to ride with any driver who has been drinking—even a family member.

COMMUNITY INVOLVEMENT Find out what your state's laws are regarding the purchase, possession, and consumption of alcohol by minors and the sale or delivery of alcohol to minors.

With school and community leaders and the police, organize a school assembly in which the legal consequences of underage alcohol use and purchase are made clear.

SCHOOL-TO-CAREER
Exploring Careers. Invite a family physician to speak to the class about his or her profession. Ask how much time in medical school was spent discussing the effects of alcohol and alcoholism. Ask what kinds of medical effects he or she sees among heavy drinkers, particularly young people.

speech, cleft palate, general weakness, slow body growth, facial abnormalities, poor coordination, and heart defects. They may also display mental retardation, poor attention span, nervousness, and hyperactivity.

9. Binge drinking can mask the reality that one has a problem with alcohol. It can also lead to alcohol poisoning and death.

10. Alcoholism begins with the need to drink to feel comfortable in social situations or to relieve stress. The next stage of alcoholism is physical and psychological dependence. The third stage is addiction and the experiencing of withdrawal symptoms if one doesn't drink.

11. Some of the symptoms of withdrawal from alcohol are hot and cold flashes, severe tremors, nightmares, hallucinations, and unreasonable fears.

12. A teen alcoholic can seek help from a school counselor, trusted adult, or support group. The teen child of an alcoholic can seek help from the same resources.

13. Consumption of alcohol in any amount decreases self-control.

14. Answers will vary.

15. Abstinence is the only responsible choice because alcohol has an immediate effect on mental and body functions even in small amounts, and the consequences of even a single bad decision made under the influence of alcohol can last a lifetime.

Thinking Critically

1.–4. Answers will vary.

Making the Connection

1.–2. Answers will vary.

Evaluate

- Use the reproducible *Chapter 25 Test* in the TCR, or construct your own using the Testmaker software.
- Use *Performance Assessment Activity 25* in the TCR.

Enrichment

Ask students to complete *Cross-Curriculum Activity 25* in the TCR.

Beyond the Classroom

Keep students involved in the community, and encourage parent participation by assigning the activities on this page for students to work on outside of class.

Illegal Drugs

		FEATURES	CLASSROOM RESOURCES

LESSON 1

Drug Use--A High-Risk Behavior

pages 574–579

Looking at the Issues

"Drug Testing: Yes or No?"
page 578

- Concept Map Activity 77
- Cooperative Learning Activity 26
- Lesson 77 Quiz
- Lesson Plan 77
- Reteaching Activity 77
- Transparency 29

LESSON 2

Psychoactive Drugs

pages 580–585

- Concept Map Activity 78
- Enrichment Activity 26
- Health Lab 26
- Lesson 78 Quiz
- Lesson Plan 78
- Reteaching Activity 78

LESSON 3

Steroids and Other Dangerous Drugs

pages 586–590

Making Responsible Decisions

"Running Scared," *page 587*

Building Health Skills

"Refusal Skills: Saying No to Drugs," *page 589*

- Concept Map Activity 79
- Decision-Making Activity 26
- Lesson 79 Quiz
- Lesson Plan 79
- Reteaching Activity 79

LESSON 4

Strategies for Preventing Substance Abuse

pages 591–595

Teens Making a Difference

"The Drive to Stay Drug Free,"
page 594

- Concept Map Activity 80
- Lesson 80 Quiz
- Lesson Plan 80
- Reteaching Activity 80
- Transparency 43

ACTIVITIES

- Cross-Curriculum Activity 26
- Health Lab 26
- Health Skills Activities 26
- Parent Letter and Activities 26

ASSESSMENT

- Chapter 26 Test
- Performance Assessment Activity 26
- Testmaker Software

STUDENT ACTIVITIES WORKBOOK

- Applying Health Skills 77–80
- Study Guide 26
- Vocabulary Activity 26

STUDENT DIVERSITY STRATEGIES

- Audiocassette Program (English)
- Audiocassette Program (Spanish)
- Spanish Parent Letters and Activities
- Spanish Summaries, Quizzes, and Activities

MULTIMEDIA COMPONENTS

- English Audiocassette Program
- Spanish Audiocassette Program
- MindJogger Videodisc and VHS program
- ABCNews InterActive™ VHS/Videodisc Series

National Health Education Standards

One of the main goals of the National Health Education Standards is to move students toward "health literacy." Health literacy is the capacity of individuals to obtain, interpret, and understand basic health information and services and the competence to use such information and services in ways which promote health. The health standards were developed by applying the characteristics of a well-educated, literate person within the context of health. The health literate person is:

- a critical thinker and problem solver
- a self-directed learner
- a responsible, productive citizen
- an effective communicator

Listed below are the Health Education Standards Performance Indicators addressed in each lesson of this chapter.

Lesson	Health Standards Performance Indicators
1	1.2, 1.7, 3.1, 3.3
2	1.2, 1.3, 3.1, 3.3
3	3.3, 5.6, 6.1, 6.3
4	3.1, 3.4, 6.3, 6.6

ONLINE RESOURCES

For a fresh approach to health topics and an in-depth look at health issues, use these online resources found under Teacher Resources at **health.glencoe.com**.

- **BLOCK SCHEDULE LESSON PLANS** Reinforce health concepts with outside readings selected especially for students. Each reading is accompanied by a lesson plan and activities to enhance
  - Reading Skills
  - Cross Curriculum
  - Media Literacy

- **TECHNOLOGY PROJECTS** Instructions and suggestions on how to use computer, Internet, and software with health lessons.

- **HEALTH UPDATES** Timely topics in health news, including late-breaking medical advances and updates on teen risk behaviors.

Out of Time?

If time does not permit teaching this chapter, you may use these features: Update on page 578; Making Responsible Decisions on page 587; and Building Health Skills on page 589.

BLOCK SCHEDULING

Block scheduling provides extended time for hands-on projects and activities. Use the following activities to engage students, provide further depth, and vary your instructional techniques:

- Update (30 minutes) **pg. 578**
- Teens Making a Difference (30 minutes) **pg. 594**
- Health Skills Activity (60–90 minutes) **pg. 596**

Illegal Drugs

CHAPTER OVERVIEW

Chapter 26 discusses the dangers of medicine misuse and substance abuse. The chapter explains how various drugs affect the body and provides strategies for preventing substance abuse.

LESSON 1 Drug abuse by teens has leveled off, but certain drug trends by teens show disturbing increases. Drug use does nothing to enhance life or help users deal with their problems, but instead introduces a host of dangers, including dependence, tolerance, withdrawal symptoms, and addiction.

LESSON 2 Psychoactive drugs affect the central nervous system and can result in mental and/or behavioral problems. Stimulants, depressants, and narcotics have medicinal value. Hallucinogens have no medicinal value. Each type of drug presents specific risks to the user's health.

LESSON 3 Common drugs, such as steroids, marijuana, inhalants, and designer drugs, have been determined to be dangerous to one's health. Each drug carries its own set of health risks, ranging from lack of concentration and impaired judgment to severe damage to the body and even death.

LESSON 4 The best preparation for teens to be drug-free is to make a commitment to resist peer pressure, avoid people who use drugs and places where drugs are found, and focus on what is meaningful for their happiness, health, and future.

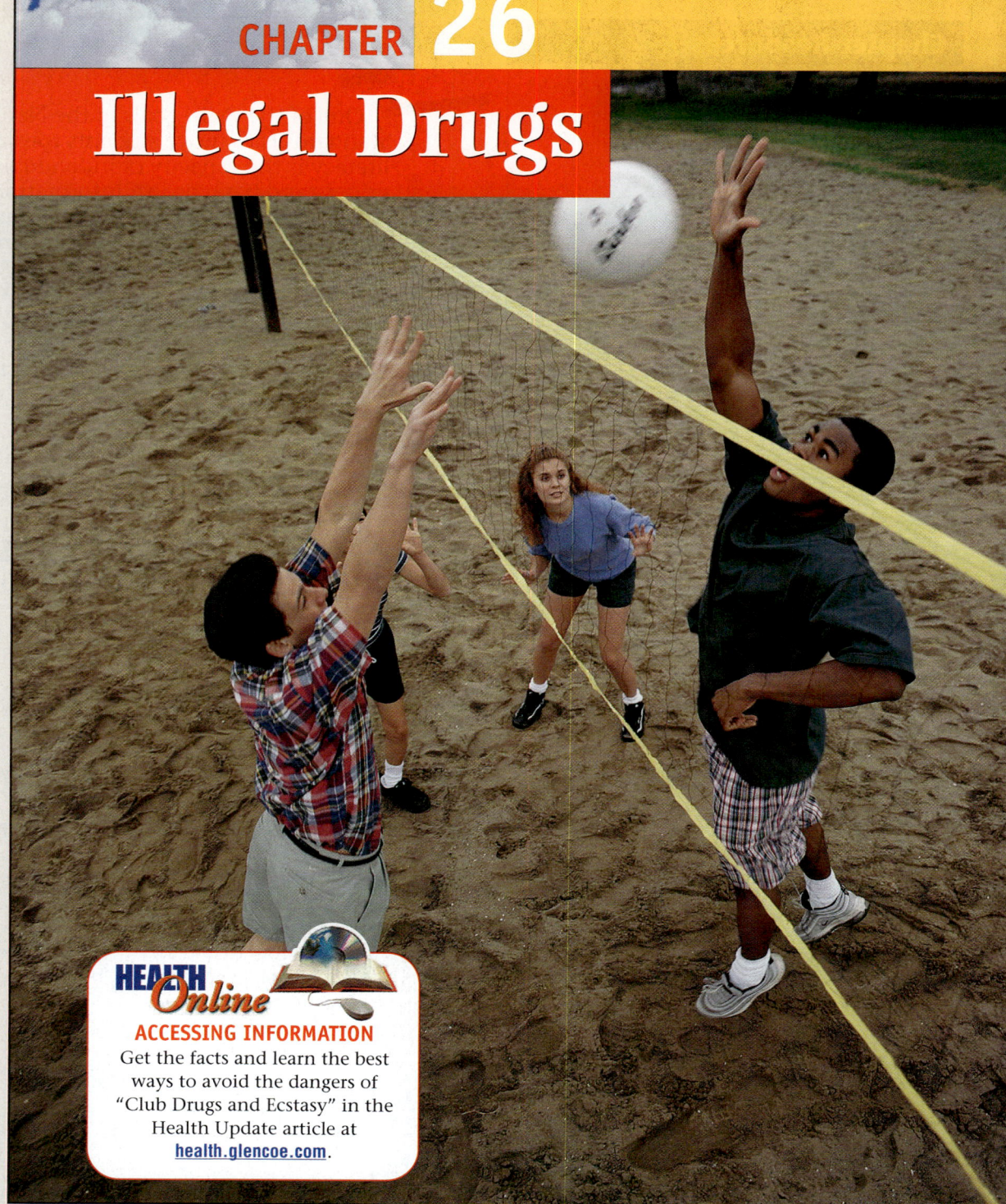

CHAPTER **26**

Illegal Drugs

HEALTH *Online*

ACCESSING INFORMATION
Get the facts and learn the best ways to avoid the dangers of "Club Drugs and Ecstasy" in the Health Update article at **health.glencoe.com**.

Hands-On Health

TEACHING STRATEGY

Risks of Alcohol and Other Drugs Let students review facts about alcohol and other drugs as they play this variation of a familiar TV game show. See Activity 22, "Jeo-Party," in the *Hands-On Health: Creative Teaching Strategies* booklet.

Time Needed
20 minutes

Supplies
• "Jeo-Party" transparency, projector
• 16 stick-on notes
• 4 or more small bells

Personal Health Inventory

Self-Inventory Write the numbers 1–10 on a sheet of paper. Read each statement below and respond by writing *yes*, *no*, or *sometimes* for each item. Write a *yes* only for items that you practice regularly. Save your responses.

1	I avoid any type of illegal or improper drug use.
2	I choose friends who avoid drug use.
3	I feel comfortable saying no to peers who offer me drugs.
4	I take only medicines that are prescribed by a doctor and never abuse or combine them.
5	I do not abuse over-the-counter drugs for any reason.
6	I stay away from areas and events where I know drugs are likely to be used or sold.
7	I never cover for a friend or peer who uses drugs.
8	I don't attend parties where I know there will be drug use.
9	I know where to get help for drug problems and would feel comfortable passing the information along to someone who needed it.
10	I understand the dangers of drugs, avoid high risks, and know healthier ways to relax.

Follow-up After completing the chapter, retake this self-inventory. Pick two items that you need to work on and set a goal to improve your health behaviors.

CHAPTER 26 ILLEGAL DRUGS **573**

> 66
> *The unexpected consequence of drug use is what I have called 'the oops phenomenon.' Why oops? Because the harmful outcome is in no way intentional.* 99
>
> —Alan I. Leshner, Ph.D.
> Director, National Institute on Drug Abuse
> National Institutes of Health

Quick Write The word *oops* implies a small, unintentional mistake. Write in one or two sentences why experimentation with drugs is not a small mistake, but is irresponsible and leads to dangerous outcomes.

INTRODUCING THE CHAPTER

Personal Health Inventory

Ask students: Why is it important for you to be honest with yourself about your attitudes toward drug use? about your drug awareness and any potential for drug-related behavior? After a brief discussion, have students read the Self-Inventory statements and record their own responses in their private Health Journals on a page labeled "My Level of Commitment to Drug Abstinence." Remind students that they will use these responses as part of the follow-up activity at the end of the chapter.

- Tell students that while alcohol abuse is the most prevalent drug abuse problem among teens, medicine misuse and illegal drugs also pose very serious problems. Tell them that after studying this chapter, they will be able to explain the effects of various drugs and problems associated with their use. Have students write on file cards any questions they want answered. Collect the cards and, after discussing the chapter, read the questions and have students answer them.

- Let students read and discuss the statement made by Dr. Leshner. Ask: What do you think the former Director of the National Institute on Drug Abuse meant when he said this? Have students complete the Quick Write, and explain that the lessons in Chapter 26 will help them recognize the risks involved with drug use.

- Distribute Parent Letter 26 in the *Parent Letters and Activities* booklet in the TCR. ☛

TECHNOLOGY OPTIONS

 You may wish to use *Drugs and Substance Abuse* with this chapter. For your convenience, use the separate *ABCNews InterActive™ Bar Code Correlation* that accompanies the *Glencoe Health* program. ◐

MINDJOGGER
VIDEOQUIZ

To preview or review chapter content, you may wish to use the *MindJogger Videoquiz* that accompanies Chapter 26. ◐

Drug Use—A High-Risk Behavior

LESSON 1

FOCUS

LESSON OBJECTIVES

After studying this lesson, students should be able to

- identify reasons that people use drugs.
- describe the dangers of substance abuse.
- discuss the costs of drug use to the user, to the user's family and friends, and to society in general.

MOTIVATOR

Write the following on the chalkboard for students to work on while attendance is being taken: *List as many of the dangerous effects of drugs as you can think of that affect the user, the user's family and friends, and the rest of society.*

INTRODUCING THE LESSON

Collect students' responses to the Motivator. On the chalkboard, write some of their responses. Explain that drug use affects almost everyone, not just the user. This lesson will focus on the dangerous effects of drugs and the physical and psychological problems that are likely to occur to anyone who uses drugs.

INTRODUCING HEALTH TERMS

- Have students discuss the definition of *gateway drugs*. Discuss how some drugs "open the way" for other drugs. Ask how and why they think this happens.
- Ask students to complete Vocabulary Activity 26 and Chapter Study Guide 26 in the *Student Workbook*. ☞

Drug Use—A High-Risk Behavior

What is a prime contributing factor in many homicides, suicides, domestic abuse, absenteeism, and accidents? The answer is substance abuse. Substance abuse has effects on individuals and on society as a whole. You will learn strategies for avoiding and preventing substance abuse. Staying drug-free will help you to reach your goals.

HEALTH TERMS

substance abuse
illegal drugs
synthetic drugs
illicit drug use
gateway drugs
overdose

HEALTH CONCEPTS

- Substance abuse is a high-risk behavior that includes misusing legal drugs or using illegal drugs or other chemicals.
- People abuse drugs for a variety of reasons, none of them healthful.
- Substance abuse can harm a person's physical, mental, emotional, and social health and even lead to death.
- Substance abuse has far-reaching consequences for the abuser, for others in the abuser's life, and for society at large.

Substance Abuse

As noted in Chapter 23, when medicines are used in ways other than intended, a problem called **medicine misuse** exists. In many cases, medicine misuse results from carelessness. Sometimes, however, medicines are misused intentionally. People will

hotlink

medicine misuse For more information on medicine misuse and its dangers, see Chapter 23, page 520.

Lesson 1 Resources

TEACHER'S CLASSROOM RESOURCES

☞ **Concept Map** Activity 77
☞ **Cooperative Learning** Activity 26
☞ **Lesson 77 Quiz**
☞ **Lesson Plan 77**
☞ **Parent Letter and Activities 26**
☞ **Reteaching** Activity 77

STUDENT WORKBOOK

☞ **Applying Health Skills 77**
☞ **Chapter Study Guide 26**
☞ **Vocabulary** Activity 26

TRANSPARENCIES AND MULTIMEDIA

🖐 **Transparency 29**
🔴 **ABCNews InterActive™,** *Drugs and Substance Abuse*

take them deliberately to achieve a "high" from one or more of the known effects or reactions. In such cases, the user is guilty not only of *mis-use* but of *abuse*. **Substance abuse** is *any unnecessary or improper use of chemical substances for nonmedical purposes.* Substance abuse includes overuse or multiple use of a drug, including alcohol taken in combination with other drugs.

Not all substances that are abused are medicines. Many are *drugs,* chemical substances that serve no medical purpose and are simply used for recreational or other unhealthful purposes. Also known as **illegal drugs,** or *street drugs,* these substances are against the law for people of any age to manufacture, possess, buy, or sell. Their potential for harm is great.

Some drugs occur naturally, taking the form of extracts from plants, animals, or minerals. Others, called **synthetic drugs,** are *chemical substances produced artificially in a laboratory.* Regardless of their source or how they are taken, the effects of these drugs are deadly.

People who use illegal drugs are guilty of a crime called **illicit drug use.** This is *the use or sale of any substances that are illegal or otherwise not permitted.* Illicit drug use includes the selling of prescription medicines on the street. Even some drugs that are legal for adults, such as alcohol, are illegal for teens and can cause major health, safety, and social problems. For teens, alcohol and nicotine are also considered **gateway drugs,** or *drugs that often lead to other serious and dangerous drug use.*

Trends in Teen Drug Use

Even though in recent years abuse of drugs by teens has begun to level off, other drug trends suggest increases in use of some illegal substances. Consider these facts:

- Teens in the United States are now using drugs at younger ages than ever before.
- According to the National Household Survey on Drug Abuse, drug use among 12- to 17-year-olds began to decline in 1997 and has continued to stay level.
- In 1999, drug use among Americans age 12 and up fell to 6.7 percent.
- More teens are trying heroin than ever before, and more teen heroin users are showing up in hospital emergency rooms.
- Marijuana is the most commonly used illicit drug, used by 75 percent of all illegal drug users.
- More teens than ever mistakenly consider marijuana to be a safe drug.

During the 1990s, these substance abuse statistics prompted the Secretary of Health and Human Services to call this generation of teens "a generation at risk." The good news is that trends can be changed. By choosing to stay away from drugs, you can become part of a generation newly committed to getting and staying drug-free.

Did You Know?

➤ According to the National Household Survey on Drug Abuse, marijuana accounts for 75 percent of teen drug use.

➤ In 1999, tobacco use among teens had declined to around 15 percent.

◀ *You will protect your health by being physically active and avoiding substance abuse.*

TEACH

L1 Discussing

Discuss the forms of medicine misuse. Explore with students scenarios when medicine misuse becomes illegal drug use.

L3 Community Involvement

Ask for volunteers to collect current statistics on the use of illegal drugs in their local community. Also, have them find out what the statistics were five years ago. Suggest that they make a bar graph to show the increase or decrease in use for different age groups.

L1 Critical Thinking

Let students share and discuss their responses to these questions: Why do you think substance abuse is so often ignored as a dangerous activity? How are substance abuse and illegal drug abuse alike? What factor makes illegal drugs particularly dangerous?

L1 Discussing

Ask: What dangers do alcohol and nicotine themselves pose? How are those dangers increased when alcohol and nicotine lead to other serious and dangerous drug use?

L2 Community Involvement

Have students develop a handout of positive ways for teens to deal with stress in their lives. Encourage them to contact professionals in the community who work with teens for ideas or resources. Make the handouts available to teens in the school or community.

COOPERATIVE LEARNING

CONFERENCE AGENDA. Divide students into groups of five and have them pretend they are members of a steering committee for a national conference about drug abuse. Instruct each group to list the issues that should be discussed and to rank the issues in order of their importance. Tell them to prepare a proposed agenda of key topics and issues that should be discussed during the conference. Have them also identify a number of experts or leaders who should address the conference. For example, they might specify a representative from a drug abuse treatment center, the Surgeon General, an employee of a federal drug enforcement agency or city police force, the head of a university neurology department, etc. Let them explain each choice. Allow time for groups to share their agendas.

HEALTH *Online*

If your class is large, you may wish to appoint a group of volunteers to visit the Web Links for this lesson. The group can share its findings in a brief oral report that emphasizes some of the shocking statistics about drug use among teens and offers concrete recommendations on how to curtail this problem. As visual support, the group might download tables and charts from the

L3 ## Guest Speaker

Invite a member of the emergency room staff at a local hospital to speak about treatment of overdose cases. Have students write short summaries of the presentation.

L2 ## Class Activity

Have students prepare a table of signs and symptoms of drug overdose, with appropriate emergency actions. Ask for volunteers to computerize the information and to make printouts for the entire class.

L1 ## Discussing

Encourage students to share their ideas in response to these questions: How does a parent's drug use affect children? How does it affect teens? Do you think teens whose parents abuse drugs are more likely to experiment with drugs, or more likely to avoid drugs altogether? Why?

L1 ## Community Involvement

Many teens—in every kind of community—feel bored. Ask the class: What are some of the alternatives to drug use in your community? Let students work together to compile a list of fun activities and interesting places to go or things to do. They may want to publish their list in an illustrated flyer, to be shared with other local teens.

HEALTH *Online*

You know that drugs can be dangerous, but do you know how they alter the body and the mind? Find out the short-term and long-term physical and mental effects of illegal drugs at **health.glencoe.com**.

hot link

side effects For more information on the nature and types of side effects, see Chapter 23, page 516.

synergistic effect For more information on the synergistic effect and other interactions that result when medicines are combined, see Chapter 23, page 516.

hot link

HIV For more information on HIV, the virus that causes AIDS, see Chapter 30, page 656.

STDs For more information on STDs and measures you can take to avoid them, see Chapter 29, page 640.

tolerance For more information on tolerance to substances, see Chapter 23, page 517.

Why People Begin Using Drugs

If people know of the dangers of drugs, then why do so many try them? This question has different answers for different people. Many teens try drugs for one or more of the following reasons:

- They see their friends, parents, or older siblings using them.
- They feel pressured to use drugs and don't know how to say no.
- They want to fit in, relax, or seem mature.
- They see drugs glamorized on TV, in videos, in the movies, or in song lyrics.
- They seek a solution to boredom or are searching for new thrills.
- They are trying to escape from their problems.

Dangers of Substance Abuse

Like medicines, some drugs have serious **side effects**, which can range from minor to deadly. When taken in conjunction with one or more medicines or other drugs, including alcohol, they can also result in a **synergistic effect**. Illegal drugs may prove especially dangerous because, unlike medicines, there are no controls or means of monitoring these substances for quality, purity, or strength. Anyone who abuses drugs is also at risk for overdosing. An **overdose** is *a strong or even fatal reaction to taking a large amount of a drug.* Many overdoses are accidental. Often, overdoses occur when alcohol and other drugs are combined.

When drug use involves injecting substances through a needle, there may be added risks of contracting diseases such as hepatitis B, a serious and sometimes fatal liver ailment, and **HIV**, the virus that causes AIDS. Intravenous drug users often share needles, and traces of viruses in body fluids from infected people are easily spread to others who use the same needles.

People who experiment with drugs tend to lose control more readily than those who do not. This can lead to unwanted sexual encounters, **STDs**, or pregnancies. Substance abuse is also a major factor in many crimes, suicides, and both accidental and intentional deaths.

Substance abuse is like riding a "down" escalator. Taking that first step onto the moving stairway may seem harmless, but the consequences are enormous. These include the following:

- **Tolerance.** The body of the substance abuser begins to develop **tolerance** to the drug, needing more and more of it to get the same effects, and eventually needing it just to function.

SCHOOL-TO-CAREER

Sometimes drugs are abused not for a high, but in a misguided effort to accomplish something worthwhile. Assign students to research the abuse of amphetamines to stay awake for exams. Have them learn about the disadvantages to such a strategy; for example, the tendency to be careless about test details while on amphetamines. Suggest they use online sources or *Reader's Guide* to research media reports about abuse of amphetamines by workers trying to work longer hours and be more productive. Encourage students to list the effects of such amphetamine abuse both on health and on long-term student and worker performance. Have them offer the list to the school newspaper.

- **Physiological dependence.** The body develops a chemical need for a drug. A person who has developed tolerance and experiences severe effects when the drug is taken away is said to be physiologically dependent on that drug.
- **Withdrawal.** **Withdrawal** occurs when a person stops using a drug on which he or she is physiologically dependent. The symptoms of this process can include nervousness, insomnia, severe nausea, headaches, vomiting, chills, cramps, and, in some instances, even death.
- **Psychological dependence.** With psychological dependence, a person believes a drug is needed in order to feel good or to function normally. He or she has a continual desire to take the drug for its effect.
- **Addiction.** Addiction involves physiological and psychological dependence on a drug.

hotlink

withdrawal For more information on withdrawal from substances, see Chapter 23, page 517.

▼ *Helping people to understand the risks involved with drug use is one way to combat substance abuse.*

ACTIVITY *With classmates, brainstorm a list of reasons teens should avoid drug use.*

Teen Marijuana Use

% WHO USED IN PAST YEAR

12TH GRADE
10TH GRADE
8TH GRADE

'95 '96 '97 '98 '99 '00

SOURCE: University of Michigan Monitoring the Future Study, 2000.

Why Teens Use Drugs

	AGE 12	AGE 17
To be cool	49%	11%
Friends are doing it	24%	25%
To feel good	9%	23%
Substance abuse in family	7%	4%
To relieve stress	6%	22%
To escape problems	3%	7%
To rebel	1%	6%

SOURCE: National Center on Addiction and Drug Abuse.

LESSON 1   DRUG USE—A HIGH-RISK BEHAVIOR   **577**

L1 Class Activity

Have students find examples of drug-related crimes and deaths in newspaper and magazine articles. Discuss some of the examples, and list some of the victims (or probable victims) involved, such as family, friends, innocent bystanders, business owners, taxpayers, and health care workers.

L3 Class Activity

Invite a panel of employers to talk about drug use in the workplace. Ask them to discuss the use of drug tests, health insurance costs, accidents, and other costs of drug use by workers.

L2 Class Activity

Have students write and rehearse skits to teach middle school students some of the costs and problems of using drugs. With administrative approval, plan a field trip to a middle school class to present the skits. Make certain that the senior high presenters know they must be prepared to answer basic questions during any discussions that may follow the skits.

DRUGS AND SUBSTANCE ABUSE (Side 1)

Chapter 15: The Nature of Addiction

Frames 48643-53540

DRUGS AND SUBSTANCE ABUSE (Side 2)

Chapter 3: Cost to Society

Frames 2500-6492

Chapter 6: Drugs and the Community

Frames 12576-14631

HOME AND COMMUNITY CONNECTION

STORY OF ABUSE AS TOLD BY FAMILY. The effect of drug abuse on family members can be devastating. Children who depend on addicted parents are especially vulnerable and may suffer neglect or abuse. Even caring, responsible parents often feel helpless and heartbroken when they cannot prevent self-destructive behavior in teens for whom they feel love and are responsible. Encourage students to write a fictional first-person account of drug abuse from the perspective of the drug abuser's parent or child. Tell them the story should convey to the reader the effects of the abuser's drug use on the fictional narrator.

L1 Explaining

Emphasize the connections between drug use and the likelihood of contracting HIV. People under the influence of drugs act impulsively, without considering the consequences. Thus, they are likely to inject with a used needle or engage in sexual activity, even though they might avoid making those choices when not under the influence of drugs.

L2 Class Activity

Select students who will design and complete a bulletin board or exhibit portraying some of the costs of drug use.

update
▶ Looking at the Issues

Drug Testing: Yes or No?

Ask volunteers to share what they know about drug testing. Ask: Is drug testing used in our school? When and why? How—if at all—do local employers use drug testing? What do you think of drug testing? Is it fair? Is it effective? Then have students read the Update feature to learn more about drug testing and to explore three different viewpoints. Finally, have students meet in small groups to discuss their responses to the Views questions; encourage students to offer facts and examples to support their opinions.

L2 Cooperative Learning

Assign *Cooperative Learning Activity 26* for more on deadly drugs. ▶

HEALTH Online

To learn more about substance abuse visit Web Links at **health.glencoe.com**.

Costs of Substance Abuse

In a teen's life, substance abuse can negatively affect performance in school, in sports, in relationships with peers, and in family life. It can affect a teen's emotional, social, and physical health. It can add undue pressure and stress to a period of life that is already filled with both. Furthermore, experimenting even once with a drug can get a teen in trouble with the law or even ruin his or her life. Educational goals may be interrupted and substance abuse can slow the progress toward becoming a mature adult.

update
▶ Looking at the Issues

Drug Testing: Yes or No?

It is estimated that substance abuse costs employers $90 billion a year in decreased productivity, absenteeism, and accidents. In the interest of health, safety, and economics, many companies are now testing employees for drug use. This has triggered a debate over whether people should be tested, who should do the testing, and whether the results are reliable.

ANALYZING DIFFERENT VIEWPOINTS

▶ **Viewpoint One**
Some groups claim that randomly testing people for drug use without just cause is an invasion of their rights, including their right to privacy.

▶ **Viewpoint Two**
Others believe that drug testing should be restricted to those who are in jobs where public safety is involved—such as pilots or bus drivers—or to cases where there is reason to suspect substance abuse, such as after a workplace accident.

▶ **Viewpoint Three**
Still other people argue that drug tests are not always accurate. They point out that people sometimes have others give drug-free urine samples in their place. Such situations can have severe consequences for the person being tested and for those in his or her life. The consequences for those incorrectly testing positive include job loss or damaged reputations.

EXPLORING YOUR VIEWS

1. Who, if anyone, do you think should be tested for drugs in the workplace? Why? In what kinds of situations?

2. When people do test positive for drugs, what do you think should happen to them? Why?

3. What do you think about schools testing students for drugs? What about testing for athletes?

4. What other means of identifying and getting help for students who are in trouble with drugs can you suggest?

CURRICULUM CONNECTIONS

LANGUAGE ARTS. Have students write a fictional first-person story which assumes that they are the victim of a drug-related crime. Ask them to set the stage of the crime, the persons involved, the kind of crime committed, the effects of the crime on the victim and the victim's family and friends, and the cost of the crime to those involved.

Select the best stories to submit to the school newspaper or to form a book of short stories.

SCIENCE. Ask for volunteers to research the types of chemical tests for blood, breath, and/or urine that are currently being used in different parts of the United States to test for use of drugs.

COSTS TO OTHERS

Substance abuse affects not just the abuser but others in his or her life. Think about the number of drug-related crimes and deaths you read or hear about. According to the National Clearinghouse for Alcohol and Drug Information, illegal drugs burden American society with an estimated $67 billion in health, social, and criminal costs every year.

DRUGS AND PREGNANCY

Substance abuse can do serious harm to developing fetuses and to babies who ingest the substance through breast milk from nursing mothers who use drugs. Despite this, nearly 7 percent of babies born each year in this country have been exposed to one or more illegal drugs passed along through the mother's blood supply. Babies born to mothers who used depressants during pregnancy may be physically dependent on them and show withdrawal symptoms at birth. Birth defects and behavioral problems among these infants are common. Babies born to women who drink too much suffer from fetal alcohol syndrome. In addition, babies are often born addicted to the drugs their mothers have ingested. Those whose mothers used cocaine, heroin, or other narcotics go into severe withdrawal a few days after birth. Hearing the cries of a newborn going through withdrawal is a graphic reminder of the high and sometimes tragic costs of substance abuse.

▲ *Using illegal drugs can lead to serious trouble.*

ACTIVITY *Make a list of warnings about the dangers of substance abuse.*

EVALUATING THE LESSON

Assign and discuss the Lesson 1 Review; then administer, grade, and discuss the *Lesson 77 Quiz* in the TCR. 🔖

RETEACHING

- Have students list ways in which drugs affect both the user and others.
- Ask students to complete *Reteaching Activity 77* in the TCR. 🔖
- Use *Transparency 29* to review the reasons teens use drugs. 🧴

ENRICHMENT

Assign each student to read a report, article, or book (or to watch a movie) about true experiences of Americans imprisoned in foreign countries for drug offenses. Ask students to find answers to these questions: What rights do the offenders have, if any? What kinds of punishments are handed out in various parts of the world? Afterward, have students share what they learned with the class.

CLOSE

Ask students to state the lesson's most important concepts.

Review

Reviewing Facts and Vocabulary

1. Define the terms *substance abuse, illegal drugs,* and *gateway drugs,* and use them in a single paragraph.
2. Describe three trends in teen drug use in recent years.
3. Identify five different reasons why a teen might start using drugs.

Thinking Critically

4. *Synthesizing.* List three costs of drug use in society, and give examples of how each of these costs might affect you.
5. *Evaluating.* Find examples of drug-related crimes and deaths in the newspaper and magazine articles. List some of the types of victims involved, such as family, friends, innocent bystanders, business owners, taxpayers, or health care workers. Evaluate the way in which each crime was handled by the criminal justice system. Do you think this strategy was effective in preventing further drug-related crimes? Why or why not?

Applying Health Skills

6. *In Your Home.* Write down three of your personal goals. Next to each goal, write a statement about how substance abuse would interfere with your ability to reach that goal. Post this list somewhere in your home where you will read it frequently.

Lesson 1 Review

Answers to Reviewing Facts and Vocabulary

1. See the Glossary for definitions. Paragraphs will vary.
2. Teens are using drugs at younger ages than ever before. More teens than ever before are trying heroin. More teens than ever before consider marijuana a safe drug.
3. See page 576 for a list of reasons people use drugs.

Answers to Thinking Critically

4.–5. Answers will vary.

Psychoactive Drugs

LESSON 2

Psychoactive Drugs

FOCUS

LESSON OBJECTIVES

After studying this lesson, students should be able to

- explain the effects of stimulants and depressants and the risks of misuse or abuse of each.
- describe the effects of narcotics and hallucinogens on the body.

MOTIVATOR

Write the following on the chalkboard for students to work on while attendance is being taken: *Write a definition for each of the following terms:* stimulants, depressants, narcotics, *and* hallucinogens.

INTRODUCING THE LESSON

Ask volunteers to share their responses to the Motivator. Tell students that stimulants, depressants, and narcotics may be used for medicinal purposes, but hallucinogens have no medical value. All of these drugs can be very dangerous when not used in a controlled medical situation.

INTRODUCING HEALTH TERMS

- Have students write a sentence explaining the difference between stimulants and depressants. Next, ask them to write a sentence contrasting narcotics and hallucinogens.
- Ask students to complete Vocabulary Activity 26 and Chapter Study Guide 26 in the *Student Workbook.* ☞

Like drugs used as medicines, drugs of abuse are grouped according to their effects on the body. Psychoactive drugs are one such group. **Psychoactive drugs** are *chemicals that affect the central nervous system and interfere with the normal functioning of the brain*. The use of psychoactive drugs among teens has increased alarmingly.

HEALTH TERMS

psychoactive drugs
stimulants
paranoia
euphoria
depressants
narcotics
hallucinogens

HEALTH CONCEPTS

- Psychoactive drugs affect the central nervous system and interfere with the normal functioning of the brain.
- Some psychoactive drugs have medicinal value whereas others do not, though all can be misused and abused.
- Misused or abused psychoactive drugs can have dangerous effects on the health and lives of their users.

Types of Psychoactive Drugs

There are four main groups of psychoactive drugs: stimulants, depressants, narcotics, and hallucinogens (huh-LOOS-ih-nuh-juhns). The first three groups have medicinal value when properly used. Hallucinogens, however, have no medical use. It is important to note that, when abused, *any* of these drugs can lead to serious health problems and even death.

 Lesson 2 Resources

TEACHER'S CLASSROOM RESOURCES
☞ **Concept Map** Activity 78
☞ **Enrichment** Activity 26
☞ **Health Lab** 26
☞ **Lesson 78 Quiz**
☞ **Lesson Plan** 78
☞ **Reteaching** Activity 78

STUDENT WORKBOOK
☞ **Applying Health Skills** 78
☞ **Chapter Study Guide** 26
☞ **Vocabulary** Activity 26

MULTIMEDIA
 ABCNews InterActive™ VHS/Videodisc, *Drugs and Substance Abuse*

Stimulants

Stimulants are *drugs that speed up the central nervous system.* Commonly abused stimulants are amphetamines (am-FET-uh-meens), methamphetamine (meth-uhm-FET-uh-meen), and cocaine. The **nicotine** in tobacco products is also a well-known stimulant, as is the caffeine in coffee, colas, tea, and chocolate.

Stimulants cause increased heart and respiratory rates, high blood pressure, dilated pupils, and decreased appetite. In addition, users may experience sweating, headaches, blurred vision, dizziness, and sleeplessness. Extremely high doses can cause irregular heartbeat, shaking or trembling, loss of coordination, and even physical collapse. Inhalation or injection of stimulants can cause a sudden increase in blood pressure that can result in stroke, high fever, or heart failure.

The psychological effects of stimulant use include moodiness, restlessness, and anxiety. Chronic users can experience hallucinations, delusions, and paranoia. **Paranoia** is *irrational suspiciousness or distrust of others.* These symptoms disappear when drug use ceases.

Amphetamines

Amphetamines are stimulants that have an effect similar to that of the **sympathetic nervous system**. Medical use of amphetamines has declined greatly in recent years. Some people use amphetamines illegally to stay awake and alert, to improve athletic performance, to lose weight, and to offset the effects of depressant drugs. Some use them for a temporary high and for **euphoria** (yoo-FOR-ee-uh), *a feeling of intense well-being or elation that may be followed by a complete "crash" or letdown.* These temporary highs, however, come at great cost to a person's physical and mental well-being, because once the craving begins, it may not go away. Tolerance to amphetamines can easily develop. Psychological dependence also can result. The user can experience exhaustion and depression as the effect of the drug wears off.

hot link

nicotine For more information on nicotine, the addictive drug found in tobacco, see Chapter 24, page 529.

hot link

sympathetic nervous system For more information on the sympathetic nervous system and its function, see Chapter 16, page 370.

◀ *What do you and your peers think can be done to stop the increase of drug use among teens?*

ACTIVITY *List some ideas you think of that could convince teens that drugs are dangerous.*

LESSON 2 PSYCHOACTIVE DRUGS **581**

CHAPTER 26 • LESSON 2

TEACH

L1 Class Activity

Display three or four cans of food or other household items with the labels removed. Let students examine the cans carefully and then guess what is in each can. Record all answers. Open the cans and find out what is inside. Compare this to the frequent deceptiveness involved in buying or selling drugs based on appearance.

L1 Explaining

Tell students there are many risks associated with putting chemicals into the body. One never knows how the body will react. Compare this to mixing chemicals in a laboratory. Discuss the health risks of using the body as a chemical lab.

L2 Discussing

Talk about the different weight-loss systems advertised in the media. Have students research which systems are most likely to be healthy and permanent approaches to losing weight. Also, ask them to find out if any of the systems that use drugs for weight loss are regulated. Lead a discussion of their findings.

L1 Explaining

Tell students that amphetamines for losing weight are usually unsuccessful because, if eating habits do not change, the weight is regained as soon as one quits taking the pills or products.

L2 Health Lab

Distribute *Health Lab 26* and have students answer the question "Can You Detect the Drug?" ▱

PERSONAL HEALTH

OBESITY DRUGS. In the 1990s, federal health officials declared obesity a disease that, above a certain level, justified the use of prescribed drugs. Have students conduct research about the drugs used to control obesity. Ask: Are amphetamines still used? If not, how do the drugs in current use differ from amphetamines? Suggest that students use the *Physicians' Desk Reference* or other source to research the adverse effects of widely used obesity drugs. After losing weight, can people stop taking the drugs without regaining the weight? If they keep taking them, do they develop tolerance? What are the health effects of long-term use? Would students use the drugs to treat their own obesity? If so, which drugs do students believe are less harmful than remaining obese?

Chapter 26 **581**

L1 Explaining

Stress that people who abuse drugs often become dependent on several different types of drugs. They may take amphetamines to get high and then take a depressant to settle down or to go to sleep. Discuss the implications of this type of abuse on the body's ability to function on its own.

L3 Cooperative Learning

Divide the class into groups. Ask each group to develop a brief skit depicting codeine's symptoms. *(drowsiness, anxiety, euphoria, slurred speech, impaired coordination, depressed reflexes, constricted pupils, loss of appetite, constipation)*

DRUGS AND SUBSTANCE ABUSE (Side 1)

Chapter 7: Cocaine and Crack

Frames 17526-22109

Chapter 10: Narcotics

Frames 28913-32535

Chapter 11: Stimulants

Frames 32569-36737

Chapter 12: Depressants

Frames 36762-40560

Chapter 14: Hallucinogens

Frames 44084-48627

hotlink

Parkinson's disease For more information on Parkinson's disease and its symptoms, see Chapter 16, page 374.

obesity For more information on the problem of obesity, see Chapter 6, page 133.

Did You Know?

➤ Passive smoke, smoke harmful to those around a smoker, does not involve just tobacco; it also applies to cocaine.

➤ About six out of every 100 children treated in emergency rooms have cocaine in their systems from breathing in the smoke from adult crack-cocaine smokers.

Methamphetamine

Methamphetamine is a stimulant that has been used medically in treating certain diseases, including **Parkinson's disease** and **obesity**. When used illegally, this drug, which is also called *crank, speed,* or *ice,* may cause a person to turn paranoid or even violent. Because crank is made in labs, it is readily available. Crank can be smoked, "snorted"—sniffed up the nostrils—injected, or swallowed. The effects of this drug are long-lasting. Food and water become unimportant after taking crank and often just the fumes alone prove deadly.

Cocaine

Cocaine is a white powder made from the coca bush, which grows in parts of South America. Cocaine use and possession is now illegal under state and federal laws.

Cocaine is a rapid-acting, powerful stimulant. Its effects can last from 20 minutes to several hours. The feelings of confidence that come from cocaine use are often followed by a letdown. Regular use can lead to depression, edginess, weight loss, and physiological dependence. Repeated cocaine use can cause tissue damage in the nose and even holes in the nasal septum, the wall dividing the two halves of the nose.

Cocaine use can cause malnutrition and, especially among those with cardiac problems, an increase in the risk of heart attack. Even in healthy individuals who are not heavy users, the drug may disturb the electrical impulses of the heart and cause death. An additional risk of cocaine use is the possibility of being infected with HIV when injecting cocaine with a shared needle.

CRACK

Crack is a form of cocaine that can be smoked. Processing converts cocaine into lumps or rocks—a form of the drug known as *freebase.* Preparing freebase may involve the use of dangerous solvents and can result in injury or death from an explosion or fire.

Crack is extremely addictive. Because it is smoked, its stimulant effects are felt within seconds. Crack users may develop a sore throat, hoarseness, and lung damage. Using crack can cause death by cardiac or respiratory failure. The drug is considered both extremely addictive and extremely dangerous.

Depressants

Depressants, or sedatives, are *drugs that tend to slow down the central nervous system.* As noted in Chapter 25, alcohol is a depressant. It is also the most commonly used psychoactive drug. Other commonly abused depressants are barbiturates (bar-BICH-uh-ruhts), tranquilizers, and methaqualone (muh-THA-kwuh-lohn).

Depressants relax muscles, relieve feelings of tension and worry, and bring on sleep. They slow down the heart and breathing rates

CURRICULUM CONNECTIONS

LANGUAGE ARTS. After reviewing literature and personal accounts of people using crack and cocaine, have each student write a short essay on cocaine and crack. The essay should explore their personal feelings about this drug and its effects on individuals.

LANGUAGE ARTS. Have each student research the history of one psychoactive drug and prepare a one-page report to share with the class. Ask students to consider such questions as these: Does the drug have any positive, useful purposes? What effects does this drug produce? Is this drug addictive? How widespread is the abuse of this drug?

and reduce blood pressure. Depressants can easily cause physical and psychological dependence.

Barbiturates

Barbiturates belong to the family of sedative-hypnotic drugs—drugs that induce sleepiness. Barbiturate use can result in mood changes, more sleep than normal, or even a coma. Barbiturates are rarely used for medical purposes. They are used illegally to produce a feeling similar to that of intoxication and to counteract the effects of stimulants. Combined with alcohol, they sometimes prove fatal.

Tranquilizers

Tranquilizers are depressants that reduce muscular activity, coordination, and attention span. Anti-anxiety tranquilizers, such as diazepam, are used medically to relieve anxiety, muscle spasms, sleeplessness, and nervousness. However, when tranquilizers are used in excess, physiological and psychological dependence occurs.

Methaqualone

The form of depressant known as methaqualone was originally prescribed to reduce anxiety and to help with insomnia. Known for producing temporary euphoria, the feeling does not last, and withdrawal from the drug is extremely unpleasant. Serious effects of using the drug include rapid dependence, headaches, diarrhea, dizziness, convulsions, and coma. Many people die by combining this depressant with alcohol.

Narcotics

Narcotics are *drugs derived from the opium plant that have a sedative effect.* The most commonly abused narcotics are morphine, heroin, opium itself, and codeine. Formerly, the term *narcotic* referred only to drugs made from the opium poppy flower. These drugs are called *opiates.* Narcotics now also include medicines used to relieve pain. Narcotics cause drowsiness and can result in physiological dependence. Drugs made from opium can cause stupor or sleep so deep that they depress respiration and can result in coma or death.

Morphine

Morphine is a natural narcotic compound that is contained in opium. It is sometimes used to reduce severe pain, for example, in terminal cancer patients. It can act as an appetite suppressant, cause severe constipation, and lead to addiction.

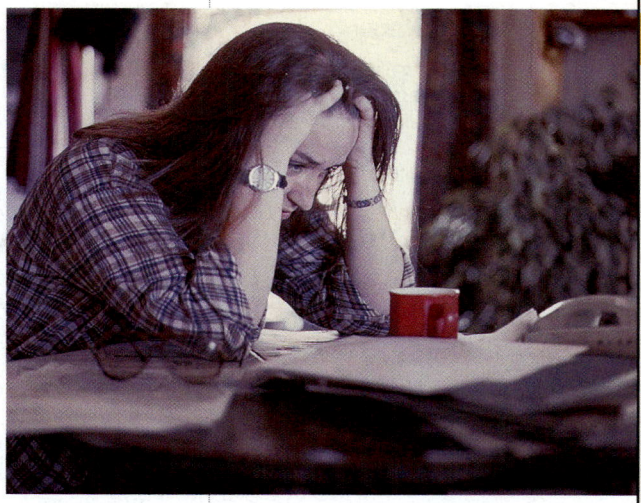

▲ *Turning to drugs is never a solution when you feel pressured or overwhelmed. Substance abuse only leads to more complex problems.*
ACTIVITY *List positive ways you can respond to stress.*

L2 Community Involvement

Ask for volunteers to visit a local pharmacy to examine labels on cough syrups. Have them find out what is used other than codeine to stop a cough. Request that they make an appointment to talk with the store's pharmacist to learn about the drugs used in cough medicines, which drugs actually suppress a cough, and the purpose of the other ingredients.

L1 Explaining

Tell students that the life expectancy of heroin addicts is quite short. The risks of overdose, hepatitis, AIDS (drug addicts have the second highest incidence of AIDS), and getting a bad mix are great. The monetary cost of maintaining the habit increases the abuser's risk of bodily harm through association with criminals. Many resort to crime to support their habit.

L3 Guest Speaker

Invite a hospice worker or intensive care nurse into class to talk about those narcotics and medicines most commonly and effectively used with dying patients to alleviate pain. Ask the speaker to discuss the average doses, how frequently and in what form they are administered, and what role the patients play in deciding on their dosage and use.

HEALTH LITERACY

SELF-DIRECTED LEARNER. Suggest that students interview a pharmacist who has been in practice for several decades, or invite a historically knowledgeable pharmacist to speak with the class about medically approved drug use during the 1960s. Encourage students to ask about any trends of prescription misuse over the years, such as the abuse of psychoactive drugs.

The pharmacist might mention such misuses as the use of amphetamines to control weight, barbiturates for sleep problems, and tranquilizers to cope with routine daily stresses. Have students ask how amphetamines, barbiturates, and tranquilizers differ from drugs now in use to treat similar problems.

L1 Discussing

Guide a class discussion of how the symptoms of heroin use differ from those of cocaine use. Are there any positive uses for either heroin or cocaine? Compare the risks of abusing the two drugs.

L1 Discussing

Why did PCP get the nickname "bad drug"? *(Its effects were extreme and varied, causing bizarre, unpredictable behaviors in users.)*

L1 Class Activity

Have students develop a bulletin board describing information about psychoactive drugs. *(Possible information to be included: street names, other descriptive information, how the drug is taken, and its effects on a person.)*

L3 Community Involvement

Assign students to find out what types of drug rehabilitation programs are available both locally and nationwide. Stress the fact that almost all of these treatment programs involve the entire family, not just the person with the drug problem. Ask why this would be important to the success of a treatment program. Encourage students to share their findings with the class.

Did You Know?

➤ A recent survey funded by National Institute of Drug Abuse found an alarming increase in the use of club drugs, including ecstasy, by teens of all ages.

➤ Ecstasy (MDMA) is similar in structure to the stimulant methamphetamine, and produces hallucinogenic effects similar to LSD.

➤ Health risks of ecstasy include confusion, depression, sleep problems, paranoia, and addiction.

➤ Ecstasy is a neurotoxin, causing damage to thought and memory processes.

➤ Serious physical effects can include muscle breakdown, kidney failure, and sudden cardiovascular system failure.

Codeine

A weaker cousin to morphine, codeine is also a narcotic compound derived from opium. Codeine is sometimes used in cough medications to stop coughing, and, like morphine, it can lead to dependence and abuse.

Heroin

Heroin is made from morphine and has no accepted medical use in the United States. It is an illegal drug. Heroin depresses the central nervous system and slows breathing and pulse rate. Coma or death may occur with large doses. Tolerance develops very quickly. Pregnant females who use heroin risk having babies who are born addicted. Retardation and delayed growth of these babies' muscular and nervous systems can result. Withdrawal from this drug is very painful. As with any drug that is injected, there are risks of HIV infection from using contaminated needles.

Until recent years, heroin was thought to be a drug of the inner city, used by hard-core drug addicts. According to the Drug Enforcement Administration, or DEA, its use is higher in the United States now than it has ever been, and it is moving to the suburbs and to rural areas. In fact, in 1997, the reported heroin use among American teens was approximately two to three times higher than in 1991. The dangers now are greater than ever in part because the drug's purity is now sometimes 10 times higher than it was in the 1980s.

Hallucinogens

Some people who have suffered from mental disorders such as schizophrenia suffer from hallucinations and other distorted perceptions of the world around them. They may see and hear things that are not really there. People who use hallucinogenic drugs may have similar experiences. **Hallucinogens** are *drugs that alter moods, thoughts, and sense perceptions, including vision, hearing, smell, and touch.* The most commonly abused narcotics are PCP, LSD, and mescaline.

PCP

Phencyclidine, also known as *PCP* or *angel dust,* is a powerful and dangerous hallucinogen. It is prepared synthetically. PCP is considered to be one of the most dangerous of all drugs. Users report that PCP makes them feel distant and detached from their surroundings. Time seems to pass slowly; body movements slow down. Muscle coordination is impaired, and the sensations of touch and pain are dulled. PCP can make the user feel strong and powerful. This feeling has resulted in tragic deaths, serious accidents, and terrible acts of violence.

Even though overdoses of PCP can cause death, most PCP-related deaths are caused by the strange, destructive behavior that the drug produces in the user. PCP users have drowned in shallow water because

584 CHAPTER 26 ILLEGAL DRUGS

Myths & Realities

MYTH. Drugs affect all people the same way.

FACT. Specific hazards of drug abuse differ from person to person. However, drug abuse can affect a person's physical and emotional health and social life.

MYTH. "Drug overdoses can't happen to me. I'm always in control of the situation."

FACT. An overdose can happen due to the drug's uncertain purity or strength, or even to the type of drug you get illegally. It can also happen due to increased tolerance, because you need more and more of a drug to get the same effect.

MYTH. "Depressants are the safest of all drugs, because they just make you relax."

FACT. Depressants can easily cause physical and psychological dependence.

they were so disoriented they could not tell where they were or which direction was up. Others have died in fires because they were disoriented and had no sensitivity to the pain of burning.

LSD

LSD is the shortened name for lysergic acid diethylamide. Commonly referred to as *acid,* it is one of the most potent of all mood-altering chemicals. A hallucinogen, LSD comes in tablet, capsule, and sometimes liquid form and is colorless, tasteless, and odorless. LSD's effects are wildly unpredictable. It can cause a false sense of security and power that has resulted in the deaths of users who, for example, believed they could fly or could stop a train by standing on the train tracks. Hallucinations may lead to panic, anxiety, or accidental suicide. Use of hallucinogens is illegal.

Mescaline

Mescaline is the psychoactive ingredient of the peyote cactus. Like LSD, it can lead to "bad trips," or frightening imagined phenomena and may lead to vicious stomach cramps and vomiting.

LESSON 2 *Review*

Reviewing Facts and Vocabulary

1. Define the term *psychoactive drugs* and use it in a well-developed paragraph about this class of drugs.
2. What are some legitimate medical uses for narcotics? What are their dangers to those who abuse them?
3. What unusual effects do hallucinogens have on their users?
4. In what ways may these effects be long-lasting?

Thinking Critically

5. *Synthesizing.* Some teens use amphetamines to lose weight. This is not an effective weight management technique. Give some of the reasons why and tell what, in addition to weight, a person might lose by using amphetamines.
6. *Comparing and Contrasting.* How do the effects of stimulants differ from those of narcotics? For what reasons do you think each has had some of its legal medical uses removed?
7. *Analyzing.* Street drugs such as LSD and heroin are often mixed with other chemicals. How does that differ from what you can expect when you buy aspirin, acetaminophen, or a prescription in a pharmacy?

Applying Health Skills

8. *In Your School.* Drug users often start experimenting occasionally with drugs and then become dependent on them. With classmates, brainstorm ways to teach preteens how to live drug-free and all of the benefits to be derived from doing so. Put your ideas in the form of a video, public service announcement, or comic book that will speak to children of that age.

ASSESS

EVALUATING THE LESSON

Assign and discuss the Lesson 2 Review; then administer, grade, and discuss the *Lesson 78 Quiz* in the TCR.

RETEACHING

- Direct each student to make a cause-and-effect chart regarding psychoactive drugs. Have students title the left side of the chart *Cause,* with a list underneath each drug discussed in the lesson. Ask them to title the right side of the chart *Effects,* followed by physical and mental effect(s) of each drug.
- Ask students to complete *Reteaching Activity 78* in the TCR.

ENRICHMENT

- Allow students to research endorphin *(produced in the brain and believed to be the body's own morphine)* to find out where and when it is produced and its effects on the body. Ask them to summarize their findings in a short paper.
- Give students additional information on the high cost of addiction by having them complete *Enrichment Activity 26,* "Substance Abuse: A Matter of Economics," in the TCR.

CLOSE

Divide the class into four groups. Assign one of the following types of drugs to each group: stimulants, depressants, narcotics, and hallucinogens. Ask each group to write a one-sentence summary of their assigned type of drug. Share the summaries with the class.

Lesson 2 Review

Answers to Reviewing Facts and Vocabulary

1. See the Glossary for definition. Paragraphs will vary.
2. Narcotics may be used to relieve severe pain, as appetite suppressants, or to stop coughing. They are dangerous because they are very powerful and very addictive.
3. They distort perception and cause the person to see and hear things that are not really there.
4. These effects may cause the user to engage in bizarre or violent behavior that is dangerous, and sometimes fatal, to himself or herself or others.

Answers to Thinking Critically

5.–7. Answers will vary.

Steroids and Other Dangerous Drugs

LESSON 3

Steroids and Other Dangerous Drugs

FOCUS

LESSON OBJECTIVES

After studying this lesson, students should be able to

- describe the dangers of anabolic steroids.
- explain the effects of marijuana and hashish on the body.
- describe the health consequences of inhalants.
- compare designer and look-alike drugs.

MOTIVATOR

Write the following on the chalkboard for students to work on while attendance is being taken: *List the following drugs in a vertical column: anabolic steroids, marijuana, hashish, inhalants, designer and look-alike drugs. Beside each drug, write a sentence or two describing it.*

INTRODUCING THE LESSON

Ask students to share some of their responses to the Motivator. Tell the class that this lesson will focus on the drugs listed on the chalkboard and how they affect a person's body and behavior.

INTRODUCING HEALTH TERMS

- Assign students to write a short commercial directed at teens, contrasting young people who are drug-free and those who use drugs. Ask for volunteers to present their commercials to the class.
- Ask students to complete Vocabulary Activity 26 and Chapter Study Guide 26 in the *Student Workbook.*

A number of misconceptions surround illegal drugs and their use. Many of these are created by drug pushers whose unsuspecting victims, all too often, are teens. This lesson will examine three other drug groups—anabolic steroids, cannabis (KAN-uh-bus) derivatives, inhalants, and designer drugs.

HEALTH TERMS

marijuana
hashish
inhalants
designer drugs
look-alike drugs

HEALTH CONCEPTS

- The damaging effects of anabolic steroids far outweigh their perceived athletic benefits.
- Marijuana and other psychoactive drugs have the properties and risks of hallucinogens, stimulants, and depressants.
- Inhalants are not meant for human consumption and can be deadly the first time they are abused.

hotlink

anabolic steroids For more information on other risks associated with the use of anabolic steroids, see Chapter 4, page 80.

Anabolic Steroids

The first stories about steroid abuse made news some two decades ago and involved professional athletes. Nowadays, sadly, some of these stories are unfolding in school locker rooms. What are **anabolic steroids**, and what is all the fuss about?

As noted in Chapter 4, anabolic steroids are synthetic derivatives of the male hormone testosterone. When used as medicine, these substances help build muscles in patients with chronic

Lesson 3 Resources

TEACHER'S CLASSROOM RESOURCES
- **Concept Map** Activity 79
- **Decision-Making** Activity 26
- **Lesson 79 Quiz**
- **Lesson Plan 79**
- **Reteaching** Activity 79

STUDENT WORKBOOK
- **Applying Health Skills 79**
- **Chapter Study Guide 26**
- **Vocabulary** Activity 26

MULTIMEDIA
- **ABCNews InterActive™ VHS/Videodisc,** *Drugs and Substance Abuse*

diseases. When used as an illegal drug, as they are by some athletes, anabolic steroids can exact a terrible price on the user in terms of both health and behavior. Steroid use causes mood swings and abnormally violent and aggressive behavior, sometimes referred to as "roid rage." Other serious side effects include **high blood pressure**, acne, baldness, increased risk of liver damage, heart disease, increased growth of body hair and facial hair, and stroke resulting from clogged arteries. In addition, males can experience depression, a decrease in sperm production and testicle size, and an increase in breast size; females can experience breast shrinkage.

One of the most tragic aspects of steroid abuse among teens is that their use is often based on the misguided belief that they make a person stronger. Although these drugs do cause muscles to look bigger, added strength comes only from working the muscles. In the meantime, the risks the drugs pose to life and limb are great.

Cannabis Derivatives

Cannabis is the scientific name for the hemp plant, which is used as an illegal drug in two forms. **Marijuana**, the more widely used form, is *cannabis that is smoked, eaten, or drunk for intoxicating effects.* **Hashish** (hah-SHEESH), or "hash," is *the dark brown resin collected from the tops of the cannabis plant.* Hashish is usually sold in small brown chunks that are smoked in a pipe. It is sometimes boiled to make hashish oil, which is then combined with tobacco and smoked for even stronger effects.

hot link

high blood pressure For more information on high blood pressure and ways of reducing its risk, see Chapter 31, page 678.

HEALTH Online

Visit **health.glencoe.com** to learn about the health effects of crack and cocaine, heroin, marijuana, and other drugs. Review the hazards of steroid abuse in athletes and teens.

Making Responsible Decisions

Running Scared

Today after practice, Jared, a new member of the school track team, was approached by Hank, one of the team's co-captains. Hank told Jared that he thought Jared had great potential, but he needed a little "help."

At this point, Hank held open his hand to reveal some pills. "Take them just before the all-city meet," Hank instructed, "and remember, the team is counting on you." Jared, who doesn't "do drugs," is worried about letting down his team.

What Would You Do?

Apply the six steps of the decision-making process to Jared's problem.

1. **State the situation.**
2. **List the options.**
3. **Weigh the possible outcomes.**
4. **Consider your values.**
5. **Make a decision and act.**
6. **Evaluate the decision.**

LESSON 3   STEROIDS AND OTHER DANGEROUS DRUGS   **587**

MEETING STUDENT DIVERSITY

ATTITUDES AND MENTAL HABITS. In general, a student's success will depend as much on his or her attitudes and mental habits as on the use of information and appropriate thinking skills. Performance tasks allow both students and teachers to observe what attitudes and habits are operating as work progresses. Examples include the following:

- showing individual responsibility
- valuing team work
- having initiative and being diligent
- being an intellectual risk-taker
- planning actions rather than being impulsive
- showing concern for the global community

TEACH

L1 Guest Speaker

Invite a doctor, athletic coach, or trainer to speak with the class about his or her observations of steroid use.

Making Responsible Decisions

1. One of the co-captains of the track team has given Jared some pills and told him to take them just before an important meet.
2. Jared could (a) take the pills as the co-captain instructed; (b) discard the pills but not say anything about them; (c) tell the co-captain that he won't take the pills; (d) talk with the team coach about the pills and the instructions from the co-captain.
3. Jared might (a) take serious risks with his health, but not offend the co-captain; (b) not risk his health, but probably worry about what the co-captain might say or do next; (c) stand up for what he knows is right, but risk making the co-captain very angry; (d) possibly prevent health risks for himself and even other team members, but risk making the co-captain very angry.
4. Jared values his health and his drug-free status; he also values fitting in with the rest of the track team.
5. Responses will vary.
6. Students should discuss both short- and long-term consequences of their decisions.

L2 Decision Making

For further study on making responsible decisions, assign *Decision-Making Activity 26* in the TCR.

L2 Class Activity

Have students use class and/or library resources to learn more about the body's immune system. Afterward, ask them to consider this question: If marijuana affects the immune system, how might it contribute to other diseases or health problems?

L1 Self-Esteem

Talk about how personality problems and marijuana use can be a vicious cycle. *(Using marijuana because of problems may further develop and intensify personality problems such as loss of willpower and motivation, lack of energy, paranoia, and memory problems.)* Brainstorm actions that would result in reinforcing a teen's self-esteem and break the cycle.

Driving and Marijuana

keeping Fit

Explain how marijuana slows down the ability to react, interferes with the proper function of muscles, and impairs good judgment. Review the examples of marijuana's effects on drivers that are provided in the feature. Discuss how driving under the influence endangers the public.

L2 Class Activity

Assign students to design advertisements for a teen magazine, warning about the use of inhalants. Display the ads and use them as the basis for a discussion about inhalants.

L1 Guest Speaker

Invite a police officer, mental health worker, and/or counselor to speak with the class about the use of inhalants in the community. Ask the speaker to share information about the types of users of inhalants, effects on the users, and legal consequences.

⇨ **When you get behind the wheel you take on added responsibility to yourself and others to be safe and alert at all times.**

keeping Fit

Driving and Marijuana

Driving under the influence of marijuana can be as dangerous as driving under the influence of alcohol. Marijuana puts added "blindfolds" on a driver by:

➤ interfering with the perception of distance,

➤ interfering with the perception of depth,

➤ impairing thinking and judgment skills,

➤ slowing reflexes, thus affecting one's ability to brake and negotiate curves, and

➤ impairing the ability to stay in the proper lane.

Physical and Psychological Effects of Cannabis

Cannabis is a hallucinogen that also has the effects of both a depressant and a stimulant. Despite a widespread misconception that people can use marijuana or hashish and still seem and act normal, cannabis used in any form alters your senses, coordination, and reaction time and can interrupt your ability to make rational and healthful decisions. The drug lowers body temperature but increases the heart rate and blood pressure. It stimulates the appetite. Some people may become talkative and giddy, others quiet and withdrawn. The effects vary from person to person and can be influenced by a person's mood and surroundings. Regular marijuana and hashish users tend to have personality problems that include loss of willpower and motivation, lack of energy, and paranoia.

Studies have shown that cannabis affects memory, making it more difficult to recall things and to pay attention. Drivers under the influence of marijuana or hashish react slower and make more accident-causing mistakes than drivers who are not under the influence.

CURRICULUM CONNECTIONS

SOCIAL STUDIES. The National Center on Addiction and Substance Abuse recently concluded a survey which showed that 80 percent of all crimes and incarcerations in the United States can be linked to drug and alcohol use. Other facts revealed by the survey include:

• 80 percent of the billion-dollar prison budget in the United States was spent to house substance-involved criminals.

• If the current trend continues, by the year 2000, the U.S. will spend more than $100 million a day to incarcerate individuals with a history of substance abuse.

• The number one substance abuse crime in the United States is drunk driving.

• Alcohol is associated more often with violent crimes, including murder, rape, assault, and spouse abuse, than any other drug.

Cannabis smoke contains more cancer-causing chemicals than cigarette smoke. Because marijuana users often inhale unfiltered smoke deeply and hold it in the lungs, it is damaging to the respiratory system, making breathing difficult. Smoking cannabis also interferes with the immune system and may cause permanent damage, making the user more highly susceptible than normal to infections from bacteria.

Regular use of marijuana or hashish lowers levels in the blood of the male hormone testosterone and decreases sperm production. Females of childbearing age should avoid cannabis use, since the drug can result in stillbirths, decreased birth weight, and a condition in the infant similar to fetal alcohol syndrome.

Inhalants

Inhalants are *substances with breathable fumes that are sniffed and inhaled to give a hallucinogenic or mind-altering high.* Included among the inhalants are glue, spray paints, aerosols, lighter fluid, and gasoline. Most inhalants depress the central nervous system and produce effects similar to those of alcohol. Immediate effects of inhalants include nausea, sneezing, coughing, nosebleeds, fatigue, lack of coordination, and loss of appetite. Heavy use of inhalants can result in liver and kidney damage, changes in bone marrow, and permanent brain damage. Inhalant use can also lead to hearing loss, limb spasms, and blood oxygen depletion. A person can go into a coma from a single use and be in a vegetative state, on a respirator, the rest of his or her life. High concentrations of inhalants can cause suffocation.

HEALTH Online

Link to the National Inhalant Prevention Coalition at **health.glencoe.com** to learn about the damaging effects of inhaling common substances.

Building Health Skills

Refusal Skills: Saying No to Drugs

LEARNING TO SAY NO effectively to drugs can be an important component in maintaining a drug-free life. Here are some effective ways to help you in your efforts to refuse drugs.

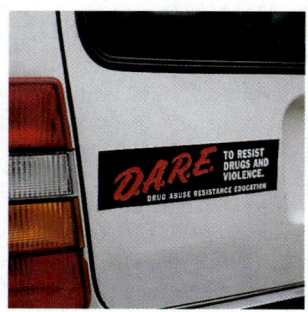

1. Make a firm commitment to stay drug-free. You may even want to write it down in contract or pledge form or make a drug-free pact with a close friend.

2. Learn and practice effective lines to use in refusing drugs. Possibilities include: "No thanks, I don't do drugs"; "That stuff makes me sick"; or "I'm on medication." Once you have said no, stick to your guns.

3. Avoid being around drugs and people who use them. If you are at a party or other gathering where drugs are being used, leave. Stick with friends who support your drug-free commitment. Create a life that is active, full, and contrary to a life of drug use.

LESSON 3   STEROIDS AND OTHER DANGEROUS DRUGS   **589**

MORE ABOUT . . . . .

MARIJUANA. Marijuana contains 421 different chemicals. The carcinogens in marijuana smoke are more abundant than those in tobacco smoke. Marijuana is considered addictive, with a three- to six-month withdrawal period. When smoked, over 150 chemicals are combusted and turned into more than 2,000 chemicals.

The chemical that produces the psychoactive effects in these cannabis derivatives is delta-9-tetrahydrocannabinol, or THC. Scientists measure the strength of marijuana and hashish by testing how much THC they contain. The THC does not dissolve in water, and it is not easily flushed out of the body. It may take many weeks after heavy use for the body to excrete it.

Building Health Skills

Saying No to Drugs
Skill: Refusal Skills

Display several antidrug bumper stickers, posters, and/or buttons. Ask students to share what they know about the programs represented. How do they help teens—and others—remain committed to drug-free living? After a brief discussion, have students work in small groups to read the Building Health Skills feature and discuss the three suggestions for refusing drugs. Let group members role-play situations in which they can use these refusal techniques effectively.

ABCNEWS INTERACTIVE™

DRUGS AND SUBSTANCE ABUSE (Side 1)

Chapter 6: Marijuana

Frames 13174-17513

Chapter 7: Cocaine and Crack

Frames 17526-22109

Chapter 8: Steroids

Frames 22130-25202

Chapter 9: Inhalants

Frames 25229-28897

Chapter 12: Depressants

Frames 36762-40560

Chapter 13: Designer Drugs

Frames 40576-44073

ASSESS

EVALUATING THE LESSON

Assign and discuss the Lesson 3 Review; then administer, grade, and discuss the *Lesson 79 Quiz* in the TCR. 👈

RETEACHING

- Assign groups of students one drug presented in the lesson. Ask each group to prepare a presentation on their topic, including information from sources other than the text.
- Ask students to complete *Reteaching Activity 79* in the TCR. 👈

ENRICHMENT

Have students prepare charts on the risks marijuana poses to various body systems, such as the lungs, brain, immune system, and the reproductive system.

CLOSE

Write the terms *anabolic steroids, marijuana, inhalants, designer drugs,* and *look-alike drugs* on separate slips of paper. Place the slips in a box. Divide the class into five groups, and let a student from each group draw a slip. Next, ask each group to write a short summary of their type of drug to present to the entire class.

Behavior while under the influence of an inhalant has been the cause of many accidental deaths. Inhalants have also been shown to be gateway drugs, and teens often used them first before moving on to "hard" drugs such as heroin. The peak age for inhalant use is about 14.

Designer and Look-Alike Drugs

To avoid using illegal substances, underground or street chemists make **designer drugs**, *synthetic substances meant to imitate the effects of narcotics and hallucinogens.* One of the most well-known designer drugs is called *ecstasy,* or *MDMA,* which has a chemical composition similar to that of methamphetamine and mescaline. A combination stimulant and hallucinogen, ecstasy may give a short-term feeling of euphoria but can result in confusion, depression, paranoia, psychosis, increases in heart rate and blood pressure, and even long-term damage to brain cells.

These drugs can be several hundred times stronger than the drugs they are meant to imitate. Symptoms of designer drug use include uncontrollable tremors, drooling, impaired speech, paralysis, and irreversible brain damage.

An equally dangerous group of street drugs is **look-alike drugs**, *drugs made so as to physically resemble specific illegal drugs.* With these drugs, the user never knows exactly what he or she is getting. Look-alike "speed," for example, might contain high doses of caffeine plus cold medicines. Such mixtures can cause dangerously fast heart rates, changes in blood pressure, strange behavior, nervousness, and breathing problems. Using these kinds of drugs or mixing them with other drugs is very dangerous. Sometimes a sugar substitute is put in a capsule and sold as an illegal drug—at a huge profit.

The use of look-alikes is hard to diagnose. This makes treatment very difficult. If look-alikes are taken with other drugs, such as alcohol, serious reactions can occur. If a user is admitted to an emergency room, the medical staff may not be able to treat the patient successfully because no one can know for sure what drugs the user took.

LESSON 3 *Review*

Reviewing Facts and Vocabulary

1. Identify some short-term and long-term risks of using marijuana or hashish.
2. Explain why designer and look-alike drugs are dangerous.

Thinking Critically

3. *Analyzing.* Analyze and discuss some of the reasons why teens are using more marijuana these days, and how this trend might be effectively reversed.

Applying Health Skills

4. *In Your Home.* Share with your family information from this lesson about the dangers of inhalants. Then, working as a team, survey your home for all household products with a potential for inhalant abuse.

590 CHAPTER 26 ILLEGAL DRUGS

Lesson 3 Review

Answers to Reviewing Facts and Vocabulary

1. See pages 588–589.
2. These drugs are dangerous because they can be extremely powerful, and their actual chemical content is unknown.

Answers to Thinking Critically

3.–4. Answers will vary.

Strategies for Preventing Substance Abuse

Strategies for Preventing Substance Abuse

When a person gets caught in the web of drug abuse, it becomes extremely difficult to get out. The best course of action therefore, is to identify the problem before it begins. This is true not only for yourself but for other people in your life whom you care about.

HEALTH TERMS

therapeutic communities

Drug-Free School Zones

drug watches

HEALTH CONCEPTS

- The decision to abstain from drug use is one of the most important a person can make.
- Programs and facilities are available nationwide for people who want to become drug-free.
- School and community drug watches help curb substance abuse.

FOCUS

LESSON OBJECTIVES

After studying this lesson, students should be able to

- describe what is involved in making a commitment to be drug-free.
- identify help that is available for individuals who presently use drugs.

MOTIVATOR

Write the following on the chalkboard for students to work on while attendance is being taken: *Why do some people have a difficult time saying no to a friend's offer or suggestion?*

INTRODUCING THE LESSON

Encourage students to share some of their responses to the Motivator. Discuss how most people want to please their friends and be accepted, and how some people are even willing to compromise their own integrity and health to do so. Explain that such decisions often reflect poor self-esteem and a lack of confidence. Such decisions can also come from being unprepared for the situation or being without goals or clear values. Tell students that this lesson will focus on some of these issues as it discusses making a commitment to being drug-free.

hotlink

peer pressure For more information on peer pressure and ways to avoid negative influence, see Chapter 2, page 29.

Drugs and Peer Pressure

As a teenager, you may already have been confronted with situations where drugs were involved. You may even have been pressured to try, buy, or sell drugs. **Peer pressure** can be intense during the teen years, particularly in settings where using drugs and drinking seem "the norm."

INTRODUCING HEALTH TERMS

- Ask students to complete Vocabulary Activity 26 and Chapter Study Guide 26 in the *Student Workbook.*

Lesson 4 Resources

TEACHER'S CLASSROOM RESOURCES

- **Concept Map** Activity 80
- **Lesson 80 Quiz**
- **Lesson Plan 80**
- **Reteaching** Activity 80

STUDENT WORKBOOK

- **Applying Health Skills 80**

- **Chapter Study Guide 26**
- **Vocabulary** Activity 26

TRANSPARENCIES

- **Transparency 43**

MULTIMEDIA

- **ABCNews InterActive™ VHS/Videodisc,** *Drugs and Substance Abuse*

CHARACTER IN ACTION

Asking for Help

Explain that there are many signs that may indicate a serious problem with drugs. Discuss the following signs after students read the feature: (1) needing more of the drug to get the same effect, (2) talking about substances a lot, (3) thinking that you have to drink or use drugs to have fun, (4) pressuring others to join in the drinking or drug use, (5) getting into trouble with the law, (6) participating in high-risk behaviors such as driving under the influence, (7) feeling depressed, hopeless, worn down, even suicidal.

TEACH

L1 Critical Thinking

Let students discuss their responses to these questions: To what extent can you control the peer pressure that is exerted on you? on the teens around you? How important are the choices you make? Why? How important are the choices your friends make? Why?

L1 Personal Involvement

Ask students to write private Health Journal entries about their own commitment to abstain from drugs. Ask: What barriers, if any, stand in the way of that commitment? What are the benefits of making, or maintaining, a commitment to drug-free living?

CHARACTER IN ACTION

Asking for Help

Asking for help with a drug problem demonstrates **courage** and strength of character.

Character Check To get help for a drug problem:

➤ Talk to a trusted adult.

➤ Look in the Yellow or Blue Pages under headings such as *Drug Abuse and Addiction* or *Alcoholism Information*.

A healthful lifestyle includes staying drug-free.
ACTIVITY *Name ways you show you are committed to a drug-free lifestyle.*

592   CHAPTER 26   ILLEGAL DRUGS

You may hear that "everyone's doing it." The fact of the matter is that for most teens, illegal drugs never become a part of their lives. The National Clearinghouse for Alcohol and Drug Information reports that over 96 percent of 12- to 17-year-olds in this country have never tried marijuana, and over 80 percent have never tried cocaine. So the claim that "everyone's doing it" is simply not true.

The Commitment to Be Drug-Free

The first step in staying free of drugs is to make a clear and deliberate decision to stay drug-free. The only way to avoid the pitfalls and dangers of substance abuse and addiction is to be firmly committed to the idea of not using them *before* they are offered. In many cases, that also means steering clear of people who use drugs and of where drugs are likely to be used or offered.

Making the commitment to abstain from drugs is a positive, life-enhancing decision. It does not mean, as some teens fear, that you will be deprived of friends or fun. Quite the opposite, being drug-free means being able to savor life's true pleasures and deal with its problems. Living a drug-free life means:

- Finding healthful ways to have fun and enjoy your life.
- Sticking with people who know how to have fun without chemicals and who make you feel good about yourself.
- Figuring out what else makes you feel good about yourself and doing more of it.
- Thinking about your true purpose and how you can put your life and talents to good use.
- Tapping into your creativity.

Myths & Realities

MYTH. Teens with high self-esteem and ambition are more likely to use drugs than their peers who are less ambitious and less sure of themselves.

FACT. Those who have a high regard for themselves are more likely to resist group pressure to use drugs. Also, drugs can interfere with schoolwork and career plans. Teenagers with a strong desire to achieve are less likely to let drugs get in their way.

MYTH. "If I choose to use drugs, it's nobody's business but my own."

FACT. Others can get hurt, too. This is especially true for family and friends who care about the user's health and happiness.

- Learning healthful ways to relax and to manage stress.
- Staying connected socially and reaching out to others.
- Learning new skills, hobbies, and crafts, developing your talents, and expanding your mind.
- Connecting to the world and its many needs and issues.
- Getting lots of physical exercise.
- Caring for your body in other ways, including healthful nutrition and adequate rest.

Remember that no one's life is completely problem-free or full of natural "highs." Accept the ups and downs of life without chemicals, and live your life with kindness, attention, and a clear head. You won't be sorry.

How to Become Drug-Free

For those teens already in trouble with drugs, it is never too late to get help. The first thing to do is to talk with a trusted adult. Self-help programs, support groups, and treatment facilities exist across the country that can help a teen in trouble with drugs to get and stay drug-free. There are facilities that provide medical supervision while a person goes through withdrawal and detoxification, getting the drug out of his or her system. These include both **therapeutic communities**, or *residential treatment centers,* and outpatient programs. In addition, there are support groups such as Cocaine Anonymous, Marijuana Anonymous, Narcotics Anonymous, and Alcoholics Anonymous. With the increase in public awareness that addiction is indeed a disease, more and more people are willing to admit to and get help for their drug-related problems and chemical dependencies.

School Efforts to Stop Drugs

All over America there are now **Drug-Free School Zones.** These are *areas within 1,000 feet of schools and designated by signs, within which people caught selling drugs receive especially tough penalties.* Sometimes the penalties are even double what they might otherwise be for the same drug offense elsewhere. Among other efforts in and around schools to cut down on drugs are classes in drug education,

⚠ *Taking a wrong turn at any moment can derail your plans for the future.*

ACTIVITY *List three places a teen can turn to for help with a drug problem.*

▣ L2 Discussing

Have students list characteristics of persons who use illegal drugs. Discuss how these characteristics may limit a person's potential to be the best that he or she can be.

▣ L1 Discussing

Discuss how adolescents who use addictive, illegal drugs remain emotionally at the same age as when they began using the drug, even though these same adolescents mature physically. What repercussions might this fact have in the successful drug recovery of youths?

▣ L1 Community Involvement

Point out that when teens who have been in trouble with drugs get help, they need to make some important changes in their lives. In most cases, they need new social contacts and opportunities to develop friendships with other drug-free teens. Ask: What do you think you could do to help teens recovering from drug-related problems? Encourage students to put some of their ideas into practice.

▣ L1 Discussing

Encourage students to share their own ideas about Drug-Free Zones. Ask: Is our school in a Drug-Free Zone? If so, what does that mean here? If not, why not? What suggestions would you make for keeping our school free of drugs?

PERSONAL HEALTH

WARNING SIGNS OF SUBSTANCE ABUSE.

- tantrums, aggressiveness, or other unpredictable behavior
- bloodshot or glassy eyes; dazed, unfocused look
- sleeping and/or eating pattern changes; weight loss
- keeping secrets from family or friends

- hanging around with drug users
- having trouble remembering or concentrating
- stealing, borrowing, or spending a lot of money
- sniffing or runny nose; irritated nostrils
- denial or anger at the suggestion of a problem with drugs

Teens Making a Difference

The Drive to Stay Drug-Free

Discussion. Have students read the feature and answer the questions that follow it. Then read the following words spoken by Bobbie Jo: *I'm committed personally to not using drugs and alcohol. My close friends have made the same commitment, and that helps. Look, if you use drugs, you can't show your caring for your family or your friends because you are not in the right state of mind. Using drugs and alcohol makes people do a 180, makes them walk in the <u>opposite</u> direction they were originally heading in terms of goals, careers and values.*

Ask: Once a teen becomes involved in drug use, what happens to his or her values? Goals? Health? How might a teen like Bobbie Jo, willing to stay drug-free and talk about her decision openly, help a student in trouble with drugs? Educate other teens on the subject? How can having drug-free friends or the support of an organization like YELL or SADD make that reaching out easier? More effective? What steps can you and your friends take to reach out and teach others about the dangers of drugs?

Class Activity. Have students make a giant circle montage or collage. One half of the circle (180 degrees) should contain pictures or phrases that suggest a loss of values, goals, and health due to drug use; the other half, pictures and phrases that suggest healthful, drug-free living based on core values.

Answers. *Bobbie Jo's Story*
1. Bobbie Jo has joined and headed an organization dedicated to staying drug and alcohol free.
2. She has organized and participated in related projects with peers and younger children, spoken out in the community, and worked to change legislation.

Responses. *Your Story* **1–2.** Responses will vary. Let students work in groups to share and discuss their ideas.

Teens Making a Difference

...CARING...RESPONSIBILITY ...CITIZENSHIP

Bobbie Jo's passion right now is her involvement in YELL—Youth to Eliminate Lost Lives—a group dedicated to helping teens make healthful decisions and prevent accidents and deaths due to drug and alcohol use. A high school senior, she is currently president of her school's YELL chapter and an example of a teen putting her highest values into practice.

TEACHING AND REACHING Bobbie Jo puts caring into action by reaching out to educate other teens. "At YELL," she begins, "we do programs like Prom Promise to get students to think about ways to have fun that don't involve drugs or alcohol. We also do a program in the elementary school called Milk Mustaches, where we talk about the dangers of drugs and alcohol. We sponsor a White-Out Day, in the high school, when we pull students out of class at the same rate that students are killed in our country due to drug or alcohol related crashes. Once they have their faces painted—these students can't speak for the rest of the day. At the end of the day, YELL announces the total number of deaths these students represent."

AGAINST DRUGGED DRIVING Bobbie Jo works to heighten others' awareness that drugged driving can be just as dangerous as drinking and driving. The dangers of impaired driving are close to home for her: her stepmother was pregnant and lost her baby when hit by an impaired driver; the former president of YELL at her school was also killed in the same way. "Kids who drive and use drugs or alcohol don't realize what's happening until after the fact when it's too late," she says. "Driving and using drugs or alcohol can hurt not only you but everyone around you, and the people in the other car, their family, their friends. If you want to be responsible, you can't use drugs."

She has taken her message to the community, speaking at a university conference on drug and alcohol abuse and addiction. Recently, she went to a national conference about drugs, alcohol, and driving where teens made policy suggestions to the United States Congress. Among the suggestions made were to have more sobriety checks—not just for alcohol but for other drugs as well.

BOBBIE JO'S STORY
1. What are some of the ways Bobbie Jo has demonstrated the values of caring and responsibility?
2. How has she reached out to the community to advocate against drugged driving?

YOUR STORY
1. What values are you exercising when avoiding drug and alcohol use?
2. What steps can you take to teach others about the dangers of drugs and the negative effects they have on one's values, goals, and health?

PROMOTING COMPREHENSIVE SCHOOL HEALTH

IDENTIFYING MAJOR PROBLEMS. Once a committee has been founded to serve the school health program, members will need to consider specific problems to address. One method of receiving input regarding areas for action is through a survey. After the surveys have been collected and the information processed, the committee should brainstorm a priority list of concerns. The priority ratings are: (1) critical problems; (2) moderate problems; (3) minor problems. The top two or three issues can become candidates for priority action. For more information about drafting such a survey, consult *Promoting a Comprehensive School Health Program* in the TCR.

suspensions and expulsions for drug use, police or security guards in halls, drug and alcohol counselors on the premises, locker searches, school uniforms, the banning of beepers and certain kinds of clothing, and more. Of course, the best way to keep any school drug-free is for each person attending the school to make a personal pledge to be drug-abstinent. Have you done your part?

Community Efforts to Stop Drugs

Communities across the nation are taking positive action. **Drug watches**, *organized community efforts by neighborhood residents to patrol, monitor, report, and otherwise help try to stop drug deals and drug use,* utilize volunteers with noisemakers, megaphones, civilian street patrols, and cellular phones to report drug deals and drug-related problems. Taking an interest in the welfare of your environment is both an indicator of a health-literate person and a **developmental task** of adolescence. Becoming involved in stopping drug use by instituting a drug watch in your community is one way to meet both these goals. Making and keeping your own personal commitment to staying drug-free is a healthful place to start.

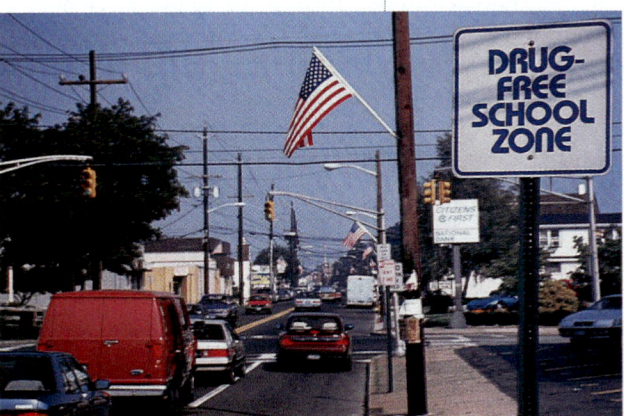

hotlink

developmental task For more information on meeting the developmental tasks of adolescence, see Chapter 21, page 482.

▼ *There are many ways to get involved in your school or community's efforts to stop substance abuse.*

ACTIVITY With a partner, make a list of five ways teens can help to promote and build drug-free environments.

ASSESS

EVALUATING THE LESSON

Assign and discuss the Lesson 4 Review; then administer, grade, and discuss the *Lesson 80 Quiz* in the TCR. 👈

RETEACHING

- Ask students to write a brief paper on what living a drug-free life means to them. Have them include their papers in their private Health Journals.
- Ask students to complete *Reteaching Activity 80* in the TCR. 👈
- Use *Transparency 43* to review refusal skills. 🧴

ENRICHMENT

Plan for a speaker from a residential treatment center to visit the class and discuss the process of drug rehabilitation. Ask the students to come to class with any questions they may have and to take notes. Instruct students to prepare a detailed outline of the presentation as an assignment.

CLOSE

Have students identify the value of being drug-free and the best ways to keep that commitment.

LESSON 4 *Review*

Reviewing Facts and Vocabulary

1. What steps can a teen take to increase his or her chances of staying drug-free?
2. Identify some of the strategies schools and communities have taken to decrease the availability of drugs.

Thinking Critically

3. *Synthesizing.* With classmates, brainstorm a list of "boredom busters," or exciting and pleasurable ways for teens to socialize without having to rely on drugs.
4. *Synthesizing.* Develop a list of strategies that might help to reduce drug use in your school. Write these up in the form of a formal proposal, and submit it to the school principal or school board.

Applying Health Skills

5. *In Your School.* Prepare a pamphlet or article for your school newspaper entitled "Marijuana: Weeding Out the Problem" about the dangers of marijuana use and how teens in your school might join together in an anti-marijuana campaign.

Lesson 4 Review

Answers to Reviewing Facts and Vocabulary

1. A person can make a firm commitment to remain drug-free and practice refusal skills before drugs are offered. He or she can choose friends who have made the same commitment. One can also avoid situations where drugs will be present.

2. See pages 593 and 595.

Answers to Thinking Critically

3.–4. Answers will vary.

Health Skills Activities

Health Skills Activities

ACTIVITY 1
HEALTH SKILLS
Communication, Health Advocacy

➤ **National Standards**
This activity meets these National Health Standards: 5.4; 7.3.

Teach
- Explain that there is often a barrier to overcome—that for an outreach to succeed, both parties must be willing to participate.
- Explain that students will be applying this metaphor to the problem of substance abuse among teens.
- Discuss and assign the activity.
- To stimulate group thought about reasons why teens might or might not seek help, invite groups to think about consequences to oneself and to others when a substance abuse problem exists.

ACTIVITY 2
HEALTH SKILLS
Communication, Health Advocacy

➤ **National Standards**
This activity meets these National Health Standards: 2.3; 7.1.

Teach
Present students with a letter that might be written to them by a younger cousin expressing fears about fitting in at high school. The following is a sample text:

Dear _____:

I will be in ninth grade next year but am worried about fitting in. I know all the kids will be bigger than I am because I am small for my age. I was thinking about going out for football but am kind of shy because of my size.

A neighbor of mine who is in high school told me about these pills called steroids that are supposed make a person get big fast. He told me if I took these, nobody would give me a hard time. He also said I'd have lots of girlfriends. These pills sound almost too good to be true. What should I do?

Activity 1 — Getting Help

It is often difficult for young persons to reach out to others when they have a serious problem. How can people with drug problems overcome these communication barriers and get the help and support they need?

Directions
1. Working in small groups, brainstorm reasons why an addicted person might not seek help.
2. Using markers and newsprint divided into two columns, list your reasons in the left-hand column. Then, in the right-hand column, list all the reasons why a teen with a drug problem might finally reach out for help.
3. Share your findings with the class. Examine and compare your list with other group's lists.

Time
40 minutes
Materials
newsprint, markers

Self-Assessment
✓ Highlighted the difficulty of asking for help for drug-related problems.
✓ Demonstrated that young people can overcome communication barriers and get help with their problems.

Activity 2 — Dangers of Steroids

Middle school students are often worried they are not going to fit in at high school. They might at times consider high-risk behavior in an effort to impress peers. How could you persuade a younger relative or friend that this thinking is harmful?

Directions
1. Read the letter your teacher hands out.
2. Review the effects of steroids on the body, as noted in the chapter. Then write a letter to your cousin advising him of these dangers. Suggest healthful ways he could fit in with his peers.
3. Share and compare your letter with those of classmates. Compile all of your letters, along with the fictional letter by Marcus, into an original book titled *Dear Cousin* to be printed on the classroom computer.

Time
45 minutes
Materials
pen, paper, computer (optional)

Self-Assessment
✓ Demonstrated knowledge of health risks related to anabolic steroids.
✓ Described alternative ways to have fun with peers and fit in that do not involve drugs.

ASSESSMENT SCORING

Using a four-level rubric, the student has achieved a 4 if:

ACTIVITY 1
✔ Student demonstrated an understanding of the problems associated with asking for help.
✔ Student showed the ability to apply a metaphor to a real-world event.
✔ Student took part in helping group develop paired lists.
✔ Student demonstrated how young people can overcome communication barriers.

ACTIVITY 2
✔ Student demonstrated an understanding of the many risks associated with steroid use.
✔ Student letter demonstrated knowledge of health risks related to anabolic steroids.
✔ Student took active role in discussion of alternative ways of fitting in.
✔ Student described alternative ways to have fun and fit in that do not involve drugs.

HEALTH NEWS
VIDEO

No Joy in Ecstasy

Some of the dangerous effects of illegal drugs occur right away. Disorientation, impaired speech, and clouded thinking can lead to immediate and critical problems. Some effects, however, build up over time. The full impact of taking a drug can take years, or even decades, to become apparent. Scientists have conducted the first human study of the drug Ecstasy. The results show that people who use Ecstasy are taking huge risks. The consequence can be permanent brain damage.

Ecstasy is an amphetamine that affects the way the brain handles a chemical called serotonin. Researchers know that this chemical is linked to mood and thinking ability. They predict that using Ecstasy could lead to devastating anxiety and depression.

Play the Video ▶

Think About It

◗ What is an amphetamine? Why is Ecstasy classified in this category?

◗ This study is the first one that analyzes the use of Ecstasy in humans. Why is this an important step?

◗ How can the results of this study be used to persuade teens not to use this dangerous drug?

CNN HEALTH NEWS **597**

MORE ABOUT . . . . .

ECSTASY. You may wish to share some of Ecstasy's damaging short-term effects with students. Physical side effects include shaking, nausea, blurred vision, sweating, chills, and increased heart rates and blood pressure. Psychological side effects run from confusion and sleeplessness to depression, anxiety, and paranoia.

Because Ecstasy is a stimulant, it can make users feel as if they have unlimited energy. This misconception can lead users to overexert themselves and can lead to dehydration, high body temperature, and heart or kidney failure.

No Joy in Ecstasy
Video Segment 16 (Time –1:47)

Objectives. After viewing the video, students should identify how the drug Ecstasy can damage the brain and use that information to decide not to take this illegal drug.

Motivator. Write the word *ecstasy* on the chalkboard and ask students to define it. Explain that the word means "a state of overwhelming emotion." Students might also point out that this word has been used to name an illegal drug. Point out that illegal drugs are not approved for use because they are unsafe. Then have students view Video Segment 16, "No Joy in Ecstasy," which explains how researchers are exploring the damaging effects of Ecstasy.

Teach

- Ask students to explain why Ecstasy is an illegal drug. Emphasize that the drug is not safe and can have short- and long-term damaging effects.
- You may wish to point out that Ecstasy is sometimes referred to as X, E, XTC, Adam, or by its scientific name, MDMA.
- Have students explain how an amphetamine like Ecstasy affects the nervous system. Have them consider why repeated use of these stimulants can create permanent brain damage. Ask students to suggest metaphors that define the problem. For example, they might think of the brain as an electric circuit which is overcharged when a stimulant is used. Repeated overcharging weakens the circuit even when the stimulation is absent.

Decision Making. Have students write a script that would help a friend decide not to use Ecstasy. Encourage students to use specific details from the video to support the decision-making process.

Close. Ask students to explain the importance of research about the effects of Ecstasy and other drugs on the brains of drug users. Their answers should describe the goals of the research detailed in the video and explain how information learned in this study could help prevent people from using this dangerous, illegal drug.

CHECKING COMPREHENSION

- Assign and discuss the chapter review.
- Use the MindJogger Videoquiz to review the chapter. 🔴

CHAPTER 26 REVIEW ANSWERS

Using Health Terms

1. gateway drugs
2. synthetic drugs
3. illegal drugs
4. substance abuse
5. hallucinogens
6. psychoactive drugs
7. depressants
8. narcotics
9. look-alike drugs
10. hashish
11. designer drugs
12. Drug-Free School Zones
13. therapeutic communities

Recalling the Facts

1. They see their friends, parents, or older siblings using them. They feel pressured to use drugs and don't know how to say no. They want to fit in, relax, or seem mature. They see drugs glamorized on TV, in videos, in the movies, or in song lyrics. They're bored and want new thrills. They are trying to escape from their problems.
2. Physiological dependence occurs when the body goes through withdrawal symptoms if you don't take the drug. Psychological dependence is the belief that you can't feel good or function without the drug.
3. The body of the substance abuser needs more and more of the drug to get the same effects. The person then needs the drug just to function. When the drug is withheld, the body goes through severe withdrawal symptoms.
4. Psychoactive drugs are chemicals that affect the central

Using Health Terms

On a separate sheet of paper, write the term that best matches each definition below.

LESSON 1

1. Drugs that often lead to other serious and dangerous drug use.
2. Chemical substances produced artificially in a laboratory.
3. Street drugs.
4. Any unnecessary or improper use of chemical substances for nonmedical purposes.

LESSON 2

5. Drugs that alter moods, thoughts, and sense perceptions, including vision, hearing, smell, and touch.
6. Chemicals that affect the central nervous system and interfere with the normal functioning of the brain.

7. Drugs that tend to slow down the central nervous system.
8. Drugs derived from the opium plant that have a sedative effect.

LESSON 3

9. Drugs made so as to physically resemble specific illegal drugs.
10. The dark brown resin collected from the tops of the cannabis plant.
11. Synthetic substances meant to imitate the effects of narcotics and hallucinogens.

LESSON 4

12. Areas within 1,000 feet of schools and designated by signs, within which people caught selling drugs receive especially tough penalties.
13. Residential treatment centers.

Recalling the Facts

Using complete sentences, answer the following questions.

LESSON 1

1. What are some of the reasons why teens begin using drugs?
2. Distinguish between physiological dependence and psychological dependence.
3. What are three of the signs of physical dependence?

LESSON 2

4. What are psychoactive drugs?
5. Define the word *stimulants* and give three different examples.
6. What is crack, and what makes it so dangerous?
7. What problems can result from regular cocaine use?
8. Define *depressants* and give two examples.

9. Define *narcotics* and *hallucinogens* and give two examples of each.

LESSON 3

10. What are the risks of using anabolic steroids?
11. Why does hashish affect a user more strongly than marijuana does?
12. Why is it dangerous to ride in a car with a driver who has been smoking marijuana?
13. What health problems do look-alike drugs present?

LESSON 4

14. What is a drug watch?
15. What are some of the steps schools and communities are taking to stop substance abuse?

---

nervous system and interfere with the normal functioning of the brain.
5. Stimulants are drugs that speed up the central nervous system. Examples are amphetamines, methamphetamine, and cocaine.
6. Crack is a form of cocaine that can be smoked. It is dangerous because it is extremely addictive and can cause death by cardiac or respiratory failure.

7. Regular cocaine use can lead to depression, edginess, weight loss, physiological dependence, malnutrition, and increased risk of heart attack.
8. Depressants are drugs that slow down the central nervous system. Examples are barbiturates, tranquilizers, and methaqualone.
9. Narcotics are drugs derived from the opium plant that have a sedative

Thinking Critically

LESSON 1

1. *Analyzing.* Drug use takes an enormous toll on society as well as on the individual. Explain this statement and provide several illustrations of the costs to both the individual and society.

LESSON 2

2. *Analyzing.* Some parents who used drugs feel conflicted about whether or not to tell their own children about their drug histories. Analyze the pros and cons of talking about past drug use with one's offspring.

LESSON 3

3. *Evaluating.* Research more of the harmful effects of steroid use to the body. List the serious, long-term, potentially fatal consequences. Then write a one-page report describing the symptoms that may indicate the presence of steroid use.

LESSON 4

4. *Synthesizing.* One way to stop the spread of drugs in your school is to recognize the signs of drug use. Write, edit, design, and print an informational leaflet called "Signs of Possible Drug Use."

Making the Connection

1. *Social Studies.* Investigate several important laws passed in the twentieth century regarding control of the sale and possession of psychoactive sustances, including the 1906 Pure Food and Drug Act and the United States Controlled Substances Act of 1970. Report on the content of these laws to the class.

2. *Language Arts.* Write a fictional, first-person story in which you imagine that you are the victim of a drug-related crime. Set the stage of the crime. Then in a dramatic court scene, through a Victim's Rights program, face the criminal who made you a victim and tell him or her what the crime has done to you.

BEYOND THE CLASSROOM

PARENTAL INVOLVEMENT With a parent or guardian, visit a hospital emergency room on a Saturday night. Observe what kinds of injuries people have. Talk with emergency room workers when there is a lull, or a break in the action. Find out how many and which kinds of injuries seem to be drug- and alcohol-related.

COMMUNITY INVOLVEMENT Learn more about Neighborhood Watch or a drug-watch effort in your neighborhood or community. Become involved in civilian patrols, anti-drug marches, and other efforts to rid your area of drugs.

SCHOOL-TO-CAREER
Exploring Careers. Invite a pharmacist to speak to your class. Ask him or her to tell you about the education and training required to become a pharmacist, and what kinds of licensing and updating of training are required. Ask about the kinds of abuses or misuses he or she has seen regarding prescribed and over-the-counter medications.

effect. Examples are morphine, codeine, and heroin. Hallucinogens are drugs that alter moods, thoughts, and sense perceptions, including vision, hearing, smell, and touch. Examples are PCP, LSD, and mescaline.

10. The risks of using anabolic steroids include mood swings, abnormally violent and aggressive behavior, high blood pressure, acne, baldness, liver damage, heart disease, and depression. Males experience a decrease in sperm production and testicle size and an increase in breast size; females experience breast shrinkage.

11. Hashish is the more concentrated form of the substance.

12. Driving with someone who has been smoking marijuana is dangerous because marijuana affects a person's senses, coordination, reaction time, and ability to make rational decisions.

13. With look-alike drugs, the user never knows exactly what he or she is getting. The mixture of ingredients could be deadly.

14. A drug watch is an organized community effort by neighborhood residents to patrol, monitor, report, and otherwise try to stop drug deals and drug use by equipping civilian street patrols with noisemakers, megaphones, and cellular phones to report drug deals and drug-related problems.

15. Some communities and schools are establishing drug watches and Drug-Free School Zones.

Thinking Critically

1.–4. Answers will vary.

Making the Connection

1.–2. Answers will vary.

Evaluate

- Use the reproducible *Chapter 26 Test* in the TCR, or construct your own using the Testmaker software.
- Use *Performance Assessment Activity 26* in the TCR.

Enrichment

Ask students to complete *Cross-Curriculum Activity 26* in the TCR.

Beyond the Classroom

Keep students involved in the community, and encourage parent participation by assigning the activities on this page for students to work on outside of class.

Recovering from Addiction and Codependency

	FEATURES	CLASSROOM RESOURCES

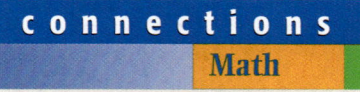

Chapter Resources

ACTIVITIES

- Cross-Curriculum Activity 27
- Health Lab 27
- Health Skills Activities 27
- Parent Letter and Activities 27

ASSESSMENT

- Chapter 27 Test
- Performance Assessment Activity 27
- Testmaker Software

STUDENT ACTIVITIES WORKBOOK

- Applying Health Skills 81, 82
- Study Guide 27
- Vocabulary Activity 27

STUDENT DIVERSITY STRATEGIES

- Audiocassette Program (English)
- Audiocassette Program (Spanish)
- Spanish Parent Letters and Activities
- Spanish Summaries, Quizzes, and Activities

MULTIMEDIA COMPONENTS

- English Audiocassette Program
- Spanish Audiocassette Program
- MindJogger Videodisc and VHS program
- ABCNews InterActive™ VHS/Videodisc Series

MODULES

- *The Reality of Drugs,* Student Edition
- *The Reality of Drugs,* Teacher's Annotated Edition

National Health Education Standards

One of the main goals of the National Health Education Standards is to move students toward "health literacy." Health literacy is the capacity of individuals to obtain, interpret, and understand basic health information and services and the competence to use such information and services in ways which promote health. The health standards were developed by applying the characteristics of a well-educated, literate person within the context of health. The health literate person is:

- a critical thinker and problem solver
- a self-directed learner
- a responsible, productive citizen
- an effective communicator

Listed below are the Health Education Standards Performance Indicators addressed in each lesson of this chapter.

Lesson	Health Standards Performance Indicators
1	2.3, 2.4, 2.6, 3.4
2	1.4, 2.4, 6.1, 7.4

ONLINE RESOURCES

For a fresh approach to health topics and an in-depth look at health issues, use these online resources found under Teacher Resources at **health.glencoe.com**.

- **BLOCK SCHEDULE LESSON PLANS** Reinforce health concepts with outside readings selected especially for students. Each reading is accompanied by a lesson plan and activities to enhance
  - Reading Skills
  - Cross Curriculum
  - Media Literacy

- **TECHNOLOGY PROJECTS** Instructions and suggestions on how to use computer, Internet, and software with health lessons.

- **HEALTH UPDATES** Timely topics in health news, including late-breaking medical advances and updates on teen risk behaviors.

Out of Time?

If time does not permit teaching this chapter, you may use these features: Update on page 603; Making Responsible Decisions on page 610; and Building Health Skills on page 612.

BLOCK SCHEDULING

Block scheduling provides extended time for hands-on projects and activities. Use the following activities to engage students, provide further depth, and vary your instructional techniques:

- Update (30 minutes) **pg. 603**
- Connections (30 minutes) **pg. 604**
- Health Skills Activity (60–90 minutes) **pg. 614**

Recovering from Addiction and Codependency

CHAPTER OVERVIEW

Chapter 27 presents the addiction continuum and how those close to the addict become protective in the situation—a problem called codependency. Both the addict and the codependent require professional help and support in their recovery.

LESSON 1 Intervention is the initial step in stopping the downward slide of addiction. It involves the support of family or close friends and the assistance of a drug or alcohol counselor in helping the addict recognize his or her problem. The process of recovering from addiction has emotional and social hurdles. Remaining drug free is an ongoing concern for addicts. Treatment choices include counseling, support groups, and an assortment of treatment centers.

LESSON 2 Someone who is codependent is overly concerned with other people's behaviors and problems and feels driven to fix and control those problems. In an effort to help the addict, the codependent actually makes the problem worse. Intervention may be required to recover from codependency. Support groups for substance addicts offer the codependent individual a support system for coping and structured programs for regaining emotional and social health.

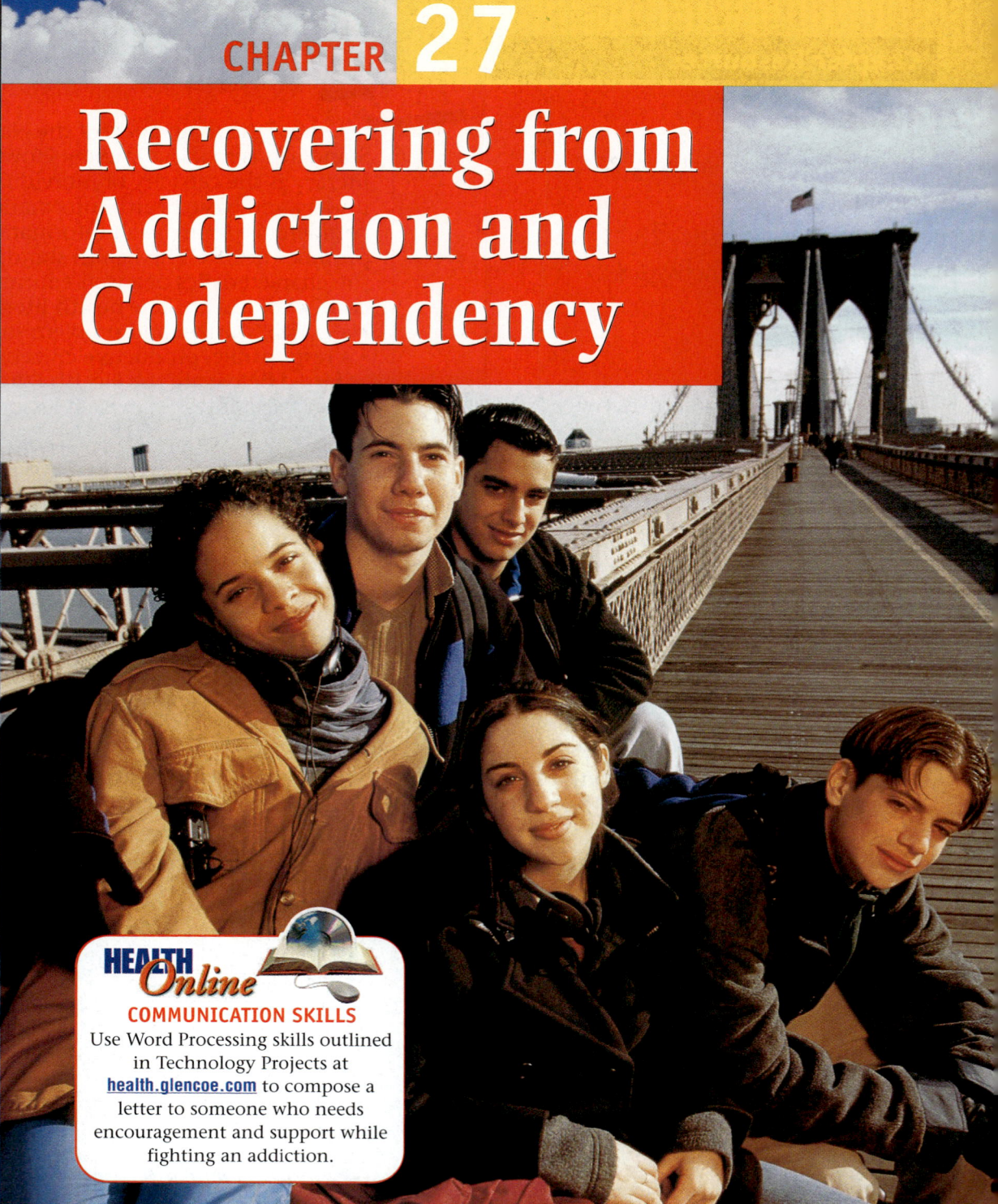

CHAPTER 27

Recovering from Addiction and Codependency

HEALTH *Online*

COMMUNICATION SKILLS
Use Word Processing skills outlined in Technology Projects at **health.glencoe.com** to compose a letter to someone who needs encouragement and support while fighting an addiction.

Hands-On Health

TEACHING STRATEGY

Reinforcing and Reviewing Bring your health classroom to life with interactive teaching strategies and classroom management techniques that keep your students interested and involved. The unique *Hands-On Health: Creative Teaching Strategies* booklet that accompanies the *Glencoe Health* program offers fun, motivating activities. 👉

The following Classroom Management Ideas can be used to reinforce chapter concepts:

- Beach Ball
- Trivia Questions
- Paper Exchange
- Mental Outburst

> **Just as no one starts out to have lung cancer when they smoke, or no one starts out to have clogged arteries when they eat fried foods...no one starts out to become a drug addict when they use drugs.**

—Alan I. Leshner, Ph.D.
Director, National Institute on Drug Abuse
National Institutes of Health

Quick Write Quickly jot down what you might say to a friend who is in trouble with drugs and needs to get help.

Personal Health Inventory

Self-Inventory Write the numbers 1–10 on a sheet of paper. Read each statement below and respond by writing *yes, no,* or *sometimes* for each item. Write a *yes* only for items that you practice regularly. Save your responses.

1	I do not live with a person who suffers from an addiction.
2	I do not have a close friend who is an alcoholic or addict.
3	My life and emotions are not totally wrapped up in the addiction of a person I care about.
4	I do not spend a great deal of time, energy, or money trying to fix the person's problems.
5	My involvement with this person is not affecting my sleep habits, appetite, or mental or physical health.
6	I never lie or cover up for the person about his or her smoking, drinking, or drug use.
7	I don't feel overly responsible for other people's behavior.
8	I don't feel comfortable or useful only when I'm trying to rescue someone in trouble.
9	I do not try to control other people or situations.
10	I do not feel as if I have to please everyone all the time.

Follow-up After completing the chapter, retake this self-inventory. Pick two items that you need to work on and set a goal to improve your health behaviors.

CHAPTER 27 RECOVERING FROM ADDICTION AND CODEPENDENCY **601**

INTRODUCING THE CHAPTER

Personal Health Inventory

Let students read and briefly discuss the Self-Inventory statements: Which of the behaviors identified here are in your control, even though exerting that control can be extremely difficult? Which are not in your control? After a brief discussion, have students use a page labeled "My Level of Codependency" in their private Health Journals to record their *yes, no,* or *sometimes* responses to the Self-Inventory statements.

- Tell students that for a long time, addiction was a misunderstood problem considered only to be a consequence of behavior. Research has led scientists to a better understanding of the causes of addiction and the problems an addict and his or her family face. This chapter will present some of these findings.
- Let students read the quotation about addiction, and ask these questions: What difference do you think it makes that addiction is now recognized as a disease? To whom is this difference important? Why? How can you recognize an addicted person? What can you do to help addicted friends or family members? In addition to the person who suffers from an addiction, who else needs help? Why?
- Distribute Parent Letter 27 in the *Parent Letters and Activities* booklet. ✏

TECHNOLOGY OPTIONS

ABCNEWS INTERACTIVE You may wish to use *Drugs and Substance Abuse* with this chapter. For your convenience, use the separate *ABCNews InterActive™ Bar Code Correlation* that accompanies the *Glencoe Health* program. ⬤

MINDJOGGER
VIDEOQUIZ

To preview or review chapter content, you may wish to use the *MindJogger Videoquiz* that accompanies Chapter 27. ⬤

Recovering from Addiction

LESSON 1

LESSON OBJECTIVES

After studying this lesson, students should be able to

- describe the process of intervention and how it helps the alcoholic or drug addict get into recovery.
- describe the process of recovery from addiction.
- identify sources of help for the addict who wishes to enter recovery.

MOTIVATOR

Write the following on the chalkboard for students to answer on paper while attendance is being taken: *How do you know if someone is addicted to a drug, such as alcohol or cocaine? How does the addicted person behave?*

INTRODUCING THE LESSON

Refer to the Motivator. Ask volunteers to share their responses. Emphasize that addiction is really a process and that someone may be on his or her way to becoming drug dependent even through "social" use of the drug.

INTRODUCING HEALTH TERMS

- Ask students to write a concise paragraph that shows they understand how these three terms are related: *recovery, detoxification,* and *relapse.*
- Ask students to complete Vocabulary Activity 27 and Chapter Study Guide 27 in the *Student Workbook.*

Recovering from Addiction

Addiction is a disease that knows no limits. Anyone can become addicted, and the source of the addiction can vary. A person can become addicted to alcohol, nicotine, drugs, gambling, or even food. Yet, of all possible addictions, none is more serious—or has more devastating consequences—than a dependence on alcohol or another drug.

HEALTH TERMS

intervention
recovery
detoxification
relapse
inpatient treatment
outpatient treatment
halfway house

HEALTH CONCEPTS

- A number of clear warning signs indicate that a substance abuse problem exists.
- You can help someone you care about recover from drug addiction by seeking help on the person's behalf.
- Recovery from addiction occurs gradually in a series of steps.

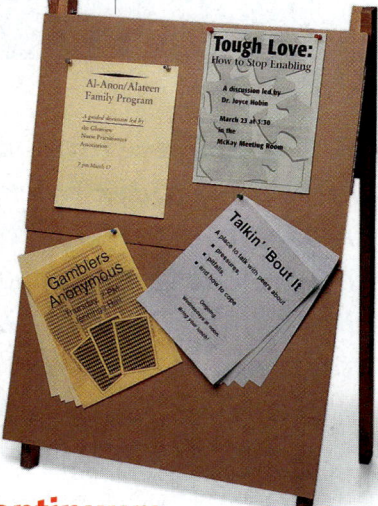

The Addiction Continuum

Addiction is a process—a series of gradual changes that happen over time. This process happens more quickly to some than to others. Some people get hooked on a drug from the first time they take a drink, a pill, or an injection. For other people, an addiction develops more slowly, perhaps over a period of many years. Others do not become addicted at all. For this reason, it is difficult to predict exactly when the use of an addictive substance—or how much of it—might lead to a problem.

This much is clear, however. Once an addiction to alcohol or some other drug sets in, the person needs help if he or she is to have any hope of returning to a normal, drug-free life.

Lesson 1 Resources

TEACHER'S CLASSROOM RESOURCES
- **Concept Map** Activity 81
- **Cooperative Learning** Activity 27
- **Health Lab** 27
- **Lesson 81 Quiz**
- **Lesson Plan** 81
- **Parent Letter and Activities** 27
- **Reteaching** Activity 81

STUDENT WORKBOOK
- **Applying Health Skills** 81
- **Chapter Study Guide** 27
- **Vocabulary** Activity 27

TRANSPARENCIES AND MULTIMEDIA
- **Transparency 45**
- **ABCNews InterActive™ VHS/Videodisc,** *Drugs and Substance Abuse*

Addiction: Recognizing the Problem

The first step in getting help with an addiction is to recognize that a problem exists. Sometimes it is the people close to the addict or alcoholic who first recognize and point to the problem. Sometimes, it is the addict himself or herself. In either case, there are clear-cut warning signs of possible addiction. These include:

- continual concern about where the next "fix"—drink or pill, for example—will come from.
- choosing friends who can supply the addictive substance.
- changes in appearance or personal habits.
- irritability, nervousness, personality changes, or mood swings.

up date
▶ Looking at the Issues

Teen Gambling: Addiction, Compulsion, or Bad Habit?

Teen gambling is now a major problem in the United States, with an estimated 40 to 70 percent of teens under 18 having gambled at one time or another. Whether flipping quarters or betting on football games, teens bet an estimated $500 million to $1 billion a year. Are these teens addicted? Opinions on the subject are divided.

ANALYZING DIFFERENT VIEWPOINTS

▶ **Viewpoint One**
Studies sponsored by the National Institutes of Health, using positron emission tomography (PET) scans, are attempting to establish a link between brain chemistry and compulsive gambling. Those who support the claim that gambling is an addictive disease note that gamblers experience an adrenaline rush and a "high" much as drug addicts do when their craving is temporarily satisfied by a drug.

▶ **Viewpoint Two**
Some experts now make a distinction between problem gamblers and compulsive gamblers just as they do between problem drinkers and alcoholics. The *problem gambler* is someone whose gambling is no longer just recreation. He or she might have difficulty controlling the money spent or the time gambling. The *compulsive gambler's* life is completely taken over by the need to gamble.

EXPLORING YOUR VIEWS

1. Do you believe that gambling for some can be an addiction, just like being hooked on other substances? Why or why not?

2. Do you gamble or know other teens who do? If you gamble, has it caused any trouble in your life? If you know teens who gamble, has it caused trouble in their lives? What kinds of additional trouble might it cause down the road?

TEACH

L1 Discussing

Have students identify the warning signs of addiction. Discuss how these characteristics or behaviors reveal the lack of control that the individual experiences.

up date
▶ Looking at the Issues

Teen Gambling: Addiction, Compulsion, or Bad Habit?

To introduce this feature, let students share their current thinking about gambling. Ask: Are you surprised that a lesson on addiction raises the issue of gambling? Why or why not? Then have students read the Update feature to learn more about teen gambling and about different viewpoints on gambling. After students have discussed their responses to each viewpoint, ask them to use their private Health Journals to record their responses to the Exploring Your Views questions.

ABCNEWS INTERACTIVE™

DRUGS AND SUBSTANCE ABUSE (Side 1)
Chapter 15: The Nature of Addiction

Frames 48643-53540

MORE ABOUT . . . . .

ALCOHOLISM. Though alcoholic beverages have been manufactured and consumed for thousands of years, the acceptance and use of alcohol vary widely. In some countries, such as France and Nigeria, alcoholic beverages are consumed daily and play an important role in social interactions. On the contrary, in other cultures, such as Mormon and Muslim, drinking alcoholic beverages is forbidden.

The introduction of alcohol to people who did not use it before European contact, notably Pacific Islanders and Native North Americans, has had long-range repercussions, leading to widespread addiction and contributing to social disruption.

CHARACTER IN ACTION

Dangerous to the Core

Have students read the Character in Action feature. Write on the board the following signs that, according to the National Clearinghouse for Alcohol and Drug Information, are among the indicators that a person may be in trouble with alcohol or other drugs: getting high or drunk regularly; avoiding people to get high or drunk; lying about the amount of drugs being used; giving up regular activities like after-school sports, homework, or socializing with teens who are substance-free. Ask students to provide other signs that a person may be in trouble with drugs.

L2 Class Activity

Encourage volunteers to act out a scenario for the class in which an addicted individual is confronted by a family member or close friend about his or her abuse of alcohol or other drugs.

connections
Math

Begin by having students share their reactions to the feature title, "The High Costs of Addiction." Ask: What kinds of costs do you think addiction involves? Then let students read the introductory paragraph to learn more about the different kinds of costs. Divide the class into four or more groups, and have group members work cooperatively to complete the lists, research, and graph. Provide guidance in selecting reputable sources if necessary. Allow class time during which the groups can share and discuss their graphs with the rest of the class.

CHARACTER IN ACTION

Dangerous to the Core

A person who uses alcohol, marijuana, or other illegal drugs is not living up to his or her **core ethical values**. Losing sight of the highest values can lead a person to cheat, lie, steal, and head for all kinds of danger to obtain the drug. By considering the highest values, a person can more easily make the right decision to stay drug-free.

Character Check Write a short script or develop a comic strip showing how a person battles the temptation to use drugs. Depict your character upholding his or her highest values as a defense against the dangers of illegal drugs.

- violent behavior.
- black-outs.
- needing increasing amounts of a substance to feel "normal."

Intervention

In the past, it was believed that the alcoholic or addict had to "reach bottom" before he or she would be willing to accept help. Recently, that thinking has changed, and nowadays many families—recognizing that a problem exists—stop the downward slide through a process called **intervention**. This is *interruption of the addiction continuum before the addict or alcoholic hits bottom.* Intervention begins with meetings between family members or other significant people involved in the life of the chemically dependent person and a certified drug or alcohol counselor. These meetings take place without the addicted person's knowledge. At the meetings, family members learn about addiction and the ways in which they have become affected by it. They make a list of all the episodes they can remember involving the person's drinking and drug use and how it made them feel.

The next step in the process is a surprise meeting with the addict that forces the person to face the seriousness of his or her addiction and how unmanageable his or her life has become because of it. The group then presents the addict with a plan for immediate treatment.

connections
Math

The High Costs of Addiction

The costs of addiction are staggering. For example, illicit drug and alcohol use in the workplace in this country costs businesses an estimated $140 billion a year in lost productivity, accidents, and medical claims. Sadly, that is just a fraction of the overall cost in the lives of the addicted, in the lives of their families, and in society at large.

1. With classmates or in small groups, brainstorm some of the costs of addiction to individuals and society. List these costs in two columns, one under *Cost in Dollars*, the other under *Other Kinds of Costs*.

2. Using print or on-line resources, gather statistics relating to some of the costs in dollars. Reputable sources of such information include the National Institute on Alcohol Abuse and Alcoholism, the NIH National Institute on Drug Abuse, and SAMSA National Clearinghouse for Alcohol and Drug Information.

3. Use the statistics you gather to create a bar graph showing the costs of alcohol and drug use to society. Share and compare your graph with those of other groups.

HEALTH LITERACY

SELF-DIRECTED LEARNER. Sometimes the example set by a person who has recovered from drug dependency or alcohol dependency can encourage others. One person's success makes it clear that recovery is possible. Personal accounts of recovery from addiction often include details about what helped the addict withdraw from the substance and stay substance free. In many cases, the strategies can be applied successfully in the lives of readers. Encourage students to research such personal accounts. They may be particularly interested in famous people who have overcome addiction. Have students read a personal account of recovery, list the actions that helped the person recover, and identify those actions that could be applied widely and successfully.

If the person refuses to get this needed help, the family, boss, or others taking part in the intervention process tell the person what steps they plan to take in response to the refusal. For example, a wife might say, "If you won't get help, I'll move out." Such ultimatums let the chemically dependent person know that he or she must now face the consequences of his or her addiction. It is only when the person has decided to do so that recovery is possible. **Recovery** means *learning to live an alcohol-free or drug-free life.*

The Recovery Continuum

Like addiction, recovery is a process that happens over time. In fact, a recovering person never says, "I am cured," but rather, "I am recovering." This is because recovery is an ongoing, lifelong process. This process happens at different rates and in different ways for different people. Yet, there are certain characteristics common to most recovery stories.

The first step in the recovery process is **detoxification**, *the removal of all drugs from the body.* This process should take place under medical supervision. In addition to the addict's regaining physical health, recovery also involves restoring one's mental health by learning to build healthy relationships and by taking responsibility for one's own life. It is generally recognized that people can begin the recovery process at any point on the downward slide into addiction—even before they suffer major losses.

Most experts in the field of addiction recommend total **abstinence** from any mood-altering drugs, including alcohol, for the recovering alcoholic or addict. Long-term studies show that attempts at controlled drinking and drug use usually fail. Even small amounts of alcohol or other drugs can send an addict back into addiction.

Many people in recovery manage to stay drug-free for the rest of their lives. Others may have **relapses**, *slips from recovery, or periodic returns to drinking and drug use.* Yet, despite how far down the addiction continuum a person goes or how many times that person relapses, the choice of and chance for recovery are always there.

Treatment Options

Where can a person with an addiction problem turn for help? As with any problem, a good starting point is to talk with someone the person trusts and who can point him or her in the direction of professional help. For a teen, this might be a parent, teacher, school counselor, or peer counselor. He or she might also directly contact a drug and alcohol treatment center. Such facilities specialize in drug and alcohol counseling. Depending at which point the person is along the addiction continuum and his or her previous experience with addictive problems, the person may be directed to a **support group** or an alcohol and drug treatment center.

🔺 ***Teens with addiction in the family often suffer in silence.***
ACTIVITY *Give three reasons why it is very important that children of alcoholics or other addicts get help for themselves.*

hotlink

abstinence For more information on abstinence and strategies for abstaining from harmful behaviors, see Chapter 21, page 484.

hotlink

support group For more information on the benefits of a support group, see Chapter 9, page 227.

L1 Discussing

Ask students to identify the steps involved in the process of recovery from addiction.

L1 Explaining

Explain why we say of alcoholics and other drug addicts that they are "in recovery," not that they "have recovered." *(Recovery is a life-long process.)*

L2 Researching

Ask students to research the studies that have been done on controlled drinking and drug use versus total abstinence. What have these studies found? Why does it seem to be more difficult to control alcohol and other drug use than to abstain entirely?

L1 Discussing

Discuss why a relapse while in recovery from drug addiction does not mean that the person is hopelessly addicted to the drug.

L3 Guest Speaker

Invite a drug counselor to class to share his or her experiences in dealing with recovering alcoholics and other drug addicts.

L2 Health Lab

Distribute *Health Lab 27* and have students investigate the use of nicotine patches. 🔳

DRUGS AND SUBSTANCE ABUSE (Side 2)
Chapter 3: Cost to Society

Frames 2500-6492

Chapter 4: Drugs and the Family

Frames 6501-9777

SCHOOL-TO-CAREER

RECOVERY PROGRAMS. Some employers have recovery programs for workers fighting addiction. In other cases, they may provide insurance that covers treatment for drug or alcohol dependency. However, some insurance policies exclude coverage for drug or alcohol problems. Have students contact several major employers, including local government agencies. Tell them to find out what recovery programs, if any, they provide for their workers. Does the insurance they provide include treatment for alcohol or drug dependency? Does discovery of drug use or addiction result in automatic termination of the employee? Encourage students to make a chart showing the employers they contacted, how they respond to addiction or substance abuse, and what recovery programs were covered by the employers' insurance.

L3 Guest Speaker

Invite a representative from the Alcoholics Anonymous central office in your area to speak with the class about the role of AA in recovery from alcoholism.

L2 Discussing

Ask students how residential treatment centers differ from outpatient treatment centers. What are some advantages and drawbacks of each?

L2 Discussing

In addition to the withdrawal from physical addiction to alcohol or another drug, what are some of the mental and social aspects of recovery from addiction?

L1 Community Involvement

Ask students to locate the names, addresses, and phone numbers of sources of help in their local community for people with alcohol and other drug addictions. Which, if any, are particularly oriented to teens? Have students make a poster or flyer that informs other students in their school of where to go for help for themselves, for friends, or for family members.

L1 Writing

Direct students to write a brief account of how someone typically recovers from addiction to alcohol or another drug. Have them describe how counseling, a support group, or a treatment center plays a role in the recovery process.

L2 Cooperative Learning

Have students complete *Cooperative Learning Activity 27,* "School Support Group," in the TCR.

Support Groups

A support group is a group of people who share a common problem and work together to help one another and themselves cope with and recover from that problem. Regular attendance at such support groups is the most popular form of ongoing treatment for addictions. Support groups such as Alcoholics Anonymous (AA) have played a major role in helping people to become and stay alcohol- and drug-free. At meetings, which are held frequently all over the world, members provide support and help one another stay sober or otherwise drug-free. Such meetings are confidential—members can remain anonymous because no one has to give his or her last name—and also free of charge. Each AA office can direct people to local AA meetings or to other support groups such as Narcotics Anonymous or Cocaine Anonymous.

Alcohol and Drug Treatment Centers

Alcohol and drug treatment centers offer a wide range of services to addicts who want to recover. Many centers specialize in treating teens with addictions or have special units solely for adolescents.

▼ *Recovery from addiction can mean new hope and happiness for every member of the family.*
ACTIVITY *List some of the short-term and long-term effects of recovery on the family.*

Some treatment centers are privately owned, but there are also state and community alcoholism and mental health clinics that offer professional care at little or no cost. Since drug and alcohol dependence are considered diseases, some health insurance plans may cover at least some of the costs.

DETOX UNITS

In some hospitals or treatment centers, there are medical detox units for alcoholics and addicts undergoing the detoxification process. During this process, the person is under a doctor's care and may be given some medication to ease the symptoms of withdrawal. Some people go directly from detox to ongoing involvement in a support group.

INPATIENT OR RESIDENTIAL TREATMENT CENTERS

Inpatient treatment is *medical and psychological care during which a person stays at a medical or rehabilitation facility.* Inpatient centers offer peaceful time and attractive surroundings away from the person's usual environment so that full concentration on recovery can take place. The first

COOPERATIVE LEARNING

INTERVENTION STRATEGY. Have students work in groups. Have each group create a fictional scenario in which a person is abusing drugs or alcohol and is developing an addiction. Tell them to describe the abuser's circumstances in detail. Suggest that they include details about the abuser's family members, friends, and colleagues. Some of the family members or friends should be developing symptoms of codependent behavior. Have groups exchange scenarios, then create written intervention strategies for each other's fictional addicts. Allow time for groups to read their scenarios and intervention strategies to the class. Strategies should include suggestions to arrest and reverse the developing trends toward codependence.

few days are spent in detox. After that, people spend a month or more taking part in drug and alcohol education, individual and group counseling, and support group meetings.

OUTPATIENT TREATMENT CENTERS

Outpatient treatment is *on-site medical and psychological care for a person trying to become alcohol-free and drug-free.* Outpatient programs often allow the recovering person to go to work or school and to live at home during the treatment process. It is less expensive than inpatient treatment, but it takes place over a longer period of time.

CONTINUING PROGRAMS

Many rehabilitation centers have long-term programs of counseling and support for people in recovery who have gone through their standard short-term treatment programs. These programs usually involve follow-up sessions, individual and group counseling, and counseling that involves the entire family in the recovery process.

HALFWAY HOUSES

Halfway houses are *continuing care facilities that offer people housing, counseling, and support meetings as they are recovering from a severe addiction.* People are generally admitted to halfway houses only after having completed at least a 28-day program of recovery at a treatment center. They stay for six months to a year as they learn coping and living skills they will need when they return to society. Residents are also sometimes channeled into vocational rehabilitation or job training programs.

Did You Know?

➤ People in recovery sometimes develop transfer addictions. That means they go from being addicted to one substance to being addicted to another substance or behavior. For example, recovering alcoholics sometimes develop eating disorders or become compulsive gamblers.

➤ People in recovery do not concentrate on the fact that they will have to live a lifetime without drugs. Instead, they talk about staying sober or clean one day at a time.

LESSON 1 *Review*

Reviewing Facts and Vocabulary

1. In what ways is addiction both a physical and psychological disease?
2. For what reasons do people in recovery describe themselves as *recovering* instead of *recovered?*
3. Outline some of the treatment choices for an alcoholic who wants to recover.

Thinking Critically

4. **Synthesizing.** What explanations can you give for why some people become addicts and some people do not?
5. **Comparing and Contrasting.** Explore the similarities and differences between inpatient and outpatient treatment centers.

6. **Evaluating.** What would be your impression of a recovery program that focused only on physical detoxification?

Applying Health Skills

7. **In Your School.** Evaluate the current services available for someone with a smoking, drinking, or other drug problem in your school. Consider such factors as accessibility, confidentiality, the competency of providers, types of services, and cost. Share the above, along with any other information you can gather, in a brochure to be distributed to students in your school.

LESSON 1 RECOVERING FROM ADDICTION **607**

ASSESS

EVALUATING THE LESSON

Assign and discuss the Lesson 1 Review; then administer, grade, and discuss the *Lesson 81 Quiz* in the TCR. 📁

RETEACHING

- Ask students to research Alcoholics Anonymous. What are the basic principles it follows? What is the nature of its recovery program? What is a typical AA meeting like? What are the roles of anonymity and confidentiality? Have students find out where and when AA meetings take place in their local community.
- Ask students to complete *Reteaching Activity 81* in the TCR. 📁
- Use *Transparency 45* to review where to go for help with an addiction. 🖌

ENRICHMENT

Select students to research the history of alcohol use and how alcoholics have been regarded at different times in the past.

CLOSE

Tell students that in this lesson they learned how family members and friends can help to get the alcoholic or drug addict into recovery through the process of intervention. Reinforce that the process of recovery is difficult and lifelong but that there are many sources of help available for the recovering addict. Explain that the next lesson will focus on the needs of family or friends who have been affected by someone dependent on alcohol or another drug.

Lesson 1 Review

Answers to Reviewing Facts and Vocabulary

1. Answers will vary. See page 605.
2. Abstaining from using a drug is a continuing, lifelong process once one stops using it.
3. See pages 606 and 607.

Answers to Thinking Critically

4. Answers will vary. May include: reasons related to the psychological, emotional, genetic, and physiological differences among people.
5. See pages 606 and 607.
6. The emotional and psychological health of the person must also be addressed in treatment to successfully break an addiction.

Recovering from Codependency

LESSON 2

FOCUS

LESSON OBJECTIVES

After studying this lesson, students should be able to

- describe codependent behavior and its relationship to alcoholism and other drug addictions.
- summarize the process of recovery from codependency.
- identify sources of help for the codependent.

MOTIVATOR

Write the following on the chalkboard for students to work on while attendance is being taken: *Write a definition of the word* codependency. *What does codependency have to do with alcoholism and other drug addictions? Can there be codependency without drug abuse?*

INTRODUCING THE LESSON

Refer to the Motivator. Ask volunteers to share their responses with the class. Explain that codependency refers to a certain type of behavior—being overly concerned with other people's problems and driven to fix them. Such behavior often characterizes people involved in relationships with alcoholics and other drug addicts.

INTRODUCING HEALTH TERMS

- Have students define *codependency*. Ask why codependent individuals might sometimes be referred to as co-addicts.
- Ask students to complete Vocabulary Activity 27 and Chapter Study Guide 27 in the *Student Workbook.*

Recovering from Codependency

Addiction is like a fire raging out of control. It extends beyond the addict, sometimes spreading to those in his or her life. In many cases, these people fan the flames of addiction, ultimately becoming part of the problem rather than part of the solution.

HEALTH TERMS
codependent
enabling
Al-Anon
detachment
Alateen

HEALTH CONCEPTS

- Codependency is a problem that occurs when those in an addict's life become part of the problem rather than part of the solution.
- In efforts to help the addict, codependents actually make the problem worse.
- The codependent did not cause the addiction and cannot cure it, but he or she can get help whether or not the addict decides to get well.

Common Traits of Codependents

People who become overly concerned with another's addiction problem and feel driven to fix or control it are called **codependents**, or "co-addicts." Though each person who exhibits codependent behavior does so in a unique way, codependents have many traits in common. Typically such people:

- feel lost, bored, or bad about themselves when not rescuing someone in trouble.
- feel responsible for other people's feelings, actions, and happiness.
- have difficulty having fun, relaxing, or taking good care of themselves.

Lesson 2 Resources

TEACHER'S CLASSROOM RESOURCES
- **Concept Map** Activity 82
- **Decision-Making** Activity 27
- **Enrichment** Activity 27
- **Lesson 82 Quiz**
- **Lesson Plan 82**
- **Reteaching** Activity 82

STUDENT WORKBOOK
- **Applying Health Skills 82**
- **Chapter Study Guide 27**
- **Vocabulary** Activity 27

MULTIMEDIA
- **ABCNews InterActive™ VHS/Videodisc,** *Drugs and Substance Abuse*

- constantly seek others' approval.
- do not meet their own needs and may not even know what their own needs are.

This much is for sure. Whatever behaviors or emotions they may exhibit on the outside, the spouses, children, and close friends of the addict suffer terribly and often in silence.

What Codependency Is Not

Codependent people are not physically addicted to a drug the way an addict is. Though codependency is often referred to as an addiction, it is neither an addiction nor a disease in the physical sense. It is, instead, a very damaging emotional and social preoccupation, or obsession, which often can have physical consequences. This type of obsession is different from drug addiction.

Codependents can suffer from a variety of stress-related mental or physical disorders, from depression and eating disorders to high blood pressure and digestive disorders. They may also be at increased risk for addictions.

Enabling: Hurting by Helping

One of the most common traits of codependency is enabling. **Enabling** means *trying to protect the person having trouble with alcohol or drugs from facing the consequences of his or her drug-related problems.* Codependent people enable an addict in many ways, including lying or covering up for the addict's mistakes; lending money, which may be used to purchase more drugs or alcohol; making excuses for him or her being late, absent, or irresponsible; doing the person's homework or other work for the addict; or trying to deflect attention from the person's addiction or bad behavior through humor, understatement, diverting attention, or denial.

What many people do not realize is that enabling is not healthful caring. Such actions do not help the addict. They just make it more comfortable and possible for the alcoholic or addict to keep on drinking or using drugs. In this way, enabling may actually help the addict to become more sick.

CHARACTER IN ACTION

No Excuses

An enabler is someone who shields the alcoholic or addict from the consequences of his or her behaviors. Problems can arise when an addictive person turns to another person for refuge instead of taking **responsibility** for his or her own actions. The enabler can be a better friend by encouraging the addict to take on his or her own responsibilities.

Character Check Make a *Dos and Don'ts List* for a person who lives with or is close to an alcoholic or addict. Include at least one example of how to guide the addictive person to take responsibility for his or her own health and wellness.

⚠ *Individuals who care about one another sometimes find themselves caught in the circle of codependency.*

TEACH

L1 Discussing

Discuss responses to the following: What are some of the characteristics and behaviors commonly found in people who are codependent?

L2 Cooperative Learning

Ask a group of students to prepare and present a short skit to the rest of the class that demonstrates a codependent relationship. Have the audience identify particular dialogue or actions that reveal the codependency.

CHARACTER IN ACTION

No Excuses

Discuss with students the role of the codependent in an addiction. How does the codependent person in a relationship or family often hurt by helping? Point out how, when it comes to another's addiction, responsibility means not enabling or playing into the addict's manipulations, not making excuses for the person's absences, lateness, or unacceptable behaviors, and saying no to the addict's unhealthful demands. It also means getting help for one's self.

L2 Class Activity

Divide the class into two groups. Have one group make a list of ways in which a codependent person might act to enable a spouse or other family member to continue with an alcohol or other drug problem. Then have the other group revise the list so that it shows helpful, not hurtful, behaviors—those that encourage the addicted person to accept and get treatment for the addiction.

Community Involvement

Ask students to investigate local sources of information, support groups, and other assistance for children of alcoholics. Have students make a poster or bulletin board to inform other students of their findings.

Making Responsible Decisions

1. Pete's best friend, Carmine, is very irritable because his father is drinking.
2. Pete could (a) stay away from Carmine until Carmine's mood improves; (b) be friendly but ignore Carmine's problem; (c) be friendly and encourage Carmine to discuss his situation with a counselor or another trusted adult.
3. Pete might (a) avoid being hurt by Carmine's bad mood but have to deal with the fact that he is not helping his friend and that he might lose the friendship; (b) keep the friendship going but realize that he is not helping his friend and perhaps watch as Carmine's problems get worse; (c) risk making Carmine angry that he is "interfering" but possibly guide his friend to assistance.
4. Pete values his friendship with Carmine; he also values Carmine's good mental/emotional and social health.
5. Responses will vary.
6. Students should consider both short- and long-term consequences of their decisions.

Decision Making

For further study on making responsible decisions, assign *Decision-Making Activity 27* in the TCR. 📁

Addiction as a Family Problem

In a family where there is alcoholism or other drug dependence, both addicts and codependent family members are hurting and need help. That is why alcoholism and drug dependence are sometimes referred to as *family diseases*. They affect everyone in the family.

People in a family with drug or alcohol dependency may experience shame, fear, disappointment, guilt, and anger. They are embarrassed to admit these feelings, not realizing that millions of other families suffer from the effects of drug dependency.

Families Dealing with Addiction

In a healthful **family system**, rules are flexible and members play many roles based on changing situations and needs. When someone in a family has a drug dependency, other members of the family must learn to cope with the addict's problems. Some individuals tend to act out roles to deal with the situation.

Different people react in different ways. They adjust their needs, emotions, and behaviors to the unhealthy demands, behaviors, and emotions of the addicted person. In the process they also become unhealthy.

The Codependency Continuum

As a family member's alcoholism or addiction progresses, his or her family's codependency becomes more complex. Some family members may become overly involved in others' problems, taking the

hotlink

family system For more information on the family system and ways of maintaining its health, see Chapter 12, page 276.

Making Responsible Decisions

When Help Is Needed

Lately, Pete's best friend Carmine has been unusually quiet and withdrawn. At first Carmine refused to tell Pete what was wrong, but yesterday he finally blurted out, "It's my dad. He lost his job and has been drinking a lot." Pete really cares about Carmine and would like to help his friend get his life straightened out. Yet, when he asked Carmine what he could do, his friend angrily snapped, "Nothing! It's none of your business!" Pete has never seen Carmine act like this. What can he do to help?

What Would You Do?

Apply the six steps of the decision-making process to Pete's problem.

1. **State the situation.**
2. **List the options.**
3. **Weigh the possible outcomes.**
4. **Consider your values.**
5. **Make a decision and act.**
6. **Evaluate the decision.**

MORE ABOUT . . . . .

CHILDREN OF ALCOHOLICS. One of the strongest feelings of children of alcoholics is a sense of powerlessness. This has three major causes. First, the child is powerless over the parent's drinking—the child can't stop the drinking or get sober for the parent. Second, the child is powerless over the relationship between the parents, which is often abusive.

Unfortunately, the child usually doesn't believe that he or she is powerless in these first two cases, so the child may try almost anything to make things better—often leading to a greater sense of powerlessness. Finally, children of alcoholics feel powerless because they can't leave the dysfunctional situation.

focus off themselves. Other family members may simply withdraw. In either case, family members put their lives on hold hoping the addiction will go away, but it does not. In turn, they may demonstrate unhealthful behaviors. Like the alcoholic or addict, they may also be in denial, not realizing or being able to admit just how bad things at home have become.

However, there is good news and hope for all families with addiction. There are many ways for families with chemical dependency to get help.

Recovering from Codependency

Just as addiction is not hopeless, neither is codependency. The downward slide into codependency can be turned around and changed into a process of recovery. Like recovery from chemical dependency, recovery from codependency takes time and effort. Different people may recover at different speeds and in different ways. Regardless of the timetable for recovery, the personal and family rewards can be great.

Recovery from Codependency

THE UPWARD CLIMB

A codependent's recovery might progress like this as the person:

- Hits an emotional bottom as a result of involvement with someone else's addiction
- Desires and goes for help
- Gets educated about the diseases of addiction
- Accepts the disease concept and his or her part in the disease
- Stops trying to control others, including the addict
- Focuses on self instead of the addict
- Begins to pay attention to personal appearance
- Experiences improvement in own physical, mental, and social health
- Rebuilds self-esteem
- Helps family become more flexible; aids in the process of redefining roles
- Continues to attend support group meetings, helping other codependents and self
- Takes full responsibility for his or her own life

Strategies for Getting Well

There are many ways that a person from a family with addiction as well as the addicted family member can get help. The first step is to admit that there is a problem. The next step is to reach outside the family system for help. This can seem like an impossibility to many people, since families of active alcoholics and drug addicts usually have lived by three unspoken rules: "Don't talk, don't trust, don't feel."

Reaching outside the family for the first time can feel like a betrayal. However, it is a healthy step to take, and a sense of relief often results. Whatever the risks are in seeking outside help, not seeking it holds greater risks. Continuing to adapt to an unhealthy family system can be far more damaging to everyone involved.

Sometimes only one person in a chemically dependent family seeks and gets outside help. Because of this, that person may feel very lonely. When everyone in the family seeks help and assumes responsibility for his or her own role in the family, recovery can occur more quickly.

L1 Discussing

Ask: What is the process of recovery like for the codependent?

L1 Discussing

What are some sources of help for codependent people who wish to start the recovery process? Why is it important to go outside the family for help? Encourage student responses.

DRUGS AND SUBSTANCE ABUSE (Side 2)

Chapter 11: Ways to Say No

Frames 30762-32673

Chapter 12: Why We Say No

Frames 32676-35020

Chapter 14: Helping Yourself and Others

Frames 37714-41658

HOME AND COMMUNITY CONNECTION

CODEPENDENCE. Behavior typical of codependents can manifest in situations other than addiction. Have students write in their private Health Journals about any evidence of codependent tendencies or personalities in family members. Suggest that they write a list of typical codependent traits and behaviors, as well as a list of better ways to handle problems involving family members and close friends. Encourage them to share the information with their families. If such communication would be difficult, suggest that they ask family members for help with the report as a means of sharing the information.

L2 Discussing

Discuss how the following elements of all addictions apply both to the alcoholic or other drug abuser and to the codependent involved with the abuser: denial, loss of control or powerlessness, continued usage without regard for consequences, repression of feelings, obsessive-compulsive thoughts and behaviors, and withdrawal symptoms.

LD Discussing

Describe the structures of each of the treatment programs, and have students consider the pros and cons of each.

L1 Researching

Select students to use library and on-line resources to research the topic of family therapy.

Building Health Skills

Helping Someone Who Needs Help
Skill: Obtaining Help

Ask: How do friends help each other? What do you do when a friend needs more help than you can give? What steps are you willing to take to see that a friend with a serious problem gets help? After volunteers have shared their thoughts, have students read the Building Health Skills feature to learn about specific steps they can take to help a friend in need. Let students work in small groups to discuss each listed guideline and to offer specific examples of putting that guideline into action.

hotlink

psychiatrist For more information on the services provided by the mental health care professionals known as psychiatrists, see Chapter 10, page 249.

psychologist For more information on the services provided by the mental health care professionals known as psychologists, see Chapter 10, page 250.

social worker For more information on the services provided by the mental health care professionals known as social workers, see Chapter 10, page 251.

Counseling

Many codependents need professional care. Individual and group counseling may be available with a **psychiatrist**, **psychologist**, **social worker**, or therapist trained in chemical dependency and codependency. Family therapy is often recommended and may help the family even if the alcoholic or addict refuses to participate.

Support Groups

There are many support groups for people involved in the lives of alcoholics and other drug addicts. The most widely known of these groups is Al-Anon. Structured similarly to Alcoholics Anonymous, **Al-Anon** is *a worldwide self-help organization for people who are close to alcoholics.* It welcomes family members and friends of alcoholics. It is open to the codependent whether or not the chemically dependent person decides to get well. Like AA meetings, Al-Anon meetings offer a support system for coping and a structured program for regaining emotional and social health. The program encourages **detachment**—*the process of pulling back or separating from involvement with someone else's addiction and refusing to let that addiction rule one's life any longer.* Al-Anon meetings are free, and what is said at the meetings remains confidential.

Building Health Skills

Obtaining Help: Helping Someone Who Needs Help

SOMETIMES, GETTING A PERSON you care about to make that first call for help can be the most important step you can take to aid in the recovery process. If someone you know needs help, consider guiding them to the following resources:

1. **Talk to people.** Encourage the person to talk with a parent, teacher, coach, clergy person, or a trusted adult.

2. **Locate support groups.** Look in the phone book under Alcoholics Anonymous, Cocaine Anonymous, or Narcotics Anonymous. The local AA office or volunteer phone counselor can help you or your friend find help.

3. **Investigate medical facilities.** Have the person call his or her family physician or a local hospital or medical center. If there is no drug or alcohol treatment program on-site, they may be able to direct you to the nearest facility.

4. **Contact information-giving organizations.** If all other efforts fail, you or the person you're trying to help can contact a reputable information source, such as the National Council on Alcoholism and Drug Dependence; the National Clearinghouse for Alcohol and Drug Information; or Partnership for a Drug-Free America.

612 CHAPTER 27 RECOVERING FROM ADDICTION AND CODEPENDENCY

PERSONAL HEALTH

INTERVENTION AND CODEPENDENCE. Some steps described in the intervention process are similar to the actions of a codependent. For example, the textbook lists ultimatums as a possible step in the intervention process. It also lists nagging and threatening among the actions of a codependent. To help students clarify in their own minds the differences between intervention and the behavior of codependents, have them create a Venn diagram comparing and contrasting the actions taken in the intervention process with those taken by codependents. Have them finish with a paragraph describing what distinguishes a codependent from a person who is attempting an intervention.

Other support groups such as Codependents Anonymous, the National Association for Adult Children of Alcoholics, the National Association for Children of Alcoholics, and Children of Alcoholics offer information and support at both national and local levels.

An offshoot of Al-Anon, **Alateen** is *a support program for people ages 12 to 20 whose parents, other family members, or friends have drinking problems.* Like Al-Anon, Alateen's members come together to share their experiences and discuss how the addiction of someone close to them has affected their lives and how they can cope and recover. Information about Al-Anon and Alateen can be found by calling the local Al-Anon office listed in the phone book. Other similar programs such as Nar-Anon and Coc-Anon are available to help families and close friends of narcotics and cocaine addicts.

◀ *Teens do not have to face problems alone when dealing with a friend or family member who has an addiction.*
ACTIVITY *List people you can turn to and support groups such as Alateen where teens can go for support.*

ASSESS

EVALUATING THE LESSON

Assign and discuss the Lesson 2 Review; then administer, grade, and discuss the *Lesson 82 Quiz* in the TCR. ☞

RETEACHING

- Tell students to list the common traits of codependents and explain how they may contribute to addicts' dependence on alcohol or other drugs.
- Ask students to complete *Reteaching Activity 82* in the TCR. ☞

ENRICHMENT

- Have students research the connection between alcohol or other drug abuse and physical abuse, particularly of wives and children of addicts. Ask them to summarize their findings in a written report.
- Give students a look at the experience of being in treatment for drug addiction by having them complete *Enrichment Activity 27*, "You CAN Beat Drugs," in the TCR. ☞

LESSON 2 *Review*

Reviewing Facts and Vocabulary

1. Define *codependent* and list some of the common traits of codependents.
2. Give three examples of enabling behavior.
3. List three places where the family of an addict or alcoholic might turn to get treatment information for the addict and help for themselves.

Thinking Critically

4. *Comparing and Contrasting.* In what ways are addiction and codependency similar? In what ways are they different?

5. *Analyzing.* What factors make it possible for the codependent person to recover even if the alcoholic or addict in his or her life does not?

Applying Health Skills

6. *In Your Home and School.* Think about times in your life you have enabled a family member or friend in an unhealthful way. List three other, more healthful ways that you might have dealt with the situation and how these alternative behaviors might have benefited both you and the other person.

CLOSE

Explain to students that in this lesson they learned how codependents, that is, people involved in unhealthy relationships with alcoholics and other drug addicts, can get help with recovery. They saw that the recovery process for codependents requires time and effort, much like the recovery process for alcoholics and other drug addicts described earlier in this chapter.

Lesson 2 Review

Answers to Reviewing Facts and Vocabulary

1. See pages 608 and 609.
2. Enabling behavior includes lying or covering up, lending money, making excuses for the person's behavior, doing the person's work for him or her, and denial.
3. Places a person can get help include Alcoholics Anonymous, Al-Anon, and Alateen.

Answers to Thinking Critically

4. Similar: Drug use becomes the center of attention and affects every aspect of living and coping. Different: The codependent isn't actually using the substance.
5. The codependent doesn't have a physiological addiction. In addition, his or her perception of the situation isn't distorted by drug use.

Health Skills Activities

ACTIVITY 1
HEALTH SKILLS
Communication, Decision Making, Health Advocacy

➤ **National Standards**
This activity meets these National Health Standards: 5.1; 6.1; 7.3.

Teach
- Review with students the addictive powers of drugs. Remind groups to include these factors in their discussions of the problems that might compromise communication of their message.
- Have groups develop their reports into a campaign to be shared with the rest of the school and/or community in the form of posters, advertisements, and other mass communication media.

ACTIVITY 2
HEALTH SKILLS
Communication, Health Advocacy

➤ **National Standards**
This activity meets these National Health Standards: 5.1; 7.3.

Teach
- Share PSAs with students that you have taped from TV or the radio. Let groups note details of these announcements, summarizing the main message.
- Prior to groups' developing their own PSAs, you may want to hold a discussion to make sure all groups understand that these messages are to be addressed not to the person with the addiction but to those whose job it is to intervene on behalf of that person.

Activity 1 — Helping a Friend Overcome Addiction

Convincing someone you know to seek assistance for drug use can be tough. Yet, it could also save this person's life. What would you say and do to help a friend overcome addition?

Directions
1. Working in a group of at least five, list ways to approach an individual who has an addictive problem with a drug. Think of as many strategies as you can to help this person change his or her behavior and get help.
2. Write down the potential negative consequences of each strategy.
3. Decide what would be the best strategy to employ. Write down why you believe this would be the best method.
4. Write a brief report detailing your group's recommendations and reasons. Present your report to the class.

Time
50 minutes
Materials
pen, paper

Self-Assessment
✓ Showed evidence that several realistic strategies and negative consequences were considered.
✓ Gave support of intervention strategy chosen.

Activity 2 — Intervention Public Service Announcement (PSA)

Structured interventions are often a first step toward convincing a drug-addicted individual to seek help. Unfortunately, many people do not know what an intervention is or how effective it can be. How would you describe an intervention?

Directions
1. In a group, review the information on interventions on pages 604-605.
2. Try to reach an agreement on what the essential elements of an intervention are. For example, the more key people who are involved, the less likely it is that the drug-addicted person can make excuses for his or her actions.
3. Discuss how this information could be woven into a 1- or 2-minute PSA for the general public.
4. Compose your intervention PSA.
5. Read your group's PSA to the class.

Time
50 minutes
Materials
audiocassette player (optional)

Self-Assessment
✓ Accurately described elements of an intervention.
✓ Indicated at least three benefits of an intervention and persuasively communicated this in PSA.

614 CHAPTER 27 RECOVERING FROM ADDICTION AND CODEPENDENCY

ASSESSMENT SCORING

Using a four-level rubric, the student has achieved a 4 if:

ACTIVITY 1
✔ Student demonstrated an understanding of the special communication skills involved in reaching out to an addicted individual.
✔ Student listed the addictive powers of drugs.
✔ Student considered several realistic strategies and negative consequences.
✔ Student took part in devising a workable intervention strategy.

ACTIVITY 2
✔ Student understood the purpose of an intervention.
✔ Student accurately described elements of an intervention.
✔ Student indicated at least three benefits of an intervention.
✔ Student persuasively communicated these benefits in PSA.

HEALTH NEWS VIDEO

Your Brain and Drugs

How do drugs actually work in the brain? Why do some people become addicts? These are just two of the questions researchers hope to answer using complex new technology.

A scanning camera and a cyclotron are the essential components of the brain imaging center. The cyclotron produces radioactive tracers that can follow brain activity. Scientists can use this device to gain a clear picture of which parts of the brain are active.

Researchers hope that this new center will help them understand how drug use damages and changes people's brains. They already know that drugs like cocaine and heroin reduce brain activity. Soon they will have more answers about the terrible toll of drug use.

Play the Video

DRUG ABUSER GREATER ACT ORBITOFRONTA
Control

CNN. All Rights Reserved.

Think About It

- Do you think the brains of people who are addicted to drugs have anything in common? Why or why not?
- How does this research emphasize the dangers of using illegal drugs? Tell how you could use information from this report to persuade a friend not to use drugs.

MORE ABOUT . . . . .

TECHNOLOGY AND SCIENCE. The imaging center uses a cyclotron to help produce brain images. A cyclotron, also called a particle accelerator, creates tracers that measure the body's use of radioactively tagged sugars. The high cost of a cyclotron limits the use of PET scanning. With current technology, labs need their own cyclotron to create these images.

Radioactive materials are unstable. Some of the radioactive tracers created by a cyclotron only are usable for about two minutes. These tracers cannot be stored or shipped. Scientists hope to develop inexpensive cyclotrons or tracers that will have longer lives.

CNN HEALTH NEWS

Your Brain and Drugs
Video Segment 17 (Time – 2:18)

Objectives. After viewing the video, students should be able to recognize the physical consequences of addiction and its effects on the brain.

Motivator. Ask students to speculate about how the brain uses natural chemicals in the body. Remind students that the brain is nourished by blood and receives chemical messages through nerves and hormones. Then discuss how this delicate system can be damaged through the use of illegal drugs. View Video Segment 17, "Your Brain and Drugs" to show how researchers are studying the effects of drugs on the brain.

Teach
- Draw a diagram of the brain on the chalkboard and have students suggest different ways to show how drugs affect the natural chemical balance of the nervous system. Then discuss possible long-term effects of drug use on the nervous system.
- Invite students to consider why journalists chose to report on this new research laboratory. Point out the beneficial impact of such reports, which inform the public about the dangers of illegal drugs. The reports also make it easier for people to make healthy choices about drug use.

Role Play. Encourage students to use their answers to the final question in Think About It as the basis for a role-playing scenario. For example, students might enact one side of a phone conversation in which they try to persuade the student to whom they are talking not to use drugs.

Close. Ask students to work together to write a two- or three-sentence summary of the video report. Help them find precise words to highlight the key details of the video.

CHAPTER **27** *Review*

CHECKING COMPREHENSION

- Assign and discuss the chapter review.
- Use the MindJogger Videoquiz to review the chapter.

CHAPTER 27 REVIEW ANSWERS

Using Health Terms

1. relapses
2. recovery
3. intervention
4. detoxification
5. inpatient treatment
6. outpatient treatment
7. halfway houses
8. Al-Anon
9. detachment
10. enabling
11. codependents
12. Alateen

Recalling the Facts

1. The addiction continuum is a process of changes that happens over time. Some people are addicted the first time they use a drug, others develop an addiction more slowly, and some do not become addicted at all.
2. The amount of time it takes to become addicted varies from person to person.
3. Answers will vary. May include: Could be inherited or lifestyle decisions.
4. In intervention, family members meet with counselors and other health care professionals to discuss the addiction of the family member and how they are affected by it. They then confront the addicted family member and require that the problem be addressed.
5. Recovery involves becoming physically free of the substance and recognizing the problems brought upon oneself and others by the addiction. It then requires a daily commitment to remain drug free.

Using Health Terms

On a separate sheet of paper, write the term that best matches each definition below.

LESSON 1

1. Slips from recovery, or periodic returns to drinking and drug use.
2. Learning to live an alcohol-free or drug-free life.
3. Interruption of the addiction continuum before the addict or alcoholic hits bottom.
4. The removal of all drugs from the body.
5. Medical and psychological care during which a person stays at a medical or rehabilitation facility.
6. On-site medical and psychological care for a person trying to become alcohol-free and drug-free.
7. Continuing care facilities that offer people housing, counseling, and support meetings.

LESSON 2

8. A worldwide self-help organization for people who are close to alcoholics.
9. The process of pulling back or separating from involvement with someone else's addiction and refusing to let that addiction rule one's life any longer.
10. Trying to protect the person having trouble with alcohol or drugs from facing the consequences of his or her drug-related problems.
11. People who become overly concerned with another's addiction problem and feel driven to fix or control it.
12. A support program for people ages 12 to 20 whose parents, other family members, or friends have drinking problems.

Recalling the Facts

Using complete sentences, answer the following questions.

LESSON 1

1. Describe the addiction continuum and how it varies for different people.
2. How long does it take for one to become addicted?
3. What factors might contribute to addiction?
4. What is intervention, and how does it work?
5. What is meant by the statement "Recovery is a process"?
6. Why do experts on addiction recommend total abstinence for the alcoholic or drug addict?
7. What happens at a detoxification unit?

8. Besides regaining physical health, what factors are involved in an addict's recovery?
9. What is a halfway house? How does the facility help in the treatment of the addict?

LESSON 2

10. Name and describe three roles a codependent might play in a family with addiction.
11. List some emotions people in a family living with an addict might experience.
12. How might being a codependent adversely affect a person's physical and mental health?
13. What part might a family play in an addict's recovery program?
14. Describe some of the functions of Al-Anon and Alateen.

6. They recommend abstinence because even a single use of the substance can undermine one's judgment and cause one to relapse.
7. At a detoxification unit, use of the substance stops and the person is given medication and counseling to help him or her through withdrawal.
8. In addition to gaining physical health, the recovering addict then gains the control over his or her life that was lost to the drug.
9. A halfway house is a continuing-care facility that offers people housing, counseling, and support meetings as they recover from severe addiction.
10. A codependent might lie or cover up for the addict's mistakes, lend him or her money for drugs or alcohol, make excuses for his or her irresponsible

Review

Thinking Critically

LESSON 1

1. **Comparing and Contrasting.** What factors might be responsible for one person becoming an addict and another not?
2. **Evaluating.** Cigarette ads were banned from television in the 1970s. Do you think ads for alcohol should be banned? Support your answer.
3. **Analyzing.** Some say that addiction is a social disease. What is the thinking behind this statement?

LESSON 2

4. **Evaluating.** Years ago, people often hid the problem of addiction within a family and suffered in silence. How are things beginning to change? What do you think is causing the change? How is this change for the better?
5. **Comparing and Contrasting.** Describe similarities and differences in the recovery process from alcoholism and from codependency.

Making the Connection

1. **Language Arts.** In the past, newspaper obituaries often did not specify, or point out specifically, that a person died from drug addiction, drug or alcohol overdose, or alcoholism. Often just the phrase "heart failure" was given as the cause of death. Write an editorial column expressing your viewpoint on this practice.

2. **Social Studies.** Using library resources, learn about residential treatment centers and their origins in the 1950s. Investigate the types of health professionals who staffed such facilities in the early days and what methods they used. Explain changes that have been made since, as well as factors that have prompted reforms.

BEYOND THE CLASSROOM

PARENTAL INVOLVEMENT In recent years, programs have been developed encouraging young people not to get started using alcohol or drugs. Make some collective judgments about the effectiveness of these programs, emphasizing how your parents feel about them.

COMMUNITY INVOLVEMENT Research two support groups for addicts and codependents within your community. Interview a facilitator or member from each group to learn all you can about the program. If no group presently exists, research the need for such a group in your area and ways to go about getting one started.

SCHOOL-TO-CAREER

Exploring Careers. Invite a certified drug or alcoholism counselor to your class. In advance, prepare questions asking about kinds of education and training required. Ask about how a person gets certified and what he or she must do to keep that certification up to date. Ask what drew the person to this field of work in the first place and what its rewards and frustrations are. Ask him or her to tell one anonymous and unidentifiable story of hope about an addict, alcoholic, or codependent with whom he or she has successfully worked.

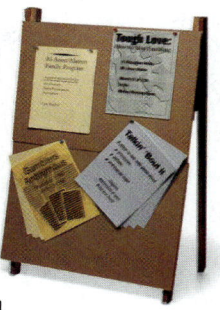

behavior, do the person's work for him or her, or try to deflect attention through denial or other means.

11. A family member might feel fear, mistrust, guilt, anger, disappointment, abandonment, or shame.

12. A codependent's mental and physical health may be harmed because the focus is on the addict, and his or her own needs are neglected.

13. A family can support the addicted family member by stopping enabling behavior, by going to Al-Anon or Alateen meetings, and by ensuring that the family member sticks to the recovery program.

14. Al-Anon and Alateen provide support, self-help guidance, and encouragement to those who are close to alcoholics.

Thinking Critically

1. The factors that make a difference are heredity, environment, and physical makeup.
2. Answers will vary.
3. Addiction is a social disease in that it affects the family, friends, and co-workers of the one who has the disease.
4. There is now a greater openness about discussing such problems. Part of the reason is that addiction is now thought of as a disease. This makes a medical and psychological approach to the problem possible.
5. The main similarity is that both the addict and the codependent must acknowledge the problem. The main difference is that the codependent doesn't have to deal with physical dependence on a substance.

Making the Connection

1.–2. Answers will vary.

Evaluate

- Use the reproducible *Chapter 27 Test* in the TCR, or construct your own using the Testmaker software.
- Use *Performance Assessment Activity 27* in the TCR.

Enrichment

Ask students to complete *Cross-Curriculum Activity 27* in the TCR.

Beyond the Classroom

Keep students involved in the community and encourage parent participation by assigning the activities on this page for students to work on outside of class.

Infectious Diseases

	FEATURES	CLASSROOM RESOURCES
LESSON 1 **What Causes Infectious Diseases?** *pages 620–626*	**Building Health Skills** "Goal Setting: Reducing Infectious Disease Risk," *page 622*	☞ Concept Map Activity 83 ☞ Cooperative Learning Activity 28 ☞ Enrichment Activity 28 ☞ Lesson 83 Quiz ☞ Lesson Plan 83 ☞ Reteaching Activity 83
LESSON 2 **Common Infectious Diseases** *pages 627–631*		☞ Concept Map Activity 84 ☞ Lesson 84 Quiz ☞ Lesson Plan 84 ☞ Reteaching Activity 84
LESSON 3 **Preventing Infectious Diseases** *pages 632–635*	**Making Responsible Decisions** "Letting the Team Down," *page 634*	☞ Concept Map Activity 85 ☞ Decision-Making Activity 28 ☞ Health Lab 28 ☞ Lesson 85 Quiz ☞ Lesson Plan 85 ☞ Reteaching Activity 85

ACTIVITIES

- Cross-Curriculum Activity 28
- Health Lab 28
- Health Skills Activities 28
- Parent Letter and Activities 28

ASSESSMENT

- Chapter 28 Test
- Performance Assessment Activity 28
- Testmaker Software

STUDENT ACTIVITIES WORKBOOK

- Applying Health Skills 83–85
- Study Guide 28
- Vocabulary Activity 28

STUDENT DIVERSITY STRATEGIES

- Audiocassette Program (English)
- Audiocassette Program (Spanish)
- Spanish Parent Letters and Activities
- Spanish Summaries, Quizzes, and Activities

MULTIMEDIA COMPONENTS

- English Audiocassette Program
- Spanish Audiocassette Program
- MindJogger Videodisc and VHS program

National Health Education Standards

One of the main goals of the National Health Education Standards is to move students toward "health literacy." Health literacy is the capacity of individuals to obtain, interpret, and understand basic health information and services and the competence to use such information and services in ways which promote health. The health standards were developed by applying the characteristics of a well-educated, literate person within the context of health. The health literate person is:

- a critical thinker and problem solver
- a self-directed learner
- a responsible, productive citizen
- an effective communicator

Listed below are the Health Education Standards Performance Indicators addressed in each lesson of this chapter.

Lesson	Health Standards Performance Indicators
1	1.4, 3.1, 4.2, 4.4
2	1.3, 3.3, 2.6, 6.3
3	1.7, 1.8, 3.3, 3.4

ONLINE RESOURCES

HEALTH Online

For a fresh approach to health topics and an in-depth look at health issues, use these online resources found under Teacher Resources at **health.glencoe.com**.

- **BLOCK SCHEDULE LESSON PLANS** Reinforce health concepts with outside readings selected especially for students. Each reading is accompanied by a lesson plan and activities to enhance
  - Reading Skills
  - Cross Curriculum
  - Media Literacy

- **TECHNOLOGY PROJECTS** Instructions and suggestions on how to use computer, Internet, and software with health lessons.

- **HEALTH UPDATES** Timely topics in health news, including late-breaking medical advances and updates on teen risk behaviors.

Out of Time?

If time does not permit teaching this chapter, you may use these features: Building Health Skills on page 622 and Making Responsible Decisions on page 634.

BLOCK SCHEDULING

Block scheduling provides extended time for hands-on projects and activities. Use the following activity to engage students, provide further depth, and vary your instructional techniques:
- Health Skills Activity (60–90 minutes) **pg. 636**

Infectious Diseases

CHAPTER OVERVIEW

Chapter 28 explains what infectious diseases are and details both their means of transmission and how the risk of infection can be decreased. Some common infectious diseases are also described.

LESSON 1 Infectious diseases are spread by pathogens that invade the body and attack its cells and tissues. Bacteria and viruses are common pathogens. Others include rickettsias, protozoans, and fungi. For disease to develop, a pathogen needs an intermediary host, a means of transportation, and a host with lowered resistance to the pathogen. The body has physical, chemical, and biological barriers to prevent pathogens from entering; the immune system assists in fighting pathogens once they have invaded.

LESSON 2 This lesson focuses on common infectious diseases. Diseases of the respiratory and nervous systems are discussed. Measles, mononucleosis, and hepatitis are also studied.

LESSON 3 A person can prevent being infected by avoiding contact with pathogens, by becoming immune through having had the disease, or by vaccination.

CHAPTER 28

Infectious Diseases

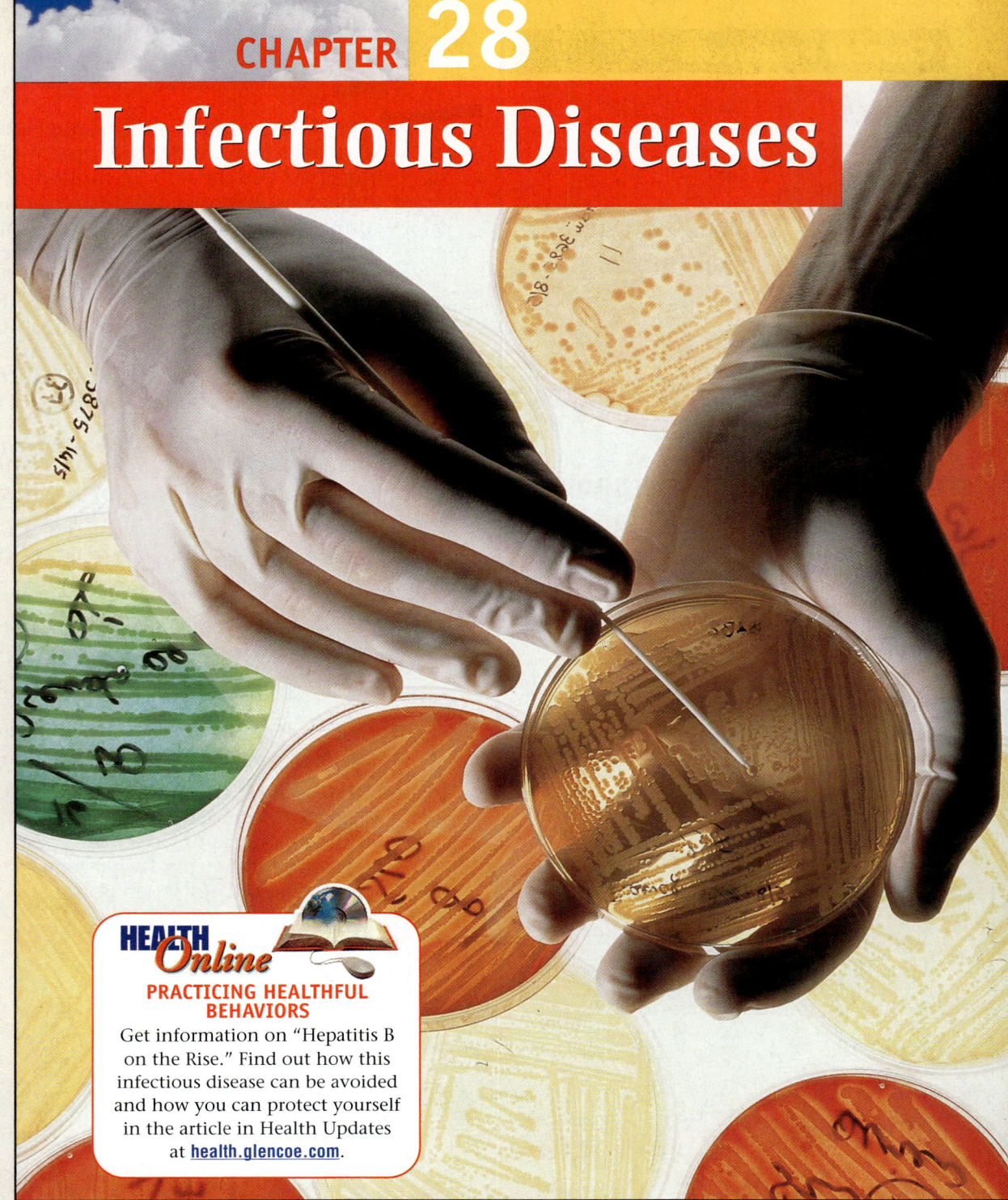

HEALTH Online

PRACTICING HEALTHFUL BEHAVIORS

Get information on "Hepatitis B on the Rise." Find out how this infectious disease can be avoided and how you can protect yourself in the article in Health Updates at **health.glencoe.com**.

TEACHING STRATEGY

Hands-On Health

Identifying Characteristics and Examples
Guide students in playing a game that involves higher-level thinking, gathering and organizing facts to define and explore the concept of diseases and their causes or cures. See Activity 27, "T-Chart Guessing Game," in the *Hands-On Health: Creative Teaching Strategies* booklet.

Time Needed
20–30 minutes

Supplies
- bulletin board
- cards with names of diseases and modes of transmission on them

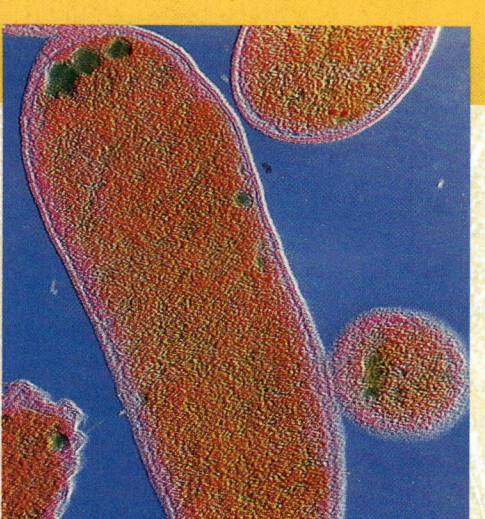

> *Prosperous nations must work in partnership with developing nations to help remove the cloud of disease from our world's future.* **99**
>
> —GEORGE W. BUSH
> PRESIDENT OF THE UNITED STATES, 2001

Quick Write List three health behaviors you practice to protect yourself against infections or to prevent spreading infections to others.

Personal Health Inventory

Self-Inventory Write the numbers 1–10 on a sheet of paper. Read each statement below and respond by writing *yes*, *no*, or *sometimes* for each item. Write a *yes* only for items that you practice regularly. Save your responses.

1	I keep my immunizations up to date.
2	I avoid contact with people who currently have a cold or the flu.
3	I bathe or shower every day.
4	I wash my hands after using the bathroom, before preparing or serving food, and before meals.
5	I practice good nutrition.
6	I get at least eight hours of sleep each night.
7	I do not share eating utensils or glasses with other people.
8	I avoid eating foods—especially dairy products and poultry—that might not have been refrigerated.
9	I cover my mouth when I cough or sneeze.
10	I stay home at least the first day that I have the symptoms of an illness.

Follow-up After completing the chapter, retake this self-inventory. Pick two items that you need to work on and set a goal to improve your health behaviors.

INTRODUCING THE CHAPTER

Personal Health Inventory

After students have read the Self-Inventory statements, ask: How do the behaviors identified here relate to your physical health? When you maintain good physical health, how do you affect your mental and emotional health? your social health? After a brief discussion, have students record their Self-Inventory responses in their private Health Journals on a page labeled "Infectious Diseases."

- Ask students how many of them have had to miss school due to a cold or the flu. Discuss the impact of lost days from school and work and the costs of treating the symptoms of cold or flu on our society. Explain that to avoid being plagued by these mild diseases, as well as more serious ones, it will help to understand our bodies' defenses against diseases and preventive measures that can be taken to avoid infectious diseases.
- Have students discuss the photographs on these two pages. Then have students read the statement from the President made during his visit to China in 2001 about curing disease around the world. Explain that students will learn more about infectious disease, their causes, and their treatment as they study the lessons in Chapter 28.
- Distribute Parent Letter 28 in the *Parent Letters and Activities* booklet.

What Causes Infectious Diseases?

LESSON 1

FOCUS

LESSON OBJECTIVES

After studying this lesson, students should be able to

- describe the types of pathogens that cause disease.
- discuss the spread of bacterial infection through cell division.
- explain how viruses differ from other pathogens.
- identify the major routes for the spread of infectious diseases and give examples of diseases spread through each route.
- describe the two main types of defenses used by the immune system.

MOTIVATOR

Write the following on the chalkboard for students to work on while attendance is being taken: *Describe your last cold. Tell how you believe you caught it and how you treated it.*

INTRODUCING THE LESSON

Have students share their responses to the Motivator. Point out that colds are one type of disease that a person can catch or give to someone else. Such diseases are called infectious diseases. Tell students that this lesson explains how some of these diseases are spread.

INTRODUCING HEALTH TERMS

- Instruct students to find medical definitions of *infectious disease* and *immunity*.
- Ask students to complete Vocabulary Activity 28 and Chapter Study Guide 28 in the *Student Workbook.* 🖛

What Causes Infectious Diseases?

When you catch a cold, you may sneeze, cough, and run a fever. You probably feel discomfort but do not think of yourself as having a disease. Yet, the common cold is a type of disease. More specifically, it is an **infectious disease,** *a disease caused by organisms that enter and multiply within the human body.*

HEALTH TERMS

infectious disease
parasites
virus
transmission
immunity
mucous membranes
phagocytosis
neutrophils
antibodies

HEALTH CONCEPTS

- Infectious diseases are caused by tiny organisms called *pathogens.*
- Infectious diseases are transmitted, or spread, through contact with a person, an animal, a contaminated object, or the environment at large.
- The body offers several layers of protection against infection by pathogens.
- You can take measures to maintain the health of your immune system.

Protozoan

E. coli bacterium

Causes of Infectious Diseases

Every infectious disease is caused by one of several types of small, microscopic organisms (microorganisms) known as *pathogens.* Pathogens invade the body and attack its cells and tissues. Most pathogens are **parasites,** *organisms that live in or on another organism and derive nourishment from it.* Among the forms pathogens can take are bacteria, viruses, rickettsias (rik-ET-see-uhs), protozoans, and fungi.

Bacteria

A bacterium is a single-celled microorganism. Bacteria can live almost anywhere. They are abundant in the air, soil, and water. Some bacteria produce poisons that are harmful to human cells. If there are enough bacteria and the person is not immune, disease results.

Lesson 1 Resources

TEACHER'S CLASSROOM RESOURCES
🖛 **Concept Map** Activity 83
🖛 **Cooperative Learning** Activity 28
🖛 **Enrichment** Activity 28
🖛 **Lesson 83 Quiz**
🖛 **Lesson Plan 83**
🖛 **Parent Letter and Activities 28**
🖛 **Reteaching** Activity 83

STUDENT WORKBOOK
🖛 **Applying Health Skills 83**
🖛 **Chapter Study Guide 28**
🖛 **Vocabulary** Activity 28

Most diseases caused by bacteria begin when microorganisms not usually present in the body invade it. When bacteria enter the body, they multiply at a rapid rate through cell division. If conditions are perfect—the right temperature and sufficient nourishment—division can take place every 20 minutes. After just 15½ hours, one bacterium can have multiplied into more than 4 billion bacteria! This rarely happens, however. In a healthy individual, the body's immune system destroys the invading bacteria. Also, perfect conditions rarely occur.

Viruses

A **virus** is *the smallest known type of infectious agent.* Viruses are about one-half to one-hundredth the size of the smallest bacterium. These organisms are also one of our worst enemies. One of the deadliest viruses known today is **HIV**, the virus that causes AIDS.

Viruses are not living cells. They consist of an inner core of genetic material surrounded by a protective protein shell and are entirely dependent on living cells for survival and reproduction. Viruses invade all known forms of life—mammals, birds, reptiles, insects, plants, and even bacteria. Viruses are highly specific in the kinds of cells they invade. Only certain viruses invade animal cells, and these viruses can attack only specific types of cells.

When a virus enters the body, it attaches itself to a cell—called the *host*—and injects its genetic material into that cell. The virus then makes copies of itself, using materials within the host cell. The copies then spread to other body cells, where the process is repeated. Viruses usually run their course and are eventually killed by the immune system.

Rickettsias

Rickettsias are organisms that resemble small bacteria but, like viruses, are able to multiply only by invading the cells of another life form. Most rickettsias are found in the intestinal tracts of insects—notably fleas—as well as in mice, ticks, and mites. Rickettsias are passed on to human and animal hosts through bites or through feces deposited on the skin. Human diseases caused by rickettsias include typhus, mentioned in the chapter-opening paragraph, and Rocky Mountain spotted fever.

Protozoans

Protozoans are single-celled organisms that are larger than bacteria and have a more complex cell structure. Most protozoans are harmless, but about 30 different types cause disease in humans. Disease-producing protozoans are most common in tropical areas that have poor sanitation.

"Friendly" Bacteria

Far from harming your body, certain bacteria—known as resident bacteria—live within or on your body and assist its normal functions. Among these "helpful" bacteria are:

- **LACTOBACILLI.** Found in the gastrointestinal tract, these bacteria produce lactic acid from simple carbohydrates, which aids in digestion.
- **COLIFORM BACILLI.** Found in the intestines, these bacteria help break down carbohydrates and combat disease-causing bacteria.

---

hotlink

HIV For more information on HIV, the virus that causes AIDS, see Chapter 30, page 656.

▼ *The smallest forms of life on earth, these microorganisms can be the most threatening to your health.*

ACTIVITY *Describe the differences that you see among the microorganisms on these pages.*

Ebola Zaire virus

Protozoan

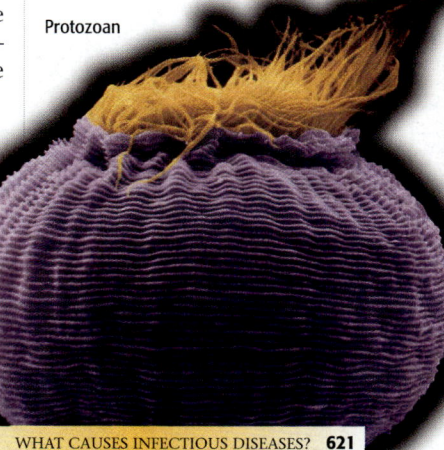

SCHOOL-TO-CAREER

HEALTH INSPECTOR. Most counties and some cities have regulations designed to prevent the spread of pathogens. Various public facilities are inspected by city or county health inspectors. For example, restaurants may be inspected to check for proper equipment, sanitation procedures, and hygiene among workers. School buildings may be checked for proper plumbing and sewage disposal. Encourage students to find out about the specific duties of health inspectors in your area. Encourage students to obtain descriptions of several positions related to public health inspection, and the qualifications for each position.

TEACH

L1 Discussing

Ask students what pathogens are. What is their role in infectious diseases?

LEP Class Activity

Have students locate magazine and newspaper photographs illustrating places in the environment where pathogens might be found.

L1 Explaining

Remind students that there are three basic types of bacteria and that they are known by their shapes: spherical or round, rod-shaped, and spiral or corkscrew. Each type causes diseases and responds differently to drug treatment.

L2 Researching

Ask students to use classroom and library resources to research some of the resident bacteria and their functions in the body.

L2 Discussing

Ask students why it is that viruses, unlike bacteria, cannot be treated with antibiotics.

L1 Explaining

Point out some of the complex problems presented by viruses. *(There are so many different types causing different diseases, therefore making it difficult to pinpoint the type of disease to be treated. The diseases they cause cannot be prevented through vaccinations or treated with antibiotics. The diseases can be treated, but they cannot be cured.)*

L1 Discussing

Ask students to explain how rickettsias are different from bacteria and viruses.

L2 Researching

Help students use classroom and library materials to research disease-producing protozoans.

L1 Guest Speaker

Ask a family and consumer sciences teacher or county extension agent to speak with the class about trichinosis and ways to prevent it by proper cooking of pork and other meat.

L1 Discussing

Ask students what fungi are. In what ways can fungi cause problems for humans?

L1 Discussing

Have students explain why they should wear shower shoes when showering in public facilities, such as school locker rooms. *(This is to prevent picking up fungi that can live on the base of shower stalls.)*

Building Health Skills

Reducing Infectious Disease Risk
Skill: Goal Setting

Ask: What is food poisoning? When and why is it likely to occur? How can you avoid food poisoning? After volunteers have shared their ideas, have students read the feature to learn more about the bacteria that can cause food poisoning and about the precautions they can take to protect themselves from food poisoning. Let students meet in groups to discuss each precaution for avoiding the bacteria that cause food poisoning.

Did You Know?

➤ Water particles expelled through a sneeze can travel at speeds up to 100 miles an hour (161 km).

➤ Your toothbrush should be discarded after a cold or sore throat.

➤ Antibiotics work well against bacteria because both bacteria and antibiotics work outside of the body's own cells.

➤ Viruses pass inside cells where antibiotics can't reach them; therefore, antibiotics have no effect on curing viral infections.

Fungi

Fungi are simple organisms that cannot make their own food. Many are *saprophytes* (SAP-ruh-fyts)—organisms that feed off dead animals, insects, and leaves. Fungi prefer dark, damp environments. The most common disease-causing fungi invade mainly deep tissues of the hair, nails, and skin and cause infections of the scalp or feet, such as ringworm and athlete's foot.

How Infectious Diseases Are Spread

There are several well-defined means of **transmission**, or *spread*, of infectious pathogens. Transmission can occur through direct contact with an infected person, an animal, or a contaminated object. Some pathogens can also reside in the environment at large.

People

Many infectious diseases are spread as a result of direct or indirect contact with an infected person.

■ **Direct Contact.** Pathogens may be spread when an uninfected person comes into physical contact with an infected person. Sexually transmitted diseases are spread in this way. The human

Building Health Skills

Goal Setting: Reducing Infectious Disease Risk

SOME OF THE COMMON bacteria associated with food poisoning are *Salmonella, Staphylococcus aureus,* and *Clostridium perfringens.* Although home kitchens are breeding grounds for these potentially life-threatening microorganisms, the risk of infection exists outside the home as well. There are precautions you as a health-literate consumer can take to protect yourself. Exercise care when:

1. **Eating out.** Avoid restaurants that do not look clean or that you think might not practice safe cooking and food storage procedures. Refuse any food that does not smell right or tastes bad.

2. **Cooking out.** If you are camping or planning a cookout at the beach or park, remember to keep all perishable foods chilled. Cook meats thoroughly and place them on a clean platter, not one that held raw meat.

3. **Buying prepared foods.** Although you might expect fresh-cut deli meats, mayonnaise-based salads, and other such foods to be free of bacteria, they are not always. Many local newspapers publish lists of food sellers that fail to pass periodic health inspections. Learn to consult such lists from time to time, and avoid establishments that "make the list."

622 CHAPTER 28 INFECTIOUS DISEASES

CURRICULUM CONNECTIONS

FAMILY AND CONSUMER SCIENCES. Invite a family and consumer sciences teacher or a local health representative to talk with the class about salmonella, trichinosis, and other food-related bacterial problems. Ask the speaker to include information about methods of prevention.

SOCIAL STUDIES. Guide students in researching and giving reports on the great epidemics of infectious diseases throughout history, such as the Black Death in Europe in the fourteenth century and the Spanish influenza of 1918.

MATH. Have students calculate how many bacteria there would be four hours after a single bacteria cell begins to divide if division occurs every 30 minutes.

bite is another, and especially dangerous, mode of transmission. A pregnant woman may also transmit an infection to her unborn child.

- **Indirect Contact.** Both bacteria and viruses can enter the body through the lungs if droplets—exhaled, coughed, or sneezed out by an infected person—are inhaled. The common cold, influenza, and tuberculosis are spread in this way.

Animals

Animals, including insects, spread many infectious diseases. The bite of an infected dog or other animal can spread rabies, a disease that can be fatal. When a bloodsucking insect, such as a mosquito, ingests blood from an infected person or animal, the insect may take pathogens into its own body. When the insect later takes blood from an uninfected person, it injects some of the pathogens into that person's body, thus spreading the disease. Malaria and dengue fever, infectious diseases common to tropical regions, are spread in this fashion.

Contaminated Objects

Certain pathogens are spread when an uninfected person touches objects that an infected person has used. These objects can include eating utensils, glasses, or toothbrushes. They also include needles used to inject drugs that are shared with another person.

The Environment

Food, water, soil, and even the air we breathe contain potentially harmful pathogens. Some forms of infectious disease are the direct result of human negligence, such as the careless disposal of infectious waste materials from hospitals, which constitutes a form of toxic dumping. This form of pollution can be deadly. Yet another way in which pathogens in the environment are spread is through the careless handling of food, which is a main source of food poisoning.

▲ **Diseases are often spread through contact with contaminated objects such as eating utensils and even pens and pencils.**

ACTIVITY *Name ways the items pictured should be handled to prevent the spread of diseases.*

L1 Guest Speaker

Invite a veterinarian or veterinarian's assistant to speak with the class about animal diseases that humans may contract. Ask the speaker to address questions such as: Who is most at risk? Which animals pose the greatest danger? How can one avoid contracting diseases without isolating oneself from animals?

L1 Explaining

Explain that most of us are constantly fighting pathogens in many ways. We do not get sick every time we come in contact with a pathogen because our immune system protects us on several fronts. People are most likely to get sick when their immune systems are compromised for some reason—lack of sleep, lack of food, use of some medications, stress, infection with HIV, etc.

L1 Self-Esteem

Ask students what responsibility they feel an infected person has to tell other people that he or she may be contagious. Discuss what influence a person's level of self-esteem would have on his or her ability to act responsibly about the risks of spreading disease.

L1 Explaining

Explain that a person can be contagious both before and after having symptoms of an infectious disease.

MORE ABOUT . . . . .

INFECTIOUS DISEASES. Deer ticks can transmit Lyme disease to humans. This is a condition that begins with a rash and is then followed by muscle and joint aches, which can lead to the development of rheumatoid arthritis.

Rat fleas can transmit tapeworms and even bubonic plague to humans.

Psittacosis, a lung infection, is spread by parakeets, parrots, and canaries. Human exposure occurs through inhalation of cage dust.

Salmonella is transmitted through turtles and hamsters, undercooked pork and fowl, and in eggs and egg products.

Mosquitoes, through their bites, can spread malaria and encephalitis.

Common (Cold) Sense

Explain that coming up with a vaccine for colds has had poor results due to the fact that cold viruses constantly undergo changes. However, scientists are investigating another means of preventing colds by blocking the cellular receptor sites that viruses need to enter the cell, replicate, and cause illness.

L2 Class Activity

Ask one student to volunteer as scribe at the chalkboard. Have the rest of the class work together to name and give examples of the types of nonspecific resistance that help us fight off infections.

L2 Class Activity

Have students use class and library resources to research mucous membranes and where they are found in the body. Follow up with a discussion of the role of mucous membranes in the fight against invading pathogens.

L3 Discussing

Ask the class what *specific* means in the phrase *specific resistance to infection.* Continue by asking why it is so valuable to have antibodies that can "remember" a pathogen.

L2 Cooperative Learning

Assign *Cooperative Learning Activity 28,* "Immune Response Analogy," in the TCR.

---

keeping
Fit

Common (Cold) Sense

Colds, though they are minor inconveniences for most people other than those with chronic respiratory conditions, are nothing to sneeze at. Colds are caused by any number of viruses, all of which, like the deadly HIV, continue to change their genetic "fingerprint" as they move from host to host. This is why a cure for the common cold has never been discovered.

When you experience symptoms of a cold—mild fever, sneezing, runny nose—treat it as the disease it is. Be sure to

➤ get plenty of rest.

➤ drink plenty of fluids.

➤ maintain proper nutrition.

Keeping your body healthy will also make it more resistant to infection, possibly reducing the number of colds you get. Again, good nutrition, combined with regular physical activity and adequate rest, is the cornerstone of a prevention plan. Controlling stress levels and not smoking are other steps a person can take.

hot link

cilia For more information on the role cilia play in resisting infection, see Chapter 17, page 402.

How Your Body Defends Against Infectious Disease

Pathogens are everywhere in numbers beyond comprehension. If they are so widespread, why are we not constantly sick? This question can be answered in one word: *immunity.* **Immunity** is *the body's natural defenses against infection.*

The Immune Response

Although you cannot see them, your body is exposed each day to millions of pathogens. Pathogens are in the air you breathe, and they cling to the surfaces you touch. Your body is constantly fighting pathogens that enter it. When they enter your body, pathogens attack your body cells and use these cells to grow and multiply. The end result of such an attack is an infection.

Most of the time, your body manages to stay free of infection because of your immune system. Your immune system includes two main types of defenses. The *innate immune system*—your inborn defenses—provides nonspecific resistance. The *adaptive immune system* provides specific resistance. Both types work together to protect your body against pathogens that could harm you.

Nonspecific Resistance

Each of us has lines of inborn, nonspecific—or "general"—defenses against infection. Body defenses that are nonspecific respond in the same way each time your body is invaded by a foreign substance. Your body's nonspecific defenses include physical and chemical barriers, body cells, and the inflammatory response.

■ **Physical Barriers.** Your body's first line of defense against invading pathogens consists of physical barriers, the main barrier being your skin. Unbroken skin helps prevent pathogens from entering body tissues. The tough dead cells that make up the outer layer of skin form an effective barrier. **Mucous membranes**—*the soft, skinlike lining of many parts of the body*—in your mouth, nose, and bronchial tubes produce a sticky substance called *mucus* that traps pathogens. Some mucous membranes have **cilia**, tiny hairs, that also trap pathogens, which are then expelled when you cough or sneeze.

■ **Chemical Barriers.** Enzymes in tears and saliva are chemical barriers that can destroy bacteria. The acidic digestive juices of the stomach are also chemical barriers. These juices destroy pathogens that are swallowed with food. Other chemicals cause body changes that help cells inside the body fight pathogens.

■ **Body Cells.** Once pathogens reach your bloodstream, certain types of white blood cells, called *phagocytes,* travel through the blood and group together to destroy them. *The process by which*

HOME AND COMMUNITY CONNECTION

PREVENTIVE MEASURES AT HOME. Let students work individually or in groups to brainstorm a checklist to use in assessing the home for risks of infectious diseases and adequate preventive measures. In particular, have students assess steps taken to prevent the spread of disease when one member of the household is ill. For example, does the ill person use only certain eating utensils, or are all eating utensils washed in very hot water? What steps are taken to prevent members of the household from touching items contaminated by the infected person? What precautions are taken against spreading infection through airborne particles? Students may wish to recommend additional preventive measures.

phagocytes engulf and destroy pathogens is called **phagocytosis** (FAG-uh-suh-TOH-suhs). **Neutrophils** (NOO-truh-filz) are *the chief type of phagocyte involved in the process of phagocytosis.*

■ **Inflammatory Response.** If pathogens break through the body's outermost barriers, your body then goes into a "red alert" stage known as the *inflammatory response*. Chemical mediators are released that cause the blood vessels to dilate and allow increased blood flow. This permits phagocytes to leave the blood and enter the body tissues. This process continues until the pathogens are destroyed. Once the pathogens are destroyed, tissues can be repaired. Symptoms of inflammation confined to a specific area include heat, redness, and swelling, which result from increased blood flow.

Specific Resistance

The general response of your nonspecific defenses is not always enough to protect your body from disease. The adaptive immune system mounts specific attacks against particular types of pathogens. When this happens, another body defense goes to work in the form of cells called *lymphocytes.*

Examine microscopic images and learn about the cell activities of streptococcus and other infectious diseases. At **health.glencoe.com** link to animations that show how the body defends itself against infectious diseases.

In order to access the animations at this site, your classroom computer will need to be equipped to run QuickTime movie (MOV) files. If you are not certain whether your computer has this capability, you may wish to visit the site prior to assigning the activity and attempt to play one of the animations. If a message comes up informing you that your computer lacks the needed application, follow the on-screen directions.

L2 ## Cooperative Learning

Divide the class into three or four groups of several students each. Have each group produce a diagram that illustrates the action of lymphocytes, including the roles of both T cells and B cells, in fighting off pathogens. Circulate the drawings. Have students give each other feedback on their diagrams to correct errors and misconceptions.

Visual Learning

The Body's Barriers Against Disease

Refer students to the picture on this page. Discuss how the innate immune system acts to block or combat *all* viruses that the body is exposed to and effectively prevents many illnesses. The adaptive immune system, however, is very specific in the types of viruses it can control. Once the body is exposed to a particular virus, the specialized white blood cells of the adaptive immune system are able to recognize and destroy that strain during any subsequent exposures, thus preventing illness. This protection lasts for an extended period of time.

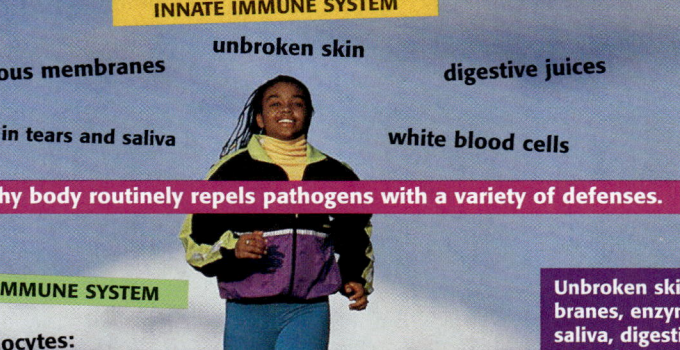

THE BODY'S BARRIERS AGAINST DISEASE

INNATE IMMUNE SYSTEM

mucous membranes

unbroken skin

digestive juices

enzymes in tears and saliva

white blood cells

A healthy body routinely repels pathogens with a variety of defenses.

ADAPTIVE IMMUNE SYSTEM

lymphocytes:

T cells

B cells

Unbroken skin, mucous membranes, enzymes in tears and saliva, digestive juices, and white blood cells all help keep unwanted bacteria at bay. But when a pathogen does elude these stalwarts of the innate immune system, the adaptive immune system provides further aid by sending out lymphocytes, cells that stalk and neutralize invading pathogens.

PERSONAL HEALTH

STAYING HOME. Students are advised in this chapter to stay home when they have illnesses such as colds, both to recover and to protect others from infection. Have students examine the consequences of staying home from school or work. What are teachers' policies regarding absence due to illness? Does absence affect their grades? Realistically, is it possible to make up missed work? If students hold jobs, they might wish to consider such questions as these: Is paid sick leave provided? Do workers sometimes lose their jobs because of excessive absence due to illness? Is the workload such that it is impossible for workers to meet performance standards if they stay home? Have students write realistic entries in their private Health Journals about the costs of staying home when ill, as well as the benefits.

ASSESS

EVALUATING THE LESSON

Assign and discuss the Lesson 1 Review; then administer, grade, and discuss the *Lesson 83 Quiz* in the TCR. 📖

RETEACHING

- Have students write a detailed outline of the material in the lesson using the lesson's major headings.
- Ask students to complete *Reteaching Activity 83* in the TCR. 📖

ENRICHMENT

- Have students research how malaria is transmitted. Based on their research, they should draw a diagram illustrating the transmission process and the organisms involved *(malaria pathogen, mosquito vector, and human host)*. They also should provide a brief explanation of the role of each organism in the transmission cycle.
- Distribute *Enrichment Activity 28*, "The Treatment for Disease in the Past," in the TCR. 📖

CLOSE

Write the lesson's major concepts on separate slips of paper. Place the slips into a box, and let each student draw one. Next, have students define and summarize the concept written on the slip of paper they selected.

lymphatic system For more information on the lymphatic system and its other functions, see Chapter 17, page 394.

ultraviolet rays For more information on protecting yourself against the sun's ultraviolet rays, see Chapter 7, page 163.

LYMPHOCYTES

Lymphocytes are a type of white blood cell that fights pathogens. Lymphocytes travel through your body along two networks of vessels. One of these networks is your blood vessels. The other network is your lymph vessels, which are a part of your **lymphatic system**. There are two main types of lymphocytes—B cells and T cells.

- **B Cells.** When B cells encounter pathogens, they are stimulated to enlarge and multiply. The B cells turn into cells called *plasma cells,* which in turn produce **antibodies**—*proteins that destroy or neutralize invading pathogens.* The antibodies for a particular pathogen remain in your blood to become active if you encounter the specific pathogen again.

- **T Cells.** There are two main groups of T cells—killer cells and helper cells. Killer T cells are stimulated to multiply by the presence of abnormal body cells. They attach to these cells and release toxins that help destroy the abnormal cells. Helper T cells aid the activity of the B cells and killer T cells and control other aspects of the body's immune system.

Care of the Immune Response

The ability of your immune system to fight off invading pathogens varies, depending on a number of preventive factors. Perhaps the most important is good nutrition. When you fail to take in adequate nutrients, you can jeopardize your immune system. This is one reason poorly planned weight-loss programs can make a person ill. Overexposure to **ultraviolet rays** also affects your immune response.

LESSON 1 *Review*

Reviewing Facts and Vocabulary

1. Use the terms *infectious disease* and *antibodies* in a paragraph.
2. In what ways can direct contact with an animal spread disease?
3. List the body's nonspecific defenses.

Thinking Critically

4. *Comparing and Contrasting.* Tell how viruses are different and more difficult to deal with than other pathogens.
5. *Analyzing.* Explain why the presence of antibodies is often used to determine whether an individual has an infectious disease.

6. *Synthesizing.* Explain the factors that would cause one person to have a healthy immune system and another person not to have one.

Applying Health Skills

7. *In Your Home and School.* Contact a local veterinarian to find out about parasites such as fleas and ticks that affect pets. How do these insects function? What problems or illnesses can they cause to pets or people? What steps can a pet owner take to prevent problems associated with fleas and ticks? Share your findings with your class and your family.

626 CHAPTER 28 INFECTIOUS DISEASES

Lesson 1 Review

Answers to Reviewing Facts and Vocabulary

1. Paragraphs will vary. See the Glossary for definitions of terms.
2. An infected dog or other animal can spread rabies through its bite. Mosquitoes and other bloodsucking insects can also spread disease.
3. Physical barriers, chemical barriers, body cells, and inflammatory response.

Answers to Thinking Critically

4. Viruses are smaller. They attack only specific types of cells; unlike bacteria, they move into the interior of cells.
5. The body produces antibodies in response to specific invading pathogens.
6. Answers may include: heredity, disease, good nutrition, and exposure to ultraviolet rays.

Common Infectious Diseases

Some 40 types of infectious disease, including the common cold and the flu, commonly occur in the United States. Many of them are preventable or can be treated with medication. In this lesson, you will learn about some of these diseases, their causes and symptoms, and how to treat them.

HEALTH TERMS

pneumonia
tuberculosis (TB)
strep throat
vaccine
immunization
rubella

HEALTH CONCEPTS

- New cases of infectious diseases once believed to be stamped out are recurring.
- Although some infectious diseases are better understood than others, all have a well-defined course of treatment that includes rest.

Respiratory Infections

Respiratory tract infections are infections of the breathing passages, which range from the nose to the alveoli of the lungs. Most of these illnesses are caused by viruses or bacteria.

Common Cold

The common cold is a viral infection that causes inflammation of the mucous membranes lining the nose and throat. Its symptoms include a stuffy, runny nose, sneezing, and sometimes a sore throat and headache. Most colds are contracted by breathing in virus-containing droplets that have been sneezed or coughed out by an infected person. Another method of transmission is rubbing the eyes or nose with fingers that have picked up the virus by hand-to-hand contact or by handling contaminated objects.

LESSON 2 COMMON INFECTIOUS DISEASES **627**

Lesson 2 Resources

TEACHER'S CLASSROOM RESOURCES
- **Concept Map** Activity 84
- **Lesson 84 Quiz**
- **Lesson Plan 84**
- **Reteaching** Activity 84

STUDENT WORKBOOK
- **Applying Health Skills 84**
- **Chapter Study Guide 28**
- **Vocabulary** Activity 28

Common Infectious Diseases

FOCUS

LESSON OBJECTIVE

After studying this lesson, students should be able to

- describe the cause, means of transmission, symptoms, and treatment for common infectious diseases.

MOTIVATOR

Write the following on the chalkboard for students to work on while attendance is being taken: *Make a list of three infectious diseases that you are aware of and identify how each is spread.*

INTRODUCING THE LESSON

Refer to the Motivator. Ask volunteers to share their responses. Most students will come up with diseases that affect the respiratory system, since they are most common, or childhood diseases like measles. STDs may also be mentioned. Tell students that this lesson will discuss common infectious diseases. Explain that STDs will be discussed in Chapters 29 and 30.

INTRODUCING HEALTH TERMS

- Copy each vocabulary term and its definition on separate 3" x 5" index cards. Place the cards facedown on a table. Have pairs of students take turns flipping over two index cards at a time, trying to match each term with its definition.
- Ask students to complete Vocabulary Activity 28 and Chapter Study Guide 28 in the *Student Workbook*.

Invite interested students to explore the subject of viruses by doing additional research. Encourage the students to share their findings in an oral report that addresses, among other topics, the mechanism by which viruses cause infection and why they are so difficult to combat.

TEACH

L1 Community Involvement

Ask students to survey friends, neighbors, and family members about how they think one can get a cold (e.g., getting chilled, not getting enough sleep, etc.). Have them compile their answers in a list. Discuss the validity of each cause listed. Point out that, while the ultimate cause of a cold is a virus, many other factors can play a contributing role by weakening the body's ability to fight off infection.

L1 Community Involvement

Have students gather information about clinics and other public sites where free or low-cost flu vaccinations are offered. If appropriate, have a group of volunteers prepare and distribute flyers with up-to-date information on the dates, times, and locations for these vaccination opportunities.

"**I**'ve got the flu" is a commonly heard complaint, especially during the winter. Links at **health.glencoe.com** provide detailed influenza information, including symptoms and treatments. Identify the three types of influenza viruses.

hotlink

antibiotic For more information on the antibiotic medicines and their uses, see Chapter 23, page 513.

▶ *Infections caused by bacteria can be treated with antibiotic medications.*
ACTIVITY *Name as many diseases as you can that are commonly treated with antibiotics.*

Most colds clear up within a week or so. There is no cure. The best treatment for a cold is rest, maintaining proper nutrition, and drinking plenty of fluids.

Influenza

Influenza is a viral infection of the respiratory tract. Symptoms of the flu include chills, fever, headache, muscle ache, and weakness. Like the common cold, flu is spread by virus-infected droplets coughed or sneezed into the air by an infected person. Major outbreaks of the flu tend to occur every few years, usually in the winter. Treatment for the flu is the same as for the common cold—rest, proper nutrition, and drinking plenty of fluids. Secondary bacterial infection may accompany the flu, particularly in the elderly and people with lung or heart problems. Flu may then develop into **pneumonia** (noo-MOHN-yuh), *a serious inflammation of the lungs.* Many people die each year from pneumonia. Secondary infections need **antibiotic** treatment.

Tuberculosis

Tuberculosis (TB) is *a highly contagious bacterial infection that most often affects the lungs.* TB is spread by airborne droplets produced by coughing or sneezing. The bacteria breathed into the lungs then multiply. In the majority of cases, the body's immune system stops the infection and healing takes place. When this does not happen, the infection spreads through the lymphatic system to the lymph nodes. Bacteria may then enter the bloodstream and spread to other parts of the body. In some people, the bacteria become inactive and may stay that way for years. When they are reactivated, damage may occur.

Because TB usually affects the lungs, the main symptoms include coughing (sometimes bringing up blood), chest pain, shortness of breath, fever, sweating, poor appetite, and weight loss. Before the development of antibiotics, TB was a major cause of death in the United States. Modern medicines have proved highly effective in treating the disease. During the 1980s, however, antibiotic-resistant strains of the bacterium that causes TB appeared. This made the standard treatment ineffective, and the incidence of TB began to rise.

Strep Throat

Strep throat is *a bacterial infection of the throat.* It is spread by droplets coughed

COOPERATIVE LEARNING

DIAGNOSIS OF INFECTIOUS DISEASES. Divide students into groups of four. Tell each group member to write, on separate cards, symptoms for two specific diseases described in the textbook, one set of symptoms for each disease. Allow students to use the textbook for reference. Tell them to mix up the cards and place them facedown. Have one member of each group draw a card and examine the symptoms. Next, the student is to identify a disease that fits the symptoms, the type of pathogen that causes it, and the appropriate treatment. Other students will discuss the response and agree, disagree, or suggest modifications. Students may refer to the textbook as necessary. All group members must agree on the diagnosis and treatment before another group member draws a card.

or breathed into the air. Symptoms may include a sore throat, fever, a general feeling of illness, and enlarged lymph nodes in the neck. An untreated strep throat infection may lead to serious complications, such as inflammation of the kidneys or rheumatic fever, which can cause permanent heart damage. Strep throat can be cured with antibiotics.

Infectious Diseases of the Nervous System

The nervous system is subject to a variety of infectious diseases. Some of these can have serious consequences if not caught and treated at an early stage.

Encephalitis

Encephalitis is an inflammation of the brain, usually caused by a virus carried by mosquitoes. Encephalitis often starts with a headache and fever. Untreated, it can progress to hallucinations, confusion, paralysis, and disturbances of speech, memory, behavior, and eye movement. There is a gradual loss of consciousness and sometimes coma. If encephalitis is caused by the herpes simplex virus, the antiviral medicine acyclovir may be effective. When the disease is caused by other viral infections, there is no known treatment.

Meningitis

Meningitis is an inflammation of the meninges, the membranes that cover the brain and spinal cord. Viral meningitis is relatively mild, but meningitis caused by bacterial infection is life-threatening. The organisms that cause meningitis usually reach the meninges through the bloodstream from an infection elsewhere in the body. The main symptoms are fever, severe headache, nausea and vomiting, sensitivity to light, and a stiff neck. In viral meningitis, the symptoms may resemble those of the flu. Viral meningitis requires no treatment. Bacterial meningitis is treated with antibiotics.

Poliomyelitis

Poliomyelitis (POHL-ee-oh-my-uh-LY-tuhs), more commonly known as *polio,* is an infectious disease of the central nervous system caused by a virus. In serious cases, the disease may lead to extensive paralysis, including paralysis of the muscles used in breathing, and death. During the mid-1950s, medical researchers Jonas Salk and Albert Sabin, working independently, each developed a polio **vaccine**—*a preparation based on a weakened or dead pathogen that provides immunity by causing the body to produce antibodies to the pathogen.* These new wonder medicines all but eliminated the disease from the United States and Europe. However, the disease has begun to reemerge among people who have not been vaccinated against it.

▲ *Certain diseases can be spread through the bite of insects such as a mosquito.*
ACTIVITY *Tell why the protective barrier of your skin is not effective against diseases carried by mosquitos.*

L2 Researching

Let interested students research and report on the sanatoriums that were once used as treatment centers for TB.

L3 Community Involvement

Select students to investigate the type of mosquito control, if any, used by the local or state health agency.

L1 Researching

Have a volunteer research the relationship between strep throat and scarlet fever (or scarlatina). Ask this volunteer to share his or her findings with the rest of the class.

L1 Community Involvement

Ask students to interview family members, friends, or neighbors who are old enough to remember the threat posed by polio before the polio vaccine became available. Have them find out what attitudes these people remember toward the possibilities of contracting polio. Have students ask the following questions in their interviews: What special precautions were taken? With what results? Did the people interviewed know, or know of, any individuals who did contract polio? If so, how were they affected by the disease? Let students share their interview findings in discussion groups.

L1 Researching

Have students research post-polio syndrome. Who suffers from it? What are the symptoms? What treatments are available? Ask students to write summaries of their findings.

CURRICULUM CONNECTIONS

FAMILY AND CONSUMER SCIENCES. Choose students to survey local pharmacies to investigate types of available medical home-testing kits. Ask students to suggest advantages and disadvantages of using these kits.

SCIENCE. Select students to present reports on diphtheria and tetanus. Ask them to explain the two diseases, their symptoms, methods of treatment, and any long-term effects. Have students conclude by discussing vaccines that are available to protect against these diseases.

L1 Explaining

Help students understand that mononucleosis is spread by means other than kissing. Explain that indirect contact with an infected person (e.g., drinking from the same glass, coughing, or sneezing) can also result in infection.

L1 Discussing

Tell students that one of the symptoms of mononucleosis is malaise. Ask: What is malaise? Why do you think it is difficult to look for this kind of symptom in diagnosing an illness?

L1 Analyzing

Ask students to identify similarities between hepatitis B and the HIV virus.

L1 Personal Involvement

Suggest that students respond to these questions in their private Health Journals: Have you been vaccinated against hepatitis B? Do you think you should be vaccinated? Why or why not?

L3 Community Involvement

Ask volunteers to visit the local blood donor center. Have them request information about current efforts taken to prevent the transmission of serum hepatitis by means of blood transfusions.

Measles

Measles is a highly contagious viral disease characterized by fever and a rash that covers the entire body. Measles mainly affects children but can occur at any age. The illness starts with a fever, runny nose, sore eyes, and cough. After three to four days, a red rash appears. The most common complications of measles are ear and chest infections. Prevention of the disease is important, because measles can have rare but serious complications. One of these is encephalitis, which was discussed earlier in this lesson.

Measles was largely eliminated through widespread **immunization**, *a program whereby communities or other large populations are systematically made immune to a disease.* During the 1990s, however, there was a brief rise in incidence of the disease because of a drop in Federal funding for immunization programs.

A viral disease with similar symptoms, **rubella**, or *German measles*, causes only a minor infection in children. However, the disease has serious consequences when it affects a woman in the early months of pregnancy. The virus may infect the fetus and cause a range of severe birth defects.

Mononucleosis

Mononucleosis (mon-oh-noo-klee-OH-sis)—or *mono*—is a viral infection common among young people in their teens. Its symptoms include chills, fever, sore throat, fatigue, and swollen lymph nodes. Mononucleosis spreads primarily through direct contact, which has given it its popular name, "the kissing disease." Once in the body, the virus multiplies in the lymphocytes. When infected with the virus, the lymphocytes change in appearance. Complete bed rest is needed in the care of mono. Treatment and recovery can take three to six weeks.

Hepatitis

Hepatitis is an inflammation of the liver. Toxic hepatitis may be caused by certain drugs, chemicals, or poisons. The most frequent cause of hepatitis is viral infection. The most obvious symptom is jaundice—yellowing of the skin and the whites of the eyes. Other symptoms include fever, nausea, loss of appetite, pain in the abdomen, aching muscles, and sometimes joint pain. In severe cases, hepatitis can result in permanent liver damage. Symptoms usually appear three to four weeks after exposure to the virus and last from two to six weeks. There are three main types of viral hepatitis.

- **Hepatitis A.** Hepatitis A results from eating food or drinking water that has been contaminated with the virus from an infected person's feces. Many cases occur among people who have traveled to areas where standards of hygiene are low.

MEETING STUDENT DIVERSITY

PROJECT: Have students create "State of Health" addresses to enhance public awareness of the status of infectious diseases.

LANGUAGE DIVERSITY. Students with language diversity might contact organizations such as the Centers for Disease Control and Prevention and the U.S. Department of Health and Human Services for various language versions of publications they produce in the area of communicable-disease control. Such students might work with English-proficient students to develop program notes in alternative languages.

LEARNING STYLES. Students in need of sheltering might benefit by a brief orientation in which the goals and expectations of the activity are discussed.

- **Hepatitis B.** Hepatitis B is found in all body fluids of an infected person, especially blood. Hepatitis B used to be spread mainly by contaminated blood transfusions and blood products. However, tests that detect the virus in the blood have helped eliminate transfusion as a means of transmission. Contaminated medical instruments, sexual contact with an infected person, and hypodermic needles shared by infected drug users are the main ways hepatitis B is spread. Hepatitis B is more serious than hepatitis A. In some cases, the virus may lead to a chronic infection and eventually to liver damage.

- **Hepatitis C.** Like hepatitis B, hepatitis C is spread through infected blood. Discovered in 1989, hepatitis C can cause liver cancer. The virus can be detected in the blood, and blood is now screened before transfusion.

As with most other viral infections, there is no cure for hepatitis, although a vaccine for hepatitis B is now available. The treatment for hepatitis is rest, proper nutrition, and ingesting plenty of fluids.

Did You Know?
> Reye's syndrome is a rare but sometimes fatal illness that occurs in children after certain viral infections such as flu. Although its exact cause is unknown, there seems to be a tie-in with taking aspirin. Therefore, it is recommended that children and teens under 18 avoid aspirin.

The best way to treat a cold is also the best way to prevent it—rest, good nutrition, and drinking lots of fluids.
ACTIVITY *Explain why drinking fluids is important when you have a cold or other infectious disease.*

LESSON 2 Review

Reviewing Facts and Vocabulary

1. Name four common infectious diseases and the type of pathogen that causes each.
2. In what ways might a person contract viral hepatitis?

Thinking Critically

3. **Analyzing.** How do you think bacteria become resistant to antibiotics?

Applying Health Skills

4. **In Your Home and School.** Take a survey of family members and classmates to determine favorite ways of treating a cold. Use the results to create a bar graph to share at home and in school. What treatments are the most popular? Why?

LESSON 2 COMMON INFECTIOUS DISEASES **631**

CHAPTER 28 • LESSON 2

ASSESS

EVALUATING THE LESSON

Assign and discuss the Lesson 2 Review; then administer, grade, and discuss the *Lesson 84 Quiz* in the TCR.

RETEACHING

- Assign students to make a chart identifying the cause, means of transmission, symptoms, and treatment for the infectious diseases presented in the lesson.
- Have students make sets of flash cards to review the diseases and the pathogens that cause them.
- Ask students to complete *Reteaching Activity 84* in the TCR.

ENRICHMENT

Have students research and report on the types of diseases caused by bacteria and on the treatments for these diseases.

CLOSE

Tell students that in this lesson they studied many of the common diseases that can be transmitted by pathogens. Explain that the next lesson will focus on how to prevent the spread of infectious diseases.

Lesson 2 Review

Answers to Reviewing Facts and Vocabulary

1. Answers will vary. Possible answers: common cold, virus; influenza, virus; tuberculosis, bacteria; strep throat, bacteria.
2. Eating food or drinking water contaminated with the virus; contaminated blood transfusions and blood products; contaminated medical instruments; sexual contact with an infected person; hypodermic needles shared by infected drug users.

Answer to Thinking Critically

3. Answers will vary.

LESSON 3

Preventing Infectious Diseases

FOCUS

LESSON OBJECTIVES

After studying this lesson, students should be able to

- differentiate between active and passive immunity.
- describe three major types of vaccines.
- cite specific ways to avoid contracting or spreading pathogens.

MOTIVATOR

Write the following on the chalkboard for students to work on while attendance is being taken: *Try to remember all the immunizations you have received, and list them on a sheet of paper.*

INTRODUCING THE LESSON

Check with a school nurse regarding immunizations required for school attendance. Refer to the Motivator by asking students what immunizations or booster shots they can remember having before they could enter school. As each immunization for a disease is mentioned, ask what some of the basic symptoms of the disease are. (It may become necessary for you to add information.) Lead into a discussion of the material in this lesson by differentiating between active and passive immunities.

INTRODUCING HEALTH TERMS

- Have students differentiate the terms *active immunity* and *passive immunity* by creating concept maps for each term.
- Ask students to complete Vocabulary Activity 28 and Chapter Study Guide 28 in the *Student Workbook.* ☞

632 Chapter 28

Preventing Infectious Diseases

Between the years 1347 and 1351, bubonic plague raged through western Europe, killing nearly half the population. In 1918, an outbreak of influenza affected 2 billion people worldwide and killed more than 22 million of them! Medical science has come a long way toward preventing such disasters.

HEALTH TERMS

active immunity
passive immunity

HEALTH CONCEPTS

- Science has developed strategies to help combat infectious diseases.
- Some common sense measures can be used to help prevent the spread of infectious diseases.

Immunity

As noted in Lesson 2, your body creates lines of defenses against disease. Immunity is the body's natural resistance to many pathogens. Certain pathogens cannot live in the body, whereas others are quickly destroyed when they enter the body.

Active Immunity

One important feature of the body's immune system is that it remembers the pathogens it meets. This gives the body long-term protection—immunity—against many infectious diseases. For example, if you had chicken pox, your immune system remembers the chicken pox virus. If the virus enters your system again, cells designed specifically to combat the chicken pox virus will attack it

Lesson 3 Resources

TEACHER'S CLASSROOM RESOURCES

☞ **Concept Map** Activity 85
☞ **Decision-Making** Activity 28
☞ **Health Lab** 28
☞ **Lesson 85 Quiz**
☞ **Lesson Plan** 85
☞ **Reteaching** Activity 85

STUDENT WORKBOOK

☞ **Applying Health Skills** 85
☞ **Chapter Study Guide** 28
☞ **Vocabulary** Activity 28

immediately. In most cases, the virus does not get a chance to make you sick again.

This *immunity your body develops to protect you from disease* is called **active immunity.** Some types of immunity last a lifetime. Others last only a short period of time. A single virus causes chicken pox, so once a person has had the disease, the body is usually protected against chicken pox for life. Many different kinds of virus cause the common cold. Because the body is continually exposed to different pathogens, immunity to colds is limited.

Passive Immunity

At birth, babies carry in their blood small amounts of the antibodies that protected their mothers. Babies are thus protected from the same diseases as their mothers. This immunity lasts for a few months after birth until the baby can produce antibodies of its own. *The temporary immunity that an infant acquires from its mother* is called **passive immunity.**

Immunization

Sometimes the body needs help to establish immunity against specific pathogens. This help can come in the form of immunization to give the body the ability to fight off the disease. There are two main types of immunization: passive and active.

Passive Immunization

Passive immunization provides immediate, short-lived protection against specific disease-causing pathogens. Blood is taken from a person (or sometimes an animal) that has been exposed to a specific microorganism. The blood contains antibodies that work against that organism. An extract of the blood is then injected into the person to be protected. If the pathogen is present in the person's blood or enters it within a few days, the antibodies help destroy it.

Active Immunization

Also known as *vaccination,* active immunization involves the introduction into the body of a vaccine. Vaccines provide immunity by causing the body to produce antibodies against the pathogen. Each vaccine contains substances that are strong enough to cause the production of the desired antibodies but not strong enough to cause the disease.

Researchers are constantly at work to find ways to fight infectious disease. You can also play a role in this.
ACTIVITY *How can healthy habits and physical activity help you to win the race against the spread of infectious diseases?*

LESSON 3 PREVENTING INFECTIOUS DISEASES **633**

TEACH

L1 Discussing
Ask students what types of immunity last a lifetime. What is the difference between active immunity and passive immunity?

L1 Guest Speaker
Invite a representative from the state health department and/or a travel agent who specializes in foreign travel to speak with the class. Ask him or her to discuss special health precautions that are necessary to travel to various parts of the world. Have the speaker list immunizations or vaccines that are needed and why.

L1 Discussing
Have students explain vaccines and how they cause the body to develop immunity against a disease.

L3 Class Activity
Select students to read and report on the annual development of vaccines to protect against various strains of influenza.

L1 Demonstrating
Invite the school nurse to demonstrate the difference between a conventional needle and an injection gun used in giving group vaccinations.

L1 Parental Involvement
If possible, have students review their immunization records. Discuss the importance of keeping them up to date. Stress that as students get older, keeping medical records becomes their responsibility.

Myths & Realities

MYTH. All children in the United States receive vaccinations for most childhood diseases.

FACT. The successful use of vaccines for many childhood diseases has caused a complacency about getting regular immunizations. Some parents even withhold immunizations, thinking the risks associated with them are greater than those of getting the disease. This can prove dangerous. Some immunizations, such as those for measles and mumps, require only one inoculation for lifelong immunity. Others require boosters. For example, tetanus boosters are required every ten years throughout life. A smallpox vaccination is no longer required in the United States because the disease has been eliminated in this country.

L1 Discussing

Ask students in what ways live-virus vaccines, killed-virus vaccines, and toxoids are different.

L2 Health Lab

Distribute *Health Lab 28* and have students investigate the best way to wash their hands. ☞

Making Responsible Decisions

1. Enrique has the initial symptoms of a bad cold, but he wants to go to school so he can compete in an important wrestling meet.
2. Enrique could (a) go to school and compete in the meet in spite of his cold; (b) stay home from school and get the rest his body needs.
3. Enrique would probably (a) not feel well all day, infect others at school—including his wrestling teammates—and be unable to wrestle as well as he could if he were healthy; (b) be unable to compete in the wrestling meet, but get the rest he needs to treat his cold.
4. Enrique values his own good health; he also values his ability to make an important contribution to the wrestling team.
5. Responses will vary.
6. Encourage students to discuss both the short- and long-term consequences of their decisions.

L2 Decision Making

For further study on making responsible decisions, assign *Decision-Making Activity 28* in the TCR. ☞

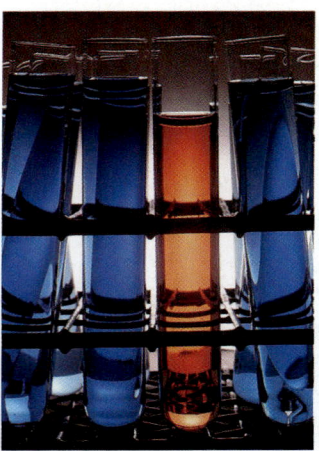

▲ *Although vaccination may cause reactions ranging from a mild fever or rash to more serious responses, the risks from vaccines are far less than the risks from the diseases themselves.*

ACTIVITY *Name as many diseases as you can that children are commonly vaccinated against.*

There are three major types of vaccines:

- **Live-virus vaccines.** These are made from weakened viruses. Scientists develop live-virus vaccines by artificially altering the genetic material of the virus or by infecting laboratory animals over and over until the organisms can no longer cause the disease but can still stimulate the production of antibodies. Measles, rubella, and oral polio vaccines all contain live viruses.
- **Killed-virus vaccines.** These contain viruses that have been killed. The killed-virus vaccine causes the body to produce antibodies, but it is not as powerful as a live-virus vaccine. Because the vaccine is less powerful, people need booster shots from time to time. Booster shots are follow-up injections given to reinforce the effect of the first injection. Cholera, typhoid fever, rabies, and Salk injected polio vaccines contain killed viruses.
- **Toxoids.** Some diseases are caused by bacteria that release a toxin. Scientists have discovered that by chemically treating bacteria toxins, they can make very effective vaccines. The treated toxins, called toxoids, stimulate the production of antibodies and establish active immunity against these diseases.

Immunization for All

Immunization is more than just a good idea—the law often requires it. Each state has its own laws governing immunizations and school attendance. In most states, students cannot enter kindergarten without up-to-date immunizations. Several states now enforce laws that prevent teenagers from attending school without complete

Making Responsible Decisions

Letting the Team Down

Enrique woke up this morning with a bad cold. He is heavily congested, has a runny nose, and keeps coughing. He knows he should stay home and rest, both for his own sake and to avoid infecting other students.

However, Enrique is a key member of the school's wrestling team. There is an important meet this afternoon with one of their toughest opponents. If Enrique does not compete, his team will lose by default in his weight class. Enrique does not want to let the team down. What should he do?

What Would You Do?

Apply the six steps of the decision-making process to Enrique's problem.

1. **State the situation.**
2. **List the options.**
3. **Weigh the possible outcomes.**
4. **Consider your values.**
5. **Make a decision and act.**
6. **Evaluate the decision.**

634 CHAPTER 28 INFECTIOUS DISEASES

HEALTH LITERACY

SELF-DIRECTED LEARNER. Have students conduct research about nutrients and other nonmedical substances that have been shown to correlate with improved immune function and/or faster recovery from illnesses such as colds. In some cases they may wish to include nutrients for which the need is greatly increased during illness or stress. They might use the *Reader's Guide* or online sources. They may wish to examine articles written by doctors about the role of nutrients or herbs in disease prevention. Suggest that they find out how the cited studies were funded. Drug studies are usually funded by drug companies, for example, and some herbs or nutrients are studied in hope of using them in drugs. Suggest that students construct a chart listing the substances they investigated and summarizing their findings about each.

immunization. Why do you think immunizations are important in the school setting?

Some infectious diseases are more common than others. Diseases that once were dreaded can now be controlled through immunization, and some have been totally eradicated. However, because some diseases are no longer the threat they used to be, people have become lax in obtaining immunization. Isolated cases of some diseases, such as polio, are being reported. An immunization program is essential to prevent the kinds of plagues and pestilences that wiped out entire populations in the past.

Common Sense Measures

What can you do to protect yourself from being infected by disease? You have several choices. You can avoid contact with pathogens and you can avoid spreading pathogens to others. Follow these common sense guidelines to reduce the spread of infection.

- Keep your body healthy so that it can better resist infection. Good nutrition, regular exercise, adequate sleep, and good health care all contribute to prevention.
- Bathe or shower every day to keep your skin, hair, and nails clean.
- Avoid sharing eating or drinking utensils.
- Store and prepare food in a safe way to prevent food poisoning.
- Wash your hands after using the bathroom, after changing diapers, and before preparing, serving, or eating food.
- If you know you are sick, avoid giving your illness to someone else. Get medical treatment for your illness. Cover your mouth when you cough or sneeze to prevent spreading the pathogens. Use tissues only once and dispose of them in a waste container.
- If you are well, avoid contact with people who are sick.

▲ *Pathogens are expelled into the air when a person coughs or sneezes.*

ACTIVITY *Tell what this person should do to prevent the spread of pathogens.*

EVALUATING THE LESSON

Assign and discuss the Lesson 3 Review; then administer, grade, and discuss the *Lesson 85 Quiz* in the TCR. ✍

RETEACHING

- Suggest that students design a comic book for grade-school students featuring ways to prevent infectious diseases. When completed, display and discuss some of the comic books. Then ask volunteers to take the comics home, share them with their younger siblings, and report their siblings' reactions to the class.
- Ask students to complete *Reteaching Activity 85* in the TCR. ✍

ENRICHMENT

Ask volunteers to locate, design, or adapt a computer program for keeping personal medical records and dates of immunizations. Have them show their results to the class.

CLOSE

Divide the class into small groups. Assign each group part of this lesson to rewrite in their own words, using their own case studies or examples. Afterward, duplicate each group's work, and distribute it to the class. Close by having one person from each group summarize the major ideas within its part of the lesson.

LESSON 3 *Review*

Reviewing Facts and Vocabulary

1. Define *active immunity* and *passive immunity.*
2. Name three major types of vaccines.
3. What is the difference between active immunization and passive immunization?

Thinking Critically

4. **Analyzing.** Each year, as flu season approaches, a flu vaccine is made available. Elderly people and people with weakened immune systems are advised to receive this vaccine. Why do you suppose this is recommended?

Applying Health Skills

5. **In Your Home and School.** Make an informational poster listing ways to protect yourself from infectious disease. Post copies of the poster in your home and school.

LESSON 3   PREVENTING INFECTIOUS DISEASES   **635**

Lesson 3 Review

Answers to Reviewing Facts and Vocabulary

1. See the Glossary for definitions.
2. Live-virus vaccines, killed-virus vaccines, and toxoids.
3. Active immunization—the introduction of a vaccine into the body. Passive immunization—the introduction of antibodies into the body; it provides immediate, short-lived protection.

Answer to Thinking Critically

4. Answers should reflect an awareness that the flu can be especially dangerous for individuals with weakened immune systems, including elderly people.

Health Skills Activities

ACTIVITY 1
HEALTH SKILLS

Comprehending Health Concepts, Self Management

➤ **National Standards**
This activity meets these National Health Standards: 1.3; 3.2; 3.4.

Teach

- From the list on the chalkboard, have each group choose one disease to research, For the broadest possible coverage, strike through the name of each disease selected so that each group researches a different disease.
- Have the class as a whole brainstorm locations for completed posters. Possibilities might include the cafeteria (including the kitchen), restrooms, locker rooms, and the gym.

ACTIVITY 2
HEALTH SKILLS

Accessing Health Information

➤ **National Standards**
This activity meets this National Health Standard: 2.2.

Teach

- Have groups choose a different form of representation, with one group researching literary mentions, another music, and so on. Possibilities to which you might direct students are English novelist Daniel Defoe's *Journal of the Plague Years.*
- If time permits, allow students to present their findings in an "art share" that features readings, songs, and an art gallery. Invite other classes to attend.

Health Skills Activities

Activity 1 — Infectious Disease Handbook

Despite progress in the war on infectious diseases, millions of people become ill every year. Building knowledge about the causes, modes of transmission, and prevention of these diseases is the key to an all-out victory.

Directions

1. In groups, gather information on one of the infectious diseases discussed in this chapter.
2. Do research to identify the following: pathogen, means of transmission, symptoms, and treatment. Record your findings.
3. Using either markers or computer design software, develop a poster identifying ways to prevent contracting this disease as well as steps to take in the event of symptoms.
4. Brainstorm places in the school where your posters might be displayed.

Time
40 minutes
Materials
paper, pen or pencil, markers, poster board, computer (optional)

Self-Assessment

✓ Described routes of transmission, signs, and symptoms of the infectious disease selected.
✓ Identified prevention strategies and treatments for the disease.

Activity 2 — Art and Diseases Through the Ages

Quilts for remembering people who have died of AIDS are considered an art form that reflects the problems of a society. What art forms could best convey a message about other infectious diseases?

Directions

1. In small groups, investigate infectious diseases of the past, such as bubonic plague. Learn about the causes as well as early myths and superstitions about the disease.
2. Locate and obtain a depiction of this disease in the visual arts, music, or literature. The bubonic plague, for example, was described in medieval songs, artwork, and poems. You might contact a local archive or museum or download a sound or image file from a Web site.
3. Share the artwork in a class discussion of diseases then and now.

Time
50 minutes plus outside research
Materials
library, or Internet health resources, poster board

Self-Assessment

✓ Highlighted a disease of the past and explained beliefs and superstitions.
✓ Identified art forms that depicted the illness.
✓ Showed advances in diagnosis and treatment of disease.

ASSESSMENT SCORING

Using a four-level rubric, the student has achieved a 4 if:

ACTIVITY 1

✔ Student described routes of transmission, signs, and symptoms of the infectious disease.
✔ Student identified prevention strategies and treatments.
✔ Student was active in group discussion and preparation.
✔ Student helped produce a poster that was informative and creative in its design.

ACTIVITY 2

✔ Student highlighted a disease of the past and explained beliefs and superstitions.
✔ Student identified an art form that depicted a disease.
✔ Student located and displayed an art form related to a past disease.
✔ Student showed advances in diagnosis and treatment of the disease in question.

CNN HEALTH NEWS VIDEO

Disease Detectives

Every person has unique fingerprints. Detectives use these fingerprints to solve mysteries. A new tool called PFGE helps scientists use a bacteria's "fingerprints" to solve medical mysteries.

PFGE can analyze the genetic pattern of a bacteria. Every strain of bacteria has its own unique genetic "fingerprint."

Public health officials read these fingerprints to track infectious disease. In Atlanta, Georgia, a toxic strain of the E. coli bacteria infected 26 young people. PFGE showed that all of them carried exactly the same E. coli strain. These results helped pinpoint the site of this epidemic: a popular local water park.

Play the Video

CNN. All Rights Reserved.

Think About It

- What are the steps in the PFGE process?
- Why can't genetic fingerprinting identify the first source of an outbreak? Could this limitation restrict the value of PFGE?
- How will Pulse Net, the electronic database of genetic fingerprints, help public health officials track diseases?

CNN HEALTH NEWS **637**

Disease Detectives
Video Segment 18 (Time – 3:05)

Objectives. After viewing the video, students should be able to explain the use of technology as a tool to identify and control outbreaks of specific strains of infectious disease.

Motivator. Display a mug or glass. Ask five or six students to pass it from the front to the back of the classroom. Then take the glass and ask: How could detectives discover which students held this glass? Students should suggest that they might use fingerprints to track the path of the glass. Then show Video Segment 18, "Disease Detectives," which reports on how scientists use genetic "fingerprinting" to track the spread of an infectious disease.

Teach

- Have students compare conventional fingerprinting used by detectives with genetic fingerprinting used to track disease. Point out that every person has a unique set of fingerprints. Every strain of a disease has a unique genetic pattern, which can be thought of as a genetic fingerprint.

- Ask students to create a flowchart that illustrates the steps in the PFGE process. After reviewing each of the major steps, ask students to summarize how this technology can help researchers track and control the spread of infectious diseases.

Group Activity. Ask a team of students to work together to create a series of diagrams or a comic book that explains how the PFGE process can help public health officials learn more about the spread of illness. Students can use their flowcharts to help plan their work. Each team member should choose a specific job, such as artist, writer, editor, or layout designer.

Close. Ask students to describe how technology has improved the accuracy of tracking the spread of diseases. Then have them describe the types of diseases that are traceable using the PFGE technology.

MORE ABOUT . . . . .

E. COLI. A common bacteria, E. coli is normally found in the intestinal tracts of healthy humans and animals. It has many beneficial functions, including protecting the digestive system from infection and producing small amounts of vitamins B_{12} and K.

While most E. coli bacteria are beneficial, some are dangerous. Toxic strains of E. coli damage cells in the lining of the intestine. Symptoms of E. coli poisoning include diarrhea, abdominal pain, vomiting, and fever. In extreme cases, the infection can lead to kidney failure and death, especially in children. Prevention strategies include cooking meat thoroughly and observing careful hygiene near infected individuals.

CHAPTER 28 Review

CHECKING COMPREHENSION

- Assign and discuss the chapter review.
- Use the MindJogger Videoquiz to review the chapter.

CHAPTER 28 REVIEW ANSWERS

Using Health Terms

1. immunity
2. transmission
3. infectious disease
4. virus
5. parasites
6. phagocytosis
7. mucous membranes
8. neutrophil
9. antibodies
10. tuberculosis
11. strep throat
12. pneumonia
13. rubella
14. immunization
15. vaccine
16. passive immunity
17. active immunity

Recalling the Facts

1. The body's immune system destroys the invading bacteria.
2. It attaches itself to a host cell and injects its genetic material into that cell. Then the virus uses materials within the host cell to make copies of itself.
3. It involves general defenses against infection; these defenses respond the same way each time the body is invaded by a foreign substance.
4. It is the immune system's specific attack against a particular type of pathogen; it involves lymphocytes, a type of white blood cell.
5. Antibodies are made when B cells (one main type of lymphocyte) turn into plasma cells, which produce antibodies. Antibodies remain in the blood to fight off any future attacks by a specific pathogen.

Using Health Terms

On a separate sheet of paper, write the term that best matches each definition below.

LESSON 1

1. The body's natural defenses against infection.
2. Spread.
3. A disease caused by organisms that enter and multiply within the human body.
4. The smallest known type of infectious agent.
5. Organisms that live in or on another organism and derive nourishment from it.
6. The process by which phagocytes engulf and destroy pathogens.
7. The soft, skinlike lining of many parts of the body.
8. The chief type of phagocyte involved in the process of phagocytosis.
9. Proteins that destroy or neutralize invading pathogens.

LESSON 2

10. A highly contagious bacterial infection that most often affects the lungs.
11. A bacterial infection of the throat.
12. A serious inflammation of the lungs.
13. German measles.
14. A program whereby communities or other large populations are systematically made immune to a disease.
15. A preparation based on a weakened or dead pathogen that provides immunity by causing the body to produce antibodies to the pathogen.

LESSON 3

16. The temporary immunity that an infant acquires from its mother.
17. Immunity your body develops to protect you from disease.

Recalling the Facts

Using complete sentences, answer the following questions.

LESSON 1

1. Bacteria can multiply rapidly enough to take over one's body in a short time. What usually prevents this from happening?
2. How does a virus work?
3. Explain nonspecific resistance.
4. Explain specific resistance.
5. Describe how antibodies are made and their role in the blood.

LESSON 2

6. Name four diseases caused by viruses and two diseases caused by bacteria.
7. What disease is a possible complication of measles, and what part of the body does it affect?

8. Name two possible complications of an untreated strep throat.

LESSON 3

9. What are some behaviors that will help a person avoid infectious diseases?
10. In what two ways can a person become immune to an infectious disease?
11. Name and briefly describe the three types of vaccines.

6. Viruses cause (any four) common cold, influenza, encephalitis, viral meningitis, poliomyelitis, measles, rubella, mononucleosis, hepatitis. Bacteria cause (any two) tuberculosis, strep throat, bacterial meningitis.
7. Encephalitis, which affects the brain.
8. Inflammation of the kidneys and rheumatic fever, which can cause permanent heart damage.

9. See the list on page 635.
10. Natural immunity, either active or passive, and immunization.
11. Live-virus vaccines are made from weakened viruses. Killed-virus vaccines contain viruses that have been killed. Toxoids contain chemically treated bacteria toxins.

Thinking Critically

LESSON 1

1. ***Comparing and Contrasting.*** Make a chart that reflects similarities and differences among the five types of pathogens discussed in this lesson.

2. ***Comparing and Contrasting.*** Compare and contrast the function of phagocytes during nonspecific resistance and lymphocytes during specific resistance.

LESSON 2

3. ***Analyzing.*** Many people think they can catch a cold by becoming chilled, getting caught in the rain, or not dressing warmly enough in cold weather. Why might people think this way?

LESSON 3

4. ***Synthesizing.*** Why is it important to have a child immunized?

5. ***Synthesizing.*** What are some of the major reasons that there is now more of a focus on wellness?

Making the Connection

1. ***Social Studies.*** Write a one-page report about a protozoan-caused infectious disease, such as malaria or dysentery. How did the disease affect people in the past? What measures were taken to prevent or control it? Is it still affecting people today? What conditions contribute to the disease's decreased or increased incidence?

2. ***Science.*** The chapter mentioned several notable "microbe hunters," people whose pioneering work has combated the spread of infectious disease. Learn about another, Louis Pasteur, founder of the science of microbiology. Learn about Pasteur's specific contributions to this field, and report your findings.

BEYOND THE CLASSROOM

PARENTAL INVOLVEMENT Ask your parents to share with you the immunization records for yourself, other family members, and any family pets. Determine whether these are complete and up to date. Share any suggestions you may have about improving your family's disease-prevention efforts.

COMMUNITY INVOLVEMENT Tuberculosis is a disease that is on the rise again in the United States. Groups with the highest incidence of TB include the homeless, people who are in prison, and people infected with HIV. Interview a local public health official about cases of TB in your community. Find out about testing and treatment programs for persons who are most at risk. If there are homeless shelters in your community, ask how TB is tracked among the transient population.

SCHOOL-TO-CAREER
Interpersonal. Invite someone in or knowledgeable about the field of epidemiology—the branch of medical science that deals with the incidence, distribution, and control of disease in a population—to speak with the class about career possibilities and requirements, such as educational background and skills required.

CHAPTER 28 REVIEW **639**

Thinking Critically

1. Charts should reflect information presented about bacteria, viruses, rickettsias, protozoans, and fungi on pages 620–622.
2. Both destroy pathogens. Lymphocytes produce specific antibodies that remain in the blood.
3. Answers will vary.
4. Answers should reflect an understanding of the fact that immunization is often legally required and that immunization can prevent a child from contracting or spreading dangerous diseases.
5. Answers will vary.

Making the Connection

1.–2. Answers will vary.

Evaluate

- Use the reproducible *Chapter 28 Test* in the TCR, or construct your own using the Testmaker software. 📁 💾
- Use *Performance Assessment Activity 28* in the TCR. 📁

Enrichment

Ask students to complete *Cross-Curriculum Activity 28* in the TCR. 📁

Beyond the Classroom

Keep students involved in the community, and encourage parent participation by assigning the activities on this page for students to work on outside of class.

Sexually Transmitted Diseases

	FEATURES	**CLASSROOM RESOURCES**

ACTIVITIES

- ☛ Cross-Curriculum Activity 29
- ☛ Health Lab 29
- ☛ Health Skills Activities 29
- ☛ Parent Letter and Activities 29

ASSESSMENT

- ☛ Chapter 29 Test
- ☛ Performance Assessment Activity 29
- 💾 Testmaker Software

STUDENT ACTIVITIES WORKBOOK

- ☛ Applying Health Skills 86, 87
- ☛ Study Guide 29
- ☛ Vocabulary Activity 29

STUDENT DIVERSITY STRATEGIES

- 🎧 Audiocassette Program (English)
- 🎧 Audiocassette Program (Spanish)
- ☛ Spanish Parent Letters and Activities
- ☛ Spanish Summaries, Quizzes, and Activities

MULTIMEDIA COMPONENTS

- 🎧 English Audiocassette Program
- 🎧 Spanish Audiocassette Program
- 💿 MindJogger Videodisc and VHS program
- 💿 ABCNews InterActive™ VHS/Videodisc Series

MODULES

- • *Education in Sexuality,* Student Edition
- • *Education in Sexuality,* Teacher's Annotated Edition

National Health Education Standards

One of the main goals of the National Health Education Standards is to move students toward "health literacy." Health literacy is the capacity of individuals to obtain, interpret, and understand basic health information and services and the competence to use such information and services in ways which promote health. The health standards were developed by applying the characteristics of a well-educated, literate person within the context of health. The health literate person is:

- • a critical thinker and problem solver
- • a self-directed learner
- • a responsible, productive citizen
- • an effective communicator

Listed below are the Health Education Standards Performance Indicators addressed in each lesson of this chapter.

Lesson	Health Standards Performance Indicators
1	3.1, 3.4, 5.6, 6.2
2	1.3, 2.6, 3.3, 6.1

ONLINE RESOURCES

For a fresh approach to health topics and an in-depth look at health issues, use these online resources found under Teacher Resources at **health.glencoe.com**.

- **BLOCK SCHEDULE LESSON PLANS** Reinforce health concepts with outside readings selected especially for students. Each reading is accompanied by a lesson plan and activities to enhance
  - • Reading Skills
  - • Cross Curriculum
  - • Media Literacy

- **TECHNOLOGY PROJECTS** Instructions and suggestions on how to use computer, Internet, and software with health lessons.

- **HEALTH UPDATES** Timely topics in health news, including late-breaking medical advances and updates on teen risk behaviors.

Out of Time?

If time does not permit teaching this chapter, you may use these features: Building Health Skills on page 644 and Making Responsible Decisions on page 648.

BLOCK SCHEDULING

Block scheduling provides extended time for hands-on projects and activities. Use the following activity to engage students, provide further depth, and vary your instructional techniques:

- • Health Skills Activity (60–90 minutes) **pg. 652**

Sexually Transmitted Diseases

CHAPTER OVERVIEW

Chapter 29 presents the incidence of STDs in the United States and how adolescents and young adults are the population most at risk. Abstinence from sexual activity is introduced as the best means of preventing infection. The symptoms, diagnoses, and treatments for common sexually transmitted diseases are also explored.

The CDC has begun to use the term "Sexually Transmitted Infection" in place of Sexually Transmitted Disease. This is because a person can have an infection, and be infectious, without necessarily having the actual diease, a phenomenon seen with HIV/AIDS distinctions. Some prevention experts also feel that people are more likely to consider themselves susceptible to an "infection" versus a "disease," hence they believe the word change might lead to more persons seeking testing and treatment.

LESSON 1 The incidence of STDs has reached epidemic proportions in the United States, with two-thirds of all cases occurring in adolescents and young adults. The sexual behavior of some teens puts them at particular risk of infection and consequences that could affect their future. More and more teens are practicing abstinence, resulting in the decline of some STDs.

LESSON 2 The symptoms, diagnoses, and treatments for common sexually transmitted diseases are presented in this lesson. Learning the symptoms of STDs can help infected individuals seek appropriate treatment and enable them to notify past partners.

Sexually Transmitted Diseases

HEALTH Online

ADVOCACY
Create a teen 'zine with information from this chapter to raise awareness of the dangers of STDs. Learn more about how to use the functions of Word Processing software in Technology Projects at health.glencoe.com.

Hands-On Health

TEACHING STRATEGY

Risks of Sexual Activity Let students see how failing to practice abstinence is actually like "rolling the dice," taking the chance of contracting an STD or beginning a pregnancy. See Activity 36, "The Dice Game," in the *Hands-On Health: Creative Teaching Strategies* booklet.

Time Needed
30 minutes

Supplies
- 1 die for each student
- small plastic or paper cups

> **Only one in five teens recognizes that a person puts him or herself at risk for STD infection with just one sexual encounter.**

—Sexually Transmitted Disease Information Center
Centers for Disease Control and Prevention

Personal Health Inventory

Self-Inventory Write the numbers 1–10 on a sheet of paper. Read each statement below and respond by writing *yes*, *no*, or *sometimes* for each item. Write a *yes* only for items that you practice regularly. Save your responses.

1	I know the facts about sexually transmitted diseases.
2	I can recognize the symptoms of a sexually transmitted disease.
3	I practice abstinence from sexual activity to reduce my risk of contracting an STD.
4	I am able to use assertive refusal to say no to sex.
5	I know and use alternatives to sexual intimacy in relationships.
6	I know the medical names for sexually transmitted diseases.
7	I know the medical symptoms of sexually transmitted diseases.
8	I know how to avoid getting a sexually transmitted disease.
9	I know how to advise someone infected with a sexually transmitted disease on where and how to seek medical help immediately.
10	I am aware of the responsibilities a person infected with a sexually transmitted disease has to his or her partner.

Follow-up After completing the chapter, retake this self-inventory. Pick two items that you need to work on and set a goal to improve your health behaviors.

Quick Write List five ways you can remind yourself, your friends, and other teens that taking risks even once during your teen years can have lifelong negative consequences.

INTRODUCING THE CHAPTER

Personal Health Inventory

Have students read the Self-Inventory statements, and ask: Why is knowledge about sexually transmitted diseases so important? Then let students use their private Health Journals to record their responses to the inventory statements on a page labeled "My Knowledge of STDs." Remind students that they will return to this inventory later, after they have studied the lessons in this chapter.

- Introduce this chapter by contrasting people's reactions to various infectious diseases. For example, if an individual were diagnosed as having chicken pox, he or she would be comfortable telling family, friends, and acquaintances. However, if the same individual were diagnosed as having an STD, he or she would probably be hesitant to tell others. Because of the social stigma attached to STDs, many people ignore their illness and hope that the STD will just go away. In this chapter, students will learn how dangerous this approach is. They will also gain specific, helpful information about STDs.

- Let students read and discuss the quotation on this page. Ask: What decisions do you face every day that could affect your entire future? How can knowledge and decision-making skills help you when you are faced with a critical choice regarding risky behaviors?

- Distribute Parent Letter 29 from the *Parent Letters and Activities* booklet in the TCR. ✒

Preventing STDs

LESSON OBJECTIVES

After studying this lesson, students should be able to

- define the term *sexually transmitted disease.*
- identify reasons why teens as a group are at particularly high risk for infection of STDs.
- describe how contracting an STD can change the course of one's life.
- identify abstinence as the 100 percent effective way to avoid contracting an STD.

MOTIVATOR

Write the following on the chalkboard for students to work on while attendance is being taken: *List three problems that can result from sexual contact.*

INTRODUCING THE LESSON

Have volunteers share their responses to the Motivator. Students should understand that unplanned pregnancies, lowered self-esteem, feelings of guilt, and sexually transmitted diseases can be prevented by avoiding sexual contact.

INTRODUCING HEALTH TERMS

- Have students write a paragraph explaining how the spread of STDs has become epidemic in the United States.
- Ask students to complete Vocabulary Activity 29 and Chapter Study Guide 29 in the *Student Workbook.* 👉

Preventing STDs

Some infectious diseases such as the flu or a virus can be transmitted through actions as simple as sharing a fork. Other infectious diseases, however, are not so easily spread. Sexually transmitted diseases, or STDs, are 100 percent avoidable. **Sexually transmitted diseases** are *infectious diseases spread from person to person through sexual contact.*

HEALTH TERMS

sexually transmitted diseases (STDs)
epidemic

HEALTH CONCEPTS

- Sexually transmitted diseases (STDs) are spread from person to person, primarily by means of sexual contact.
- Although the rate of transmission of STDs has been steadily declining, the problem remains an epidemic in this country.
- The only sure way to avoid contracting or spreading an STD is by abstaining from sexual activity and other high-risk behaviors.

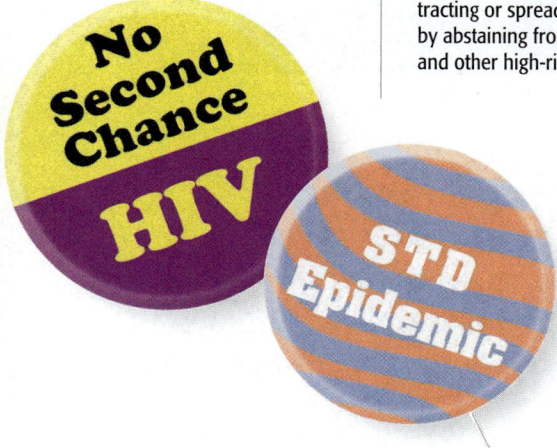

STDs: The Silent Epidemic

At the turn of the twentieth century, this country was faced with an epidemic of typhoid fever, an infectious disease caused by bacteria acquired through infected water. An **epidemic** is *an outbreak of an infectious disease that affects a large population.* With intervention on the part of health officials at the state and county level, the typhoid epidemic was wiped out.

Today our country faces another epidemic. This one is an epidemic of STDs. About 13 million new cases of STDs are reported each year in the United States. What is perhaps even more alarming is that numerous other cases go unreported. This is because STDs carry a social stigma, or mark of shame. Many people are embarrassed to talk about them, especially those who become infected. For

---

Lesson 1 Resources

TEACHER'S CLASSROOM RESOURCES

- 👉 **Concept Map** Activity 86
- 👉 **Enrichment** Activity 29
- 👉 **Health Lab** 29
- 👉 **Lesson 86 Quiz**
- 👉 **Lesson Plan** 86
- 👉 **Parent Letter and Activities** 29
- 👉 **Reteaching** Activity 86

STUDENT WORKBOOK

- 👉 **Applying Health Skills** 86
- 👉 **Chapter Study Guide** 29
- 👉 **Vocabulary** Activity 29

MULTIMEDIA

- 💿 **ABCNews InterActive™ VHS/Videodisc,** *Teenage Sexuality* this reason, STDs are often referred to as the "silent" epidemic. Partly because of this silence, a number of myths and misconceptions have arisen around STDs and how they are spread.

STDs and Adolescents

One common myth surrounding STDs is that they are not a problem among teenagers, when in reality two-thirds of all STD cases occur in adolescents and young adults. The Centers for Disease Control and Prevention has noted that one in four sexually active teens will contract an STD before graduating from high school.

Why are teens as a group at particularly high risk for infection from STDs? One reason is that teens who are sexually active are likely to exhibit one or more of the following behaviors:

- Having more than one sexual partner rather than committing to a single, long-term relationship.
- Engaging in unprotected sex.
- Selecting partners at higher risk, such as those with a history of multiple sex partners or intravenous drug use. An additional risk for teen females is that they lack an **immunity** to some of the pathogens that cause STDs.

These risk factors are magnified by the fact that when teens do contract an STD, they are less likely than adults to seek medical attention. Some teens are simply unaware of what action to take, though in many cases the reluctance to seek help stems from a fear of disapproval by parents or other adults at home. Other teens refuse to believe that they could have an STD. Through denial and rationalization, they ignore the signs and symptoms of infection.

Partly because of this silence, a number of myths and misconceptions have arisen around STDs and how they are spread.

hotlink

immunity For more information on immunity and how it protects the body from pathogens, see Chapter 28, page 631.

MORE MYTHS ABOUT STDs

MYTH You can get STDs only if you have lots of sexual partners.
FACT You can get an STD from your first sexual experience.

MYTH STDs can easily be cleared up with antibiotics.
FACT Some types of STDs are incurable and last a lifetime.

MYTH If you have an STD, you would have symptoms of the disease.
FACT In some cases, especially early in the disease, no symptoms are present.

MYTH Once the symptoms of an STD go away, the disease is cured.
FACT You can still have an STD, even if the symptoms go away.

MYTH You can have only one type of STD at a time.
FACT It is possible to have more than one kind of STD infection.

MYTH Once infected with an STD, you cannot get it again.
FACT No one can become immune to STDs. Anyone can be reinfected.

MYTH A vaccine can prevent the spread of STDs.
FACT No vaccine exists for STDs, except for hepatitis B.

MYTH Having a Pap test is one way a female can find out if she has an STD.
FACT A Pap test detects cancer cells, not the presence of an STD.

SCHOOL-TO-CAREER

PHLEBOTOMIST. Testing for sexually transmitted diseases is sometimes accomplished by blood tests. The blood may be drawn by a doctor or nurse, but sometimes it is drawn by a specialist called a phlebotomist. A phlebotomist needs training from a doctor, university, or trade school. Many phlebotomists are already lab technicians or nurses. However, some training programs are available without a college degree. Encourage interested students to call doctors, teaching hospitals, and medical trade schools in the area to find out what qualifications are needed to be accepted for training. Employers vary in their requirements, so they should call hospitals, doctors, and laboratories in the area to find out what they require of phlebotomists they employ.

TEACH

L1 Discussing

Guide a class discussion of how STDs are spread from one person to another through sexual contact. Then discuss how to prevent the spread of these diseases.

L1 Discussing

Explain that since the development of the birth control pill, cases of STDs have increased in number. Discuss how this development has affected public health.

L1 Discussing

Ask students to form groups and discuss the following: If you were a parent, would you expect your teenager to tell you that he or she has contracted an STD? Why? Why not? How would you feel about your teenager receiving treatment without your permission? Encourage groups to share their responses with the rest of the class.

L2 Researching

Guide students in researching the response of federal, state, and local health departments in the early decades of the 1900s to the epidemic of what was then called *venereal disease*. How did it differ from today's response to this public health problem? In what ways was it similar?

L1 Community Involvement

Suggest that students send for materials from the local health department and area health clinics to prepare posters and a bulletin board on STDs.

Building Health Skills

Setting Limits for Expressing Physical Attraction
Skill: Communication

After students have read the feature "Setting Limits for Expressing Physical Attraction," ask: Why do you think it is important to have clear limits for the expression of physical attraction? How and when can you set those limits? Then have students meet in groups to read and discuss the feature and the four steps in the suggested plan of action. Finally, ask students to write entries in their private Health Journals, explaining their own limits for expressing physical attraction and discussing how they intend to enforce those personal limits.

L2 Health Lab

Distribute *Health Lab 29* and have students investigate the transmission of STDs. ⬛

TEENAGE SEXUALITY (Side 2)

Chapter 10: Deciding Not to Have Sex

Frames 19097-20260

Chapter 11: Saying No

Frames 20262-22477

Chapter 15: Fears, Risks and Consequences

Frames 28337-30076

---

hot link

sterility For more information on sterility and other conditions that can cause it, see Chapter 19, page 440.

hot link

AIDS For more information on AIDS and the virus that causes it, see Chapter 30, page 656.

STDs and Your Future

Contracting an STD can dramatically change the course of your life. Consider:

- Some STDs can cause **sterility**, the inability to reproduce.
- Infants born to mothers with STDs can be infected at birth and suffer consequences such as blindness and deformities.
- Some STDs are incurable, meaning that the individual must live with the reoccurrence of painful genital sores for the rest of his or her life.
- Individuals with STDs are at a greater risk for cancer, and some STDs such as **AIDS** are fatal.

Being informed with facts about STDs can help you avoid behaviors that lead to infection. In the pages that follow, you will learn critical facts about STDs. For now, it is enough to be aware of the most important fact: *The primary means of transmission of STDs is sexual contact.* A person who practices abstinence from sexual activity reduces his or her risk of contracting an STD.

Building Health Skills

Communication Skills: Setting Limits for Expressing Physical Attraction

THERE ARE MANY WAYS of expressing positive feelings for another person. When affection turns physical, however, there is a danger of acting impulsively—or "on the spur of the moment." Casual kissing and hugging may intensify sexual feelings when dating couples express physical affection.

How can you set limits on mutual displays of affection with someone you are dating? Here is a plan of action:

1. **Recognize that there are degrees of "liking."** Wanting to be liked is one of life's basic needs. One form liking can take is affection; another is respect. When a date respects you, he or she will act in your best interests. This includes *never* asking you to do something you are not ready to do.

2. **Discuss your limits.** Let your partner know in advance that sexual intimacy is not in your plans. Back up your words with your actions.

3. **Keep your brain in charge of your actions.** Express your affection in ways that will allow you to remain in control of your actions and your decisions.

4. **Avoid alcohol and other drugs.** Insist that your date do the same. The last thing either of you needs when emotions are running high is a substance that can cloud your judgment.

644   CHAPTER 29   SEXUALLY TRANSMITTED DISEASES

HOME AND COMMUNITY
CONNECTION

EDUCATING DROPOUTS. Have students chart the STDs covered in this chapter, the symptoms, and the dangers if untreated. Suggest that they end with a paragraph about the importance of contacting all present and former sexual partners. Have them compile the information into a pamphlet. The pamphlet should also include a directory of addresses and telephone numbers for government agencies and free or low-cost clinics that offer confidential treatment for STDs. Encourage them to distribute pamphlets, with permission, where they might be read by teens who have dropped out of high school and missed health education. Such locations might include trade schools, job training programs, movie theaters, fast-food restaurants, and other places frequented by students.

Practicing Abstinence

You have probably learned about cause-and-effect relationships. Touching a hot iron, for example, can be a *cause* of sustaining a burn, which is the *effect*.

A clear cause-and-effect relationship exists between sexual intercourse and sexually transmitted diseases. If you have sexual contact with an infected person, you will be at high risk of contracting an STD. Sexual activity is the cause; an STD is the effect.

Having sexual relations during the teen years can lead to other unwanted consequences as well, including an unplanned or unintentional pregnancy and the responsibility of becoming a parent. Having sexual contact can complicate relationships with family members and friends. Remaining abstinent will allow teenagers to focus more clearly on their goals for the future.

Fortunately, more and more teens are learning about the realities of STDs and practicing **abstinence**. Their actions have resulted in a decrease in the rates of STD infection over the past several years. The recent decline in the most prevalent STD of them all, chlamydia, is one example of this positive trend.

hotlink

abstinence For more information on abstinence from sexual activity before marriage and other high-risk behaviors, see Chapter 21, page 484.

LESSON 1 *Review*

Reviewing Facts and Vocabulary

1. What is an epidemic?
2. How do STDs differ from the infectious diseases discussed in Chapter 28?
3. What high-risk behaviors can lead teens to become infected with an STD?
4. What is the best way to avoid getting an STD?

Thinking Critically

5. *Analyzing.* Determine whether the following statements are myths or facts. Rewrite any myths to make them factual statements: (a) The body builds immunities to certain STDs. (b) A person could have an STD and not know it. (c) Having a Pap test is one way a female can find out if she has an STD. (d) Once the symptoms of an STD go away, the disease is cured.
6. *Synthesizing.* Explain what steps public health agencies can take to prevent the further spread of STDs in the United States.
7. *Evaluating.* Some say that those who are sexually active before marriage have poor self-esteem. Is this a fair statement? Explain your answer.

Applying Health Skills

8. *In Your Home.* Share what you are learning about sexually transmitted diseases with your parents. You might want to show them what you are reading and tell them how you feel about learning the facts about sexually transmitted diseases. Ask them to share any additional information they know about STDs.

ASSESS

EVALUATING THE LESSON

Assign and discuss the Lesson 1 Review; then administer, grade, and discuss the *Lesson 86 Quiz* in the TCR. ☞

RETEACHING

- Have students outline the lesson, detailing important facts.
- Tell students to list reasons why practicing abstinence is the only reliable means of avoiding becoming infected with an STD.
- Ask students to complete *Reteaching Activity 86* in the TCR. ☞

ENRICHMENT

Point out influences that have shaped and reshaped society's standards of intimate behavior and the resulting changes in health and social structure by having students complete *Enrichment Activity 29*, "The Sexual Revolution and Its Consequences," in the TCR. ☞

CLOSE

Ask students to summarize the most important concepts in this lesson.

Lesson 1 Review

Answers to Reviewing Facts and Vocabulary

1. An outbreak of an infectious disease that affects a large population.
2. STDs are spread through sexual contact.
3. Having more than one sexual partner, engaging in unprotected sex, and selecting partners at higher risk.
4. Practicing abstinence from sexual activity.

Answers to Thinking Critically

5. (a) Myth. No one can become immune to any STD. (b) Fact. (c) Myth. A Pap test does not detect the presence of an STD. (d) Myth. You could still have an STD.
6. Answers should reflect an awareness of the importance of practicing abstinence and of knowledge of the facts about STDs.
7. Answers will vary.

Common STDs and Their Treatments

FOCUS

LESSON OBJECTIVES

After studying this lesson, students should be able to

- identify the symptoms and treatments for some of the common STDs.
- discuss the importance of seeking medical attention for any sign of an STD and notifying any past sexual partners.

MOTIVATOR

Write the following on the chalkboard for students to work on while attendance is being taken: *Imagine that you have just received a letter from a friend saying that he or she may have a sexually transmitted disease. Write a brief response to the letter.*

INTRODUCING THE LESSON

Refer to the Motivator. Ask volunteers to share their responses. Explain that all sexually transmitted diseases have the potential to be very dangerous and that anyone at risk of having one should know to seek treatment and prevent further spread of the disease. Tell students that they will learn about the symptoms and treatment of STDs in this lesson.

INTRODUCING HEALTH TERMS

- Have each student use the vocabulary terms and their definitions to create a crossword puzzle.
- Ask students to complete Vocabulary Activity 29 and Chapter Study Guide 29 in the *Student Workbook.* ☞

Common STDs and Their Treatments

You have probably heard the saying, "An ounce of prevention is worth a pound of cure." This saying certainly holds true when it comes to sexually transmitted diseases. This lesson will provide the facts about common STDs, including their symptoms and treatment. Chapter 30 will contain information on the most deadly STD of them all, AIDS.

HEALTH TERMS

chlamydia

nongonococcal urethritis

gonorrhea

trichomoniasis

vaginitis

genital warts

genital herpes

syphilis

HEALTH CONCEPTS

- Knowing the risk and symptoms of common STDs is an important first step toward prevention for sexually active people.

- Learning to identify the symptoms of STDs can help infected individuals seek appropriate treatment.

- People who discover that they have been infected with an STD have a responsibility to seek treatment and to inform any and all past sexual partners.

- Common sense, positive values, and good decision-making skills all contribute to the prevention of STDs.

Chlamydia

Chlamydia (kluh-MID-ee-uh) is *an infection caused by a bacterium that affects the vagina in females and the urethra in males.* The U.S. Centers for Disease Control and Prevention estimates that more than 4 million new cases of chlamydia infection occur each year. Chlamydia is a common cause of sterility and, if untreated, can lead to **nongonococcal urethritis** (non-gon-uh-KOK-uhl yur-ih-THRYT-uhs). Also known as *NGU,* this is *an infection caused by several different kinds of bacteria-like organisms that infect the urethra in males and the cervix in females.*

In males, the symptoms of chlamydia include pain and burning during urination and an unusual discharge from the penis. In

---

Lesson 2 Resources

TEACHER'S CLASSROOM RESOURCES
- ☞ **Concept Map** Activity 87
- ☞ **Cooperative Learning** Activity 29
- ☞ **Decision-Making** Activity 29
- ☞ **Lesson 87 Quiz**
- ☞ **Lesson Plan 87**
- ☞ **Reteaching** Activity 87

STUDENT WORKBOOK
- ☞ **Applying Health Skills 87**
- ☞ **Chapter Study Guide 29**
- ☞ **Vocabulary** Activity 29

MULTIMEDIA
- 🔴 **ABCNews InterActive™ VHS/Videodisc,** *Teenage Sexuality*

females, the symptoms are not always obvious. If symptoms do occur, they may include an unusual discharge from the vagina, pain in the pelvic region, and painful urination. Untreated chlamydia in females can cause **pelvic inflammatory disease** (PID), a painful infection of the ovaries, fallopian tubes, and/or uterus. A pregnant female who has chlamydia can transmit it to her baby during delivery. In infants, the disease can cause eye infection, blindness, and sometimes even pneumonia.

Chlamydia is diagnosed through a laboratory test. Certain antibiotics can cure chlamydia. However, if scar tissue has already formed, treatment cannot undo that damage. Chances of sterility in the male and the female will remain.

Gonorrhea

Gonorrhea (gon-uh-REE-uh) is *an STD caused by bacteria that affect the genital mucous membrane, primarily in the lining of the urethra of the male and in the cervix and vagina of the female.* The bacteria are transmitted during sexual contact. A person cannot pick up the pathogens from towels or toilet seats because the bacteria cannot live outside the body. A pregnant female can, however, transmit the infection to her unborn child.

Symptoms of gonorrhea are not always obvious, especially in females. In the female, symptoms may include a slight discharge from the vagina, a burning sensation during urination, abnormal menstruation, and abdominal pain or tenderness. In the male, symptoms may include a whitish discharge from the penis and a burning sensation during urination. The lymph nodes in the groin may also become enlarged and tender. These symptoms usually appear between three days and three weeks after sexual contact with an infected person. These symptoms may go away on their own, but the disease is still present in the body.

Gonorrhea can be confirmed only by a medical diagnosis. In a male, gonorrhea is diagnosed by examining discharge from the penis under a microscope. In a female, a culture test of the vagina is done to make the diagnosis. This involves taking a sample of cells from the vagina and examining them under a microscope. Gonorrhea can be treated with antibiotics.

hotlink

pelvic inflammatory disease For more information on pelvic inflammatory disease, see Chapter 19, page 447.

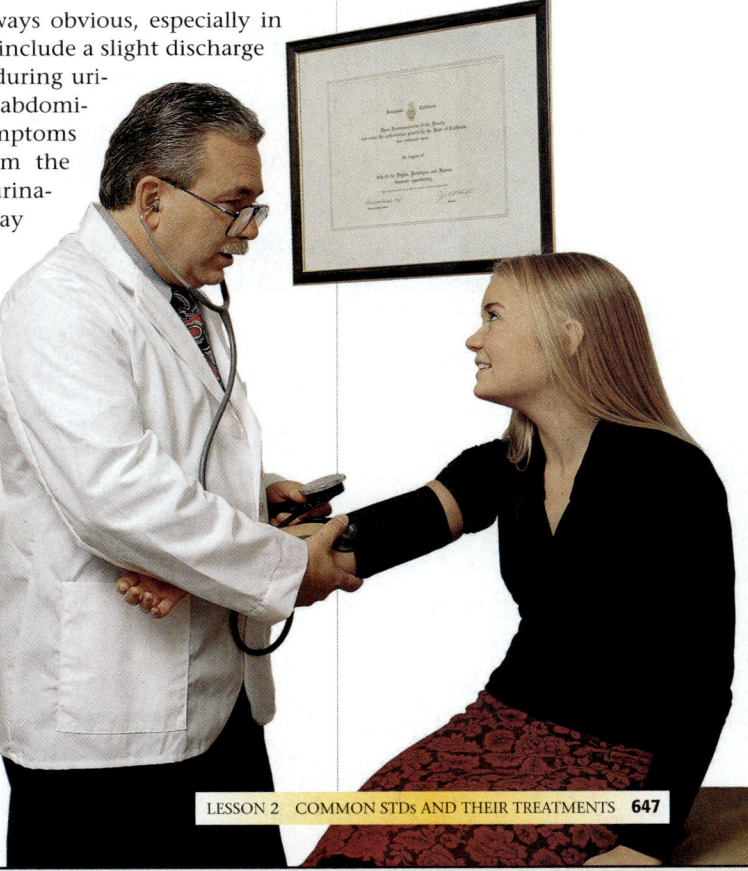

▼ *Your family physician, school nurse, your parents, and other health-care professionals can give you accurate health information.*

LESSON 2   COMMON STDs AND THEIR TREATMENTS   **647**

MORE ABOUT . . . . .

PID. Pelvic inflammatory disease is caused by untreated chlamydia or gonorrhea in females. This disease can lead to reproductive damage by causing obstruction and scarring of the fallopian tubes, resulting in involuntary infertility. Thousands of females are affected each year by PID. In addition, females who have had PID are more likely to experience ectopic pregnancies. An ectopic pregnancy occurs when the fallopian tubes are partially blocked and a fertilized egg becomes implanted in one of the tubes rather than in the uterus. As the cells multiply, there is danger of rupturing the fallopian tube, causing a serious health risk to the female.

TEACH

L1 Demonstrating

Borrow slides from the science department showing the different organisms that cause STDs. Share them with the class.

L1 Class Activity

Compare and contrast the symptoms of chlamydia in males and in females. Ask students to list reasons a female with chlamydia is less likely than a male to exhibit signs of the disease until it is in the advanced stage.

L2 Class Activity

Ask students to form debate groups. Help them prepare to debate whether tests for STDs should be required during all physical examinations conducted by a doctor.

L1 Explaining

Point out to the class that there is no blood test for gonorrhea. Usually a male knows that he has the disease because of obvious symptoms. Because the female is asymptomatic, a simple test similar to a Pap smear is done in the doctor's office to detect the bacterium gonococcus.

TEENAGE SEXUALITY (Side 1)
Chapter 9:   What Is Sexuality?

Frames 17909-20348

Chapter 10: Evolution of American Attitudes

Frames 20363-23965

L1 **Discussing**

L1 **Discussing**

Discuss with students why medical professionals have recently decided not to distinguish between herpes 1 and 2.

Making Responsible Decisions

1. Angel has learned that a friend, who formerly dated a boy Angel has known since middle school, has genital herpes.
2. Angel could (a) do nothing; (b) urge her friend to tell the boy she dated (if they had sexual contact); (c) tell the boy about her friend's genital herpes; (d) talk over the situation with a school health professional or another trusted adult.
3. Angel might (a) avoid making anyone uncomfortable, but worry about the health of both of her friends; (b) risk making her friend angry, but perhaps help the friend overcome her reluctance; (c) risk making both her friend and the boy angry, but perhaps help protect the boy's health; (d) risk making her friend angry, but get assistance in helping both her friend and the boy.
4. Angel values the health of the people she knows. She also values getting along well with them.
5. Responses will vary.
6. Students should consider both the short- and long-term consequences of their decisions.

L2 **Decision Making**

For further study on making responsible decisions, assign *Decision-Making Activity 29* in the TCR. ☞

L1 **Discussing**

Ask students why the rate of genital herpes is increasing, even with widespread education about STDs.

Trichomoniasis

Trichomoniasis (trik-uh-muhn-EYE-uh-suhs) is *a vaginal infection that can lead to urethra and bladder infections.* Males are rarely infected with trichomoniasis, but they can be carriers. Like chlamydia, this STD can lead to nongonococcal urethritis. In females, symptoms of trichomoniasis include burning and itching in the vagina, a yellowish-green discharge, and pain upon urination. In males, symptoms include itching of the penis, a clear discharge, and pain upon urination. Trichomoniasis can be cured with a medicine that can be prescribed only by a physician.

Trichomoniasis can also cause vaginitis, another secondary infection, in females. **Vaginitis** is *a common inflammation of the female genitals* that can be carried by males. Vaginitis is rare in young women who are not yet sexually active. In more than 90 percent of all cases, vaginitis is caused by a bacterium, protozoan, or virus transmitted through semen and certain other body secretions. Medication is now available that can be taken in a single dose and that cures vaginitis within 24 hours.

Genital Warts

Genital warts are *pink or reddish warts with cauliflowerlike tops that appear on the genitals.* Genital warts are caused by a virus called the human papilloma virus (HPV). Once infected, a person has the virus for the rest of her or his life. The warts appear on the genitals one to three months after infection. A physician can remove the warts, but they may reappear. Medical treatment may also include

Making Responsible Decisions

Getting Treatment for an STD

One of Angel's friends has just confided in Angel that she has herpes. She was dating a boy that Angel has known for several years, but Angel heard that they have recently stopped seeing each other. The friend told Angel that she is embarrassed and does not want her reputation to suffer by having people find out that she has a sexually transmitted disease. She is also afraid to discuss it with her old boyfriend. What should Angel do?

What Would You Do?

Apply the six steps of the decision-making process to Angel's problem.

1. **State the situation.**
2. **List the options.**
3. **Weigh the possible outcomes.**
4. **Consider your values.**
5. **Make a decision and act.**
6. **Evaluate the decision.**

PROMOTING COMPREHENSIVE SCHOOL HEALTH

COMMUNITY SUPPORT. Tapping into local resources is a key to effectively working a comprehensive school health plan. It is important to involve local health agencies, parents, churches, youth groups, and other organizations. By enlisting local groups and individuals, the committee establishes grassroots support. Community involvement provides the resources and support needed to reduce fragmentation of efforts or duplication of programs. Ongoing collaboration and cooperation between the team and other community members prevent unwarranted controversy. For information about community support, consult *Promoting a Comprehensive School Health Program* in the TCR.

application of a prescription skin medication. This STD is known to be one of the causes of cervical cancer in women.

Genital Herpes

Genital herpes appears as *blisterlike sores in the genital area* that are caused by the herpes simplex type 2 virus. Like genital warts, genital herpes cannot be cured. The virus remains in the body for a lifetime. The sores usually appear two to twenty days after contact with an infected person and may last as long as three weeks. Other symptoms include fever and a burning sensation during urination. With the help of moisture and friction, the virus can spread to other areas of the body. This is why a person with herpes is told not to rub the skin and to keep the skin dry. The blisters can break out at any time and often occur during periods of stress.

Herpes is diagnosed by a medical examination of genital sores and verified by lab tests. Medications are used to treat the symptoms. To avoid spreading genital herpes, an infected person should avoid having sexual contact when blisters are present and right after they disappear.

Syphilis

Syphilis (SIH-fuh-luhs) is *an STD that attacks many parts of the body and is caused by a small bacterium called a spirochete.* When left untreated, it can damage vital organs, such as the heart, the liver, the kidneys, and the central nervous system, including the brain. It can cause heart disease, blindness, paralysis, and insanity.

Syphilis is different from other STDs in that it develops in stages. Symptoms appear and then go away on their own. However, if treated in the early stages, the disease can be cured.

- **Primary Stage.** The first sign of syphilis is a *chancre* (SHAN-kuhr), a painless, reddish sore at the place where the pathogen enters the body, usually the genitals. It appears within 10 to 90 days after contact with an infected person. The chancre lasts one to five weeks and will then go away, even if untreated. However, the disease remains in the body.

- **Secondary Stage.** If not treated, the pathogen will be circulated in the blood. Within one to six months after contact, the highly contagious second stage of syphilis appears. This stage is commonly characterized by a non-itching rash on the chest, backs of the arms, and legs. In females, the rash is most often found on the outer edges of the vagina. Sores may develop from the rash. These sores will likely give off a clear liquid filled with infectious spirochetes. Swelling may occur in the lymph nodes under the arms and around the groin. Fever, sore throat, and a general sick feeling are common symptoms. Without treatment, these symptoms will disappear, but the disease continues to develop.

genital wart

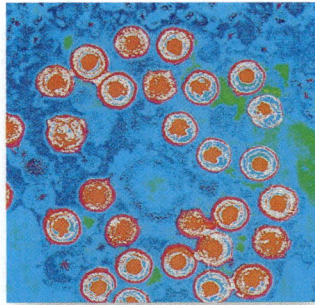
herpes blister

▲ *Genital warts (top) and genital herpes (bottom) are caused by virus.*

ACTIVITY *Tell how genital warts are different from genital herpes.*

L1 **Discussing**

Explain why people can't tell for sure when herpes 2 is in its contagious state.

L1 **Discussing**

Ask what syphilis is. Why is it considered one of the most dangerous of all the sexually transmitted diseases?

L2 **Researching**

Have students research how requiring a test for syphilis when applying for a marriage license and during pregnancy has affected the spread of syphilis in the United States. Ask: What are the advantages and disadvantages of STD testing?

L1 **Discussing**

Lead a discussion of when and how syphilis got to the United States.

L3 **Class Activity**

Tell students that, although antibiotics can cure many STDs, some STD pathogens have become resistant to current medications. Have students define *resistant* in this context, and then have them each write a paragraph about the problems this poses to individuals and society.

TEENAGE SEXUALITY (Side 2)

Chapter 10: Deciding Not to Have Sex

Frames 19097-20260

Chapter 11: Saying No

Frames 20262-22477

L1 Discussing

Ask students why it might not be wise to share clothes and towels with others, even brothers and sisters. *(Some STDs, such as pubic lice and scabies, can be transmitted by sharing towels and clothes.)*

L1 Community Involvement

Instruct students to survey your local area for a list of doctors and clinics that have facilities for STD testing.

L1 Activity

Have students imagine that they are an adult giving advice about STDs to a young teenager. Encourage them to list what they think are the most important points to mention.

L3 Researching

Challenge students to learn about other STDs, including the different types of vaginitis, their symptoms, and their treatment.

L2 Researching

Ask students to research the effects of STDs on an unborn child. Contact the March of Dimes for information relating to birth defects and other conditions related to STDs and newborns.

L2 Cooperative Learning

Assign *Cooperative Learning Activity 29* in the TCR for more on STDs. ✎

Hepatitis B

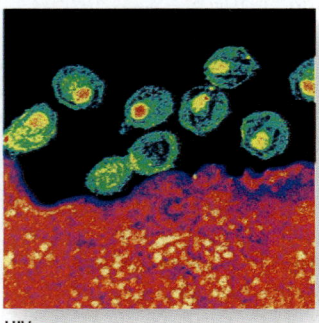
HIV

⚠ *Hepatitis B and HIV are caused by viruses carried in the bloodstream.*

hotlink

hepatitis B For more information on hepatitis B and other forms of this infectious disease, see Chapter 28, page 629.

- **Latent Stage.** The third stage of syphilis usually begins about two or more years after the initial infection. All signs disappear, leading the individual to think that he or she is cured or perhaps never had the disease. However, it is in this stage that syphilis begins to attack the heart and blood vessels and the central nervous system. The damage to these areas is slow and steady. Even though people have reached the latent stage, they can relapse into the second stage, and sores will reappear.

- **Neurosyphilis Stage** (NOOR-uh-SIH-fuh-luhs). If untreated, syphilis moves into the neurosyphilis stage within 10 to 30 years, and the heart, skin, brain, and spinal cord are affected. A person loses the ability to coordinate muscular movements and may experience blindness or insanity. The central nervous system is affected, resulting in a loss of mental abilities. A person in this stage of syphilis may experience paralysis and convulsions. Syphilis in this stage can be treated but not cured.

The medical test for syphilis is a blood test. The presence of the spirochete bacteria in the blood or in sores indicates the presence of the disease. Penicillin is the main drug used in the treatment of syphilis. No matter how effective the treatment is, it cannot undo any harm that has already been done. Early treatment is crucial.

Other STDs

Several other problematic infectious diseases are spread through sexual contact:

- Chancroid (SHAN-kroyd) is a bacterial infection with many similarities to the primary stage of syphilis. Deep sores show up near the genitals. Contact with these sores will spread the disease. Chancroid is treated with antibiotics.

- Candidiasis (kan-duh-DY-uh-suhs) is a yeast infection of the vagina. This condition usually occurs without sexual contact, but is often passed to a partner during sexual contact. Symptoms include a yellowish discharge, strong odor, and itching. It can be cured through medicated creams and tablets sold over the counter.

- Pubic lice are tiny insects that attach themselves to skin and hair in the pubic area. The lice feed on blood and cause intense itching. Treatment consists of using a special medicated shampoo.

- Scabies is an infestation of the skin by mites that cause red, swollen, itchy bumps similar to those found during the primary stage of syphilis. Itching begins four to six weeks after infection. Treatment includes hot baths and medicated creams.

- **Hepatitis B** is caused by a virus that attacks the liver. It also can be spread through contact with infected blood. Symptoms do not show up for six months, during which time a person may not

---

PERSONAL HEALTH

DIALOGUE. Abstinence followed by marriage does not guarantee protection from STDs. A married person is only as safe as the spouse is honest and responsible. The media are filled with stories of people who believed themselves in monogamous marriages yet contracted STDs. Have students write in their private Health Journals a dialogue between themselves and a prospective marriage partner. The dialogue should include questions to ask about sexual history and behavior, whether tests for STDs are advisable, and the need for absolute trust and honesty throughout the relationship. The dialogue should make clear that the partners are trusting each other with their health and their lives, as well as their emotional well-being.

know that he or she is infected. Treatment includes bed rest and a healthy diet. A **vaccine** is available.

- Human immunodeficiency virus (HIV) is the virus that causes AIDS. **HIV** also can be spread through contact with infected blood. Once the virus is contracted, it remains in the body. At this time there is no cure for HIV or AIDS, and the disorder is considered fatal.

Responsibilities of Infected Individuals

Treatment for sexually transmitted diseases is an important personal as well as social responsibility. Having an STD is not like having a cold. It will not simply go away if a person waits long enough. The individual must take action to have the disease treated. Although a person may feel embarrassed about having an STD, he or she should seek treatment from a private doctor or a public health clinic immediately. By law, it is guaranteed that all information will remain confidential.

It is also important for a person infected with an STD to notify all people with whom he or she has had sexual contact. The infected person has a responsibility to educate partners about the symptoms and risks of the STD and encourage them to have a medical checkup. Informing someone else about the possibility of having an STD could save that person's life. A doctor or a public health clinic can help an infected person take these steps.

hotlink

vaccine For more information on vaccines and their role in combating infectious diseases, see Chapter 28, page 632.

HIV For more information on HIV/AIDS, see Chapter 30, page 656.

ASSESS

EVALUATING THE LESSON

Assign and discuss the Lesson 2 Review; then administer, grade, and discuss the *Lesson 87 Quiz* in the TCR. ✏️

RETEACHING

- Have students create a chart that identifies the symptoms and treatment of each STD.
- Ask students to complete *Reteaching Activity 87* in the TCR. ✏️

ENRICHMENT

Have students research the number of reported cases of the STDs presented in this lesson during five-year intervals from 1950 to present. They should present their findings in bar graphs.

CLOSE

Have students explain how taking responsibility for their behavior can prevent the possibility of contracting an STD.

LESSON 2 *Review*

Reviewing Facts and Vocabulary

1. Which STD is characterized by reddish cauliflowerlike warts? Which STD, if left untreated, can affect the brain?
2. Why is it important for someone who suspects he or she is infected with an STD to seek treatment?
3. Identify two responsibilities of an individual who suspects he or she is infected with an STD.

Thinking Critically

4. *Comparing and Contrasting.* Divide the STDs in this lesson into two lists—one for STDs that can be cured if immediate treatment is sought, the other for STDs that cannot be cured. Describe the treatment for each.

5. *Synthesizing.* Tell how you would advise a friend who confides that he or she is experiencing pain during urination and itching in the genital area.

Applying Health Skills

6. *In Your Home and School.* Invite your school nurse or a community health official to speak to your class about STDs in your community. Find out if any of the STDs are more common than others. Ask the speaker to explain what occurs when a teenager comes forward to seek help with a possible STD.

Lesson 2 Review

Answers to Reviewing Facts and Vocabulary

1. Genital warts; syphilis.
2. An STD will not go away, even if symptoms may disappear. Anyone infected with an STD can spread the disease to others through sexual contact.
3. Seek treatment and inform any and all past and present sexual partners.

Answers to Thinking Critically

4. Answers should reflect an awareness that genital warts, genital herpes, and HIV cannot be cured.
5. Answers should reflect an awareness that the friend should seek advice from a health professional.

Health Skills Activities

ACTIVITY 1
HEALTH SKILLS
Accessing Health Information, Health Advocacy

➤ **National Standards**
This activity meets these National Health Standards: 2.4; 7.6.

Teach

- Prior to assigning the activity, contact a local department of health or a federal health agency such as the Centers for Disease Control and Prevention to request brochures on STDs and their prevention.
- Have students compare the language in the pamphlets provided with the language in their health textbooks. Have them note, in particular, the average number of words per sentence, the choice of words, and so on.
- Groups should develop several drafts of their brochure. These should be exchanged with and assessed fairly by other groups.

ACTIVITY 2
HEALTH SKILLS
Communication—Refusal Skills, Health Advocacy

➤ **National Standards**
This activity meets these National Health Standards: 5.6; 7.1.

Teach

- Steer the direction of the first step in the student activity so as not to involve real names of students either within or outside the class.
- Students may have an easier time writing letters if actual scenarios are developed that involved peer pressure. You may want to devote an additional 20 minutes of a class period to having students work in groups to develop such scenarios.

Activity 1 — Evaluating STD Information

Teens who fear they have an STD can benefit from knowing what steps to take. The most effective way to reach an audience is to speak to them in their own language. What would you say to other teens about the dangers of STDs?

Directions

1. In a group, evaluate one of the STD brochures provided by your teacher. Is the approach as effective as it could be? In what ways might the language or other aspects appeal more to teens?
2. Use your ideas to create a more effective, persuasive brochure by hand or on the classroom computer.
3. Exchange a first draft of your brochure with another group. Share and implement useful criticism. Distribute the finalized brochures around the school.

Self-Assessment

✓ Analyzed health information for effective communication and appeal to specific audience.
✓ Included accurate information about the prevention of STDs.

Time
50 minutes
Materials
paper, pen or pencil, pamphlets and brochures about STDs, computer with design software and color printer

---

Activity 2 — Helping a Friend Choose Abstinence

The most effective way to prevent contracting a sexually transmitted disease is to practice abstinence. Fortunately, more and more teens are choosing to abstain from sexual activity before marriage. You can help promote this trend.

Directions

1. Imagine that your best friend, who is usually talkative and lively, has been quiet and withdrawn lately. Since the beginning of the school year your friend has been dating a classmate. When you ask your friend what's wrong, your friend explains that he or she is being pressured to engage in sexual activity.
2. Write a letter to your friend explaining the importance of practicing abstinence. Convince your friend to resist the pressure and make the healthy decision. Point out the risks involved in making the wrong choice, and mention the positive things you want for your friend's future.

Self-Assessment

✓ Explained the benefits of practicing abstinence from sexual activity before marriage.
✓ Identified persuasively the risks involved in engaging in sexual activity before marriage.

Time
30 minutes
Materials
paper, pen or pencil

ASSESSMENT SCORING

Using a four-level rubric, the student has achieved a 4 if:

ACTIVITY 1
✔ Student analyzed health information for effective communication and appeal to specific audience.
✔ Student played a role in developing pamphlet.
✔ Student was open to and gave positive criticism during class discussion.
✔ Student included accurate information about the prevention of STDs.

ACTIVITY 2
✔ Student identified features of persuasion used to appeal through letters.
✔ Student explained the benefits of practicing abstinence.
✔ Student identified persuasively the risks of engaging in sexual activity before marriage.
✔ Student presented arguments in ways that would be likely to appeal to a peer.

Study Rates STDs in U.S.

A new study shows that the United States has an "astronomical number" of new cases of sexually transmitted diseases, or STDs, per year.

Experts say the study, done by the American Social Health Association and Kaiser Family Foundation, indicates it's time the nation confront the issue–particularly because everyone who is sexually active is at risk.

"There are about 15 million new cases of STDs in the U.S. each year," said Linda Alexander of the American Social Health Association. "That's an astronomical number. It's one of the highest rates of all industrialized countries in the world."

Having any STD greatly increases a person's risk of developing a disease that cannot be cured. Alexander explains this dangerous connection: "If you have a sexually transmitted disease, you're more likely to acquire HIV if you're exposed to it and you're more likely to transmit HIV if you have it."

According to the study, STDs affect one in four U.S. citizens over a lifetime. The risks associated with STDs range from sterility to cancer to death. The top STDs include these four that can be treated with antibiotics: Chlamydia, gonorrhea, syphilis and trichomoniasis. They also include viral infections that have no cure: genital herpes, genital warts (also known as human papilloma virus), hepatitis B, and HIV, which causes AIDS.

Experts say a national discussion on the issue could help change social attitudes toward STDs.

Experts also say some major challenges must be overcome to beat back the high rate of STDs. Those challenges include getting doctors to talk about STDs with their patients and convincing both men and women to get tested.

Think About It

1. Summarize the findings of the recent study on sexually transmitted diseases in the United States.
2. What are some of the strategies that might effectively limit the trend identified by this study?

CNN HEALTH NEWS **653**

CNN HEALTH NEWS

Study Rates STDs in U.S.

Objectives. After reading the article, students should be able to recognize the widespread problems of STDs in this country, some of which are incurable.

Motivator. Write this item on the chalkboard: "True or False? Sexually transmitted diseases are mostly found in underdeveloped countries with limited national health care systems." Share student responses. Then ask them to read "Study Rates STDs in U.S."

Teach

- After students read the article, return to the true/false query on the chalkboard. Help students understand that the statement is clearly false. STDs can pose a significant problem to industrialized countries like the United States.
- Ask students to review methods to avoid getting STDs. Emphasize that abstinence from sexual activity is the best way to avoid getting an STD.
- Have students consider how discussion about this topic can help prevent future infections. Discuss the role of the media and articles like this one in raising public awareness of the dangers of STDs.

Research. Have students find out more about the rate of STD infections in the United States. Encourage students to create charts, graphs, and tables to illustrate their data.

Close. Ask students to describe the purpose and intended audience of the article. Then ask students to evaluate the effectiveness of the author's work.

MORE ABOUT . . . . .

RELIABLE SOURCES. The American Social Health Association was founded in 1914 to help improve public health. This private organization is a trusted source of information about sexually transmitted diseases. In addition to sponsoring sociological research, the association publishes informative pamphlets and books and helps health providers and caregivers communicate about risk, transmission, prevention, testing, and treatment.

All information on its Internet site and all of its publications follow the approved treatment guidelines recommended by the Centers for Disease Control and Prevention.

CHECKING COMPREHENSION

- Assign and discuss the chapter review.
- Use the MindJogger Videoquiz to review the chapter. 🔴

CHAPTER 29 REVIEW ANSWERS

Using Health Terms

1. epidemic
2. sexually transmitted diseases (STDs)
3. trichomoniasis
4. genital warts
5. chlamydia
6. genital herpes
7. nongonococcal urethritis (NGU)
8. syphilis
9. gonorrhea
10. vaginitis

Recalling the Facts

1. Because they affect a large population—about 12 million new cases are reported each year.
2. Some don't know what kind of help to get or how to get help; others refuse to believe they could have an STD.
3. Abstaining from sexual activity is the best way to avoid STDs and their consequences.
4. Chlamydia.
5. Gonorrhea is treated with antibiotics.
6. Both have the same symptom: sores near the genitals.
7. Hepatitis B and HIV.
8. Nongonococcal urethritis and pelvic inflammatory disease.
9. The reason is that the symptoms are not always obvious.
10. It is treated with medicine prescribed by a physician.
11. Genital herpes is diagnosed by medical examination of genital sores; the diagnosis is verified by lab tests.

Using Health Terms

On a separate sheet of paper, write the term that best matches each definition below.

LESSON 1

1. An outbreak of an infectious disease that affects a large population.
2. Infectious diseases spread from person to person through sexual contact.

LESSON 2

3. A vaginal infection that can lead to urethra and bladder infections.
4. Pink or reddish warts with cauliflowerlike tops that appear on the genitals.
5. An infection caused by a bacterium that affects the vagina in females and the urethra in males.

6. Blisterlike sores in the genital area.
7. An infection caused by several different kinds of bacterialike organisms that infect the urethra in males and the cervix in females.
8. An STD that attacks many parts of the body and is caused by a small bacterium called a spirochete.
9. An STD caused by bacteria that affect the genital mucous membrane, primarily in the lining of the urethra of the male and in the cervix and vagina of the female.
10. A common inflammation of the female genitals.

Recalling the Facts

Using complete sentences, answer the following questions.

LESSON 1

1. Why are STDs considered an epidemic?
2. Why are teens less likely than adults to seek medical attention for an STD?
3. Why is it important for teens to say no to sexual activity?

LESSON 2

4. Which STD is the most prevalent in the United States today?
5. How is gonorrhea treated?
6. How are the symptoms of chancroid similar to those of the primary stage of syphilis?
7. Which STDs also can be contracted through another means of contact?
8. What two infections can result from untreated chlamydia?
9. Why is it possible for a female not to know that she has an STD?
10. How is trichomoniasis treated?
11. How is genital herpes diagnosed?

Thinking Critically

LESSON 1

1. ***Comparing and Contrasting.*** Which of the following teens is more likely to get an STD? Explain your answer. (a) Robert loves the thrills of taking risks. He is usually the one who takes on a dare given by members of his clique, even when it involves dangerous behaviors. (b) Tim is a member of Students Against Destructive Decisions (SADD) at school. He often gives talks about abstaining from alcohol. He socializes with other members of SADD and with family friends.

2. ***Comparing and Contrasting.*** Compare and contrast assertive and aggressive styles in letting others know that you don't want to be part of a situation where sexual activity is practiced openly.

LESSON 2

3. ***Evaluating.*** Some states have a law requiring couples who apply for marriage licenses to be tested for syphilis. Explain the purpose of this law. Then develop a law of your own that you think would be effective in the control of STDs. Explain your thinking.

4. ***Synthesizing.*** Prepare a chart that explains the stages of syphilis. Include symptoms for each stage of the disease. Do additional research to fill in any information not provided in the text.

Making the Connection

1. ***Math.*** Use current, up-to-date resources to research the number of cases of gonorrhea during five-year intervals from 1950 to the present. Present your findings in a bar graph. Develop a comparable bar graph for population increases during the same period. Compare the two graphs.

2. ***Language Arts.*** Use a dictionary to find the etymology, or origin, of the words *gonorrhea, syphilis,* and *herpes.* Which of these words has an alternate spelling, and what is it?

BEYOND THE CLASSROOM

PARENTAL INVOLVEMENT Ask your parents or other adults at home how they learned about STDs. Ask about the quality of that information. Talk with them about the best ways for young people to learn about STDs.

COMMUNITY INVOLVEMENT Find out what kinds of assistance are available to help people who have STDs in your community. Prepare a report to share your findings with your classmates.

SCHOOL-TO-CAREER

Interpersonal. Some artists build a career as a medical illustrator, one who draws illustrations used in medical writings, such as brochures or textbooks. Determine what kinds of preparation and experience are required in both art and science for a career as a medical illustrator. Share your findings with the class in a brief oral report.

CHAPTER 29 REVIEW **655**

Thinking Critically

1. Robert, because he is more likely to engage in risk behaviors. Complete explanations will vary.
2. Answers will vary.
3. A person with syphilis may have no symptoms but can still pass on the disease to a sexual partner. Suggested laws will vary.
4. Charts should show an understanding of the information on pages 649 and 650.

Making the Connection

1.–2. Answers will vary.

Evaluate

- Use the reproducible *Chapter 29 Test* in the TCR, or construct your own using the Testmaker software.
- Use *Performance Assessment Activity 29* in the TCR.

Enrichment

Ask students to complete *Cross-Curriculum Activity 29* in the TCR.

Beyond the Classroom

Keep students involved in the community, and encourage parent participation by assigning the activities on this page for students to work on outside of class.

HIV and AIDS

	FEATURES	CLASSROOM RESOURCES

ACTIVITIES

- Cross-Curriculum Activity 30
- Health Lab 30
- Health Skills Activities 30
- Parent Letter and Activities 30

ASSESSMENT

- Chapter 30 Test
- Performance Assessment Activity 30
- Testmaker Software

STUDENT ACTIVITIES WORKBOOK

- Applying Health Skills 88, 89
- Study Guide 30
- Vocabulary Activity 30

STUDENT DIVERSITY STRATEGIES

- Audiocassette Program (English)
- Audiocassette Program (Spanish)
- Spanish Parent Letters and Activities
- Spanish Summaries, Quizzes, and Activities

MULTIMEDIA COMPONENTS

- English Audiocassette Program
- Spanish Audiocassette Program
- MindJogger Videodisc and VHS program
- ABCNews InterActive™ VHS/Videodisc Series

MODULES

- *HIV/AIDS and Society,* Student Edition
- *HIV/AIDS and Society,* Teacher's Annotated Edition
- *El VIH/SIDA y la Sociedad*

National Health Education Standards

One of the main goals of the National Health Education Standards is to move students toward "health literacy." Health literacy is the capacity of individuals to obtain, interpret, and understand basic health information and services and the competence to use such information and services in ways which promote health. The health standards were developed by applying the characteristics of a well-educated, literate person within the context of health. The health literate person is:

- a critical thinker and problem solver
- a self-directed learner
- a responsible, productive citizen
- an effective communicator

Listed below are the Health Education Standards Performance Indicators addressed in each lesson of this chapter.

Lesson	Health Standards Performance Indicators
1	1.3, 3.3, 5.6, 6.1
2	1.8, 3.1, 2.4, 2.6

ONLINE RESOURCES

For a fresh approach to health topics and an in-depth look at health issues, use these online resources found under Teacher Resources at **health.glencoe.com**.

- **BLOCK SCHEDULE LESSON PLANS** Reinforce health concepts with outside readings selected especially for students. Each reading is accompanied by a lesson plan and activities to enhance
  - Reading Skills
  - Cross Curriculum
  - Media Literacy

- **TECHNOLOGY PROJECTS** Instructions and suggestions on how to use computer, Internet, and software with health lessons.

- **HEALTH UPDATES** Timely topics in health news, including late-breaking medical advances and updates on teen risk behaviors.

Out of Time?

If time does not permit teaching this chapter, you may use these features: Making Responsible Decisions on page 661; Update on page 665; and Building Health Skills on page 668.

BLOCK SCHEDULING

Block scheduling provides extended time for hands-on projects and activities. Use the following activities to engage students, provide further depth, and vary your instructional techniques:

- Update (30 minutes) **pg. 665**
- Health Skills Activity (60–90 minutes) **pg. 670**

HIV and AIDS

CHAPTER OVERVIEW

Chapter 30 explains how HIV attacks the immune system and can ultimately result in AIDS, a state in which the body is open to a host of opportunistic illnesses. Means of transmission, symptoms, research and treatment, and prevention of HIV infection are also discussed.

LESSON 1 AIDS is a fatal communicable disease with no known cure. The HIV virus, which causes AIDS, attacks the body's immune system. HIV must enter a person's bloodstream to infect the person. The primary means of transmission include having sexual intercourse with an infected person or sharing a contaminated needle. Teenagers are a primary risk group for contracting AIDS if they engage in high-risk behaviors.

LESSON 2 Testing for HIV is recommended for foreign service employees, the medical profession, and individuals who have practiced risk behaviors. Infection can be detected by the presence of HIV antibodies. Its symptoms may not appear for six months to 10–12 years. Diagnosis of AIDS is based on the presence of HIV antibodies, the presence of opportunistic diseases, and a T-helper cell count below 200. Researchers continue to search for treatment and vaccines. Prevention can be achieved by staying informed and avoiding high-risk behaviors.

CHAPTER 30

HIV and AIDS

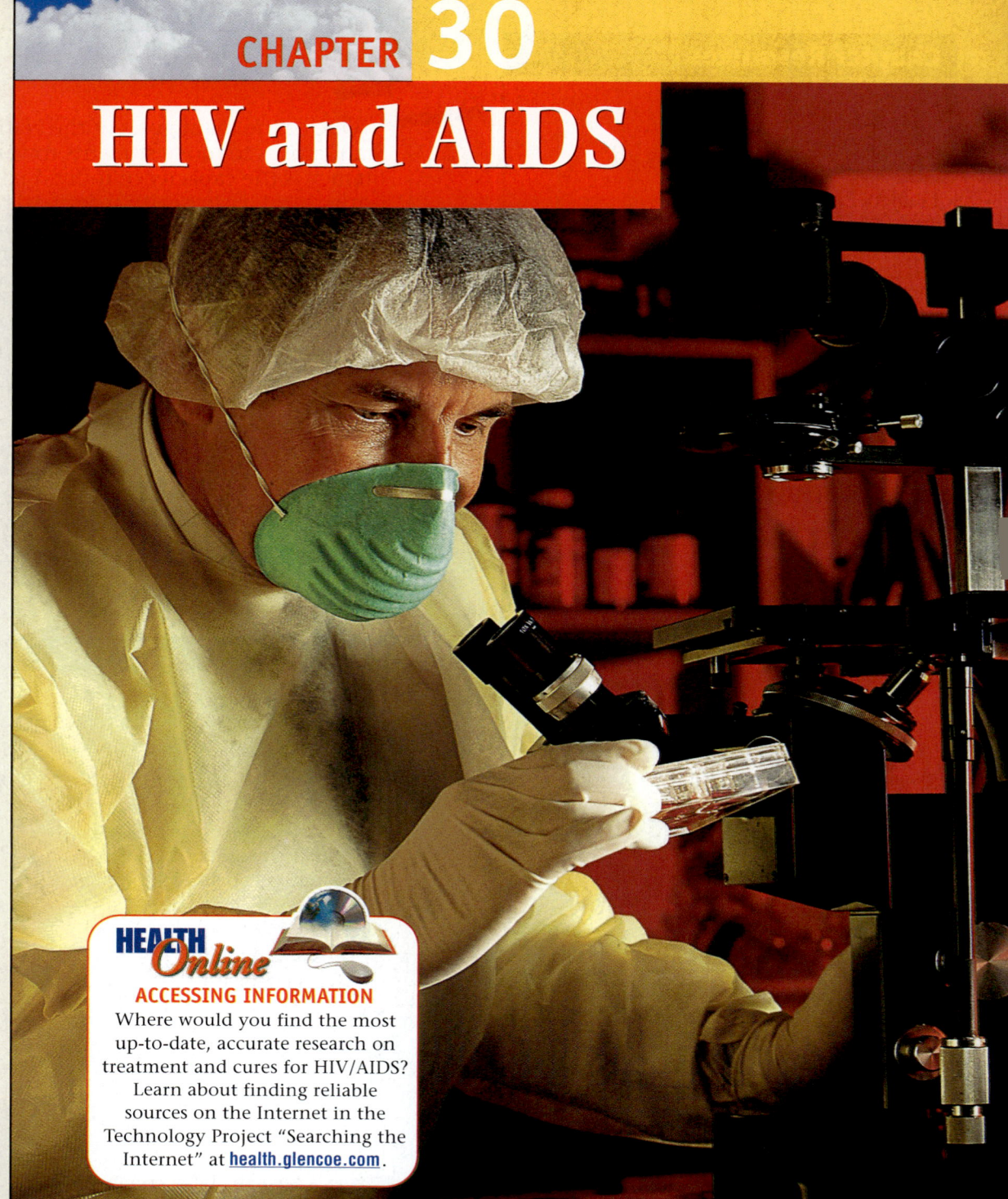

HEALTH Online

ACCESSING INFORMATION
Where would you find the most up-to-date, accurate research on treatment and cures for HIV/AIDS? Learn about finding reliable sources on the Internet in the Technology Project "Searching the Internet" at **health.glencoe.com**.

Hands-On Health

TEACHING STRATEGY

Understanding the Effects of AIDS Provide an opportunity for students to commemorate individuals who have died of AIDS. See Activity 40, "Candle Ceremony," in the *Hands-On Health: Creative Teaching Strategies* booklet.

Time Needed
20 minutes

Supplies
- 1 candle for each student
- video or photographs of the AIDS quilt

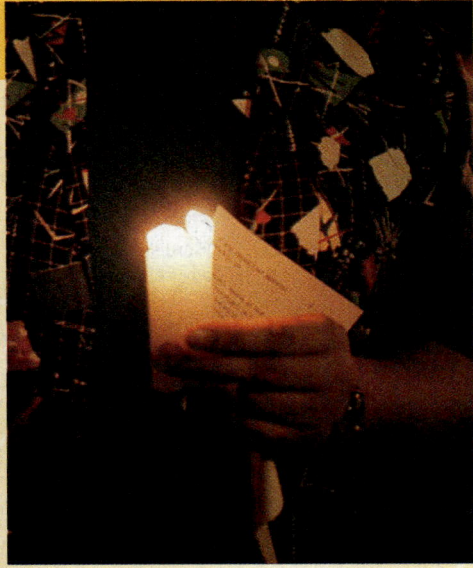

> **The underlying reality...
> is that the HIV epidemic in
> our country is far from over.**
>
> —DIVISIONS OF HIV/AIDS PROTECTION
> CENTERS FOR DISEASE CONTROL AND PREVENTION

Quick Write   List five myths or misconceptions about HIV or AIDS that you think teens often mistakenly believe to be true. Discuss these with your teacher and classmates.

Personal Health Inventory

Self-Inventory Write the numbers 1–10 on a sheet of paper. Read each statement below and respond by writing *yes*, *no*, or *sometimes* for each item. Write a *yes* only for items that you practice regularly. Save your responses.

1	I keep informed about HIV infection and AIDS.
2	I know which behaviors pose the highest risk for infection from HIV.
3	I know with whom to talk and where to get information when I have questions about HIV infection and AIDS.
4	I avoid all behaviors that can transmit HIV.
5	I can say no to something I do not want to do or do not feel ready for.
6	I do not use illegal drugs.
7	I abstain from sexual activity.
8	I do not use needles, including tattoo needles, razors, or other items that have been used by someone else.
9	I am not easily influenced by peer pressure.
10	I know the relationship between HIV and AIDS.

Follow-up After completing the chapter, retake this self-inventory. Pick two items that you need to work on and set a goal to improve your health behaviors.

TECHNOLOGY OPTIONS

ABCNEWS INTERACTIVE™ You may wish to use *Health: AIDS* with this chapter. For your convenience, use the separate *ABCNews InterActive™ Bar Code Correlation* that accompanies the *Glencoe Health* program.

MINDJOGGER
VIDEOQUIZ

To preview or review chapter content, you may wish to use the *MindJogger Videoquiz* that accompanies Chapter 30.

INTRODUCING THE CHAPTER

Personal Health Inventory

Focus students' attention on the first Self-Inventory statement and ask: Why is it important to keep informed about HIV infection and AIDS? Emphasize that researchers continue to look for new ways to treat, and even to cure, AIDS; health-literate individuals take the time to learn about new approaches and experimental treatments. Then have students read all ten inventory statements and record their responses on a page labeled "HIV and AIDS" in their private Health Journals.

- Tell students that this chapter will investigate AIDS, a disease that attacks the body's immune system. Ask them to brainstorm what they already know about AIDS. List their statements on paper and distribute photocopies to all students. Have them verify facts and identify any misinformation or misconceptions as they study the chapter.
- Let volunteers describe the photographs on these two pages and discuss what each shows or suggests about HIV and AIDS. Then have students read the quotation and do the Quick Write on this page. Ask: How has public knowledge about HIV and AIDS grown? What remains to be learned about HIV and AIDS? Explain that students will explore these and related questions as they study the lessons in Chapter 30.
- Distribute Parent Letter 30 in the *Parent Letters and Activities* booklet.

LESSON 1

HIV Infection

FOCUS

LESSON OBJECTIVES

After studying this lesson, students should be able to

- list body fluids through which HIV is known to be transmitted.
- list behaviors known to transmit HIV.
- identify myths regarding HIV transmission.

MOTIVATOR

Write the following on the chalkboard for students to work on while attendance is being taken: *Write an example of how your immune system helps prevent you from getting diseases.*

INTRODUCING THE LESSON

Have volunteers share their responses to the Motivator. Tell students that the virus that causes AIDS attacks the body's immune system. This lesson discusses how the immune system is affected by the virus, ways the virus is transmitted, and how to avoid becoming infected.

INTRODUCING HEALTH TERMS

- Instruct volunteers to use a dictionary to find the meanings of these words/word parts: *acquired, immuno-, deficiency, syndrome, intra-, venous.* Have another volunteer write the meanings on the board. Have each student write a sentence about each vocabulary term that demonstrates its meaning.
- Ask students to complete Vocabulary Activity 30 and Chapter Study Guide 30 in the *Student Workbook.* ☞

Of all STDs, none has received more attention—and deservedly so—than AIDS. The costs of this deadly affliction—in both monetary cost and the loss of human potential—have been enormous. AIDS is now the leading cause of death in people between the ages of 25 and 44.

HEALTH TERMS

acquired immune deficiency syndrome (AIDS)

human immunodeficiency virus (HIV)

intravenous (IV) drugs

HEALTH CONCEPTS

- AIDS is a disorder that interferes with the body's ability to fight off infections.
- Viruses are the simplest form of life.
- HIV plays a central role in the AIDS epidemic.
- The human immunodeficiency virus (HIV) is transmitted mainly through semen, secretions from the female's vagina, blood, and breast milk, sharing needles, and transfusions.

hotlink

immune system For more information on the immune system and how it protects the body from infection, see Chapter 28, page 624.

AIDS and HIV

Acquired immune deficiency syndrome (AIDS)—defined formally as *HIV infection combined with severe immune deficiency*—is the final stage of infection with HIV. Short for **human immunodeficiency** (im-myuh-noh-duh-FIH-shuhn-see) **virus**, HIV is *a virus that attacks the body's immune system.* This lesson will look at how people become infected with HIV—and how they do not.

HIV and the Human Body

In order to understand how HIV attacks the body's **immune system**, it is necessary to review the function of lymphocytes—white blood cells made in bone marrow. The human body contains billions of lymphocytes, found in the blood, spleen, lymph nodes, appendix, tonsils, and adenoids.

Lesson 1 Resources

TEACHER'S CLASSROOM RESOURCES
- ☞ **Concept Map** Activity 88
- ☞ **Cooperative Learning** Activity 30
- ☞ **Decision-Making** Activity 30
- ☞ **Health Lab** 30
- ☞ **Lesson 88 Quiz**
- ☞ **Lesson Plan 88**
- ☞ **Parent Letter and Activities** 30

- ☞ **Reteaching** Activity 88

STUDENT WORKBOOK
- ☞ **Applying Health Skills** 88
- ☞ **Chapter Study Guide** 30
- ☞ **Vocabulary** Activity 30

MULTIMEDIA
- 🔴 **ABCNews InterActive™ VHS/Videodisc,** *Health: AIDS*

Lymphocytes help your body fight disease-causing organisms, or pathogens. There are two major types of lymphocytes: B cells, which mature in bone marrow, and T cells, which mature in the thymus gland. T-helper cells, a type of T cell, stimulate B cells to produce antibodies. Antibodies are proteins that help destroy pathogens that enter the body.

When HIV enters the bloodstream, it enters certain cells, including T-helper cells. Here HIV reproduces its genetic material. More T-helper cells become infected and are destroyed. This decrease in the number of T-helper cells reduces the ability of the immune system to fight pathogens, making the body vulnerable to certain illnesses.

HIV can be present anywhere in the body—the bloodstream, lymph nodes, even brain cells.

How HIV Is Transmitted

There are many myths about how HIV is or is not spread. The fact is, HIV must enter a person's bloodstream in order to infect the person. HIV has been found in body fluids such as blood, semen, and vaginal secretions of infected persons. Small concentrations have also been found in saliva, sweat, tears, feces, urine, and breast milk. To date, HIV is known to be transmitted only through semen, blood, vaginal secretions, and breast milk. Certain behaviors and situations are known to transmit HIV from an infected person to an uninfected person because the exchange of body fluids is involved.

▲ *This microscopic photograph shows HIV reproducing from a host cell.*

ACTIVITY *Describe the process by which HIV invades the immune system.*

Risk Behaviors Known to Transmit HIV

About 93 percent of adults and teenagers revealed through testing to be infected with HIV have acquired the virus through sexual intercourse or the use of **intravenous (IV) drugs**—*drugs that are injected into the veins.* These two actions are high-risk behaviors for HIV infection.

- **Sexual Intercourse.** HIV can be transmitted during any form of sexual intercourse. During intercourse, secretions containing HIV can enter a partner's blood through tiny cuts in the body. The risks of HIV infection increase with the number of sexual partners a person has or by having sexual contact with someone

TEACH

L2 Discussing

Have the class discuss why AIDS is the most serious communicable disease known today.

L2 Discussing

Ask students what AIDS is. Discuss how HIV affects and changes the normal function of the T4 lymphocyte cell. How does this affect our immune system?

L2 Health Lab

Assign *Health Lab 30* and have students investigate how the AIDS virus replicates. ☞

L3 Class Activity

Ask volunteers to make a chart that includes diagrams of how HIV enters the body, the action of the immune system, development of AIDS, and development of opportunistic diseases that result ultimately in death.

HEALTH: AIDS (Side 1)

Chapter 3: What is AIDS?

Frames 2477-4590

Chapter 4: Your Immune System and AIDS

Frames 4603-8648

Chapter 5: How You Can Become Infected

Frames 8661-11745

L2 Explaining

Does everyone infected with HIV develop AIDS? Tell students that it is hard to explain the course of infection for all individuals. Recent studies indicate that 20 to 30 percent of those who carry HIV developed AIDS within five years, and 35 to 40 percent within eight years.

L2 Discussing

Discuss how the use of alcohol and drugs other than IV drugs would be considered a risk behavior associated with contracting AIDS.

L1 Guest Speaker

Invite a health care professional who deals with AIDS patients to talk with the class. Ask the speaker to talk about these patients' unique problems and the precautions that he or she must take when treating these patients.

L1 Guest Speaker

Recruit a speaker from an AIDS support organization to speak with the class. Prior to the visit, have students prepare questions about all the aspects of this disease: scientific, economic, social, and emotional.

L2 Cooperative Learning

Distribute *Cooperative Learning Activity 30* for more on HIV. ☛

HEALTH: AIDS (Side 1)

Chapter 7: How to Protect
    Yourself

Frames 14415-16613

Chapter 10: Needle Sharing:
    IV Drug Abuse

Frames 21390-23456

who has had many sexual partners. Having an STD that results in sores and bleeding or discharge also increases the risk of HIV entering the blood.

■ **Sharing Needles.** If a person who is infected with HIV injects drugs into his or her veins with a syringe, drops of that person's blood are left on the needle. If another person uses the same needle, it is very likely that the infected blood will be passed to this person's blood. Sharing any needle, including one used to inject steroids, make tattoos, or pierce ears, puts a person at risk of becoming infected with HIV.

MYTHS ABOUT HIV TRANSMISSION

MYTH
You can get HIV from a mosquito bite if that mosquito has bitten an HIV-infected person.

FACT
Although mosquitoes can spread diseases such as malaria and yellow fever, HIV is not spread through a mosquito's salivary glands.

MYTH
You can get HIV by touching a glass from which a person infected with HIV has drunk.

FACT
HIV is spread primarily through blood, semen, and vaginal secretions.

MYTH
You can get HIV from swimming in a pool with someone who is infected.

FACT
Even if an HIV-infected person bled into a swimming pool, the blood would be so diluted it would be harmless.

MYTH
You can get HIV from being sneezed on by someone who is infected.

FACT
HIV is not spread through airborne droplets.

660 CHAPTER 30   HIV AND AIDS

PROMOTING COMPREHENSIVE SCHOOL HEALTH

MEASURING PROGRESS ASSESSMENT.
Evaluating the committee's progress will help identify what works, what has been successfully changed, and how the community is instrumental in the process of change. Assessment might take any of the following forms: ongoing evaluation of the action plan, a comparison of the program against a set of voluntary guidelines or statewide objectives, reviewing the health statistics in the community, or asking committee members to retake the survey that originally led to the priority list of problems. For more information, consult *Promoting a Comprehensive School Health Program* in the TCR. ☛

Making Responsible Decisions

Is Honesty the Best Policy?

Stuart, a high school freshman, found out that he is infected with HIV. He contracted the virus through a blood transfusion years ago. Because Stuart has hemophilia, his blood does not clot properly. As a result, he may bleed excessively from a minor injury. Stuart has been receiving a clotting factor through injections and transfusions. Stuart is aware from other cases like his that there is a great deal of fear and misunderstanding related to HIV infection. If people know he is infected, there may be a negative reaction to his being on the school team. Yet he wants to lead as normal a life as possible, and he wants to be honest. He is uncertain how to handle the situation.

What Would You Do?

Apply the six steps of the decision-making process to Stuart's problem.

1. **State the situation.**
2. **List the options.**
3. **Weigh the possible outcomes.**
4. **Consider your values.**
5. **Make a decision and act.**
6. **Evaluate the decision.**

OTHER MODES OF TRANSMISSION

Two other modes of HIV transmissions are blood transfusions and mother-to-child transfer during birth. Combined, however, these modes account ultimately for less than 3 percent of all cases of AIDS. Since March of 1985, all blood donated in the United States has been tested for the presence of HIV antibodies. This testing has greatly reduced—although not eliminated—the risk of receiving contaminated blood or blood products from a transfusion. There is no risk when donating blood because disposable needles are used. These needles are used only one time.

A pregnant female who is infected with HIV can pass the virus to the fetus in blood exchanged through the umbilical cord. This occurs between 20 and 35 percent of the time when the mother is infected with HIV. There is a treatment available that can reduce the risk of HIV being transmitted from an infected woman to her unborn child. Therefore, it is important for all pregnant women to get early prenatal care to protect their infants. A baby also could be infected with HIV during birth if the virus enters through a cut on the baby's body. A nursing baby could receive HIV while breast-feeding.

Teenagers at Risk

Unlike other STDs whose rates are decreasing among adolescents, the incidence of HIV infection among teenagers is on the rise, especially among African Americans, Hispanic Americans, and

---

1. Stuart wonders whether he should be honest about the fact that he is infected with HIV.
2. Stuart could (a) tell only a few close friends that he is infected with HIV; (b) make his HIV infection completely public; (c) keep his HIV infection completely secret.
3. Stuart might (a) get support from many of his close friends, but find that the fact of his infection does not remain private for long; (b) risk facing very negative reactions from a few people, but probably get strong support from others; (c) find that he cannot keep his infection completely secret, and thus have to face very negative reactions from at least some people.
4. Stuart values honesty. He also values being able to live as normal a life as possible.
5. Responses will vary.
6. Students should consider both short- and long-term consequences of their decisions.

L2 Decision Making

For further study on making responsible decisions, assign *Decision-Making Activity 30* in the TCR.

HEALTH: AIDS (Side 1)

Chapter 11: Mother to Child

Frames 23462-25455

Chapter 12: Infected Blood Products: Hemophilia

Frames 25460-27227

MORE ABOUT . . . . .

DEALING WITH SENSITIVE ISSUES.
Students may be reluctant to discuss HIV and AIDS. For some, AIDS may be too frightening a topic for discussion. For others, it may be a moral issue. Other students may have experienced the pain of watching a family member or friend suffer and even die of AIDS. As appropriate, remind students that AIDS is a serious disease. The best protection against HIV and AIDS is to have as much information about them as possible.

ASSESS

EVALUATING THE LESSON

Assign and discuss the Lesson 1 Review; then administer, grade, and discuss the *Lesson 88 Quiz* in the TCR. ☞

RETEACHING

- Have students describe the changes in the function of the T-helper cells in the immune system when HIV enters the body.
- Tell students to explain how AIDS is not transmitted.
- Ask students to complete *Reteaching Activity 88* in the TCR. ☞

ENRICHMENT

Encourage a group of students to contact the Centers for Disease Control and Prevention and the Public Health Department. Have them request the latest information on AIDS. Instruct them to make a poster using this information to share with the class.

CLOSE

Have students describe responsible behaviors that can prevent a teen from getting AIDS.

---

females. The Centers for Disease Control and Prevention (CDC) reports the following:

- AIDS is now the leading cause of death in the 25- to 44-year-old age group. Many of those in their 20s probably became infected with HIV as teenagers.
- As of June 1997, the CDC reported 3,359 cases of HIV infection among people 13–19 years old. Considering that many cases go unreported, the numbers may be substantially higher.
- AIDS is now the leading cause of death for women in 15 of the largest cities in the United States.

HIV infection can be prevented, as will be seen in the lesson that follows. A teen who chooses to abstain from sexual intercourse and who does not use IV drugs greatly reduces the risk of HIV infection. In addition, abstaining from the use of alcohol and other drugs, which can impair a person's judgment in regard to sexual activity and drug use, can also reduce the risk of HIV infection. Making responsible decisions about your own activities and behaviors is your most valuable tool for protecting yourself against HIV infection. As scientists continue to search for a cure for this disease, you have a responsibility to yourself and to others to avoid any behaviors that could put you at risk of infection.

LESSON 1 *Review*

Reviewing Facts and Vocabulary

1. What is AIDS?
2. What is the function of T-helper cells?
3. Explain the ways HIV is known to be transmitted.

Thinking Critically

4. **Evaluating.** Do you think it is wrong for an individual who is infected with HIV to remain silent about her or his condition while being sexually active with another person?
5. **Synthesizing.** Why are there so many myths surrounding AIDS?
6. **Analyzing.** We live in a society that does not encourage open discussion of sex. How does this contribute, if at all, to the misunderstandings surrounding AIDS and how HIV is spread?

Applying Health Skills

7. **In Your Home and School.** Interview family members and five people in your school or neighborhood. Ask them what they think are the five primary causes of infection with HIV. Are their ideas based on fact or fiction? Share and discuss your findings with classmates.

Lesson 1 Review

Answers to Reviewing Facts and Vocabulary

1. AIDS is HIV infection combined with severe immune deficiency.
2. T-helper cells stimulate B-cells to produce antibodies.
3. Through semen, blood, vaginal secretions, and breast milk.

Answers to Thinking Critically

4. Answers should reflect an understanding of the risks of transmitting HIV to sexual partners.
5. Answers will vary.
6. Answers will vary.

Treatment for HIV-Related Illnesses and AIDS

Following the initial outbreak of AIDS cases in the early 1980s, researchers set to work developing tests that would indicate infection with HIV. This lesson will describe the testing process. It will also examine what happens to an individual who tests **HIV-reactive,** or "positive"– that is, *infected with HIV.*

HEALTH TERMS

HIV-reactive

ELISA (EIA)

confirmatory test

asymptomatic stage

AIDS-opportunistic illnesses (AIDS-OIs)

HEALTH CONCEPTS

- A number of tests are used to detect the presence of HIV antibodies.
- AIDS interferes with the normal functioning of the immune system, making patients prey to a host of AIDS-opportunistic illnesses that seldom appear in people with healthy immune systems.
- AIDS education can help stem the AIDS pandemic.
- Choosing abstinence from high-risk behaviors is the 100 percent effective way to limit the spread of HIV infection.

Detecting HIV Antibodies

Just as there are misconceptions about how HIV is spread, there are also misunderstandings about the tests used to indicate whether a person is HIV-reactive. There are two phases of testing that may be done in suspected cases of HIV infection. Together, the tests have an accuracy level of greater than 99 percent.

HIV Testing

Persons who suspect they are infected with HIV due to high-risk behaviors are urged to seek testing. It takes anywhere from two weeks to six months for the body to produce antibodies following infection. Individuals are advised to see a health professional right away and to

LESSON 2 TREATMENT FOR HIV-RELATED ILLNESSES AND AIDS **663**

Lesson 2 Resources

TEACHER'S CLASSROOM RESOURCES

- **Concept Map** Activity 89
- **Enrichment** Activity 30
- **Lesson 89 Quiz**
- **Lesson Plan 89**
- **Reteaching** Activity 89

STUDENT WORKBOOK

- **Applying Health Skills 89**
- **Chapter Study Guide 30**
- **Vocabulary** Activity 30

MULTIMEDIA

- **ABCNews InterActive™ VHS/Videodisc,** *Health: AIDS*

Treatment for HIV-Related Illnesses and AIDS

FOCUS

LESSON OBJECTIVES

After studying this lesson, students should be able to

- describe the two tests that detect the presence of HIV antibodies.
- explain the factors that determine a diagnosis of AIDS.
- identify ways to protect against HIV transmission.

MOTIVATOR

Write the following on the chalkboard for students to work on while attendance is being taken: *Why is it important that at-risk individuals get tested for AIDS?*

INTRODUCING THE LESSON

Have students share their responses to the Motivator. Explain that there are special groups of people that are required to be tested for AIDS to prevent the spread of the disease. For instance, pregnant women, people who donate blood, body organs, or tissues, and those who join the armed forces are required to be tested. Tell students that this lesson discusses testing for HIV infection and treatment for infected persons.

INTRODUCING HEALTH TERMS

- Discuss the meaning of *opportunistic,* and identify the AIDS-OIs presented in the lesson.
- Ask students to complete Vocabulary Activity 30 and Chapter Study Guide 30 in the *Student Workbook.*

TEACH

LD Discussing

Ask students if they believe health care workers should be tested for the AIDS virus and why. Use this opportunity to correct any misinformation they have acquired.

L2 Discussing

How is a person tested for HIV? Does a negative test always mean that a person is not infected? If the first test is negative, what procedure is used next to determine if a person is infected? Ask students to explain their responses.

HEALTH: AIDS (Side 1)

Chapter 15: Past Epidemics

Frames 33724-37822

Chapter 17: United States Statistics

Frame 45783

Chapter 18: World Statistics

Frame 45841

Chapter 20: Minorities and AIDs

Frames 45899-47698

CHARACTER IN ACTION

Honesty and Responsibility

When it comes to HIV/AIDS and other STDs, **honesty** and responsibility are both critical, central, and ethical values that need to be upheld. Sexual activity outside of marriage is a high-risk behavior that has grave consequences. When a person has been sexually active or knows that he or she may have been infected with HIV/AIDS or another STD, withholding information is not only unethical for unsuspecting partners; it can prove deadly.

Staying abstinent is a decision that is based on the highest values, including self-respect and responsibility. It is the only reasonable and responsible decision for protecting your health and the health of others.

Character Check Fold a piece of paper into four columns. Then list respectively: Physical, Emotional, Social, and Ethical Benefits of remaining sexually abstinent.

avoid all behaviors known to transmit HIV. After six months, testing should indicate accurately whether infection is present in the body.

The first test performed, **ELISA**—or **EIA**—is *a test that screens for the presence of HIV antibodies in the blood,* not a test for HIV infection or AIDS. The ELISA (EIA) is very sensitive and will be reactive even if there are only one or two antibodies in the blood sample. Because certain health conditions such as hemophilia, hepatitis, and pregnancy can cause "false" reactive readings, the ELISA (EIA) may be repeated if the first test proves reactive. A reactive ELISA (EIA) will be followed up by a second **confirmatory test,** *a highly accurate test used to confirm the results of a reactive ELISA (EIA).* One of three different tests—the Western blot test, the IFA, or the RIA—will be administered for this purpose. A reactive confirmatory test result means that the person has HIV antibodies in his or her blood. This person is infected with HIV, although he or she may show no signs of infection at the time of the test. A non-reactive test means that there were no HIV antibodies in the sample of blood and that the person is not infected. If, however, a person subsequently becomes exposed to HIV through a risk behavior—or if the test was done within six months of the suspected risk incident—he or she will need to be retested.

Symptoms of HIV Infection

A person infected with HIV may or may not experience illness. In fact, a person infected with HIV can feel and look healthy. However, this individual can still infect others when practicing behaviors known to transmit HIV. A person can be infected with HIV for years before showing signs of infection. The earliest phase of HIV infection is the **asymptomatic** (AY-sim-tuh-MAT-ik) **stage.** This is *a period of months or years during which the virus is present in the blood but there are no symptoms or signs of disease.*

Although symptoms of HIV infection may not appear for six months to 10–12 years, a person infected with HIV will almost always develop AIDS. During that period, a person infected with HIV will go through a number of stages, each accompanied by different signs and symptoms. In the symptomatic stage, symptoms—which include fever, rash, headache, body aches, and swollen glands—may be mistaken for those of flu. Although these symptoms may pass over time, the person's ability to fight pathogens decreases, along with his or her T-helper cell count.

Diagnosis of AIDS

Yet another misconception is that AIDS itself is a disease. In point of fact, AIDS is a disorder associated with the last stage in the course of HIV infection. Once the immune system fails, the person's body is open to a host of infections that can attack other systems and create serious illness.

COOPERATIVE LEARNING

ACTIVITY. Persons infected with HIV might be unfairly judged. Organize students into groups to make a videotape that raises awareness and compassion for people with HIV infection and AIDS. In a panel discussion that includes the video, they should point out that anyone can contract HIV. Students can illustrate ways that HIV can be spread that are not related to high risk behaviors on the part of an infected individual. For example, HIV can be transmitted by a careless tattoo artist. Students could also point out that many people have been infected with HIV as a result of one incident and not a pattern of at-risk behavior. Have them emphasize that all persons with AIDS need compassion and support, not judgment.

Looking at the Issues

HIV Testing Through In-Home Collection Kits

In May of 1996, the FDA approved the first in-home collection kit for HIV testing. An individual draws a small amount of his or her own blood. The dried blood spot is mailed to a laboratory where it is tested for the presence of HIV antibodies through standard tests such as ELISA and Western blot. To get the results of the test, the person calls a toll-free number. Telephone counseling services are provided when the test result is positive. Issues surrounding in-home collection kits include questions related to counseling services and the quality, accuracy, and reliability of testing.

ANALYZING DIFFERENT VIEWPOINTS

▶ **Viewpoint One**
According to the National Center for Health Statistics, less than 15 percent of adults in the United States have been tested for HIV. Findings from surveys showed that, of people who have not taken HIV tests, 24 percent would undergo testing if it could be done at home. Clearly, in-home access to testing would increase the number of people tested for HIV who would not otherwise seek testing.

▶ **Viewpoint Two**
Some people feel that to assure proper collection and treatment of blood samples, the samples should be collected only by a health care professional. The laboratory doing the testing has no control over the conditions under which samples are collected in the home. Individuals may fail to follow accurately the instructions that come with the kit. They may delay mailing the sample to the laboratory for a period of time, which could affect test results.

▶ **Viewpoint Three**
Of major concern to some people is the issue of pretest and posttest counseling. Quality in-person counseling services can decrease anxiety over test results, can link individuals to other services, and may reduce high-risk behaviors. Counseling over the telephone with no face-to-face contact, however, may not provide intervention support or address risk-reduction activities, which in some cases could be dangerous for the consumer.

▶ **Viewpoint Four**
Other people recognize that for some, remaining anonymous is extremely important. For such people, in-home collection and phone counseling provide an easily accessible, highly private, and confidential form of testing.

EXPLORING YOUR VIEWS

1. If you feared you were at risk for HIV infection, what would be the advantages and disadvantages of being tested by your physician, being tested at a public clinic or other site, or using an in-home collection kit?

2. What do you think the advantages and disadvantages would be in receiving counseling on the phone or in person about a positive HIV test?

3. How careful do you think people would be about taking their own blood sample and mailing it to a laboratory in a timely manner? Explain your answer.

Looking at the Issues

HIV Testing Through In-Home Collection Kits

Ask: What do you think prevents many people from being tested? After a brief discussion, have students read the Update feature to learn about HIV testing with in-home collection kits and to explore the various viewpoints. Let volunteers share their ideas in response to the views questions, and then have students record their own responses in their private Health Journals.

L3 Interview

Ask students who know (or perhaps are related to) general-practice health professionals to interview those individuals about their HIV-related interactions with patients. Under what circumstances do they suggest HIV testing? How often do they raise the issue of HIV infection and/or HIV risk behaviors with their patients? Allow these students to discuss the results of their interviews with the rest of the class.

L2 Class Activity

Ask students to write a paragraph explaining the following statement: *People do not actually die from HIV.*

L3 Researching

AIDS is affecting all countries in the world. Let students form cooperative learning groups, and have the members of each group select one country. Group members should work together to compile statistics about the rates of HIV infection in that country and gather information on how HIV is affecting family and social structures there. Let group members present their findings in written or oral reports.

L1 Discussing

According to a recent study by the United Nations AIDS agency, one out of every 100 sexually active adults under the age of 49 is infected with HIV. Of those infected, only one in ten is aware of having HIV. Share this information with students, and help them discuss the implications of these facts.

L2 Research

Let students work in groups to gather more information about the listed AIDS-OIs. Have each group prepare a chart, graph, or other pictorial summary of their findings to be shared with the rest of the class.

L2 Discussing

People visiting AIDS patients often wear gauze masks and protective gowns—not to protect themselves from the patient, but to protect the patient from visitors. Have students discuss why this is necessary.

keeping Fit

Good News, Bad News

It is true that some people with HIV/AIDS are living healthier and longer lives than a few years ago. This is in large part due to new potent medicines and combinations of medicines. However, the news about HIV/AIDS is definitely not all good. No one should be fooled into thinking HIV/AIDS is no longer a terrible and deadly threat. Consider these facts:

➤ Potent new medicines and combinations of medicines do not work for everyone.

➤ Many of these cause terrible side effects—so terrible that some infected people stop using them.

➤ Many of these new medicines are too expensive for some people.

➤ Medicine therapies often involve complex schedules of pill-taking, including large numbers of pills to take throughout the day and night and at exact times.

AIDS-opportunistic illnesses (AIDS-OIs) are *infections and other diseases caused by organisms that do not usually produce illness in healthy people with unimpaired immune systems.* Several infectious diseases, as well as a number of cancers and diseases that damage the heart and nervous system, are typically associated with AIDS. In addition to a reactive test result for HIV antibodies and a T-helper cell count of under 200, diagnosis of AIDS is based on the presence of one or more AIDS-OIs. AIDS-OIs are the eventual cause of death in AIDS patients.

Common AIDS-OIs

Some of the more common AIDS-OIs are diseases that have been discussed in other chapters, or variations of such diseases. These include tuberculosis as well as the following:

- **Mycobacterium Avium Complex (MAC or MAI).** MAC is a bacterial infection. Its symptoms include persistent fever, night sweats, fatigue, weight loss, chronic diarrhea, anemia, abdominal pain, weakness, dizziness, and nausea.

- **Cryptococcosis (Cryptoccal Disease).** Cryptococcosis (krip-tuh-kaw-KOK-sis) is a fungal infection that may cause meningitis—inflammation of the coverings of the brain—or a form of pneumonia. The symptoms of meningitis include headache, stiffness in the neck, fever, blurred vision, a staggering gait, and fatigue. Untreated, the infection may end in coma and death.

- **Pneumocystis Carinii Pneumonia (PCP).** PCP is a protozoal infection that causes a form of pneumonia. Its symptoms include difficulty in breathing, fever, and persistent cough.

- **Toxoplasmosis Gondii (Toxo).** Toxo is a protozoal infection that can cause encephalitis. It is characterized by an altered mental state—confusion, lethargy, and delusional behavior—as well as paralysis on one side of the body, seizures, severe headaches, fever, and coma.

- **Cytomegalovirus (CMV).** CMV is a viral infection with symptoms that include blurry vision, blindness, pain and difficulty swallowing, lesions in the esophagus, fever, diarrhea, abdominal pain, wasting, and eventual blindness.

- **AIDS-Related Cognitive Motor Dysfunction.** Formerly known as AIDS dementia complex, this condition is a progressive disorder in which brain tissue is destroyed. Symptoms range from mild confusion to inability to control one's muscular movement.

- **Peripheral Nerve/Spinal Cord Dysfunction.** This is an inflammation of the nerves connecting the central nervous system to the sensory organs, muscles, glands, and internal organs. Symptoms include numbness, tingling, pain, and muscle weakness.

Many of these illnesses are accompanied by wasting syndrome, an infection of the cells lining the intestine. The symptoms include

COOPERATIVE) LEARNING

AN UNFOLDING DRAMA. The history of battles waged and won in the area of public health includes many dramatic breakthroughs (e.g., the discovery of bacteria; the development of penicillin and various vaccines; the treatment of diabetes; the cures for pellagra, scurvy, and rickets) as well as heartbreaking setbacks. In the field of HIV/AIDS research, the story is unfolding before our eyes on television and radio and in the pages of newspapers, journals, and magazines. Encourage students to start a class scrapbook of current developments in AIDS research, consisting of articles clipped from a variety of sources.

extreme weight loss, weakness, fever, diarrhea, nausea, and inability to absorb food.

Research and Treatment

The search for a vaccine to prevent HIV infection is ongoing. Research is also being done on medical treatments to prolong the life of persons infected with HIV and even reverse symptoms of HIV-related illnesses and AIDS. Scientists have isolated chemicals that need to be present in a person's body in order for HIV to infect that person's cells. Understanding how the virus works is a key to finding out how to stop it from reproducing.

Once HIV enters the body, it begins producing copies of itself at a rate of about one billion a day. Every day the body produces new immune cells to fight the virus, and eventually the immune system becomes exhausted and overwhelmed by the virus. To prevent this from occurring, researchers have geared their treatment efforts toward attacking the virus as soon as possible after the initial infection.

The U.S. Food and Drug Administration has approved several new medications that interfere with HIV's ability to reproduce. A new class of medications, *protease inhibitors* (PROH-tee-ayz in-HIB-uh-tuhrs), when used in combination with other antiviral medications such as zidovudine (zih-DOH-vyoo-deen) (AZT) and 3TC, has considerably reduced the amount of HIV in infected individuals. A recently completed clinical trial has determined that giving AZT to a pregnant woman significantly reduces the rate of maternal-fetal transmission of HIV. Effective treatments for AIDS-OIs are prolonging the lives—and improving the quality of life—of people with HIV.

▼ *Trace the reaction of HIV as it is blocked by medications used in treatment of the virus.*

TRIPLE THREAT

Combining these drugs seems to be the most effective strategy in halting the virus. Current research shows that the cocktail works best when administered within a few months of infection.

AZT   3TC   PROTEASE DRUG

DNA

1. HIV enters a cell

2. AZT and 3TC disrupt an early stage of the virus' reproduction

3. Protease inhibitors block the final stage of reproduction

4. As a result, no additional virus is produced

Good News, Bad News

keeping Fit

Discuss with students how a person's life might be affected if the person were HIV infected. Draw the health triangle on the chalkboard, labeling its sides with the areas of health. Ask students to consider how each side could be negatively affected by HIV infection. Summarize their ideas according to each side.

Draw a second health triangle and have students think of personal characteristics and systems of support that would help the HIV-infected person respond positively to the circumstance. Again, summarize their ideas. Conclude by pointing out that HIV infection can affect all areas of a person's health, but personal strength and support can help the individual cope.

L3 Writing

Have students research and report on the latest developments in the research for a vaccine, treatments, and a cure for AIDS. Have them summarize their findings in the form of a research paper.

L1 Researching

Ask students to locate and read magazine articles that relate the experiences of AIDS patients and/or the relatives and friends of AIDS patients. Let students meet in groups to summarize and discuss these articles.

SCHOOL-TO-CAREER

AIDS AND THE WORKPLACE. People with AIDS have at times faced discrimination at school and work. In most cases, laws prevented employers from firing them. However, discrimination can take other forms. Have students research media reports dating back to 1990. Have workers been treated so badly they were forced to quit? Have colleagues or customers shunned or avoided them? Upon leaving work because of harassment or extreme illness, did they lose their badly needed insurance benefits? After they research media reports, suggest that students create a list of questions to ask large employers in the area about their policies regarding workers who contract AIDS. Suggest that they include questions about insurance coverage and what happens when AIDS workers become too ill to work.

Building Health Skills

Classroom Resource Folder for AIDS Information
Skill: Assessing Health Information

Help the class review some of the most recent findings about the prevention and treatment of HIV and AIDS. Ask: Why is it so important to be familiar with reliable new information about HIV and AIDS? After a brief discussion, let students read the feature to find out how they can compile their own information resource folder on a classroom computer. Guide students in discussing the importance of each listed guideline, and then ask volunteers to be in charge of setting up the classroom folder. Other students should be encouraged to contribute to the folder, and it should be made available to all class members, as well as to other interested students.

L3 Class Activity

Have a group of students develop a questionnaire to be used in their school to poll students as to how they feel about AIDS. Have another group design a questionnaire to determine how much students in their school know about AIDS. Distribute the questionnaires to volunteer respondents. Respondents should not put their names on the questionnaires. Have the group work together to post the responses under the categories "age/grade" and "number of health education classes taken." Then ask students to make a graph of the information gathered.

Building Health Skills

Assessing Health Information: Classroom Resource Folder for AIDS Information

INFORMATION ABOUT HIV, AIDS, and the number of people they affect is being revised almost constantly. Having information that is up-to-the-minute is critical in preventing the spread of this dreaded virus and educating the public at large. One way of doing so is by maintaining an AIDS information resource folder on your classroom computer. Here are some guidelines for getting started:

1. **Contact reputable sources.** These include organizations such as the Centers for Disease Control and Prevention and the National Institutes of Health.

2. **Communicate your needs.** In requesting information, remember that much of the literature published by scientific organizations is intended for health professionals and may, therefore, be beyond your level of comprehension. Specify fact sheets, press releases, and other print materials intended for a non-scientist audience.

3. **Update the contents of your file regularly.** In the world of HIV/AIDS research, nothing stays the same for long. The CDC updates statistics at 6-month intervals. Make sure to do the same with your resource folder.

Obstacles to Research and Treatment

Despite the supposed promise of cutting-edge research and treatment, a number of obstacles remain in the fight against HIV and AIDS. One is the nature of the virus itself. HIV belongs to a family of viruses called *retroviruses*, which reproduce in a manner that makes them difficult to combat. Since HIV was first detected, moreover, several new strains of the virus have emerged, further complicating the already enormous difficulties of developing an effective vaccine. Another obstacle to research is lack of appropriate animal models. Still another roadblock is the issue of affordability of treatment. The combination therapies cost tens of thousands of dollars a year, putting them out of the financial reach of many patients.

Preventing the Spread of HIV

Although the hopes of ever finding a cure or vaccine for HIV infection are uncertain at this point, there is some cause for optimism. HIV is, for the most part, preventable. By avoiding high-risk behaviors, staying informed, and making responsible decisions, you can protect yourself and others from infection.

HEALTH LITERACY

RESPONSIBLE/PRODUCTIVE CITIZEN. Encourage students to investigate community organizations that provide support for AIDS patients. Such organizations might include local chapters of national AIDS groups, hospices, support groups, medical clinics, and testing sites. Suggest that they find out what type of volunteer help might be needed. Volunteers may wish to perform such tasks as stuffing envelopes, delivering flyers, or answering telephones. Most such organizations need money. Encourage students to hold a fund-raiser for organizations that support AIDS patients. They might raise funds through such activities as crafts sales, talent shows, car washes, pancake breakfasts, a booth outside a busy market, or door-to-door collections. They might also conduct a food drive for a hospice or other residential facility.

AIDS Education

As opposed to a mere epidemic, AIDS is a *pandemic*—an outbreak of infectious disease of global proportions. The first step toward altering the picture is educating the public. As Dr. C. Everett Koop, former U.S. Surgeon General, has said, "It is important that we all understand this disease, but it is particularly important for young people who are more often involved in behaviors that put them at risk for getting AIDS."

Abstinence and HIV/AIDS

As noted earlier, a person infected with HIV can look and feel healthy for months or years. As a result, a person can be lured into a false sense of security regarding physical intimacy. The only solution is **abstinence**. You need to say no not only to sexual activity but also to drugs. The following tips can help you practice abstinence from sexual activity and drugs:

- Avoid situations and events where drug use or the pressure to have sexual activity is likely to occur. If you are at a party where things are getting out of control, leave immediately.
- Choose your relationships carefully. Avoid forming a dating relationship with someone whom you know to be sexually active. Avoid known drug users or people who approve of drug use.
- Learn and practice **refusal skills**. Information on strategies for saying no may be found in Chapter 13.

▲ *The AIDS quilt, spread over 24 acres in Washington, D.C.*

hotlink

abstinence For more information on abstinence and its importance, see Chapter 21, page 484.

refusal skills For more information on refusal skills and ways of saying no, see Chapter 13, page 304.

ASSESS

EVALUATING THE LESSON

Assign and discuss the Lesson 2 Review; then administer, grade, and discuss the *Lesson 89 Quiz* in the TCR.

RETEACHING

- Invite a health educator from the Public Health Department and an administrator from your school into class to discuss efforts that are being made to control the spread of AIDS in the community. Ask students to report on treatment available and testing procedures used to determine HIV infection.
- Ask students to complete *Reteaching Activity 89* in the TCR.

ENRICHMENT

- Assign each student to investigate one or more of the following subjects surrounding the AIDS issue: confidentiality of test results; mandatory AIDS testing; legal suits against people who have transmitted the disease; the FDA and the unavailability of certain experimental drugs; group homes for AIDS children; hospices for AIDS patients; and prejudice against people with the virus. Have students report their findings to the class. If possible, plan a panel discussion in which several or all of these issues are addressed in detail.
- Raise students' awareness and have them complete *Enrichment Activity 30*, "AIDS and Discrimination," in the TCR.

CLOSE

Tell students to determine what role they can play in preventing the spread of AIDS.

LESSON **2** *Review*

Reviewing Facts and Vocabulary

1. What tests are used to determine if a person is HIV-reactive?
2. List two medicines currently being used to treat AIDS.
3. Why is confidentiality an important aspect of HIV testing?

Thinking Critically

4. *Analyzing.* HIV/AIDS is not treated like other infectious diseases in the United States. What aspects of the disorder account for its unique status?
5. *Evaluating.* Should information about HIV and AIDS be part of the regular health education curriculum in public schools? Why or why not?

6. *Synthesizing.* Why might someone armed with knowledge about HIV/AIDS choose to continue to engage in high-risk behaviors?

Applying Health Skills

7. *In Your School.* Develop a one-minute public service announcement (PSA) to inform others about the importance of avoiding the spread of HIV by never doing drugs and remaining abstinent at this time in their lives. Submit the PSA to your school office to be read over the intercom during announcements.

LESSON 2   TREATMENT FOR HIV-RELATED ILLNESSES AND AIDS   **669**

Lesson 2 Review

Answers to Reviewing Facts and Vocabulary

1. ELISA screens for the presence of HIV antibodies. A reactive ELISA is followed by a confirmatory test (Western blot test, IFA, or RIA).
2. Any two: protease inhibitors, AZT, 3TC.
3. Answers will vary but should reflect an understanding of privacy issues.

Answers to Thinking Critically

4. Answers should reflect an understanding of the means by which HIV is spread and the fact that there is no currently known cure.
5. Answers will vary.
6. Answers will vary.

Health **Skills** Activities

Health Skills Activities

ACTIVITY 1
HEALTH SKILLS

Comprehending Health Concepts, Health Advocacy

➤ **National Standards**
This activity meets these National Health Standards: 1.7; 1.8; 7.4.

Teach

- Based on the information provided about the TV documentary, students should form documentary groups based on assigned tasks, including writing, editing, research, and public speaking.
- If graphs are to be created by hand or on computer, groups should also contain individuals responsible for this task.
- Challenge groups to include information in their documentaries on where health experts envision the HIV/AIDS epidemic in another ten, 15, and 20 years.

ACTIVITY 2
HEALTH SKILLS

Communication—Refusal Skills

➤ **National Standards**
This activity meets these National Health Standards: 5.4; 5.5; 5.6.

Teach

- Bring to class or assign students to bring to class a pair of dice, discarded buttons, shirt cardboards, and other materials that will be used in the activity.
- Urge students with art and design skills to team with students who have strong organization skills. Both are vital to the design of an effective game.
- Students who are to function as judges should be well-versed in refusal skills and key points of the chapter. They should be prepared, when called upon, to explain their decisions.

Activity 1 — HIV/AIDS in the United States

The United States is among the world's most advanced nations, yet we continue to see new cases of HIV/AIDS reported.

Directions

1. With several classmates, create a live documentary presentation on the problem of HIV/AIDS. Use information in the chapter and gathered through research.
2. Note the problem's extent, how it is being dealt with, and your evaluation of the costs associated with ongoing research, caring for the sick, and loss in productivity.
3. Perform your documentary for the class.
4. Offer time for a question-and-answer session.

Time
50 minutes

Materials
paper, pen or pencil, library or Internet information

Self-Assessment

✓ Identified at least three risks of contracting HIV/AIDS in your documentary.
✓ Frankly evaluated the HIV/AIDS problem.
✓ Listed at least two prevention strategies.

Activity 2 — Lines of Defense

Abstaining from sexual intercourse is the only 100-percent effective way to protect yourself from HIV/AIDS. Yet, standing your ground under intense peer pressure can be difficult. The board game you are about to create may help.

Directions

1. Write each of 15 or so high-pressure come-ons on one side of an index card. Brainstorm responses for each. Write these on a sheet of paper.
2. Rule off squares around the outside of a sheet of poster board. Label some squares "Pick a card." Others should have to do with navigating the board (e.g., "Lose a turn," "Advance 3 spaces").
3. Place the cards face-down at the center. Two players take turns rolling dice and answering come-ons. A third student compares each response with the answer sheet. First to circle the board wins.

Time
50 minutes

Materials
poster board, pair of dice, colored markers, ruler, index cards, buttons

Self-Assessment

✓ Suggested responses that support the decision to practice abstinence for each high-pressure come-on presented.
✓ Created a colorful and interesting board game.

ASSESSMENT SCORING

Using a four-level rubric, the student has achieved a 4 if:

ACTIVITY 1

✔ Student identified risk practices that could lead to the contracting of HIV/AIDS.
✔ Student frankly evaluated the HIV/AIDS problem.
✔ Student accurately reported costs associated with this problem.
✔ Student listed at least two prevention strategies.

ACTIVITY 2

✔ Student was able to develop come-ons or at least stimulate development of these lines.
✔ Student suggested responses that support the decision to practice abstinence for each pressure line presented.
✔ Student helped create an interesting game.
✔ Game worked as intended and was clearly organized.

A New Image of HIV

How can you fight something if you don't know what it looks like? That's the problem scientists face when they treat a new disease. Now scientists have developed a computer model that presents a close-up of a deadly virus.

A recent experimental lab has created the first three-dimensional image of HIV, the virus that causes AIDS. The image can be rotated, color-coded, and analyzed to find weaknesses in the structure of the virus. Researchers hope this model will help them develop medicines that will take advantage of these once-invisible weaknesses.

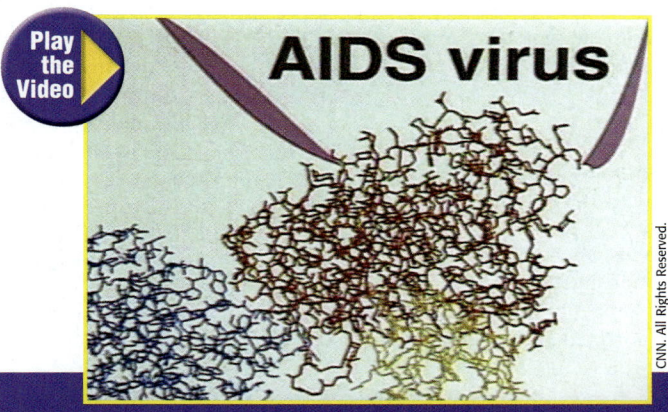

Play the Video

AIDS virus

CNN. All Rights Reserved.

Think About It

- How can this imaging technology contribute to preventing and curing AIDS?

- Researchers explain that the HIV virus wears an outer layer of sugar molecules. Why do they compare this strategy to "a criminal wearing a disguise"?

- What is an "Achilles heel"? What do researchers at the Dana-Farber Cancer Institute believe might be the Achilles heel of HIV?

CNN HEALTH NEWS **671**

Objectives. After viewing the video, students should be able to assess the potential of three-dimensional image technology as a step toward the prevention and cure of HIV and AIDS.

Motivator. Draw a square on the chalkboard. Then draw a three-dimensional picture of a cube. Ask students to tell which picture provides more detail. Then show Video Segment 19, "A New Image of HIV," which demonstrates how using three-dimensional imaging can help give scientists a clearer picture of the HIV virus, which causes AIDS.

Teach

- Review the terminology used in the video. Explain that HIV is a virus that causes an STD called AIDS (Acquired Immunodeficiency Syndrome).
- Discuss how generating images of viruses can help scientists understand how the virus works. This can help them discover treatments that effectively interfere with the virus's functions.

Decision Making. Have students contemplate whether they could learn more about HIV by studying a photograph or a computer model of the virus. Through discussion, students should recognize that a photograph can be difficult to read and may not make the elements or processes of the virus clear; a computer model is a dimensional diagram that simplifies the structure of the virus to make the essential elements clear. Compare the two types of viral data with an aerial photograph and a map of the same region.

Close. Have students explain whether the three-dimensional imaging described in this video might be useful when researching diseases other than HIV. Students should understand that this type of image could help scientists find treatments or cures for many different diseases with unknown or unfamiliar structures.

MORE ABOUT . . . . .

ASK THE EXPERTS. Many imaging projects use the expertise and knowledge of a medical or scientific illustrator. These artists use their graphic skills to create clear and accurate depictions of elements and processes from biology, chemistry, or other fields of science.

Most medical illustrators have a master's degree from a graduate school program. High school students interested in this field should select coursework focusing on both arts and sciences. College students on this career track typically major in fine arts and minor in a specific science.

Today, practicing medical illustrators receive accreditation from the Commission on Accreditation of Allied Health Educational Programs (CAAHEP).

CHECKING COMPREHENSION

- Assign and discuss the chapter review.
- Use the MindJogger Videoquiz to review the chapter. 🔴

CHAPTER 30 REVIEW ANSWERS

Using Health Terms

1. human immunodeficiency virus (HIV)
2. intravenous (IV) drugs
3. acquired immune deficiency syndrome (AIDS)
4. latency
5. HIV-reactive
6. confirmatory test
7. AIDS-opportunistic illnesses (AIDS-OIs)
8. ELISA (EIA)

Recalling the Facts

1. AIDS is the final stage of infection with HIV.
2. It decreases the number of T-helper cells.
3. Semen, blood, vaginal secretions, and breast milk.
4. The ability of the immune system to fight pathogens is reduced, and the body becomes more vulnerable to certain illnesses.
5. ELISA (EIA). A confirmatory test is performed.
6. Two weeks to six months.
7. From six months to 10–12 years.
8. The virus is a retrovirus, difficult to combat; there are several strains; lack of appropriate animal models; combination therapies are very costly.
9. AIDS education and abstinence from sex and drugs.
10. Abstain from sex and abstain from the use of drugs.
11. They impair judgment in regard to sexual activity and drug use.
12. It is the primary means by which HIV is spread.

CHAPTER 30 Review

Using Health Terms

On a separate sheet of paper, write the term that best matches each definition below.

LESSON 1

1. A virus that attacks the body's immune system.
2. Drugs that are injected into the veins.
3. HIV infection combined with severe immune deficiency.

LESSON 2

4. A period of months or years during which the virus is present in the blood but there are no symptoms or signs of disease.

5. Infected with HIV.
6. A highly accurate test used to confirm the results of a reactive ELISA.
7. Infections and other diseases caused by organisms that do not usually produce illness in healthy people with unimpaired immune systems.
8. A test that screens for the presence of HIV antibodies in the blood.

Recalling the Facts

Using complete sentences, answer the following questions.

LESSON 1

1. What is the connection between HIV infection and AIDS?
2. How does HIV attack the body's immune system?
3. Through which body fluids is HIV known to be transmitted?
4. What happens when T-helper cells become infected and are destroyed?

LESSON 2

5. What is the first test used for detecting HIV? What happens if the results of this test are reactive?
6. How long may the body take to develop antibodies to HIV after being infected?
7. How long can HIV stay in the body before a person shows signs of infection?
8. What are some of the obstacles that stand in the way of research and treatment for AIDS patients?

9. AIDS is not curable, but it is preventable. What are the best methods of prevention?
10. Name two ways teens can reduce their risk of HIV infection.
11. How can using alcohol and illegal drugs increase a person's risk of HIV infection?
12. What role does sexual intercourse play in the spread of HIV?
13. What are two suggestions for practicing abstinence when pressure to engage in sexual activity arises? For practicing abstinence when it comes to drugs?

---

13. Any two for each form of abstinence: avoid situations where pressure to have sex (or use drugs) is likely; choose relationships carefully; learn and practice refusal skills.

Thinking Critically

LESSON 1

1. *Analyzing.* Indicate which of the following behaviors are known to transmit HIV from an infected person to an uninfected person.
   a. sexual intercourse
   b. kissing with the mouth closed
   c. sharing contaminated needles
   d. sharing bathroom facilities
   e. receiving a blood transfusion
   f. being stung by a wasp
   g. donating blood
   h. breast-feeding a baby

2. *Evaluating.* Why do you think many people are uninformed about HIV infection and AIDS?

LESSON 2

3. *Analyzing.* What makes opportunistic infections more dangerous for individuals who are HIV-reactive than for persons who are not infected with HIV?

4. *Synthesizing.* Outline an HIV-prevention program aimed at teens entering high school, emphasizing not doing drugs, ever, and not becoming sexually active before marriage.

Making the Connection

1. *Math.* Through June of 1997, the CDC had received reports of 612,078 cases of AIDS. By exposure category, 84 percent were adult or adolescent males, 15 percent were adult or adolescent females, and 1 percent were children under 13 years of age. Create a pie graph that reflects this information.

2. *Science.* Find out about the important discoveries made by one or more of the following researchers: Dr. David Ho, Dr. Robert Gallo, Flossie Wong-Staal, Irving Sigal, or Dr. Peter Piot. Report your findings to the class.

BEYOND THE CLASSROOM

PARENTAL INVOLVEMENT Ask your parents or other adults at home how they learned about HIV and AIDS. Ask them to discuss the quality of the information they were given. Talk with them about the best ways for young people to learn about HIV and AIDS.

COMMUNITY INVOLVEMENT Find out what organizations in your community are helping people with HIV infection and AIDS. Make a list of these organizations and include information about the services each provides. Use the information you have gathered to produce a pamphlet on the classroom computer that can be made available through the school health office.

SCHOOL-TO-CAREER
Resources. Investigate the educational requirements, special skills—including interpersonal skills—time, experience, and other important information about the work of an epidemiologist specializing in HIV and AIDS research. You might start by contacting the American Medical Association, 515 North State Street, Chicago, IL 60610.

CHAPTER 30 REVIEW **673**

Thinking Critically

1. Sexual intercourse, sharing contaminated needles, receiving a blood transfusion, and breast-feeding a baby.
2. Answers should reflect an understanding of the fear many feel, of the tendency toward denial, and of widespread misunderstanding.
3. Those infected with HIV have a reduced ability to fight pathogens.
4. Outlines will vary.

Making the Connection

1. Graphs should reflect appropriate proportions.
2. Reports will vary according to topic.

Evaluate

- Use the reproducible *Chapter 30 Test* in the TCR, or construct your own using the Testmaker software.
- Use *Performance Assessment Activity 30* in the TCR.

Enrichment

Ask students to complete *Cross-Curriculum Activity 30* in the TCR.

Beyond the Classroom

Keep students involved in the community, and encourage parent participation by assigning the activities on this page for students to work on outside of class.

Noninfectious Diseases and Disabilities

	FEATURES	CLASSROOM RESOURCES

ACTIVITIES

- Cross-Curriculum Activity 31
- Health Lab 31
- Health Skills Activities 31
- Parent Letter and Activities 31

ASSESSMENT

- Chapter 31 Test
- Performance Assessment Activity 31
- Testmaker Software

STUDENT ACTIVITIES WORKBOOK

- Applying Health Skills 90–93
- Study Guide 31
- Vocabulary Activity 31

STUDENT DIVERSITY STRATEGIES

- Audiocassette Program (English)
- Audiocassette Program (Spanish)
- Spanish Parent Letters and Activities
- Spanish Summaries, Quizzes, and Activities

MULTIMEDIA COMPONENTS

- English Audiocassette Program
- Spanish Audiocassette Program
- MindJogger Videodisc and VHS program

National Health Education Standards

One of the main goals of the National Health Education Standards is to move students toward "health literacy." Health literacy is the capacity of individuals to obtain, interpret, and understand basic health information and services and the competence to use such information and services in ways which promote health. The health standards were developed by applying the characteristics of a well-educated, literate person within the context of health. The health literate person is:

- a critical thinker and problem solver
- a self-directed learner
- a responsible, productive citizen
- an effective communicator

Listed below are the Health Education Standards Performance Indicators addressed in each lesson of this chapter.

Lesson	Health Standards Performance Indicators
1	1.3, 1.4, 1.6, 3.3
2	1.6, 1.8, 2.6, 4.3
3	1.1, 1.6, 2.6, 6.1
4	2.6, 3.5, 3.6, 6.1

ONLINE RESOURCES

For a fresh approach to health topics and an in-depth look at health issues, use these online resources found under Teacher Resources at **health.glencoe.com**.

- **BLOCK SCHEDULE LESSON PLANS** Reinforce health concepts with outside readings selected especially for students. Each reading is accompanied by a lesson plan and activities to enhance
  - Reading Skills
  - Cross Curriculum
  - Media Literacy

- **TECHNOLOGY PROJECTS** Instructions and suggestions on how to use computer, Internet, and software with health lessons.

- **HEALTH UPDATES** Timely topics in health news, including late-breaking medical advances and updates on teen risk behaviors.

Out of Time?

If time does not permit teaching this chapter, you may use these features: Building Health Skills on page 685; Update on page 687; and Making Responsible Decisions on page 691.

BLOCK SCHEDULING

Block scheduling provides extended time for hands-on projects and activities. Use the following activities to engage students, provide further depth, and vary your instructional techniques:

- Health Lab (30 minutes) **pg. 678**
- Update (30 minutes) **pg. 687**
- Health Skills Activity (60–90 minutes) **pg. 698**

Noninfectious Diseases and Disabilities

CHAPTER OVERVIEW

Chapter 31 discusses the symptoms, causes, treatments, and prevention of common noninfectious diseases.

LESSON 1 Cardiovascular disease is closely related to one's lifestyle. The symptoms and causes of various cardiovascular diseases and stroke are presented in this lesson, along with the advances made in treating the diseases. Prevention is best achieved through lifestyle intervention.

LESSON 2 Generally, all cancers constitute abnormal, uncontrolled cell growth. Diagnosis is best achieved by a medical exam, though early warning signs can alert one to its presence. The treatments for cancer include surgery, radiation, and chemotherapy.

LESSON 3 This lesson describes how diabetes functions and the types of diabetes. Diabetes cannot be cured, though it can be controlled. The types of arthritis and treatments for it are also presented in this lesson.

LESSON 4 Disability can interfere with an individual's performance of everyday tasks. A few of the more common disabilities that result from physical and mental impairments are identified. The importance of eliminating barriers that hinder individuals with a disability from reaching their potential is also addressed.

CHAPTER 31

Noninfectious Diseases and Disabilities

HEALTH Online

ACCESSING INFORMATION

What can a piece of clothing do to help a person suffering from a disease? An exciting new technology incorporates medical technology into a Lifesaving Vest. Read the facts in "Dressed to Live" in Health Updates at health.glencoe.com.

Hands-On Health

TEACHING STRATEGY

Making Healthy Choices Help students recognize how their own health-related choices and lifestyle decisions affect their futures. See Activity 1, "Three Wishes," in the *Hands-On Health: Creative Teaching Strategies* booklet. ▱

Time Needed

15 to 20 minutes

Supplies

• decorated stick for "magic wand"
• copies of "Letter from a Doctor"

CHAPTER 31

> **The more serious the illness, the more important it is for you to fight back, mobilizing all your resources— spiritual, emotional, intellectual, and physical.**
>
> —NORMAN COUSINS
> WRITER, HUMANITARIAN, (1915-1990)

Quick Write Jot down five steps you can take regularly to increase the chances you will stay healthy and avoid the risks of preventable diseases. How many of these steps are you already taking each day?

Personal Health Inventory

Self-Inventory Write the numbers 1–10 on a sheet of paper. Read each statement below and respond by writing *yes, no,* or *sometimes* for each item. Write a *yes* only for items that you practice regularly. Save your responses.

1	I avoid being around people who are smoking.
2	I abstain from using tobacco products myself.
3	I avoid adding salt to my food without first tasting it.
4	I eat foods high in fiber, including fruits and vegetables.
5	I keep my weight at an acceptable level.
6	I use some effective ways to relax.
7	I use a sunscreen when participating in activities out of doors.
8	I exercise aerobically at least three times a week.
9	I can identify some of the special challenges that people with disabilities face.
10	I am aware of ways in which my community has met or failed to meet the needs of people with special challenges.

Follow-up After completing the chapter, retake this self-inventory. Pick two items that you need to work on and set a goal to improve your health behaviors.

CHAPTER 31 NONINFECTIOUS DISEASES AND DISABILITIES **675**

TECHNOLOGY OPTIONS

MINDJOGGER
VIDEOQUIZ

To preview or review chapter content, you may wish to use the *MindJogger Videoquiz* that accompanies Chapter 31.

INTRODUCING THE CHAPTER

Personal Health Inventory

Let students read and discuss the Self-Inventory statements: How do these behaviors relate to protecting your physical health? your mental and emotional health? your social health? After a brief discussion, have students record their own *yes, no,* or *sometimes* responses in their private Health Journals on a page labeled "Noninfectious Diseases and Disabilities." Remind students that they will review and revise their responses in the follow-up activity at the end of Chapter 31.

- Ask students to make a list of any ten diseases. Remind them that a disease that can be passed from one person to another is called an infectious disease. Have students identify the diseases on their lists that a person cannot "catch" from another person. Explain that those diseases are noninfectious diseases. Tell students that they will learn about these conditions in this chapter.

- Have students read the quotation and share their thoughts on this attitude expressed by Cousins. Have them complete the Quick Write and discuss ways that they can influence their health by their attitudes. Then tell students that, as they study the lessons in Chapter 31, they will learn more about the link between lifestyle choices and specific diseases.

- Distribute Parent Letter 31 in the *Parent Letters and Activities* booklet.

Chapter 31 **675**

FOCUS

LESSON OBJECTIVES

After studying this lesson, students should be able to

- identify the risk factors of cardiovascular disease.
- describe hypertension and identify factors related to it.
- define and describe arteriosclerosis.
- describe diseases of the heart.
- identify the signs of stroke.
- explain the means of treating cardiovascular diseases.

MOTIVATOR

Write the following on the chalkboard for students to work on while attendance is being taken: *Write a definition for the term noninfectious disease and list three examples of this type of disease.*

INTRODUCING THE LESSON

Refer to the Motivator. Ask volunteers to share their responses. On the chalkboard, write the correct definition and the correct examples given by the students. Explain that this lesson will focus on two noninfectious diseases—cardiovascular disease and stroke. Tell students this lesson will help them learn the types and causes of these noninfectious diseases, which are the leading causes of death in the United States.

INTRODUCING HEALTH TERMS

- Have students define each vocabulary term and use it in a sentence.
- Ask students to complete Vocabulary Activity 31 and Chapter Study Guide 31 in the *Student Workbook.*

LESSON 1

Lifestyle Diseases

When people hear the word *disease,* they often think of a condition that is contagious, or "catching." Yet, one of the greatest threats today is a group of *diseases that are not transmitted by means of a pathogen.* While you cannot "catch" a heart attack or "come down" with a stroke, these and other **noninfectious diseases** are linked to real risk factors.

HEALTH TERMS

noninfectious diseases

cardiovascular diseases (CVDs)

hypertension

arteriosclerosis

angina pectoris

fibrillation

congestive heart failure

stroke

HEALTH CONCEPTS

- Many cardiovascular diseases relate to a person's habits and lifestyle.
- Adopting positive habits now, while you are young, can help set you on the road to good health for life.

hotlink

circulatory system For more information on the circulatory system and its functions, see Chapter 17, page 388.

What Is Cardiovascular Disease?

What do you think is the number one killer in the United States today? It is cardiovascular disease, or *CVD.* **Cardiovascular diseases** are *medical disorders that affect the heart and blood vessels.* The heart and blood vessels are two key parts of the **circulatory system**.

According to the Centers for Disease Control and Prevention, CVDs account for over 45 percent of all deaths among persons in the United States aged 45 years or over. The lifestyle choices and health habits you adopt now can

---

Lesson 1 Resources

TEACHER'S CLASSROOM RESOURCES

- Concept Map Activity 90
- Health Lab 31
- Lesson 90 Quiz
- Lesson Plan 90
- Parent Letter and Activities 31
- Reteaching Activity 90

STUDENT WORKBOOK

- Applying Health Skills 90
- Chapter Study Guide 31
- Vocabulary Activity 31

have a direct influence on whether you will be a candidate for a CVD in the future.

Risk Factors for Cardiovascular Disease

A number of risk factors have been identified that increase a person's chances of developing a CVD. Five of these risk factors—heredity, ethnicity, gender, age, and environment—are beyond a person's control.

■ **Heredity.** A tendency toward heart disease runs in families. If one or both parents had a CVD, one's chances of developing it are higher. Children of parents with **hypertension**, or *high blood pressure,* are also more likely to develop this CVD.

■ **Ethnicity.** Some ethnic groups are at greater risk than others for developing CVDs. For example, African Americans are twice as likely as whites to develop high blood pressure. The reasons for this remain unknown at present.

■ **Gender.** Males have a greater risk of heart disease and stroke than females. At the same time, the latest studies indicate that heart attack is the number one killer among American women and that their chances of survival are lower than those of men.

■ **Age.** Risk of CVDs increases with age. Heart attack death rates increase markedly after the age of 45, with 55 percent of all heart attack victims being 65 or older. Risk of stroke also increases dramatically with age.

■ **Environment.** Environmental factors such as smog are beyond your control, another form of air pollution—tobacco smoke from another person's cigar, pipe, or cigarette—is often avoidable. Stress, likewise, is a controllable environmental risk factor.

Behavior

Although the factors identified in the previous section are beyond the individual's ability to control, a fifth risk factor is not. That factor is behavior. Making the right healthful choices now, while you are young, can reduce your risk of developing a CVD later in life. These choices include ample physical activity, electing not to smoke, and moderation and balance in your food selections. Because of the link between lifestyle and CVDs, these diseases are sometimes referred to as "lifestyle diseases."

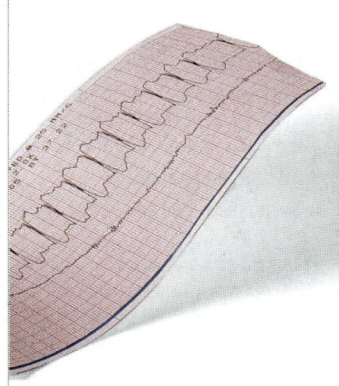

TEACH

LD Class Activity

LD students may have difficulty reading this lesson independently. Provide a skeletal outline for them to follow and fill in during class discussion.

L1 Discussing

Lead a discussion of how the lifestyle choices students make today (the health habits they have developed and practiced) relate directly to their potential for developing a cardiovascular disease. Ask: Is it easier to change unhealthy habits now or when recovering from a heart attack?

L1 Cooperative Learning

Divide students into groups. Give each group a poster and have them divide the poster into three sections. Label one section *Risk Factors for Cardiovascular Disease.* Label the next section *Factors I Cannot Change* and the third, *Factors I Can Change.* Have each group discuss specific ways to reduce the risk factors of its members. Ask each group to develop a plan on how to reduce risk factors for cardiovascular disease.

L2 Researching

Have students make a chart of foods preferred by teens and society as a whole. Make sure they include the number of calories and amount of cholesterol in each food.

CURRICULUM CONNECTIONS

PHYSICAL EDUCATION. Set aside a time when students can meet in the gym to practice taking their target heart rates. Explain the importance of exercise in preventing cardiovascular disease and steps that should be taken for them to receive optimal benefit from the exercise. Using the formula in Chapter 3, have students calculate their target heart rates. Select an aerobic activity for the students. Have them check at intervals to see if they are performing in the effective, beneficial range. After returning to the classroom, compare the resting heart rates of athletes and others who participate in regular aerobic exercise programs with those who do not.

health lab

HOW MUCH IS ENOUGH?

Time Needed: About 20 minutes on each of two days

Understanding Objectives:
Students will compare their own concepts of serving sizes with those identified in the Food Pyramid Guide.

Focus on the Health Lab:
Show students some favorite foods, or pictures of favorite foods, and ask: To which food group does each belong? How many servings are recommended as part of your daily diet? What constitutes a single serving?

Observation and Analysis:
Let students work in small groups to follow the Health Lab steps. Have group members work cooperatively to estimate the correct serving size for each food. Ask students to form the same groups about a week later, to repeat the experiment.

In Conclusion Answers:
Answers will vary. Let group members discuss and record their ideas.

Further Investigation:
Suggest that students measure correct serving sizes for other foods they commonly choose.

L1 Class Activity

Ask the class to explain this statement: *High blood pressure is a "silent killer."* Point out that high blood pressure makes the heart work harder. Challenge students to compare the action in the heart and arteries that creates blood pressure to a water hose and nozzle in respect to water pressure. *(The smaller the nozzle opening is, the more pressure is put on the inside walls of the hose.)*

---

health lab

HOW MUCH IS ENOUGH?

When it comes to food, a problem for many Americans is not only *what* they eat but *how much.* Learning to identify healthful portions can be a first step in controlling the tendency to overeat—not to mention the risk of CVDs in the future.

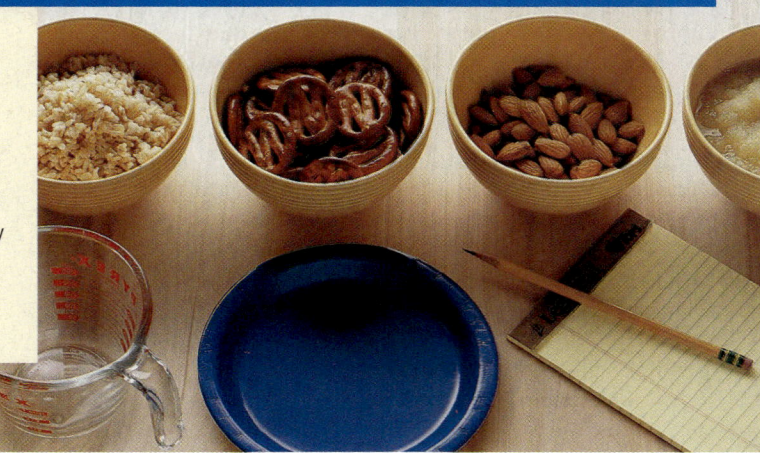

What you will need

- Large bowls of the following foods: applesauce, cooked rice or pasta, unsalted pretzels, and shelled nuts.
- A 1-cup measuring cup
- Paper plate, pad and pencil

What you will do

1. Begin by consulting the Food Guide Pyramid on page 114 for suggested single servings of each of the foods you have assembled.

2. Transfer what you imagine to be a single serving of one of the foods onto a paper plate. Let your eyes alone judge quantity.

3. Using the measuring cup, measure out a 1-cup portion of the same food onto a second paper plate. Record any differences you observe between the two portions.

4. Repeat the procedure with the other three foods. Again, note any differences.

5. After several days, repeat the entire experiment again.

In conclusion

1. How close were you at estimating correct serving sizes? Did you become more proficient at "eye-balling" correct amounts when you repeated the experiment?

2. Were the recommended serving sizes less or more of each food than you normally eat?

Types of Cardiovascular Diseases

The heart, blood, and arteries are the principal parts of the circulatory system. When these parts work together properly, the circulatory system runs efficiently. When a problem affects one part, the entire system is threatened.

Hypertension

Blood pressure is the force of blood against the walls of blood vessels as blood flows through the circulatory system. The force is created by the contraction of the heart muscle and the resistance of the vessel walls. Normal blood pressure varies with age, height, weight, and other factors. If a person's blood pressure stays above his or her

---

MORE ABOUT . . . . .

BLOOD PRESSURE. Blood pressure is expressed as two numbers, *X* over *Y*. *X* is the blood's pressure against the arteries when the heart is contracting and is called the systolic pressure. *Y* is the pressure against the arteries between contractions, when the heart is resting; it is called the diastolic pressure. The blood pressure range of a healthy teen or adult is 120/80, read "120 over 80." During heavy exercise, both the systolic and diastolic pressures rise. The instrument for measuring blood pressure is called a sphygmomanometer. Low blood pressure can be as unhealthy as high blood pressure. It causes transient lightheadedness, dizziness, and even fainting.

normal pressure, the person is said to have hypertension. An estimated 60 million Americans suffer from hypertension, which is both a disease and a causative factor in other CVDs. Because an individual may show no symptoms in the early stages, hypertension often goes undetected. Hypertension is, therefore, known as the "silent killer."

In many cases, the exact cause of hypertension is not known. However, many factors have been identified as being related to it, including the uncontrollable risk factors noted earlier. Controllable factors include obesity, alcohol use, inactivity, smoking, and excessive intake of salt or sodium.

Hypertension cannot be cured but can be controlled through basic lifestyle changes, such as eating well, losing excess weight, and exercise. In more extreme cases, medications are sometimes prescribed.

Diseases of the Arteries

At birth, the lining of the blood vessels is smooth. Over the years, fatty deposits, called *plaque,* build up along the inner lining of the arteries. This buildup is due mainly to food choices. If this buildup is permitted to continue, **arteriosclerosis** (ahr-tir-ee-oh-skluh-ROH-suhs), or *hardening of the arteries,* occurs. Arteriosclerosis is a condition in which the walls of the arteries become thick and lose their elasticity. It is the most common cause of death in the United States. Hypertension is a factor that contributes to arteriosclerosis.

As fatty deposits accumulate, blood vessels narrow. This condition, called *atherosclerosis* (ath-uh-roh-skluh-ROH-suhs), can result in blockage of the arteries. Foods high in fat and **cholesterol** are key contributing factors to atherosclerosis.

Diseases of the Heart

When atherosclerosis becomes severe enough, the blood vessels leading to the heart become blocked. Normal oxygen supply is cut off. The heart sends out a warning in the form of **angina pectoris** (AN-juh-nuh PEK-tuh-ris), or *pain and tightness in the chest caused by the lack of oxygen to the heart.* Angina is like an SOS from the body warning that the heart is in distress. Angina pain usually lasts a few minutes. Treatment includes medications that relax the blood vessels.

HEART ATTACK

If the distress of angina continues over time, eventually heart attack occurs. A heart attack is caused by insufficient oxygen and nutrients to the heart muscle cells. One and a half million people in the United States each year suffer heart attacks.

A heart attack can occur at any time and usually happens without warning. However, immediate response to the early signs, which include discomfort in the center of the chest, can mean the difference between life and death. The sensation of a heart attack may be one of pressure, fullness, squeezing, or aching. This distress may extend into one or both arms, the neck, jaw, upper abdomen, and even the back.

Are you "heart smart"? Visit **health.glencoe.com** to learn how to lower your risk of heart disease and recognize warning signs of heart attack and stroke. Take an online quiz to see how much you have learned.

hotlink

cholesterol For more information on the risks associated with elevated cholesterol levels, see Chapter 5, page 106.

Encourage students with home computers to share the self-quiz on protecting against heart attacks with adults in the home.

L1 Discussing

Refer to Chapter 3 on physical fitness. Ask students to discuss the effects of regular exercise on the heart.

L1 Discussing

Ask students to name some of the signs of a heart attack. Why do some people misinterpret the signs of a heart attack, thus denying and delaying medical attention?

L2 Researching

Tell students to determine the steps of first aid for a person complaining of chest pain, shortness of breath, and weakness. Have students make a chart of the ABCs of CPR. Students can contact the American Red Cross or the American Heart Association for materials, including posters for the class. Have them share and display the materials.

L2 Demonstrating

Bring an anatomical model of a heart to class and demonstrate the chambers of the heart and how cardiovascular problems can occur. Display a chart of the circulatory system and explain how the blood is pumped throughout the body, carrying oxygen and nutrients to each cell.

L3 Researching

Select volunteers to read about the Framingham Heart Studies. Ask them to report on the purpose and the findings of the studies.

L1 Discussing

Discuss reasons why some people fail to attach importance to the findings of scientific studies that examine the relationship between disease and lifestyle.

Myths & Realities

MYTH. Only old people have heart attacks.
FACT. Congenital heart defects, diseases, and use of drugs can cause heart attacks at an early age.

MYTH. Most people with heart disease die suddenly.
FACT. Heart disease is a silent killer; the progression of the disease can take years before actually causing a heart attack.

MYTH. Cigarette smokers do not have a higher death rate from heart attack than nonsmokers do.
FACT. Smoking does increase the risk of heart attack. It causes the blood vessels to constrict, decreasing blood flow to the cells. It increases blood pressure and strains the heart. It releases carbon monoxide into the blood, decreasing the oxygen supply in the blood.

L1 Discussing

Ask class members to list some of the major signs of a stroke. Under what conditions is a cerebral hemorrhage likely to occur? What are some of the effects of stroke on the body?

L2 Researching

Have students research and report on local medical assistance available to stroke victims.

L3 Researching

Select students to research the relationship of strokes to the following risk factors: obesity, high-fat diets, and smoking.

L2 Discussing

Ask the class what a catheter is. How is it used in coronary angiography?

L1 Explaining

Explain the procedure of coronary bypass surgery. What is its purpose?

L1 Writing

Have students write essays about specific steps they can take to make their own lifestyles more heart-healthy. Ask them to share their essays during a round-table discussion.

L1 Community Involvement

Encourage students to become involved with an organization such as the American Heart Association. They could join or initiate a fund-raising campaign (such as a bike-a-thon or walk-a-thon). Have them consider involving other class-rooms, schools, neighborhoods, or the PTA.

hotlink

cardiopulmonary resuscitation (CPR) For more information on the lifesaving technique of cardiopulmonary resuscitation (CPR), see Chapter 35, page 781.

Early signs of a heart attack can include a tightness in the chest, sensation in the arms or back, and shortness of breath.

ACTIVITY *List the causes of heart attack and of congestive heart failure.*

Nausea, vomiting, sweating, and shortness of breath may accompany the attack. A person with these symptoms should seek medical attention immediately.

Depending on the amount of tissue death, a heart attack can cause death or a decrease in heart function. An immediate cause of death in many heart attacks is **fibrillation**—*the rapid ineffective beating of the heart in one of two chambers called ventricles.* Ventricular fibrillation is also known as "cardiac arrest." When this occurs, **cardiopulmonary resuscitation (CPR)** should be initiated as soon as possible.

Heart attack is related to many risk factors, such as high levels of cholesterol in the blood. Cholesterol builds up inside the scarred arteries, which can lead to fatal blockages. Studies also link excess levels in the blood of *homocysteine* (hoh-moh-SIS-teen), a potentially deadly amino acid, to heart disease. Stress, another major risk factor, can increase other existing risk factors, such as overeating, smoking, and hypertension. People with Type A personalities may also be at higher risk.

CONGESTIVE HEART FAILURE

Heart attack is an immediate event in response to stress on the heart. Sometimes the result of years of arteriosclerosis and hypertension result not in heart attack but in **congestive heart failure,** *a slow, gradual weakening of the heart muscle from overwork.* Congestive heart failure can also be brought about by the use of certain illegal drugs.

Stroke

Sometimes arterial blockage affects the blood supply to the brain. When the blockage is severe, **stroke**—*an interruption of the flow of blood to any part of the brain*—may occur. Stroke can affect different parts of the body. The warning signs of stroke are:

- sudden weakness or numbness of the face, arm, and leg on one side of the body
- loss of speech, or trouble in speaking or understanding people
- sudden dimness or loss of vision, particularly in only one eye
- unexplained dizziness, unsteadiness, or sudden falls

There are various causes of stroke. One of the most common is the blocking of a cerebral artery by a blood clot, or *thrombus,* that forms inside the artery. Sometimes a diseased artery in the brain can burst and flood the surrounding brain tissue with blood. This damaging condition, called a *cerebral hemorrhage* (suh-REE-bruhl HEM-uh-rihj), is more likely to occur when a person suffers from a combination of atherosclerosis and hypertension.

HEALTH LITERACY

SELF-DIRECTED LEARNER. Encourage students to research the connection between diet, specific nutrients, and homocysteine levels. For example, suggest that they investigate the connection between consumption of meat and other methionine-rich foods with high levels of homocysteine. Have them read about studies linking betaine, vitamin B_6, vitamin B_{12}, and folic acid with lowered levels of homocysteine.

What evidence proves that these or other nutrients lower homocysteine levels? Do they work best individually or together? What levels of each nutrient are needed to lower homocysteine levels? Can these amounts be obtained from balanced meals, or would it require supplements to reach effective levels? Have them write a news article summarizing their findings.

Treating Cardiovascular Diseases

In recent decades there have been amazing advances in treating heart disease. These include new instruments and techniques for measuring electrical activity of the heart and the extent of the disease, as well as new surgical procedures.

- **Electrocardiogram.** An electrocardiogram (ih-lek-troh-KAR-dee-uh-gram)—or *EKG*—produces a graph of the electrical activity of the heart's rhythm. An EKG can help detect the nature of a heart attack and how the heart is behaving.

- **Radionuclide** (RAY-dee-oh-NOO-klyd) **imaging.** This process includes several tests that involve the injection of substances called *radionuclides* into the blood. Following the progress of the radionuclides on a computer screen, technicians are able to determine how much blood is being supplied to the heart, how well its chambers are functioning, and whether any part of the heart has been damaged by heart attack.

- **Phonocardiography** (FOHN-uh-kar-dee-OG-ruh-fee). This process involves placing a microphone on a person's chest to record heart sounds and signals, which are transferred through photography to graph paper. A professional can then examine the tracings for heartbeat irregularities.

- **Coronary angiography** (KOR-uh-nayr-ee an-jee-OG-ruh-fee). This procedure is used to help evaluate the extent of coronary artery disease. This procedure uses a *catheter*, a thin, flexible tube that can be guided through blood vessels to the heart. When dye is injected into the catheter, motion X rays can be taken, by which narrow or obstructed areas of the heart can be detected.

- **Artificial pacemaker.** If the heart's natural pacemaker fails, an artificial one is implanted in the chest and wired to the heart. The pacemaker can be set to work on demand when the natural heartbeat is too slow or at a fixed rate to work all the time.

- **Magnetic resonance imaging (MRI).** This test uses powerful magnets to look inside the body. Images of the heart muscle are transferred to a computer, allowing technicians to identify damage from a heart attack and diagnose certain congenital heart defects.

Surgical Procedures

Many surgical procedures have saved the lives of people with heart problems. Only since the middle of the twentieth century, however, have these procedures been available. Some, such as the implantation of artificial hearts and blood vessels, are still on the cutting edge. Procedures currently in use include:

- **Heart transplant.** If a patient's heart is badly damaged by heart disease, doctors may remove the weak heart and replace it with a heart from a person who has recently died.

Did You Know?

- There are about 1.5 million heart attacks each year in the United States.

- About 13.5 million Americans have had a heart attack, have chest pain, or experience both.

- According to the Kentucky Heart Institute, among the most common heart attack triggers are angry outbursts; strenuous tennis playing or other exercise; panic or fear; and emotional stress. Many other triggers are yet to be identified.

L1 Parental Involvement

Ask students to obtain a copy of the RISCO health appraisal from the American Heart Association. Have them explain the factors on the health appraisal to their parents. Tell them to take the RISCO health appraisal with their parents to determine their risk of cardiovascular disease, and have them urge their parents to determine their own level of risk. Encourage students to discuss with their parents ways to reduce their risk of heart disease.

L3 Reading

Select students to read about and report on the roles sodium and cholesterol play on cardiovascular disease. Have them explain the importance of reading food labels.

L2 Researching

Ask students to research athletes who have suffered heart attacks at a young age while playing their particular sport. Were any related to drug use, including steroids?

L2 Researching

Instruct students to research changes in the leading causes of death since 1900 in the United States. Ask them to explain what this tells us about how lifestyles have changed over the decades. How has the environment changed?

L2 Health Lab

Distribute *Health Lab 31* and have students investigate further what an electrocardiogram says about your heart.

MORE ABOUT . . . . .

STROKE. Due to improving diagnosis and treatment of strokes, the survival rate has increased by more than 50 percent in the last 20 years. As with heart attacks, early recognition and medical intervention are keys to surviving a stroke. With increasing survival rates, stroke victims are requiring more rehabilitative assistance. When speech is lost, a stroke victim requires speech therapy to relearn spoken language. When muscle strength and coordination are lost, a stroke victim requires physical therapy. When job skills are lost, occupational therapy is needed to learn new job skills. For fun and motivation, recreational therapy provides sports, games, and mental activities.

ASSESS

EVALUATING THE LESSON

Assign and discuss the Lesson 1 Review; then administer, grade, and discuss the *Lesson 90 Quiz* in the TCR. 🖝

RETEACHING

- Ask students to define *cardiovascular disease* and list the types and causes of the disease studied in this lesson. Relate high blood pressure to heart disease and stroke.
- Ask students to complete *Reteaching Activity 90* in the TCR. 🖝

ENRICHMENT

Have each student choose a particular congenital heart disease and write a brief report about it, including what causes it and what types of treatment are available.

CLOSE

Have students recall the major concepts of this lesson. Clarify any misconceptions.

⚠ *Balloon angioplasty inside a blocked artery will open a path for blood flow.*

ACTIVITY *What measures can you take to keep your arteries free of plaque buildup?*

- **Coronary bypass surgery.** Coronary bypass surgery creates detours around obstructed or narrowed coronary arteries so that more blood can reach the heart. In this operation a large vein from the patient's leg is grafted onto the heart. This allows blood to flow to the area that was not getting enough blood.
- **Balloon angioplasty.** Balloon angioplasty involves threading a balloon-tipped catheter through the body to the site of the blockage. As the balloon is inflated, it pushes the plaque against the artery wall, opening a path for the blood to flow through.
- **Heart valve surgery.** Valves control the proper flow of blood through the heart. Defective valves may be present at birth or develop later in life. A valve may be too tight, which can restrict the flow of blood, or it may not close tightly enough, which can cause blood to flow backward. A surgical procedure replaces a defective valve with an artificial one made of metal or plastic.

Prevention of Cardiovascular Disease

Adopting healthful habits now, while you are young, can help prevent your risk of heart disease in the future. Practice the following:

- Avoid the use of tobacco products, alcohol, and drugs.
- Reduce your intake of cholesterol. Choose an eating plan that has plenty of vegetables, fruits, and grain products.
- Maintain a weight that is healthful for you.
- Limit your intake of salty foods. Avoid adding salt to food.
- Get plenty of physical activity.
- Manage stress in your daily life.

LESSON 1 Review

Reviewing Facts and Vocabulary

1. What are the five uncontrollable risk factors associated with cardiovascular diseases?
2. Use the terms *hypertension, arteriosclerosis, atherosclerosis,* and *angina pectoris* in a paragraph that discusses the progression of heart disease.
3. List three techniques or procedures for treating heart disease.

Thinking Critically

4. *Analyzing.* Why do you think the noninfectious diseases have replaced the infectious diseases as the leading causes of death?

5. *Synthesizing.* Denial is the major reason why someone who is suffering the warning signs of a heart attack does not seek medical attention. Why would someone deny having a heart attack? How can denial of the warning signs of a heart attack cost someone his or her life?

Applying Health Knowledge

6. *In Your Home.* If you or someone in your home is in a high-risk group for heart disease, what lifestyle changes could you suggest to reduce the risks of heart attack?

Lesson 1 Review

Answers to Reviewing Facts and Vocabulary

1. Heredity, ethnicity, gender, age, and environment.
2. Paragraphs will vary. Review lesson for definitions of terms.
3. See the bulleted lists on pages 681 and 682 for possible answers.

Answers to Thinking Critically

4. Answers should reflect an understanding of uncontrollable risk factors and the risk behaviors related to noninfectious diseases.
5. Answers will vary.

Cancer

Human life begins as a single cell that divides millions of times. Cell division occurs throughout life as old dead cells are replaced by new ones. Sometimes the normal forces regulating cell growth are disrupted. Abnormal cells grow and spread to healthy cells. These *uncontrolled abnormal cell growth*s are called **cancers.**

HEALTH TERMS

cancers

tumors

benign

malignant

metastasis

carcinogen

melanoma

biopsy

chemotherapy

HEALTH CONCEPTS

■ Risk factors for cancer include heredity, environment, and lifestyle.

■ There are seven warning signs of cancer.

■ The earlier a cancer is diagnosed, the greater the range of treatment options that are available.

Tumors

All cancers are **tumors**, *masses of tissue,* but not all tumors are cancers. Some tumors are **benign**, or *noncancerous.* Noncancerous tumors are characterized by abnormal cells, but their growth is less aggressive than that of cancerous ones. Also, these tumors are surrounded by membranes that prevent them from spreading.

Malignant, or *cancerous*, tumors—by contrast—have no such membranes. Sometimes cancerous cells break away from a malignant tumor and move through **lymph** or blood vessels to other healthy tissues. This *spread of cancer from the point where it originated to other parts of the body* is known as **metastasis.**

hotlink

lymph For more information on lymph and the role of the lymphatic system, see Chapter 17, page 393.

Lesson 2 Resources

TEACHER'S CLASSROOM RESOURCES

☞ **Concept Map** Activity 91

☞ **Lesson 91 Quiz**

☞ **Lesson Plan 91**

☞ **Reteaching** Activity 91

STUDENT WORKBOOK

☞ **Applying Health Skills 91**

☞ **Chapter Study Guide 31**

☞ **Vocabulary** Activity 31

Cancer

FOCUS

LESSON OBJECTIVES

After studying this lesson, students should be able to

• explain how cancer develops.
• identify known carcinogens.
• describe the types of cancer.
• identify the warning signs of cancer.
• discuss the basic approaches to treating cancer.

MOTIVATOR

Write the following on the chalkboard for students to work on while attendance is being taken: *List three types of cancer.* (Examples: skin, colon, rectum, lung, breast, prostate, cervix, leukemia.)

INTRODUCING THE LESSON

Ask students to share their responses to the Motivator. Introduce this lesson by stating that cancer is the second leading cause of death among adults in the United States. Cancer is unique because it is not a single disease but many diseases. Tell students that this lesson will examine the basics of what is currently known about various kinds of cancer, the known causes of cancer, treatment for the disease, and the little that is known regarding prevention.

INTRODUCING HEALTH TERMS

• Have students locate the vocabulary terms in the Glossary and define each term.

• Ask students to complete Vocabulary Activity 31 and Chapter Study Guide 31 in the *Student Workbook.* ☞

TEACH

L2 Discussing

Ask students how cancer cells differ from normal cells. What do cancer cells do during their growth process?

L1 Discussing

Ask students to explain the process of metastasis.

L1 Explaining

Inform the class that cancer is classified in two ways: (1) from the part of the body where the cancer cells first developed; (2) from the type of body tissue where the cancer begins.

L1 Discussing

Have students explain the difference between a benign tumor and a malignant one. *(A benign tumor is not cancerous; a malignant tumor is.)* Stress that any tumor should be examined by a doctor.

ABCD of Skin Care

keeping Fit

Review the signs of skin cancer that are presented in the feature. Discuss the importance of reducing exposure to sun as the most prudent means of preventing skin cancer. Have students use classroom and library resources to find answers to the following questions: What factors influence the total amount of UV radiation that reaches the earth at any given time? During what hours of the day are you most likely to get a sunburn?

keeping Fit

ABCD of Skin Care

Catching melanoma early can mean the difference between life and death. An important part of cancer prevention, therefore, is to periodically check any skin moles for the "ABCDs":

➤ **A**symmetry—or unevenness;

➤ **B**order—look for telltale features such as notched, scalloped, or indistinct edges;

➤ **C**olor—be alert for the following colors and patterns: tan and brown, black, or red and white; and

➤ **D**iameter—a mole larger than 6 mm should be reported to a physician.

Lymphocytes attacking cancer cell

Causes of Cancer

A number of risk factors have been associated with cancer, among them heredity, environment, and lifestyle. Some cases of cancers are caused by exposure to a **carcinogen** (kar-SIN-uh-jihn), *a cancer-causing substance in the environment.* Carcinogens include chemicals found in tobacco smoke, asbestos, and toxic wastes. Exposure to certain forms of radiation, including X rays, radon, and the sun's ultraviolet rays, is another known cause of cancer. Some viruses and contaminated water have also been found to be carcinogenic.

Not everyone is equally susceptible to the same carcinogens. You can control your exposure to and ingestion of many carcinogens.

Types of Cancer

Cancers are classified in two ways: by the part of the body where the cancer cells first develop, and by the type of body tissue within which the cancer begins.

Cancers that develop in *epithelial tissue,* tissue that forms the skin and linings of body organs, are called carcinomas (KAR-suh-NOH-muhs). Sarcomas are cancers that develop in connective and

Different Types of Cancer

BODY-SITE TYPE	ORGAN(S) MOST OFTEN AFFECTED	OCCURRENCE
Skin cancer	Skin	Most common type in the United States
Digestive system	Colon (large intestine) and rectum (excreting tract)	Most common type in United States next to skin cancer
Respiratory system	Larynx and lungs	Mainly occurs in men: increase in incidence of lung cancer in women
Breast	Breast	Mostly women
Reproductive system	*Males*—prostate gland *Female*—cervix, ovaries, uterus	
Blood and lymph system	Bone marrow, lymph (cancer of the bone marrow is called *leukemia*)	Occurs in men and women

684   CHAPTER 31   NONINFECTIOUS DISEASES AND DISABILITIES

HOME AND COMMUNITY CONNECTION

ASSESSING EXPOSURE. Have students obtain a list of carcinogens from the EPA or from on-line and print sources. Have volunteers contact agencies that monitor water, air, and sanitation in the community for a list of carcinogens that might put residents at risk. Discuss their findings in class. Explain that students cannot control exposure from local sources, but they can reduce total exposure by reducing risk factors at home. Suggest that students assess their homes. How often are pesticides used inside or outside? What types of chemicals are used? What other factors, such as paint or dry-cleaned clothing, create indoor pollution? Have them suggest improvements, such as non-toxic substitutes for pesticides and toxic chemicals.

supportive tissues such as bones, muscles, and tendons. Lymphomas are cancers that develop in the lymphatic system. Hodgkin's disease is a type of lymphoma.

Skin Cancer

There are three types of skin cancer: **melanoma**, the *often deadly type of skin cancer,* the more curable basal cell, and squamous cell skin cancers. There are 100,000 new cases of melanoma every year. While there is an increased awareness about the dangers of exposure to the sun, people develop skin cancers because they fail to protect themselves by using sunscreens.

▼ *When it is used correctly, sunscreen protects your skin from the sun's ultraviolet rays.*
ACTIVITY *Find which SPF (sun protection factor) found in sunscreen offers the greatest amount of protection from the sun's rays for the longest period of time. How often should you apply sunscreen while in the sun?*

L1 Explaining

On the chalkboard, list several known carcinogens, such as radiation, tobacco, toxic waste, and certain food additives.

L2 Discussing

Have students debate this statement: *A suntan is a sign of good health.*

L2 Discussing

Explain to students that excessive use of alcohol can lead to cancer of the liver, larynx, esophagus, and stomach. Discuss why this is possible.

Building Health Skills

Reducing the Risks of Cancer

SOME CANCER RISK FACTORS such as age and family history cannot be changed. However, other risk factors such as eating patterns and use of known carcinogens can be controlled. The following guidelines can help lower your chances of developing cancer.

1. Be physically active.

2. Achieve and maintain a healthful weight.

3. Eat plenty of fruits, vegetables, and whole grains.

4. Reduce the amount of fat in the foods you eat, particularly from animal sources, to no more than 30 percent of your total daily calorie intake.

5. Limit your time in the sun. Use sunscreen when exposed to the sun for any length of time.

6. Avoid using all forms of tobacco and alcohol.

7. Know your body and recognize the warning signs of cancer. Visit your doctor immediately if you suspect a problem.

LESSON 2   CANCER   **685**

Building Health Skills

Reducing the Risks of Cancer
Skill: Goal Setting

Help students review cancer risk factors, and ask: What would you be willing to do to reduce your chances of getting cancer? Then guide students in reading and discussing the guidelines in the Building Health Skills feature. Let volunteers suggest specific steps that teens can take to follow each of the guidelines. As a follow-up, have students write entries in their private Health Journals, identifying at least two specific behaviors they want to develop to reduce their own cancer risks.

MORE ABOUT . . . . .

RADIATION AND CANCER. Students may be confused by what seems to be a contradiction regarding cancer and radiation. Radiation and X rays are listed in this chapter as common sources of carcinogens, yet both also serve as treatments for cancer. Logically, students may wonder how radiation can be both harmful and beneficial. Tell them that radiation is a risk factor for cancer when a person is exposed to large doses of it or for prolonged periods of time. When used as a treatment for cancer, it is targeted directly at cancer cells in small doses that kill the affected cells but generally spare damage to normal cells.

L1 Discussing

Ask students to identify the two main factors accounting for the increase in lung cancer.

L1 Parental Involvement

Ask students to share the seven warning signs of cancer with their parents. Have students ask their parents if they know someone who has had cancer and recovered. Has a member of the family had cancer? What kind was it, and what type of treatment was used? How were the families affected? Ask students to write a report on their findings.

L1 Guest Speaker

Invite a school nurse to speak with the class about do-it-yourself home tests for colon-rectal cancer.

L1 Explaining

Explain that the Pap test is used to detect cancer in the female reproductive system. Secretions on the cervix are placed on a slide and examined under a microscope for cancerous cells.

L2 Class Activity

Direct students to read about self-examinations in this lesson. On a sheet of paper, have the girls write the procedure for breast self-examination, and have the boys write the procedure for testicular self-examination. They may wish to refer to Chapter 19 to review the procedures. Ask students when a person should begin self-examination. If possible, have a school nurse present to discuss any questions that might arise.

L2 Explaining

Point out that leukemia is a disease of the parts of the body that make blood, affecting the body's production of white blood cells. Ask students to explain how blood transfusions and bone marrow transplants would benefit persons with leukemia.

A Word of Caution About Cancer

Every individual should be alert to the seven warning signs of cancer. As a way of remembering these signs, you might note that their first letters, when combined, spell the word *caution*.

C hange in bowel habit (either loose stools or constipation).

A sore that does not heal.

U nusual bleeding or discharge (as from the uterus, bladder, bowels, or with coughing).

T hickening or a lump in the breast or elsewhere (let your doctor decide what the lump means).

I ndigestion or difficulty swallowing.

O bvious change in a wart or mole.

N agging cough or hoarseness.

Other symptoms include fatigue and unexplained weight loss. If you experience any of these symptoms, contact your physician.

hotlink

reproductive system For more information on the reproductive system and its care, see Chapter 19, page 434.

breast self-examination (BSE) For more information on how to perform breast self-examination, see Chapter 19, page 444.

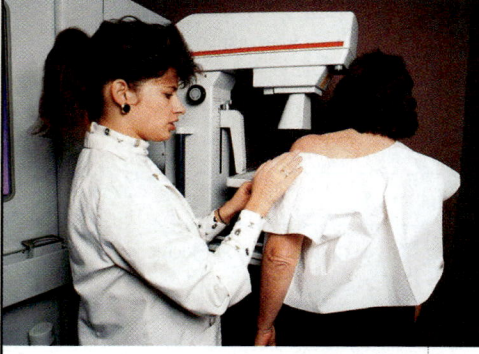

▼ *Regular mammogram checks provide early detection of breast cancer.*

Lung Cancer

The American Cancer Society reports that cigarette smoking is the single greatest cause of cancer in the United States today, accounting for 85 percent of lung cancer cases among males and 75 percent among females. Males who start smoking before the age of 15 are five times more likely to die of lung cancer than those who started after age 25. Among women, lung cancer has tripled in the last 20 years. This is a direct result of the increasing numbers of women who now smoke. Survival rate is only 13 percent.

Oral Cancer

Oral cancer affects the mouth and throat area. Risk factors for oral cancer include smoking of cigarettes, cigars, or a pipe, and the use of smokeless tobacco. These cancers form where tobacco has touched the person's lips, mouth, and throat tissues. Excessive use of alcohol is another risk factor for oral cancer.

Cancer of the Colon and Rectum

Cancer of the colon and rectum is the third most commonly occurring cancer in the United States today. This cancer usually develops in the lowest part of the colon, near the rectum. As the cancer grows larger, it either blocks the colon or causes bleeding, often during elimination. Cancers of this type are slow to spread. Seeking early medical help greatly increases a person's chance of survival. An eating plan low in fat and high in fiber decreases a person's risk of this cancer.

Reproductive Cancer

Most new cancer cases in the United States are found in the **reproductive system**—breast cancer in women and prostate cancer in men. In women, cancerous tumors can develop in the ovaries and uterus as well. Early detection through regular pelvic examinations and a Pap test has reduced the death rate from uterine and cervical cancers. **Breast self-examination (BSE),** regular medical checkups, and mammography are ways that breast cancer is detected.

Prostate cancer can often be detected during a rectal exam. Cancer in males can also develop in the testes. Testicular cancer, the leading type of cancer among males aged 15 to 34, can be detected during regular testicular self-examination. Any lumps or thickening detected by a male or female through a reproductive self-examination should be reported to a doctor.

MEETING STUDENT DIVERSITY

CANCER. Teens with cancer say one of the most difficult things about living with cancer is the loneliness. They often feel isolated and set apart. They look different—surgical scars, lost weight, lost hair. Their lives are different—missed school, some restrictions on recreation. If their friends do treat them differently or ostracize them, it is usually out of ignorance or fear.

Friends often want to know if cancer is contagious, which of course it is not. They want to know if it hurts. Sometimes it does, and sometimes the treatments are uncomfortable and frustrating. They may be afraid of getting close to someone who is ill, in pain, and possibly going to die.

Leukemia

Leukemia is cancer of the blood-forming tissue in the bone marrow. In leukemia, immature white blood cells multiply too rapidly and crowd out mature white cells. This weakens the body's immune system. Although often thought of as primarily a childhood disease, leukemia strikes people of all ages and both genders. Childhood leukemia is very curable, with a success rate of 95 percent.

Detecting Cancer

Early detection of cancer is the most critical factor in combating the disease. Many types of cancer can be detected during a routine physical examination. This is one reason why regular physical checkups are important. If a tumor is found, a physician may do a **biopsy,** *a laboratory analysis of a section of tissue taken from a site where abnormal cell growth is suspected.* Ultrasound, which uses sound waves, can be used to locate abnormal growths when they are small and more easily treatable. This diagnostic procedure can also help determine the best method of treatment.

Treating Cancer

Treatment of cancers is directed at confining and killing the cancerous cells. At present, this is accomplished by three basic approaches: surgery, radiation, and chemotherapy.

▼ *Due to constant improvements in medicine and technology, today cancer patients experience a high rate of recovery.*

ACTIVITY *Explain ways you could support a friend or relative who is undergoing treatment for cancer.*

L1 Discussing

Have students explain the three basic strategies of treating cancer. Ask: What are the shortcomings of surgery as a method of treating cancer? Describe how radiation is used to treat cancer cells. What are some of the risks of radiation?

L1 Discussing

Ask students what chemotherapy is. What is its goal? What advantage does it have over surgery or radiation?

L2 Researching

Have students investigate hospices and their role in the lives of cancer victims. Ask students to share their findings with the class.

update
▶ *Looking at Technology*

The Cyberknife

A new technological advancement in the war on cancer is the *cyberknife.* A blend of robotics, computers, and radiation therapy, the cyberknife is used to blast away cancerous tumors deep in the brain. A robotic arm is programmed to fire beams of low-level gamma rays toward specific targets—in this case, tumors. Much like a guided missile, the cyberknife is able to hit the tumor with maximum accuracy and without damaging surrounding tissue. The cyberknife compensates for any slight movement of the patient's head by automatically and constantly readjusting its fix on the target. This capability has rendered obsolete the bulky, uncomfortable metal devices that brain tumor patients were once forced to wear when undergoing gamma radiation. What is more, the cyberknife is lighter, faster, more flexible, and more powerful than past "gamma knife" treatments.

update
▶ *Looking at Technology*

The Cyberknife

Let students share what they know about brain cancers, and ask: What special problems are involved in treating tumors on or in the brain? After a brief discussion, have students read the Update feature to learn what a cyberknife is and how it is used. Ask: What benefits does this new technology offer? As a follow-up activity, have students use magazines, journals, or on-line resources to read about the experiences of patients who have been treated with cyberknife technology.

LESSON 2 CANCER **687**

MORE ABOUT . . . . .

CANCER THERAPIES. Several new cancer treatments are being researched.

- Transplant: Cancerous organs or parts of organs can be removed and replaced with healthy tissue.

- Chemoprevention: Using controlled megadoses of vitamins and minerals may prevent cancer recurrences and reduce chances for high-risk persons.

- Transfusion: Giving blood cells and platelets controls the symptoms of cancer and the side effects of some treatments.

- Hyperthermia: Applying localized or total body heat destroys some tumors without damaging surrounding healthy tissue.

ASSESS

EVALUATING THE LESSON

Assign and discuss the Lesson 2 Review; then administer, grade, and discuss the *Lesson 91 Quiz* in the TCR. ▱

RETEACHING

- Have students make lists of the following information: three health steps that help prevent cancer, the seven warning signs of cancer, and three treatments for cancer.
- Ask students to complete *Reteaching Activity 91* in the TCR. ▱

ENRICHMENT

Ask students to read about the controversies surrounding animal testing in medical research, particularly in cancer research. Have students use the following questions to guide their research: What are both sides of the controversy? What do you think of each? What is the Ames test, a test sometimes viewed as an alternative to animal testing? What are its benefits? What are its drawbacks?

CLOSE

Have students recall the major concepts of the lesson. Clarify any misconceptions.

▾ *Surgery, radiation, and chemotherapy are techniques used to treat and control many types of cancers.*

ACTIVITY *Describe how different treatments destroy or stop the growth of cancer cells.*

Surgery

Surgery has been a standard method in removing tumors and affected areas. Today, with improved surgical techniques, cancer patients have a longer life expectancy and an improved quality of life. Whereas amputation used to be standard practice for treating cancer of arm and leg bones, now doctors are able to treat many such cancers by removing only the diseased bone tissue and transplanting healthy tissue from another part of the patient's body.

Radiation

Radiation energy from cobalt or radium can penetrate a tumor. The energy destroys the tumor cells by damaging DNA in the nuclei. DNA is the genetic material responsible for cell division. Radiation therapy is very successful in arresting—or slowing the growth of—certain kinds of cancer, such as cervical cancer. It is also very helpful in areas of the body where surgery is difficult, such as the head and neck.

Chemotherapy

Chemotherapy is *the use of anti-cancer medications in the treatment of cancer.* Its goal is to destroy malignant cells without excessive destruction of normal cells.

Chemotherapy works by interfering with cell division of the cancer cells and, by doing so, preventing the cancer from spreading. Unfortunately, some unpleasant side effects such as nausea and vomiting may occur with the use of these strong medicines. However, new techniques are allowing doctors to administer chemotherapy more safely and with fewer complications and side effects.

LESSON 2 *Review*

Reviewing Facts and Vocabulary

1. What is the difference between a benign tumor and malignant tumor?
2. Why is early diagnosis and treatment of cancer so important?

Thinking Critically

3. *Synthesizing.* Find out if there is such a thing as a "safe" tan. Compare tanning that results from the sun's rays to tanning from a tanning salon. Share your findings in a report.
4. *Comparing and Contrasting.* Use information from the chapter as well as other current resources to make a three-column chart. The first column should note the body system or organ affected by the cancer, the second should note the number of people affected by it annually, and the third should describe the success rate of treatment.

Applying Health Knowledge

5. *In Your Home and School.* Interview someone at home or in your school or community who has successfully undergone cancer treatment. Get details about the treatment, any side effects, and time needed for recovery. Share your findings in a report.

688 CHAPTER 31 NONINFECTIOUS DISEASES AND DISABILITIES

Lesson 2 Review

Answers to Reviewing Facts and Vocabulary

1. Benign tumors are noncancerous; malignant tumors are cancerous.
2. Treatment—confining and killing the cancerous cells—is more likely to be effective if the cancer is diagnosed early.

Answers to Thinking Critically

3. Research should indicate that the only "safe" tans are artificial, as from cosmetic products.
4. Charts will vary.

Other Noninfectious Diseases

S ome noninfectious diseases can seem to strike without warning. Others tend to "build" in the body over time, eventually leading to poor health. Regardless of the manner in which a disease presents itself, having information about these diseases is a first step toward prevention and recognition of their signs and symptoms.

HEALTH TERMS

diabetes

insulin

impaired glucose tolerance (IGT)

arthritis

rheumatoid arthritis

osteoarthritis

HEALTH CONCEPTS

- Knowing the differences between type 1 and type 2 diabetes is essential to treatment of the diseases.
- Arthritis can affect people of any age.
- Treatment programs to ease the discomfort of arthritis are available.

Diabetic's insulin kit

hotlink

glucose For more information on glucose and its role in nutrition, see Chapter 5, page 102.

Diabetes

D iabetes is *a chronic disease that affects the way body cells convert food into energy.* It is the seventh leading cause of death by disease in the United States, affecting 16 million Americans. Each day approximately 2,200 new cases are diagnosed.

Diabetes can lead to a host of other major illnesses and health conditions, including blindness, kidney disease, nerve disease and amputations, and heart disease and stroke.

What Causes Diabetes

In the normal digestive process, carbohydrates are changed to the sugar **glucose**, then absorbed into the blood and delivered to body

Lesson 3 Resources

TEACHER'S CLASSROOM RESOURCES

- **Concept Map** Activity 92
- **Cooperative Learning** Activity 31
- **Decision-Making** Activity 31
- **Lesson 92 Quiz**
- **Lesson Plan 92**
- **Reteaching** Activity 92

STUDENT WORKBOOK

- **Applying Health Skills 92**
- **Chapter Study Guide 31**
- **Vocabulary** Activity 31

Other Noninfectious Diseases

FOCUS

LESSON OBJECTIVES

After studying this lesson, students should be able to

- describe diabetes and its progression.
- identify the types of diabetes.
- describe the two most common types of arthritis.

MOTIVATOR

Write the following on the chalkboard for students to work on while attendance is being taken: *What is diabetes? How can knowledge of diabetes be helpful?*

INTRODUCING THE LESSON

Have students share their responses to the Motivator. Quickly survey the class to see how many have a diabetic in their family. More than likely there will be several. Tell students that they will learn about diabetes and another disease, arthritis, in this lesson. Explain that both diseases combined affect more than 56 million people in the United States alone.

INTRODUCING HEALTH TERMS

- Have students use each of the vocabulary terms in paragraphs describing diabetes and arthritis.
- Ask students to complete Vocabulary Activity 31 and Chapter Study Guide 31 in the *Student Workbook.*

TEACH

L1 Cooperative Learning

Divide the class into groups and give each a poster board. Assign each group one of the following and have them create a display for the poster board: (1) List all of the types of diabetes and symptoms/characteristics of each. (2) Describe healthful habits, such as diet and exercise, needed to control diabetes. (3) Provide pictures of unhealthful habits that contribute to diabetes. (4) Describe the types of treatment available for diabetics besides diet and exercise.

L1 Discussing

Have students explain how diabetes functions. What happens when glucose is unable to enter the body cells?

L3 Researching

Encourage students to read about hypoglycemia, sometimes referred to as low blood sugar. Then, have them compare and contrast hypoglycemia with diabetes. How are their symptoms, treatments, diagnoses, and long-term effects on the body similar and different? What roles does insulin play in each? How can hypoglycemia lead to diabetes? What does it mean to be "prediabetic"? Ask them to present their findings in writing.

cells. **Insulin,** *a hormone that is produced in the pancreas and that helps the body convert glucose to energy,* is an essential link in this process. In the case of diabetes, sufficient insulin is not produced or is not used efficiently. When glucose is unable to enter the cells, it accumulates in the blood until the kidneys filter out some of the surplus, which is passed off in urine. High sugar content in urine and in the blood is one of the surest signs that a person has diabetes.

In Case of a Diabetic Emergency

TYPE I	TYPE II
SOURCE	**SOURCE**
■ Low blood sugar (Insulin reaction/*hypoglycemia* (high-poh-gly-**see**-mee-uh), an abnormal decrease of sugar in the blood)	■ High blood sugar
TIME SPAN	**TIME SPAN**
■ Sudden onset (minutes to hours)	■ Gradual onset (hours to days)
SIGNS	**SIGNS**
■ Staggering, poor coordination	■ Thirst
■ Irritability, belligerence, hostility	■ Very frequent urination
■ Pale color	■ Flushed skin
■ Sweating	■ Vomiting
■ Eventual stupor or unconsciousness	■ Fruity or winelike odor or breath
	■ Eventual stupor or unconsciousness
CAUSES	**CAUSES**
■ Delayed or missed meals	■ Undiagnosed diabetes
■ Too much insulin, by overdose or error	■ Insulin forgotten or omitted
■ Extreme exercise	■ Stress, such as illness or injury
	■ Overindulgence in food or drink
TREATMENT	**TREATMENT**
■ Provide sugar.	■ Get the person to a hospital.
■ If the person can swallow without choking, offer *any* food or drink containing sugar, such as soft drinks, fruit juice, candy.	■ If you are uncertain whether the person has high blood sugar or low blood sugar, give some food or drink containing sugar. If the person does not respond in 10 to 15 minutes, he or she needs a physician's help.
■ Do not use diet drinks!	■ Do not give food or drink if the person is unable to swallow. Take the person to a hospital if he or she has no response to treatments.
■ If the person does not respond in 10 to 15 minutes, take him or her to a hospital.	
■ Look for a diabetic identification bracelet or necklace.	
■ The diabetic may carry candy or special quick-sugar commercial preparations in plastic, soft-tipped containers. Squeeze the contents into the person's mouth.	

690 CHAPTER 31 NONINFECTIOUS DISEASES AND DISABILITIES

MEETING STUDENT DIVERSITY

PROJECT: Have students create a magazine that focuses on promoting healthful lifestyles for teens.

LEARNING STYLES. Students with special learning needs may benefit from working together with mainstream students on a variety of tasks, including fact gathering. At the time of assessment, pairs may be evaluated in terms of positive interdependence and individual accountability.

VISUALLY IMPAIRED. Students with visual impairments may want to supervise publication of a large-type version of the magazine. These students should work with illustrators in choosing a typeface that is open and easy-to-read and in making other design-related decisions.

Types of Diabetes and Risk Factors

There are two main classifications of diabetes: type 1, or immune-mediated (formerly known as *insulin-dependent*) diabetes, and type 2 (formerly known as *non-insulin-dependent*) diabetes. Type 1 usually occurs during childhood or adolescence. Type 2, the most common form of the disease, usually occurs after age 40.

Like CVDs, some risk factors for diabetes are related to lifestyle, principally obesity and physical inactivity, while others are genetic. For reasons not entirely understood, whites are more likely than other groups to develop type 1 diabetes, while African Americans, Hispanics, and Native Americans are more likely to develop type 2. Yet another major risk factor for type 2 diabetes is **impaired glucose tolerance (IGT),** *a condition in which blood sugar levels are higher than normal but not high enough to be classified as diabetes.*

Type 1 Diabetes

Type 1 diabetes, which accounts for about 10 percent of all cases of the disease, appears abruptly and progresses rapidly. Most often, type 1 diabetes results from a malfunction of the **immune system**—the system that defends the body against invading pathogens. In an individual with type 1 diabetes, the immune system mistakenly attacks and destroys the insulin-producing cells of the pancreas. The body's cells become "starved" for insulin.

Symptoms of type 1 diabetes include frequent urination, abnormal thirst, unusual hunger, weight loss, weakness, fatigue, irritability, and nausea. Because the pancreas is unable to produce insulin,

h⊙tlink

immune system For more information on the functions of the immune system, see Chapter 28, page 624.

Making Responsible Decisions

1. Sylvie is concerned because her mother, who is at risk for type 2 diabetes, has begun eating very little and has lost 25 pounds very rapidly.
2. Sylvie could (a) ignore the situation and hope someone else helps her mother; (b) discuss her concerns with her mother and urge her mother to see a health professional; (c) discuss the problem with her father, either by phone or as soon as he comes home.
3. Sylvie might (a) avoid "interfering" or irritating her mother, but continue to worry that her mother is increasing her health risks; (b) risk making her mother angry, but possibly succeed in getting her mother to seek medical help; (c) know that her father will try to help her mother, but continue to worry and perhaps have to wait until he comes home.
4. Sylvie values her mother's physical health and her own good relationship with her mother.
5. Decisions will vary.
6. Remind students to consider both short- and long-term consequences of their decisions.

L2 Decision Making

For further study on making responsible decisions, assign *Decision-Making Activity 31* in the TCR. ☞

Making Responsible Decisions

Confronting Diabetes

Diabetes runs in Sylvie's family on her mother's side. Last month, her aunt was diagnosed as having type 2 diabetes. Sylvie has seen the effect the disease has had on other family members. Her grandfather lost a leg to the disease, and an uncle went blind. Now a new problem has arisen in the family, and it has Sylvie worried. Her mother, afraid of becoming the next victim of diabetes, has stopped eating. She has lost over 25 pounds. Sylvie's father is away much of the time on business, and Sylvie feels there is no one else she can turn to for help for her mother. What should she do?

What Would You Do?

Apply the six steps of the decision-making process to Sylvie's problem:

1. **State the situation.**
2. **List the options.**
3. **Weigh the possible outcomes.**
4. **Consider your values.**
5. **Make a decision and act.**
6. **Evaluate the decision.**

COOPERATIVE LEARNING

PARTY MENU. Group students and have them plan beverages and hors d'oeuvres for a family reunion that includes people with cardiovascular disease, high blood pressure, and diabetes. Colon cancer runs in the family. Suggest they use this chapter, and on-line sources and print dietary recommendations for each condition. Have them obtain resources such as food composition and nutrition tables and list some of the most common party foods; then, look up the sodium, fat, and sugar content of each, and find out which contain aspartame. Decide which foods should be eliminated and brainstorm possible substitutes. Search the tables for foods that seem healthy for people who wish to avoid the diseases listed. Which are particularly tasty? Encourage groups to duplicate their menus and share them with other groups.

L1 Class Activity

Ask students to make a chart of common types of arthritis, and the prevention and treatment for each.

L1 Explaining

Tell the class that arthritis is seen more often in women than in men. It is likely to strike persons in the age groups of 20 to 50 years of age. However, it can start at any age.

L3 Researching

Assign volunteers to visit a pharmacy and look at medicines that are recommended for the pain and inflammation of arthritis. Have them compare the ingredients on the labels, looking for similarities. Ask students to write down the ingredients and brand names of the medicines. Is there one common ingredient in all over-the-counter medicines for arthritis? Is there a difference in price? Have students ask the pharmacist for names of prescription medicines used for arthritis. Are generic brands available?

L3 Researching

Have students research the use of artificial joints to replace those damaged by arthritis. Have them answer the following question with their research: How successful is this surgery in easing the pain and lack of movement or motion caused by arthritis?

L2 Cooperative Learning

Assign *Cooperative Learning Activity 31*, "Use of Animals in Research," in the TCR. ☞

People with diabetes must pay close attention to the foods they eat and monitor the amount of sugar in their blood to avoid diabetic emergencies.

ACTIVITY *Find out what you would need to do for a friend with diabetes in case of emergency.*

patients must take daily doses of insulin either through injection or by means of a special pump that is attached to the body via tubing or surgically implanted. Today, because of advanced methods of treatment, many persons with diabetes live near-normal lives.

Emergencies can arise for people with diabetes that necessitate immediate medical attention. It is, therefore, important for a person with diabetes to wear an identification device, such as a bracelet or necklace, advising of this medical condition so that passersby can act quickly and get help that can be the difference between life and death.

Type 2 Diabetes

Type 2 diabetes is a metabolic disorder resulting from the body's inability to make enough, or properly use, insulin. In type 2 diabetes, the pancreas produces some insulin, but because of a cell receptor defect, the cells cannot use the insulin effectively. Symptoms of type 2 diabetes include excess weight, drowsiness, blurred vision, tingling or numbness in the hands and feet, slower than normal healing of cuts and bruises, itching, and recurring skin, gum, or bladder infections.

About 80 percent of all type 2 patients are overweight at the time of diagnosis. Type 2 diabetes can usually be controlled by eating patterns, exercise, and—when necessary—by losing excess weight. In some cases, oral medications or injections of insulin are also required. Problems related to circulation are common in this type of diabetes. Because the onset of type 2 diabetes is gradual, the disease often goes undetected for years. In fact, of the estimated 15.3 million Americans currently inflicted with the disease, roughly half are unaware they have it.

Arthritis

Arthritis covers *at least 100 different conditions that cause aching, pain, and swelling in joints and connective tissue throughout the body.* The term *arthritis* itself means "inflammation of a joint." Arthritis can and does occur at all ages, from infancy on. The National Center for Health Statistics estimates that over 40 million people have arthritis severe enough to require medical care.

The two most common types of arthritis are rheumatoid (ROOM-uh-toyd) arthritis and osteoarthritis. Like type 1 diabetes, these are *autoimmune diseases,* conditions in which the body's immune system turns on itself. Why this occurs is still a mystery.

MORE ABOUT . . . . .

ARTHRITIS. In the early 1900s, people who had arthritis had very limited options for treatment. In fact, it was believed that participation in any kind of exercise was the wrong thing to do. It was thought that exercise would aggravate joint problems. As a result, arthritic patients were told that rest was the only option they had. Today the thinking is much different. Researchers have studied the effects of vigorous exercise on people with arthritis. The results indicate that aerobic exercise is safe and beneficial. Brisk walking is encouraged as an excellent form of exercise for people with arthritis.

Rheumatoid Arthritis

The most serious type of arthritis, **rheumatoid arthritis** is mainly *a destructive and disabling inflammation of the joints.* It affects primarily the joints of the hands and arms, the hips, and the feet and legs. Rheumatoid inflammation also attacks connective tissue, causing symptoms such as fever, fatigue, and swollen lymph glands. Rheumatoid arthritis causes the joints to stiffen, then swell and become tender. The inflammation can do progressive damage inside the joint if it is not diagnosed and properly treated.

Scientists do not know the cause of rheumatoid arthritis, and at present there is no cure. A full treatment program for rheumatoid arthritis depends on the physician and may include anti-inflammatory medicines such as aspirin and ibuprofen, rest, exercise, weight control, splints, walking aids, heat, surgery, and rehabilitation.

Osteoarthritis

Osteoarthritis is *a disease that affects primarily the weight-bearing joints of the knees and hips, causing aches and soreness especially when moving.* It is the most common type of arthritis, affecting about 16 million people. Osteoarthritis results from wear and tear in the mechanical parts of a joint. Inflammation is rarely a problem.

In osteoarthritis, the cartilage becomes pitted and frayed and, in time, may wear away completely. Bone ends then become thicker and bony spurs may develop. As a result, surrounding ligaments and membranes become thickened, changing the whole structure and shape of the joint. There is no cure for arthritis, but early detection and diagnosis is essential to managing the disease. The treatment program includes exercise, weight control, eating a balanced assortment of foods, and pain medications.

▼ *Compare the appearance of normal bone tissue (top) with tissue affected by osteoarthritis (bottom).*

LESSON 3 *Review*

Reviewing Facts and Vocabulary

1. What is a sure sign that a person has diabetes?
2. What are the early signs of arthritis?
3. How is arthritis treated?

Thinking Critically

4. ***Comparing and Contrasting.*** Review the similarities and differences of type 1 and type 2 diabetes. Explain why type 2 diabetes is considered a lifestyle disease for most people.

5. ***Analyzing.*** Compare rheumatoid arthritis and osteoarthritis.

Applying Health Knowledge

6. ***In Your School.*** Invite to class an individual with diabetes. Find out how the disease has affected his or her life. What special precautions must he or she take to stay healthy? How are these precautions the same as and different from measures you take to stay healthy?

LESSON 3   OTHER NONINFECTIOUS DISEASES   **693**

ASSESS

EVALUATING THE LESSON

Assign and discuss the Lesson 3 Review; then administer, grade, and discuss the *Lesson 92 Quiz* in the TCR. ☞

RETEACHING

- Have students label a sheet of paper *Type 1 Diabetes* and another *Type 2 Diabetes,* then fill in the causes, signs, and treatments for each type. Have students refer to the lesson as they complete each outline.
- Direct students to make a chart that compares and contrasts rheumatoid arthritis with osteoarthritis.
- Ask students to complete *Reteaching Activity 92* in the TCR. ☞

ENRICHMENT

Have students investigate lupus (systemic lupus erythematosus). What is the disease? How many lives does it claim each year in the United States? How did the disease get its name? What populations does the disease most commonly affect? What are the treatments, recent research findings, and advancements? Why is the disease so difficult to diagnose? Why is it sometimes associated with arthritis? Why do people with lupus get sent to rheumatologists, as arthritics do? Ask students to summarize their findings in writing.

CLOSE

Have students recall major concepts of the lesson. Clarify any misconceptions.

Lesson 3 Review

Answers to Reviewing Facts and Vocabulary

1. High sugar content in urine or in the blood.
2. Stiffening in the joints.
3. Exercise, weight control, eating a balanced assortment of foods, and pain medication.

Answers to Thinking Critically

4. Although heredity can be a risk factor, other factors that lead to type 2 diabetes include obesity and physical inactivity.
5. See descriptions of each on page 693.

Physical and Mental Challenges

FOCUS

LESSON OBJECTIVES

After studying this lesson, students should be able to

- identify the most common types of physical and mental disabilities.
- describe ways in which progress has been made to better integrate individuals with disabilities into society.

MOTIVATOR

Write the following on the chalkboard for students to work on while attendance is being taken: *When you hear the term disability, what first comes to mind?*

INTRODUCING THE LESSON

Have students share their responses to the Motivator. Discuss how people with disabilities are often viewed as different because of their disability, when in fact they have the same needs as everyone else and would like to enjoy the same privileges. Tell students that this lesson will look at the challenges that individuals with disabilities face and how society is taking steps to better accommodate their needs, enabling them with more independence and interaction.

INTRODUCING HEALTH TERMS

Ask students to complete Vocabulary Activity 31 and Chapter Study Guide 31 in the *Student Workbook.* 🖝

Physical and Mental Challenges

oes your school have ramps and special bathroom facilities to accommodate people in wheelchairs? Are there telephones for the hearing or vision impaired? Such aids for people with physical and mental challenges began to appear in recent decades.

HEALTH TERMS

disability

profound deafness

mental retardation

Americans with Disabilities Act

HEALTH CONCEPTS

- Depending on its nature and severity, a disability can interfere with an individual's performance of tasks that nondisabled people may take for granted.
- Understanding the realities of physical and mental challenges is important for all people.

Disabilities

A disability is *any physical or mental impairment that limits normal activities, including seeing, hearing, walking, or speaking.* It is estimated that between 9 and 10 percent of the population in this country has a disability.

People with a disability sometimes have difficulty doing things other people take for granted. They may have difficulty riding buses and subways, climbing stairs, or even using certain household appliances. However, the greatest challenge facing people with a disability is the misguided view society has long held. Historically, people with disabilities have been seen as a "breed apart." They have been pitied, ignored, and even placed in institutions that offered mere custodial care.

Physical Challenges

The most common types of physical challenges affect a primary sense or ability to move and get around easily. These include sight impairment, hearing impairment, and motor impairment.

Lesson 4 Resources

TEACHER'S CLASSROOM RESOURCES

🖝 **Concept Map** Activity 93

🖝 **Enrichment** Activity 31

🖝 **Lesson 93 Quiz**

🖝 **Lesson Plan 93**

🖝 **Reteaching** Activity 93

STUDENT WORKBOOK

🖝 **Applying Health Skills 93**

🖝 **Chapter Study Guide 31**

🖝 **Vocabulary** Activity 31

Sight Impairment

As with other disabilities, sight impairment can be moderate, as is the case with the more than 5 million Americans who are vision-impaired, or it can be severe, as with the 1 million who are blind. About 10 percent of people fitting this description are under 20 years old.

The leading cause of blindness today is from complications due to diabetes. Whereas everyone must take care of their vision and have regular eye examinations, those with diabetes must take special care to have more frequent exams in addition to maintaining a special diet and taking medication. Other causes of blindness are macular degeneration, **glaucoma**, and **cataracts**. Early diagnosis means that treatment can begin sooner to prevent blindness.

Hearing Impairment

Hearing impairment affects 20 million Americans. Like blindness, hearing impairment can range from minor to severe. **Profound deafness** is *a hearing loss so severe that a person affected cannot benefit from mechanical amplification such as a hearing aid.*

Deafness can be inherited or caused by injury or disease. Most hearing impairments are caused by infections, obstructions, or nerve damage. Obstructions may block sound waves traveling to the inner ear. If obstruction is the cause of hearing impairment, the hearing loss may involve only one ear. Obstructions may be due to a buildup of wax, bone blockage, or something stuck in the ear.

A person born with abnormal bone growth in the inner ear may have inherited an obstruction that results in impaired hearing or deafness. Surgery can cure many of these cases.

Nerve damage usually distorts hearing in both ears. Exposure to loud noise can cause nerve damage. It may also occur with aging. Hearing impairments from nerve damage and obstruction may be gradual. If your hearing has changed, it may be time for a visit to your doctor or to an *audiologist,* a specialist in hearing problems.

HEALTH Online

Visit **health.glencoe.com** to learn about eye care, diseases, and the responsibilities of eye care professionals.

hotlink

glaucoma For more information on glaucoma, a disease that damages the optic nerve of the eye, see Chapter 7, page 174.

cataracts For more information on cataracts, a clouding of the lens of the eye, see Chapter 7, page 174.

Learning sign language can give you the ability to communicate with the hearing impaired.

ACTIVITY *List organizations in your area that offer special classes for sign language or for Braille, a system that allows blind people to read through the sense of touch.*

TEACH

L1 Discussing

Pose these questions: What specific indications do you see that people with disabilities are no longer considered "different"? How do you think this current attitude benefits people with disabilities? people without disabilities?

L2 Researching

Let volunteers research macular degeneration and then explain this disease, its effects, and treatment possibilities to the rest of the class.

L2 Critical Thinking

Let volunteers research the concept of a deaf culture, in which people with serious hearing impairment are considered not as disabled but as members of a unique cultural group. Encourage these volunteers to share their findings, and then have the entire class discuss their responses to the concept of deaf culture.

HEALTH Online

You may want to divide the class into groups, assigning each a different link to explore at this rich site. One group, for example, might research aspects of daily preventive care, another group eye safety during sports, another eye diseases and conditions, and so on. Have groups work on a time share basis if computer access is limited. Set aside class time for an information share.

SCHOOL-TO-CAREER

OCCUPATIONAL HAZARDS. A person's work situation may affect risk factors. For example, tobacco smoke may be present in the work environment. Farm laborers, factory workers, and exterminators handle pesticides. Construction workers may be exposed to lead or asbestos when stripping or tearing down old buildings. Dry cleaners inhale toxic chemicals all day. Many workers are at risk for potentially disabling accidents. Divide students into groups and have them pretend that they have been assigned to a congressional subcommittee to study health hazards in the workplace. Have each group choose an area to research, such as farm labor, construction workers, factory workers, etc. Have them conduct research on their subjects and report their findings while the class role-plays a larger congressional committee.

L1 Discussing

Ask students to share their ideas about helping other people with motor impairment. Ask: When and how do you think you should offer assistance to someone you don't know? to someone you know casually? to a friend?

L2 Research/Writing

Instruct students to research fetal alcohol syndrome. What is it, and how can it be recognized? What causes it, and how can it be avoided? How many babies are born with fetal alcohol syndrome each year? Ask students to use their findings in writing short stories or plays. Encourage them to share their completed compositions with the rest of the class.

L2 Community Involvement

How has the Americans with Disabilities Act affected your school district, your community, and your state? Have students work in cooperative learning groups to explore and discuss answers. Then have group members work together to write a summary of their findings.

L2 Self-Esteem

How does one's level of self-esteem help in struggling with a disability? Elicit responses from the class.

▶ *A visit to someone who is chronically ill can help make them feel better.*

ACTIVITY *Write the name of someone you know who is chronically ill, and next to the name write at least two things you can do to help that person feel better.*

Motor Impairment

An injury to the brain or a disorder of the nervous system can affect the body's range of movement and coordination, including that of the hand and eye. Sometimes, especially when there is trauma to the brain, motor impairment of this sort may be accompanied by mental impairment.

Advances have been made to assist people with motor impairments. For example, people with limb amputations are fitted with *prosthetic,* or artificial, limbs. Motorized wheelchairs also allow many people with motor impairment to get around without assistance.

Mental Challenges

Some challenges affect a person's ability to live independently in society. This is the case with some of the physical challenges mentioned above. It is also true of the mental challenge called *mental retardation.* **Mental retardation** is *below-average intellectual ability present from birth or early childhood and associated with difficulties in learning and social adaptation.* Mental retardation affects about 3 percent of the population. The four levels of mental retardation are mild, moderate, severe, and profound. Mildly affected individuals make up about 75 percent of the mentally retarded population and often cannot be outwardly distinguished from nonretarded people.

Several factors have been isolated as causes of mental retardation. One is heredity. Symptoms of **genetic disorders** such as Down syndrome, PKU, or Tay-Sachs disease include mental retardation. Lifestyle of the mother-to-be during pregnancy is another factor. Women who use alcohol or other addictive drugs greatly increase the risk that

hotlink

genetic disorders For more information on genetic disorders and health conditions associated with each, see Chapter 20, page 464.

696 CHAPTER 31 NONINFECTIOUS DISEASES AND DISABILITIES

PERSONAL HEALTH

PREDICTING EFFECTS. Health effects of high-risk lifestyles are long-term. Moreover, the effects of one person's unhealthful lifestyle can influence the health of many people. Children may suffer from the premature loss or disability of parents, or be burdened as adults by care of ailing parents. Individuals may be widowed or become caregivers for terminally or chronically ill spouses. A family may be bankrupted by medical bills; taxpayers may cover the medical costs. Employers may be let down by unhealthy workers who cannot perform. Invite students to write entries in their private journals, listing the risky activities and lifestyle factors to which they are most prone. Tell them to predict the effects in 50 years on spouses, offspring, friends, and employers.

their babies will be born with retardation. Yet another preventable risk factor is infection with rubella, or German measles, during pregnancy. Immunization against this disease either during a female's childhood or within three months of her becoming pregnant reduces this risk.

Eliminating Barriers

People with physical and mental challenges have the same needs and interests as the rest of the population. They also have many of the same abilities. In recent decades, strides have been made toward eliminating barriers of stereotyping and prejudices. These trends have been the result in part of lobbying efforts by people with physical and mental challenges themselves. In securing their rights, these individuals have worked to establish several important principles:

- that society make certain changes—such as wheelchair access to public transportation and building entrances—that allow people with physical or mental challenges to take part more readily in business and social activities;
- that people be evaluated on the basis of individual merit, not on stereotyped assumptions about disabilities; and
- that, to the extent each is able, these people be integrated among persons who do not have physical or mental challenges.

A major action toward achieving these goals was the passage by Congress in 1990 of the **Americans with Disabilities Act.** This is *a law prohibiting discrimination against people with physical or mental disabilities in the workplace, transportation, public accommodations, and telecommunications.*

LESSON 4 *Review*

Reviewing Facts and Vocabulary

1. Define *disability*.
2. Describe the possible causes of deafness.
3. Name one way a mother-to-be can decrease the risk of mental retardation in her baby.

Thinking Critically

4. *Analyzing.* Make a list of ways in which people use their eyes and ears each day. Next to each item, list the problems that might be associated

with each task for persons with sight impairment or hearing impairment.

Applying Health Knowledge

5. *In Your Home.* Loud noise over a long period of time can cause permanent hearing loss. Loud noise also causes temporary hearing loss, but over the years a permanent high-tone hearing loss develops. Name some hobbies or activities that you and your friends participate in that include loud noise. What can you do to protect your hearing?

LESSON 4   PHYSICAL AND MENTAL CHALLENGES   **697**

ASSESS

EVALUATING THE LESSON

Assign and discuss the Lesson 4 Review; then administer, grade, and discuss the *Lesson 93 Quiz* in the TCR. ☞

RETEACHING

- Have students outline the lesson using Roman numerals for the headings. Ask that they provide at least two facts to support each Roman numeral entry.
- Ask students to complete *Reteaching Activity 93* in the TCR. ☞

ENRICHMENT

- Have students form groups to review the contents of the Americans with Disabilities Act of 1990. Assign each group a category, such as employment, public transportation, public accommodations, telecommunications, and miscellaneous provisions. Ask each group to prepare a presentation of provisions guaranteed to disabled individuals under this law.
- Get students to think about some of the practical and ethical implications of losing heart, kidney, liver, or other essential organ function by having them complete *Enrichment Activity 31,* "Organ Transplants," in the TCR. ☞

CLOSE

Have students recall the incidence and causes of common physical and mental disabilities and discuss the challenges a person with a disability may face.

Lesson 4 Review

Answers to Reviewing Facts and Vocabulary

1. Any physical or mental impairment that limits normal activities, including seeing, hearing, walking, or speaking.
2. Infections, obstructions, and nerve damage.
3. Any one: abstain from alcohol and other addictive drugs, avoid exposure to rubella, be immunized against rubella during childhood.

Answer to Thinking Critically

4. Lists will vary.

Health Skills Activities

ACTIVITY 1
HEALTH SKILLS

Accessing Health Information, Analyzing Influences

➤ **National Standards**
This activity meets these National Health Standards: 1.5; 4.4 .

Teach

- Help students approach this problem by thinking of specific buildings in the community—including the school building—that have stairs and other features that might pose a problem to those with disabilities.
- Suggest that students also consider internal items: the height of tray rails in the cafeteria and whether restrooms have accommodations for those in wheelchairs.
- While some students are compiling details for the report card, others might research the names and addresses of state and United States representatives.

ACTIVITY 2
HEALTH SKILLS

Comprehending Health Concepts, Health Advocacy

➤ **National Standards**
This activity meets these National Health Standards: 1.6; 7.2

Teach

- Suggest that researchers gather as much information as they can from the text, as well as from Web sites you have prescreened that offer useful information. Links to such sites may be obtained by visiting Glencoe's Health Web site (health.glencoe.com).
- Once a first draft of a script has been completed and reviewed by student reviewers, the individual who is to read the script should read the broadcast while others time the reading to ensure it can be done within the allotted time frame.

Activity 1 — Community Report Card

Since passage of the Americans with Disabilities Act, many communities have instituted changes such as greater wheelchair accessibility. What does your community do to meet the special needs of its members?

Directions

1. With several classmates, develop a checklist of ways your community meets the special needs of the physically and mentally challenged.
2. Make an inspection tour of community buildings and facilities. Note ramps, Braille signage, and other features you find at a location.
3. Assign your community a grade based on the presence of helpful features. Devise a total grade based on the section grades. Suggest improvements, if any, your community could make.
4. Discuss your findings in class. You may also want to send your Community Report Card to a local legislator.

Time
20 minutes, plus outside research time

Materials
paper, pen or pencil

Self-Assessment

✓ Identified community services or features available to the physically and mentally challenged.
✓ Suggested improvements your community could undertake.

Activity 2 — Radio Broadcast to Stop Cancer

There are many different types of cancer. Each has warning signs and risk factors. You can help inform others of the risks and of the healthful behaviors that will reduce those risks.

Directions

1. As a class, review types of cancers most likely to affect teens. Appoint members to write a script for a two-minute radio broadcast about one type of cancer. Other members are to gather additional information about the disease, as needed. Include warning signs and steps that can be taken to reduce the risk of that cancer.
2. Still other group members should review the broadcast to make sure the language is powerful and effective.
3. If possible, broadcast your message over the school public address system.

Time
40 minutes

Materials
paper, pen

Self-Assessment

✓ Identified cancer warning signs, risk factors, and prevention strategies.
✓ Created a broadcast that is clear and persuades the listener of the importance of practicing disease prevention.

ASSESSMENT SCORING

Using a four-level rubric, the student has achieved a 4 if:

ACTIVITY 1
✔ Student identified community services or features available to the physically and mentally challenged.
✔ Student was thorough in features compiled.
✔ Student suggested improvements your community could undertake.
✔ Student communicated information clearly in a form to be sent to officials.

ACTIVITY 2
✔ Student successfully researched a cancer common among teens.
✔ Student identified warning signs, risk factors, and prevention strategies for the cancer.
✔ Student created a broadcast showing the importance of practicing disease prevention.
✔ Student broadcast met the time constraints and format of broadcast samples provided.

Adult Diseases, Young Bodies

Many teens are eager to accept adult responsibilities. Unfortunately, poor lifestyle choices make some teens susceptible to adult diseases as well.

Type 2 diabetes is often called "adult-onset diabetes" because it usually occurs in people over 40. Because of an alarming new trend, doctors may need to change the name of this hazardous condition.

The number of teenagers who develop type 2 diabetes has increased dramatically. This rise is tied to risk factors such as high-fat diets, skipping breakfast, obesity, and lack of exercise.

Once diagnosed with diabetes, teens can manage their condition by adopting a balanced, healthy diet and limiting inactivity. Making these choices now can help everyone avoid this unwanted part of growing up.

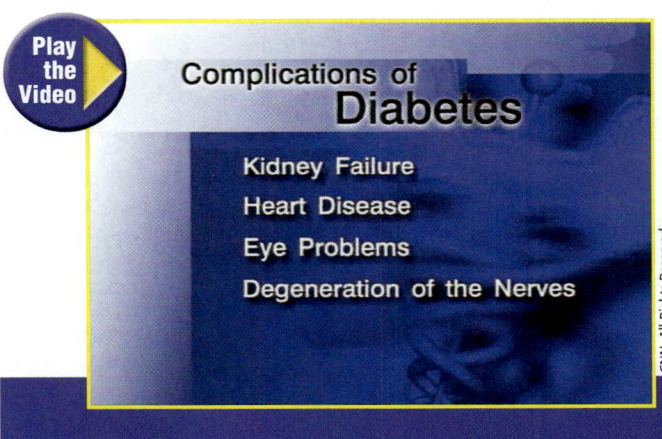

Play the Video ▶

Complications of **Diabetes**

Kidney Failure

Heart Disease

Eye Problems

Degeneration of the Nerves

CNN. All Rights Reserved.

Think About It

▶ Nigel was diagnosed with adult-onset diabetes when he was 15. What risk factors do you think made him vulnerable to this disease?

▶ What steps has Nigel taken to manage the disease?

CNN HEALTH NEWS **699**

MORE ABOUT . . . . .

TEEN DIABETES. Researchers believe that the increase of type 2 diabetes among teens is directly related to the increase in obesity in the United States. A survey published in the Archives of Pediatrics and Adolescent Medicine indicated that the number of overweight children aged 6 to 17 has risen from 5 percent in the 1960s to 11 percent in the 1990s.

Analysts at the Centers for Disease Control and Prevention (CDC) concluded that the most important key to reversing this trend is increased physical activity and exercise.

Adult Diseases, Young Bodies
Video Segment 20 (Time – 2:11)

Objectives. After viewing the video, students should be able to recognize the impact that diabetes has on teen sufferers and identify the symptoms and treatments of the disease, including lifestyle changes that can control it.

Motivator. Ask students to name some diseases that affect adults more commonly than teens. Help students assess their lists to identify reasons why many diseases tend to occur in later stages of life. Then screen Video Segment 20, which describes the growing trend of teenagers diagnosed with adult-onset diabetes.

Teach

• Use a Venn diagram to review the similarities and differences between type 1 and type 2 diabetes. Emphasize that both types of diabetes affect the way the body converts food into energy. Type 1 diabetes usually occurs during childhood and adolescence. It almost always is treated with daily insulin injections. Type 2 is more common, usually occurs after age 40, and is usually controlled by changing diet and exercise patterns.

• Have students list the risk factors that increase a teen's chances of developing type 2 diabetes, such as high-fat diets, lack of exercise, and poorly balanced meals. Next to each factor, ask students to suggest three specific changes that might help someone develop healthier habits.

Investigate. Encourage students to share information about type 2 diabetes and teenagers with their family and friends. As students discuss this trend with others, encourage them to note comments and suggestions presented in health news reports. Allow time for students to share their observations with classmates.

Close. Write the phrase *adult-onset diabetes* on the chalkboard. Ask students to describe the condition and explain why this name is not entirely accurate.

CHECKING COMPREHENSION

- Assign and discuss the chapter review.
- Use the MindJogger Videoquiz to review the chapter. 🔴

CHAPTER 31 REVIEW ANSWERS

Using Health Terms

1. hypertension
2. stroke
3. cardiovascular diseases (CVDs)
4. congestive heart failure
5. benign
6. melanoma
7. cancers
8. biopsy
9. impaired glucose tolerance (IGT)
10. insulin
11. rheumatoid arthritis
12. Americans with Disabilities Act
13. disability

Recalling the Facts

1. Discomfort in the center of the chest, possibly extending into one or both arms, the neck, jaw, upper abdomen, and/or back; nausea; vomiting; sweating; and/or shortness of breath.
2. Arteriosclerosis, or hardening of the arteries.
3. Hypertension is both a disease and a causative factor in other CVDs.
4. Sudden weakness or numbness of the face, arm, and leg on one side of the body; loss of speech, or trouble in speaking or understanding people; sudden dimness or loss of vision, particularly in only one eye; unexplained dizziness, unsteadiness, or sudden falls.
5. Cigarette smoking.
6. Change in bowel habits; a sore that does not heal; unusual bleeding or discharge;

Using Health Terms

On a separate sheet of paper, write the term that best matches each definition below.

LESSON 1

1. High blood pressure.
2. An interruption of the flow of blood to any part of the brain.
3. Medical disorders that affect the heart and blood vessels.
4. A slow, gradual weakening of the heart muscle from overwork.

LESSON 2

5. Noncancerous.
6. Often deadly type of skin cancer.
7. Uncontrolled abnormal cell growths.
8. A laboratory analysis of a section of tissue taken from a site where abnormal cell growth is suspected.

LESSON 3

9. A condition in which blood sugar levels are higher than normal but not high enough to be classified as diabetes.
10. A hormone that is produced in the pancreas and that helps the body convert glucose to energy.
11. A destructive and disabling inflammation of the joints.

LESSON 4

12. A law prohibiting discrimination against people with physical or mental disabilities in the workplace, transportation, public accommodations, and telecommunications.
13. Any physical or mental impairment that limits normal activities, including seeing, hearing, walking, or speaking.

Recalling the Facts

Using complete sentences, answer the following questions.

LESSON 1

1. What are the early signs of a heart attack?
2. What happens as a result of plaque building up in the arteries?
3. To what health problems does hypertension often lead?
4. What are the signals that indicate a stroke may be occurring?

LESSON 2

5. What factor is the leading cause of lung cancer?
6. What are the seven warning signs of cancer?
7. What is an advantage of chemotherapy over surgery or radiation in the treatment of cancer?

LESSON 3

8. Which groups are most likely to suffer from type 1 diabetes?
9. Why might a case of type 2 diabetes go undetected for years?
10. What are the goals of treatment of rheumatoid arthritis?

LESSON 4

11. Name two physical challenges a person might face.
12. What are some causes of mental retardation?
13. Explain what strides have been made toward eliminating barriers for the physically and mentally challenged.

700 CHAPTER 31 NONINFECTIOUS DISEASES AND DISABILITIES

thickening or a lump in the breast or elsewhere; indigestion or difficulty swallowing; obvious change in a wart or mole; nagging cough, hoarseness.
7. Avoids excessive destruction of normal cells.
8. Whites.
9. Onset is gradual.

10. Relieve pain, reduce inflammation, prevent damage to joints, and prevent deformities.
11. Any two: sight impairment, hearing impairment, motor impairment.
12. Heredity, lifestyle of the mother-to-be during pregnancy, and infection with rubella during pregnancy.

Thinking Critically

LESSON 1

1. *Synthesizing.* What lifestyle decisions are associated with the development of hypertension or heart disease?

LESSON 2

2. *Synthesizing.* How is early detection of cancer related to the likelihood of cure?

LESSON 3

3. *Synthesizing.* Although persons with diabetes can die because of too much or too little sugar in their blood, they are more likely to die from complications of heart or kidney disease that has progressed over the years. What is the connection between diabetes and these other life-threatening illnesses?

LESSON 4

4. *Evaluating.* Which of the following statements would you say is more appropriate: (a) The disabled are special people. (b) The disabled are normal people. Defend your selection.

Making the Connection

1. *Language Arts.* Using print or on-line newsmagazine or other sources, research the history of one of the treatments for heart disease. How did the treatment develop? How long did research continue before the treatment was tried on humans? How effective has this particular treatment proven?

2. *Social Studies.* Read about countries that have lower incidences of certain types of cancer—for example, the lower incidence of breast cancer in Japan and the higher incidence of colon cancer in Western nations. Chart how the types of foods people eat in these countries may contribute to these trends.

BEYOND THE CLASSROOM

PARENTAL INVOLVEMENT Encourage your family to participate in a "save your heart" week. Make a chart that lists at least four lifestyle behaviors family members can adopt during a seven-day period, such as taking a walk after dinner or eating fruit instead of a high-fat dessert. At the end of the week, report in your private Health Journal on the success of your experiment.

COMMUNITY INVOLVEMENT Speak with a public official or law enforcement officer in your community about the issue of handicapped parking spaces. Learn how the number of such spaces for a given facility is determined, what the fine or punishment is for abusing such a space, and whether fines are levied against nonchallenged individuals driving a car with handicapped license plates. Share your findings in an oral report.

SCHOOL-TO-CAREER

Exploring Careers. Interview an oncologist about the possibilities of a career in the area of oncology. Determine what preparation, including schooling, is necessary, the various settings in which oncologists work, and the types of interpersonal skills needed for the job. Share your findings with the class in an oral report.

Thinking Critically

1. Lifestyle decisions such as not enough physical activity, smoking, and unhealthful food selections.
2. Early detection makes successful treatment more likely.
3. Lack of sufficient insulin leads to excess glucose in the blood; the glucose affects the heart and kidneys.
4. Statements and defenses will vary.

Making the Connection

1.–2. Answers will vary.

Evaluate

- Use the reproducible *Chapter 31 Test* in the TCR, or construct your own using the Testmaker software.
- Use *Performance Assessment Activity 31* in the TCR.

Enrichment

Ask students to complete *Cross-Curriculum Activity 31* in the TCR.

Beyond the Classroom

Keep students involved in the community, and encourage parent participation by assigning the activities on this page for students to work on outside of class.

---

13. Barriers of stereotyping and prejudices are being overcome; society is making changes that allow people with physical or mental challenges to take part more readily in business and social activities; to the extent each is able, people with special challenges are being integrated among those who do not have physical or mental challenges; the Americans with Disabilities Act was passed in 1990.

Consumer Choices and Public Health

	FEATURES	CLASSROOM RESOURCES

LESSON 1

Selecting Health Care and Services

pages 704–708

- Concept Map Activity 94
- Lesson 94 Quiz
- Lesson Plan 94
- Reteaching Activity 94
- Transparencies 32, 33

LESSON 2

Being an Alert Health Consumer

pages 709–712

Making Responsible Decisions

"Choosing a Health Plan,"
page 710

- Concept Map Activity 95
- Decision-Making Activity 32
- Lesson 95 Quiz
- Lesson Plan 95
- Reteaching Activity 95

LESSON 3

Strategies for Dealing with Consumer Problems

pages 713–716

Building Health Skills

"Obtaining Help: When You're Unhappy with a Health Service or Product,"
page 714

- Concept Map Activity 96
- Cooperative Learning Activity 32
- Enrichment Activity 32
- Health Lab 32
- Lesson 96 Quiz
- Lesson Plan 96
- Reteaching Activity 96

LESSON 4

Community Health

pages 717–719

- Concept Map Activity 97
- Lesson 97 Quiz
- Lesson Plan 97
- Reteaching Activity 97

ACTIVITIES

- Cross-Curriculum Activity 32
- Health Lab 32
- Health Skills Activities 32
- Parent Letter and Activities 32

ASSESSMENT

- Chapter 32 Test
- Performance Assessment Activity 32
- Testmaker Software

STUDENT ACTIVITIES WORKBOOK

- Applying Health Skills 94–97
- Study Guide 32
- Vocabulary Activity 32

STUDENT DIVERSITY STRATEGIES

- Audiocassette Program (English)
- Audiocassette Program (Spanish)
- Spanish Parent Letters and Activities
- Spanish Summaries, Quizzes, and Activities

MULTIMEDIA COMPONENTS

- English Audiocassette Program
- Spanish Audiocassette Program
- MindJogger Videodisc and VHS program

National Health Education Standards

One of the main goals of the National Health Education Standards is to move students toward "health literacy." Health literacy is the capacity of individuals to obtain, interpret, and understand basic health information and services and the competence to use such information and services in ways which promote health. The health standards were developed by applying the characteristics of a well-educated, literate person within the context of health. The health literate person is:

- a critical thinker and problem solver
- a self-directed learner
- a responsible, productive citizen
- an effective communicator

Listed below are the Health Education Standards Performance Indicators addressed in each lesson of this chapter.

Lesson	Health Standards Performance Indicators
1	1.7, 2.2, 2.3, 2.5
2	2.1, 2.3, 2.5, 6.1
3	2.4, 5.3, 7.3, 7.6
4	1.7, 3.4, 7.5, 7.6

ONLINE RESOURCES

For a fresh approach to health topics and an in-depth look at health issues, use these online resources found under Teacher Resources at **health.glencoe.com**.

- **BLOCK SCHEDULE LESSON PLANS** Reinforce health concepts with outside readings selected especially for students. Each reading is accompanied by a lesson plan and activities to enhance
  - Reading Skills
  - Cross Curriculum
  - Media Literacy

- **TECHNOLOGY PROJECTS** Instructions and suggestions on how to use computer, Internet, and software with health lessons.

- **HEALTH UPDATES** Timely topics in health news, including late-breaking medical advances and updates on teen risk behaviors.

Out of Time?

If time does not permit teaching this chapter, you may use these features: Making Responsible Decisions on page 710 and Building Health Skills on page 714.

BLOCK SCHEDULING

Block scheduling provides extended time for hands-on projects and activities. Use the following activities to engage students, provide further depth, and vary your instructional techniques:

- Health Skills Activity (60–90 minutes) **pg. 720**

Consumer Choices and Public Health

CHAPTER OVERVIEW

Chapter 32 presents information to inform consumers of the service providers in the health care system. Guidelines are provided for selecting services and products, and agencies that receive complaints are identified.

LESSON 1 A variety of health care providers work in both short- and long-term facilities to meet the public's medical needs. Insurance programs can be purchased to protect individuals from the high cost of health care services, and government programs are available to specific groups.

LESSON 2 The responsibility for selecting and maintaining health coverage has fallen on the shoulders of the private health consumer. This lesson introduces factors that should be considered when selecting a health plan and health care provider. Developing patient skills to fulfill the individual's role in their health care is also discussed.

LESSON 3 Consumers should be aware of the types of treatments and products that are most susceptible to false claims. Consumers depend upon others to provide them with products and services to protect their health. They should, however, become aware of the agencies that can assist them in any claims against a product or company.

LESSON 4 Agencies are available at local, national, and international levels to administer public health.

HEALTH *Online*

GOAL SETTING
You can make a difference in someone's life, offer help in the community, or put your communication skills to work by choosing a health services profession. Browse the Career Corner at **health.glencoe.com** for ideas for your future.

Hands-On Health

TEACHING STRATEGY

Accessing Reliable Health Resources
Provide an opportunity for students to gather and share information about reliable health resources for teens. See Activity 28, "Hot Line," in the *Hands-On Health: Creative Teaching Strategies* booklet.

Time Needed
2 hours in class

Supplies
- local phone books
- art supplies
- computer with graphics options

Personal Health Inventory

Self-Inventory Write the numbers 1–10 on a sheet of paper. Read each statement below and respond by writing *yes*, *no*, or *sometimes* for each item. Write a *yes* only for items that you practice regularly. Save your responses.

1	I have a doctor that I see regularly for checkups.
2	I trust my physician and can communicate easily with him or her.
3	I understand the roles played by various health care professionals, such as therapists and laboratory technicians.
4	I know my medical history and keep a written record of it.
5	In case of a medical emergency, I know what action to take.
6	I have health insurance and know how to use it.
7	I pay attention to the effectiveness of the medical treatments I receive.
8	I avoid using unproven or useless over-the-counter remedies.
9	I follow instructions when taking over-the-counter or prescription medications.
10	I pay attention to side effects from taking medications and report these to my doctor.

Follow-up After completing the chapter, retake this self-inventory. Pick two items that you need to work on and set a goal to improve your health behaviors.

> ❝ *Our nation is strong, and our people resilient. We have a well-earned reputation for pulling together in the worst of times to help each other.* ❞
>
> —LAURA BUSH
> FIRST LADY, SEPTEMBER 12, 2001

Quick Write In the photo on the facing page, volunteers are lined up at the American Red Cross building in Washington, D.C., to donate blood for emergencies. Make a quick list of the ways you can contribute to the health and well-being of others.

TECHNOLOGY OPTIONS

MINDJOGGER
VIDEOQUIZ

To preview or review chapter content, you may wish to use the *MindJogger Videoquiz* that accompanies Chapter 32. 🔴

INTRODUCING THE CHAPTER

Personal Health Inventory

After students have read the Self-Inventory, encourage them to discuss the importance of the behaviors and attitudes identified in the inventory statements. How do they help you protect all aspects of your health? Then provide time during which students can record their own statement responses in their private Health Journals on a page labeled "My Understanding of Health Care." Remind students that they will return to this Self-Inventory in the follow-up activity at the end of Chapter 32.

- Help students develop a list of health care facilities and services available in the community. The list should include hospitals and clinics (general and specialized), private doctors, dental offices and clinics, nursing homes, etc. In an urban area, the list will be extensive. In a rural area, discuss the availability of health care, travel required to reach specialty health care facilities, and the availability of such transportation.
- Let students read the introductory quotation on this page, and have them complete the Quick Write. Have volunteers identify some of the ways public service workers help others. Then ask: If you had a health problem, who would you turn to? What are ways to become familiar with health services in your community? Explain that students will explore these topics as they study the lessons in Chapter 32.
- Distribute Parent Letter 32 in the *Parent Letters and Activities* booklet. 👉

Selecting Health Care and Services

FOCUS

LESSON OBJECTIVES

After studying this lesson, students should be able to

- describe the basic groups of health care providers.
- discuss the roles of short- and long-term health care facilities.
- describe the types of health insurance currently available.
- distinguish between the types of managed care.

MOTIVATOR

Write the following on the chalkboard for students to work on while attendance is being taken: *If you had a sudden attack of appendicitis, to which hospital would you go? How long would you be likely to stay in the hospital? What would it cost? Who would pay for it?*

INTRODUCING THE LESSON

Refer to the Motivator. Ask volunteers to share their responses. Most teens have relatively limited experience with the health care system. Tell them that this lesson will discuss health care providers, facilities, and insurance.

INTRODUCING HEALTH TERMS

- Tell students to remember that *Medicare* is intended to "care" for people over age 65, while *Medicaid* is intended to "aid" anyone who can't afford medical care.
- Ask students to complete Vocabulary Activity 32 and Chapter Study Guide 32 in the *Student Workbook.*

Selecting Health Care and Services

As you move toward your adult years, you will become increasingly responsible for making decisions about your health care. Knowing about the vast complex of services and institutions that make up our nation's health care system will better prepare you to make these decisions.

HEALTH TERMS

health care providers

primary care physician

specialist

health care facility

outpatient surgical facility

health insurance

Medicare

Medicaid

health maintenance organization (HMO)

preferred provider organization (PPO)

HEALTH CONCEPTS

- Health care providers offer many different types of health services.
- Health care facilities include medical offices, hospitals, and nursing homes.
- Health insurance is a participatory program that covers some of the costs of health care.

Ophthalmologist's equipment

Health Care Providers

The foundation of the nation's health care system is a group of *professionals trained in the health fields* called **health care providers.** This group includes physicians, nurses, and allied health care professionals. Each plays an important role in providing comprehensive health care for the American public.

Physicians

When you think of health care, perhaps the provider that most often comes to mind is the physician. The physician has traditionally been the backbone of the American health care system. *A medical professional who provides the first line of health care* is called a **primary care physician.** You see a primary care physician for checkups or when a health problem arises.

Lesson 1 Resources

TEACHER'S CLASSROOM RESOURCES

- **Concept Map** Activity 94
- **Lesson 94 Quiz**
- **Lesson Plan 94**
- **Parent Letter and Activities 32**
- **Reteaching** Activity 94

STUDENT WORKBOOK

- **Applying Health Skills 94**
- **Chapter Study Guide 32**
- **Vocabulary** Activity 32

TRANSPARENCIES

- **Transparencies 32, 33**

A primary care physician may refer you to a **specialist**, *a physician who has received additional training in a particular area of medicine.* Dermatologists, for example, specialize in treating diseases and problems of the skin. Oncologists specialize in treating cancer. The chart below lists other specialists.

Nurses

Nurses provide care for sick people. Their responsibilities vary according to the amount of training they have received. Licensed practical nurses (LPNs) assist physicians and provide direct care such as bathing or changing bandages. Registered nurses (RNs) take more responsibilities for patients and sometimes supervise LPNs. Nurse practitioners have advanced training that enables them to work independently of a physician. A nurse practitioner may specialize in a field such as childbirth or public education. Nurse practitioners can assume the role of a primary care physician in examining and treating patients.

Health Care Specialists

PHYSICIAN	SPECIALIZES IN...
Allergist	allergies
Dermatologist	skin diseases
Gynecologist	female reproductive system problems
Internist	internal, nonsurgical diseases
Neurologist	nervous system problems, such as strokes
Oncologist	cancer
Ophthalmologist	eye disease
Orthopedist	skeletal deformities or injuries
Pediatrician	primary care for children
Psychiatrist	mental health
Rheumatologist	pain and stiffness in muscles or joints
Urologist	urinary problems

An ophthalmologist will give a thorough eye exam and check for diseases.

ACTIVITY *Describe the difference between a primary care physician and a specialist.*

MORE ABOUT . . . . .

THE MEDICAL HIERARCHY. The medical division of labor in the United States is very elaborate, with many practitioners filling roles other than that of physician. Nonetheless, physicians are the preeminent practitioners, and they are further subdivided into more than 20 specialties. These vary by the body parts treated and the techniques used, as well as by the earnings, status, and power accorded to the practitioner. Doctors of internal medicine are at the top of the physician hierarchy; within internal medicine, higher status goes to cardiology than to urology or proctology, reflecting the cultural symbolism we attach to the corresponding body parts.

TEACH

L1 Class Activity

Ask students to write sentences that describe the ideal doctor. Have the students share their responses with the class. Explain that everyone should be careful in choosing the right doctor for specific health problems.

L1 Discussing

Discuss with students the advantages and disadvantages of seeing a doctor who is in a group practice versus choosing one who is in practice alone.

L1 Discussing

Explore the issue of why a person might choose to go to a family doctor with a specific problem rather than to a specialist *(familiarity, doctor knows family history, etc.).* Why might a person choose instead to go to a specialist? *(greater expertise about a specific ailment, more sophisticated equipment, etc.)*

L1 Parental Involvement

Ask students to discuss with their parents the types of medical specialists that are available. Have them ask how their parents would go about choosing a particular specialist if one were needed. Encourage students to share their findings with the class.

L1 Reading

Have students read about the legal aspects of medical care for minors, including treatment with and without parental consent and doctor-patient confidentiality.

L2 Discussing

Help the class consider reasons why outpatient surgery and second opinions are becoming more frequent in medical practice.

L3 Researching

Instruct students to find out what the average daily cost (or the actual cost) at a particular facility is for a patient in each of the following types of facilities: private hospital, community hospital, alcoholism treatment center, psychiatric hospital, and nursing home. Have them present this information as a bar graph.

L1 Guest Speaker

Invite a speaker from a local nursing home to talk about his or her health care facility. Ask the speaker to describe a typical patient and the reason the patient is there. The speaker should address what the nursing home provides that is not available in the patient's own home.

L1 Guest Speaker

Invite an insurance agent to discuss the types of medical insurance available and the cost of the insurance for single individuals and families. Ask: How is group insurance beneficial?

L3 Parental Involvement

Ask students to interview their parents about the types of medical facilities that are currently used or have been used in the past by family members. What factors determined how these facilities were selected? What kind of medical insurance does the family have?

△ *This registered nurse is giving the patient specialized, personal care.*

ACTIVITY *Name several duties of an RN and a nurse's aid.*

hotlink

clinical psychologist For more information on clinical psychologists and the health services they perform, see Chapter 10, page 250.

Allied Medical Professionals

ALLIED MEDICAL PROFESSIONAL	SPECIALIZES IN...
Clinical psychologist	treating emotional or behavioral disorders
Dental hygienist	cleaning and polishing teeth
Dietitian	nutritional counseling; planning specialized menus
Emergency medical technician (EMT)	emergency treatment
Laboratory technician	lab tests, such as urine or blood workup
Nurse's aide	making beds, feeding and bathing patients
Occupational therapist	training persons with disabilities for daily activities and jobs
Optometrist	testing vision for eyeglasses
Pharmacist	dispensing medicines
Physical therapist	physical rehabilitation after injury, accidents, strokes, other disorders
Radiology technician	X rays
Social worker	counseling people with health problems
Speech therapist	helping people overcome speech problems

Allied Health Care Professionals

Other health care professionals cover a broad range of job descriptions from dentist to physical therapist to **clinical psychologist**. Some allied health professionals work closely with and under the supervision of physicians in medical settings.

Health Care Facilities

A **health care facility** is *any place staffed by health care professionals and equipped for delivery of health services.* A doctor's office is one type of health care facility. Generally speaking, however, the term is used to denote two main types of institutions—*short-term facilities,* such as hospitals, and *long-term facilities,* such as nursing homes.

Short-Term Health Care Facilities

The hospital is perhaps the most familiar type of short-term health facility in a community. Hospital stays are usually measured in days or weeks, although sometimes a patient must stay longer, depending on the condition.

706 CHAPTER 32 CONSUMER CHOICES AND PUBLIC HEALTH

MEETING STUDENT DIVERSITY

GIFTED. Although no formal definition exists, gifted students can be described as having above-average ability, task commitment, and creativity. They usually finish work more quickly than other students and are capable of divergent thinking. Tips for instructing gifted students include the following:

• Make arrangements for students to work on independent projects.

• Encourage creative avenues of expression.

• Make resources (print, visual, and multimedia) available for additional investigation.

• Emphasize concepts, theories, ideas, relationships, and abstract thinking.

Hospital care is provided on both an inpatient and outpatient basis. Inpatients are people who are admitted to a treatment facility and occupy a bed in it. Outpatients receive various services such as X rays or other diagnostic tests and return home the same day.

Various clinics may be part of a hospital setting. A clinic provides medical tests and treatment that does not require an overnight stay. Urgent care clinics provide emergency care on a walk-in basis. Due to breakthroughs in postsurgical treatment, which have shortened hospital stays, a new type of clinic has emerged. The **outpatient surgical facility** is *a place where surgery is performed on patients who are released the same day.*

Long-Term Health Care Facilities

Long-term health care facilities provide care for patients over an extended period of time. Persons recovering from serious accidents or crippling illnesses may spend time at a rehabilitation center. There they receive physical therapy and, where necessary, relearn basic living skills, such as feeding themselves and bathing. A hospice, another type of long-term health care facility, provides care for the terminally ill. Through a team effort of loved ones, hospice nurses, and a participating physician, a dying patient can live out the rest of his or her life in a homelike setting.

Nursing homes are facilities in which care is provided for medical and nonmedical needs. Though most residents are 65 years of age or older, these facilities are used by people of all ages. A person with a serious long-term illness or recovering from surgery may also live in a nursing home.

▲ *Often physical therapy can be provided in an outpatient facility.*

ACTIVITY *Name an injury or illness that might require physical therapy.*

Health Insurance

Health insurance is *a plan to cover part or most costs of expenses and care associated with medical treatment.* To maintain membership in such a plan, the insured person pays a periodic *premium,* or fee, for his or her coverage. In conventional insurance plans, the insured person pays for doctor's visits and other forms of treatment out of pocket and is then reimbursed by the insurance company for a predetermined portion of the cost, often 80 percent.

Soaring costs of health care in this country in recent decades have driven up the costs of insurance and prompted some alternatives to

L1 Explaining

Distinguish among the kinds of services and products that health insurance policies typically cover.

L3 Researching

Guide students in researching the two government-sponsored health insurance programs, Medicare and Medicaid. Have them determine the origin of each, how they are utilized by the population, and how they are frequently abused. Select several students to present their information orally. Have the class discuss ways to prevent abuse within the system.

L1 Discussing

Ask students to explain why more and more health consumers are joining health maintenance organizations (HMOs). Why do students think more doctors are also becoming part of these organizations?

L2 Community Involvement

Have students research community resources for information regarding HMOs. Compare and contrast private and group practices with HMOs.

L3 Researching

Let volunteers research the health costs involved for an individual who is hospitalized for a life-threatening illness, such as a heart attack. Have them determine how one catastrophic illness can affect a person financially. Ask the volunteers to share the information with the class.

SCHOOL-TO-CAREER

INSURANCE AGENT. An insurance agent sells insurance and helps clients select the health care plan that best suits their needs. Because insurance agents are licensed by the state, qualifications vary from state to state. A typical state may require an examination to qualify for the license. Some states require training from a trade school before sitting for the exam. A high school graduate can usually complete the training in a week or a little longer. The state may permit candidates to complete training through correspondence schools. Some states require renewal every few years, and they may require additional study as a condition of renewal. Students with good communication skills may wish to find out about their state's requirements for an insurance license.

EVALUATING THE LESSON

Assign and discuss the Lesson 1 Review; then administer, grade, and discuss the *Lesson 94 Quiz* in the TCR. 📕

RETEACHING

- Ask students to work in small groups and to imagine that they are answering calls to an information hot line for foreigners settling in the United States. Ask each group to act out what they would say to the inquiring person about the types of health facilities available in the United States and the kinds of medical insurance available to pay for them.
- Ask students to complete *Reteaching Activity 94* in the TCR. 📕
- Use *Transparencies 32* and *33* to review careers in the health care area. 🖌

ENRICHMENT

Encourage students to compare the health care system in the United States with that of Canada. Have them identify the advantages and disadvantages of each system. Can they think of ways to combine the advantages of each into one improved health care system?

CLOSE

Ask students to summarize the most important points in this lesson. Have them identify different kinds of health care providers and facilities and describe the various kinds of health insurance programs.

---

conventional coverage. Two alternate programs are provided by the government. **Medicare** is *a health insurance program that is available to people who are 65 years of age or older and to people who receive Social Security disability benefits.* Some people who receive Medicare also are eligible for Medicaid. **Medicaid** is *an assistance program of medical aid for people of all ages who are unable to afford medical care.*

Other approaches to health insurance include *managed health care.* Under a managed care plan, a person must choose a physician affiliated with the plan. This physician, usually a primary care physician, "manages" the person's health care. If the primary care physician thinks the patient needs to see a specialist, a referral will be made.

Health maintenance organizations (HMOs) are the most common type of managed care. A **health maintenance organization (HMO)** is *a group of physicians of different specialties who work together to provide medical services to members.* Members pay a monthly fee but receive most or all medical services without paying an additional charge or by making a small *co-payment* fee at the time of an office visit.

Another kind of managed care is the **preferred provider organization (PPO)**, *a type of health insurance in which medical providers agree to charge less to members of the plan.* The patient, however, can still choose to see a physician outside the plan, but at a higher cost.

LESSON 1 *Review*

Reviewing Facts and Vocabulary

1. Which medical professional provides the first line of health care?
2. Give a definition for a health care facility.
3. How is a preferred provider organization different from a health maintenance organization?

Thinking Critically

4. **Analyzing.** Explain why it is important to have health insurance. What risks does one take by not having health insurance?
5. **Evaluating.** Conventional health care is expensive. In managed care or in programs where health care is free, patients may not choose their own doctors and may have to wait for care. Some specialized care may not be available to everyone. Is it better to have good care at high cost for some, or minimal care for everyone at low cost? Explain your response.

Applying Health Skills

6. **In Your Home.** Talk with your parents or other adults at home about the kind of health coverage your family has. What services are covered, and what restrictions apply, if any? Also, find out what costs are covered and what costs are paid by the patient. Determine, finally, whether the adults are pleased overall with this coverage, and if not, why.

Lesson 1 Review

Answers to Reviewing Facts and Vocabulary

1. Primary care physician.
2. Any place staffed by health care professionals and equipped for delivery of health services.
3. PPO offers members a wider choice of physicians, including those outside the plan; however, PPO members have to pay more for visits to physicians who are not part of the plan.

Answers to Thinking Critically

4. Answers should reflect an awareness of the high costs of health care.
5. Answers will vary.

Being an Alert Health Consumer

Have you ever taken cough medicine or a pain reliever? If so, you have experience as a **health consumer,** *a person who uses health products or services.* As a health consumer, you have a right to be informed about the products or services you buy. This is true whether you are shopping for medicine or a health plan.

HEALTH CONCEPTS

- A health consumer is anyone who shops for and purchases health products and services.
- Being an alert health consumer includes knowing and standing up for your rights.

Choosing a Health Plan

In the past, the task of shopping for a health plan was one many Americans never needed to face. The decision was often made for them by their employer; health coverage in a group plan was often a standard job benefit. Today, however, with the cost of such coverage reaching unprecedented highs, many companies have cut back drastically on health benefits to employees or eliminated them altogether. Increasingly, in recent years, the responsibility for selecting and maintaining health coverage has fallen on the shoulders of the private health consumer.

Although this may seem like an awesome responsibility, an awareness of several key factors can help. These factors, which need to be taken into account when considering enrollment in any health plan, include:

Lesson 2 Resources

TEACHER'S CLASSROOM RESOURCES
- **Concept Map** Activity 95
- **Decision-Making** Activity 32
- **Lesson 95 Quiz**
- **Lesson Plan 95**
- **Reteaching** Activity 95

STUDENT WORKBOOK
- **Applying Health Skills 95**
- **Chapter Study Guide 32**
- **Vocabulary** Activity 32

LESSON 2

Being an Alert Health Consumer

FOCUS

LESSON OBJECTIVES

After studying this lesson, students should be able to

- identify important considerations when selecting a health plan.
- discuss guidelines for choosing a health provider.
- describe the responsibilities that a good patient assumes, including the purchase and use of medicines.

MOTIVATOR

Write the following on the chalkboard for students to work on while attendance is being taken: *Define consumer. Then make a list of ten products or services you buy or use at least once a week.*

INTRODUCING THE LESSON

Have students share their responses to the Motivator. Point out that everyone is a consumer of products and services. Explain that this lesson will focus on guidelines for making wise choices as a private health consumer.

INTRODUCING HEALTH TERMS

- Have students write a paragraph describing the type of information that would likely be found in a person's medical history.
- Ask students to complete Vocabulary Activity 32 and Chapter Study Guide 32 in the *Student Workbook.*

TEACH

L1 Family Involvement

Encourage students to discuss their family's health insurance with parents and ask the following questions: What kind of health insurance do we have? What eligibility requirements, if any, does our family meet to be enrolled in our current insurance plan? Ask students to write one-paragraph summaries of their family discussions.

Making Responsible Decisions

1. Gilbert's employer has announced that the employees' health benefits package will be reduced.
2. Gilbert could (a) hope that his family can get by on the limited health benefits; (b) look for another job with full health benefits; (c) arrange to pay more to get full health benefits for his family.
3. Gilbert might (a) find that his family has very high medical costs that are not covered by insurance; (b) get a job at which he will have lower seniority but that offers full medical benefits; (c) have to spend part of his wages to be sure his family has full medical benefits.
4. Gilbert values good medical care for his family. He also values his family's financial security.
5. Decisions will vary.
6. Guide students in considering the short- and long-term consequences of their decisions.

L2 Decision Making

For further study on making responsible decisions, assign *Decision-Making Activity 32* in the TCR. ☞

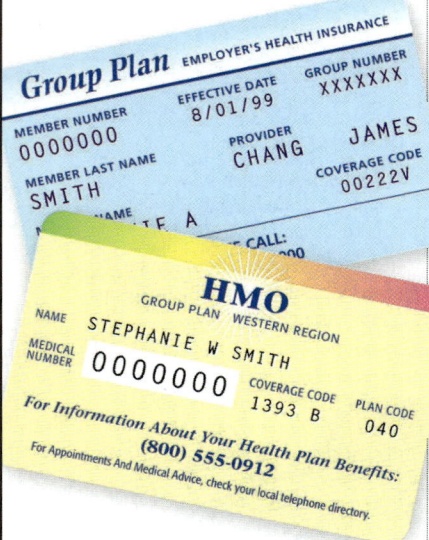

■ **Cost.** Some 46 million Americans have responded to the rising costs of health care by enrolling in HMOs. An advantage to HMOs is that the premiums are generally far lower than those associated with conventional coverage. A disadvantage is that such plans limit your choice of health care providers to doctors who are affiliated with the plans.

■ **Special needs.** Certain health conditions and forms of treatment are not covered by some insurance policies. Most, for example, deny coverage for treatment with an experimental medication. Many, moreover, have "ceilings"—dollar amounts after which a condition, such as a catastrophic illness, will no longer be covered.

■ **Eligibility.** Some health plans have attractive rates and coverage but are limited to people affiliated with a certain group. Religious and professional organizations are two examples. It is important to be aware of eligibility requirements when choosing a plan.

Choosing a Health Care Provider

When choosing a health care provider, the following guidelines will be helpful:

■ Ask friends or relatives outside your immediate family for recommendations.
■ Ask other health care professionals you know for a referral. These people know who can provide you with the best medical care.
■ Call your local medical society. Most medical societies will provide three names, chosen in rotation from the society's membership roster.

Making Responsible Decisions

Choosing a Health Plan

The plant at which Gilbert has worked for 12 years recently announced that they will be offering a limited health benefits package to its employees. For Gilbert and his wife, this is a special hardship, because their two-year-old daughter, Sara, was born with a heart valve defect, which has required ongoing treatment. What should Gilbert do to make sure his family has the health coverage they need?

What Would You Do?

Apply the six steps of the decision-making process to Gilbert's problem.

1. **State the situation.**
2. **List the options.**
3. **Weigh the possible outcomes.**
4. **Consider your values.**
5. **Make a decision and act.**
6. **Evaluate the decision.**

PERSONAL HEALTH

FOLLOWING RESEARCH. The body of knowledge about nutrients and botanicals grows every day. As of 1993, the FDA had approved only one health claim for a nutrient: calcium to prevent osteoporosis. By the end of the 1990s, it had approved many more. Before the FDA approved the claim that folic acid could reduce the risk of neural tube defects in an embryo, the U.S. Public Health Service was recommending 400 micrograms of folic acid daily for all women of child-bearing age, and scientific evidence was available in libraries. Encourage students to keep abreast of studies suggesting a relationship between nutrients and conditions in the body. Eventually, if confirmed by numerous studies, these findings may become part of the accepted scientific body of knowledge.

- Ask a local librarian or consumer protection agency if a directory of doctors has been compiled in your community, or use the *American Medical Directory* at your local library to get detailed information about specific doctors, including their professional credentials and areas of specialization.

In getting referrals, make any personal preferences and needs known. Some people feel more comfortable going to a physician of the same gender. Others prefer to start a relationship with a doctor who is relatively young and is likely to be practicing well into the future. Yet another consideration is personality—what kind of "bedside manner" does the person have? Is he or she easy to talk with?

Patient Skills

Many people choose a physician according to his or her level of skill, then place themselves in the hands of the physician, feeling that their job is done. As a health consumer, however, a patient continues to bear responsibility for his or her own care. Good health care requires an active partnership between the health care provider and the patient. It requires skills not only on the part of the health professional but also on the part of the patient. Good "patient skills" begin with an awareness of one's own **medical history**. This is *complete and comprehensive information about immunizations and any health problems to date.* A good patient is also one who:

- *is prepared when visiting a physician.* Write down the reasons for your visit, including any specific health complaints such as pains or discomfort.
- *asks questions of the doctor when necessary.* If the doctor explains a problem, make sure you understand what he or she is saying. Ask for a repetition of any points that are sources of confusion. If

keeping Fit

For the Record: Your Rights

Your medical records are your doctor's property. What can you do if you need to get access to the health information your physician has on file?

➤ Remember that you have the right to get copies of all records.

➤ You also have the right to have copies of these records sent to another doctor of your choosing.

➤ If a person is under age or seen as incompetent, then a parent, legal guardian, or other authorized person may have to sign for the documents to be released.

➤ If a doctor can't find your records, mixes your records with someone else's, or has recorded very little information about you, you should be concerned.

➤ Check to see what the law is in your state regarding confidentiality. More than 50 percent of states now have laws requiring patient access.

➤ Ask who else can be given copies of your records, such as insurance companies, government agencies, and others.

keeping Fit

For the Record: Your Rights

Discuss individuals' rights to get access to their medical records as described in the feature. Ask: What medical information is required by schools? (*immunization record to be admitted, physical exam results for sports participation*) Suggest that students ask their parents to request a copy of their medical records to establish their own file of their medical history.

L1 **Personal Involvement**

Have each student write a private Health Journal entry about his or her own primary health provider. How did you select that provider, or who selected that provider for you? What do you like about your health care provider? What would you like to change? If you are interested in selecting a new provider, what specific steps will you take?

L1 **Guest Speaker**

Invite a primary care provider, such as a general practice physician or a family nurse practitioner, to speak with the class about his or her interactions with patients: What "patient skills" do most patients seem to have? Which do many lack? How does the health care provider try to encourage improved patient skills? What recommendations does he or she have for teen patients?

HOME AND COMMUNITY
CONNECTION

MANAGED CARE PROVIDERS. One factor of concern for health insurance consumers is the choice of physicians. Students may benefit from examining a list of HMO and PPO providers in the community. Have students assess how much membership in managed care would restrict their choices. Provide PPO or HMO membership lists for students to examine. You may be able to use a list provided by your district plan. Let students

compare the list of providers for both HMOs and PPOs with the Yellow Pages list of physicians in the area. How many physicians are included on each list? Are students' family physicians on the lists? How many are excluded? Have students discuss their observations and whether they would feel restricted by managed care in your community.

ASSESS

EVALUATING THE LESSON

Assign and discuss the Lesson 2 Review; then administer, grade, and discuss the *Lesson 95 Quiz* in the TCR. ☞

RETEACHING

- Ask students to set up a chart identifying factors that are important when considering a health plan and a health care provider.
- Ask students to complete *Reteaching Activity 95* in the TCR. ☞

ENRICHMENT

- Have students discuss with their parents the type of health plan their family is enrolled in and what program choices they had available to them.
- Ask students to research the cost and availability of health plans for individuals who are self-employed or unemployed.

CLOSE

Remind students that it is important to recognize the responsibilities that they will face as adult health consumers. The decisions they make could greatly affect their health maintenance and finances.

---

hotlink

medicines For more information on medicines and their role in health, see Chapter 23, page 512.

hotlink

over-the-counter (OTC) medicines For more information on over-the-counter (OTC) medicines and their use, see Chapter 23, page 519.

---

medication is prescribed, make sure you understand how it is to be taken and why you are taking it.

- *follows up on a visit as needed.* If a problem for which you have been treated persists or recurs, inform the doctor.

Although patients do not have a major role in choosing the **medicines** a doctor prescribes, there are some important consumer skills in this area. Be sure you understand the doctor's instructions regarding prescription medicines, and know why you are taking a particular medicine. It is also important to make sure you are taking a medicine as intended and to report any problems or side effects.

As a patient, it is also your right to inquire about taking a **generic** equivalent of a medicine. This is *a less-expensive version of a medicine that may be substituted for a brand-name medication*. In some cases, a doctor may insist on a patient's taking a nongeneric medicine because the generic equivalent lacks *buffers*—added ingredients that make the medicine easier to tolerate. As a patient, you have a right to this information as well.

Over-the-Counter Medicines

When shopping for **over-the-counter (OTC) medicines**—those that can be bought without a doctor's prescription—it is important to use the same skills as when shopping for any other product. This includes a careful reading of the label to make sure you understand how the medicine is meant to be used. Another consideration when shopping for OTC medicines is price comparison.

LESSON 2 *Review*

Reviewing Facts and Vocabulary

1. What is a health consumer?
2. Identify three patient skills.
3. What is the difference between generic medicines and nongeneric medicines?

Thinking Critically

4. **Analyzing.** Interpret the following statement: The doctor *cannot* do what the patient *will* not do.
5. **Synthesizing.** Beth has had severe cramps for several days. John is seeing his doctor for a follow-up visit after suffering a concussion in a football game last Friday night. Write several questions that each teen might want to ask his or her physician.

Applying Health Skills

6. **In Your Home.** Find out about your own medical history. Ask your parents or other adults in your home to show you any records they have on doctor visits and health problems you have had. Also, check to see if they have a list of your immunizations. If not, work with them and your family physician to compile a list of immunizations and health treatments, and keep these in a safe place where they are easily accessible.

Lesson 2 Review

Answers to Reviewing Facts and Vocabulary

1. A person who uses health products or services.
2. Any three: being aware of one's own medical history; being prepared when visiting a physician; asking questions of the doctor when necessary; following up on a visit when needed.
3. Generic medicines are less expensive substitutes for brand name medicines.

Answers to Thinking Critically

4. Answers should reflect an understanding of the fact that the patient is in control of his or her own behavior, including taking prescribed medications and altering risk behaviors.
5. Questions will vary.

Strategies for Dealing with Consumer Problems

H ave you ever purchased a health-care product that did not fulfill its claim? When it comes to health care, receiving quality health care and products is important. Sometimes a consumer will receive poor, ineffective, or even harmful products and services. This lesson will tell you what steps a consumer can take when this happens.

HEALTH TERMS

quackery

advocate

HEALTH CONCEPTS

- Developing an awareness of the potential for fraud and deception in health care is one of the keys to being an alert consumer.
- A consumer who suspects fraud has several actions to choose from.

Medical Fraud

I t is illegal to make false claims, promising that a medicine or medical treatment can do something that it cannot do. Yet, there are people looking to benefit from other people's misfortune. You may have heard such people referred to as "quacks." **Quackery** is *a type of medical fraud* that plays on human emotion, weakness, and fear. Quackery is used to extract money from people who want fast cures or relief from pain. Quacks may appeal to consumers' emotions by using techniques such as testimonials, personal stories from individuals who claim to have been cured by a particular product or treatment.

LESSON 3   STRATEGIES FOR DEALING WITH CONSUMER PROBLEMS   **713**

Lesson 3 Resources

TEACHER'S CLASSROOM RESOURCES

- **Concept Map** Activity 96
- **Cooperative Learning** Activity 32
- **Enrichment** Activity 32
- **Health Lab** 32
- **Lesson 96 Quiz**
- **Lesson Plan** 96
- **Reteaching** Activity 96

STUDENT WORKBOOK

- **Applying Health Skills** 96
- **Chapter Study Guide** 32
- **Vocabulary** Activity 32

Strategies for Dealing with Consumer Problems

FOCUS

LESSON OBJECTIVES

After studying this lesson, students should be able to

- identify popular types of product and treatment fraud.
- identify agencies and organizations that exist to help health consumers with complaints.

MOTIVATOR

Write the following on the chalkboard for students to work on while attendance is being taken: *Write the names of two health-related products or services you have seen advertised that you do not think would really do what the advertising promises.*

INTRODUCING THE LESSON

Have students share their responses to the Motivator. (*Possibilities might include wrinkle creams, weight-loss clinics, diet supplements, etc.*) Tell students that this lesson describes different forms of quackery and where complaints can be filed.

INTRODUCING HEALTH TERMS

- Tell students to define *quackery* and identify techniques used to appeal to consumers' emotions.
- Ask students to complete Vocabulary Activity 32 and Chapter Study Guide 32 in the *Student Workbook.*

TEACH

L1 Discussing

Ask students to relate personal experiences in which they bought worthless products or services. Have students discuss what convinced them to make the purchases in the first place. Follow up by brainstorming ways to avoid quackery.

L2 Cooperative Learning

Distribute *Cooperative Learning Activity 32,* "Truth in Advertising," in the TCR. 📖

Building Health Skills

When You're Unhappy with a Health Service or Product
Skill: Obtaining Help

To introduce this feature, let students brainstorm a list of specific health services and health products they might use; record their ideas on the board. Then ask: What could happen that would make you unhappy with one of these services or products? What would you do then? Divide the class into groups, and assign one of the listed services or products to each group. Have the members of each group work together to read the Building Health Skills feature and to discuss how they would apply each tip to their assigned situation.

L2 Health Lab

Assign *Health Lab 32* and have students discover what moisturizer is most effective. 📖

Fraudulent Products and Remedies

Among the many useless products sold over-the-counter to vulnerable consumers are anti-aging aids. In our youth-oriented society, many middle-aged adults are interested in stopping the processes of aging such as wrinkling or balding. However, no product can reverse the process of aging. The best way to stay healthy and fit is to exercise, avoid tobacco and other drugs, limit your hours in the sun, and eat a balance of foods from the different sections of the Food Guide Pyramid.

Another lucrative area for health quackery is weight-loss formulas. Popular weight-loss products claim that using them can cause weight loss without the hard work of exercising or reducing calories. Unlike most quack remedies, many of these products may, if faithfully followed, lead to an actual loss of weight. The real "secret," however, is not in the product itself but in the fact that most involve a cutback in the amount of food consumed.

Building Health Skills

Obtaining Help: When You're Unhappy with a Health Service or Product

EVEN THE MOST CAREFUL health consumers find themselves buying products or securing services that do not work right or serve them well. This is why it is necessary for you, as a health consumer, to know what to do and where to go for help. Here are some tips to follow:

1. **Identify the problem.** Decide on what you feel would be a fair way to resolve it.

2. **Have some documentation available to back up your complaint.** This might be an invoice or canceled check. Include a list of symptoms.

3. **Go back to the source.** Contact or visit the health care provider or, in the case of medication, the pharmacy or store that sold it to you. State the problem and how you would like to have it solved.

4. **Go to a higher authority.** If the first person you contact is not helpful, ask to speak to a supervisor or, in the case of medications, a store manager. Repeat your story. Most problems are resolved at this level.

5. **Write a letter.** If you are still not satisfied with the response at the higher level, do not give up. If the health facility operates nationally or the product is a national brand, write a letter to the president or the director of consumer affairs of the company.

714 CHAPTER 32 CONSUMER CHOICES AND PUBLIC HEALTH

HEALTH LITERACY

RESPONSIBLE/PRODUCTIVE CITIZEN. In some cases, the damage to consumers from specific health care products is extreme. After exhausting other remedies, consumers may resort to class action suits or boycotts. Encourage students to research some instances of health care consumers who suffered extreme damage, such as women with silicone implants or daughters of women who took diethylstilbestrol while pregnant. How are the victims addressing the manufacturers? In the case of adversarial actions, such as the boycotts and class action suits against Dow Corning, what attempts were made to persuade the manufacturers to accept responsibility before taking extreme measures? Have students decide whether any current boycotts or class action suits are worthy of their support.

Fraudulent Treatment

Among the people most susceptible to fraudulent treatments are those with chronic illnesses such as Alzheimer's disease and osteoporosis, for which there is no cure or instant relief. Because many older adults fall into this category, they are likely targets for fraud. Although some fraudulent treatments may not cause physical harm, they may be dangerous because the patient delays seeking sound medical advice and treatment until it is too late. Cancer and arthritis are two areas where many kinds of fraudulent and useless treatments are offered.

Help for Consumer Problems

Several agencies and organizations exist to help consumers with complaints against health providers or products. These include licensing boards, consumer affairs bureaus, media action programs, private consumer groups, and government services.

- **Licensing Boards.** If you have a problem with a professional health care provider, you may be able to get help from a state licensing or regulatory board such as the American Medical Association (AMA), which licenses physicians and provides peer review when problems arise.

HEALTH Online

Locate articles on consumer protection and learn how to avoid product scams and to protect your consumer rights at **health.glencoe.com**.

Government Services

AGENCY	PURPOSE	ADDRESS
Consumer Product Safety Commission (CPSC)	protects consumers against harmful products; can ban or recall a dangerous product	Director, Office of Communications Consumer Product Safety Commission Washington, DC 20207
Consumer Information Center (CIC)	distributes consumer information materials; provides free copies of the Catalog of Consumer Information	Consumer Information Center Pueblo, CO 81009
Food and Drug Administration (FDA)	ensures that medicines are properly labeled and safe and effective for their intended uses; determines whether a medicine should be prescription or over-the-counter	Director, Consumer Communications Food and Drug Administration 5600 Fishers Lane Rockville, MD 20857
Federal Trade Commission (FTC)	prevents unfair, false, or deceptive advertising of consumer products and services	Office of the Secretary Federal Trade Commission Washington, DC 20580

Myths & Realities

MYTH. Because of government regulations, all advertising must be accurate.

FACT. Many forms of advertising praise an item by using inflated opinions and exaggerations. This practice is called "puffery," and it uses words to make products seem far better than they really are. Puffery statements are not illegal because they cannot be proven false by the Federal Trade Commission. They cannot be proven true either, and can be very misleading to consumers. Here are some examples of puffery: "Three out of four doctors recommend _____ ." (How many were surveyed?) "_____ gives fast relief." (How fast is it?)

L1 Family Involvement

Direct students to ask their parents, grandparents, or other adult relatives about types of product fraud that they have observed over the years. Have students ask questions such as: Did you or your friends or family members use any of the products? What were some of the claims made about the products? What were the results, if the products were used? Request that students share some of their interviews with the class.

HEALTH Online

If you can devote all or part of a class period to this activity, you may want to visit the consumer protection site and list main topic links on the chalkboard. Then invite students to sign up to investigate one of those areas based on individual interests. Note that the documents accessed at each link are available in both text and PDF (full-graphic) versions, the latter requiring Adobe Acrobat® Reader, which can be obtained at the Adobe® Web site.

L1 Discussing

Ask the class why some people do not file formal complaints or return merchandise even when they have received poor service or defective merchandise.

L2 Community Involvement

Choose students to visit the local or state consumer office to research educational materials and information available on fraud and quackery regarding health providers or products.

Avoiding Quackery

keeping Fit

Have students find and bring to class examples of quackery and unsupported claims to discuss.

ASSESS

EVALUATING THE LESSON

Assign and discuss the Lesson 3 Review; then administer, grade, and discuss the *Lesson 96 Quiz* in the TCR. ☞

RETEACHING

- Collect a variety of newspaper and magazine ads for products that are susceptible to quackery. Have students analyze the ads and make a list of reasons why they think the product is legitimate and another list of reasons why they think the product is fraudulent. Discuss their analyses as a class.
- Ask students to complete *Reteaching Activity 96* in the TCR. ☞

ENRICHMENT

- Organize students into groups to formulate three laws that would make it more difficult for quacks to operate. Have students discuss as a class their legislative suggestions. Which would be most effective? Why?
- Have students complete *Enrichment Activity 32,* "How Drugs Get FDA Approval," in the TCR. ☞

CLOSE

Stress that consumers have both rights and responsibilities. A complaint must be genuine. When consumers handle a problem in an organized way, they are more likely to achieve a satisfactory resolution.

---

keeping Fit

Avoiding Quackery

Medical quackery can result in a waste of money. Even more serious, it can result in injury, illness, or death. Be on the lookout for the following "red flags":

➤ "secret formula"

➤ "miracle cure"

➤ "overnight results"

➤ "limited offer"

➤ endorsements by famous persons

➤ availability only through mail order

➤ foreign medicine not usually available in the United States

➤ passionate testimonials of those supposedly "cured"

➤ hard-sell approaches

If you contact a state board for help, it will usually bring your complaint to the attention of the person whom you filed against. The board will seek a satisfactory solution to your problem and can conduct an investigation if necessary.

- **Consumer Affairs Bureaus.** Local consumer affairs offices are easy to contact by phone or in person, and they are usually familiar with local regulations and procedures. The Better Business Bureau (BBB) is a nonprofit organization sponsored by private businesses that provides general information on products and services, reliability reports, and background information on local businesses and organizations.

- **Media Action Programs.** If you live in or near a large city, you may be aware of one of the more than 100 newspapers and 50 radio and TV stations that offer action groups or phone-in services for consumers who need help.

- **Private Consumer Groups.** In addition to the many government and business organizations that can be of assistance to the consumer, private consumer groups exist in all 50 states. In almost all cases, these are made up of individual consumer members who join together to support consumer interests. They are called *advocates.* An **advocate** is *someone who speaks out for another person or a cause.*

- **Government Services.** The federal government has established a number of specialized agencies that deal with health-related products and services. See the chart on page 715. You have a right as a citizen to make use of their services, and these agencies have a responsibility to help you.

LESSON 3 *Review*

Reviewing Facts and Vocabulary

1. What is quackery? Which products and treatments are often at the midst of quackery?
2. How can an advocate help a consumer with a complaint?
3. What does the Consumer Product Safety Commission (CPSC) do to help health care consumers?

Thinking Critically

4. *Evaluating.* List several criteria you could use to distinguish between an effective complaint against a health care provider or product and an ineffective complaint.

Applying Health Skills

5. *In Your School.* Prepare a survey on the kinds of over-the-counter medicines used by students in your school. Ask students to complete the survey on a confidential basis. Determine which medicines are most used by students you surveyed. Compile the results and share them with the class.

Lesson 3 Review

Answers to Reviewing Facts and Vocabulary

1. A type of medical fraud that plays on human emotion, weakness, and fear; anti-aging aids and weight-loss products.
2. By speaking out for other consumers or for specific causes.
3. Protects consumers against harmful products; can ban or recall a dangerous product.

Answer to Thinking Critically

4. Answers should reflect an understanding of the importance of accessing help through government agencies and private consumer groups.

Community Health

P eople today are living longer than ever. This is due partly to the advent in this country in the late 1800s of a system of **public health,** *a community-wide effort to monitor and promote the welfare of the population.* Thanks to developments in public health, American citizens can be reasonably sure that their drinking water, food, and medicines are safe.

HEALTH TERMS

public health
epidemiology
famine

HEALTH CONCEPTS

- Public health is a community-wide effort to monitor and promote the welfare of the population.
- Organizations and agencies that promote the health of the public exist at the local, state, and national levels, as well as in the private sector.
- Every member of a society has a responsibility toward the health of the community at large.

Public Health Agencies

A lthough public health is defined as a community health effort, the term *community* may have a variety of connotations. You probably think of a neighborhood or an organized group of people when you hear this term. Yet, a community—especially with regard to health matters—may also include an entire city, a state, a nation, or even the world at large. As a result, many organizations and agencies have been formed for administering public health on all levels.

Public Health at the Local Level

You are undoubtedly familiar with the names of such organizations as the March of Dimes and the American Lung Association. These groups are private agencies usually devoted to a particular

Lesson 4 Resources

TEACHER'S CLASSROOM RESOURCES
- **Concept Map** Activity 97
- **Lesson 97 Quiz**
- **Lesson Plan 97**
- **Reteaching** Activity 97

STUDENT WORKBOOK
- **Applying Health Skills 97**
- **Chapter Study Guide 32**
- **Vocabulary** Activity 32

Community Health

FOCUS

LESSON OBJECTIVE

After studying this lesson, students should be able to

- identify public health agencies and their functions.

MOTIVATOR

Write the following on the chalkboard for students to work on while attendance is being taken: *Name a public health agency of which you are aware. What services does it provide to the public?*

INTRODUCING THE LESSON

Have students share their responses to the Motivator. Most students will be aware of local organizations such as the March of Dimes, which concentrates on reducing birth defects. Explain that public health agencies are established at the local, national, and even international levels. This lesson will introduce many of these agencies and discuss their primary functions in administering public health.

INTRODUCING HEALTH TERMS

- Have students use the vocabulary terms in a written paragraph. Ask volunteers to read their paragraphs to the class.
- Ask students to complete Vocabulary Activity 32 and Chapter Study Guide 32 in the *Student Workbook.*

TEACH

L1 Critical Thinking

Let students identify some of the communities to which they belong. Then guide them in discussing the larger communities of which they are members. Ask: In what sense are all people in the United States members of the same community? How do the health problems of small numbers of people affect the entire national community? In what sense are we all members of one community, Earth? How are you affected if people in a distant region of the world are struck by a famine? How do you think you should respond to that kind of problem?

L2 Interviewing

Ask several students to interview local adults who work for (or volunteer with) local public health organizations, both private and governmental. What are the goals of the agencies? What are the responsibilities of the interviewed adults? Have these interviewers share their findings with the rest of the class.

L1 Researching

Have students work in cooperative learning groups to research the organization and functions of the Department of Health and Human Services.

L1 Guest Speaker

Invite a community member who once served with the Peace Corps to speak with students about his or her experiences.

△ *Hazardous or toxic materials need to be handled by a trained technician.*
ACTIVITY *Name the government agency responsible for controlling toxic substances.*

CHARACTER IN ACTION

Civic Duty and Public Health

Civic duty means being a responsible citizen. You are fulfilling your civic duty when you follow the law, vote, and participate in community projects. By observing basic health practices you promote your own health and the health of those around you.

Character Check Be responsible when it comes to public health:

➤ Make certain your immunizations are up-to-date.

➤ Do not expose others when you have a contagious illness.

➤ Participate in a fund-raiser like a walk or race for a particular disease.

---

health concern—in these specific cases, to birth defects and lung disease. Although many of these groups are local chapters of a national organization, they are usually run by local volunteers and funded through donations. The goals of private groups range from educating the public about a health problem to raising funds for research and treatment of particular diseases.

Government public health agencies also exist on the local level. These groups include county and state health departments that set regulations affecting the local community. For example, they may pass regulations to set standards for sanitation in restaurants, compile health statistics, and control environmental pollution.

Public Health at the National Level

The Department of Health and Human Services is a federal agency whose responsibility is public health in the United States. A division of the Department of Health and Human Service is the Public Health Service. This division is in charge of promoting the prevention of disease and enforcing health and safety standards. It has several agencies through which this work is done:

■ **The National Institutes of Health (NIH).** This Public Health Service agency conducts medical research of all kinds. It also provides grants—or funding—for other medical research done at universities or other institutions.

■ **The Centers for Disease Control and Prevention (CDC).** The CDC conducts research and collects data that help control the spread of diseases. Part of the CDC's job involves **epidemiology** (ep-uh-deem-ee-OL-uh-jee), *the scientific study of epidemics.* An epidemic, as you learned in Chapter 24, is the sudden spread of disease among many people.

■ **The Agency for Health Care Policy and Research.** This agency sets policies to improve health care, including its organization and access. It also promotes improvements in the financing of health care in the United States.

■ **The Health Resources and Services Administration.** This agency provides health resources and services for those in need, such as persons with AIDS, migrant workers, and the homeless.

■ **The Agency for Toxic Substances and Disease Registry.** The task of this agency is to investigate hazardous materials and their effects on humans.

MEETING STUDENT DIVERSITY

SUPPORT GROUPS. There are more than half a million support and self-help groups in the United States. They deal with everything from drug abuse to divorce, from mental retardation to weight control. Groups are formed by individuals with similar concerns and are designed to provide information and resources and to give emotional support. Support groups are not meant to replace health care professionals. Instead, they supplement and complement structured health care services. For information about a group that deals with a specific concern, students can contact a local hospital, doctor, or social service agency. Have students make posters with the names and phone numbers of these special groups in their area.

- **The Substance Abuse and Mental Health Service Administration.** This agency provides programs to serve substance abusers and people with mental and emotional disorders.

Public Health at the International Level

With such comprehensive and far-reaching public health policy, Americans often take public health for granted. In developing nations, however, these measures are not available. Many diseases that have all but disappeared in our society still exist in developing countries. In addition, these countries may still suffer from famines. A **famine** is *a widespread shortage of food* that results in nutritional deficiencies, starvation, and death. Several organizations work cooperatively among different sponsor nations to address world health. These include the World Health Organization, the Peace Corps, and the International Red Cross.

Public Health and You

One of the **developmental tasks** of adolescence involves developing a social intelligence, or concern for others and the environment. Being concerned about public health is part of this task. Reporting any suspected public health problems protects not only your own health but the health of your family, friends, and community members. Chapter 33 contains further information on ways of becoming an involved citizen in the interests of public health.

hotlink

developmental tasks For more information on the developmental tasks of adolescence, see Chapter 21, page 482.

developmental tasks For more information on the developmental tasks of adolescence, see Chapter 21, page 482.

LESSON 4 *Review*

Reviewing Facts and Vocabulary

1. What is public health?
2. The Public Health Service is a division of which federal government department?
3. What is the role of the National Institutes of Health?

Thinking Critically

4. **Comparing and Contrasting.** Explain the differences in the way that a media action group might handle a consumer complaint and the way a government agency might handle the same complaint.

5. **Evaluating.** Better Business Bureaus are sponsored by private businesses. Is this a good or bad arrangement? How does the term *conflict of interests* come into play here?

Applying Health Skills

6. **In Your School.** Find out what steps your school takes to stop the spread of disease among students and staff. Think of other suggestions students can follow to stop the spread of disease at school. Make a list of these suggestions and post them or publish them in the school newspaper.

Lesson 4 Review

Answers to Reviewing Facts and Vocabulary

1. A community-wide effort to monitor and promote the welfare of the population.
2. The Department of Health and Human Services.
3. Conducts medical research and provides funding for research done at universities or other institutions.

Answers to Thinking Critically

4. Answers should reflect an awareness of a media action group's interest in publicity and a government agency's interest in law and policy.
5. Opinions will vary.

CHARACTER IN ACTION

Civic Duty and Public Health

Encourage students to organize or participate in one of the activities suggested in the feature. Have them write a brief essay on their experiences.

ASSESS

EVALUATING THE LESSON

Assign and discuss the Lesson 4 Review; then administer, grade, and discuss the *Lesson 97 Quiz* in the TCR.

RETEACHING

- Ask students to explain why agencies are needed at all "community" levels to effectively function.
- Ask students to complete *Reteaching Activity 97* in the TCR.

ENRICHMENT

Assign students one of the public health agencies identified in the lesson. Have them acquire information about their organization by writing for information or locating its Web site, if available. Provide a bulletin board on which students can advertise their respective agencies.

CLOSE

Remind students that local health agencies depend upon volunteers and are funded by donations. Discuss how becoming involved benefits the organization, the people it serves, and the individual who becomes involved.

Health Skills Activities

ACTIVITY 1
HEALTH SKILLS
Self Management

➤ **National Standards**
This activity meets these National Health Standards: 3.1; 3.5.

Teach

- Introduce the activity by asking whether students have ever had a problem with something they bought and, if they did, how they dealt with it. Did they obtain satisfactory results? What methods did they use?

- Poll your class early on to find out if there are students interested in preparing and teaching a lesson plan as described in step 4 of the activity. If so, speak with a supervisor in your school district about making the necessary arrangements. Afterward, have these students report to the class on their experience.

ACTIVITY 2
HEALTH SKILLS
Accessing Health Information, Health Advocacy

➤ **National Standards**
This activity meets these National Health Standards: 2.3; 2.5; 7.5.

Teach

- As an alternative to sending students out into the community, you might bring to class and distribute flyers from a local pharmacy.

- Instruct students to begin by examining the contents of their home medicine cabinets and adding to their lists any common items they may have neglected.

- Review with students the formula for computing unit price: cost ÷ weight. Have groups of students apply the formula to the product packaging they have received. Make sure students move the decimal point in their computations as required.

Activity 1 — Letter of Complaint

When writing to a company to complain about a product or service, you need to include specific information. What would you include in such a letter?

Directions

1. With a partner, review the "Building Health Skills" activity on page 714. Then compose a complaint letter about a real or imaginary problem with a provider or product.
2. Be sure to state the problem clearly and include all necessary information.
3. Transfer your letter to poster board. Make the text large enough to be read at a distance.
4. If possible, teach a lesson on writing a complaint letter to a middle school class in your school or community. Use your enlargement as a model.

Time
50 minutes
Materials
paper, pen, poster board, colored markers

Self-Assessment

✓ Letter clearly stated the problem.
✓ Letter was respectful, yet assertive in tone.
✓ Lesson to middle school students clearly explained how to write a complaint letter.

Activity 2 — Medicine Pricing Guide

Determining the comparative costs of OTC medicines can be difficult, especially when two competing products are sold in varying sizes. You can help your family members compare and save on OTC medicines.

Directions

1. Visit a pharmacy to get information about the prices of competing brands of cough formulas, pain relievers, adhesive bandages, and other commonly used products in your home.
2. Note each type of product, the brand name, the net weight on the packaging, and the store price.
3. Determine the unit price of each product by dividing the price expressed in dollars and cents by the net weight in ounces.
4. Share your results in a pricing guide. Make copies available to family members and to classmates' families.

Time
40 minutes plus outside research
Materials
paper, pen, computer (optional)

Self-Assessment

✓ Pricing guide was well-organized and easy to read.
✓ Used mathematical equation to correctly calculate unit prices.

ASSESSMENT SCORING

Using a four-level rubric, the student has achieved a 4 if:

ACTIVITY 1
✔ Student letter clearly stated the problem.
✔ Student letter contained all necessary information to achieve a satisfactory result.
✔ Student letter was respectful, yet assertive in tone.
✔ Student lesson plan clearly explained how to write a complaint letter.

ACTIVITY 2
✔ Student pricing guide was well organized and easy to read.
✔ Student list of home remedies was complete.
✔ Student used mathematical equation to correctly calculate unit prices.
✔ Student compared like products.

HEALTH NEWS VIDEO

Internet Health Caution

Many people use the Internet to research health questions. The Net contains tons of health information. Some of it is clear, accurate, and helpful. Some of it is none of the above.

A recent study emphasizes the importance of reading Web pages cautiously and critically. When scientists studied Internet resources on one type of cancer, they found that more than half the pages had no peer review. This means the pages reflected the ideas of just one person. The study also found that 6 percent of the pages contained false information.

Surfers need to be critical of information on the Web. Look for reliable sites that have been created by more than one author. Check credentials of doctors at Web sites, and always ask your doctor about health information you find.

Play the Video

Think About It

▶ What are some of the advantages of using the Internet to research health questions? What are some disadvantages?

▶ What does Dr. J. Sybil Biermann mean when she says, "There really isn't gatekeeping on the Internet?"

MORE ABOUT . . . . .

TECHNOLOGY AND SCIENCE. In addition to presenting inaccurate or unsupported data, Internet health searches also can produce hundreds of unrelated pages and bad links. Students can compare three or four search engines and review effective search methods.

Remind students that a specific search request is likely to have more helpful results than a general one. Also explain that many search engines understand the use of quotations to search for a phrase. For example, searching for "Ewing's sarcoma" will lead to pages that contain that phrase; searching for Ewing's sarcoma will lead to pages that contain both words, together or separate.

Internet Health Caution
Video Segment 21 (Time – 2:08)

Objectives. After viewing the video, students should be able to analyze the Internet as a resource for health information and review ways to verify the reliability of the source.

Motivator. Ask students how they could answer a health question, such as "How can I prevent and treat acne?" Invite students to make lists of resources they might consult, including friends, doctors, reference books, magazines, textbooks, and the Internet. Next have students rate each source on their lists from 1 to 5 to indicate its reliability. Then screen Video Segment 21, which demonstrates how the Internet can be a source of both reliable and unreliable information.

Teach

• Discuss the results of the Internet research study. Have students share their assumptions about the Internet. They should conclude that not every fact on the Web is accurate. Therefore, researchers should carefully check data gathered from the Internet. Emphasize the importance of consulting a doctor before making any medical decisions.

• Discuss how to verify the credentials of any group or organization that sponsors a Web site. Explain that many sites have an "About" icon on their home pages. This link usually provides a brief description of the sponsor and authors.

Group Activity. Have students work together to investigate the accuracy and reliability of health Web sites that cover topics also found in this book. Each student should evaluate a different site to determine if the information agrees with other published accounts. They should list the credentials of the author or site sponsor.

Close. Ask students to tell how they can verify facts they locate on the Internet. Point out that errors can spread rapidly on the Net. Therefore, it is best to verify a fact with another source, such as a reference book, periodical, or physician.

CHAPTER **32** *Review*

CHECKING COMPREHENSION

- Assign and discuss the chapter review.
- Use the MindJogger Videoquiz to review the chapter. 🔴

CHAPTER 32 REVIEW ANSWERS

Using Health Terms

1. health insurance
2. preferred provider organization (PPO)
3. specialist
4. generic
5. medical history
6. health consumer
7. quackery
8. advocate
9. epidemiology
10. public health
11. famine

Recalling the Facts

1. Any three: physicians (primary care physicians, specialists, dermatologists, oncologists, etc.), nurses (LPNs, RNs, nurse practitioners), allied health care professionals (dentists, physical therapists, clinical psychologists, etc.).
2. Members pay a monthly fee but receive most or all medical services without paying an additional charge or by making a small co-payment fee at the time of an office visit.
3. A primary care physician provides the first line of health care; a specialist has received additional training in a particular field of medicine.
4. LPNs assist physicians and provide direct care such as bathing or changing bandages; RNs take more responsibilities for patients and sometimes supervise LPNs.
5. At an outpatient surgical facility, surgery is performed on patients who are released the same day; a hospital provides care for patients who may be admitted for longer stays.
6. Care for the terminally ill in a homelike setting.
7. Cost; special needs; eligibility.
8. Ask friends or relatives for recommendations; ask other health care professionals you know for a referral; call your local medical society; refer to a local directory of doctors or the *American Medical Directory*.
9. Quacks use testimonials and other techniques that appeal to consumers' emotions.
10. They may cause patients to delay seeking sound medical advice and treatment until it is too late.

Using Health Terms

On a separate sheet of paper, write the term that best matches each definition below.

LESSON 1

1. A plan to cover part or most costs of expenses and care associated with medical treatment.
2. Type of health insurance in which medical providers agree to charge less to members of the plan.
3. A physician who has received additional training in a particular area of medicine.

LESSON 2

4. A less-expensive version of a medicine that may be substituted for a brand-name medication.

5. Complete and comprehensive information about immunizations and any health problems to date.
6. A person who uses health products or services.

LESSON 3

7. A type of medical fraud.
8. Someone who speaks out for another person or a cause.

LESSON 4

9. The scientific study of epidemics.
10. A community-wide effort to monitor and promote the welfare of the population.
11. A widespread shortage of food.

Recalling the Facts

Using complete sentences, answer the following questions.

LESSON 1

1. Name three kinds of professionals who are health care workers.
2. How is a health maintenance organization (HMO) different from conventional health insurance?
3. How is a primary care physician different from a specialist?
4. What is the difference between a licensed practical nurse (LPN) and a registered nurse (RN)?
5. How does an outpatient surgical facility differ from a hospital?
6. What services does a hospice provide?

LESSON 2

7. What factors should you take into consideration when choosing a health plan?

8. What are some guidelines for choosing a health care provider?

LESSON 3

9. What kinds of techniques do quacks use to draw in unsuspecting patients?
10. Why might fraudulent treatments for cancer or arthritis be dangerous?
11. How could the Better Business Bureau (BBB) help a consumer with a complaint against a health care provider?
12. What does the Food and Drug Administration regulate in the field of health care?

LESSON 4

13. What is the role of county and state health departments?
14. How does the Centers for Disease Control and Prevention (CDC) help to control the spread of diseases?

Thinking Critically

LESSON 1

1. *Comparing and Contrasting.* To which specialist might a primary care physician refer a person who has: (1) acne; (2) scoliosis (curvature of the spine); (3) unrealistic fears about getting sick?

LESSON 2

2. *Synthesizing.* Write several criteria besides those listed in the lesson that you could use to choose a new primary care physician.

LESSON 3

3. *Synthesizing.* What conclusions might a person draw if he or she spent money on a weight-loss remedy and lost weight but gained it all back in a few months? Explain.

LESSON 4

4. *Analyzing.* Makers of name-brand products pay large sums of money to have their products used in movies. Do you feel this is fair advertising? Should it be permitted?

Making the Connection

Math. A conventional health insurance plan might offer the following coverage: 80 percent of expenses plus a $500 deductible—a dollar amount the insured person must pay out of pocket before health benefits begin. Under this plan, the member pays out-of-pocket the first $500 of medical expenses incurred each year. For the rest of medical expenses, if any, the member pays 20 percent and the plan pays 80 percent. What out-of-pocket expenses might a person incur if their total costs for medical expenses in one year totals $1500?

BEYOND THE CLASSROOM

PARENTAL INVOLVEMENT Interview your parents or other adults at home about their use of health insurance and health care during their adult years. Ask them what decisions they think they made wisely, as well as what they might have done differently as they look back on their lives. Write a private Health Journal entry telling what you have learned.

COMMUNITY INVOLVEMENT Ask a health clinic in your community for a brochure that describes the various health care professionals who work there. Determine whether each person listed is a physician or an allied health care professional, and tell what their specialty is or what job they perform. Share the information with your class.

SCHOOL-TO-CAREER
Interpersonal. Use a book about careers from your school's career center or from the library. Determine which interpersonal skills are needed to become a hospital administrator. Consider skills needed in both business and medicine.

Thinking Critically

1. Dermatologist; orthopedist; psychiatrist.
2. Answers will vary.
3. Answers should show an awareness of the fact that permanent weight loss is the result of exercising and reducing calories.
4. Answers will vary.

Making the Connection

Out-of-pocket expenses would be $200.

Evaluate

- Use the reproducible *Chapter 32 Test* in the TCR, or construct your own using the Testmaker software.
- Use *Performance Assessment Activity 32* in the TCR.

Enrichment

Ask students to complete *Cross-Curriculum Activity 32* in the TCR.

Beyond the Classroom

Keep students involved in the community, and encourage parent participation by assigning the activities on this page for students to work on outside of class.

---

11. The BBB provides general information on products and services, reliability reports, and background information on local businesses and organizations.
12. The FDA ensures that medicines are properly labeled and safe and effective for their intended uses; determines whether a medicine should be prescription or over-the-counter.
13. These departments set regulations that affect the local community, such as establishing standards for sanitation in restaurants, compiling health statistics, and controlling environmental pollution.
14. The CDC conducts research and collects data which helps control the spread of diseases.

The Health of the Environment

	FEATURES	**CLASSROOM RESOURCES**

LESSON 1

Air and Water
pages 726–729

CLASSROOM RESOURCES
- Concept Map Activity 98
- Health Lab 33
- Lesson 98 Quiz
- Lesson Plan 98
- Reteaching Activity 98

LESSON 2

Land
pages 730–733

FEATURES

Making Responsible Decisions
"Don't Drink the Water,"
page 731

up|date ▶ Looking at Technology
"Jason, the Sludge-Detecting
Robot," *page 732*

CLASSROOM RESOURCES
- Concept Map Activity 99
- Cooperative Learning Activity 33
- Decision-Making Activity 33
- Lesson 99 Quiz
- Lesson Plan 99
- Reteaching Activity 99

LESSON 3

Being an Involved Citizen
pages 734–737

FEATURES

Building Health Skills
"Being a Wise Consumer:
Rules of Precycling," *page 735*

CLASSROOM RESOURCES
- Concept Map Activity 100
- Enrichment Activity 33
- Lesson 100 Quiz
- Lesson Plan 100
- Reteaching Activity 100
- Transparency 31

ACTIVITIES

- 🖏 Cross-Curriculum Activity 33
- 🖏 Health Lab 33
- 🖏 Health Skills Activities 33
- 🖏 Parent Letter and Activities 33

ASSESSMENT

- 🖏 Chapter 33 Test
- 🖏 Performance Assessment Activity 33
- 💾 Testmaker Software

STUDENT ACTIVITIES WORKBOOK

- 🖏 Applying Health Skills 98–100
- 🖏 Study Guide 33
- 🖏 Vocabulary Activity 33

STUDENT DIVERSITY STRATEGIES

- 🎧 Audiocassette Program (English)
- 🎧 Audiocassette Program (Spanish)
- 🖏 Spanish Parent Letters and Activities
- 🖏 Spanish Summaries, Quizzes, and Activities

MULTIMEDIA COMPONENTS

- 🎧 English Audiocassette Program
- 🎧 Spanish Audiocassette Program
- 🔴 MindJogger Videodisc and VHS program

National Health Education Standards

One of the main goals of the National Health Education Standards is to move students toward "health literacy." Health literacy is the capacity of individuals to obtain, interpret, and understand basic health information and services and the competence to use such information and services in ways which promote health. The health standards were developed by applying the characteristics of a well-educated, literate person within the context of health. The health literate person is:

- a critical thinker and problem solver
- a self-directed learner
- a responsible, productive citizen
- an effective communicator

Listed below are the Health Education Standards Performance Indicators addressed in each lesson of this chapter.

Lesson	Health Standards Performance Indicators
1	1.5, 3.3, 4.3, 6.2
2	1.5, 4.3, 6.1, 6.2
3	1.5, 3.1, 3.3, 3.4

ONLINE RESOURCES

For a fresh approach to health topics and an in-depth look at health issues, use these online resources found under Teacher Resources at **health.glencoe.com**.

- **BLOCK SCHEDULE LESSON PLANS** Reinforce health concepts with outside readings selected especially for students. Each reading is accompanied by a lesson plan and activities to enhance
  - Reading Skills
  - Cross Curriculum
  - Media Literacy

- **TECHNOLOGY PROJECTS** Instructions and suggestions on how to use computer, Internet, and software with health lessons.

- **HEALTH UPDATES** Timely topics in health news, including late-breaking medical advances and updates on teen risk behaviors.

Out of Time?

If time does not permit teaching this chapter, you may use these features: Making Responsible Decisions on page 731; Update on page 732; and Building Health Skills on page 735.

BLOCK SCHEDULING

Block scheduling provides extended time for hands-on projects and activities. Use the following activities to engage students, provide further depth, and vary your instructional techniques:

- Update (30 minutes) **pg. 732**
- Health Skills Activity (60–90 minutes) **pg. 738**

The Health of the Environment

CHAPTER OVERVIEW

Chapter 33 discusses the forms and consequences of pollution, and emphasizes ways that the individual can make a difference through conservation and recycling.

LESSON 1 Air pollution is caused by gases and particulates that enter the atmosphere. These pollutants result in acid rain, photochemical smog, and depletion of the ozone layer. Untreated sewage, toxic industrial wastes, runoff from polluted groundwater, and oil spills pollute the earth's water sources, dwindling the amount of fresh water that is already being taxed by increasing populations and greater demands for resources.

LESSON 2 People living in concentrated areas, along with the impact of technology, are challenging the future of our global environment. Destruction of forests is creating an increase of unusable land, while industrial technology is introducing toxic wastes.

LESSON 3 Everyone has a responsibility to protect the earth. Individuals can reduce waste and conserve natural resources by following certain guidelines at home. As consumers, they can precycle by avoiding the purchase of unnecessary things that need to be disposed of, and recycle those wastes that can be reused.

CHAPTER **33**

The Health of the Environment

HEALTH Online

ADVOCACY

Get involved in a project of your choice to help save the planet. Visit **health.glencoe.com** and choose the Interactive Project on "Impacting the Environment" to find out how to get involved.

Hands-On Health

TEACHING STRATEGY

Working Together Guide students in exploring community resources and developing strategies for solving local problems. See Activity 29, "Do You Know Your Neighbor?" in the *Hands-On Health: Creative Teaching Strategies* booklet.

Time Needed
60 minutes or more in class

Supplies
- note-taking materials
- computer and school stationery

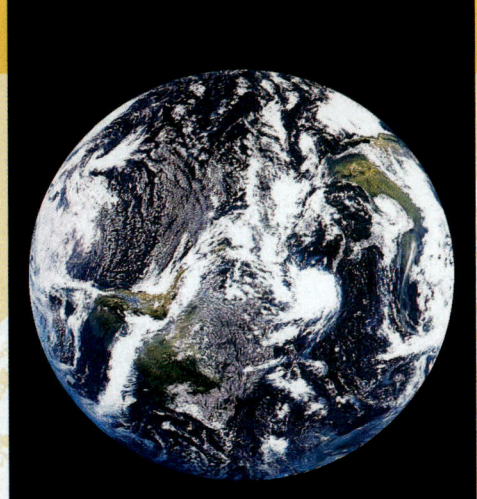

> ## You look down at this planet and it's all one living system. 99

—RUSSELL SCHWEICKART
AMERICAN ASTRONAUT, (1935–)

Quick Write Imagine being out in space and looking down at the Earth. Write a message to the planet about your personal commitment to preserving its resources and health.

Personal Health Inventory

Self-Inventory Write the numbers 1–10 on a sheet of paper. Read each statement below and respond by writing *yes*, *no*, or *sometimes* for each item. Write a *yes* only for items that you practice regularly. Save your responses.

1	I work at conserving water in my home.
2	I make a habit of turning out lights when I leave a room.
3	I try to make other people aware of the problem of littering.
4	I refuse packaging for products that already have a package.
5	I avoid buying disposable products when longer-lasting alternatives exist.
6	I read labels and buy the least toxic products available.
7	I reuse paper and plastic bags that are brought home from the store.
8	I buy recycled paper when I have the choice.
9	I actively participate in a recycling program in my community.
10	At home, I put on a second layer of clothing rather than turn up the heat when feeling cold.

Follow-up After completing the chapter, retake this self-inventory. Pick two items that you need to work on and set a goal to improve your health behaviors.

INTRODUCING THE CHAPTER

Personal Health Inventory

Let students read and discuss the statements in the Self-Inventory: How do the behaviors identified in these statements relate to your own health? To the health of others in your community? After a brief discussion, let students record their personal responses to these statements in their private Health Journals on a page labeled "The Health of the Environment." Remind students that this inventory will be most useful if they are open and honest in their responses.

- Introduce this chapter by asking for student input in listing environmental threats in their geographic area. Discuss local problems that may have received media coverage, such as landfills, city dumps, and air pollution. Then help students expand their thinking to include environmental problems associated with other localities. Help students recognize that environmental problems which face other communities may someday affect their local area.
- Help students describe and discuss the photographs on these two pages. What do they bring to mind about the topic of this chapter, "The Health of the Environment"? How does the health of the environment affect all three aspects of your own health? How can you affect the health of the environment? Explain that students will explore these issues as they study the lessons in Chapter 33.
- Distribute Parent Letter 33 in the *Parent Letters and Activities* booklet.

TECHNOLOGY OPTIONS

MINDJOGGER
VIDEOQUIZ

To preview or review chapter content, you may wish to use the *MindJogger Videoquiz* that accompanies Chapter 33.

LESSON **1**

Air and Water

FOCUS

LESSON OBJECTIVES

After studying this lesson, students should be able to

- identify the sources of air pollution.
- explain the greenhouse effect.
- explain the effect of CFCs on the ozone layer.
- name sources of water pollution.

MOTIVATOR

Write the following on the chalkboard for students to work on while attendance is being taken: *In your own words, define pollution, then list as many types of pollution as you can.*

INTRODUCING THE LESSON

Have students share their responses to the Motivator. Introduce the lesson by stating that there are many types of pollution and that pollutants in one part of the world can affect the entire global environment. Tell students that this lesson will focus on pollution of the world's air and water.

INTRODUCING HEALTH TERMS

- Have students work in pairs to write a short paper, using each of the vocabulary terms. Afterward, ask them to test each other's understanding of the terms' definitions.
- Ask students to complete Vocabulary Activity 33 and Chapter Study Guide 33 in the *Student Workbook.*

We live in a society fueled by modern technology. People once traveled by foot or on horseback. Today forms of high-speed transportation get us where we are going fast. Essential goods once made by hand are now mass-produced. These breakthroughs have not come without cost to the health of the environment. The name of this cost is *pollution.*

HEALTH TERMS

acid rain

greenhouse effect

chlorofluorocarbons (CFCs)

particulates

asbestos

biodegradable

HEALTH CONCEPTS

- Air pollution can result from gases or particles introduced into the atmosphere.
- Water pollution is largely the result of chemical wastes or poor sanitation.

Recyclable paper products

Air Pollution

Air pollution is the contamination of the earth's atmosphere by substances that pose a health threat to humans, plants, and animals. Each year industrialized countries such as the United States generate billions of tons of air pollutants. The majority of these take one of two main forms—gases or particulates.

Gases

We survive by breathing in a mixture of gases, chiefly oxygen and nitrogen. During the last 50 years, other undesirable gases have begun to pollute the air we breathe. Most of these harmful gases are

Lesson 1 Resources

TEACHER'S CLASSROOM RESOURCES

- Concept Map Activity 98
- Health Lab 33
- Lesson 98 Quiz
- Lesson Plan 98
- Parent Letter and Activities 33
- Reteaching Activity 98

STUDENT WORKBOOK

- Applying Health Skills 98
- Chapter Study Guide 33
- Vocabulary Activity 33

produced by the burning of fossil fuels such as coal, oil, wood, or natural gas. The evaporation of liquid solvents such as paint thinner is another source of air pollution.

CARBON MONOXIDE

Carbon monoxide, a colorless, odorless gas, results from the burning of most substances. Sources of carbon monoxide include tobacco smoke and the exhaust fumes from cars. A danger of carbon monoxide to humans is that it binds with hemoglobin, the oxygen-carrying part of blood, and prevents your body from receiving the oxygen it needs. When inhaled in sufficient quantities, carbon monoxide is fatal.

NITROGEN OXIDES AND SULFUR OXIDES

Produced by the burning of fossil fuels such as coal and oil, these gases can cause burning and tearing eyes. They can also lead to or trigger respiratory problems. Another serious environmental problem to which these gases are related is **acid rain.** *A by-product* of *nitrogen oxides or sulfur oxides mixed with rain,* acid rain can destroy plant life and corrode stone and metal.

CARBON DIOXIDE

As noted in Chapter 17, we produce carbon dioxide ourselves as part of the process of **respiration**. However, when large quantities of this gas are released into the atmosphere by the burning of petroleum, coal, or other fossil fuels, one possible result is *a slowdown of the rate at which the earth loses heat, causing an increase in the earth's temperature.* This condition, known as the **greenhouse effect**, has serious and far-reaching consequences. The "global warming" trends it threatens to bring about would negatively affect crop production and cause sea levels to rise significantly, leading to major flooding.

In addition to the burning of fossil fuels, the slash-and-burn method of clearing tropical forests has contributed in recent years to the 0.4-percent-a-year increase in atmospheric carbon dioxide.

HYDROCARBONS

When solvents such as turpentine evaporate or fossil fuels are incompletely burned, a combination of hydrogen and carbon called *hydrocarbons* escapes into the atmosphere. The reaction of hydrocarbons with nitric oxide in the presence of sunlight produces the form of pollution known as *smog.* Smog reduces visibility, in some parts of the country by as much as 70 percent, and causes the eyes to sting. By themselves, hydrocarbons are poisonous and have been linked to some cancers. Motor vehicle exhaust is a primary source of hydrocarbons.

▲ *Much of the air pollution in major cities comes from the burning of fuel by motor vehicles.*

ACTIVITY *World vehicle production is approaching 40 million units annually, and the total vehicle fleet is currently nearing 500 million. If this trend continues, how many cars and trucks will be on the road by the year 2020?*

h⊙t link

respiration For more information on respiration and the body organs involved in it, see Chapter 17, page 400.

TEACH

L1 Class Activity

Ask students to collect newspaper and magazine articles about global environmental issues. Discuss reasons the information in the articles is important to students and their families.

L1 Discussing

Have students describe acid rain. Talk about why it is a relatively new phenomenon.

L2 Class Activity

Select a small group of students to create a bulletin board about the effects of acid rain on the global environment.

L2 Discussing

Ask: From what sources does carbon dioxide enter the atmosphere? How do plants take carbon dioxide from the air?

L2 Discussing

Lead a discussion of why many of the world's scientists are concerned about the greenhouse effect. Ask: How might the greenhouse effect alter the global environment?

L1 Discussing

Ask students to explain what smog is. What are some of its effects on the environment?

 ## SCHOOL-TO-CAREER

REDUCING COMMUTER POLLUTION. Government agencies, organizations, and environmental groups have proposed and implemented strategies to reduce pollution caused by commuting workers. Encourage students to list strategies they have used to save energy traveling to and from school and work, such as public transportation, ride sharing, walking, or cycling. Then have them research one of the most energy-efficient strategies:

telecommuting or working at home. Tell them to examine the advantages to worker and employer of working at home, the disadvantages, and the valid or invalid reasons offered for not giving workers this option. Then have students imagine a large business, identify the jobs in which working at home would or would not be feasible, and prepare a work-at-home proposal for company managers.

L1 Discussing

Talk about some of the damaging effects of ozone depletion.

L2 Researching

Suggest that students investigate some of the uses of asbestos. Have them identify possible sources of asbestos in their current home, school, work, and recreational environments.

L1 Explaining

Talk about the fact that although about 70 percent of the earth's surface is water, water is a limited resource. Have the class identify some causes of water pollution.

L2 Class Activity

Have students use library resources to find out which parts of the world are facing a water shortage and what steps, if any, are being taken to deal with the situation. Ask them to share what they learn with the class.

LEP Writing

Instruct students to create designs for T-shirts, grocery sacks, bumper stickers, or baseball caps that promote a safe and clean water supply for the world. Ask students to set up a classroom display of their completed designs. Take photographs of some of the designs to submit to the school newspaper.

L3 Researching

Have students use classroom and library resources to research which illnesses related to water pollution are most common around the world. Ask them to share their findings with the class.

L2 Health Lab

Distribute *Health Lab 33* and have students investigate how best to clean up oil spills.

Did You Know?

➤ Today, the average visual range in much of the western United States is one-half to two-thirds of what it would be without pollution from human sources. In the eastern United States, the visual range is as little as one-fifth.

hotlink

ultraviolet rays For more information on the sun's ultraviolet rays and the damage they do, see Chapter 7, page 163.

▲ *Using a cloth bag to carry groceries eliminates the need for paper and plastic bags.*

ACTIVITY *What extra steps is this girl taking to reduce pollution?*

CHLOROFLUOROCARBONS

In the early 1970s, researchers began to consider the effect on the atmosphere of a particular group of chemicals known as **chlorofluorocarbons** (KLOHR-uh-FLOHR-uh-kar-buhns). Known as *CFCs* for short, these *compounds of chlorine, fluorine, and carbon* are odorless and invisible. Although their main industrial use—as refrigerants and propellants in aerosol spray cans—was long viewed as harmless, the effect of CFCs on the atmosphere has proved to be anything but harmless. When these chemicals rise high into the upper atmosphere, they react with sunlight to produce chemicals that destroy ozone molecules. These molecules shield the earth's surface from the harmful **ultraviolet rays** of the sun. In 1984, researchers measured drastic reductions in ozone over Antarctica, which many have linked directly to the action of CFCs. Since 1987, more than 150 countries have signed a series of international agreements calling for an eventual end to the manufacture of CFCs.

Particulates

Another main source of air pollution besides gases is **particulates** (par-TIK-yuh-luhts), *tiny particles suspended and carried through air.* Particulates can take the form of dust, soot, and mold spores. They also occur suspended in some gases. The Environmental Protection Agency (EPA) estimates that some 60,000 people in the United States die each year from respiratory problems linked to particulate emissions such as from:

- **Lead.** Lead can poison the kidneys, liver, and nervous system and can cause mental retardation in babies and young children. Paint-related lead poisoning remains a problem in older, substandard dwellings.

- **Asbestos.** *A mineral occurring in the form of fibers,* **asbestos** (az-BES-tus) was once widely used on hot-water pipes and as an insulator because of its fireproof properties. Asbestos has been linked to lung cancer, especially in people who also smoke.

Water Pollution

Each year, industry, agriculture, and private citizens threaten the planet's rapidly dwindling freshwater resources through one form of pollution or another. Much of this pollution is a result of the dumping of raw sewage or industrial waste into rivers, lakes, and streams.

MEETING STUDENT DIVERSITY

PROJECT: Have students form committees to organize a "Community Day" to raise awareness of the importance of protecting the Earth.

LEARNING STYLES. Meet with such students who have special learning needs and their committees at intervals during the period leading up to Community Day. Allow students to share information of the following nature: the kind of action their group is planning to take, what aspect of the environment the action is meant to serve, and what problems the group has encountered to date. As an alternative, these students can be paired with mainstream class members to carry out similar tasks. In assessing the performance of pairs, use the evaluative criteria that reflect the capacity of the partners to work together effectively, such as positive interdependence.

Raw Sewage and Industrial Wastes

When sewage is dumped in quantities too large to be **biodegradable** (BY-oh-duh-GRAYD-uh-buhl)—*able to be broken down by microorganisms in the environment*—the water is no longer safe for use. Disease-causing viruses and bacteria contained in the sewage become a serious health threat to humans and to aquatic life forms.

Wastes produced by industrial operations such as manufacturing and mining are another problem. Toxic, nonbiodegradable, or both, these wastes include acids, dyes, and metals such as mercury and lead.

Harmful Chemicals

Some of the pollution of our water resources happens indirectly through *runoff,* polluted groundwater that drains into streams. Pesticides and herbicides, chemicals used to kill crop pests and weeds, are toxic and contaminate drinking water. Some household cleaning products, such as bleaches and detergents, contain chlorine or phosphates, two other chemicals that are harmful to the environment.

Oil Spills

Millions of gallons of petroleum and crude oil are transported on the world's major waterways every day. There is always the risk of accidental spills. Oil pollution in ocean regions is caused by the discharging of tank flushings and the release of oil from offshore drilling rigs. By exploring alternative forms of energy, the world could greatly reduce the problem of ocean pollution.

▲ **The trash collecting on this riverbank contributes to water pollution.**

ACTIVITY *List alternative ways you would dispose of the objects pictured.*

LESSON 1 *Review*

Reviewing Facts and Vocabulary

1. Write a public service announcement about air pollution using the terms *acid rain* and *greenhouse effect.*
2. Identify three causes of water pollution.

Thinking Critically

3. *Analyzing.* Find out the major sources of air pollution in your area. Determine whether current efforts to reduce the problem are sufficient.
4. *Synthesizing.* Investigate which water pollution problems appear to be most prevalent in today's world. Prepare an oral report describing the causes and effects of these threats.

Applying Health Skills

5. *In Your Home.* Check the labels of laundry and household products being used in your home. Note any that contain chlorine or phosphates. Share your findings with family members, noting any dangers that exist. Make recommendations that will remedy the problem.

LESSON 1   AIR AND WATER   **729**

Land

FOCUS

LESSON OBJECTIVES

After studying this lesson, students should be able to

- identify environmental problems associated with waste disposal.
- describe the effects of population growth on the environment.
- explain the difference between deforestation and desertification.

MOTIVATOR

Write the following on the chalkboard for students to work on while attendance is being taken: *Imagine that you are responsible for all of the world's land. Write a short paper describing how you feel about people's treatment of your land.*

INTRODUCING THE LESSON

Have students share their responses to the Motivator. Talk about how the future of the world's land is up to each of us. Explain that this lesson will be about some of the major crises facing the planet and some of the steps being taken to deal with them.

INTRODUCING HEALTH TERMS

- Have students compare and contrast the terms *deforestation* and *desertification*.
- Ask students to complete Vocabulary Activity 33 and Chapter Study Guide 33 in the *Student Workbook*. ☞

Land

As a group of people, we are collectively making decisions about the way we use our natural resources. Our actions and attitudes toward the environment can make a difference in the health of future generations. In this lesson you will learn how the earth is impacted by our actions. You will learn how you can make decisions that will help preserve the land and its resources.

HEALTH TERMS

hazardous wastes
deforestation
desertification

HEALTH CONCEPTS

- Solid and toxic waste disposal are poisoning the land.
- Worldwide population living in concentrated areas has upset the natural balance of our planet.

Toxic Dumping

Each year, billions of tons of solid waste are dumped, burned, and buried in the United States alone. Much of this waste is deposited in landfills or canyons, a trend that has created a twofold environmental problem. The first problem is the availability of landfill space—many landfills are at or nearing full capacity. A second and perhaps more compelling problem is the nature of the wastes themselves. The Environmental Protection Agency has coined a term—**hazardous wastes**—for *any substances that are explosive, corrosive, flammable, or toxic to human or other life forms.* Some hazardous wastes are generated by the military or private industry. Other toxic wastes

Lesson 2 Resources

TEACHER'S CLASSROOM RESOURCES

☞ **Concept Map** Activity 99
☞ **Cooperative Learning** Activity 33
☞ **Decision-Making** Activity 33
☞ **Lesson 99 Quiz**
☞ **Lesson Plan 99**
☞ **Reteaching** Activity 99

STUDENT WORKBOOK

☞ **Applying Health Skills** 99
☞ **Chapter Study Guide** 33
☞ **Vocabulary** Activity 33

Making Responsible Decisions

Don't Drink the Water

For over a month now, cloudy water has been coming from the tap in Alonzo's home. When Alonzo first mentioned the problem, his father told him that the city is probably doing work on nearby pipes. This morning, Alonzo read in the newspaper about the digging of a new landfill several miles away. Alonzo now fears that the cloudiness may be a sign of groundwater contamination. He would like to find out if his concerns are justified, but he is not sure what action to take. What should Alonzo do?

What Would You Do?

Apply the six steps of the decision-making process to Alonzo's problem.

1. **State the situation.**
2. **List the options.**
3. **Weigh the possible outcomes.**
4. **Consider your values.**
5. **Make a decision and act.**
6. **Evaluate the decision.**

---

are produced by hospitals. Once dumped into landfills, these wastes release gases and other toxins that seep into the soil, polluting underground and surface water. Measures have been taken to line landfills and place them in sites not subject to flooding or high groundwater levels. Despite such measures, experts agree that more reliable means of solid waste disposal need to be explored.

Nuclear Waste Disposal

Another outcome of modern technology is nuclear energy. Today, nuclear energy power plants dot the world's landscape. Industrialized nations that are poor in energy resources rely heavily on nuclear power. Unfortunately, the widespread use of this energy has led to a new problem—the disposal of a special form of hazardous wastes called *nuclear wastes*. Nuclear wastes are a radioactive, extremely dangerous collection of materials. The decay rates of some nuclear materials is such that they must be isolated for 10,000 years or more.

Expansion and Development

Throughout history, population growth has been accelerating. Whereas it took half a million years for humankind to reach a population size of 1 billion, the next billion people were born in a span of only 80 years, and close to 1½ billion more have been born since 1975.

Too many people living in concentrated areas continues to have a dramatic impact on the land. As new cities are built to accommodate the growing masses, room for them must be cleared. This clearing has been at the expense of wilderness areas and rain forests.

TEACH

Making Responsible Decisions

1. Alonzo wants to find out whether the cloudy tap water in his home might be a sign of groundwater contamination.
2. Alonzo could (a) express his concerns to his father and leave the matter in his father's hands; (b) contact the environmental office of his local government; (c) contact the local office of a private environment-protection group; (d) contact local media.
3. Alonzo might (a) wonder how his father is taking care of the matter and feel that he, Alonzo, hasn't done his part; (b) expect the issue to be investigated but with little or no publicity; (c) find that the issue is investigated but possibly used as publicity for the private environment-protection group; (d) find that the matter gets wide publicity but that it might not be investigated thoroughly.
4. Alonzo values the safety of the environment. He also values his own ability to help protect the environment.
5. Decisions will vary.
6. Encourage students to discuss both short- and long-term consequences of their decisions.

L2 Decision Making

For further study on making responsible decisions, assign *Decision-Making Activity 33* in the TCR.

HEALTH LITERACY

CRITICAL THINKER/PROBLEM SOLVER. Many environmental problems discussed in this chapter were the result of solutions to other problems. Lead was added to gasoline to prevent knocking. Asbestos prevented fires in buildings. To reduce the use of dwindling fossil fuels and the pollution they cause, we turned to nuclear energy, which led to nuclear wastes and accidents. Have students note or predict problems that might result from solutions to a current environmental problem. For example, they might want to predict the economic effects if consumers suddenly stopped buying all disposable products, used their own cloth bags for shopping, and cut gasoline consumption in half. Would students be happy to see this happen in spite of the economic effects? What strategies might solve the problem of waste and overconsumption without serious adverse economic effects?

L2 Class Activity

Ask students to write a story about the kind of world they will live in 20 years from now if the damage to the world's environment continues unchecked. Have as many students as possible read their stories to the class.

L1 Discussing

Pose these questions: If you could pass one law to protect the global environment, what would it be? How would you enforce it? Have students explain their answers.

▼ *These teens are protecting the environment by marking water drains to warn people not to dump toxic wastes.*

update
▶ *Looking at Technology*

Jason, the Sludge-Detecting Robot

Help students review what they already know about toxic dumping: Where does it take place? What problems does it cause? Why is it important to understand these problems? Then ask: What problems do you think might be created by toxic dumping in oceans and other bodies of water? Have students read the Update feature to learn how scientists are studying possible problems caused by dumping at sea. After students have discussed their reactions to the information about Jason, have volunteers research other uses of robotic technology to study and deal with hazardous materials.

L2 Cooperative Learning

Have students complete *Cooperative Learning Activity 33*, "Manage A Forest," in the TCR. ☞

Disappearing Forests

Developing nations in Central America, Africa, and Southeast Asia are rapidly expanding in agriculture and industry. These nations have been clearing tropical forests on a massive scale to make way for farms, ranch land, and fuel. This **deforestation**, or *destruction of forests,* has upset the fragile balance of nature.

Aside from providing a home to countless plant and animal species, the world's great forests play a vital part in controlling soil erosion, flooding, and sediment buildup in rivers, lakes, and reservoirs. Deforestation interferes with these processes. It can also change regional patterns of rainfall as a result of altered rates of evaporation, transpiration (vapor exhaled from the surface of green plants), and runoff. Without trees, precipitation declines and the region grows hotter and drier. Ultimately, desertlike conditions prevail where there had once been a rich tropical grassland.

update
▶ *Looking at Technology*

Jason, the Sludge-Detecting Robot

Toxic dumping is a problem not only on land but at sea. After years of chemical dumping by industries and individuals, many waterways in the United States now have thick black sludge on their bottom, sometimes referred to as "black mayonnaise." Originally, it was assumed that such sludge buildup would occur only in shallow or landlocked waterways, but now evidence is mounting that sludge is even accumulating on the ocean floor.

Now scientists studying the problem are getting some help from Jason. Who is Jason? He is a sludge-detecting robot working on the ocean floor off the coasts of New Jersey and New York. The robot, attached by fiber-optic cables, is operated by a scientist on a research ship who maneuvers Jason by means of a joystick. Using a variety of monitors and video screens, scientists are able to watch as the remote-controlled robot moves across the ocean floor, scooping up sediment and water samples 9,000 feet below the water's surface. The samples will be studied to determine the long-term damage of the millions of tons of sewage and other pollutants that have been dumped into the ocean.

Jason is just the beginning of a high-tech trend. Increasingly, robots are being used to study and to clean up wastes, chemicals, and other hazardous materials that might prove unhealthful for humans to handle directly.

732 CHAPTER 33 THE HEALTH OF THE ENVIRONMENT

HOME AND COMMUNITY
CONNECTION

ENVIRONMENTAL THREATS. Have students work in groups and imagine they have been assigned to a committee of five to identify conditions most likely to threaten the local environment in the near future. Suggest that they first consider how global conditions such as waste disposal are likely to affect them, their families, their community, and their region.

What effects have they already observed? Then have them identify possible threats generated locally. Groups should assign each member to write a brief description of a global or local condition, where it exists, and how it threatens the local environment. Have each group rank the threats in order of importance.

Clearing large tracts of tropical forest may also have global repercussions because the trees help maintain the cycling of carbon and oxygen. When the trees are harvested or burned, carbon is released into the atmosphere in the form of carbon dioxide, which may play a role in the greenhouse effect.

Expanding Deserts

The world has always had deserts. One-third of the earth's surface is now believed to be affected by **desertification**, *the conversion of grasslands, rain-fed cropland, or irrigated cropland to desertlike conditions.* Desertification worldwide has prompted a drop in agricultural productivity.

Today, large-scale desertification is occurring mainly as a result of overgrazing. With world population on the rise and the growing demand for food supplies, scientists believe that food production must be increased by the end of the century simply to maintain present levels of nutrition. Desertification of once-productive land poses a threat to the health of the world's people.

Responding to These Environmental Trends

As the population continues to expand onto undeveloped land, care must be taken to plan this expansion to avoid destruction of land features and an undue drain on natural resources. Care must be taken to preserve the habitats of the many species of plants and animals in these regions that give our planet its rich biological diversity.

LESSON 2 *Review*

Reviewing Facts and Vocabulary

1. Use the term *hazardous waste* in a sentence that explains the seriousness of toxic dumping.
2. Explain the difference between deforestation and desertification.

Thinking Critically

3. *Synthesizing.* Find examples in newspapers and magazines of land pollution and its effects on the global environment. Write a summary of your findings.
4. *Comparing and Contrasting.* Use both a current and an older world map or atlas to compare the growing effects of deforestation and desertification.

Applying Health Skills

5. *In Your School.* Conduct an informal questionnaire in your school to find out what students know about the problem of toxic landfills. Use the results as a springboard for a campaign that could be used to raise the consciousness of all members of your community to this serious problem.

HAZARDOUS WASTE PROHIBITED

LESSON 2 LAND **733**

CHARACTER IN ACTION

Make Every Day Earth Day

Explain that the U.S. has only 5 percent of the world's population but uses 25 percent of its resources. Discuss the ideas of the feature and the values involved when a person decides to help to conserve energy and recycle resources. Brainstorm other ways to save trees and save energy.

ASSESS

EVALUATING THE LESSON

Assign and discuss the Lesson 2 Review; then administer, grade, and discuss the *Lesson 99 Quiz* in the TCR. ◗

RETEACHING

• Have students write a short article for the school newspaper, focusing on a major idea from the lesson.
• Ask students to complete *Reteaching Activity 99* in the TCR. ◗

ENRICHMENT

Have students study patterns of rainfall in different areas of the world throughout this century. Ask them to consult library resources for the changing patterns. Request that they make an illustrated report of their findings.

CLOSE

Make a poster-board copy of a world map, and cut the map into jigsaw puzzle pieces. On the back of each piece, write one of the lesson's major concepts. Have students select a concept to summarize for the class and insert their puzzle piece to re-form the world map.

Lesson 2 Review

Answers to Reviewing Facts and Vocabulary

1. Sentences will vary. (A hazardous waste is any substance that is explosive, corrosive, flammable, or toxic to human or other life forms.)
2. Deforestation is the destruction of forests. Desertification is the conversion of grasslands, rain-fed cropland, or irrigated cropland to desertlike conditions.

Answers to Thinking Critically

3. Examples and summaries will vary.
4. Comparisons should indicate an increase in deforestation and desertification.

Being an Involved Citizen

LESSON **3**

Being an Involved Citizen

FOCUS

LESSON OBJECTIVES

After studying this lesson, students should be able to

- identify ways to conserve home energy.
- discuss the rules of precycling.
- describe the guidelines for recycling.

MOTIVATOR

Write the following on the chalkboard for students to work on while attendance is being taken: *In your own words, write a definition for the term* conservation.

INTRODUCING THE LESSON

Refer to the Motivator. Ask volunteers to share their responses. Combine these responses to develop the definition used in the text. Explain to students that this lesson will explain the importance of conservation in protecting the environment and discuss ways to conserve resources.

INTRODUCING HEALTH TERMS

- Ask students to explain how conservation and recycling can help protect the environment.
- Ask students to complete Vocabulary Activity 33 and Chapter Study Guide 33 in the *Student Workbook.*

At last count, the earth's population was 6 billion. With so many people in the world, you may well wonder how you can make a difference in the health of the environment. Actually, each one of us can—and *must*—do something about the problems discussed in Lessons 1 and 2. The survival of our planet hangs in the balance, but you can make a difference.

HEALTH TERMS

conservation

recycling

HEALTH CONCEPTS

- Every citizen is responsible for doing his or her share to improve and maintain the fragile health of our planet.
- Conservation of water, energy, and natural resources and recycling are the keys to the future health of the global community.

Conservation

The health of the environment is influenced by many factors, but the actions people take can have a far-reaching effect. **Conservation,** *protection and preservation of the environment,* is more important than ever. Much of the power and responsibility for conservation today rests with you, the health-literate citizen. You can help conserve precious natural resources and reduce waste by being aware of environmental issues and by making others aware of them. You can also protect the environment through the sound decisions you make as a consumer.

734 CHAPTER 33 THE HEALTH OF THE ENVIRONMENT

Lesson 3 Resources

TEACHER'S CLASSROOM RESOURCES

- **Concept Map** Activity 100
- **Enrichment** Activity 33
- **Lesson 100 Quiz**
- **Lesson Plan 100**
- **Reteaching** Activity 100

STUDENT WORKBOOK

- **Applying Health Skills 100**
- **Chapter Study Guide 33**
- **Vocabulary** Activity 33

TRANSPARENCIES

- **Transparency 31**

Guidelines for Home Conservation

About 70 percent of the energy we use at home is for heating or cooling. An additional 20 percent is used to heat water, and the remaining 10 percent goes toward lighting, cooking, and running small appliances. What can you and the adults in your home do to conserve energy? The following are a few of the actions you can take:

HEATING AND COOLING

- Keep doors and windows shut during the air-conditioning season. Close fireplace vents.
- Keep air-conditioning at a constant temperature.
- During cold weather, turn the thermostat down at bedtime.

WATER

- Wash clothes in warm or cold, not hot, water.
- Fix leaky faucets.
- Never let hot water run unnecessarily.

LIGHTING

- Use fluorescent bulbs when possible.
- Use one higher-watt bulb instead of two lower-watt bulbs in a two-bulb fixture.

COOKING

- Be sure a gas stove has a blue flame in the pilot light.
- When possible, cook on the stove top rather than in the oven.

Building Health Skills

Being a Wise Consumer: Rules of *Precycling*

MANY COMPANIES ARE NOW doing their part in the recycling effort by taking steps to reduce the amount of waste they create. You can do your part right inside the store by *precycling* as you shop. Here are some tips:

1. **Be selective about packaging.** Determine whether the package a product comes in can be reused or refilled.

2. **Choose products packaged in recyclable materials.** These include paper, glass, aluminum, and cardboard. Avoid products packaged in polystyrene, which contains CFCs.

3. **Avoid disposable items.** These include disposable razors, diapers, cups, and plates.

4. **Buy in bulk.** In addition to saving money, bulk quantities use less packaging than small or single-serving sizes.

LESSON 3   BEING AN INVOLVED CITIZEN   **735**

TEACH

LD Discussing

Have students relate how they and their families reduce waste. Discuss ways to improve community action and awareness in recycling.

L1 Reading

Instruct students to collect magazine and newspaper articles about conservation issues on local, national, and world levels. Have students report on how and why the information in the articles is important to them.

Building Health Skills

Rules of *Precycling*
Skill: Health Consumer Skills

Display ads for such items as paper plates and napkins, single-use plastic cups, and disposable razors. Ask: Why do consumers choose these kinds of products? What problems do these products create? What other choices can consumers make? Then have students read the Building Health Skills feature to learn about precycling. (If appropriate, help students recognize that the prefix *re-* in *recycling* means "again" and the prefix *pre-* in *precycling* means "before.") Then divide students into groups to brainstorm lists of specific steps they can take to follow the tips for precycling.

PERSONAL HEALTH

ENVIRONMENTAL RESPONSIBILITY. Encourage students to list the important steps individuals can take in protecting the regional or global environment. Suggest they list those steps described in the chapter and add others from personal background and experience. Have them rank the steps from greatest to least environmental impact. Then have them rank the same steps according to how much sacrifice, expense, or inconvenience each requires. For example, turning off unused lights requires no sacrifice or inconvenience. More commitment is required to cut down on driving or to put up with cooler room temperatures in winter. Finally, tell them to rank the steps from the one they are most willing to take to the one they are least willing to take.

L1 Class Activity

Tell students to make a class list of everything that is commonly recycled. *(aluminum, batteries, cardboard, clothing and household items, glass, oil, paper, plastics, tin cans, tires, yard waste)*

L1 Explaining

Buying recycled products reduces air and water pollution and mining wastes by 70 percent. Using recycled aluminum reduces pollution by as much as 95 percent. Every ton of recycled paper bought in America saves 17 trees, 7,000 gallons of water, and enough energy to heat or air-condition a house for six months.

L2 Cooperative Learning

Arrange students into four groups. Instruct one group to discuss ways to conserve energy, another group to focus on how to conserve water, another on how to reduce waste disposal, and another on how the world will be in an ecological crisis if Americans do not concentrate on protecting their environment. Have each group put their ideas in writing and report their findings to the class.

L2 Community Involvement

Ask volunteers to make a map of the city, county, or just the neighborhood, marking all of the sites where local recycling centers are located. Include places where secondhand merchandise can be sold, such as flea markets, salvage yards, and used-book stores. Have them include the name, address, and phone number for each location. Share the map with the class and put the map in the school newspaper with an article about conservation.

HEALTH Online

How can you limit the amount of waste you create by reducing, reusing, and recycling? Learn about this and other environmental issues, such as air and water polution, at **health.glencoe.com**. Test your knowledge by solving an online crossword puzzle.

Recycling

Recycling is *the treating of waste so that it can be reused, as well as an awareness of such practices.* Recycling pays dividends to the environment in many ways:

- Recycling saves energy. For example, making a can out of recycled aluminum takes only 10 percent of the energy needed to make a brand-new can from raw materials.
- Recycling saves resources by reducing the need for cutting trees, mining, and drilling.
- Recycling can produce six times as many jobs as when landfills and incineration are used. Whatever does not have to be burned or buried, moreover, is money saved.

Guidelines for Recycling

More than 80 percent of household waste can be recycled. The following guidelines apply to individual recyclable materials.

- **Aluminum.** Rinse cans and other aluminum receptacles such as pie pans and frozen food trays. Crush them to save space.
- **Cardboard.** Flatten cardboard boxes and tie them together.
- **Clothing and household items.** Recycle these by donating them to a community organization for refurbishing and resale.
- **Glass.** Check with your recycling center to see which of the three types of glass—clear, green, and brown—it accepts. Rinse bottles and jars well, and remove any caps or lids.
- **Oil.** Take used motor oil to a service station or oil change shop for proper disposal.
- **Paper.** Reuse the backs of envelopes and paper from junk mail. Reuse grocery bags, and replace paper towels with rags.
- **Tires.** Use old tires for play equipment, gardening containers, and bumpers.
- **Computer printer toner cartridges.** Some computer printers now use recyclable toner cartridges. Consult your manual, or contact the manufacturer.

▶ *Check packaging for symbols that show the item is recyclable.*
ACTIVITY *Explain what recycling methods are used in your community.*

COOPERATIVE LEARNING

ENVIRONMENT vs. JOB. One reason often given for failure to pass regulations which protect the environment is that it would hurt business and eliminate jobs by raising the cost of doing business or discontinuing the sale of certain products. Have groups of students poll adults in your community. First, instruct students to pick an environmental problem in the community, such as harvesting old-growth forests, development that threatens wilderness and species, polluted air, or overflowing landfills. Then have them ask adults if they would support strong measures to address the problem. Would they still be supportive if such measures eliminated a large number of jobs? if such measures resulted in the loss of their own job? What percentage put the environment first? Compare the responses.

Protecting the Environment

Here are some practical suggestions for becoming involved in protecting the environment:

- **Become an informed consumer.** Evaluate advertising, labels, contents, and packaging as it relates to the environment. Give feedback to companies on positive ways they can affect the environment. Write letters also to newspapers, and seek opportunities to express your opinions about the environment.

- **Contact organizations that conserve resources, and educate people on environmental issues.** Ask for information and ideas for conservation. Review how your own habits and lifestyle affect the environment. Better still, join an environmental organization. Most of these organizations can provide you with resources for understanding current issues. Being part of such a group can often provide you with suggestions on ways you can promote environmental health.

- **Take action against local polluters.** The environmental problems in your community directly affect your health and way of life. Targeting local polluters is a very effective way of protecting your health and that of your family and neighbors. Unfortunately, this is not an easy task. Local and national laws may not be adequately enforced. Some companies continue to pollute for years before the government can make them stop. Even then, the fines are often small compared with the cost of modernizing the facilities or cleaning up toxic wastes. Joining with others to let elected officials become aware of the problem is a start.

LESSON 3 Review

Reviewing Facts and Vocabulary

1. Name two steps you can take to conserve energy and water in your home.
2. How does recycling contribute to protecting the environment?

Thinking Critically

3. *Analyzing.* At present, only 10 percent of recyclable household products are actually recycled. Why do you think this is so? How can you help implement a change in this area?
4. *Evaluating.* Explain in what ways you as an individual can most make a difference in environmental matters.

What skills and powers do you possess that could be useful?

Applying Health Skills

5. *In Your Home.* Make an inspection of your home, looking for ways in which your family currently conserves energy and water. Discuss areas that could be improved with parents or other adults in your household.

LESSON 3   BEING AN INVOLVED CITIZEN   **737**

CHAPTER 33 • LESSON 3

ASSESS

EVALUATING THE LESSON

Assign and discuss the Lesson 3 Review; then administer, grade, and discuss the *Lesson 100 Quiz* in the TCR.

RETEACHING

- Ask students to do an energy inventory with their parents to see what energy-efficient measures are used in their home to conserve energy. What could family members do to make their home more energy efficient?
- Ask students to complete *Reteaching Activity 100* in the TCR.
- Use *Transparency 31* to review the advantages of precycling and recycling.

ENRICHMENT

- Assign volunteers to investigate whether or not their community has an energy conservation program.
- Encourage students to be part of the ongoing effort to provide a life-sustaining environment for themselves and for future generations. Assign *Enrichment Activity 33,* "Environmental Political Activism," in the TCR.

CLOSE

Have students summarize the most important concepts in this lesson.

Lesson 3 Review

Answers to Reviewing Facts and Vocabulary

1. Refer to list of Guidelines for Home Conservation on page 735.
2. Recycling saves energy, reduces the demand for natural resources, and produces jobs.

Answers to Thinking Critically

3. Answers will vary.
4. Answers will vary.

Chapter 33   **737**

Health Skills
Activities

ACTIVITY 1
HEALTH SKILLS

Comprehending Health Concepts, Health Advocacy

➤ **National Standards**
This activity meets these National Health Standards: 1.5; 7.1.

Teach

- Review with students key concepts from the chapter. Make sure that students are able to recognize applications of each type of problem addressed.
- Urge students to follow up (possibly by conducting an informal student poll a day after the article's appearance). Set aside class time for a discussion of the impact of the articles.

ACTIVITY 2
HEALTH SKILLS

Comprehending Health Concepts, Health Advocacy

➤ **National Standards**
This activity meets these National Health Standards: 1.5; 7.4.

Teach

- Review the types of environmental problems discussed in the chapter. Focus on those that impact most on animal populations.
- Urge groups to develop a checklist of traits to investigate during research, such as status of species, current population range, current actions being taken to protect the species, and so on.
- Encourage students within a group to sign up for one or more of the job descriptions highlighted during the preparation phase of the activity.

Health Skills Activities

Activity 1 — Your Environmental Health

The news is filled with stories about environmental problems throughout the world. Although addressing these hazards is important, action must start "at home." How can you improve the environmental health of your community?

Directions

1. With a group, browse newspaper articles. Identify three local community health problems related to the environment. For each, describe the problem itself, how it impacts the environment, and possible solutions.
2. Prepare a brief report summarizing your findings. Include actions that can be taken now by students in you school.
3. Compile your findings into an article to be published in a school or community newspaper.

Time
50 minutes

Materials
pen, local newspapers, computer with printer (optional)

Self-Assessment

✓ Suggested at least one solution for each environmental problem.
✓ Report clearly and accurately summarized the problem and possible solutions.

Activity 2 — Save our Local Species

The health of the environment is influenced by many factors. Yet, the actions people take can have a far-reaching impact, especially on the health of other species. Imagine you were hired to develop an ad to save a species.

Directions

1. In a group, research endangered or threatened species. Choose one, and take notes on its habitat, current population size, and factors that threaten or endanger this species. Learn in addition what actions, if any, environmental groups are taking to protect this species.
2. With your group, brainstorm ways of getting others involved in a "Save the Species" campaign for the species you have researched. Possibilities might include slogans, TV commercials, or public service announcements.

Time
50 minutes, plus outside research

Materials
library or Internet resources

Self-Assessment

✓ Accurately described the problems facing a specific species.
✓ Created a persuasive message urging support for preserving remaining members of this species.

ASSESSMENT SCORING

Using a four-level rubric, the student has achieved a 4 if:

ACTIVITY 1
✔ Student recognized examples of environmental problems within the community.
✔ Student suggested at least one solution for each environmental problem.
✔ Student article clearly and accurately summarized the problem and solutions.
✔ Student assessed impact of article on community as a whole.

ACTIVITY 2
✔ Student prepared and completed a checklist for an endangered or threatened species.
✔ Student accurately described the problems facing the species chosen.
✔ Student chose tasks related to ad production.
✔ Student had a hand in creating a persuasive message urging support for preserving remaining members of this species.

HEALTH NEWS ARTICLE

Ozone Layer Will Take Time to Heal

For decades we've been cutting our use of aerosol cans and foam cups because the chemicals they use–CFCs–harm the atmosphere. Now researchers believe that the ozone layer may still take half a century or more to heal. A recent study revealed that up to 70 percent of the ozone layer over the North Pole has been lost.

"Even though levels of organic chlorine in the stratosphere are going down, we saw severe ozone depletion in the Arctic this past winter," said National Oceanic and Atmospheric Administration scientist Dale Hurst.

The extreme cold in the Arctic stratosphere intensifies ozone depletion. Atmospheric physicist Paul Newman says the cold slows the decay of CFCs and causes them to destroy ozone faster.

The ozone layer is important to the protection of human life. Ozone reduces ultraviolet radiation, the kind that burns skin. Loss of that protection has predictable results, Newman says. "Skin cancer rates will go up. Sunburns will occur at a faster rate . . . because of enhanced ultraviolet radiation from a lowering of ozone."

Read This ▼

Ozone 101

Here's a quick refresher on ozone:
- Ozone is colorless gas.
- A layer of ozone surrounds the Earth in a zone called the stratosphere. This ozone layer acts like a pair of sunglasses. It absorbs dangerous ultraviolet radiation from the sun.
- CFCs, or chloro-fluorocarbons, are chemicals that were used in refrigerants, industrial solvents, cleaning fluids, and to make foam.
- When CFCs are released at ground level, they rise into the stratosphere. When they reach the ozone layer, the molecules break down and release chlorine, which destroys ozone.

Source: Environment Canada–The Ozone Layer

"This is a wakeup call that although we have cut emissions of ozone depleting chemicals, these ozone holes may continue for a long time into the future," Hurst warns.

Think About It

1. How do CFCs affect the ozone layer?
2. How can the destruction of the ozone layer affect people's health?

MORE ABOUT . . . . .

OZONE DEPLETION. CFCs are not the only chemicals that contribute to the ozone hole. Bromine, a chemical cousin to chlorine and used for some of the same purposes -- fire fighting, infection control, and sanitation -- has not been as strictly regulated.

Experts explain that bromine is 45 times more damaging to ozone in the atmosphere than chlorine, but has not been subject to the same restrictions because many countries could not stand the loss of income from its stricter regulation. Some scientists, however, believe governments will be under growing pressure in the coming years to limit the chemical.

CNN HEALTH NEWS

Ozone Layer Will Take Time to Heal

Objectives. After reading the article, students should be able to identify the role that chlorofluorocarbons (CFCs) play in ozone depletion and explain some of the damaging health effects of this problem.

Motivator. Draw a diagram of the sun and Earth on the chalkboard. Have students list the beneficial effects of the sun, including providing energy and light. Then ask students to describe how the sun might harm us. Have students read the article "Ozone Layer Will Take Time to Heal," which describes the problem of ozone depletion, a process that increases the amount of dangerous ultraviolet radiation coming from the sun.

Teach
- Have students suggest ways to modify the chalkboard diagram to show the condition of the ozone layer as described in the video. They might add a circle around the diagram of the earth to represent the ozone layer. Then they can erase a small part of the circle to represent the thinning ozone layer above the North Pole.
- Help students understand why CFCs cause more damage at the North Pole than in other regions of the stratosphere. Emphasize that temperature can affect the speed of many chemical reactions. The cool temperatures at the North Pole slow down the chemical process which causes CFCs to dissipate. More ozone is destroyed the longer the CFCs are in the stratosphere.

Role Play. Ask students to create a skit that shows how ozone depletion can affect human health. For example, they might enact a beach scene in which people experience sunburns quicker because the thinned ozone layer allows more ultraviolet rays to reach Earth.

Close. Ask: Why does the ozone layer affect your health? Make sure that student responses explain the relationship between the uses of chemicals like CFCs and the destruction of the ozone layer, which leads to increased damaging ultraviolet radiation.

CHECKING COMPREHENSION

- Assign and discuss the chapter review.
- Use the MindJogger Videoquiz to review the chapter. 🔴

CHAPTER 33 REVIEW ANSWERS

Using Health Terms

1. biodegradable
2. particulates
3. greenhouse effect
4. asbestos
5. chlorofluorocarbons (CFCs)
6. acid rain
7. desertification
8. hazardous wastes
9. deforestation
10. recycling
11. conservation

Recalling the Facts

1. Technology, such as cars and other forms of high-speed transportation, and machines of mass-production.
2. Advantage: Carbon dioxide is produced as part of the human respiration process. Disadvantage: Carbon dioxide contributes to the greenhouse effect.
3. A by-product of nitrogen oxides or sulfur oxides mixed with rain, acid rain can destroy plant life and corrode stone and metal.
4. Chlorofluorocarbons (CFCs).
5. They react with sunlight to destroy ozone molecules, which shield the earth's surface from harmful ultraviolet rays.
6. Raw sewage and industrial wastes pose a health threat to humans and aquatic life forms; harmful chemicals contaminate drinking water; oil spills cause ocean pollution.
7. Problems include limited availability of space, problems of toxic wastes.

Using Health Terms

On a separate sheet of paper, write the term that best matches each definition below.

LESSON 1

1. Able to be broken down by microorganisms in the environment.
2. Tiny particles suspended and carried through air.
3. A slowdown of the rate at which the earth loses heat, causing an increase in the earth's temperature.
4. A mineral occurring in the form of fibers.
5. Compounds of chlorine, fluorine, and carbon.
6. A by-product of nitrogen oxides or sulfur oxides mixed with rain.

LESSON 2

7. The conversion of grasslands, rain-fed cropland, or irrigated cropland to desert-like conditions.
8. Any substances that are explosive, corrosive, flammable, or toxic to human or other life forms.
9. Destruction of forests.

LESSON 3

10. The treating of waste so that it can be reused, as well as having an awareness of such practices.
11. Concern about the preservation of the environment.

Recalling the Facts

Using complete sentences, answer the following questions.

LESSON 1

1. What aspects of modern life have led to environmental problems such as pollution?
2. What are the advantages of carbon dioxide in the atmosphere? What are the disadvantages?
3. What is acid rain?
4. What is the major cause of damage to the ozone layer?
5. Why are CFCs dangerous?
6. List three ways in which water can become polluted, and identify the effects.

LESSON 2

7. What are the pros and cons of using landfills to store solid waste?
8. What are the risks associated with the use of nuclear power?

9. How does ever-expanding development pose a threat to forests?
10. How does deforestation affect rainfall?

LESSON 3

11. Give four suggestions that can be used in support of the statement: *Each home owner has it in his or her power to help conserve precious energy.*
12. What does recycling involve?
13. Identify three actions a responsible citizen can take to help save the environment from future abuse.

8. Production of nuclear energy produces radioactive waste materials that are extremely dangerous and that must be isolated for as long as 10,000 years or more.
9. Tropical forests are being cleared to make way for farms, ranch land, and fuel.

10. Deforestation changes regional patterns of rainfall as a result of altered rates of evaporation, transpiration, and runoff; precipitation declines and the region grows hotter and drier.
11. Refer to Guidelines for Home Conservation on page 735.

Thinking Critically

LESSON 1

1. **Comparing and Contrasting.** Identify two similarities and two differences between harmful gases and particulates.
2. **Synthesizing.** Explain why the greenhouse effect poses a serious threat to the future of the planet.
3. **Analyzing.** What simple actions can the individual consumer take to reduce the pollution of the world's waterways?

LESSON 2

4. **Synthesizing.** Working alone or with several classmates, invent one or more environmentally sound ways for society to dispose of trash or garbage. Be creative. Present your plan to the class, along with illustrative pictures or diagrams of your process.

LESSON 3

5. **Evaluating.** Of the environmental problems addressed in this chapter, to which do you feel you could make the strongest commitment? Support your answer with valid reasons. Then take the next step and make the commitment.

Making the Connection

1. **Science.** Fill a shallow pan with water until it is half full. Pour in one cup of cooking oil or salad oil. Devise several ways to remove the oil from the water. You might try a lettuce leaf or a suction tube. Which of your cleanup devices worked best? Which could be best applied on a large scale?

2. **Social Studies.** The *Exxon Valdez* spill was the worst oil spill on record. It is not, sadly, the only such environmental catastrophe. Learn about another such catastrophe. Determine when the event happened, what happened, and what the long-term consequences have been. Share your findings in a brief report.

BEYOND THE CLASSROOM

PARENTAL INVOLVEMENT Observe and keep track of your trash at home for a week. Then talk to your parents or other adults at home about a family trash reduction program. Identify items thrown away that could be recycled, such as glass jars or plastic bottles. Develop a plan whereby each family member takes a responsibility for one kind of material to recycle.

COMMUNITY INVOLVEMENT Find out about the water treatment facility used by your community to treat water before it is consumed. Where is this facility located, how large an area does it serve, and what process is water exposed to before it is ready for human consumption? Report your findings to the class.

SCHOOL-TO-CAREER
Interpersonal. Rachel Carson was a marine biologist by profession. Find out about the work done by people in this field. What training—including education—and interpersonal skills are necessary for a career in this area? What are some of the struggles faced by people in this line of work? Write a report of your findings for a classroom resource folder.

Thinking Critically

1. Similarities and differences will vary.
2. Answers should reflect an understanding of the fact that the greenhouse effect can create a negative effect on crop production and an increase in flooding.
3. Answers will vary.
4. Ideas and illustrations will vary.
5. Answers will vary.

Making the Connection

1.–2. Answers will vary.

Evaluate

- Use the reproducible *Chapter 33 Test* in the TCR, or construct your own using the Testmaker software. ☞ 🖳
- Use *Performance Assessment Activity 33* in the TCR. ☞

Enrichment

Ask students to complete *Cross-Curriculum Activity 33* in the TCR. ☞

Beyond the Classroom

Keep students involved in the community, and encourage parent participation by assigning the activities on this page for students to work on outside of class.

12. Treating waste so that it can be reused and having an awareness of such practices.
13. Conserve natural resources and reduce waste by being aware of environmental issues; make others aware of environmental issues; make sound decisions as a consumer.

Your Safety and Well-Being

	FEATURES	**CLASSROOM RESOURCES**

LESSON 1

Safety at Home
pages 744–747

CLASSROOM RESOURCES:
- Concept Map Activity 101
- Lesson 101 Quiz
- Lesson Plan 101
- Reteaching Activity 101

LESSON 2

Safety Outside the Home
pages 748–753

FEATURES:
Making Responsible Decisions
"Selling Safety Short,"
page 751

CLASSROOM RESOURCES:
- Concept Map Activity 102
- Cooperative Learning Activity 34
- Decision-Making Activity 34
- Enrichment Activity 34
- Lesson 102 Quiz
- Lesson Plan 102
- Reteaching Activity 102

LESSON 3

Safety on Wheels
pages 754–759

FEATURES:
update ▶ *Looking at the Issues*
"Should More Restrictions
Be Put On Teen Drivers?"
page 756

Building Health Skills
"Being an Alert Consumer:
Helmet Hints," *page 757*

CLASSROOM RESOURCES:
- Concept Map Activity 103
- Health Lab 34
- Lesson 103 Quiz
- Lesson Plan 103
- Reteaching Activity 103
- Transparency 52

LESSON 4

Personal Safety
pages 760–763

CLASSROOM RESOURCES:
- Concept Map Activity 104
- Lesson 104 Quiz
- Lesson Plan 104
- Reteaching Activity 104

ACTIVITIES

- Cross-Curriculum Activity 34
- Health Lab 34
- Health Skills Activities 34
- Parent Letter and Activities 34

ASSESSMENT

- Chapter 34 Test
- Performance Assessment Activity 34
- Testmaker Software

STUDENT ACTIVITIES WORKBOOK

- Applying Health Skills 101–104
- Study Guide 34
- Vocabulary Activity 34

STUDENT DIVERSITY STRATEGIES

- Audiocassette Program (English)
- Audiocassette Program (Spanish)
- Spanish Parent Letters and Activities
- Spanish Summaries, Quizzes, and Activities

MULTIMEDIA COMPONENTS

- English Audiocassette Program
- Spanish Audiocassette Program
- MindJogger Videodisc and VHS program
- ABCNews InterActive™ VHS/Videodisc Series

National Health Education Standards

One of the main goals of the National Health Education Standards is to move students toward "health literacy." Health literacy is the capacity of individuals to obtain, interpret, and understand basic health information and services and the competence to use such information and services in ways which promote health. The health standards were developed by applying the characteristics of a well-educated, literate person within the context of health. The health literate person is:

- a critical thinker and problem solver
- a self-directed learner
- a responsible, productive citizen
- an effective communicator

Listed below are the Health Education Standards Performance Indicators addressed in each lesson of this chapter.

Lesson	Health Standards Performance Indicators
1	3.3, 3.5, 3.6, 6.3
2	3.5, 3.6, 6.1, 7.4
3	1.2, 1.7, 3.5, 5.8
4	3.5, 3.6, 5.5, 5.6

ONLINE RESOURCES

For a fresh approach to health topics and an in-depth look at health issues, use these online resources found under Teacher Resources at **health.glencoe.com**.

- **BLOCK SCHEDULE LESSON PLANS** Reinforce health concepts with outside readings selected especially for students. Each reading is accompanied by a lesson plan and activities to enhance
  - Reading Skills
  - Cross Curriculum
  - Media Literacy

- **TECHNOLOGY PROJECTS** Instructions and suggestions on how to use computer, Internet, and software with health lessons.

- **HEALTH UPDATES** Timely topics in health news, including late-breaking medical advances and updates on teen risk behaviors.

Out of Time?

If time does not permit teaching this chapter, you may use these features: Making Responsible Decisions on page 751; Update on page 756; and Building Health Skills on page 757.

BLOCK SCHEDULING

Block scheduling provides extended time for hands-on projects and activities. Use the following activities to engage students, provide further depth, and vary your instructional techniques:

- Update (30 minutes) **pg. 756**
- Health Skills Activity (60–90 minutes) **pg. 764**

Your Safety and Well-Being

CHAPTER OVERVIEW

Chapter 34 focuses on ways to prevent accidents and acts of violence. The chapter observes risks in the home, during recreation and work, during the operation of a vehicle, and in situations where an individual is isolated from others.

LESSON 1 Although accidents seem to be random or haphazard events, safety experts have observed a recurring pattern that is present in all mishaps. Precautions can be taken to avoid fires, falls, electrical shock, and poisoning.

LESSON 2 Recreation and work can put individuals at risk of injury. Natural disasters can also pose threats to safety. When individuals participate in activities away from home, they should be aware of possible hazards and follow basic safety rules.

LESSON 3 Vehicular safety involves obeying the rules of the road, as well as exercising common sense and good judgment. Safety considerations for motorcycles and bicycles are similar to those for automobiles, with the addition of wearing a helmet, appropriate clothing, and safety gear.

LESSON 4 Violence is on the rise. Physical attack can occur in conjunction with some other crime, but random violence in isolated situations is on the rise. Individuals should appraise the safety of situations and conduct themselves in a way that may dissuade possible attackers.

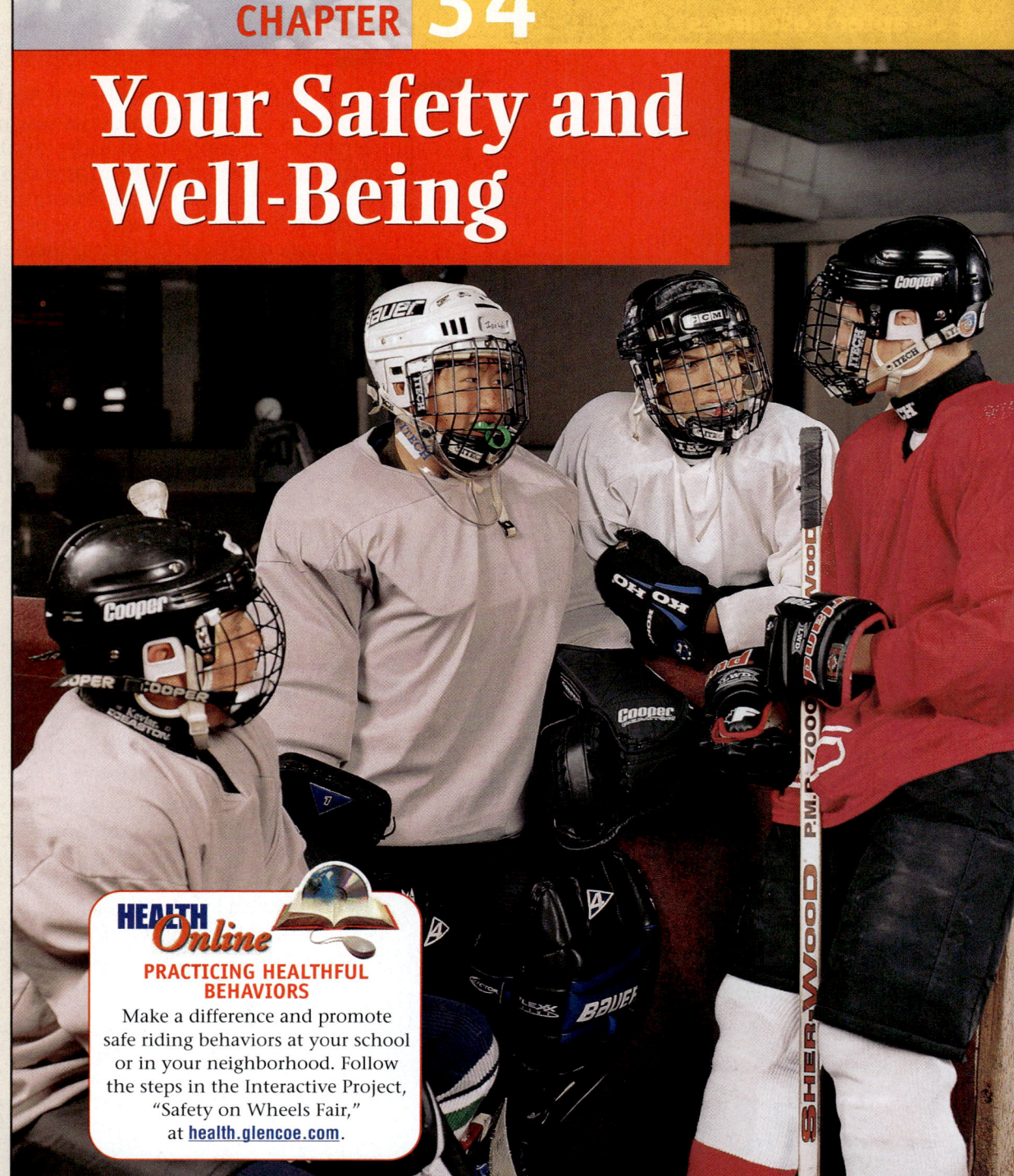

CHAPTER 34

Your Safety and Well-Being

HEALTH Online

PRACTICING HEALTHFUL BEHAVIORS

Make a difference and promote safe riding behaviors at your school or in your neighborhood. Follow the steps in the Interactive Project, "Safety on Wheels Fair," at health.glencoe.com.

Hands-On Health

TEACHING STRATEGY

Advertising Safety Help students increase awareness of safe practices by creating and sharing their own video ads. See Activity 30, "You Need to Know . . .," in the *Hands-On Health: Creative Teaching Strategies* booklet.

Time Needed

60 minutes or more in class

Supplies

- video camera
- videotape
- VCR and monitor

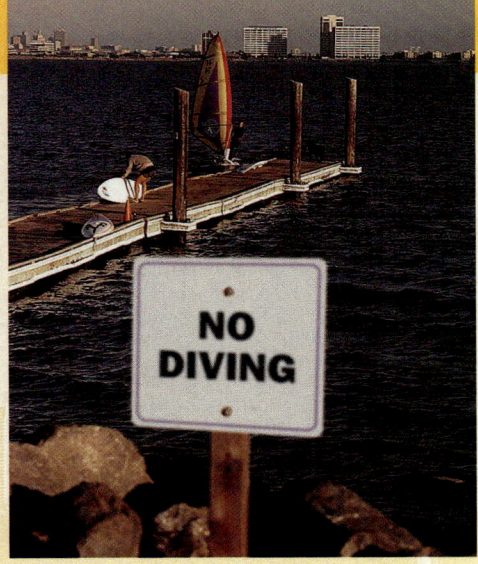

Simple things make a difference. 99

—Dr. Tedd Mitchell
Director, Wellness Program, Cooper Clinic

Quick Write Divide a sheet of paper into three columns and list the steps you can take *at home, in school,* and *in your community* to reduce the risk of accidents and other preventable injuries.

Personal Health Inventory

Self-Inventory Write the numbers 1–10 on a sheet of paper. Read each statement below and respond by writing *yes, no,* or *sometimes* for each item. Write a *yes* only for items that you practice regularly. Save your responses.

1	I do not use an electrical appliance if my body, clothing, or the floor is wet.
2	I do not rebottle or repackage products that might cause harm to someone else.
3	I stay within my abilities and limits when taking part in sports and recreational activities.
4	I don't risk my health or the health of others to show off.
5	I read and follow labels when using chemicals.
6	When I drive a vehicle or a motorcycle, I follow traffic guidelines.
7	I follow posted speed limits when driving or cycling.
8	I wear seat belts.
9	I do not open the door of my home to anyone I do not know or trust.
10	When going out with someone I do not know well, I make sure we go with other friends of mine.

Follow-up After completing the chapter, retake this self-inventory. Pick two items that you need to work on and set a goal to improve your health behaviors.

CHAPTER 34 YOUR SAFETY AND WELL-BEING **743**

INTRODUCING THE CHAPTER

Personal Health Inventory

Have students read and discuss the Self-Inventory statements. Ask: How does each behavior relate to protecting your own safety and the safety of other people? How can you affect all aspects of your health by following basic safety guidelines? After a brief discussion, let students record their inventory responses in their private Health Journals. Ask students to label this journal page "Safety and Well-Being."

- Ask students to discuss safety practices on the school campus. List on the chalkboard the rules and practices that are brought out. Ask why these rules and practices have been established. *(To protect us and to prevent accidents.)*
- Let volunteers describe the photographs on these two pages, and have students read the quote and complete the Quick Write. Ask: What risks might be associated with each scene? What guidelines do you think should be followed in each situation? Why? Explain that as they study the lessons in Chapter 34, students will explore those and related practices for protecting their safety and well-being.
- Distribute Parent Letter 34 in the *Parent Letters and Activities* booklet. ☞

TECHNOLOGY OPTIONS

  You may wish to use *Violence Prevention* with this chapter. For your convenience, use the separate *ABC News InterActive™ Bar Code Correlation* that accompanies the *Glencoe Health* program. 🔘

MINDJOGGER
VIDEOQUIZ

To preview or review chapter content, you may wish to use the *MindJogger Videoquiz* that accompanies Chapter 34. 🔘

Safety at Home

LESSON OBJECTIVES

After studying this lesson, students should be able to

- explain the elements of the accident chain.
- identify the most important causes of home accidents and how they can best be prevented.

MOTIVATOR

Write the following on the chalkboard for students to work on while attendance is being taken: *You are awakened at night in your bedroom by the high-pitched sound of a smoke detector. Your room is smoky and you start to cough. You try to turn on the light, but the power is off. What should you do?*

INTRODUCING THE LESSON

Refer to the Motivator. Ask students to share their responses. Tell them that if they do not already have a plan of action to follow in case of a home fire, they will learn how to make one in this lesson, as well as learn about other important causes of home accidents and injuries.

INTRODUCING HEALTH TERMS

- Ask students to discuss the major points that are portrayed in the accident chain and the fire chain. Why is the word *chain* so descriptive of the causes of accidents and fires? *(More than one thing must be linked for either to occur.)*
- Ask students to complete Vocabulary Activity 34 and Chapter Study Guide 34 in the *Student Workbook.*

Safety at Home

H ome should be the one place where you can feel safe and secure. Yet every year, thousands of people are injured as a result of home accidents. Accidents involving fire, falls, and electric shock cause more disabling injuries than any other kind. This lesson will look at the nature of accidents in the home and explore ways of preventing them.

HEALTH TERMS

accident chain
situation
smoke detector
fire extinguisher
electrocution

HEALTH CONCEPTS

- Although accidents do happen, exercising safety sense can help prevent accidents or at least diminish the severity of their effects.
- Safety measures in the home include the use of working smoke detectors and periodic inspection of electrical outlets and power cords.

The Accident Chain

A lthough accidents seem to be random, haphazard events, safety experts have observed an **accident chain**, *a recurring pattern that is present in all mishaps.* They have found that nearly all accidents include four steps that are connected, much like the links of a chain. In order for the accident to occur, all four of the following steps must be present:

- **The Situation.** The **situation** is *the circumstance or event leading up to an accident.* A situation can be something seemingly innocent, such as heading to your room to listen to CDs with a friend.
- **The Risk Factor.** The risk factor may be either an isolated unsafe act or an unsafe habit. An example is routinely leaving your

Lesson 1 Resources

TEACHER'S CLASSROOM RESOURCES

- **Concept Map** Activity 101
- **Lesson 101 Quiz**
- **Lesson Plan 101**
- **Parent Letter and Activities 34**
- **Reteaching** Activity 101

STUDENT WORKBOOK

- **Applying Health Skills 101**
- **Chapter Study Guide 34**
- **Vocabulary** Activity 34

books on the stairway as you go up to your room after school. Rushing is another habit that is involved in many accidents.

- **The Accident.** The accident is the result or consequence of one or more risk factors. For example, as your friend hurries down the stairs after listening to CDs, she trips over the books you have left on the stairway and falls.

- **The Aftermath.** The aftermath may take the form of personal injury, destruction of property, or both. For example, in the aftermath of your friend's fall, she might have broken her arm.

As you will see in the sections and lessons that follow, a single preventive behavior is often sufficient to break the accident chain.

Fires

What needs to be present for a fire to take place? Three elements (fuel, heat, and air) must be present. Fuel for a fire can be carelessly stored rags, wood, coal, oil, gasoline, or paper. A heat source could be a match, an electrical wire, or a cigarette. The oxygen in the air feeds and fans the flames. Recognition of the three links in the "fire chain" is the basis of fire prevention.

Fire Prevention Devices

Because household fires kill thousands of people each year, it is essential that each home be equipped with two life-saving devices: a smoke detector and a fire extinguisher. A **smoke detector** is *an alarm that is triggered by the presence of smoke.* Safety experts recommend one smoke detector on each floor or level of a home. They also advise testing the detector periodically and replacing the battery. Smoke detectors are now universally installed in new homes.

A **fire extinguisher** is *a portable device that puts out small fires by ejecting fire-extinguishing chemicals.* If you are confident that you can control a fire quickly with an extinguisher, use it promptly and properly. Stand away from the flames; aim it at the source of the fire, not at the flames; and move the spray from side to side. If you have any doubt at all, forget the extinguisher, get out of the house, and call the fire department.

When selecting a fire extinguisher for the home, be certain that you and your family understand the manufacturer's specifications and directions. Check the dial on the equipment from time to time to be certain that it still has sufficient pressure to be useful in an emergency.

Fire Safety Action

Most fatal home fires occur during the night, when it is easy to become disoriented by smoke or flame. The best protection against injury or death from home fires is to establish escape plans and conduct practice drills periodically.

keeping Fit

Think Fast!

If you are caught near or in an actual fire, acting quickly and remaining calm could save your life and the lives of others. Remember the following:

➤ Most deaths caused by fire result from smoke inhalation rather than burns. The chemical by-products of combustion combine quickly with oxygen, preventing smoke-inhalation victims from getting oxygen from the air. Because smoke rises, stay low to the floor to escape.

➤ Cover your mouth and nose with a wet towel or pillowcase to filter the smoke when evacuating a room.

➤ If you cannot escape your room, stuff towels and clothing in door cracks and vents.

➤ If a fire starts in a frying pan, put a lid on the fire. Never put water on a grease fire, because it will make the grease and the fire spread.

➤ If a fire starts in the oven, turn off the oven, and smother the fire with baking soda.

➤ Do not use water to put out an electrical fire. Use dry materials such as sand, salt, flour, or baking soda.

➤ If your clothes catch on fire, remember to *stop, drop,* and *roll.* Roll on the ground or roll up in a rug or blanket to smother the flames. If you remain upright or run, the flames will spread.

TEACH

Discussing
Ask students: Outside of driving on the highway, where are you most likely to suffer a serious injury? *(at home)* Why is the home such a dangerous place?

Discussing
What four elements are present in almost all accidents, combining to form an accident chain? How many elements must be changed in order to prevent the accident?

Writing
Allow volunteers to write a description of an accident, including a brief account of the situation, the unsafe habit or risk, the unsafe act, the accident, and the possible injuries—all the links in the accident chain.

Class Activity
Ask students to name several different sources of fuel that could start a home fire *(rags, wood, coal, oil, gasoline, paper)*. Have them describe the proper way to store each type of fuel to minimize the possibility of fire.

Think Fast!

keeping Fit

Have students review the feature to recall the major points one should remember when faced with a fire emergency. Explain that thinking fast in an emergency is easiest when you are prepared. Discuss the importance of devising a floor plan that shows alternate exits from each room. Ask what steps should be included in all home fire-escape plans.

MORE ABOUT . . . . .

ACCIDENTS. According to Tom Parker's book *In One Day:* each day in the United States numerous objects, many of which are not usually thought to be dangerous, cause emergency-room injuries.

Objects	No. of Injuries
stairs, steps, and ramps	2,100
bicycles and accessories	1,420
nails, screws, and tacks	690
drinking glasses	300
hammers	150
carpets and rugs	140
pencils, pens, desk supplies	120
toilets and sinks	90
television sets	75
paper bags and wrappers	35
ashtrays	15
aquariums and accessories	15

L1 Class Activity

Encourage the class to identify the four basic types of accidents that are likely to occur in the home (*fires, falls, electric shock, and poisoning*). Ask volunteers to describe one way in which each type of accident could occur.

L1 Discussing

What are some potential sources of heat that may start home fires? What precautions should be taken with these sources in order to lessen the risk of fire?

L1 Discussing

Which age groups are most prone to injuries from falls? Where do most falls at home occur?

L2 Explaining

Explain how electrical shocks occur. How does one become part of the circuit on which an electric current travels? What does being "grounded" mean? How is it related to shock?

L1 Discussing

What are some of the most important ways to avoid electrical shocks in the home? Elicit student responses.

L1 Community Involvement

Ask students to investigate the meaning and importance of child-proofing the home and yard. Then have them develop lists of child-proofing precautions for infants, toddlers, and preschoolers.

⚠ *Use a safe stepping-stool to reach high places.*

You and your family should draw a floor plan, including doors, hallways, and windows, of each story of your home. Use arrows to point out two ways of escape, if possible, from each room. Alternate escape routes are necessary in case one route is blocked. For example, if an upstairs door is blocked by fire, a ladder or a readily available rope coil is essential for escape through windows. Use a predetermined signal to alert everyone to the fire. Smoke detectors, which should be in every household, will do this job.

After escaping, meet outside at a safe prearranged place. Do not go back into the house. Call the fire department from a neighbor's house. If a person is trapped inside a burning building, rescue is safer and usually faster if left to the fire department.

Falls

Even though young children and the elderly are the most susceptible to injury from falls, this type of accident can happen to anyone.

Preventing Falls

Although falls are not usually serious, in some instances they can be deadly. You can take steps to help break the accident chain associated with many falls.

Stairways should be well lighted, in good repair, equipped with sturdy handrails and nonskid stair strips, and free of clutter. A loose rug is always a danger. Make sure that all bare wood and tile floors are not slippery. All bathtubs and showers should be equipped with safety rails and nonskid mats.

Outdoor steps and sidewalks should be maintained in good repair and kept free of ice, leaves, toys, and other obstacles.

If there are small children in the home, install adjustable safety latches so that windows can open only a few inches. (Be sure they are removable in case of an emergency.)

Electric Shock

Shocks from electrical appliances can kill. Each year, more than 1,000 Americans are killed by accidental **electrocution**, *death resulting from passage through the body of a high-voltage current.*

Preventing Electric Shock

You should take precautions when using home electrical appliances and power tools. Whenever anything seems to be wrong with an appliance or power tool, unplug it immediately. Inspect cords occasionally for signs of cracked insulation and have frayed cords replaced. Cords should not be

746   CHAPTER 34   YOUR SAFETY AND WELL-BEING

MORE ABOUT . . . . .

FIRE SAFETY. Along with fireplaces, woodstoves have become popular sources of heat in some parts of the United States. They're also dangerous. Like a fireplace, a woodstove's chimney may build up a lining of creosote—a gummy, highly flammable substance that is produced when wood is burned. Creosote is the most common cause of chimney fires. To avoid a chimney fire with a woodstove or fireplace, one should keep the chimney free of creosote and be prepared for emergencies. Once a year, the chimney should be cleaned by a trained chimney sweep who uses special brushes to remove the creosote. One should also keep a fire extinguisher near the fireplace or woodstove and check it regularly.

placed under a carpet or rug because they can be damaged when walked on.

Disconnect appliances by pulling on the plug, not on the cord. Never use an electrical appliance or power tool if your body, clothing, or the floor is wet. Keep outlet protectors in sockets if small children are in the home.

Poisoning

Everyday products, not just those marked with a skull and crossbones, can be poisonous. Most of these products are typically found in the kitchen, bathroom, utility area, basement, and garage. Poisoning, which is especially prevalent among young children, can result from either swallowing a toxic substance or breathing in a lethal gas. Still another type of poisoning, **food poisoning**, is covered in Chapter 6.

Preventive Behaviors

In families with children, household products and medicines should be kept in locked cabinets or out of the reach of children. Never place any **medicine** in an unlabeled vial or a container other than the one it was originally packaged in. Periodically check the medicine cabinet, read labels carefully, and discard any medicine that is past its expiration date.

keeping Fit

Medical Emergency

Be prepared for medical emergencies at home. Be sure to:

➤ Keep a short medical record of each family member in a convenient location.

➤ On separate cards, list each person's birth date, medical history, allergies, current medications, and doctor's name and phone number. Give the appropriate card to emergency medical technicians when they arrive on the scene.

hotlink

food poisoning For more information on food poisoning and ways of preventing it, see Chapter 6, page 151.

medicine For more information on medicine and precautions for its use, see Chapter 23, page 518.

---

keeping Fit

Medical Emergency

Have students design magnetic or adhesive cards with spaces for pertinent medical information. Make copies of the cards for each member of your students' families.

ASSESS

EVALUATING THE LESSON

Assign and discuss the Lesson 1 Review; then administer, grade, and discuss the *Lesson 101 Quiz* in the TCR. ☞

RETEACHING

• Provide students with copies of floor plans of several different homes. Ask them to develop emergency exit routes from all rooms in each house and indicate where smoke detectors and fire extinguishers should be placed. Have them justify their decisions.

• Ask students to complete *Reteaching Activity 101* in the TCR. ☞

ENRICHMENT

Ask students to think of examples of various child-safety devices (*safety door latches, door alarms, intercom monitors, child-safety gates, etc.*). For each device, have students determine what link in the accident chain the device is meant to break.

LESSON 1 Review

Reviewing Facts and Vocabulary

1. Explain the purpose of a smoke detector and a fire extinguisher.
2. Give some examples of hazards that cause falls in the home.

Thinking Critically

3. *Evaluating.* For a school report that is due in a month, Todd is keeping back issues of newsmagazines. He has piled a dozen copies on a stair landing leading down to the family basement. Identify at least two accidents that could result from this situation.
4. *Analyzing.* Analyze the saying: *Safety begins at home.* What assumptions does this saying make?

5. *Synthesizing.* Marta has a three-year-old brother. What special steps do Marta and her family need to take to minimize her brother's risk of injury due to a fall if the family lives in an apartment?

Applying Health Skills

6. *In Your Home and School.* Design a fire escape plan for your classroom and your home. For your home, include two escape routes from each room.

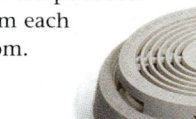

LESSON 1 SAFETY AT HOME **747**

Lesson 1 Review

Answers to Reviewing Facts and Vocabulary

1. A smoke detector alerts residents to possible fires; a fire extinguisher puts out small fires.
2. Possible answers: poorly lighted stairways, loose rugs, showers without nonskid mats, icy outdoor stairs.

Answers to Thinking Critically

3. Possible answers: Papers could catch fire; someone could trip on the papers and fall down the stairs.
4. Analyses will vary.
5. Answers will vary.

CLOSE

Tell students that if they apply what they learned in this lesson to their own home life, they and their family will decrease the chances of being seriously injured in a home accident.

Safety Outside the Home

Safety Outside the Home

FOCUS

LESSON OBJECTIVES

After studying this lesson, students should be able to

- identify basic safety rules that help prevent accidents during recreation and while at work.
- describe how best to seek protection during a natural disaster.

MOTIVATOR

Write the following on the chalkboard for students to work on while attendance is being taken: *Recall an accident that occurred during a recreational activity. Write a brief description of the accident and the steps leading up to it.*

INTRODUCING THE LESSON

Refer to the Motivator. Ask volunteers to share their responses. Have the class try to identify the cause of each accident and how it might have been prevented.

INTRODUCING HEALTH TERMS

- Tell students to explain the terms *hurricane, tornado,* and *blizzard* in their own words.
- Ask students to complete Vocabulary Activity 34 and Chapter Study Guide 34 in the *Student Workbook.* ☞

Although many accidents occur at home, the potential for danger lurks outside the home as well. Accidents occur during leisure-time activities, in the workplace, and even in acts of nature. As with accidents in the home, a single preventive behavior can often break the accident chain.

HEALTH TERMS

Occupational Safety and Health Administration (OSHA)

hurricane

tornado

blizzard

HEALTH CONCEPTS

- Many accidents, especially among teens, occur when people show off, get overly confident, or accept a dare.
- Safety on the job is the responsibility of each and every employee.
- Careful planning and preparation can help you survive a natural disaster.

Recreational Safety

Do you enjoy swimming? Maybe you participate in a sport. Recreational activities such as these can be fun, but all too often such activities are "accidents waiting to happen." By exercising common sense and caution, you can break the accident chain.

Accidents In or On Water

Drowning is the second leading cause of injury-related death for children in the United States today. Each year 4,300 people drown, and another 3,000 are hospitalized for near-drownings. The majority of drownings and near-drownings occur in residential swimming pools. Children under the age of four are especially at risk and account for over 60 percent of all pool drownings.

748   CHAPTER 34   YOUR SAFETY AND WELL-BEING

Lesson 2 Resources

TEACHER'S CLASSROOM RESOURCES

☞ **Concept Map** Activity 102

☞ **Cooperative Learning** Activity 34

☞ **Decision-Making** Activity 34

☞ **Enrichment** Activity 34

☞ **Lesson 102 Quiz**

☞ **Lesson Plan 102**

☞ **Reteaching** Activity 102

STUDENT WORKBOOK

☞ **Applying Health Skills 102**

☞ **Chapter Study Guide 34**

☞ **Vocabulary** Activity 34

Among teens, accidents involving water occur most often when a person is showing off, gets overly confident, uses alcohol near or on the water, or accepts a dare.

Water Safety

When the behaviors described above happen in or around water, the price can be high—even deadly. Whether you are swimming, diving, or boating, following these simple rules will reduce your risk of accidents:

SWIMMING

- Know your swimming abilities. Never swim so far out that you are not sure you can make it safely back to your starting point. Learn to swim well.
- Swim only in supervised areas, where a lifeguard is present. If possible, swim with a companion who knows lifesaving techniques.
- If you get a **muscle cramp**, do not panic. Relax, float, and press and squeeze the muscle until it relaxes.
- If you are pulled offshore by rapid currents or undertows, swim toward shore at a 45-degree angle until you are freed by the current.
- Never swim or dive when using any form of medication or when under the influence of alcohol or another drug.

Pool Rules

The high incidence of pool-related drownings can be greatly reduced by following a few simple, common-sense rules.

➤ Never leave a small child alone near the water.

➤ Remove toys that are in and around the pool when they are not being used. Toys can attract young children to a pool.

➤ With above-ground pools, steps and ladders leading from the ground to the pool should be secured and locked.

➤ A first-aid kit, a phone, and emergency phone numbers should be in a convenient nearby location.

➤ High fences or walls should protect outsiders from getting in your pool.

➤ For a young child, a bathtub can be as dangerous as a pool.

hot link

muscle cramp For more information on muscle cramps and ways to treat this problem, see Chapter 4, page 84.

Drowning is a constant danger for all swimmers, no matter how well they swim. That is why it is important to always swim with a lifeguard present.

ACTIVITY *What can you do to improve your swimming skills?*

TEACH

L2 Discussing

Have students discuss this statement: *We are twice as likely to have an accident when we are enjoying ourselves. Why is this so?*

L1 Class Activity

Ask students to identify three basic safety guidelines for those involved in sports and other recreational activities. *(Know your limits, warm up and cool down, learn the safety rules for your activity.)*

L1 Discussing

What are some of the causes of the more than 7,000 drownings that take place each year in the United States?

L1 Discussing

Lead a discussion of the following: How are swimming lessons related to risk of drowning?

Pool Rules

keeping **Fit**

Discuss with students the rules for pool safety that are presented in the feature. Ask what rules students have seen posted at public pools they have visited. Students interested in taking pool safety a step further may be interested in becoming certified as lifeguards. Ask volunteers to investigate lifeguard-certifying programs in the community. Such programs typically require a certain proficiency in swimming, and training will include surveillance and rescue skills. Allow students to present their findings in class.

MORE ABOUT . . . . .

AVOIDING POTENTIAL DROWNING.

Many drowning victims never intended to go into the water in the first place—they fell in while fishing, walking, playing, boating, or cycling. Many of us can't swim well enough to save ourselves or others if we do fall into the water accidentally, so the best precaution is to avoid falling into the water in the first place.

Be cautious when alongside water—banks are often wet and slippery, or they may crumble underfoot. Never disregard danger notices and don't be overconfident—even if you can swim. Swimming in an icy lake is very different from swimming in a warm pool. Finally, never go fishing or swimming by yourself.

L2 Researching

Ask students to read about swimming programs for infants and toddlers. Ask: What drowning-prevention methods are taught? What are the medical and psychological benefits and dangers of involving small children in these programs? Have students summarize their findings in writing.

L1 Discussing

What safety guidelines are important in helping to prevent camping accidents and injuries?

L1 Researching

Instruct volunteers to look through local newspapers for reports on recreational accidents. Discuss how the accidents occurred and how they could have been prevented. What unnecessary risks may have been taken in each case? Why do people take such risks?

L1 Community Involvement

Ask students to research recreational activities that are common in their area. For each recreational activity, ask them to investigate specific rules that regulate the activity; causes of the most common accidents associated with the activity; and local education sources of accident-prevention.

L1 Discussing

Ask students who have jobs to describe specific safety measures that are taken at their places of work. Discuss why employers place so much emphasis on safety *(to increase employee productivity and to reduce employee health care costs)*.

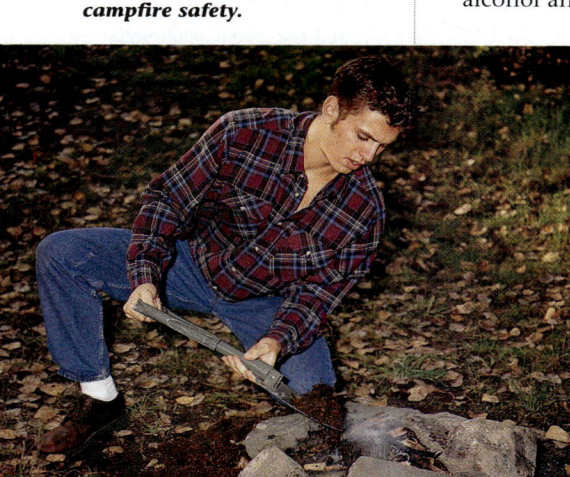

▼ *Camping can be fun when safety precautions are followed.*

ACTIVITY *Name other precautions that campers should follow in addition to campfire safety.*

hotlink

physical activity For more information on physical activity and its benefits to total health, see Chapter 4, page 72.

DIVING

- Always check the water depth before diving.
- Never dive into unfamiliar water or into shallow breaking waves. Make sure the area is clear of swimmers and floating objects.
- Always dive straight ahead and not off the side of the diving board.
- Do not jump into shallow water. This could cause a spinal injury by jolting the body.

BOATING

- Learn how to handle a boat or canoe correctly. Some states require a boating class or have age requirements.
- Wear approved flotation devices on boats and other watercraft. Rubber tubes and floats are no substitute in the event of a mishap.
- Follow basic highway and driving safety rules when it comes to alcohol and drugs: Don't drink or use drugs and drive a boat.

Accidents on the Trail

Outdoor pastimes, such as hiking, camping, hunting, and climbing are wonderful forms of **physical activity**. Yet, they can turn disastrous when rules of safety are not followed. When taking part in any nature activity or sport, keep the following safety tips uppermost in mind:

- Stay in specified campsites, and hunt only in approved areas.
- Never camp, hike, or hunt alone. Always make sure someone knows where you are going and when you will return.
- Be knowledgeable about poisonous plants, insects, and snakes in the area.
- Carry plenty of fresh water on the trail.
- Never cook inside a tent, and smother all campfires with dirt and water.
- Never include alcohol or drugs in any outdoor activity.

Safety on the Job

Do you have an after-school or weekend job? Even if you do not, some day you will be part of the workforce. Thus, it is important for you to know that precautions in the workplace are a vital part of safety.

Since the early 1990s accidental deaths on the job have been reduced by three quarters, largely due to the efforts of the **Occupational Safety and Health Administration (OSHA),** *a federal agency responsible for promoting safe and healthful conditions in the workplace.* A

COOPERATIVE LEARNING

REFUSAL SKILLS. Divide the class into groups of four. Have groups discuss reasons individuals might accept dares or other invitations to engage in unsafe behavior. Suggest that they discuss media images of daredevil heroes, as well as teen expectations of one another. Do boaters in films, for example, wear flotation devices? Should they? Then have each group brainstorm a scenario in which one teen pressures another to engage in unsafe behavior, such as diving off a cliff or swimming in heavy surf on an unsupervised beach. Choose two group members to role-play a conversation demonstrating good refusal skills. The other two members may critique the response and offer constructive suggestions. Have members switch roles, taking turns until all members have role-played refusal skills.

Making Responsible Decisions

Selling Safety Short

Herb and Ramon, two friends and classmates, are working in the same factory over the summer. During their two-week training period, the boys' supervisor emphasized the importance of wearing safety goggles at all times while in the factory. Recently, Ramon started noticing that Herb wears his goggles only when the supervisor is nearby. When confronted by Ramon, Herb made it clear that he finds the goggles uncomfortable and hot. Ramon is concerned for his friend and remembers being told during training about employees who were injured on the job. He wants to tell the supervisor but is afraid it might cost his friend his job.

What Would You Do?

Apply the six steps of the decision-making process to Ramon's problem.

1. **State the situation.**
2. **List the options.**
3. **Weigh the possible outcomes.**
4. **Consider your values.**
5. **Make a decision and act.**
6. **Evaluate the decision.**

---

division of the U.S. Department of Labor, OSHA develops and enforces health regulations and job safety. It also is involved in keeping employers and employees aware of industrial hazards. OSHA deals with fire prevention, protective clothing, and acceptable levels of exposure to asbestos and lead. OSHA workers inspect work sites to ensure compliance with their standards.

Responsibility for maintaining a safe work environment also rests with the employer and the employee. Employers can do their part by making sure that workers are adequately trained and are made aware of potential hazards and safety rules. Employees can help ensure a healthful and accident-free environment by:

- arriving at work well rested and alert.
- learning the proper use of machinery and other equipment.
- following established safety measures, including the wearing of protective gear.

Natural Disasters

The sky turns suddenly dark, an ominous funnel appears at the horizon. You are sitting at home when suddenly the floor begins to vibrate beneath your feet, and objects come crashing to the floor. These and similar situations, all acts of nature, affect not only the individual but entire communities. Yet, as with other situations, careful planning and preparation can help you survive should a natural disaster hit your area.

SCHOOL-TO-CAREER

INJURY INSURANCE AT WORK. Some worker injury insurance plans are national; for example, the Jones Act covers workers in such vehicles as trains and boats. Other plans vary from state to state. Have students investigate employer-provided injury insurance in your state. They should ask: What types of injuries are covered? What circumstances must exist for a claim to be paid? Are all injuries in the workplace covered? Are workers covered while traveling from place to place on the job? Are workers covered while working at home or at a client's location? What benefits are paid? What losses are not compensated? Have students discuss the financial and human costs of injury on the job that are not compensated.

Making Responsible Decisions

1. Ramon is concerned because his friend Herb often fails to wear his safety goggles in the factory.
2. Ramon could (a) report the problem to their supervisor; (b) tell Herb that Ramon will speak with the supervisor unless Herb starts wearing his goggles; (c) continue to remind Herb about wearing his goggles; (d) ignore the problem and hope Herb does not get injured.
3. Ramon might (a) get the supervisor to insist that Herb wear the goggles, but also risk having Herb lose his job and probably make Herb angry; (b) irritate or even anger Herb, but perhaps get Herb to start wearing the goggles; (c) irritate Herb, but have some chance of getting Herb to wear the goggles more often; (d) avoid risking Herb's anger, but continue to worry about his safety.
4. Ramon values Herb's safety and his friendship.
5. Decisions will vary.
6. Remind students to discuss both the short- and long-term consequences of their decisions.

L2 **Decision Making**

For further study on making responsible decisions, assign *Decision-Making Activity 34* in the TCR.

L1 **Discussing**

What is the purpose of the Occupational Safety and Health Act (OSHA)? When was it enacted?

L1 **Discussing**

What can a worker do personally to help ensure safety on the job?

If your community is prone to one or more specific types of natural disaster, such as hurricane, tornado, flood, and earthquake, have students compile and organize useful tips into a public service announcement. Encourage them to arrange to broadcast their PSA on the school's public address system.

L2 Researching

Have students research the natural disasters most likely to occur in their part of the country. They are to find out what to do in these emergencies, what preventive actions to take, and how to recognize possible dangers.

L2 Cooperative Learning

Divide the class into four groups. Assign each group one of the weather-related emergencies discussed. Have students research and develop a class presentation on their weather-related emergency. Presentations may include photos, drawings, past occurrences or disasters related to their weather emergency, what type of help is available, warnings, and prevention.

L1 Parental Involvement

Ask students to make plans and procedures for their families to follow during weather-related emergencies. Have students provide a plan for each family member in case parents are not at home when the emergency happens.

L2 Cooperative Learning

Assign *Cooperative Learning Activity 34*, "Safety," in the TCR.

A natural disaster can occur just about anywhere and at any time. Learn how to prepare for and stay safe during natural disasters from the American Red Cross Disaster Services at **health.glencoe.com**.

Hurricanes and Tornadoes

A **hurricane** is *a powerful rainstorm, characterized by driving winds.* Hurricanes occur near coastal areas of the United States, mainly on the eastern and southern seaboards. In general, preparation for a hurricane includes securing your property and then either going to a shelter or evacuating the area as the National Weather Service instructs. The farther inland you go, the safer you will be. Hurricanes have been known to build up enough momentum to carry their destructive winds inland for hundreds of miles.

A **tornado** is *a powerful, twisting windstorm.* Although tornadoes were once largely confined to the central United States, in recent times they have begun to strike sporadically in all areas of the country. Knowing what to do in case of a hurricane or a tornado could save your life.

A storm cellar or basement is the safest place to go for protection from a tornado. If neither option is available, a hallway or bathtub away from windows will suffice. If you are caught outside, get into a ditch and lie face down. Cover yourself with a mattress, blanket, rug, or bulky winter clothing, if possible, to protect yourself from flying objects.

Floods

Flooding is often the result of severe rains of the type that accompany hurricanes. Some streams and rivers may also overflow as a result of melting mountain snow. If you live in an area that is prone to flooding, an emergency plan is your best first course of action. It is also important to learn under what conditions to abandon your home, as well as when it is safer to stay put until help arrives. Some people refuse to leave, and they drown in their homes.

If you are in a car that stalls because of rising waters, abandon the car and seek higher ground immediately. When driving, be on the lookout as well for signs warning that bridges and roads may be "out" because of flood conditions.

Earthquakes

Heavy ground tremors from earthquakes occur often in some parts of the United States. California averages almost 5,000 weak but detectable quakes per year. Knowing what to do during and after an earthquake is important to your safety.

Most casualties during an earthquake are not a direct result of the ground movement but result from falling objects or collapsing structures. If you are inside a building and feel a tremor, follow these safety procedures:

1. Stay in the building.
2. Select a safe spot away from falling objects within a few steps of where you are standing, and go to it. If there is a heavy desk or table with enough space for you to fit underneath, crawl under it

MEETING STUDENT DIVERSITY

CULTURAL PERSPECTIVES. Explain that weather has always played a major role in shaping human life, especially in agricultural economies, where changes in weather can be very important. By the third century B.C., the Chinese had learned to measure humidity using charcoal, which absorbs water vapor from the air. By weighing pieces of charcoal and recording the differences over time, the Chinese could measure changes in relative humidity. Encourage students to investigate how other cultures sought to explain, predict, and/or control the weather.

and then hold on to it to keep it from moving away from you.

3. If you live in an area prone to tremors, safeguard your home by bolting bookcases and other tall or heavy furniture to the wall. If you are outdoors when an earthquake hits, stay away from buildings, trees, and power lines.

Blizzards

A **blizzard** is *a snowstorm with winds of 35 miles per hour (56 km per hour) or greater.* Visibility is less than 500 feet (152 m), so it is easy for a person to get lost. The safest place to be during a blizzard is indoors. If you are caught outside, try to keep your mouth and nose covered, and keep moving so that you do not freeze. Try to follow a road or a fence to the closest safe place. If you live in snow country, carry jumper cables, a blanket, and shovel in your car during the winter.

If you must go outside in a blizzard, wear protective clothing. All of the following will help protect you from freezing temperatures and **frostbite:** thermal undergarments; outer garments that repel wind and moisture; head, face, and ear coverings; extra socks; warm boots; and wool-lined mittens. Many thin layers of clothing provide the best protection from the cold.

△ *Blizzards and other natural disasters can strike without warning.*

ACTIVITY *Identify measures established in your community to prepare for disasters.*

hotlink

frostbite For more information on frostbite, see Chapter 4, page 87.

EVALUATING THE LESSON

Assign and discuss the Lesson 2 Review; then administer, grade, and discuss the *Lesson 102 Quiz* in the TCR. ☞

RETEACHING

- Request from the school principal copies of several old accident reports. Have students analyze them for the causes of the accidents and to identify ways they might have been prevented.
- Ask students to complete *Reteaching Activity 102* in the TCR. ☞

ENRICHMENT

- Encourage students to investigate the myths and facts about when people are most accident-prone *(for example, when their biorhythms are at an ebb or when there is a full moon).* Ask them to organize their findings about these myths and facts in chart form. Then have each student show the chart to ten people and ask them to describe their own "accident-proneness" in terms of the chart. Do their experiences fit better with the myth section or with the fact section?
- Tell students that the need to resolve safety issues continues into the workplace. Have them complete *Enrichment Activity 34,* "The Right to a Safe Workplace," in the TCR. ☞

Reviewing Facts and Vocabulary

1. List five rules of safety on or near water.
2. Describe the purpose of OSHA.

Thinking Critically

3. **Synthesizing.** Develop a plan that would help reduce the number of recreational accidents in your community.
4. **Analyzing.** Compare safe and unsafe behavior when camping or hiking.
5. **Comparing and Contrasting.** Tell in what ways hurricanes, tornadoes, and earthquakes are similar. In what ways are they not alike?

Applying Health Skills

6. **In Your Home.** Research the kinds of natural disasters common to your area of the United States. Speak with someone at your local chapter of the American Red Cross, Salvation Army, or National Guard about what action should be taken in disasters of this type. Summarize your findings, and share them with the class.

Have students recall the major concepts of the lesson. Ask students to analyze their favorite recreational activities or their workplace to determine areas of risk and to consider ways to protect themselves.

Lesson 2 Review

Answers to Reviewing Facts and Vocabulary

1. Refer to lists headed Swimming, Diving, and Boating on pages 749–750.
2. Develop and enforce health regulations and job safety; help keep employers and employees aware of industrial hazards; deal with issues of fire prevention, protective clothing, and acceptable levels of exposure to asbestos and lead.

Answers to Thinking Critically

3. Plans will vary.
4. Comparisons will vary.
5. Comparisons should reflect an understanding of the importance of advance preparation.

LESSON 3

Safety on Wheels

FOCUS

LESSON OBJECTIVES

After studying this lesson, students should be able to

- identify safety guidelines for travel on wheels.
- discuss the problem of road rage and driving strategies to help avoid it.

MOTIVATOR

Write the following on the chalkboard for students to work on while attendance is being taken: *Do you wear seat belts? Why or why not? If you do not wear seat belts all the time, how often do you wear them?*

INTRODUCING THE LESSON

Refer to the Motivator. Take a poll of the class and summarize their seat-belt habits on the chalkboard. Ask students who don't use seat belts to explain their reasons for not doing so.

INTRODUCING HEALTH TERMS

- Have students list driving habits that are known to set off road rage for some emotionally unstable drivers.
- Ask students to complete Vocabulary Activity 34 and Study Guide 34 in the *Student Workbook.* ☞

I t is a frightening fact that automobile accidents are the leading cause of death for people between the ages of 15 and 20 in the United States. The fatality rate for teenage drivers is about four times higher than the rate for drivers 25 to 65 years old. What is perhaps even more sobering is that many of these fatal accidents are preventable.

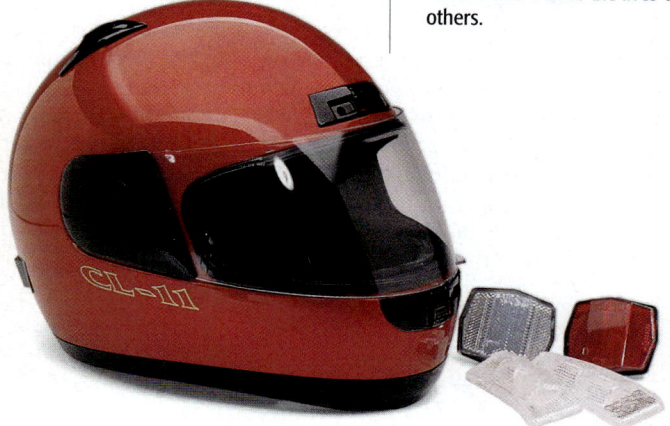

HEALTH TERMS

vehicular safety

road rage

HEALTH CONCEPTS

- Vehicular safety is obeying the rules of the road, as well as exercising common sense and good judgment.
- Most automobile accidents among teens do not involve a second vehicle.
- Every driver accepts some responsibility to protect his or her personal life as well as the lives of others.

Automobile Safety

When teenagers are entrusted with the family car, they are taking on a big responsibility to themselves, their own families, their passengers, and the passengers of other vehicles. That responsibility is to behave in a manner that reduces the risk of death or injury. Behaving responsibly means exercising **vehicular safety**—*obeying the rules of the road, as well as exercising common sense and good judgment.* Obeying the rules means driving within the speed limit, yielding the right-of-way when called for, and observing local traffic regulations. Exercising common sense and good judgment includes:

- **Paying attention to road conditions.** This means reducing your speed when the road is icy or rain-slicked, when a lane narrows, or when there is construction or congestion.

Lesson 3 Resources

TEACHER'S CLASSROOM RESOURCES

☞ **Concept Map** Activity 103

☞ **Health Lab** 34

☞ **Lesson 103 Quiz**

☞ **Lesson Plan** 103

☞ **Reteaching** Activity 103

STUDENT WORKBOOK

☞ **Applying Health Skills** 103

☞ **Chapter Study Guide** 34

☞ **Vocabulary** Activity 34

TRANSPARENCIES

🖋 **Transparency 52**

- **Paying attention to other drivers.** A popular TV commercial that aired several years ago, sponsored by the National Safety Council, advised drivers to "watch out for the other guy." This advice is still sound. When it is dark or inclement weather reduces visibility, turn on your headlights. This makes it possible for other drivers to see *you*. In general, drive as though the other driver is going to act irresponsibly. That way you will always be ready for some unforeseen action.

- **Paying attention to your physical state.** If you are tired, don't drive. Pull over at the nearest rest stop and call home. *Under no circumstances should you drive when you have been using alcohol, other drugs, or prescription or over-the-counter medications.* The National Highway Traffic Safety Administration (NHTSA) reports that almost 38 percent of young drivers killed in crashes in 1999 were **intoxicated**.

- **Paying attention to your emotional state.** If you are angry or feeling other strong emotions, don't drive. Your mental state can affect your judgment and reaction time as much as your physical state. Taking an approved driver's education course can help you develop better driving skills and habits. Such a course can help you learn to anticipate problems before they occur.

Road Rage

Sometimes people who are otherwise emotionally stable become enraged when they get behind the wheel. *When intense anger and driving mix,* the results—known as **road rage**—can be deadly. Road rage has been linked to a number of incidents, such as disputes over a parking space, obscene gestures, loud music, overuse of the horn, and slow driving. A driver consumed with road rage may run red lights, tailgate, or pass on a shoulder. Some individuals have even been known to use guns or other weapons.

If you see someone who is truly a danger on the road, keep your distance. Get the vehicle's license plate number, and report it promptly to the police.

ROAD RAGE: SOME STRATEGIES

You can protect yourself when you are behind the wheel by taking these measures:

- avoid blocking the right-hand turn lane.
- assume other drivers' mistakes are not personal.
- be polite and courteous, even if the other driver is not.
- pull over and allow traffic to pass if moving slowly.
- avoid unnecessary use of high-beam headlights.
- avoid all conflict if possible. If another driver challenges you, take a deep breath and get out of the way.

TEACH

L1 Discussing

Explain that the leading cause of death for older teens and young adults is car accidents. Ask: What do you think are the major contributing factors? *(speeding, alcohol)*

L1 Guest Speaker

Invite a driver education teacher to class to explain what defensive driving means and to give students some examples of defensive-driving techniques.

L1 Analyzing

Let students share their thoughts about road rage, either in groups or as part of a class discussion. Ask: Why do you think people are more likely to feel and express intense anger in their cars? In what sense can road rage be contagious? What can you, as a driver or as a passenger, do to diminish the risks of road rage?

hot link

intoxicated
Discuss the term *intoxicated* and the particular risks that drinking and driving presents. Ask: If alcoholism is a disease, how should drunk driving be considered—as a symptom of illness or as a serious crime?

L1 Researching

Have students research the laws and penalties for driving while under the influence of alcohol.

MORE ABOUT . . . . .

ANTI-LOCK BRAKING SYSTEMS. Anti-lock braking systems (ABS) prevent cars from skidding by using computers to sense when the car's wheels are going to lock up. When the computer determines that one wheel is beginning to spin more slowly than the others, it automatically releases and applies pressure to the braking mechanism so the wheel does not lock until the car slows down. ABS were designed to improve road safety and prevent automobile accidents. The systems are especially helpful when driving on wet, icy, or snow-covered roads.

L1 Explaining

Explain why children are at greater risk than adults in car accidents if they are not belted into a car seat.

L1 Researching

Have the class investigate the role of seat belts in reducing serious injuries and deaths in car accidents.

L2 Researching

Instruct students to find out more about state laws concerning car safety seats for children.

L2 Researching

Ask students to investigate airbag safety. Why are young children required to be seated in the back seat of a car? What are car manufacturers doing to make airbags safer for everyone?

update
▶ *Looking at the Issues*

Should More Restrictions Be Put on Teen Drivers?

Let volunteers explain the procedure for becoming a licensed driver in your state. Ask: Does our state impose any special restrictions on teen drivers? What kinds of restrictions do other states impose? After a brief discussion, have students read the Update feature to learn more about the issue of restrictions for teen drivers. Encourage volunteers to offer additional facts and examples to support the two different viewpoints on this issue. Then have students write their answers to the Exploring Your Views questions.

Other Preventive Behaviors

For every 100 young people killed in a motor vehicle accident in the United States last year, 80 would still be alive if they had been wearing a seat belt. Yet, according to the CDC's *Youth Risk Behavior Survey,* about 19 percent of students nationwide rarely, or never, use seat belts when riding in a car or truck driven by someone else. Drivers and passengers who fail to use seat belts are more likely to become flying missiles during a crash. This is true whether they are in the front or back seat.

When you use a seat belt, you are practicing accident and injury prevention. If your friends do not buckle up, ask them to do so. Most states have laws requiring the use of seat belts.

update
▶ *Looking at the Issues*

Should More Restrictions Be Put on Teen Drivers?

Although driver training helps save lives, some safety experts feel that where teens are concerned, driver's ed and safety courses are "too little, too late." Many states have now implemented measures to restrict teen drivers. These include raising the minimum driving age, revoking licenses for criminal offenses, limiting the kinds of roads on which teens may drive, and keeping teens off the roads after dark. Not everyone agrees with these policies.

ANALYZING DIFFERENT VIEWPOINTS

▶ **Viewpoint One**
Many teens believe that just because some teens drive unsafely, other law-abiding and safe-driving teens should not have to pay the price. They state that many teens are good citizens who care about their own and others' safety and are respectful of others' rights on the road.

▶ **Viewpoint Two**
Advocates of stricter driving restrictions state that some teens, unaccustomed to cars and driving, make dangerous mistakes on the road. Other teens, they say, are guilty of daredevil tactics, showing off for friends, and driving under the influence of alcohol and other drugs. They also point to statistics that reveal that 16-year-old drivers are less responsible and more likely to have accidents than 17-year-olds.

EXPLORING YOUR VIEWS

1. Do you believe that teen drivers should have restrictions placed on them? Why or why not?

2. How does the topic of driving restrictions relate to the issue of rights vs. responsibility?

756 CHAPTER 34 YOUR SAFETY AND WELL-BEING

HOME AND COMMUNITY
CONNECTION

PUBLIC TRANSIT. Have students investigate public transportation in the community to find out which vehicles do or do not provide safety restraints. Answers may be different for buses, trains, limousines, and taxicabs. If some public transit vehicles are not equipped with safety restraints, discuss with students ways to minimize the risk of injury in the event of an accident. In particular, have them discuss suggestions for parents of small children, such as seating the child next to an adult, or by holding a small child firmly on the lap. Encourage students to promote laws which call for safety restraints on public transportation, by writing to local lawmakers. Some students may prefer to write to the editor of a local newspaper.

Building Health Skills

Being an Alert Consumer: Helmet Hints

ACCORDING TO THE NHTSA, an estimated half of all cyclists between the ages of 15 and 20 who die in crashes each year were not wearing helmets. When buying a helmet, remember to consider:

1. Visibility. A helmet should be bright-colored so that motorists can see you clearly. Helmets that are black or some neutral color may be stylish, but they can also be deadly if they cause you to blend in with your surroundings.

2. Dependability. A properly fitting helmet should cover the top of your forehead. It should also have straps that prevent it from shifting or, worse still, falling off in the event you hit a bump.

3. Reliability. Buy only a helmet that is certified by the Snell Memorial Foundation or approved by the American National Standards Institute.

Use your head when buying a helmet. This is your best safeguard against losing it.

Safety on Two Wheels

Although the phrase *safety on wheels* may prompt you to think only of cars and trucks, remember that motorcycles, mopeds, and even bicycles are also vehicles. Like cars, they are subject to vehicular safety as well as traffic laws.

Motorcycle and Moped Safety

Motorcyclists and moped drivers are 17 times more likely to be killed in an accident than people traveling in a car. Part of the reason is that motorized two-wheeled vehicles slide more easily and weigh less than those with four wheels. Such vehicles are also more difficult for other motorists to see.

Besides following safety rules on the road, cyclists can increase their protection by:

- wearing safety helmets and proper clothing, including eye protection.
- being extra cautious in wet weather when tire traction on wet surfaces is poor.
- avoiding "wheelies" and other forms of showing off.
- carrying an additional rider *only* when your vehicle has an attached second seat, foot rests, and a spare helmet.
- avoiding touching or grabbing on to another moving vehicle.

keeping Fit

Glove Compartment Checklist

When you are driving alone, your car's glove compartment can be a lifesaver–provided it contains the following items:

- ➤ a flashlight with working batteries.
- ➤ a notepad and pen or pencil.
- ➤ change for a telephone call.
- ➤ a tire pressure gauge.
- ➤ number of a 24-hour towing service.
- ➤ an insurance card for the car you are traveling in.
- ➤ a pump-spray product that can be used to fix a flat tire instantly.

Building Health Skills

Helmet Hints
Skill: Health Consumer Skills

Show students several different bicycle helmets, or ads for different helmets. Ask: Which would you choose? Why? After students have shared their ideas, have them read the Building Health Skills feature to find out what they should consider when choosing a helmet. Then tell students to form groups in which they create effective ads for safe bicycle helmets (either actual helmets on the market or helmets of their own design). Groups may choose to create print ads, posters, or TV commercials. Allow time for each group to share its helmet ad with the rest of the class.

ⓛ Discussing

Elicit responses to the following: Should bicyclists and motorcyclists be required by law to wear helmets? Why or why not?

ⓛ Class Activity

Direct students to make a list on the chalkboard of safety practices to follow when riding a bicycle after dark and in wet weather.

ⓛ Discussing

Ask students who ride bicycles to discuss the behavior they expect from motorists.

Glove Compartment Checklist

keeping Fit

Encourage students to go over the checklist in the feature with a parent and collect the necessary items to prepare their family drivers for an automotive breakdown.

MEETING STUDENT DIVERSITY

ATV SAFETY. All-terrain vehicles (ATVs) and snowmobiles have become very popular recreational vehicles. They are also very dangerous. As a result, safety training and licensing for operators under 16 years of age are required in many states.

Here are two other safety tips to stress to students who want to enjoy these recreational vehicles more safely. ATVs and snowmobiles should never be ridden in unfamiliar areas at night; wires, fences, and downed trees can all cause fatal accidents. Riders should always wear specially designed clothing and equipment, including helmets, visors, shoulder and chest pads, padded boots, special gloves, and for very rough terrain, kidney belts.

L1 Researching

If there is a motorcycle helmet law in your state, have students find out if injuries and deaths to cyclists have decreased since the law was put into effect.

L3 Writing

Have several students sit (at a safe distance) at busy intersections and observe motorists, cyclists, and pedestrians. Ask students to record examples of risk-taking behavior and then write a newspaper editorial on taking unnecessary risks.

L1 Discussing

Ask students about bike lanes in the areas around their school and/or their homes. Which major roads have bike lanes? What is the best way to use a bike lane? How should riding in a bike lane affect your adherence to the guidelines for safe cycling?

L1 Community Involvement

What special areas have been set aside for trail biking, for skateboarding, and/or for in-line skating in the community? Let students work together to compile a list with relevant information; encourage them to share this list with friends, family members, and neighbors.

L1 Discussing

What safety guidelines should be followed in order to avoid injury when riding on roller skates, skateboards, and in-line skates?

L2 Health Lab

Distribute *Health Lab 34* and have students answer the question, "Does Speed at Impact Make a Difference?"

hotlink

head injury For more information on head injuries and ways to reduce their risk, see Chapter 16, page 373.

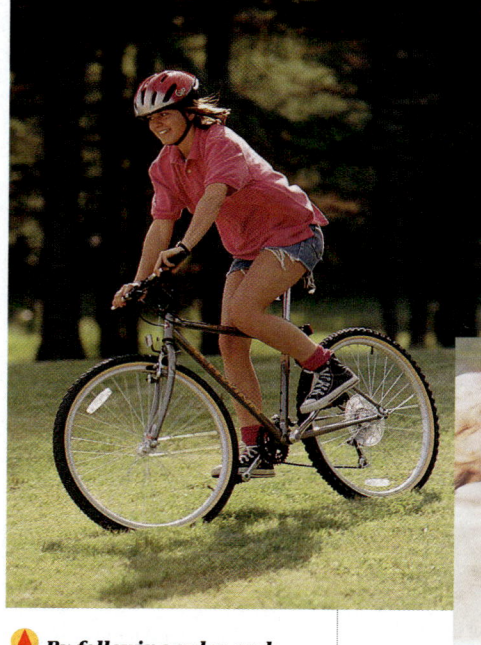

⬆ *By following rules and using proper safety equipment, you can avoid injury while enjoying the health benefits of bicycling or in-line skating.*

- being on the lookout for potential sudden hazards, such as a car door opening or pedestrians darting out from between parked cars.
- taking a motorcycle safety course, required in some states.

Bicycle Safety

Bicycles are a main form of transportation in many nations around the world, and their popularity in the United States has grown dramatically in recent years. Because bicycles use "human power" rather than motor power, they also represent a pleasant way to stay fit.

At the same time, like motorcycles and mopeds, bicycles are legitimate vehicles and need to be taken seriously. An estimated 53,000 bicycle injuries occur each year, some 750 of them fatal. The most common and potentially most serious mishap is a **head injury**, which can be as minor as a scalp wound or as serious as a traumatic brain injury. Four out of five collisions between bicycles and cars are caused by cyclists who disregard traffic rules. The most frequent mistake that cyclists make is riding on the wrong side of the road, against—rather than with—the flow of traffic.

Follow these guidelines for safe cycling:

- Ride on the right, keeping close to the side of the road. When riding with others, ride in a straight, single-file line.
- Always yield the right-of-way. You will not win against a car or truck.
- Watch for parked cars pulling into traffic and for car doors that swing open suddenly in your path.
- Obey the same rules as drivers, such as signaling before you turn and stopping for red lights and stop signs.

PERSONAL HEALTH

PERSONAL ACCIDENT CHAIN. Encourage students to examine the accident chain from a personal perspective. What situations occur often in their lives, especially those with the potential to lead up to an accident? Do students drive, swim, ski, rock climb? Are students prone to risk factors, such as careless or unsafe behaviors? Do they drink or use alcohol, leave safety restraints unfastened, leave objects on the floor or stairs, walk alone at night? Have students write entries in their private Health Journals, listing the situations and risk factors that are common in their lives. Suggest that they identify those risk factors within their control, and choose which they would consider changing.

- Except when signaling, keep both hands on the handlebars at all times.
- Wear a properly fitting hard-shell helmet.
- Make sure your bike has a bright headlight and a red rear light and reflector for night riding.
- Wear reflective, or at least light-colored, clothing when riding at dawn, dusk, after dark, or in the rain.

Skating Safety

Skateboards, roller skates, and in-line skates can be a lot of fun. They can also lead to disaster when precautions are not followed. When roller skating, skateboarding, or using in-line skates, heed the following:

- Wear protective equipment—wrist guards, elbow and knee pads, a hard-shell helmet, and light gloves.
- Watch for and slow down around pedestrians.
- Keep your speed under control.
- Do not hold anything in your hand, such as a portable radio. In the event of a fall, your natural reflex will be to save the item you are holding, rather than to protect your body.
- If you do begin to fall, try to curl up into a ball and roll, staying loose. Tensing up will increase your chances of injury.

LESSON 3 *Review*

Reviewing Facts and Vocabulary

1. What is vehicular safety?
2. List three safety tips for operators of each of the following: cars, motorcycles, and bicycles.

Thinking Critically

3. *Synthesizing.* Write a one-page editorial emphasizing the importance of wearing a helmet when riding a two-wheel vehicle or while skating.
4. *Evaluating.* Since the federal speed limit of 65 was abolished, many states have increased their speed limits to 70 or 75, and in a few states there is no daytime speed limit whatsoever. Do you feel this is a mistake? Support your views.

5. *Analyzing.* What does it mean to say that it is "better to be alive than right" when it comes to vehicular safety?

Applying Health Skills

6. *In Your Home.* Collect several newspaper articles about accidents in and around your community. Try to identify each of the links of the accident chain and ways the chain might have been broken.

LESSON 3   SAFETY ON WHEELS   **759**

ASSESS

EVALUATING THE LESSON

Assign and discuss the Lesson 3 Review; then administer, grade, and discuss the *Lesson 103 Quiz* in the TCR.

RETEACHING

- Divide the class into four groups, and assign each group one type of transportation on wheels. Ask each group to write a list of safety practices that should be followed when using that type of transportation.
- Ask students to complete *Reteaching Activity 103* in the TCR.
- Use *Transparency 52* to explore ways safety measures are portrayed in the media.

ENRICHMENT

Ask students to conduct a survey about seat-belt use. They should interview at least 10 to 20 adults and teenagers who drive. Have them design a brief questionnaire to determine patterns of seat-belt use and misconceptions about the role of seat belts in injury prevention.

CLOSE

Tell students that in this lesson they studied important safety practices to follow when using cars, motorcycles, bicycles, and skates. The practices most likely to prevent serious injury or death to teens are three safe-driving practices. They can be summed up as follows: Don't speed, never drink and drive, and always wear a seat belt.

Lesson 3 Review

Answers to Reviewing Facts and Vocabulary

1. Obeying the rules of the road, as well as exercising common sense and good judgment.
2. Any three tips from each of the lists in this lesson.

Answers to Thinking Critically

3. Editorials will vary.
4. Answers will vary.
5. Answers should reflect an understanding of the importance of safe, defensive driving (or bike or motorcycle riding).

Personal Safety

Personal Safety

FOCUS

LESSON OBJECTIVE

After studying this lesson, students should be able to

- demonstrate measures to help prevent, escape, and survive a violent personal attack.

MOTIVATOR

Write the following on the chalkboard for students to work on while attendance is being taken: *Make a list of places and/or situations that you would try to avoid because of the possibility of rape or other violent attack. If the place or situation was unavoidable, what else might you do to protect yourself from potential violence?*

INTRODUCING THE LESSON

Refer to the Motivator. Ask volunteers to share their responses with the class. Did students focus on weapons or martial arts for protection? If so, steer discussion to the inner tools of self-defense described in this lesson. Did students consider the possibility of date or acquaintance rape? If not, ask them specifically for ways to avoid it.

INTRODUCING HEALTH TERMS

- Have students find the legal definition of *rape* and then rewrite it in their own words. Does the definition apply equally to males and females?
- Ask students to complete Vocabulary Activity 34 and Chapter Study Guide 34 in the *Student Workbook*. ☞

Up until now, the focus of this chapter has been safety procedures that can minimize the risk of accidents and injury. Yet, in life there are "non-accident" situations that are every bit as serious and require the same preparedness and alert action. This lesson will explore such situations.

HEALTH TERMS

date rape
acquaintance rape

HEALTH CONCEPTS

- When safety sense is used, the likelihood of physical attack can be reduced.
- Rape and sexual assault are crimes of violence, not passion.

hotlink

violence For more information on violence in its many forms and ways to prevent it, see Chapter 14, page 324.

Physical Attack

Anyone can be a victim of physical **violence**. In fact, it is estimated that one out of three Americans will become the victim of a sexual assault or attempted attack sometime in his or her lifetime. Although this usually happens to females, males can also be victims. Teens who are involved with—or have friends who are involved with—gangs, guns, alcohol, or drugs are especially at risk.

In many instances, physical attack occurs in conjunction with some other crime, such as robbery. In other cases, the attack can be purely random and happen for no apparent reason. Such crimes, moreover, can take place anywhere, although there are well-defined circumstances under which they are more likely to occur. These include deserted streets, dark parking lots, and other isolated situations, particularly during nighttime hours.

Lesson 4 Resources

TEACHER'S CLASSROOM RESOURCES
☞ **Concept Map** Activity 104
☞ **Lesson 104 Quiz**
☞ **Lesson Plan 104**
☞ **Reteaching** Activity 104

STUDENT WORKBOOK
☞ **Applying Health Skills 104**
☞ **Chapter Study Guide 34**
☞ **Vocabulary** Activity 34

MULTIMEDIA
🔴 **ABCNews InterActive™ VHS/Videodisc,** *Violence Prevention*

Preventive Behaviors

Some suggestions for preventing and surviving physical violence are addressed in Chapter 14. Other measures include the following:

- Give up jewelry, shoes, a bike, or other personal property, if that is what the attacker is after. You are better off losing a possession, even one that at the time seems priceless, rather than risking personal injury.
- Avoid parts of town or places with a high incidence of known crime.
- Avoid walking alone at night, in wooded areas, or in dark alleys. If you must walk at night, walk under lights and by the curb. Avoid doorways.
- At night, have your car keys ready when you are going to your car. Before entering, check the back seat to make sure no one is inside your car. Lock all the doors.
- Park in well-lighted areas.
- Don't put your wallet or purse in an easy-to-grab place.
- Take down license plate numbers and descriptions of suspicious cars in your neighborhood and report them to the police.
- Stay alert to what is going on around you.
- Walk briskly; act assertively, as though you know where you are going and what you are doing.
- Be cautious with anyone who gives you undue attention.
- Avoid placing yourself in isolated, risky situations.
- Don't hitchhike or give rides to hitchhikers.
- Ask anyone giving you a ride to wait until you have safely entered where you're going.
- Get on and off buses in well-lit areas.

SOME INNER TOOLS OF SELF-DEFENSE

When people talk about self-defense, they often mean learning physical strategies for stopping attacks. They imagine quick kicks and tricky moves. However, mental or emotional strategies are also important. You may already have the following valuable self-defense tools within you.

- **Self-esteem.** This includes the confidence you have in yourself. People with high self-esteem are not likely to be bullied or chosen as easy targets, particularly by people who know them.
- **Assertiveness.** Assertiveness is bold and confident behavior. **Assertive** people speak with definite conviction, leaving no doubt as to their feelings or intentions. Many attackers want easy victims they can overpower quickly. Phrases such as "Leave me alone" or "I'm not going with you" may throw an attacker off guard.

⚠ *How are these teens demonstrating safe behavior while walking at night?*

h⊙tlink

assertive For more information on an assertive posture and how to use assertiveness in high-pressure situations, see Chapter 13, page 308.

TEACH

L1 Discussing

What are some of the factors behind the recent dramatic rise in violent crimes that affect teens?

L1 Class Activity

Ask students to make a list on the chalkboard of inner self-defense tools that will help them avoid being violently attacked. Have them explain each one.

LEP Class Activity

Ask students to demonstrate how they can use body language as a self-defense tactic.

L1 Explaining

Explain to students why assertive, self-assured behavior is a good strategy for self-defense.

L1 Discussing

What are several common sense measures you should practice in order to avoid being trapped in your car by an attacker?

L1 Explaining

Explain the best way to fight back if you are under attack. Consider a variety of situations.

HEALTH LITERACY

RESPONSIBLE/PRODUCTIVE CITIZEN.
Suggest that students find out if they have neighborhood crime prevention programs. If not, ask them to obtain literature from law enforcement offices about these programs and share it with family and neighbors. If the community law enforcement agency can send officers to homes to speak about neighborhood crime prevention, suggest that students organize meetings in their neighborhoods, get to know their neighbors, and learn their habits. For example, do delivery people regularly come and go? Do neighbors have gardeners, housekeepers, or grown children who may enter when they are not home? Suggest that they exchange phone numbers with neighbors and write down the license plate numbers of each other's cars.

L3 Self-Esteem

Pose this question to students: How is a self-protective attitude related to self-esteem? Give examples. How would you describe the level of self-esteem of a person who is continually a victim or target of violence?

L2 Discussing

What is sexual harassment? Ask students to give examples of comments and behaviors which they consider to be sexually harassing. Is there disagreement among class members? Why?

L1 Cooperative Learning

Ask students to identify behaviors and situations they should avoid to reduce the risk of rape.

L2 Discussing

What is "date rape" or "acquaintance rape"? How common is it? Does it differ from rape by a stranger? Is it more or less devastating? Why?

L2 Explaining

Explain how and why rape victims are often made to feel guilty or ashamed of what has happened to them. Elaborate on how this leads to underreporting of rapes and fewer convictions of rapists.

VIOLENCE PREVENTION (Side 1)

Chapter 6: Respecting Friends

Frames 17785-22839

Chapter 8: Preventing Crime

Frames 27033-32591

hotlink

rape For more information on rape and how to avoid becoming a victim, see Chapter 14, page 331.

▼ *Taking a class in self-defense can improve your chances of withstanding an attack.*

ACTIVITY *Name four mental and emotional self-defense tools.*

- **Body language.** Your body language can project your thoughts in a forceful way. Making direct eye contact, using a strong voice, keeping your body erect and chin held high, and using a deliberate stride can send the message that you are in charge of your safety.

- **A self-protective attitude.** Realize that you are worthy and have a right to be treated with respect and to be safe. Don't be afraid of insulting someone by walking away or by being overly cautious.

Sexual Assault and Rape

As noted in Chapter 14, some physical attacks have a sexual component. These crimes, sexual assault and **rape**, are crimes of violence, not passion. The attacker is motivated not by sexual desire but by the prospect of forcing another person to do something he or she doesn't want to do.

Often, victims of rape know their attacker. *When rape occurs between two people who are dating,* it is called **date rape. Acquaintance rape** is *rape by someone who is known casually by the victim or someone thought to be a friend.* Though these crimes are technically different, for the victim the consequences are equally devastating. These include a feeling of having been violated, which can leave deep emotional scars.

Preventive Behaviors

Sexual assault and rape can happen anywhere. They can even happen in the confines of a house—your own or someone else's. Among the measures you can take to prevent becoming a victim are the following:

- Have sexual limits and communicate them clearly.
- Do not drink or use drugs or date anyone who does.
- Do not go out alone or ride in a car with a person you do not know well.
- Do not put others' feelings ahead of your own safety.
- Take classes in karate or other forms of self-defense.
- Never open your door to anyone you do not know or trust.
- Use locks on doors and windows.
- Do not let strangers use your phone.
- Do not get into an elevator alone with a stranger.
- Do not hitchhike or pick up hitchhikers.
- Do not park your car, walk, or jog in remote areas.
- If you are being followed, hurry to a place where there are other people, such as to a store.
- If your car is rammed from behind or breaks down, stay in your car with the doors locked and flasher lights on.

762 CHAPTER 34 YOUR SAFETY AND WELL-BEING

MORE ABOUT . . . . .

WHAT TO DO IF ATTACKED. Escape if you can. Negotiate if possible. Fight only if you have no choice. These are the key rules for dealing with an attacker. Precisely what you do depends on your strength, confidence, and willingness to fight back, and your assessment of the assailant. An assailant who is drunk or using other drugs acts impulsively, so you can't predict what will happen if you try to defend yourself. In some cases, resisting violently may increase your chances of being killed. If you do fight, never give a warning. Strike as swiftly and as hard as you can and be ready to repeat the blow, and always scream for help as you fight.

Escaping and Surviving an Attack

If you become the target of a sexual attack, try to run for help. If you cannot run, decide on another course of action. Scream or yell "Fire!" If possible, physically disable or stun the person in some way. Watch for a moment when the attacker may be caught off guard so you can escape. Use your wits. Try different approaches. Don't assume you can't get away. You have a greater chance of escaping than you might think. If all else fails, you may have to submit in order to survive.

Help for Rape Victims

If you or someone you know is raped, get help from your family or a friend after an attack and get it quickly. *Call law enforcement agents immediately.* Get medical help right away. You should undergo medical tests for pregnancy, **STDs**, and **HIV** infection.

Call a rape crisis center and get counseling or join a support group. You will need help to recover from the emotional shock of being raped. Be patient. It takes time to recover from the trauma of an attack. Remember that any person who becomes a victim of rape is the *victim,* not the cause, and has no reason to be ashamed.

hot link

STDs For more information on STDs and their treatment, see Chapter 29, page 642.

HIV For more information on HIV, the virus that causes AIDS, see Chapter 30, page 656.

LESSON 4 *Review*

Reviewing Facts and Vocabulary

1. What are three ways of reducing your chances of becoming a victim of physical attack?
2. Explain the similarities and differences between date rape and acquaintance rape.

Thinking Critically

3. *Synthesizing.* Most incidences of rape are not reported. Why do you think this is so?
4. *Analyzing.* What steps can teens in particular take to prevent becoming victims of attack, sexual or otherwise?
5. *Synthesizing.* Summarize the major considerations when it comes to the decision of resisting or not resisting in the case of an assault.

6. *Evaluating.* People make a "big deal" out of sexual harassment. It really becomes an issue only when someone wants to "get back" at an individual. Is this an accurate statement? Explain.

Applying Health Skills

7. *In Your Home.* Read about crime statistics in your community. Create a public service announcement offering specific ways of reducing the incidence of physical attack (e.g., by cleaning up certain neighborhoods). If possible, broadcast the announcement over a local radio station.

ASSESS

EVALUATING THE LESSON

Assign and discuss the Lesson 4 Review; then administer, grade, and discuss the *Lesson 104 Quiz* in the TCR. 🗀

RETEACHING

- Have students apply what they learned in this lesson by describing hypothetical violent situations. For each situation, ask students to discuss ways the situation could have been avoided and, if it could not be avoided, how the situation could best be handled.
- Ask students to complete *Reteaching Activity 104* in the TCR. 🗀

ENRICHMENT

Tell students to read a book or series of articles about body language and then present what they learned. They should demonstrate what various facial expressions, gestures, postures, and movements communicate in different cultures.

CLOSE

Review with students ways to reduce their risk of being victims of violence, including rape.

Lesson 4 Review

Answers to Reviewing Facts and Vocabulary

1. Refer to the list of Preventive Behaviors on page 761.
2. Answers should reflect an understanding of the fact that the victim in a date rape is dating the attacker, and the victim in an acquaintance rape knows the attacker casually or thinks of the attacker as a friend.

Answers to Thinking Critically

3. Answers will vary.
4. Answers should reflect an understanding of the importance of avoiding risk behaviors and risky situations. See list on page 762.
5. Summaries will vary.
6. Answers will vary.

Health **Skills** Activities

Health Skills Activities

ACTIVITY 1
HEALTH SKILLS
Self Management

➤ **National Standards**
This activity meets these National Health Standards: 3.1; 3.5.

Teach

- Review with the class conditions that prevail during a real fire emergency that impedes movement. Focus on smoke, which obscures visibility, and heat, which can block certain paths.
- Work with students at making sure their plans allow for all possible obstacles, including large, immovable pieces of furniture.
- Set aside part of another class period for students to share experiences, discussing what they and family members learned.

ACTIVITY 2
HEALTH SKILLS
Self Management, Health Advocacy

➤ **National Standards**
This activity meets these National Health Standards: 3.6 7.4; 7.6.

Teach

- Review with students the information covered on pages 760-763 of their texts. Make sure they understand the emotional and physical impact of these types of attacks, as well as avoidance techniques and self-defense strategies.
- Suggest to students the possibility of doing fictionalized scenarios illustrating positive safety techniques, such as choosing well-lighted streets to travel on at night and having a driver wait until you are safely inside your home before pulling away.

Activity 1 — In Case of Fire

Does your family have a fire escape plan in place in case of an emergency? If they do not, here is your chance to help.

Directions

1. On a computer or working freehand, create a "blueprint" of your family home. Show stairways, and note windows and doors by drawing short breaks, or spaces, in walls.
2. Draw red arrows to indicate a main escape route and a secondary route (in case the main one is blocked) from every room.
3. Include a meeting spot outside the home where all family members are to gather.
4. Share your escape route with all members of your family at a family meeting. Rehearse the main and secondary routes.

Self-Assessment

✓ House "blueprint" was neat and easy to read with each room clearly labeled.
✓ Both escape routes were clearly marked and easy to use in an emergency situation.

Time
50 minutes
Materials
paper, pen, colored markers, computer with printer (optional)

Activity 2 — Personal Safety Video

Anyone can become a victim of physical violence. However, there are some preventive measures you can take to increase your personal safety. You and classmates will show these in an instructional video.

Directions

1. Using the information in your text, create a list of topics for a "Personal Safety Instructional Video." Among the topics to be explored are how to prevent and survive physical violence, tools of self-defense, reducing the risk of sexual assault, and escaping and surviving a sexual attack.
2. Group members are to convert their findings into a script detailing the kinds of measures a person can take to increase his or her chances of safety.
3. Record your video to be shared with other classes.

Self-Assessment

✓ Included all the information requested.
✓ Video was clear, engaging, and targeted to a teen audience.

Time
50 minutes
Materials
library or Internet health resources, paper, pen or pencil, video camera

---

ASSESSMENT SCORING

Using a four-level rubric, the student has achieved a 4 if:

ACTIVITY 1
✔ Student's blueprint was neat and easy to read.
✔ Student was thorough in labeling rooms in the home and noting all and any obstacles.
✔ Student clearly marked escape routes to use in an emergency situation.
✔ Student returned a signed letter affirming completion of the activity with family members.

ACTIVITY 2
✔ Student demonstrated an understanding of emotional and physical impact of attacks.
✔ Student included all the information requested.
✔ Student video was clear, engaging, and targeted to a teen audience.
✔ Student shared health message with other teens and/or members of the community.

Cell Phone Safety Survey

An estimated 3 percent of American drivers are talking on handheld cell phones at any given time, according to the first-of-its-kind survey conducted by the federal government.

The National Highway Traffic Safety Administration (NHTSA) found that about a half-million drivers are holding a phone to their ears at any given time.

The survey found that rates of use can double during times outside rush hour. The survey covered drivers of all types of passenger vehicles, including cars, vans, sport-utility vehicles, and pickups.

While the report looked at cell phone use across the country, it did not try to assess how cell phones contribute to car crashes. However, other NHTSA data suggests cell phones contribute to approximately 20 to 30 percent of all crashes.

Data collected in the survey found:
- Drivers of vans and SUVs used their cell phones the most.
- Use by drivers was highest during times outside rush hour.
- Women use their cell phones more then men. In the case of SUV drivers it was almost twice as high.
- Senior citizens use cell phones less than any other age group.
- Cell phones are used more during the week than on weekends.

The study is based on data collected nationwide by researchers who observed more than 12,000 vehicles between 8 a.m. and 6 p.m. during October and November.

Read This

No Hands? Still Risky

Some drivers have shifted to using "hands free" cell phones. They hope that these speaker phones will allow them to drive and talk safely.

Unfortunately, a new study suggests that driving with a hands-free cell phone is just as dangerous as a hand-held phone. The National Safety Council found that having any type of phone conversation slows down a driver's responses. Slower responses are directly linked to poor driving and traffic collisions.

Source: CNN.com

Think About It

1. How is driving while talking on a cell phone dangerous?
2. What is being done to curb this danger?

CNN HEALTH NEWS **765**

MORE ABOUT . . . . .

RELIABLE SOURCES. The National Highway Traffic Safety Administration (NHTSA) is a government agency dedicated to "reducing deaths, injuries and economic losses resulting from motor vehicle crashes." In addition to funding crucial research on driver behavior and traffic safety, the organization establishes and enforces safety standards for motor vehicles and equipment.

The NHTSA also investigates safety defects, sets and enforces fuel economy standards, and promotes the use of safe driving equipment, including seat belts, air bags, air child safety seats. The agency provides consumer information through publications, and their Web site, found in Web Links at **health.glencoe.com.**

CHAPTER **34** *Review*

CHECKING COMPREHENSION

- Assign and discuss the chapter review.
- Use the MindJogger Videoquiz to review the chapter.

CHAPTER 34 REVIEW ANSWERS

Using Health Terms

1. accident chain
2. fire extinguisher
3. electrocution
4. situation
5. smoke detector
6. tornado
7. Occupational Safety and Health Administration (OSHA)
8. hurricane
9. blizzard
10. road rage
11. vehicular safety
12. acquaintance rape
13. date rape

Recalling the Facts

1. Stay low to the floor.
2. Keep stairways well lighted, in good repair, equipped with sturdy handrails and nonskid stair strips, and free of clutter.
3. Keep household products in a locked cabinet or out of the reach of children. Never place any medicine in an unlabeled vial or a container other than the one in which it was originally packaged. Periodically check the medicine cabinet and discard any medicine that is past its expiration date.
4. To avoid drowning.
5. Jumping into shallow water.
6. Make sure that workers are adequately trained and made aware of potential hazards and safety rules.
7. Arrive at work well rested and alert; learn the proper use of machinery and other equipment; follow established safety measures, including the wearing of protective gear.

Using Health Terms

On a separate sheet of paper, write the term that best matches each definition below.

LESSON 1

1. A recurring pattern that is present in all mishaps.
2. A portable device that puts out small fires by ejecting fire-extinguishing chemicals.
3. Death resulting from passage through the body of a high-voltage current.
4. The circumstance or event leading up to an accident.
5. An alarm that is triggered by the presence of smoke.

LESSON 2

6. A powerful, twisting windstorm.
7. A federal agency responsible for promoting safe and healthful conditions in the workplace.

8. A powerful rainstorm, characterized by driving winds.
9. A snowstorm with winds of 35 miles per hour (56 km per hour) or greater.

LESSON 3

10. When intense anger and driving mix.
11. Obeying the rules of the road, as well as exercising common sense and good judgment.

LESSON 4

12. Rape by someone who is known casually by the victim or someone thought to be a friend.
13. When rape occurs between two people who are dating.

Recalling the Facts

Using complete sentences, answer the following questions.

LESSON 1

1. What is a good way to prevent smoke inhalation during a fire?
2. What can be done to reduce the number of falls that occur on stairways?
3. How should poisonous products in the home be stored to minimize their dangers?

LESSON 2

4. Why should everyone learn to swim?
5. What is a major cause of spinal injuries that can result in paralysis?
6. How can employers minimize the risk of work-related accidents?
7. How can employees minimize the risk of work-related accidents?

LESSON 3

8. What is the leading cause of death among people between 15 and 20?
9. How can bike riders minimize the risk of injury in case of an accident?
10. What five pieces of protective equipment should people wear when roller skating or skateboarding?
11. What should you do if you fall while using in-line skates?

LESSON 4

12. Name four inner self-defense tools you can use to help protect yourself from an attack.
13. Give examples of body language that can help protect someone from harm.
14. What measures can you take to help prevent rape?

8. Automobile accidents.
9. Wear a properly fitting hard-shell helmet.
10. Wrist guards, elbow pads, knee pads, a hard-shell helmet, and light gloves.
11. Try to curl up into a ball and roll, staying loose.

12. Self-esteem, assertiveness, body language, a self-protective attitude.
13. Making direct eye contact, keeping the body erect and chin held high, and walking with a deliberate stride.
14. Refer to the list of Preventive Behaviors on page 762.

Thinking Critically

LESSON 1

1. *Analyzing.* What parts of the accident chain are the easiest to break?

2. *Synthesizing.* Name three flammable liquids that might be used in or around a home. Tell what preventive behaviors should be taken in using each.

3. *Synthesizing.* What would you include in a home fire escape plan? Why?

LESSON 2

4. *Evaluating.* How would you measure the worth of wearing safety goggles on the job?

5. *Synthesizing.* Explain the importance of planning for a natural disaster.

LESSON 3

6. *Evaluating.* Some states have laws requiring a person to use a seat belt while driving or riding in a car and to wear a helmet while operating a motorcycle. Explain your opinion of such laws.

LESSON 4

7. *Evaluating.* List, in order, the five most important things you think a person should do after a rape. Why did you rate each one as you did?

Making the Connection

1. *Math.* Conduct a survey in your school and in your community to find out the following: how many homes have smoke detectors, how many people periodically test the battery to make sure it is in proper working order, and how many people have disengaged the battery. Compute the percentages and share your findings with the class.

2. *Social Studies.* Do research to find out how so-called push-out doors—the variety with bar handles found in gyms, schools, theaters, and public buildings—first came to be used. If possible, learn why these doors were originally called "panic doors." Share your findings in a brief report.

BEYOND THE CLASSROOM

PARENTAL INVOLVEMENT Speak with parents or other adults in your home about safety precautions that are necessary at their jobs. Ask them what they are required to do regarding safety in the workplace.

COMMUNITY INVOLVEMENT Find the telephone numbers for the fire department, the police department, and the poison control center in your community. Post these and other emergency numbers in your home by the phone. Interview a person from each of these agencies to find out what action they take when they receive a call.

SCHOOL-TO-CAREER
Technology. Learn how technology is used in the field of accident prevention and quick response time to accidents. Investigate the use of computers and other high technology to enable rescuers to arrive on the scene more quickly than ever in response to 911 calls. Write a report on your findings.

Thinking Critically

1. The risk factor and (in some cases) the situation.
2. Answers will vary.
3. Answers will vary.
4. Answers should reflect an understanding of the fact that an injury to the eyes could disable a worker for life.
5. Answers will vary.
6. Opinions will vary.
7. Ratings will vary.

Making the Connection

1. Answers will vary.
2. Reports will vary.

Evaluate

- Use the reproducible *Chapter 34 Test* in the TCR, or construct your own using the Testmaker software.
- Use *Performance Assessment Activity 34* in the TCR.

Enrichment

Ask students to complete *Cross-Curriculum Activity 34* in the TCR.

Beyond the Classroom

Keep students involved in the community, and encourage parent participation by assigning the activities on this page for students to work on outside of class.

Providing First Aid and Handling Emergencies

	FEATURES	CLASSROOM RESOURCES
LESSON 1 **Administering First Aid** *pages 770–774*		🖜 Concept Map Activity 105 🖜 Lesson 105 Quiz 🖜 Lesson Plan 105 🖜 Reteaching Activity 105
LESSON 2 **Poisonings** *pages 775–778*	**Building Health Skills** "Goal Setting: Planning a Safe Home Environment," *page 776*	🖜 Concept Map Activity 106 🖜 Enrichment Activity 35 🖜 Lesson 106 Quiz 🖜 Lesson Plan 106 🖜 Reteaching Activity 106
LESSON 3 **First Aid for Choking, Rescue Breathing, and CPR** *pages 779–784*		🖜 Concept Map Activity 107 🖜 Lesson 107 Quiz 🖜 Lesson Plan 107 🖜 Reteaching Activity 107
LESSON 4 **More Common Emergencies** *pages 785–789*	**Making Responsible Decisions** "Acting in an Emergency," *page 787*	🖜 Concept Map Activity 108 🖜 Cooperative Learning Activity 35 🖜 Decision-Making Activity 35 🖜 Health Lab 35 🖜 Lesson 108 Quiz 🖜 Lesson Plan 108 🖜 Reteaching Activity 108 🝙 Transparency 53

Chapter Resources

ACTIVITIES

- Cross-Curriculum Activity 35
- Health Lab 35
- Health Skills Activities 35
- Parent Letter and Activity 35

ASSESSMENT

- Chapter 35 Test
- Performance Assessment Activity 35
- Testmaker Software

STUDENT ACTIVITIES WORKBOOK

- Applying Health Skills 105–108
- Study Guide 35
- Vocabulary Activity 35

STUDENT DIVERSITY STRATEGIES

- Audiocassette Program (English)
- Audiocassette Program (Spanish)
- Spanish Parent Letters and Activities
- Spanish Summaries, Quizzes, and Activities

MULTIMEDIA COMPONENTS

- English Audiocassette Program
- Spanish Audiocassette Program
- MindJogger Videodisc and VHS program

National Health Education Standards

One of the main goals of the National Health Education Standards is to move students toward "health literacy." Health literacy is the capacity of individuals to obtain, interpret, and understand basic health information and services and the competence to use such information and services in ways which promote health. The health standards were developed by applying the characteristics of a well-educated, literate person within the context of health. The health literate person is:
- a critical thinker and problem solver • a self-directed learner
- a responsible, productive citizen • an effective communicator

Listed below are the Health Education Standards Performance Indicators addressed in each lesson of this chapter.

Lesson	Health Standards Performance Indicators
1	2.6, 3.4, 3.5, 3.6
2	2.4, 2.6, 3.5, 3.6
3	2.4, 2.6, 3.3, 3.4
4	2.6, 3.5, 3.6, 6.1

ONLINE RESOURCES

HEALTH Online

For a fresh approach to health topics and an in-depth look at health issues, use these online resources found under Teacher Resources at **health.glencoe.com**.

- **BLOCK SCHEDULE LESSON PLANS** Reinforce health concepts with outside readings selected especially for students. Each reading is accompanied by a lesson plan and activities to enhance
  - Reading Skills
  - Cross Curriculum
  - Media Literacy

- **TECHNOLOGY PROJECTS** Instructions and suggestions on how to use computer, Internet, and software with health lessons.

- **HEALTH UPDATES** Timely topics in health news, including late-breaking medical advances and updates on teen risk behaviors.

Out of Time?

If time does not permit teaching this chapter, you may use these features: Building Health Skills on page 776 and Making Responsible Decisions on page 787.

BLOCK SCHEDULING

Block scheduling provides extended time for hands-on projects and activities. Use the following activity to engage students, provide further depth, and vary your instructional techniques:
- Health Skills Activity (60–90 minutes)   **pg. 790**

Providing First Aid and Handling Emergencies

CHAPTER OVERVIEW

Chapter 35 presents first aid techniques to use during common medical emergencies.

LESSON 1 First aid is the immediate, temporary care given to a person who has become sick or who has been injured. It continues until a proper medical authority arrives.

LESSON 2 Between 1 and 2 million poisonings occur every year. Poison may enter the body through swallowing, through insect or animal bites, and even through touching certain substances. Each means of poisoning has specific guidelines for administering first aid.

LESSON 3 The techniques for responding to a person who is choking or who has stopped breathing differ slightly, depending on the age of the victim. Cardiopulmonary resuscitation (CPR) can be administered to victims of cardiovascular failure. Adjustments must be made when administering the technique to young children.

LESSON 4 First aid for minor mishaps, such as fractures, sprains, animal bites, bee stings, fainting, objects in the eye, burns, nosebleeds, and temperature- or weather-related emergencies, is discussed in this lesson.

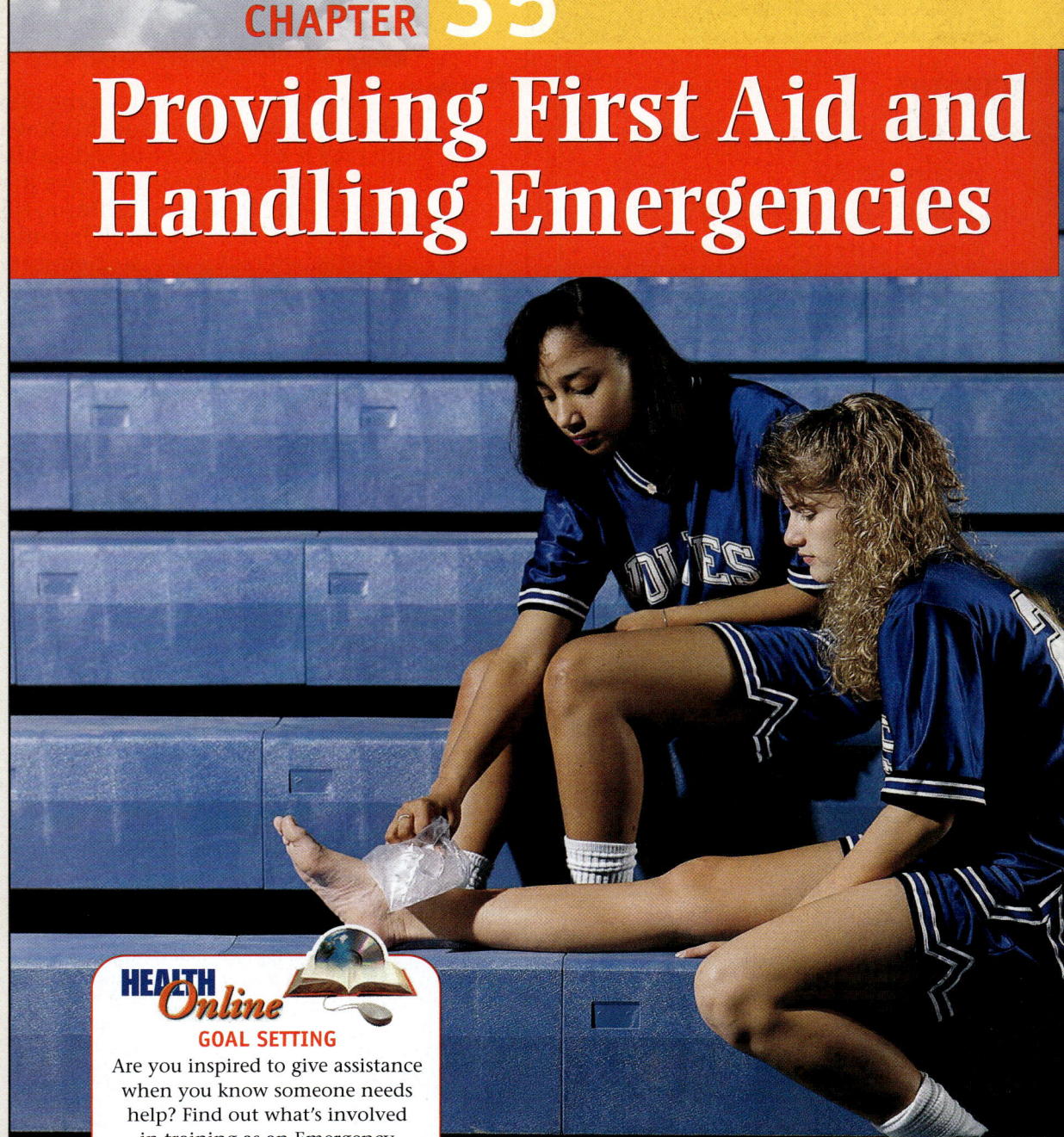

CHAPTER 35

Providing First Aid and Handling Emergencies

HEALTH Online

GOAL SETTING

Are you inspired to give assistance when you know someone needs help? Find out what's involved in training as an Emergency Medical Technician in the Career Corner at **health.glencoe.com**.

Hands-On Health

TEACHING STRATEGY

Reinforcing and Reviewing Bring your health classroom to life with interactive teaching strategies and classroom management techniques that keep your students interested and involved. The unique *Hands-On Health: Creative Teaching Strategies* booklet that accompanies the *Glencoe Health* program offers fun, motivating activities.

The following Classroom Management Ideas can be used to reinforce chapter concepts:

- Beach Ball
- Trivia Questions
- Paper Exchange
- Mental Outburst

> **The best place to find a helping hand is at the end of your own arm.**
>
> —SWEDISH PROVERB

Quick Write Think of a time when you were hurt and someone came to your aid or when you helped someone else. Write about the experience in a paragraph. Include the words *caring, responsibility,* and *safety* in your paragraph.

Personal Health Inventory

Self-Inventory Write the numbers 1–10 on a sheet of paper. Read each statement below and respond by writing *yes, no,* or *sometimes* for each item. Write a *yes* only for items that you practice regularly. Save your responses.

1	I make a point of knowing the names of all my family's health care professionals.
2	I keep a list of emergency phone numbers near a telephone in my home.
3	I can help someone who has swallowed poison.
4	I take small bites of food when eating and chew each bite slowly before swallowing.
5	I know what action to take to help victims of choking.
6	I am trained in rescue breathing for adults and children.
7	I know how to administer CPR.
8	I know what steps to take to stop heavy bleeding.
9	I am able to tell the difference between minor and serious burns and can treat each kind.
10	I know how to help with common emergencies such as nosebleed, fainting, heat cramps, or frostbite.

Follow-up After completing the chapter, retake this self-inventory. Pick two items that you need to work on and set a goal to improve your health behaviors.

CHAPTER 35 PROVIDING FIRST AID AND HANDLING EMERGENCIES **769**

INTRODUCING THE CHAPTER

Personal Health Inventory

Let students read and discuss the statements in this Self-Inventory, and ask: What first-aid or emergency-related behaviors are identified here? How can familiarity with these procedures help you protect your own health and the health of others? After students have shared their ideas, let them record their inventory responses in their private Health Journals. Have them add the title "First Aid and Emergencies," and remind students that they will consider this inventory again at the end of the chapter.

- Remind students that accident prevention is our primary concern, but when an accident does happen, we need to be prepared to reduce unnecessary suffering and to prevent further damage to the people involved. Tell students that this chapter will help them learn to administer first aid for common emergencies. As they learn what to do in an emergency, they should also think in terms of how the injury could have been prevented.
- Have students read the proverb and discuss its meaning. Ask them to create a paragraph for the Quick Write. Encourage students to take a few minutes to think about what they wrote in their paragraphs and how being prepared for emergency situations should be an important health goal for themselves and for those they care about.
- Distribute Parent Letter 35 in the *Parent Letters and Activities* booklet. ☞

TECHNOLOGY OPTIONS

MINDJOGGER

VIDEOQUIZ

To preview or review chapter content, you may wish to use the *MindJogger Videoquiz* that accompanies Chapter 35. ●

FOCUS

LESSON OBJECTIVES

After studying this lesson, students should be able to

- define *first aid*.
- identify the priorities in responding to an emergency.
- differentiate between types of wounds and know the first-aid treatment for each one.
- describe shock and its treatment.

MOTIVATOR

Write the following on the chalkboard for students to work on while attendance is being taken: *Write your own definition of first aid.*

INTRODUCING THE LESSON

Introduce the lesson by reminding students of the responsibility that they take when they administer first aid. Emphasize the fact that they must know what they are doing, or they risk doing more harm than good. Clarify the text definition of *first aid* by having students share their own definitions from the Motivator. Place emphasis on the fact that first aid takes place until a proper medical authority arrives—it does not take the place of medical treatment. Tell students that this lesson explains the basic rules of first aid.

INTRODUCING HEALTH TERMS

- Have students explain the difference between *shock* and *electrical shock*.
- Ask students to complete Vocabulary Activity 35 and Chapter Study Guide 35 in the *Student Workbook.*

LESSON 1

Administering First Aid

Imagine you happened upon the scene of a traffic accident in which people had been hurt. Suppose you were on a bus and someone fainted. Would you know what to do in either of these emergency situations? In this chapter, you will learn about responses to accidents and emergencies that could save a life.

HEALTH TERMS

first aid
poison
pressure point
shock

HEALTH CONCEPTS

- Actions taken in the first minutes of an emergency can make the difference between life and death.
- The most important considerations in treating open wounds are stopping the bleeding and seeking help.

First Aid

First aid is *the immediate, temporary care given to a person who has become sick or who has been injured.* First aid is administered in the seconds and minutes following an accident or a person's becoming sick. Administering first aid until a proper medical authority arrives on the scene can mean the difference between life and death.

Priorities in an Emergency

The first five minutes of an emergency situation are the most critical. During this crucial time, it is important to remain calm and to keep these six priorities in mind:

Lesson 1 Resources

TEACHER'S CLASSROOM RESOURCES
- **Concept Map** Activity 105
- **Lesson 105 Quiz**
- **Lesson Plan 105**
- **Parent Letter and Activities 35**
- **Reteaching** Activity 105

STUDENT WORKBOOK
- **Applying Health Skills 105**
- **Chapter Study Guide 35**
- **Vocabulary** Activity 35

1. **Check the immediate surroundings for possible dangers.** Move the victim only if his or her life is threatened. Some life-threatening conditions include water deep enough for drowning, a car that might catch on fire, or a room filled with smoke or poisonous fumes.

2. **Check to see if the victim is conscious.** If not, call for an ambulance at once.

3. **Check breathing.** Be sure the victim has an open airway. If he or she does not, attempt to clear the airway. Then administer rescue breathing if necessary. More on this lifesaving technique is presented in Lesson 3.

4. **Control severe bleeding.** If blood is bright red and spurting, an artery has been damaged. You can control the bleeding by applying direct pressure to the wound. Use gloves or other protective barrier to prevent the spread of infectious diseases.

5. **Check the victim for poisoning.** A poison is *any substance— solid, liquid, or gas—that causes injury, illness, or death when introduced into the body.* Treatment for poisoning is detailed in the next lesson.

6. **Send for medical help.** Emergency Medical Services (EMS) can be summoned in most areas by dialing either 911 or 0. Learn the numbers for EMS in your area.

Secondary Emergency Measures

Once you have taken steps to ensure the victim's safety and have administered life support procedures, you should attend to the following secondary measures:

- Learn as much as you can about what happened, and devise a plan of action.
- Look after the victim's continued safety and comfort. Keep the victim still and in the position most suited to his or her injury or condition.
- Make sure the victim maintains normal body temperature. Provide blankets or a coat for warmth, or provide shade for cooling protection from the hot sun.
- Loosen tight or binding clothing. Take care not to jar the victim's neck or spine.

As you work, keep reassuring the victim. Part of your job is to keep him or her calm. Above all else, know your own limits. Do not try to do more than you have been trained to do.

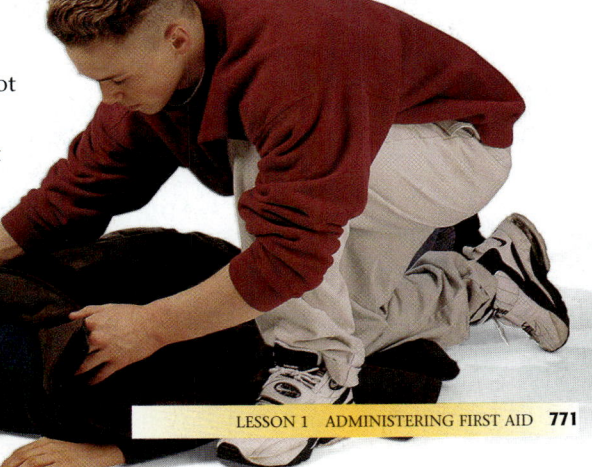

LESSON 1   ADMINISTERING FIRST AID   **771**

---

keeping Fit

Read My Wrist!

Another important procedure when treating an accident victim is to look for a piece of emergency medical identification on or near the victim. He or she may have a bracelet, necklace, or card carried in a wallet or purse advising of a medical condition that demands special attention.

People with diabetes or heart conditions and those subject to seizures or severe allergic reactions are among those who wear or carry emergency medical identification. The tag or card gives vital information to those who might be called upon to give the wearer first aid.

Dialing 911 will summon emergency help in most areas. **ACTIVITY** *Make a list of situations for which it would be appropriate to call 911. Also, make a list of those situations that require first aid but do not require that you call 911.*

TEACH

L1 Explaining

Bring a copy of the Good Samaritan Law for first aid, if your state has such a law. Explain to the class the requirements of this law, which are to protect ordinary citizens who render aid to victims in need of assistance. This law *does not* require first-aid treatment to be administered if the person is unable to provide adequate treatment. Some states require that permission from the victim be given prior to administering first aid. This law *does* require that the person stay with the victim, call for help, or render basic first aid if possible. It also protects the citizen from being sued for administering basic first aid.

Read My Wrist!

keeping Fit

Explain that emergency medical information may not be helpful to nonprofessional rescuers, but that pointing out any emergency medical identification to trained personnel as soon as they are notified or arrive could help save the victim's life.

L1 Discussing

Guide students in talking about accident situations in which the victim must be moved, such as fire, fallen wires, or nearby explosives. Then have them discuss when it would be unsafe to move the victim. *(broken bones, spinal injury)*

SCHOOL-TO-CAREER

EMERGENCY MEDICAL TECHNICIAN. Ambulance drivers must be certified as emergency medical technicians. They must take a comprehensive course in emergency care and pass an examination. Besides first aid and CPR, emergency medical technicians are allowed to begin such basic treatment as administering oxygen. Encourage interested students to investigate how to become an emergency medical technician. What requirements must be met to qualify for emergency medical technician training? Where does training take place? What employment opportunities exist? What does an emergency medical technician earn? Suggest that students write an employment ad for an emergency medical technician, specifying requirements, salary, and duties.

L1 Demonstration

Invite a school nurse to visit the class to help you demonstrate basic first aid and treatment of wounds.

L1 Discussing

Ask the class to discuss what might be used to apply pressure on a wound if a clean cloth is not available. If the cloth becomes soaked with blood, what procedure do you use to keep applying direct pressure to the wound?

L1 Discussing

Which wounds are likely to produce severe bleeding? *(Cut or avulsion. Explain that facial injuries may not be serious, but do sometimes bleed very heavily.)*

L2 Researching

Have students do library research to find out about the effects of blood loss on the body. Ask them to share their findings with the class.

L1 Discussing

Immediately following an accident, bystanders and onlookers often congregate around the injured people. Discuss how onlookers can help or hinder first-aid efforts. Should the person giving first aid rely on his or her own judgment or follow the advice of people at the scene? Explain that it is important that the person administering first aid always point to one person in the crowd to call for squads or ambulances. Often individuals assume that someone else will go, thus delaying the arrival of help.

CHARACTER IN ACTION

Proper Use of Emergency Services

Have you ever needed to call for an ambulance or paramedic? If you have, you know how important time and availability can be. One way to show your **concern for others** is to make sure that you use emergency services properly and only when truly necessary. For example, you can ensure that emergency services are there for people who need them by going to the emergency room *only* for serious ailments.

Character Check Brainstorm a *Do and Don't List* for the proper use of emergency services. Ask students to give examples of the proper use of each kind of service.

Did You Know?

➤ Removing adhesive bandages from minor cuts can be made painless by rubbing an alcohol-moistened cotton ball across the bandage.

➤ Most accidents take place between 2 A.M. and 7 A.M. and again during the period between 2 P.M. and 5 P.M.

➤ The manufacturing industry is the most dangerous in terms of worker injuries.

Types of Emergencies

There are many different kinds of emergencies. Some, such as nosebleeds and splinters, are relatively minor. Others—including situations in which an individual is rendered unconscious, as was the case with Jamal in the chapter-opening story—can be life-threatening. Among the most serious emergencies are open wounds and severe burns.

Open Wounds

Open wounds are caused by a variety of accidents, including falls and the mishandling of sharp tools and machinery. The correct response to an open wound depends on the type of wound:

- **Abrasion.** Also known as a scrape, an abrasion damages the outer layers of skin. Abrasions are accompanied by little or no bleeding but may easily become infected. Abrasions are caused by scraping or rubbing.

- **Laceration.** A laceration, or cut, is generally caused by a sharp object such as a knife or broken glass, though lacerations also can be the result of a hard blow from a blunt object. Lacerations can have jagged or smooth edges and are usually accompanied by bleeding. Deep cuts can result in heavy bleeding, as well as damage to nerves, large blood vessels, and other soft tissues.

- **Puncture.** A puncture is a wound caused by a pin, splinter, or other pointed object piercing the skin. Although external bleeding is usually limited, puncture wounds carry the potential for internal bleeding and damage to internal organs as well as an increased possibility of infection. The risk of infection becomes even greater when the object remains in the skin.

- **Avulsion.** This is a wound that results when tissue is separated partly or completely from a person's body. Avulsions often occur in auto accidents and from animal bites. Because severed body parts can sometimes be reattached surgically, they should be sent along with the victim to the hospital, packed in ice or ice water if possible to preserve the tissue.

First Aid for Open Wounds

As with any emergency, treating an open wound requires thinking quickly and remaining calm. It also requires a knowledge of four steps. These are as follows:

1. **Stop the bleeding.** Apply direct pressure to the top of the wound or to a **pressure point**, *one of a number of points along the main artery supplying blood to an affected limb.* This prevents blood loss without interfering with circulation. When applying direct pressure, use a thick, clean cloth and press firmly with the heel of your hand, adding fresh layers as the blood soaks through. To

---

HEALTH LITERACY

RESPONSIBLE/PRODUCTIVE CITIZEN. Encourage students to arrange for a certified instructor to teach a first-aid and CPR course at your school after school hours. If the instructors need to be paid for their time, hold a class fundraiser so that students may take the course free of charge. Have students make posters to display and create ads to run in the school newspaper. The posters and ads should highlight the benefits and importance of learning first aid and CPR. Assess success by the number of participants, the percentage of participants who certify successfully, and a student-generated questionnaire to be completed by participants. If any students believe that CPR courses should be included in the school curriculum, have them write letters to the state board of education, suggesting such a course.

protect yourself from **infectious diseases**, wear disposable latex gloves, and wash your hands as soon as possible after giving care.

2. **Protect the wound.** Normally, a clean cloth over an open wound will help protect it from infection. If a cloth is not available, a coat, undershirt, or any other clean covering will do.

3. **Treat for shock.** Shock is *the failure of the cardiovascular system to keep adequate blood circulating to the vital organs of the body.* Shock can result from severe bleeding, heart attack, **electrocution**, poisoning, burns, or sudden changes in temperature. Symptoms of shock include confusion, accelerated or slowed pulse rate, trembling, weakness in the arms and legs, pale or clammy skin, pale or bluish lips and fingernails, and enlarged pupils. When treating for shock, it is important to keep the victim lying down, maintain his or her normal body temperature, and get medical help as quickly as possible. Unless a head injury is suspected—in which case the person should not be moved—a shock victim should be kept on his or her back with the feet elevated on a book bag or large purse about 8 to 12 inches (20 to 30 cm) above the head. This helps return blood to the heart. Shock victims should never be given food or drink.

4. **Get help.** See to it that the wounded victim gets immediate medical attention. Send someone for help, or if you are alone, shout for help. Leave the victim only after you have performed first aid and feel that you have lessened the risk of further injury or death. If you know the victim's blood type, you will want to communicate this information to the emergency medical technician. You should also know your own blood type, in case you become the victim of an emergency.

Blood Types

Human blood is classified into four types: **TYPE A, TYPE B, TYPE AB,** and **TYPE O.** For transfusions to work, the blood types must match. Hospitals and blood banks take extreme care in checking blood types before giving transfusions. Knowing your blood type can save your life.

A person who has **TYPE O BLOOD** is referred to as a *universal donor* because that person can give blood to a person with any blood type.

A person with **TYPE AB BLOOD** is referred to as a *universal recipient* because he or she can receive any type of blood.

Another important consideration regarding blood transfusions is **RH FACTOR,** a protein present in the blood of some 85 percent of the U.S. population. Individuals with Rh-negative blood—blood that does not have the factor—should not be given Rh-positive blood.

hotlink

infectious diseases For more information on infectious diseases and how to prevent their spread, see Chapter 28, page 632.

electrocution For more on electrocution and how to prevent it, see Chapter 34, page 746.

◄ *Giving blood helps save lives.*

ACTIVITY *Find out what organizations in your community conduct blood drives.*

L1 Discussing

What are the reasons for receiving a tetanus shot following a wound? What could happen to a person who received a wound from a dirty or rusty object and did not have a current tetanus shot?

L1 Discussing

Talk about why the pressure-point technique applies pressure to arteries rather than veins. Review how students can determine if blood vessels are arteries or veins.

L1 Class Activity

Ask students to list some shocking facts about shock. *(It can kill. Its symptoms include shallow or uneven breathing; pale, cold, or moist skin; weak pulse; dull eyes; fully dilated pupils.)* Have students practice what to do when a person is in shock in situations where there is a head injury and where there is not such an injury.

L1 Parental Involvement

Ask students to look in their own homes for a first-aid kit or materials to make one. Request that students discuss with their parents the necessary materials each home should have to treat first-aid emergencies. Have students share with the class what family members do to provide first aid in their own home.

MEETING STUDENT DIVERSITY

PROJECT. Have students stage a community-wide expo on first-aid issues and techniques.

VISUALLY IMPAIRED. Visitors with visual impairment will benefit from large-print versions of any printed materials furnished. Visually impaired members of the class may function as consultants to illustrators on the size of typefaces and reproduction of graphics used.

PHYSICALLY CHALLENGED. Ask students with physical challenges to head up an information unit at the expo addressing first-aid techniques and procedures for people in wheelchairs and/or with limited muscular function. Researchers may work with these students in culling information from the local chapter of the American Red Cross and organizations for the physically challenged.

EVALUATING THE LESSON

Assign and discuss the Lesson 1 Review; then administer, grade, and discuss the *Lesson 105 Quiz* in the TCR.

RETEACHING

- Have each student present a one-minute oral summary of the five priorities in an emergency. Ask volunteers to present additional information about general procedures to further assist the victim.
- Ask students to complete *Reteaching Activity 105* in the TCR.

ENRICHMENT

Encourage students to interview a paramedic and write a job profile. Have them include the following information in the profile: job description, training, average education, average age, percentages of males and females, salary, job turnover rate, average length of service, etc. (Library research may be necessary.)

CLOSE

Have students summarize the most important concepts studied in this lesson.

Severe Burns

Burns can be a minor inconvenience, as when your finger touches a hot stove. When a burn destroys vital tissue, however, it can be a life-and-death emergency. There are three types of burns.

1. **First-degree.** These are superficial burns, like most sunburns, and involve the top layer of skin. Healing takes five to six days.
2. **Second-degree.** Second-degree burns involve the top several layers of skin. The skin will have blisters and appear blotchy. Healing takes three to four weeks.
3. **Third-degree.** The most serious burns, third-degree burns destroy all layers of skin as well as nerves, muscles, fat, and bones. The burn looks black or brown.

△ *Sunburn is typically a first-degree burn.*

ACTIVITY *How can sunburn be avoided? How should more serious burns be treated?*

FIRST AID FOR SEVERE BURNS

A severe burn—one in which more than one part of the body is affected or where the skin is blistered and charred—requires immediate medical attention. While waiting for help to arrive, ease the burn with plenty of cool water and place a clean, dry dressing over the burned area to prevent infection. If possible, raise the burned area above the level of the heart. Treat for shock. *Do not attempt to remove clothing that is stuck to the burn or to treat burns where the skin has been burned away.*

LESSON 1 *Review*

Reviewing Facts and Vocabulary

1. Use the term *first aid* in a paragraph that also specifies the six tasks that should be completed first in an emergency.
2. Name the four types of open wounds.

Thinking Critically

3. *Analyzing.* While cycling fast, your friend takes a bad spill. You rush to help and find that her skin is clammy and blood is spurting from her head. Describe the first aid you would administer.
4. *Evaluating.* If it is a stranger in need of first aid, and you ask the person if he or she wants your help, and the answer is no, should you walk away?

Should you be held accountable if you cause some harm to an injured person while trying to administer first aid?

Applying Health Skills

5. *In Your School.* Prepare a talk on first aid for younger students in a school in your community. Think about specific points to emphasize that relate to potential local accident sites.

774 CHAPTER 35 PROVIDING FIRST AID AND HANDLING EMERGENCIES

Lesson 1 Review

Answers to Reviewing Facts and Vocabulary

1. Paragraphs will vary. First aid is the immediate, temporary care given to a person who has become sick or who has been injured. The six priorities are listed on page 771.
2. Abrasion, laceration, puncture, and avulsion.

Answers to Thinking Critically

3. Keep her lying down, press a clean cloth to her head wound, cover her for warmth if possible, and get help.
4. Answers will vary.

Poisonings

W hat do medicines, snakebites, auto exhaust, household cleaners, and many plants have in common? All are potentially poisonous to the human body. Do you remember from the previous lesson what a poison is? A poison is any substance that causes injury, illness, or death when introduced into the body.

HEALTH TERMS

poison control center

emetic

venom

HEALTH CONCEPTS

- Poisoning can occur through swallowing or inhaling a toxic substance, through snakebite, or through contact with a poisonous plant or chemical.
- Victims of poisoning require immediate treatment.
- Poisoning is a life-threatening situation.

Poisons

The American Red Cross estimates that between 1 and 2 million poisonings occur in the United States every year. About half of these involve medicines or household products that are swallowed or inhaled. Poisoning can also result from insect or animal bites and even from touching certain substances, such as poison ivy and certain chemicals. Most poisonings involve children under the age of six.

Swallowing Poison

Today, most household cleaners, medications, and other potentially dangerous products come in containers with safety tops that are hard for children to remove. Yet, in spite of these precautions, many poisonings still occur.

LESSON 2   POISONINGS   **775**

Lesson 2 Resources

TEACHER'S CLASSROOM RESOURCES

- ☞ **Concept Map** Activity 106
- ☞ **Enrichment** Activity 35
- ☞ **Lesson 106 Quiz**
- ☞ **Lesson Plan 106**
- ☞ **Reteaching** Activity 106

STUDENT WORKBOOK

- ☞ **Applying Health Skills** 106
- ☞ **Chapter Study Guide** 35
- ☞ **Vocabulary** Activity 35

Poisonings

FOCUS

LESSON OBJECTIVE

After studying this lesson, students should be able to

- explain procedures for treating poisoning by swallowing, snakebite, or touching.

MOTIVATOR

Write the following sentence on the chalkboard for students to work on while attendance is being taken: *List as many poisonous substances as you can.*

INTRODUCING THE LESSON

Check in the school or public library or call your state Extension Service for information listing many common household poisons and poisonous plants. To introduce this lesson, let students share their responses to the Motivator. Ask them which of these poisonous substances are found in and around the home. Remind them that these substances should be out of the reach of any younger siblings and should be moved if necessary. Refer to this list when discussing first aid for poisons.

INTRODUCING HEALTH TERMS

- Discuss the meaning of the term *emetic* and ask students when an emetic should be administered.
- Ask students to complete Vocabulary Activity 35 and Chapter Study Guide 35 in the *Student Workbook.* ☞

TEACH

L1 Discussing

Use the following questions to launch a discussion: How can accidental poisonings occur? How can they be prevented? Why do people take such unnecessary risks?

L1 Class Activity

Pose the following situation to students: You are baby-sitting a three-year-old child. You find the child sitting in his room playing with an aspirin bottle. Some pills remain in the bottle and some are found on the floor. You suspect the child has swallowed some aspirin. Write out the first-aid steps you would take.

Building Health Skills

Planning a Safe Home Environment
Skill: Goal Setting

Let students briefly review what they know about the dangers of poisons, and ask volunteers to name poisonous materials that are commonly found in homes. Ask: What can you do to protect yourself and others from accidental poisoning with these materials? Why is preventing poisoning so important? After students have shared their ideas, have them read the Building Health Skills feature to learn about specific steps they can take to safeguard their homes. Suggest that students discuss these safeguards with other family members and then take appropriate steps to improve the safety of their own home environments. Ask students to write short essays describing the changes they made at home and explaining how these changes will benefit family members.

Even though the signs of oral poisoning are not as obvious as those in many other emergency situations, telltale symptoms do exist. These symptoms include sharp abdominal cramps, extreme drowsiness followed by a loss of consciousness, vomiting, chemical odor on the breath or chemical burns on the lips, and the presence of an open container of a potentially poisonous substance.

First Aid for Swallowing Poison

When you suspect someone has swallowed a poison, look for and save the container of the suspected poison. Then do the following:

■ Call the nearest **poison control center**, *a 24-hour hot line that provides emergency medical advice on treating poisoning victims*. Such centers are part of a nationwide network that has been set up in and around large cities. A toll-free number for the poison control center in your locality may be listed in your local telephone directory. This number should be posted in a highly visible place in your home.

■ Be prepared to give information about the victim and the poison to the person on the phone. This information should include the age and weight of the victim, the name of the suspected poison,

Building Health Skills

Goal Setting: Planning a Safe Home Environment

ALTHOUGH KNOWING WHAT TO DO in the event of a poisoning is important, a prior step that is every bit as important is *prevention*. The following are steps that can be taken to help safeguard any home against poisoning accidents.

1. **Make sure all potentially poisonous products have child-resistant caps.** Even in homes where there are no small children, the presence of such caps can alert family members to a medicine's or product's potential for poisoning.

2. **Keep household products and medicines out of children's reach.** Install childproof locks on cabinets and closets that contain anything that could poison a child.

3. **Carefully read the directions when using poisonous products and medicines.** Reseal and safely store these products after use. In the case of medicines, be mindful of the expiration date on the label, and flush away all medicines that are past this date.

4. **Be prepared.** Look in the phone book and write the phone number of the nearest poison control center on a card. Place it next to the phone on the family's emergency number list.

MORE ABOUT . . . . .

POISONING. You can suspect that a person has taken poison if any of the following are present: a poison container; observing poison ingestion or hearing the victim tell of it; sudden illness or pain; lip or mouth burns; chemical smell on the breath; pupils of the eyes abnormal for the situation.

Calling the poison control center is more advisable than following procedures noted on poison product labels. The directions for antidotes on many poison containers are not always the best practices to follow. Administering an incorrect procedure can cause more harm to the victim than the poison itself. After applying appropriate first aid, the poisoned victim should see a doctor.

the amount of poison swallowed, and the time it was swallowed, if known. The person at the control center will then offer assistance with the situation and tell you where to go for further help. Depending on the poison, you may be instructed to give the victim a substance that dilutes the poison, such as large quantities of water or milk, or you may be told to administer an **emetic** (ee-MEH-tik). This is *an agent that induces vomiting,* such as a tablespoon of salt dissolved in warm water. *An emetic should never be administered to a person who is unconscious.*

■ Treat the victim for shock. Use the same procedure you read about in the section on treating wounds in Lesson 1. It may also be necessary to help the victim maintain respiration and circulation through rescue breathing or CPR. You will learn about these techniques in the next lesson.

Snakebite

People who think of snakebites as hazards of life found only in rural areas are only partly right. Suburban environments and city parks can also be home to poisonous snakes.

Of the hundreds of varieties of snakes, only four poisonous types are found in the United States: the rattlesnake, the copperhead, the water moccasin (also called the *cottonmouth*), and the coral snake. More than half of all poisonous snakebites occur in Texas, North Carolina, Florida, Georgia, Louisiana, and Arkansas.

Only about 1 percent of the people bitten by poisonous snakes die. A large number of deformities and amputations do result from poisonous snakebites, so they should be treated immediately.

Knowing which snakes are poisonous can help you steer clear of danger.

ACTIVITY *Find out what kinds of snakes are found in your community. Share this information with classmates.*

First Aid for Snakebite

If you are unsure whether a snakebite came from a poisonous snake, treat the bite as though it had. You can administer first aid by following these steps:

➤ **Get the victim to a hospital.** This is the most important task. Keep the victim as quiet as possible, preferably in a reclining position. The more the victim moves, the greater the risk that the venom will be circulated throughout the body. **Venom** is *a poisonous substance secreted by a snake or other animal.*

➤ **Keep the bitten area at or below the level of the heart.** If the bitten area is on a limb, keep the affected part immobile.

➤ **Call, or have someone call, EMS.** Take careful note of any instructions you are given.

➤ **Delay the absorption of venom.** Because snakes are cold-blooded animals, their venom does the most damage in a cold environment. For this reason, avoid putting anything cold on the bite or giving the victim alcohol or sedatives. Aspirin, which can adversely affect blood coagulation, should also be avoided.

➤ **Maintain breathing and prevent aggravation of the wound.** If you are the victim of a snakebite and are alone, walk slowly and rest periodically. This will help to minimize blood circulation.

L1 Class Activity

Have students consider when they would call the following sources of assistance if they were baby-sitting during an emergency: When would it be most appropriate to contact a child's parents? When would it be most appropriate to call 911? When would it be most appropriate to call a poison control center? When would calling the child's doctor be the best response? Talk about how a person left in charge makes decisions in an emergency. What guidelines should sitters use in getting help?

L1 Parental Involvement

Ask students to survey their homes for the placement of medicines and poisonous substances. Have them ask their parents to look for outdated medicines in the home and dispose of them properly. What precautions are taken in their home to avoid an accidental poisoning? Are medicines and poisonous substances put out of the reach of small children? What methods are used?

L2 Researching

Instruct students to research which common houseplants or yard plants are poisonous to small children. How can the need for first-aid procedures be reduced or eliminated?

PERSONAL HEALTH

AM I PREPARED? Have students write entries in their private Health Journals about which injuries and health emergencies they are most likely to face due to their lifestyle, activities, and home situations. For example, do they swim, play contact sports, ski, rock climb? Do they have an elderly relative living at home? Does a family member have heart disease or seizures? Do students have friends or family members who abuse drugs or alcohol? Have them assess in their journals which injuries and health emergencies they feel prepared to handle. Then ask them to identify the emergencies they do not feel prepared to handle and the situations in which these are most likely to occur. Suggest that they write steps they can take to prepare themselves.

ASSESS

EVALUATING THE LESSON

Assign and discuss the Lesson 2 Review; then administer, grade, and discuss the *Lesson 106 Quiz* in the TCR.

RETEACHING

- Ask students to make a large poster for the classroom of a chart relating to poisons. Have students provide the types of poisons, how poisonings can be prevented, and the first-aid procedure for each case. Display the poster in the classroom.
- Ask students to complete *Reteaching Activity 106* in the TCR.

ENRICHMENT

- Have students research the beneficial use of venom in medicine. Why are rattlesnake hunts popular and beneficial to medicine? What is the cost of the venom, and how is it processed into a serum?
- Give students an idea of what happens when paramedics are called to an emergency. Assign *Enrichment Activity 35,* "The Front Line in Emergency Care," in the TCR.

CLOSE

Have students summarize the first-aid procedures for poisoning and review ways to avoid such emergencies.

Poison oak

Poison sumac

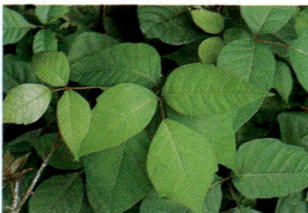
Poison ivy

▲ *Common poisonous plants.*
ACTIVITY *Describe the reaction caused by contact with these plants.*

Contact Poisoning

Poisons that come into contact with the skin fall into two categories: those found on plants and those found in some chemicals.

First Aid for Poisonous Plants

The most common poisonous plants have the word *poison* in their names. These are poison ivy, poison oak, and poison sumac. A first defense against poisoning by any of these plants is to learn what they look like. Some people have no reaction to poisonous plants. Others develop a severe skin rash at the point of contact, followed later by blistering, swelling, burning, itching, and possibly a fever.

First aid for plant poisoning begins by removing any clothing that may be contaminated. Pour large quantities of water over the affected areas and wash thoroughly with soap and water. Calamine lotion can be used to relieve itching. If pain is severe, seek medical attention.

First Aid for Poisonous Chemicals

Pesticides, solvents, household cleaning agents, and highly abrasive cleaners are among the chemicals that can cause poisoning. To protect against such poisoning, make sure safety caps on these products are securely in place when the products are not being used. In addition, the products should be stored out of the reach of small children.

Poisoning through direct contact with a chemical is usually characterized by a burning of the skin, resembling a sunburn. Treatment should begin as soon after the contact as possible.

1. Remove any clothing that has come into contact with the chemical.
2. Remove as much of the chemical from the surface of the skin as you can by flooding the area with water for 15 minutes.
3. Contact the nearest poison control center.

LESSON 2 *Review*

Reviewing Facts and Vocabulary

1. Use the terms *poison control center* and *emetic* in a paragraph that defines the terms and explains their relationship.
2. Identify three steps to take in treating the two types of contact poisoning.

Thinking Critically

3. *Comparing and Contrasting.* In what ways are first aid for swallowing a poison and touching a poison similar? How are they different?

4. *Synthesizing.* Which of the first-aid techniques covered in the lesson would be especially important for a camper or a hiker to know? Explain your choices.

Applying Health Skills

5. *In Your School.* Have a horticulturist, a person who works with plants, come to your class and discuss poisonous plants in your area, how they can be recognized, and what to do in case of exposure.

778 CHAPTER 35 PROVIDING FIRST AID AND HANDLING EMERGENCIES

Lesson 2 Review

Answers to Reviewing Facts and Vocabulary

1. Paragraphs will vary. Example: A poison control center is a 24-hour hot line that provides emergency medical advice on treating poison victims. Advice from a poison control center may include instructions to give an emetic, an agent that induces vomiting.

2. See page 778. Accept answers for either poisonous plants or chemicals.

Answers to Thinking Critically

3. Comparisons will vary.
4. Answers will vary.

First Aid for Choking, Rescue Breathing, and CPR

Each year more than 2,800 Americans choke to death, and many of the victims are children under four years of age. Choking is, in fact, the sixth leading cause of death in the overall population. What is even more sobering is that many who died could have been rescued. This lesson will explore first aid for choking, rescue breathing, and CPR.

HEALTH TERMS
abdominal thrusts
respiratory failure
rescue breathing
carotid pulse
cardiovascular failure
cardiopulmonary resuscitation (CPR)
xiphoid process

HEALTH CONCEPTS
■ The main objectives of rescue breathing are maintaining an open airway and supplying a victim with oxygen.
■ CPR is a lifesaving measure in which a heart that has stopped is forced to pump blood to the body by means of applied pressure.
■ The method for applying CPR differs between adults and children.

First Aid for Choking

In the majority of cases, choking occurs when a piece of food becomes lodged in the **trachea**. No matter what the cause, the first step in first aid for choking is recognizing the symptoms of choking and attempting to dislodge the offending particle or object. The "universal" choking signal is both hands placed at the throat.

Choking in Children and Adults

If you suspect a child or adult is choking, ask the person, "Are you choking?" If the victim is unable to breathe, cough, or speak, begin first aid immediately by administering abdominal thrusts. Also

h⭕tlink

trachea For more information on the trachea and habits that can help prevent choking, see Chapter 17, page 402.

First Aid for Choking, Rescue Breathing, and CPR

FOCUS

LESSON OBJECTIVES

After studying this lesson, students should be able to

- list the steps for aiding a choking victim.
- demonstrate how to check for breathing and pulse.
- demonstrate the process for administering rescue breathing.
- demonstrate the steps involved in administering CPR.
- compare CPR for adults with CPR for small children.

MOTIVATOR

Write the following on the chalkboard for students to work on while attendance is being taken: *List as many causes of choking as you can.*

INTRODUCING THE LESSON

Introduce this lesson by clutching your neck between the thumb and index finger, showing the universal distress signal for choking. Ask the students if anyone recognized what you were doing. Explain the importance of knowing this signal. Refer to the Motivator. Ask volunteers to share their responses.

INTRODUCING HEALTH TERMS

- Have students locate their carotid pulse. Emphasize the importance of pressing lightly to avoid disrupting blood flow to the brain.
- Ask students to complete Vocabulary Activity 35 and Chapter Study Guide 35 in the *Student Workbook.*

Lesson 3 Resources

TEACHER'S CLASSROOM RESOURCES
☞ **Concept Map** Activity 107
☞ **Lesson 107 Quiz**
☞ **Lesson Plan 107**
☞ **Reteaching** Activity 107

STUDENT WORKBOOK
☞ **Applying Health Skills 107**
☞ **Chapter Study Guide 35**
☞ **Vocabulary** Activity 35

TEACH

L1 Discussing

Why is it important to ensure that a person really is choking before you administer the abdominal thrust?

L1 Discussing

How can you tell if a child or infant is choking? Is it a good idea to proceed with the appropriate first aid even if you are not sure? *(no)* Why or why not? *(You could cause the death of the child or infant.)*

L1 Explaining

Hand positioning is very important in administering first-aid thrusts for choking. Incorrect positioning of the hands could break ribs, causing internal problems.

L1 Class Activity

Have students list foods that might cause choking in small children. *(Whole grapes, nuts, popcorn, hard candies, large bites of food, or food that hasn't been cut up are some examples.)* What else might cause a child to choke? *(eating too quickly; running or moving around while eating)*

known as the *Heimlich maneuver,* **abdominal thrusts** are *the application of sudden pressure on the victim's diaphragm so as to expel the substance blocking the airway.*

When administering abdominal thrusts to a conscious victim:

AIDING CHOKING ADULTS

STEP 1

STEP 2

1. Wrap your arms around the victim's waist, thumb side of your wrist against the victim's abdomen. Make sure the victim's feet are spread apart so that you have a good base of support. Place your hand halfway between the lower tip of the victim's breastbone, or sternum, and the navel.
2. Grasp your fist with the other hand, and press into the abdomen with quick upward thrusts until the blockage is dislodged.

If no other person is present, a choking victim can perform abdominal thrusts on himself or herself by leaning over the back of a chair or over the edge of a table.

Choking in Infants

For children age one and under, abdominal thrusts are not recommended, since this technique may result in damage to the abdomen and internal organs. Families with very small children are urged to take a course in first aid for choking from the local Emergency Medical Services (EMS) or local chapter of the American Red Cross or the American Heart Association. Briefly, the technique is as follows and should be performed only on conscious choking infants:

1. Place the infant on a downward angle over your arm.
2. Using the heel of your other hand, give four quick blows to the baby's back between the shoulder blades.
3. Turn the infant over, supporting its head, neck, and back between the shoulders. Press two fingers into the middle of the baby's sternum. This action is known as a *chest thrust.* Repeat four times.
4. Alternate administering back blows and chest thrusts until the object is dislodged.

AIDING CHOKING CHILDREN AND BABIES

STEP 1

STEP 2

STEP 3

Myths & Realities

FIRST AID FOR CHOKING. The first instinct for most people is to hit a choking victim on the back and try to dislodge the object causing the obstruction. Actually this is the worst thing the administrator of first aid can do for the person. Hitting someone on the back can actually make the object fall deeper into the windpipe, making it more difficult or impossible to dislodge the object. Tell students to remember that if the victim can cough, speak, or breathe, they should not administer abdominal thrusts. However, they should stay with the person and watch him or her closely. If they determine a person is choking, they should direct someone to call 911 and proceed to administer abdominal thrusts.

Respiratory Failure

When choking blockage is severe, **respiratory failure**—a *state in which air is unable to reach the lungs*—occurs. This condition can also result from the lungs filling with water, as in drowning, or from gas poisoning, an overdose of **narcotics**, or electrocution. Signs of respiratory failure include an absence of breathing movements, dilated pupils, and a bluish color to the lips, tongue, or fingernails. Blood and oxygen circulation must be restored to the brain within four minutes to prevent irreversible brain damage. In such an emergency, the best course of action is *artificial respiration,* or **rescue breathing**. This technique may be administered mouth to mouth or mouth to nose. The American Red Cross recommends using a special protective face shield to avoid direct contact with body fluids.

Rescue Breathing for Adults

Check to see whether the victim is conscious. Tap the person's shoulder and ask, "Are you all right?" If there is no response, direct someone else at the scene to call EMS for help. To administer rescue breathing for adults, follow these steps:

1. Tilt the victim's head backward by placing one hand under the bony part of the victim's chin and lifting while placing the other hand on the victim's forehead and pressing downward. This action moves the jaw and tongue forward, opening the airway.
   Determine whether the victim is breathing. Look, listen, and feel. Look to see whether the chest is rising and falling. Listen for air being expelled from the lungs. Feel whether air is being expelled by placing your cheek close to the victim's mouth, or hold a mirror in front of the victim's mouth.
2. If the victim is not breathing, pinch the victim's nostrils together with your index finger and thumb. Take a deep breath and, with your mouth sealed over the victim's, exhale. Give the person two full breaths (1 to 1½ seconds each).
3. Keeping the victim's head tilted, look, listen, and feel again. Determine whether the victim's heart is beating by feeling for the **carotid** (ku-RAH-tid) **pulse.** This is *the heartbeat found on each side of the neck.* To locate the carotid pulse, place your index and middle finger on the Adam's apple and slide them into the groove at the side of the neck.
4. If there is a pulse but still no breathing, continue to administer breaths at the rate of one every five seconds.

hotlink

narcotics For more information on narcotics and the dangers of using these and other drugs, see Chapter 26, page 583.

RESCUE BREATHING FOR ADULTS

STEP 1

STEP 2

STEP 3

STEP 4

L1 Discussing

What would you do if you were choking and no one was around? The abdominal thrust maneuver can be self-administered. That is, you could press your own fist into your upper abdomen by using a quick, upward thrust. What other objects might be available to administer the thrust? *(Chair or sofa arm would work; anything large and soft that will not injure the ribs and heart.)*

L1 Explaining

Tell students that the first steps in first aid are to determine if the victim is breathing. If rescue breathing is used on someone who is already breathing, a dangerous situation will occur.

L1 Class Activity

Have students practice the methods of opening the airway. Remind students of the importance of not moving the neck in case there is an injury to it.

L1 Explaining

In rescue breathing, the victim's stomach may become bloated with air, causing the victim to vomit. If this happens, make sure the victim's head is turned to the side so the vomit will not choke him or her.

L1 Parental Involvement

Request that students demonstrate and explain to their parents and family the procedures for administering first aid to choking victims and to persons who are not breathing.

COOPERATIVE LEARNING

ASSESSMENT AND EMERGENCY MEASURES. Divide the class into groups of six. Then have each group member write descriptions of health emergencies on separate cards. They should describe the symptoms, such as "choking, can/cannot speak, cough, etc." or "unconscious, pulse but no breathing," or "toddler vomiting, open container of shoe polish nearby." Tell them to collect the cards, shuffle them, and place them face down. Taking turns, each member draws a card and verbally describes the appropriate response, or if possible, role-plays the response with another member. Other group members may critique the response and offer constructive suggestions. Repeat until all cards have been drawn.

L1 Discussing

Ask: Because the procedures for rescue breathing are different for babies, children, and adults, what could happen if you used the procedure for an adult on a child? Discuss the effects of incorrectly using rescue breathing on anyone.

L1 Explaining

Tell students that CPR is to be carried out only by qualified persons. Persons not certified in CPR by an organization, such as the American Red Cross or the American Heart Association, should arrange to enroll in a class to learn the procedure. It is a skill you may never have to use, but if you are called upon to do it, you will be prepared. Persons not certified in CPR who try to perform the procedure can cause extreme harm and even death to another person.

L1 Explaining

Tell students that when a person is unconscious and you do not know the extent or cause of injury, you should always begin by doing a primary survey, checking the ABC's of first aid: A—open airway; B—check breathing; and C—check circulation.

L1 Discussing

Review the proper techniques to carry out the ABC's of first aid.

L1 Discussing

How is CPR similar to rescue breathing? How is it different? Are there times when both might be required?

Have students investigate the availability, times, and location of CPR courses in their own community. Invite them to post these times on a classroom bulletin board and/or make posters urging fellow students to learn this vital lifesaving technique.

RESCUE BREATHING FOR CHILDREN AND BABIES

STEP 1

STEP 2

STEP 3

Visit **health.glencoe.com** to review the steps for giving CPR to adults, children, and infants. Knowing how to perform CPR in an emergency can mean the difference between life and death.

Periodically, check the victim's chest to see whether it is rising and falling. If it is moving, you know that air is getting into the lungs. Continue artificial respiration until the victim has started breathing again or medical help arrives and takes over.

Rescue Breathing for Infants and Children

Rescue breathing for infants and children parallels rescue breathing for adults, with these exceptions:

1. When positioning the child's head to clear the airway, do not tilt the head as far back as you would for an adult.
2. For infants, cover and form an airtight seal by placing your mouth over *both* the infant's mouth and nose rather than only the mouth.
3. Administer not-quite-full breaths, and breathe into the infant's mouth and nose at a rate of one breath every three seconds. For a child, give one breath about every four seconds.

CPR

Among the most serious life-threatening situations a person can face is *failure of the heart to pump blood.* This condition, **cardiovascular failure**, can be brought on by respiratory failure, a drug overdose, blockage in a **blood vessel**, electric shock, or poisoning. In such situations, **cardiopulmonary resuscitation (CPR)**—*a lifesaving technique in which a heart that has stopped is forced to pump blood to the body by means of applied pressure*—is the victim's only hope. CPR requires no special tools or equipment to perform. Yet, learning this technique is like giving the gift of life.

Unlike abdominal thrusts, before a person can administer CPR, he or she must receive certification by taking an approved course with a local chapter of the American Red Cross.

CPR for Adults

CPR consists of three basic steps. A convenient way of remembering these steps and the order in which they occur is to think of them as the ABC's of CPR: **A**irway, **B**reathing, **C**irculation.

AIRWAY

When you witness a person collapsing or come upon a person who has collapsed, your first task is to determine whether the victim is conscious. Tap the person's shoulder and ask, "Are you all right?" If the victim does not respond, dial 911 or contact your local EMS before beginning CPR. If someone is nearby, direct that person to make the call.

If the victim is not lying flat on his or her back, you need to carefully roll the person into this position. Do not turn the upper body first, then the lower body. Once the victim is lying flat, open his or her airway as described in Step 2 of rescue breathing on page 781.

MORE ABOUT . . . . .

RESCUE BREATHING. Provide the following instructions to students. If a person loses consciousness while you are attempting to clear an obstructed airway, ease the person to the floor, protecting the head. Open the airway and attempt to give a breath. If you cannot ventilate, straddle the person's middle and give abdominal thrusts. Push forcefully inward and upward just above the navel. After the thrusts, do a finger sweep to remove any object inside the mouth. Retilt the head and try to give a breath. If still obstructed, continue this procedure until help arrives. If the object is removed, continue with mouth-to-mouth breathing and check pulse as recommended in CPR.

BREATHING

Check for breathing, as in Step 3 of rescue breathing. Check to see if the chest is rising and falling. Listen and feel for signs that air is being expelled from the lungs. If the victim shows no signs of breathing, you must get air into his or her lungs at once by administering Step 4 of rescue breathing.

CIRCULATION

The third and most critical step in CPR is to move blood through the body to supply oxygen to the cells. The heart is located beneath the sternum. Compressions on the sternum force blood out of the heart and into the blood vessels. *Remember that you must be properly trained before administering this procedure to anyone.*

First, check the victim's carotid pulse for 5 to 10 seconds. This is a very important step because chest compressions can harm the victim if his or her heart is beating. If you find no pulse, begin artificial circulation. *Never practice this technique on someone whose heart is beating.*

Finding the correct position to give effective compressions is essential. The pressure must be directly on the sternum to avoid injury to the ribs and above the xiphoid (ZY-foyd) process so that internal organs will not be damaged. The **xiphoid process** is *the lower part of the sternum that projects downward to the point where the sternum meets the lower ribs.*

After locating the correct position for hand placement, you should position your body so that your shoulders are directly above your hands and your elbows are locked. Push straight down. Each compression should push the sternum down 1½ to 2 inches (3.8 to 5.1 cm). When the pressure is released, blood flows into the heart. Apply compressions in short, rhythmic thrusts about one per second. Every 15 seconds or so, you should apply mouth-to-mouth respiration, alternating two full breaths for every 15 chest compressions. Even if no signs of revival are apparent, continue the procedure until help arrives.

CPR FOR ADULTS

AIRWAY

BREATHING

CIRCULATION

keeping Fit

Do's and Don'ts of CPR

When you happen upon an accident or other emergency situation, it is important to know when to jump in and help and when to wait for trained help to arrive. Here are some guidelines on administering CPR and rescue breathing.

➤ *Don't* take action unless **you know what you are doing.** This is especially true of administering CPR if you have not taken a course and become certified in the procedure. Taking the wrong action could cost a life. Call 911, and wait for help to arrive.

➤ *Do* call out for help when you lack the necessary first-aid skills. Someone at the accident scene or a passerby may have such skills.

➤ *Do* protect yourself against risk of infection with hepatitis or HIV. The American Red Cross encourages the public to use some sort of barrier between themselves and someone's blood and other body fluids when performing emergency lifesaving techniques.

L1 Class Activity

Ask someone certified in CPR, such as a trainer or nurse, to demonstrate CPR on a mannequin for the class. Allow students to practice on the mannequin, supervised by a trained professional. Emphasize that they should not practice this procedure on someone who has a heartbeat because it will put the heart into fibrillation and the person could die.

Do's and Don'ts of CPR

keeping Fit

Emphasize how being certified to administer CPR could help save a life. Have volunteers find out about CPR courses in the community. Where are they given? What does it cost? How many sessions are there? Have students share this information with the class.

L1 Discussing

Can a person have a pulse but not be breathing? Can a person breathe but not have a pulse? How does this relate to the procedures of first aid?

L1 Discussing

How is CPR different for children and infants, and why? Emphasize that when giving breaths to an infant, you only give puffs as if you were putting out a candle. An adult can force air into the stomach of an infant, doing damage to the child, if he or she is not careful.

MORE ABOUT . . . . .

WHEN TO STOP CPR. Those administering first aid should initiate CPR to the best of their knowledge and ability in cases they recognize as cardiac arrest. Resuscitation efforts should continue until one of the following occurs:

• Resuscitation efforts have been transferred to another responsible person who continues the efforts;

• Circulation and breathing have been restored;

• A doctor or doctor-directed person or team assumes responsibility;

• The victim is transferred to emergency medical services personnel;

• The rescuer is exhausted and unable to continue resuscitation.

ASSESS

EVALUATING THE LESSON

Assign and discuss the Lesson 3 Review; then administer, grade, and discuss the *Lesson 107 Quiz* in the TCR. ☞

RETEACHING

- Let volunteers demonstrate first aid for a choking victim. Ask them to role-play an adult choking victim and to use a doll to represent an infant choking victim.
- Ask students to complete *Reteaching Activity 107* in the TCR. ☞

ENRICHMENT

Ask students to identify some of the possible psychological or medical concerns associated with rendering CPR, such as catching an infectious disease. Have students describe the ways rescuers may deal with these concerns in advance so that they do not hesitate in any emergency situation.

CLOSE

Have students summarize the most important concepts learned in this lesson.

CPR FOR CHILDREN AND BABIES

AIRWAY

BREATHING

CIRCULATION

CPR for Children

Because of differences in size, some adjustments need to be made when administering CPR to infants and children up to age eight. The first two steps are the same as those for rescue breathing.

AIRWAY

Tip the child's head back only a little. Tilting the head back too far will close the airway.

BREATHING

Cover the child's mouth and nose with your mouth rather than pinching the nose shut. For infants, give small puffs of air.

CIRCULATION

In infants, check the pulse at the inner arm just above the elbow. For a child, check the carotid pulse. If no pulse is detected, administer chest compressions as follows.

For infants, draw an imaginary line between the nipples. Place two or three fingers on the sternum, one finger width below the imaginary line, and compress ½ to 1 inch (1.3 cm to 2.5 cm) at a rate of 100 compressions per minute.

For children, place the middle and index fingers of one hand on the xiphoid process, and with the heel of the other hand, compress the sternum about 1 to 1½ inches (2.5 cm to 3.8 cm) at a rate of 80 to 100 compressions per minute. For both infants and children, administer a breath after every five chest compressions.

Remember, never try this on a well person. *Do not attempt CPR at all without training!*

LESSON 3 *Review*

Reviewing Facts and Vocabulary

1. Give another name for each of the terms *abdominal thrust* and *artificial respiration,* and use each in an original sentence.
2. What is CPR, and who can administer it?

Thinking Critically

3. *Comparing and Contrasting.* Compare first aid for choking in infants with first aid for choking in children and adults.

4. *Synthesizing.* In an emergency, if plastic gloves or rescue breathing masks are not available, what could you do to avoid contact with body fluids?

Applying Health Skills

5. *In Your Home.* Discuss with your family the importance of learning CPR. Report on their reactions to your discussion.

Lesson 3 Review

Answers to Reviewing Facts and Vocabulary

1. Heimlich maneuver; rescue breathing. Sentences will vary.
2. A lifesaving technique in which a heart that has stopped is forced to pump blood to the body by means of applied pressure. Only individuals who have been trained and certified in the CPR procedure should administer it.

Answers to Thinking Critically

3. See pages 779 and 780.
4. Answers will vary.

More Common Emergencies

In addition to such life-threatening emergencies as severe bleeding and poisoning, life has its share of minor mishaps. For example, you and your friend are going out the door when your friend slips and sprains an ankle. As with major emergencies, knowing proper first aid in these and other common emergencies can help prevent further injury or complication.

HEALTH TERMS

rabies

gangrene

HEALTH CONCEPTS

- Every type of injury, minor or severe, has its own specific and general first-aid procedures.
- Animals are frequently carriers of diseases that are harmful to humans.
- Weather conditions are always a consideration when participating in any outdoor recreational activity.

Fractures

When a body part, such as a leg or an arm, is under stress and you hear a popping sound, it is usually a good indication that a bone has been fractured. Always treat such an injury as if the bone were broken.

In applying first aid to fractures, your main objective is to keep the bone end from moving. Never attempt to set the bone.

Keep the body part in the position it is in, and immobilize it by securing a splint to the body part with clean lengths of cloth. You can fashion a splint from everyday materials, such as rolled newspapers and heavy cardboard. Seek medical care immediately.

LESSON 4   MORE COMMON EMERGENCIES   **785**

Lesson 4 Resources

TEACHER'S CLASSROOM RESOURCES

- 📁 **Concept Map** Activity 108
- 📁 **Cooperative Learning** Activity 35
- 📁 **Decision-Making** Activity 35
- 📁 **Health Lab 35**
- 📁 **Lesson 108 Quiz**
- 📁 **Lesson Plan 108**
- 📁 **Reteaching** Activity 108

STUDENT WORKBOOK

- 📁 **Applying Health Skills 108**
- 📁 **Chapter Study Guide 35**
- 📁 **Vocabulary** Activity 35

TRANSPARENCIES

- 🔖 **Transparency 53**

More Common Emergencies

FOCUS

LESSON OBJECTIVES

After studying this lesson, students should be able to

- describe proper first-aid techniques for common emergencies.
- list various weather-related emergencies.

MOTIVATOR

Write the following on the chalkboard for students to work on while attendance is being taken: *Write down the first five words that cross your mind when you hear the word emergency.*

INTRODUCING THE LESSON

Have volunteers share their responses to the Motivator. *(Answers might include danger, panic, pain, injury, serious.)* Point out that emergencies are not always life-threatening or serious. Some, such as minor burns and insect bites, are very common and happen to all of us. Ask volunteers who have suffered sprains or broken bones to share their experiences with the class. Tell students that in this lesson, they will learn how to deal with these and other common injuries and emergencies.

INTRODUCING HEALTH TERMS

- Have students determine causes of gangrene.
- Ask students to complete Vocabulary Activity 35 and Chapter Study Guide 35 in the *Student Workbook.* 📁

Chapter 35   **785**

TEACH

L1 Demonstration

Bring some X rays of broken bones to class, and let students see how broken bones look underneath the skin. Most doctors will have extra X rays.

L2 Demonstration

Using an anatomical model of a skeleton, review the placement of bones. Explain how fractures occur in bones. Show the difference between a simple fracture and a compound fracture. Point out the difference between open and closed fractures. Indicate that sprains occur in joints, not bones. Demonstrate for the class the difference between a separated shoulder and a broken collar bone.

L1 Discussing

What are smelling salts, and how do they work? What other preparations have been used to help revive someone who has fainted? Are these beneficial or harmful? Why?

L1 Explaining

Because animals can transmit diseases to humans, remind students that any animal that bites should be watched for unusual signs of illness, such as rabies. If the animal appears ill, call the local health department.

L2 Cooperative Learning

Have students complete *Cooperative Learning Activity 35*, "Handling Emergencies," in the TCR. ☞

---

hotlink

sprain For more information about sprains and strategies for reducing their risk when exercising, see Chapter 4, page 85.

R.I.C.E. procedure For more information on the *R.I.C.E.* procedure, which is effective for treating sprains and other minor injuries, see Chapter 4, page 85.

☞ *Sprains are among the less serious mishaps that require medical attention.*

ACTIVITY *Speak with a member of your family or a neighbor who suffered a sprain. Find out what type of medical care was administered and how long the recovery period took. Share your findings with classmates.*

Sprains

A **sprain** is a condition caused by a stretching or tearing of the soft tissue bands, or ligaments, that hold bones together at a joint. Wrists, knees, and ankles are among the areas most frequently sprained. To treat a sprain, use the **R.I.C.E. procedure** outlined in Chapter 4.

Fainting

Fainting is a temporary loss of consciousness brought on by a reduced supply of blood to the brain. People who faint usually recover within a few minutes. First aid for fainting includes the following steps:

1. Do not prop the person up. Leave the individual lying down on her or his back. If possible, elevate the legs 8 to 12 inches.
2. Loosen any tight or binding clothing.
3. Maintain an open airway, as explained in Lesson 3.
4. Sponge the person's face with water. Do not splash water over the face, because this may cause the person to choke.
5. If the person fails to revive promptly, seek medical help.

Animal Bites

Dogs and other animals can transmit diseases to humans by biting them. Any animal bite, and especially one in which the animal's teeth have pierced the skin, should be washed with soap and warm water, then covered with a clean dressing or bandage. It is also important to get the person to a hospital or doctor's office at once. Some animals carry **rabies**—*a viral disease of the nervous system that eventually causes madness and death.* In addition to dogs, common carriers of the disease include cats, squirrels, skunks, foxes, bats, raccoons, and rats.

If you find the animal that inflicted the wound, do not try to capture it yourself. Contact the proper authorities to capture the animal and call the local health center to learn where the animal has been taken for examination. If the animal is not captured, the bitten individual will need to undergo a series of daily injections with a rabies vaccine. If this vaccine is not administered to a person who is indeed infected with the rabies virus, the person will die.

Bee Stings

In most cases, bee stings are minor emergencies and are easily treated. For people who are allergic to bee

---

MORE ABOUT . . . . .

ANIMAL BITES. Infection is the guaranteed result of any bite unless it is cleaned thoroughly. Most bites are puncture wounds and should be treated accordingly.

A wild animal, such as a raccoon, that appears unusually friendly or domesticated may well be rabid. If the animal is sick, the result can be a bite that will infect an individual with rabies. A series of rather painful shots is the treatment.

Do not assume that a dog or cat that is young or especially friendly cannot be rabid. An animal should be tested for rabies if it has bitten anyone—even if it is your own pet.

Making Responsible Decisions

Acting in an Emergency

Sally and several friends were driving along the interstate. It was raining, and the road was slick. As Sally was approaching her exit, she saw a recreational vehicle spin out of control ahead of her and veer off the road. Upon reaching the accident scene, Sally and her friends discovered two people in the RV. Neither of them was responsive. Neither Sally nor her friends knew what steps to take at this point, though all agreed something needed to be done—and fast.

What Would You Do?

Apply the six steps of the decision-making process to the problem facing Sally and her friends.

1. **State the situation.**
2. **List the options.**
3. **Weigh the possible outcomes.**
4. **Consider your values.**
5. **Make a decision and act.**
6. **Evaluate the decision.**

stings, however, stings can be serious and sometimes even fatal. To treat bee stings, use a piece of cardboard, a credit card, or other flat, sharp-edged object to scrape the stinger away from the skin until you pull out the venom sac. Wash the area thoroughly with soap and water.

Once the stinger is out, watch for allergic reactions. An allergic person will usually carry a kit with adrenaline to open the airways.

Objects in the Eye

If a foreign object comes into contact with the surface of your eye, resist the impulse to rub the eye or you may scratch the cornea. Instead, gently flush the eye with water, starting at the edge nearest the nose and working outward. If this measure fails to dislodge the object, cover both eyes and seek medical attention.

Minor Burns

When burns are severe, they are potentially life-threatening. When burns are minor, do the following:

1. Stop the burning by removing the victim from the source of the burn.
2. Cool the burn by soaking the burned area in cool water or using wet towels.
3. Cover the burn with dry, sterile dressings. This action helps prevent infection and reduces pain.

Chemical burns should be flushed with large quantities of cool running water. Remove any clothing that has the chemical on it.

HEALTH *Online*

What should you do if one of your friends needs first aid? Learn about first aid for emergencies such as broken bones, burns, cuts, and insect stings at **health.glencoe.com**.

HOME AND COMMUNITY CONNECTION

LOCAL EMERGENCIES. Have students decide which of the emergencies is most likely to occur in your community or immediate area. For example, do rough waters often result in near drownings? Do fractures occur at a nearby ski resort? Are bees, wasps, and ticks frequently encountered? Does heat exhaustion or heatstroke occur frequently? Have students research first aid for additional health emergencies to which your area is prone. For example, if frostbite is a common problem, students may wish to research treatment for hypothermia. Have them write a pamphlet of first-aid measures for emergencies common in your area, including numbers for local emergency services such as lifeguards, paramedics, and emergency rooms, and share it with family members.

Making Responsible Decisions

1. Sally and her friends have to decide how to help two nonresponsive victims of an accident.
2. Once they have made sure there is no danger of the RV catching on fire, they could (a) wait beside the RV and try to get someone else to stop or call for help on a cellular phone; (b) leave the scene to get help; (c) have someone go to the nearest phone to call 911 while the others wait with the accident victims.
3. Sally and her friends might (a) get capable help soon, or perhaps have to wait a long time for someone else to stop; (b) risk the safety of the accident victims by leaving them alone; (c) get help as quickly as possible and avoid leaving the victims alone.
4. Sally and her friends value the safety of others; they also value their own ability to help others.
5. Decisions will vary.
6. Guide students in considering both the short- and long-term consequences of their decisions.

L2 Decision Making

For further study on making responsible decisions, assign *Decision-Making Activity 35* in the TCR.

HEALTH *Online*

As an alternative to designing posters, students may prefer to consolidate information from the various articles on the site into a first-aid pamphlet to be distributed among family members and friends. Urge students to customize information on topics such as poisonous plants and animal bites for your locality.

L1 Discussing

How should stings be treated? *(Cold applications and soothing lotions, such as calamine lotion, can bring relief. A person allergic to bee stings should seek medical attention immediately.)*

L1 Explaining

Emphasize that in cases where chemicals enter the eyes, flush the eyes with water for at least 15 minutes and seek medical treatment immediately.

L1 Explaining

Tell students that burns are described in terms of the extent of the body surface that is covered. An adult who has suffered burns on 15 percent of the body surface, or a child who has received burns on 10 percent of the body, usually requires hospitalization. Burns on or around the face require prompt medical attention because swelling could obstruct breathing.

L1 Explaining

Explain that a common misconception in treating nosebleeds is to tilt the head back. This risks blood running into the throat and windpipe, which can cause the victim to choke or vomit.

L1 Discussing

During cold weather, it is vital to wear several layers of clothing to retain body heat. Footwear and headgear are also important.

L1 Discussing

Ask students to contrast heat cramps and heatstroke.

L2 Health Lab

Distribute *Health Lab 35* and have students answer the question, "Can Newspaper Serve as Insulation?"

Nosebleeds

Nosebleeds can happen when the nose is struck or when the mucous membranes in the nose become dried out. Occasional minor nosebleeds are not a cause for alarm. People whose noses bleed often, however, should see their health care professional.

To treat a nosebleed, do the following:

1. Keep the person quiet. Walking, talking, and blowing the nose may cause an increase in bleeding.
2. Place the person in a sitting position and have him or her lean forward. You do not want to tilt the head back, because doing so may cause the person to choke as the blood runs down the throat.
3. Use a protective barrier and apply direct pressure by pressing on the bleeding nostril.
4. Apply a cold towel to the person's nose and face.
5. Place a piece of cotton or gauze between the upper lip and teeth to stop the bleeding.

If these measures fail to stop the bleeding, the person should seek medical help immediately.

Weather-Related Emergencies

Extremes of heat and cold can bring on conditions that require immediate care. You should be familiar with these problems.

Frostbite

In extremely cold conditions, the body tries to conserve heat for its more vital internal organs. As a result, less blood is sent to the extremities. If the temperature in body cells gets low enough, frostbite may occur. Frostbite is a condition in which ice crystals form in the spaces between the cells. This ice expands and kills tissue and, in the process, causes the skin to lose color and become numb.

Frostbitten skin is yellowish or gray in color and feels clammy or doughy. Treat frostbite by doing the following:

1. Never rub the affected area. Rewarm the frozen body part by soaking it in lukewarm water (about 100° to 105° F [37.8° to 40.6° C]).
2. Bandage the injured part, placing sheets of gauze between the warmed fingers and toes.
3. Seek professional medical attention as soon as possible.

▼ *Frostbite occurs only when exposure to extreme temperatures is prolonged.*

ACTIVITY *Identify four measures people can take during cold weather to guard against frostbite.*

Cold Weather Advisory

When you plan to spend prolonged periods outdoors during cold weather, it is vital to dress properly. Wearing several layers of clothing will help retain body heat. Footgear and headgear are also important.

Be mindful, too, of the windchill. Any windchill of -25° F (-31° C) or colder presents a danger, with -72° F (-57.8° C) presenting a critical danger.

Myths & Realities

MYTH. Seek help immediately upon arriving at the scene of a medical emergency.

FACT. You are to assess the scene and check for breathing. If there is no breathing, administer rescue breathing and follow the steps outlined in this chapter.

MYTH. If someone is suffering from heat exhaustion, they should take salt tablets.

FACT. To replace lost fluids, drink small sips of water. The rate is one pint per hour for every 70 pounds of body weight if you are exercising heavily at an air temperature of 92°F.

MYTH. For frostbite, submerge the body in hot water.

FACT. This is not only wrong, but also dangerous. The water temperature should be lukewarm, only 100° to 105°F.

If a frostbitten body part goes untreated, gangrene may set in. **Gangrene** is *the death of tissue in a part of the body.* Gangrene often requires amputation of the affected part.

Heat Cramps

When a person is exposed to high temperatures over a prolonged period of time, the body loses essential water and salt. The resulting condition is known as **heat cramps**. Heat cramps are characterized by muscle cramps, heavy sweating, headache, and dizziness.

Here are some procedures to follow when heat cramps strike:

1. Move the victim, or help the victim move, out of the heat.
2. Using your hands, apply firm pressure to the cramped muscle. Gently massage the muscle to relieve the spasm.
3. Give the victim sips of plain water or a commercial sports drink, which will replace the lost salt and water. The victim should consume about 4 ounces (118 ml) every 15 minutes. Be careful that the victim does not take in too much of the liquid at once.

Heatstroke

In some cases, prolonged exposure to extremely high heat causes a life-threatening condition known as *heatstroke.* Unlike heat cramps, which are accompanied by profuse sweating, a warning sign of heatstroke is *lack* of perspiration. Other signs include vomiting, confusion, and an irregular pulse. The victim may lose consciousness.

Prompt action is essential. Get the person to a shaded area immediately and, if possible, immerse the victim in cold water or place ice packs around the neck, in the groin, and under the arms. Monitor the person's symptoms while waiting for emergency help to arrive.

hotlink

heat cramps For more information on heat cramps and precautions against them, see Chapter 4, page 87.

LESSON 4 *Review*

Reviewing Facts and Vocabulary

1. What should you *not* do in treating a fracture? In treating frostbite?
2. Describe first aid for minor burns.

Thinking Critically

3. ***Evaluating.*** Of the first-aid measures mentioned in the chapter, which are most important for someone living in your locality? Explain your answer.
4. ***Synthesizing.*** While out hiking, Simon is bitten by a raccoon. Tell what health risk Simon faces, what type of treatment he can expect, and what information he needs to provide to authorities.

Applying Health Skills

5. ***In Your School.*** Interview at least ten students and teachers in your school about common emergencies the person has faced in the past six months. Learn about the steps the person took and the way in which the problem was resolved. Share your findings with the class in a report on the general level of safety knowledge in your school.

ASSESS

EVALUATING THE LESSON

Assign and discuss the Lesson 4 Review; then administer, grade, and discuss the *Lesson 108 Quiz* in the TCR.

RETEACHING

- Ask each student to make a collage showing the aftermath of one kind of weather-related emergency. Have students use pictures from newspapers and magazines in their collages. Then ask other students to assess what kind of natural event caused the damage pictured in each collage.
- Ask students to complete *Reteaching Activity 108* in the TCR.
- Use *Transparency 53* to discuss methods for handling emergencies.

ENRICHMENT

Most communities have civil defense shelters. Ask students to find out where the shelters are in the community. How do people know which one to go to? What qualifies a place to serve as a shelter? When have such shelters been used in the past? Ask students to summarize their findings in written reports.

CLOSE

Have students summarize the most important concepts learned in this lesson.

Lesson 4 Review

Answers to Reviewing Facts and Vocabulary

1. Fracture: Never try to set the bone. Frostbite: Never rub the affected area.
2. Remove victim from source of burn; cool burn by soaking area in cool water or using wet towels; cover burn with dry, sterile dressings.

Answers to Thinking Critically

3. Answers will vary.
4. Health risk: rabies. Treatment: series of daily injections. He needs to tell authorities that he was bitten and by what kind of animal; also, where the animal is—so that authorities can capture it.

ACTIVITY 1
HEALTH SKILLS
Accessing Health Information, Health Advocacy

➤ **National Standards**
This activity meets these National Health Standards: 2.1; 2.3; 7.5.

Teach
- Make sure to have necessary health consumer information resources on hand the day you plan to assign the activity. This might include a copy of the Yellow Pages of your local phone directory, the American Red Cross First Aid Handbook, magazines and/or catalogues geared toward the hospital or health-care industry, and the addresses of pre-screened Web sites that provide this type of information.

ACTIVITY 2
HEALTH SKILLS
Self Management

➤ **National Standards**
This activity meets this National Health Standard: 3.5.

Teach
- Prior to the class period during which you will assign the activity, write along the top of the chalkboard the various topic headings noted in step 1 of the student activity. Invite students on a first-come, first-served basis to sign up for work on the topic area that holds the most interest for them.
- Students should attempt as much as possible to customize the handbook for your area. They should note, for example, types of snakes found in the area, the presence of a large deer population (deer ticks carry lime disease), and the like.

Activity 1 — Prepared for Emergencies

Since the outbreak of deadly HIV in the early 1980s, emergency medical teams have worn plastic gloves and rescue breathing masks when attending to accident victims. Do you have the proper equipment for an emergency situation?

Directions

1. Work in pairs to locate supply facilities in your community where one could obtain the protective gear mentioned at the left.
2. Determine the average cost for each item.
3. Research different types of breathing masks that may be available.
4. Present your findings to the class in an oral presentation, using illustrations or visual aids.
5. After your presentation, ask classmates to list items that should be included in a well-stocked first-aid kit.

Time
50 minutes plus outside research

Materials
paper, pen, illustrations of protective gear

Self-Assessment
✓ Collected information on at least three different protective devices.
✓ Explained how each protective item should be properly used.

Activity 2 — First Aid Handbook

Administering first aid in an emergency situation can mean the difference between life and death. Would you know what to do in an emergency situation? You and members of your community will after your class publishes a "First Aid Handbook."

Directions

1. In groups, review or research these topics: "First Steps to Take," "Wounds," "Treating Shock," "Burns," "Bites and Stings," "Poisons," and "CPR."
2. Discuss the most effective way of communicating each topic (i.e., through lists, illustrations, or both).
3. Appoint one or more class members to input the handbook on the classroom computer.
4. Include an appendix with emergency telephone numbers for your area.
5. Share copies of your handbook with family and community members.

Time
50 minutes

Materials
library or Internet health resources, computer with design software and color printer

Self-Assessment
✓ Covered various areas of first aid.
✓ Included accurate emergency telephone numbers.
✓ Completed book is clear, well-organized, and attractively designed.

790 CHAPTER 35 PROVIDING FIRST AID AND HANDLING EMERGENCIES

ASSESSMENT SCORING

Using a four-level rubric, the student has achieved a 4 if:

ACTIVITY 1
✔ Student made effective use of one or more health consumer information sources.
✔ Student collected information on at least three protective devices.
✔ Student explained proper use of each item.
✔ Student gave evidence of having shared information on a well-stocked first-aid kit with adults in the home.

ACTIVITY 2
✔ Student covered in depth an area of first aid.
✔ Student included accurate emergency telephone numbers.
✔ Student was instrumental in producing a book that was clear, well-organized, and attractively designed.
✔ Student made an effort to share copies of the handbook with members of the community.

HEALTH NEWS VIDEO

Coping with Emergencies Every Day

When a medical crisis hits, the experts are ready. Emergency workers arrive at the scene. Trauma surgeons and operating room staff wait at the hospital, ready to tend wounds. Later, others nurses and doctors take over to help patients heal. But who takes care of these caregivers? Working in urgent medical situations takes a heavy emotional toll.

All trauma workers need to find their own ways of coping with the daily stress of handling emergencies. Off-the-job relaxation is key. Talking about job stress with a counselor is another essential tool.

Play the Video

CNN. All Rights Reserved.

Think About It

- What are the particular stressors linked with providing emergency medical care? Describe the programs that often are available to help workers handle these stressors.

- Suppose that you are interviewing someone who wants to be an emergency medical worker. What strengths would you look for?

- Make a list of the kinds of workers who might be involved in one emergency medical situation. Consider each person's unique perspective on the event.

CNN HEALTH NEWS **791**

MORE ABOUT . . . . .

REPORTING THE STORY. Discuss how media attention to stress, such as this video report, can help raise public awareness of this crucial issue. Have students consider some of the positive effects of this journalism. For example, viewers might take action to improve the programs available to emergency workers in your area; they can also learn to incorporate stress management strategies into their own lives.

Encourage students to write editorials for school or local newspapers that describe the importance of understanding and handling stress issues for emergency workers.

CHAPTER 35 *Review*

CHECKING COMPREHENSION

- Assign and discuss the chapter review.
- Use the MindJogger Videoquiz to review the chapter. ⦿

CHAPTER 35 REVIEW ANSWERS

Using Health Terms

1. pressure point
2. first aid
3. shock
4. emetic
5. venom
6. poison control center
7. cardiovascular failure
8. respiratory failure
9. xiphoid process
10. cardiopulmonary resuscitation (CPR)
11. carotid pulse
12. gangrene
13. rabies

Recalling the Facts

1. Wording will vary. Learn as much as you can about what happened, and devise a plan of action; look after the victim's continued safety and comfort; make sure the victim maintains normal body temperature; loosen tight or binding clothing.
2. Stop the bleeding; protect the wound; treat for shock; get help.
3. Symptoms include confusion, accelerated or slowed pulse rate, trembling, weakness in arms and legs, pale or clammy skin, pale or bluish lips or fingernails, and enlarged pupils.
4. Call the nearest poison control center. Give information about the victim and the poison, and follow the instructions you receive. Treat the victim for shock.
5. The age and weight of the victim, the name of the suspected poison, the amount of

poison swallowed, and the time it was swallowed, if known.
6. A burning of the skin, resembling sunburn.
7. Perform abdominal thrusts on oneself by leaning over the back of a chair or over the edge of a table.
8. Tilt victim's head back and determine whether the victim is breathing. If

Using Health Terms

On a separate sheet of paper, write the term that best matches each definition below.

LESSON 1

1. One of a number of points along the main artery supplying blood to an affected limb.
2. The immediate, temporary care given to a person who has become sick or injured.
3. The failure of the cardiovascular system to keep adequate blood circulating to the vital organs of the body.

LESSON 2

4. An agent that induces vomiting.
5. A poisonous substance secreted by a snake or other animal.
6. A 24-hour hot line that provides emergency medical advice on treating poisoning victims.

LESSON 3

7. Failure of the heart to pump blood.
8. A state in which air is unable to reach the lungs.
9. The lower part of the sternum that projects downward to the point where the sternum meets the lower ribs.
10. A lifesaving technique in which a heart that has stopped is forced to pump blood to the body by means of applied pressure.
11. The heartbeat found on each side of the neck.

LESSON 4

12. The death of tissue in a part of the body.
13. A viral disease of the nervous system that eventually causes madness and death.

Recalling the Facts

Using complete sentences, answer the following questions.

LESSON 1

1. In your own words, describe the four secondary measures one should attend to in an emergency situation.
2. Explain the four steps in treating an open wound.
3. What are the symptoms of shock?

LESSON 2

4. What is the proper first aid for poisoning by swallowing?
5. What information should you give when you call a poison control center?
6. What is a characteristic of chemical poisoning by touch?

LESSON 3

7. What is the best thing to do if one is alone and choking?
8. Outline the steps in giving artificial respiration.
9. What are the two main objectives in rescue breathing?
10. What is the purpose of CPR?

LESSON 4

11. If one suspects someone has suffered a fracture, should the victim be told to move the injured part to see if it works? Why or why not?
12. What is the first-aid procedure for fainting?
13. What factors can play a role in frostbite? Which of these factors is within a person's control?

the victim is not breathing, pinch victim's nostrils together, seal your mouth over the victim's, and give two full breaths. Check again for breathing and for heartbeat. If there is pulse but still no breathing, continue to administer breaths at the rate of one every five seconds.

Review

Thinking Critically

LESSON 1

1. **Analyzing.** Methods of first aid sometimes change as new information becomes available. What implications does this hold for people who have studied first aid?

LESSON 2

2. **Analyzing.** How would treatment for poison ivy and treatment for a battery-acid burn on the skin differ?

LESSON 3

3. **Analyzing.** Why is it important to know any universal distress signal?
4. **Synthesizing.** Analyze this statement: *Two people are better than one when it comes to administering CPR.*

LESSON 4

5. **Evaluating.** In some areas, emergency medical technicians decide whether to transport victims to a hospital for further treatment. In other areas, anyone in an emergency is transported to a hospital. Which procedure do you feel is better?

Making the Connection

1. **Science.** Using information from Chapter 17 and the current chapter, draw a diagram of the respiratory system that shows how abdominal thrusts force the diaphragm upward, dislodging a foreign object.
2. **Language Arts.** Research the universality of body language by interviewing individuals in your community who speak languages in addition to English. Make a poster showing eight foreign words and drawings of their body language equivalents. Present your poster to the class. Consider how interpreting body language in emergency situations would be important in the case of language differences.

BEYOND THE CLASSROOM

PARENTAL INVOLVEMENT Share with your parents or other adults in your home information you learned in this chapter. Then, together, make your home more first-aid ready. Find and post the phone numbers for the nearest poison control center and other emergency numbers. Assemble or update a first-aid kit.

COMMUNITY INVOLVEMENT In this chapter, you have learned first aid for many different kinds of wounds and situations. Make a separate poster for each kind of first aid discussed. Post each one in a location in the school where it is most appropriate. For example, a poster on how to treat chemical burns may be best suited for the chemistry lab.

SCHOOL-TO-CAREER
Exploring Careers. Interview an emergency medical technician in your community. Learn about the training and interpersonal skills needed for this job. Share your findings with the class in a brief report. If a video camera is available, you may want to record your interview so classmates can learn firsthand about this important profession.

9. Restore blood and oxygen circulation to prevent brain damage.
10. Force a stopped heart to pump blood to the body.
11. No, the main objective is to keep the bone end from moving.
12. Leave victim lying down and, if possible, elevate legs. Loosen any tight or binding clothing. Maintain an open airway. Sponge the victim's face with water. If the person fails to revive promptly, seek medical help.
13. Extreme cold. People can control risks of frostbite by dressing appropriately and limiting time spent in extremely cold conditions.

Thinking Critically

1. Answers should reflect an understanding of the fact that people need to update their first-aid knowledge regularly.
2. Treatment for poison ivy involves removing affected clothing, washing affected area with soap and water, and applying calamine lotion if necessary to relieve itching. Treatment for a battery-acid burn involves removing affected clothing, flooding burned area with water for at least 15 minutes, and contacting the nearest poison control center.
3. Answers should reflect an understanding of the importance of being able to request help, even when you are unable to speak or unable to speak the language of those around you.
4. Answers should reflect an understanding of the vigorous nature of CPR.
5. Answers will vary.

Evaluate

- Use the reproducible *Chapter 35 Test* in the TCR, or construct your own using the Testmaker software. 🖎 💾
- Use *Performance Assessment Activity 35* in the TCR. 🖎

Enrichment

Ask students to complete *Cross-Curriculum Activity 35* in the TCR. 🖎

Beyond the Classroom

Keep students involved in the community, and encourage parent participation by assigning the activities on this page for students to work on outside of class.

Glossary

A

Abdominal thrusts   The application of sudden pressure on the victim's diaphragm so as to expel the substance blocking the airway. (Ch. 35, 780)

Absorption   The passage of digested food from the digestive tract into the circulatory system. (Ch. 18, 412)

Abstinence   The conscious decision to avoid harmful behaviors, including sexual activity before marriage and the use of tobacco, alcohol, and other drugs. (Ch. 1, 21; Ch. 21, 484)

Abuse   The intentional physical, emotional, sexual, and/or verbal maltreatment or injury of one person by another. (Ch. 14, 330)

Accident chain   A recurring pattern that is present in all mishaps. (Ch. 34, 744)

Acid rain   A by-product of nitrogen oxides or sulfur oxides mixed with rain. (Ch. 33, 727)

Acne   A clogging of the pores of the skin. (Ch. 7, 165)

Acquaintance rape   Rape by someone who is known casually by the victim or someone thought to be a friend. (Ch. 14, 330)

Acquired immune deficiency syndrome (AIDS) HIV infection combined with severe immune deficiency. (Ch. 30, 658)

Action plan   A multi-step strategy for identifying and achieving goals. (Ch. 2, 38)

Active immunity   Immunity your body develops to protect you from disease. (Ch. 28, 633)

Active listening   Really paying attention to what someone is saying and feeling. (Ch. 11, 265)

Addiction   A physiological or psychological dependence on a substance or activity. (Ch. 24, 529)

Additive interaction   When medicines work together in a positive way. (Ch. 23, 516)

Adolescence   The stage between childhood and adulthood. (Ch. 21, 478)

Adrenal glands   Two glands located on the top of the kidneys. (Ch. 16, 379)

Adrenaline   The "emergency hormone" secreted by the adrenal glands to prepare the body to respond to a stressor. (Ch. 9, 216)

Advocate   Someone who speaks out for another person or a cause. (Ch. 32, 716)

Aerobic exercise   Vigorous activity in which oxygen is continuously taken in for a period of at least 20 minutes. (Ch. 3, 57)

Aesthetic   Artistic. (Ch. 8, 193)

Affective disorder   A psychological illness or condition that relates to emotions and involves mood swings or mood extremes that interfere with everyday living. (Ch. 10, 241)

Affirmation   Positive input that helps others feel appreciated and supported. (Ch. 12, 281)

Aggravated assault   Unlawful attack with an intent to hurt or kill. (Ch. 14, 325)

Aggressive   Overly forceful, pushy, hostile, or otherwise attacking in approach. (Ch. 13, 307)

Agility   The ability to control the body's movements and to change the body's position quickly. (Ch. 4, 74)

AIDS-opportunistic illnesses (AIDS-OIs)   Infections and other diseases caused by organisms that do not usually produce illness in healthy people with unimpaired immune systems. (Ch. 30, 666)

Al-Anon   A worldwide self-help organization for people who are close to alcoholics. (Ch. 27, 612)

Alarm   The first stage in the stress response when the body and mind go on high alert. (Ch. 9, 216)

Alateen   A support program for people ages 12 to 20 whose parents, other family members, or friends have drinking problems. (Ch. 27, 613)

Alcohol poisoning   A dangerous toxic condition that occurs when a person drinks a large amount of alcohol in a short period of time. (Ch. 25, 563)

Alcoholism   A physical and psychological dependence on the drug ethanol. (Ch. 25, 563)

Americans with Disabilities Act   A law prohibiting discrimination against people with physical or mental disabilities in the workplace, transportation, public accommodations, and telecommunications. (Ch. 31, 697)

Amino acids   Chemical substances that make up body proteins. (Ch. 5, 103)

Amniocentesis   A procedure in which a syringe is inserted through the pregnant female's abdominal wall into the amniotic fluid surrounding the developing fetus. (Ch. 20, 466)

Anabolic steroids   Chemicals similar to the male hormone testosterone. (Ch. 4, 80)

Anaerobic exercise   Intense bursts of activity in which the muscles work so hard that they produce energy without using oxygen. (Ch. 3, 58)

Analgesics   Pain relievers. (Ch. 23, 515)

Angina pectoris   Pain and tightness in the chest caused by the lack of oxygen to the heart. (Ch. 31, 679)

Anorexia nervosa   A disorder in which the irrational fear of becoming obese results in severe weight loss from self-induced starvation. (Ch. 6, 142)

Antagonistic interaction   When the effect of a medicine is canceled or reduced when taken with another medicine. (Ch. 23, 517)

Antibodies   Proteins that destroy or neutralize invading pathogens. (Ch. 28, 626)

Anxiety disorder   An illness or condition in which real or imagined fears prevent a person from enjoying life. (Ch. 10, 239)

Apgar test   Diagnostic test that determines an infant's physical condition at birth. (Ch. 20, 460)

Appendicitis   Inflammation of the appendix. (Ch. 18, 421)

Appendicular skeleton   The 126 bones of the shoulders, arms, hands, hips, legs, and feet. (Ch. 15, 346)

Appetite   A desire, rather than a need, to eat. (Ch. 5, 97)

Arteries   The blood vessels that carry blood away from the heart. (Ch. 17, 392)

Arteriosclerosis   Hardening of the arteries. (Ch. 31, 679)

Arthritis   At least 100 different conditions that cause aching, pain, and swelling in joints and connective tissue throughout the body. (Ch. 31, 692)

Asbestos   A mineral occurring in the form of fibers. (Ch. 33, 728)

Assailant   A person who commits a violent act against another. (Ch. 14, 324)

Assertive   Standing up for your own rights, in firm but positive ways. (Ch. 13, 307)

Asthma   An inflammatory condition in which the small airways in the lungs become narrowed, causing difficulty in breathing. (Ch. 17, 404)

Athlete's foot   A fungal infection of the skin between the toes. (Ch. 15, 343)

Autonomy   The confidence that one can control one's own body, impulses, and environment. (Ch. 20, 469)

Axial skeleton   The 80 bones of the skull, spine, ribs, and sternum, or breastbone. (Ch. 15, 346)

B

Balance   The ability to remain upright while either standing still or moving. (Ch. 4, 74)

Basal metabolism   The minimum amount of energy required to maintain the life processes in a body. (Ch. 3, 54)

Benign   Noncancerous. (Ch. 31, 683)

Bile   A yellowish green, bitter fluid important in the breakdown of fats. (Ch. 18, 416)

Binge drinking   Periodic excessive drinking. (Ch. 25, 562)

Biodegradable   Able to be broken down by microorganisms in the environment. (Ch. 33, 729)

Biopsy   A laboratory analysis of a section of tissue taken from a site where abnormal cell growth is suspected. (Ch. 31, 687)

Bipolar disorder   A psychological illness characterized by extreme mood swings between depression and extreme happiness, or mania. (Ch. 10, 241)

Bladder   A hollow, muscular organ that acts as a reservoir for urine. (Ch. 18, 426)

Blizzard   A snowstorm with winds of 35 miles per hour (56 km per hour) or greater. (Ch. 34, 753)

Blood alcohol concentration (BAC)   The amount of alcohol in a person's blood expressed as a percentage. (Ch. 25, 557)

Body composition   The ratio of body fat to lean body tissue, including muscle, bone, water, and connective tissue such as ligament, cartilage, and tendons. (Ch. 3, 47)

Body language   Nonverbal communication through gestures, facial expressions, and behaviors. (Ch. 11, 266)

Body mass index (BMI)   The ratio of weight to height. (Ch. 6, 135)

Brain stem   A 3-inch-long (7.6-cm-long) stalk of nerve cells and fibers that connects the spinal cord to the rest of the brain. (Ch. 16, 369)

Bronchi   The airways that connect the trachea to the lungs. (Ch. 17, 402)

Bulimia nervosa   A disorder in which cycles of overeating are followed by some form of purging or clearing of the digestive tract. (Ch. 6, 142)

C

Calories   Units of heat. (Ch. 3, 54)

Cancer   Uncontrolled abnormal cell growth. (Ch. 31, 683)

Capillaries   The vessels that carry blood between arterioles and small vessels called venules. (Ch. 17, 392)

Carbohydrate loading   Storing extra glycogen in the muscle. (Ch. 6, 148)

Carbohydrates   The starches and sugars found in foods. (Ch. 5, 101)

Carbon monoxide   A colorless, odorless, poisonous gas in cigarette smoke that passes through the lungs into the blood. (Ch. 24, 530)

Carcinogens   Cancer-causing substances. (Ch. 24, 530; Ch. 31, 684)

Cardiac muscle   A special type of striated tissue that forms the walls of the heart. (Ch. 15, 354)

Cardiopulmonary resuscitation (CPR)   A lifesaving technique in which a heart that has stopped is forced to pump blood to the body by means of applied pressure. (Ch. 35, 782)

Cardiorespiratory endurance   The ability of the heart, lungs, and blood vessels to send fuel and oxygen to the body's tissues during long periods of vigorous activity. (Ch. 3, 48)

Cardiovascular diseases (CVDs)   Medical disorders that affect the heart and blood vessels. (Ch. 31, 676)

Cardiovascular failure   Failure of the heart to pump blood. (Ch. 35, 782)

Carjacking   Hijacking or stealing a car by force. (Ch. 14, 328)

Carotid pulse The heartbeat found on each side of the neck. (Ch. 35, 781)

Cartilage Strong, flexible connective tissue. (Ch. 15, 346)

Cerebellum The second largest part of the brain. (Ch. 16, 368)

Cerebral palsy A group of nonprogressive neurological disorders that are the result of damage to the brain before birth, during birth, in the newborn period, or in early childhood. (Ch. 16, 376)

Cerebrum The largest, most complex part of the brain. (Ch. 16, 367)

Cervix Neck of the uterus. (Ch. 19, 444)

Chemotherapy The use of anti-cancer medications in the treatment of cancer. (Ch. 31, 688)

Child abuse Physical harm, including sexual abuse, or emotional harm to a child. (Ch. 12, 287)

Chlamydia An infection caused by a bacteria that affects the vagina in females and the urethra in males. (Ch. 29, 646)

Chlorofluorocarbons (CFCs) Compounds of chlorine, fluorine, and carbon. (Ch. 33, 728)

Cholesterol A fatlike substance produced in the liver of all animals and, therefore, found only in foods of animal origin. (Ch. 5, 106)

Chorionic villi sampling A test in which a small piece of membrane is removed from the chorion, a layer of tissue that develops into the placenta. (Ch. 20, 467)

Choroid The middle layer of the eyeball wall. (Ch. 7, 172)

Chromosomes Tiny structures within the nuclei of cells that carry information about hereditary traits. (Ch. 20, 461)

Chyme A creamy, fluid mixture of food and gastric juices. (Ch. 18, 415)

Circumcision Surgical removal of the foreskin of the penis. (Ch. 19, 438)

Cirrhosis A condition in which liver tissue is destroyed and then replaced with useless scar tissue. (Ch. 25, 559)

Clinical psychologist A psychologist who diagnoses and treats emotional and behavioral disorders but cannot prescribe medications. (Ch. 10, 250)

Clique A small, narrow circle of friends, usually with similar backgrounds or tastes, that excludes people they view as outsiders. (Ch. 13, 300)

Closure A coming to an end of the most intense parts of the grieving process. (Ch. 9, 231)

Cluster suicides A rash of suicides occurring within a short space of time and involving several people in the same school or community. (Ch. 10, 246)

Codependents People who become overly concerned with another's addiction problem and feel driven to fix or control it. (Ch. 27, 608)

Cognition The ability to reason and think out abstract solutions. (Ch. 21, 479)

Commitment A promise or a pledge. (Ch. 22, 498)

Communication A process through which you send messages to and receive messages from others. (Ch. 11, 263)

Compromise The result of each person's giving up something in order to reach a solution that satisfies everyone. (Ch. 11, 261)

Confidentiality Respecting the privacy of both parties and keeping details secret. (Ch. 14, 323)

Confirmatory test A highly accurate test used to confirm the results of a reactive ELISA (EIA). (Ch. 30, 664)

Conflict Any disagreement, struggle, or fight. (Ch. 14, 316)

Conflict resolution The process of ending a conflict by cooperating and problem solving. (Ch. 14, 320)

Congenital Occurring at birth. (Ch. 17, 397)

Congestive heart failure A slow, gradual weakening of the heart muscle from overwork. (Ch. 31, 680)

Conservation Concern about the preservation of the environment. (Ch. 33, 734)

Constructive criticism Nonhostile comments that point out problems and have the potential to help a person change. (Ch. 11, 268)

Contaminant A substance that spoils or infects. (Ch. 6, 151)

Cool-down Engaging in activity to gradually decrease activity. (Ch. 3, 64)

Cooperation Working together for the good of all. (Ch. 11, 261)

Coordination The ability to use two or more body parts together well, or to use the senses along with the body parts. (Ch. 4, 74)

Cornea The main lens of the eye that performs most of the focusing. (Ch. 7, 172)

Crisis An extreme change in a person's life. (Ch. 12, 287)

Crisis center A facility equipped to handle emergencies and make referrals for persons who need help. (Ch. 12, 288)

Cross-contamination The spreading of bacteria from one food to another. (Ch. 6, 153)

Cross-training Combining various exercise routines to help work different body systems. (Ch. 3, 62)

Culture The collective beliefs, customs, and behaviors of a group. (Ch. 1, 14)

Custody A legal decision about who has the right to make decisions that affect the children and who has the physical responsibility of caring for them. (Ch. 12, 286)

Cystitis A bacterial infection of the bladder that occurs most frequently in females. (Ch. 18, 428)

D

Dandruff A condition in which the outer layer of dead skin cells is shed from the scalp. (Ch. 7, 166)

Date rape When rape occurs between two people who are dating. (Ch. 34, 762)

Defense mechanisms Strategies used to deal with strong or stressful emotions and situations. (Ch. 8, 204)

Deforestation Destruction of forests. (Ch. 33, 732)

Delayed grief response A putting off of the most intense stages of grief. (Ch. 9, 231)

Delirium tremens (DTs) The dramatic physical and psychological effects of alcohol withdrawal. (Ch. 25, 565)

Depressants Drugs that tend to slow down the central nervous system. (Ch. 26, 582)

Depression Feelings of helplessness, hopelessness, and sadness. (Ch. 10, 243)

Dermis The inner, thicker layer of skin. (Ch. 15, 341)

Desertification The conversion of grasslands, rain-fed cropland, or irrigated cropland to desertlike conditions. (Ch. 33, 733)

Designated drivers People in social settings who choose not to drink so that they can safely drive themselves and others. (Ch. 25, 559)

Designer drugs Synthetic substances meant to imitate the effects of narcotics and hallucinogens. (Ch. 26, 590)

Detachment The process of pulling back or separating from involvement with someone else's addiction and refusing to let that addiction rule one's life any longer. (Ch. 27, 612)

Detoxification The removal of all drugs from the body. (Ch. 27, 605)

Developmental task Something that needs to occur during a particular stage for a person to continue his or her growth toward becoming a healthy, mature adult. (Ch. 20, 468)

Diabetes A chronic disease that affects the way body cells convert food into energy. (Ch. 31, 689)

Diaphragm A muscle that separates the chest and abdominal cavities. (Ch. 17, 401)

Digestion The mechanical and chemical breakdown of foods for use by the body's cells. (Ch. 18, 412)

Disability Any physical or mental impairment that limits normal activities. (Ch. 31, 694)

Distress Negative stress. (Ch. 9, 215)

Domestic violence Any acts of violence involving family members. (Ch. 12, 286)

Drug watches Organized community efforts by neighborhood residents to patrol, monitor, report, and otherwise help try to stop drug deals and drug use. (Ch. 26, 595)

Drug-Free School Zones Areas within 1,000 feet of schools and designated by signs, within which people caught selling drugs receive especially tough penalties. (Ch. 26, 593)

E

Electrocution Death resulting from passage through the body of a high-voltage current. (Ch. 34, 746)

Electrolytes Nutrients that become electrically charged when in solution. (Ch. 6, 146)

Elimination The expulsion of undigested food or body wastes. (Ch. 18, 412)

ELISA (EIA) A test that screens for the presence of HIV antibodies in the blood. (Ch. 30, 664)

Embryo Cluster of developing cells following implantation. (Ch. 20, 455)

Emetic An agent that induces vomiting. (Ch. 35, 777)

Emotional abuse A pattern of behavior that attacks a child's emotional development and sense of self-worth. (Ch. 12, 287)

Emotional intimacy The ability to experience a caring, loving relationship with another person with whom you can share your innermost feelings. (Ch. 22, 497)

Emotional maturity The state at which the mental and emotional capabilities of an individual are fully developed. (Ch. 22, 495)

Emotions Signals that tell your mind and body how to react. (Ch. 8, 197)

Empathy The ability to imagine and understand how someone else feels. (Ch. 8, 199; Ch. 11, 262)

Empty-nest syndrome Feelings of despair or loneliness that accompany children leaving home and entering adulthood. (Ch. 22, 504)

Enabling Trying to protect the person having trouble with alcohol or drugs from facing the consequences of his or her drug-related problems. (Ch. 27, 609)

Endocrine glands Ductless, or tubeless, structures that secrete hormones. (Ch. 16, 377)

Enriched food A food in which nutrients lost in processing have been added back. (Ch. 5, 123)

Environment The sum total of your surroundings—your family, where you grew up, where you live now, and all of your experiences. (Ch. 1, 11)

Epidemic An outbreak of an infectious disease that affects a large population. (Ch. 29, 642)

Epidemiology The scientific study of epidemics. (Ch. 32, 719)

Epidermis The outer, thinner layer of skin. (Ch. 15, 341)

Epilepsy A disorder of the nervous system that is characterized by recurrent seizures—sudden episodes of uncontrolled electrical activity in the brain. (Ch. 16, 376)

Escalate Grow into a situation that is unhealthful and even unsafe. (Ch. 14, 318)

Ethanol   The type of alcohol found in alcoholic beverages. (Ch. 25, 550)

Euphoria   A temporary feeling of intense well-being or elation that may be followed by a complete "crash" or letdown. (Ch. 26, 581)

Eustress   Positive stress. (Ch. 9, 215)

Exploitation   Being used for someone else's benefit. (Ch. 12, 287)

Extensors   Muscles that open out a joint. (Ch. 15, 354)

External auditory canal   A passageway in the ear about 1 inch (2.5 cm) long. (Ch. 7, 176)

F

Fallopian tubes   A pair of tubes with fingerlike projections that draw the ovum in. (Ch. 19, 443)

Family counseling   Therapy to restore healthy relationships in a family. (Ch. 12, 290)

Famine   A widespread shortage of food. (Ch. 32, 719)

Fatigue   The third stage of the stress response, resulting in a tired feeling that lowers one's level of activity. (Ch. 9, 218)

Fatty liver   A condition in which fats build up in the liver and cannot be broken down. (Ch. 25, 559)

Feedback   Messages from others that indicate who they think you are or what they think you are like. (Ch. 8, 189)

Fermentation   The chemical action of yeast on sugars. (Ch. 25, 550)

Fertilization   The union of a reproductive cell from a male and one from a female. (Ch. 19, 438)

Fetal alcohol syndrome (FAS)   A condition in which a fetus has been adversely affected mentally and physically by its mother's heavy alcohol use during pregnancy. (Ch. 25, 561)

Fetus   The name by which the embryo is known from the end of the eighth week until birth. (Ch. 20, 455)

Fibrillation   The rapid, ineffective beating of the heart in one of two chambers called ventricles. (Ch. 31, 680)

Fire extinguisher   A portable device that puts out small fires by ejecting fire-extinguishing chemicals. (Ch. 34. 745)

First aid   The immediate, temporary care given to a person who has become sick or who has been injured. (Ch. 35, 770)

Flexibility   The ability to move a body part through a full range of motion. (Ch. 3, 47)

Flexors   Muscles that close a joint. (Ch. 15, 354)

Follicles   Tiny pits in the skin. (Ch. 7, 165)

Food additives   Substances added to food intentionally to produce a desired effect. (Ch. 5, 123)

Food allergy   A condition in which the body's immune system overreacts to substances in some foods. (Ch. 6, 154)

Foodborne illness   Food poisoning. (Ch. 6, 151)

Food intolerance   A negative reaction to a food or an ingredient in food that is not related to the body's immune system or to food poisoning. (Ch. 6, 155)

Fortification   The addition of nutrients that are not naturally present. (Ch. 5, 123)

Foster care   Under the guidance and supervision of a family headed up by parents or a parent who is not related to the child by birth. (Ch. 12, 289)

Friendship   A significant relationship between two people based on caring, consideration, and trust. (Ch. 11, 259)

Frostbite   A condition that results when body tissue becomes frozen. (Ch. 4, 87)

G

Gametes   Reproductive cells produced by the gonads. (Ch. 21, 479)

Gangrene   The death of tissue in a part of the body. (Ch. 35, 789)

Gastric juices   Secretions from the stomach lining that contain pepsin and hydrochloric acid. (Ch. 18, 414)

Gateway drugs   Drugs that often lead to other serious and dangerous drug use. (Ch. 26, 575)

Generativity   A shift of attention away from oneself in the present to concerns for future generations. (Ch. 22, 502)

Generic   A less-expensive version of a medicine that may be substituted for a brand-name medication. (Ch. 32, 712)

Genes   Segments of DNA molecules. (Ch. 20, 461)

Genital herpes   Blisterlike sores in the genital area. (Ch. 29, 648)

Genital warts   Reddish warts with cauliflowerlike tops that appear on the genitals. (Ch. 29, 648)

Glucose   A simple sugar and the body's chief fuel. (Ch. 5, 102)

Glycogen   A starchlike substance. (Ch. 5, 102)

Goal   Something you aim for that takes planning and work. (Ch. 2, 36)

Gonads   The ovaries and testes. (Ch. 16, 378)

Gonorrhea   An STD caused by bacteria that affect the genital mucous membrane, primarily in the lining of the urethra of the male and in the cervix and vagina of the female. (Ch. 29, 647)

Greenhouse effect   A slowdown of the rate at which the earth loses heat, causing an increase in the earth's temperature. (Ch. 33, 727)

Grief reaction   An individual's total response to a major loss. (Ch. 9, 229)

H

Halfway houses   Continuing-care facilities that offer people housing, counseling, and support meetings as they are recovering from a severe addiction. (Ch. 27, 607)

Hallucinogens Drugs that alter moods, thoughts, and sense perceptions, including vision, hearing, smell, and touch. (Ch. 26, 584)

Hardy personality A personality type that seems able to stay healthy despite major or even traumatic stressors. (Ch. 9, 220)

Hashish The dark brown resin collected from the tops of the cannabis plant. (Ch. 26, 587)

Hazardous wastes Any substances that are explosive, corrosive, flammable, or toxic to human or other life forms. (Ch. 33, 730)

Health The combination of your physical, mental/emotional, and social well-being. (Ch. 1, 4)

Health-care facility Any place staffed by health-care professionals and equipped for the delivery of health services. (Ch. 32, 706)

Health-care providers Professionals trained in the health fields. (Ch. 32, 704)

Health consumer A person who uses health products or services. (Ch. 32, 709)

Health insurance A plan to cover part or most costs of expenses and care associated with medical treatment. (Ch. 32, 707)

Health literacy An individual's capacity to obtain, interpret, and understand basic health information and services and use such information to promote his or her health and wellness. (Ch. 1, 10)

Health maintenance organization (HMO) A group of physicians of different specialties who work together to provide medical services to members. (Ch. 32, 708)

Health skills Specific tools and strategies that lead to better and more informed health choices. (Ch. 2, 28)

Heat cramps Muscle spasms that are the result of loss of large amounts of salt and water through perspiration. (Ch. 4, 87)

Heat exhaustion An overheating of the body resulting in cold, clammy skin and symptoms of shock. (Ch. 4, 87)

Hemodialysis A technique in which an artificial kidney machine removes waste products from the blood. (Ch. 18, 429)

Hemoglobin The oxygen-carrying part of blood. (Ch. 17, 390)

Heredity All the traits and properties that are passed along biologically from parent to child. (Ch. 1, 11)

Hernia Protrusion of an organ or tissue through a weak area in the muscle. (Ch. 15, 357)

Hiatal hernia A condition in which part of the stomach pushes through an opening in the diaphragm. (Ch. 18, 419)

Hierarchy of needs A ranked list of those needs essential to human growth and development presented in ascending order from most basic to most fulfilling or satisfying. (Ch. 8, 191)

HIV-reactive Infected with HIV. (Ch. 30, 663)

Homicide The willful killing of one human being by another. (Ch. 14, 324)

Hormones Chemical substances produced by ductless glands that regulate the activities of different body cells. (Ch. 16, 377)

Hostility The intentional use of unfriendly or nasty behavior. (Ch. 8, 200)

Human immunodeficiency virus (HIV) A virus that attacks the body's immune system. (Ch. 30, 658)

Hunger A natural drive that protects us from starvation. (Ch. 5, 97)

Hurricane A powerful rainstorm, characterized by driving winds. (Ch. 34, 752)

Hydration The addition of body fluids. (Ch. 4, 80)

Hypertension High blood pressure. (Ch. 31, 677)

Hypochondria Preoccupation with the body and fear of diseases that are not present. (Ch. 10, 240)

Hypothermia A condition in which body temperature becomes dangerously low. (Ch. 4, 87)

I

"I" message A statement in which a person tells how he or she feels using the pronoun "I." (Ch. 11, 264)

Illegal drugs Street drugs. (Ch. 26, 575)

Illicit drug use The use or sale of any substances that are illegal or otherwise not permitted. (Ch. 26, 575)

Immunity The body's natural defenses against infection. (Ch. 28, 624)

Immunization A program whereby communities or other large populations are systematically made immune to a disease. (Ch. 28, 630)

Impaired glucose tolerance (IGT) A condition in which blood sugar levels are higher than normal but not high enough to be classified as diabetes. (Ch. 31, 691)

Incontinence The inability of the body to control the bladder and the elimination of waste. (Ch. 18, 428)

Indigestion A burning discomfort in the upper abdomen. (Ch. 18, 418)

Infatuation Exaggerated feelings of passion for another person. (Ch. 13, 301)

Infectious disease A disease caused by organisms that enter and multiply within the human body. (Ch. 28, 620)

Infertility The inability of a woman to become pregnant. (Ch. 19, 445)

Ingestion The taking of food into the body. (Ch. 18, 413)

Inhalants   Substances with breathable fumes that are sniffed and inhaled to give a hallucinogenic or mind-altering high. (Ch. 26, 589)

Inpatient treatment   Medical and psychological care during which a person stays at a medical or rehabilitation facility. (Ch. 27, 606)

Insulin   A hormone that is produced in the pancreas and that helps the body convert glucose to energy. (Ch. 31, 690)

Integrity   A feeling of wholeness and contentment. (Ch. 22, 505)

Integumentary system   The body system that includes your skin, hair, nails, sebaceous glands, and sweat glands. (Ch. 15, 340)

Internal conflicts   Struggles within yourself. (Ch. 14, 317)

Interpersonal conflicts   Disagreements between groups of any size, from two people to entire nations. (Ch. 14, 316)

Intervention   Interruption of the addiction continuum before the addict or alcoholic hits bottom. (Ch. 27, 604)

Intoxication   Physical and mental impairment resulting from the use of alcohol. (Ch. 25, 550)

Intravenous (IV) drugs   Drugs that are injected into the veins. (Ch. 30, 659)

Isokinetic exercise   Activity that involves resistance through an entire range of motion. (Ch. 3, 58)

Isometric exercise   Activity that uses muscle tension to improve muscular strength with little or no movement of the body part. (Ch. 3, 58)

Isotonic exercise   Activity that combines muscle contraction with repeated movement. (Ch. 3, 58)

L

Labyrinth   Inner ear. (Ch. 7, 177)

Lacrimal gland   The gland responsible for producing tears. (Ch. 7, 171)

Larynx   Voice box. (Ch. 17, 402)

Latency   A stage when the virus is present but not active. (Ch. 30, 664)

Leukoplakia   Thickened, white, leathery-appearing spots on the inside of a smokeless tobacco user's mouth that can develop into cancer of the mouth. (Ch. 24, 535)

Lifestyle activities   Forms of physical activity that are a normal part of your daily routine or recreation that promote good health throughout a lifetime. (Ch. 4, 73)

Lifestyle factors   Personal behaviors and habits related to the way a person lives that help determine his or her level of health. (Ch. 1, 8)

Ligaments   Tough bands of fibrous, elastic tissue that bind the bone ends at the joint. (Ch. 15, 348)

Linoleic acid   An essential fatty acid not made in the body but that is essential for growth and healthy skin. (Ch. 5, 105)

Lipid   A fatty substance that does not dissolve in water. (Ch. 5, 105)

Look-alike drugs   Drugs made so as to physically resemble specific illegal drugs. (Ch. 26, 590)

Lymph   A clear yellow fluid that fills the spaces around body cells. (Ch. 17, 393)

Lymphocytes   White blood cells that protect the body against pathogens. (Ch. 17, 394)

M

Mainstream smoke   The smoke that a smoker blows off. (Ch. 24, 536)

Malignant   Cancerous. (Ch. 31, 683)

Manipulation   A sneaky or dishonest way to control or influence others. (Ch. 13, 305)

Marijuana   Cannabis that is smoked, eaten, or drunk for intoxicating effects. (Ch. 26, 587)

Marital adjustment   How well people adjust and adapt to marriage and to each other. (Ch. 22, 499)

Mastication   The process of chewing. (Ch. 18, 413)

Mediation   A process in which specifically trained people help others to resolve their conflicts peacefully. (Ch. 14, 323)

Mediator   A person who helps others resolve issues to the satisfaction of both parties. (Ch. 12, 290)

Medicaid   An assistance program of medical aid for people of all ages who are unable financially to afford medical care. (Ch. 32, 708)

Medical history   Complete and comprehensive information about immunizations and any health problems to date. (Ch. 32, 711)

Medicare   A health insurance program that is available to people 65 years of age or older and to people who receive Social Security disability benefits. (Ch. 32, 708)

Medicine misuse   Using a medicine in a way other than the one intended. (Ch. 23, 520)

Medicines   Substances that, when taken internally or applied to the body, help prevent or cure a disease or other medical problem. (Ch. 23, 512)

Megadoses   Very large amounts of nutrient supplements. (Ch. 6, 150)

Melanin   The pigment that gives skin, hair, and the iris of the eyes their coloring. (Ch. 15, 341)

Melanoma   Often deadly type of skin cancer. (Ch. 31, 685)

Menopause   The stopping of ovulation and menstruation. (Ch. 22, 503)

Menstrual cycle   The time from the beginning of one menstrual period to the onset of the next. (Ch. 19, 444)

Mental disorder   An illness of the mind that can affect the thoughts, feelings, and behaviors of a person, preventing him or her from leading a happy, healthful, and productive life. (Ch. 10, 238)

Mental health   Generally having a positive outlook, being comfortable with yourself and others, and being able to meet life's challenges and demands. (Ch. 8, 186)

Mental retardation Below-average intellectual ability present from birth or early childhood and associated with difficulties in learning and social adaptation. (Ch. 31, 696)

Metabolism The process by which your body gets energy from food. (Ch. 3, 54)

Metastasis Spread of cancer from the point where it originated to other parts of the body. (Ch. 31, 683)

Minerals Inorganic substances that the body cannot manufacture but that act as catalysts, regulating many vital body processes. (Ch. 5, 109)

Miscarriage A spontaneous abortion. (Ch. 20, 460)

Modeling Copying the behaviors of those you are exposed to. (Ch. 8, 196)

Mucous membranes The soft, skinlike lining of many parts of the body. (Ch. 28, 624)

Muscle cramp A spasm or sudden tightening of a muscle. (Ch. 4, 84)

Muscle tone The natural tension in the fibers of a muscle. (Ch. 15, 355)

Muscular endurance The ability of the muscles to do difficult physical tasks over a period of time without causing fatigue. (Ch. 3, 48)

Muscular strength The amount of force a muscle can exert. (Ch. 3, 47)

N

Narcotics Drugs derived from the opium plant which have a sedative effect. (Ch. 26, 583)

Neglect A failure to provide a child's physical or emotional needs. (Ch. 12, 287)

Negotiation A process in which compromise is used to reach agreement. (Ch. 14, 322)

Nephrons The functional units of the kidneys. (Ch. 18, 425)

Neurologist A physician who specializes in organic disorders of the brain and nervous system. (Ch. 10, 250)

Neurons Nerve cells. (Ch. 16, 365)

Neutrophils The chief phagocyte involved in the process of phagocytosis. (Ch. 28, 625)

Nicotine The addictive drug in cigarettes. (Ch. 24, 529)

Nicotine substitutes Manufactured forms of nicotine that deliver small amounts of the drug into the user's system while he or she is trying to give up the tobacco habit. (Ch. 24, 539)

Nicotine withdrawal The process that occurs when nicotine, an addictive drug, is no longer used. (Ch. 24, 539)

Nongonococcal urethritis An infection caused by several different kinds of bacterialike organisms that infect the urethra in males and the cervix in females. (Ch. 29, 646)

Noninfectious diseases Diseases that are not transmitted by means of a pathogen. (Ch. 31, 676)

Nutrient supplements Pills, powders, liquids, and other synthetic forms of nutrients. (Ch. 6, 149)

Nutrient-dense Foods high in nutrients relative to their caloric content. (Ch. 6, 138)

Nutrients Substances in food that your body needs to function properly, such as in growing, in repairing itself, and in having a supply of energy. (Ch. 5, 96)

Nutrition The process by which the body takes in and uses food. (Ch. 5, 100)

O

Obesity Excess body fat, or adipose tissue. (Ch. 5, 99; Ch. 6, 133)

Occupational Safety and Health Administration (OSHA) A federal agency responsible for promoting safe and healthful conditions in the workplace. (Ch. 34, 750)

Ossicles Three tiny, linked, movable bones behind the eardrum. (Ch. 7, 176)

Ossification The process by which bone is formed, renewed, and repaired. (Ch. 15, 346)

Osteoarthritis A disease in the weight-bearing joints of the knees and hips, causing aches and soreness especially when moving. (Ch. 31, 693)

Otosclerosis A hereditary disorder in which an overgrowth of bone causes the ossicles to lose their ability to move. (Ch. 7, 179)

Outpatient surgical facility A place where surgery is performed on patients who are released the same day. (Ch. 32, 707)

Outpatient treatment On-site medical and psychological care for a person trying to become alcohol-free and drug-free. (Ch. 27, 607)

Ova Female reproductive cells. (Ch. 19, 442)

Ovaries The female sex glands that house the ova and produce female sex hormones. (Ch. 19, 443)

Overdose A strong or even fatal reaction to taking a large amount of a drug. (Ch. 26, 576)

Overexertion Overworking the body. (Ch. 4, 86)

Overload Working the body harder than it is normally worked. (Ch. 3, 62)

Over-the-counter (OTC) medicines Medicines you can buy without a doctor's prescription. (Ch. 23, 519)

Overweight Weighing more than 10 percent over the standard weight for height. (Ch. 6, 133)

Ovulation The process of releasing one mature ovum each month. (Ch. 19, 443)

P

Pancreas A gland that serves two systems—the digestive and the endocrine. (Ch. 16, 380)

Paranoia   Irrational suspiciousness or distrust of others. (Ch. 26, 581)

Parasites   Organisms that live in or on another organism and derive nourishment from it. (Ch. 28, 620)

Parathyroid glands   Structures that produce parathyroid hormone, which regulates the body's calcium and phosphorus balance. (Ch. 16, 379)

Particulates   Tiny particles suspended and carried through air. (Ch. 33, 728)

Passive   Giving up, giving in, or backing down without standing up for your own rights and needs. (Ch. 13, 306)

Passive immunity   The temporary immunity that an infant acquires from its mother. (Ch. 28, 633)

Passive smoke   Cigarette, cigar, or pipe smoke inhaled by nonsmokers as well as smoke that remains in a closed environment after the smoker is through smoking. (Ch. 24, 536)

Pasteurized   Treated by a process of heating to destroy or slow the growth of pathogens. (Ch. 6, 152)

Peer mediators   Students trained to help other students in conflict find fair ways to settle their differences. (Ch. 14, 323)

Peer pressure   The control and influence people your age may have over you. (Ch. 1, 14; Ch. 13, 304)

Peers   People the same age who share a similar range of interests. (Ch. 1, 14)

Penis   A tube-shaped organ attached to the trunk of the body just above the testes. (Ch. 19, 437)

Peptic ulcer   A sore in the lining of the digestive tract. (Ch. 18, 422)

Periodontal disease   An inflammation of the periodontal structures. (Ch. 7, 168)

Periodontium   The area immediately around the teeth. (Ch. 7, 167)

Perishable   Liable to spoil. (Ch. 6, 153)

Peristalsis   A series of involuntary muscular contractions. (Ch. 18, 414)

Personal identity   The factors you believe make you unique, or unlike anyone else. (Ch. 21, 482)

Personality   A complex set of characteristics that makes you unique and sets you apart from everyone else. (Ch. 8, 194)

Personality disorders   A variety of psychological illnesses and conditions that affect a person's ability to get along with others. (Ch. 10, 241)

Phagocytosis   The process by which phagocytes engulf and destroy pathogens. (Ch. 28, 625)

Pharynx   Throat. (Ch. 17, 402)

Phobias   Irrational fears. (Ch. 8, 200)

Physical activity   Any form of movement, whether purposeful, as in exercise and sports or recreation, or incidental, as when carrying out domestic chores. (Ch. 4, 72)

Physical fitness   The ability to carry out daily tasks easily and have enough reserve energy to respond to unexpected demands. (Ch. 3, 46)

Physical maturity   The state at which the physical body and all its organs are fully developed. (Ch. 22, 495)

Pituitary gland   Structure that regulates and controls the activities of all other endocrine glands. (Ch. 16, 378)

Placenta   A blood-rich tissue developed from an outer layer of cells from the embryo and tissue from the mother (Ch. 20, 455)

Planned pregnancy   Making a decision to get pregnant before the baby is conceived. (Ch. 22, 500)

Plaque   A sticky, colorless film that acts on sugar to form acids that destroy tooth enamel and irritate gums. (Ch. 7, 168)

Plasma   The fluid in which the other parts of blood are suspended. (Ch. 17, 390)

Platelets   The cells that prevent the body's loss of blood. (Ch. 17, 391)

Platonic friendship   A relationship with a member of the opposite gender in which there is affection, but no sexual activity. (Ch. 13, 299)

Pleurisy   An inflammation of the membrane lining the lungs and chest cavity. (Ch. 17, 405)

Pneumonia   Inflammation of the lungs. (Ch. 28, 628)

Poison   Any substance—solid, liquid, or gas—that causes injury, illness, or death when introduced into the body. (Ch. 35, 771)

Poison control center   A 24-hour hot line that provides emergency medical advice on treating poisoning victims. (Ch. 35, 776)

Power   The ability to use force with great speed. (Ch. 4, 74)

Preferred provider organization (PPO)   A type of health insurance in which medical providers agree to charge less to members. (Ch. 32, 708)

Prejudice   Negative feeling toward someone or something that is based not on experience but, rather, on stereotypes. (Ch. 13, 300)

Prescription medicines   Medicines that cannot be used safely without the written approval of a licensed physician. (Ch. 23, 519)

Pressure point   One of a number of points along the main artery supplying blood to an affected limb. (Ch. 35, 772)

Prevention   Practicing healthy habits to keep a person well and free from disease and other ailments. (Ch. 1, 9)

Primary care physician   A medical professional who provides the first line of health care. (Ch. 32, 704)

Priorities   Those goals, tasks, or activities that you judge as more important to do than others. (Ch. 9, 227; Ch. 21, 484)

Profound deafness A hearing loss so severe that a person affected cannot benefit from mechanical amplification such as a hearing aid. (Ch. 31, 695)

Progression A gradual increase in overload necessary for achieving higher levels of fitness. (Ch. 3, 63)

Proteins Nutrients that help build and maintain body tissues. (Ch. 5, 103)

Psychiatric social worker One who has concentrated on psychiatric casework, doing fieldwork in a mental hospital, mental health clinic, or family service agency that provides guidance and treatment for clients with emotional problems. (Ch. 10, 251)

Psychiatrist A medical doctor who specializes in diagnosing and treating mental disorders and can prescribe medications. (Ch. 10, 249)

Psychoactive drugs Chemicals that affect the central nervous system and interfere with the normal functioning of the brain. (Ch. 26, 580)

Psychologists Professionals with doctoral degrees who diagnose and treat emotional and behavioral disorders. (Ch. 8, 194)

Psychosomatic response A physical disorder that results from stress rather than from an injury or illness. (Ch. 9, 222)

Puberty The period of time when males and females become physically able to reproduce. (Ch. 21, 478)

Public health A community-wide effort to monitor and promote the welfare of the population. (Ch. 32, 717)

Pulp The living tissue inside the tooth. (Ch. 7, 167)

Q

Quackery A type of medical fraud. (Ch. 32, 713)

R

Rabies A viral disease of the nervous system that eventually causes madness and death. (Ch. 35, 786)

Random violence Violence committed for no particular reason. (Ch. 14, 325)

Rape Sexual intercourse by force. (Ch. 14, 331)

Reaction time The rate of movement once a person realizes the need to move. (Ch. 4, 74)

Rechanneling Transferring or redirecting your energies. (Ch. 9, 226)

Recommended Dietary Allowances (RDA) The amounts of nutrients that will prevent deficiencies and excesses in most healthy people. (Ch. 5, 112)

Recovery Learning to live an alcohol-free or drug-free life. (Ch. 27, 605)

Recycling The treating of waste so that it can be reused, as well as having an awareness of such practices. (Ch. 33, 736)

Reflex A spontaneous response of the body to a stimulus. (Ch. 16, 371)

Refusal skills Techniques that can help you refuse when you are urged to take part in unsafe or unhealthful behaviors. (Ch. 2, 29; Ch. 13, 308)

Rehydration Restoring lost body fluids. (Ch. 6, 146)

Relapses Slips from recovery, or periodic returns to drinking and drug use. (Ch. 27, 605)

Relationship A bond or connection between people. (Ch. 11, 258)

Relaxation response A state of deep rest that can be reached if one or more relaxation techniques are practiced regularly. (Ch. 9, 226)

Repetitive motion injury Damage to tissues caused by prolonged, repeated movements. (Ch. 15, 352)

Rescue breathing Artificial respiration. (Ch. 35, 781)

Resilience The ability to adapt effectively and recover from disappointment, difficulty, or crisis. (Ch. 8, 207)

Resistance The second stage in the stress response, when the body tries to repair its damage from the stressful event and return to its normal state. (Ch. 9, 216)

Respiration The exchange of gases between your body and your environment. (Ch. 17, 400)

Respiratory failure A state in which air is unable to reach the lungs. (Ch. 35, 781)

Resting heart rate The number of times your heart beats in one minute when you are not active. (Ch. 3, 65)

Retina The light-sensitive membrane on which images are cast by the cornea and lens. (Ch. 7, 172)

Rheumatoid arthritis A destructive and disabling inflammation of the joints. (Ch. 31, 692)

Risk factors Actions or behaviors that represent a potential health threat. (Ch. 1, 17)

Road rage When intense anger and driving mix. (Ch. 34, 755)

Role A part that you play in a relationship. (Ch. 11, 260)

Rubella German measles. (Ch. 29, 630)

S

Schizophrenia A serious mental illness disorder meaning "split mind." (Ch. 10, 242)

Sclera The tough white outer coat of the eye. (Ch. 7, 172)

Sebaceous glands Structures within the skin that produce an oily secretion called sebum. (Ch. 7, 165)

Sedentary lifestyle A way of life that requires little movement or exercise. (Ch. 3, 54)

Self-actualization The striving to become the best that you can be. (Ch. 8, 193)

Self-control A person's ability to use sense to override emotions. (Ch. 21, 485)

Self-directed Making correct decisions about behavior when adults are not there to enforce rules. (Ch. 22, 501)

Self-esteem The confidence and worth that you feel about yourself. (Ch. 2, 30)

Semen A thick fluid containing sperm and other secretions from the male reproductive organs. (Ch. 19, 438)

Sex characteristics Those traits related to one's gender. (Ch. 21, 478)

Sexual assault Any intentional sexual attack against another person. (Ch. 14, 331)

Sexually transmitted diseases (STDs) Infectious diseases spread from person to person through sexual contact. (Ch. 21, 486; Ch. 29, 642)

Shock The failure of the cardiovascular system to keep adequate blood circulating to the vital organs of the body. (Ch. 35, 773)

Sibling Brother or sister. (Ch. 12, 279)

Side effects Reactions to medicine other than the one intended. (Ch. 23, 516; Ch. 34, 744)

Sidestream smoke The smoke that comes from burning tobacco. (Ch. 24, 536)

Situation The circumstance or event leading up to an accident. (Ch. 34, 744)

Skeletal muscles The striped, or striated, muscles attached to bones that cause body movements. (Ch. 15, 354)

Smoke detector An alarm that is triggered by the presence of smoke. (Ch. 34, 745)

Smokeless tobacco Tobacco that is sniffed through the nose or chewed. (Ch. 24, 531)

Smooth muscles The type of muscle concerned with the movements of internal organs. (Ch. 15, 354)

Somatoform disorder An illness or condition in which a person complains of disease symptoms, but no physical cause can be found. (Ch. 10, 240)

Specialist A physician who has received additional training in a particular area. (Ch. 32, 703)

Specificity Principle that states that particular exercises and activities improve particular areas of health-related fitness. (Ch. 3, 63)

Speed The ability to move a distance or complete a body movement in a short period of time. (Ch. 4, 74)

Sperm Male reproductive cells. (Ch. 19, 436)

Sprain An injury to tissues surrounding a joint. (Ch. 4, 85)

Spousal abuse Domestic abuse directed at a spouse. (Ch. 12, 287)

Stereotype An exaggerated and oversimplified belief about an entire group of people. (Ch. 13, 300)

Sterility A condition in which a person is unable to reproduce. (Ch. 19, 440)

Stillbirth The birth of a dead fetus. (Ch. 20, 460)

Stimulant A drug that increases the action of the central nervous system, the heart, and other organs. (Ch. 24, 530; Ch. 26, 581)

Strain A condition in which muscles have been overworked. (Ch. 4, 85)

Strep throat A bacterial infection of the throat. (Ch. 28, 628)

Stress The body's and mind's demands and reactions to everyday demands or threats. (Ch. 9, 214)

Stress tolerance The amount of stress that you can handle before you reach a state of too much stress. (Ch. 9, 219)

Stressor Any stimulus that produces a stress response. (Ch. 9, 215)

Stroke An interruption of the flow of blood to any part of the brain. (Ch. 31, 680)

Substance abuse Any unnecessary or improper use of chemical substances for nonmedical purposes. (Ch. 26, 575)

Suicide The taking of one's own life. (Ch. 10, 243)

Support group An informal or a formal gathering of people who meet and share experiences, feelings, and trust. (Ch. 9, 227)

Sweat glands Structures within the skin that secrete perspiration through ducts to pores on the skin's surface. (Ch. 7, 163)

Synergistic effect The interaction of two or more medicines that results in a greater effect than when the medicines are taken independently. (Ch. 23, 516)

Synthetic drugs Chemical substances produced artificially in a laboratory. (Ch. 26, 575)

Syphilis An STD that attacks many parts of the body and is caused by a small bacterium called a spirochete. (Ch. 29, 649)

T

Tar A thick, sticky, dark fluid produced when tobacco burns. (Ch. 24, 530)

Tartar A hard, crustlike substance. (Ch. 7, 169)

Tendinitis The inflammation of a tendon. (Ch. 15, 357)

Tendons Fibrous cords that join muscle to bone or to other muscles. (Ch. 15, 348)

Testes Two small glands that produce sperm. (Ch. 19, 437)

Testosterone Male sex hormone. (Ch. 19, 436)

Therapeutic communities Residential treatment centers. (Ch. 26, 593)

Thyroid gland Structure that produces hormones that regulate metabolism—the use of nutrients by the body's cells—body heat production, and bone growth. (Ch. 16, 379)

Time management skills Specific strategies for planning and using time in effective, healthful ways. (Ch. 9, 227)

Tinnitus A condition in which a ringing, buzzing, whistling, hissing, or other noise is heard in the ear in the absence of external sound. (Ch. 7, 179)

Tolerance Accepting others' differences and allowing them to be who they are without expressing disapproval. (Ch. 14, 321)

Tolerance A condition in which the body becomes used to the effect of a medicine. (Ch. 23, 517)

Tornado A powerful, twisting windstorm. (Ch. 34, 752)

Trachea Windpipe. (Ch. 17, 402)

Training program A program of formalized physical preparation for participation in a sport. (Ch. 4, 79)

Transitions Critical changes that occur at all stages of life. (Ch. 22, 502)

Transmission Spread. (Ch. 28, 623)

Trichomoniasis A vaginal infection that can lead to urethra and bladder infections. (Ch. 29, 647)

Tuberculosis (TB) A highly contagious bacterial infection that most often affects the lungs. (Ch. 28, 628)

Tumors Masses of tissue. (Ch. 31, 683)

Type A personality A competitive, high-achieving personality type most likely to develop heart disease. (Ch. 9, 220)

Type B personality A "laid back," noncompetitive personality type less likely to suffer from heart disease. (Ch. 9, 220)

U

Ultrasound A test in which sound waves are used to project light images on a screen. (Ch. 20, 467)

Umbilical cord A tube through which nutrients and oxygen pass from the mother's blood into the embryo's blood. (Ch. 20, 455)

Undernutrition Not consuming enough essential nutrients or calories for normal body functions. (Ch. 6, 134)

Underweight Being 10 percent or more below normal weight. (Ch. 6, 134)

Unit pricing A strategy for recognizing the relative cost of a product based on the cost of a standard unit, such as an ounce or a gram. (Ch. 5, 125)

Ureters Tubes that connect the kidneys with the bladder. (Ch. 18, 425)

Urethra The tube that leads from the bladder to the outside of the body. (Ch. 18, 426)

Urethritis An inflammation of the urethra. (Ch. 18, 428)

Urine Liquid waste material. (Ch. 18, 424)

Uterus A small, muscular, pear-shaped organ, about the size of a fist. (Ch. 19, 443)

V

Vaccine A preparation containing weakened or dead pathogens that provides immunity by causing the body to produce antibodies to the pathogen. (Ch. 23, 513; Ch. 28, 629)

Vagina A muscular, elastic passageway that extends from the uterus to the outside of the body. (Ch. 19, 442)

Vaginitis A common inflammation of the female genitals. (Ch. 29, 648)

Values Beliefs and standards of conduct that you find important. (Ch. 1, 20)

Vegans Vegetarians who eat only foods of plant origin. (Ch. 6, 148)

Vehicular safety Obeying the rules of the road, as well as exercising common sense and good judgment. (Ch. 34, 754)

Veins The vessels that return deoxygenated blood toward the heart from the body's organs and tissues. (Ch. 17, 393)

Venom A poisonous substance secreted by a snake or other animal. (Ch. 35, 777)

Violence The use of physical force to injure or abuse another person or persons. (Ch. 14, 324)

Virus The smallest known type of infectious agent. (Ch. 28, 621)

Vitamins Compounds that help regulate many vital body processes, including the digestion, absorption, metabolism, and use of other nutrients. (Ch. 5, 107)

W

Warm-up Engaging in activity that prepares the muscles for the work that is to come. (Ch. 3, 63)

Weight cycling The cycle of losing, regaining, losing, and regaining weight. (Ch. 6, 140)

Wellness An overall state of well-being, or total health. (Ch. 1, 7)

Withdrawal The process that occurs when a person stops using a medicine or other substance to which he or she has a physiological dependence. (Ch. 23, 517)

X

Xiphoid process The lower part of the sternum that projects downward to the point where the sternum meets the lower ribs. (Ch. 35, 783)

Z

Zygote The cell that results from the union of sperm and ovum. (Ch. 19, 443)

Glossary/Glosario

A

Abdominal thrusts/compresiones abdominales La aplicación de presión brusca sobre el diafragma de la víctima para expulsar la sustancia que está bloqueando la tráquea.

Absorption/absorción Paso del alimento digerido desde el sistema digestivo al sistema circulatorio.

Abstinence/abstinencia Decisión consciente de evitar conductas nocivas, incluyendo las relaciones sexuales prematrimoniales y el consumo de tabaco, alcohol y otras drogas.

Abuse/maltrato El maltrato o daño físico, emocional, sexual y/o verbal que una persona causa intencionalmente a otra.

Accident chain/concatenación de eventos previos a un accidente Patrón recurrente de acontecimientos que se presenta en todos los percances.

Acid rain/lluvia ácida Derivados del óxido de nitrógeno o sulfuro mezclados con la lluvia.

Acne/acné Oclusión de los poros de la piel.

Acquaintance/conocido Persona que te resulta superficialmente familiar.

Acquaintance rape/violación por un conocido Violación por alguien a quien la víctima conoce superficialmente, o por alguien a quien considera un amigo.

Acquired immune deficiency syndrome (AIDS)/síndrome de inmunodeficiencia adquirida (sida) Infección por VIH combinada con inmunodeficiencia severa.

Action plan/plan de acción Estrategia de etapas múltiples para identificar y lograr objetivos.

Active immunity/inmunidad activa Inmunidad que desarrolla el cuerpo para protegerse de las enfermedades.

Active listening/escucha activa Prestar verdadera atención a lo que alguien dice y siente.

Addiction/adicción Dependencia fisiológica o psicológica respecto de una sustancia o actividad.

Additive interaction/interacción aditiva Situación en la que dos medicamentos obran juntos de manera positiva.

Adolescence/adolescencia Etapa entre la niñez y la edad adulta.

Adrenal glands/glándulas suprarrenales Dos glándulas ubicadas sobre los riñones.

Adrenaline/adrenalina La "hormona de la emergencia" secretada por las glándulas suprarrenales que prepara al cuerpo para responder a una situación de estrés.

Advocate/defensor Alguien que habla en nombre de otra persona o de una causa.

Aerobic exercise/ejercicio aeróbico Actividad vigorosa en la que se inhala y exhala oxígeno de forma continua por un período de por lo menos 20 minutos.

Aesthetic/estético ArtÌstico.

Affective disorder/trastorno afectivo Trastorno o enfermedad psicológica relacionada con las emociones que se presenta con cambios de humor o variaciones extremas del estado anímico que interfieren con la vida cotidiana.

Affirmation/reafirmación Proveer apoyo que ayude a otros a sentirse apreciados y respaldados.

Aggravated assault/agresión grave Ataque ilegal cometido con la intención de herir o matar.

Aggressive/agresivo Excesivamente brusco, insistente, hostil, o que se conduce con agresividad.

Agility/agilidad La destreza para controlar el movimiento del cuerpo y para cambiar la posición del cuerpo con rapidez.

AIDS-opportunistic illnesses (AIDS-OIs)/enfermedades oportunistas del sida Infecciones y otras enfermedades que no suelen afectar a personas sanas inmunocompetentes.

Al-Anon/Al-Anon Organización mundial de autoayuda para familiares y amigos de alcohólicos.

Alarm/alarma La primera etapa en la respuesta al estrés, cuando el cuerpo y la mente entran en alerta.

Alateen/Alateen Programa de apoyo para personas entre 12 y 20 años de edad cuyos padres, parientes o amigos tienen problemas de alcoholismo.

Alcohol poisoning/intoxicación alcohólica Grave trastorno tóxico que ocurre cuando alguien consume gran cantidad de alcohol en poco tiempo.

Alcoholism/alcoholismo Dependencia física y psicológica de la droga etanol.

Americans with Disabilities Act/Ley sobre Discapacitados de Estados Unidos Ley que prohíbe la discriminación de personas discapacitadas física o mentalmente en el lugar de trabajo, los medios de transporte, instalaciones públicas y telecomunicaciones.

Amino acids/aminoácidos Sustancias químicas que componen las proteínas del cuerpo.

Amniocentesis/amniocentesis Procedimiento en el que se introduce una jeringa a través de la pared abdominal de la mujer embarazada para extraer algo del líquido amniótico que rodea al feto en desarrollo.

Anabolic steroids/esteroides anabólicos Sustancias químicas similares a la hormona masculina testosterona.

Anaerobic exercise/ejercicio anaeróbico Arranques de actividad intensa en los que los músculos se esfuerzan tanto que producen energía sin utilizar oxígeno.

Analgesics/analgésicos   Medicinas para aliviar el dolor.

Angina pectoris/angina de pecho   Dolor y presión en el pecho causada por la falta de oxígeno en el corazón.

Anorexia nervosa/anorexia nerviosa   Trastorno en el que el miedo irracional a la obesidad resulta en la pérdida severa de peso debido al ayuno autoimpuesto.

Antagonistic interaction/interacción antagónica   Cuando el efecto de una medicina se cancela o reduce al combinarla con otra medicina.

Antibodies/anticuerposp   Proteínas que destruyen o neutralizan los patógenos invasores.

Anxiety disorder/trastornos de ansiedad   Enfermedad o trastorno en el que los miedos reales o imaginarios impiden a alguien disfrutar la vida.

Apgar test/prueba de Apgar   Examen diagnóstico de rutina que determina la condición física de un recién nacido.

Appendicitis/apendicitis   Inflamación del apéndice.

Appendicular skeleton/esqueleto apendicular   Los 126 huesos de los hombros, los brazos, las manos, las caderas, las piernas y los pies.

Appetite/apetito   El deseo, más que la necesidad, de comer.

Arteries/arterias   Los vasos sanguíneos que transportan la sangre desde el corazón.

Arteriosclerosis/arterioesclerosis   Endurecimiento de las arterias.

Arthritis/artritis   Al menos 100 trastornos diferentes que causan molestia, dolor e hinchazón en las articulaciones y el tejido conjuntivo de todo el cuerpo.

Asbestos/asbesto   Mineral fibroso

Assailant/atacante   Aquel que comete un acto violento en contra de otra persona.

Assertive/firme   Defender los derechos propios de manera enérgica pero positiva.

Asthma/asma   Trastorno inflamatorio en el que se angostan los pequeños conductos de los pulmones, llamados bronquiolos, causando dificultad para respirar.

Athlete's foot/pie de atleta   Infección por hongos de la piel entre los dedos de los pies.

Autonomy/autonomía   La seguridad de poder controlar el propio cuerpo, impulsos y medio ambiente.

Axial skeleton/esqueleto axial   Los 80 huesos del cráneo, la columna vertebral, las costillas y el esternón.

B

Balance/equilibrio   La capacidad de mantenerse erguido, ya sea parado o en movimiento.

Basal metabolism/metabolismo basal   La cantidad mínima de energía requerida para mantener los procesos vitales del cuerpo.

Benign/benigno   Que no es canceroso.

Bile/bilis   Fluido verde amarillento y amargo que desempeña un papel importante en la descomposición de las grasas.

Binge drinking/borrachera   Tomar alcohol en exceso periódicamente.

Biodegradable/biodegradable   Que puede ser descompuesto por los microorganismos del medio ambiente.

Biopsy/biopsia   Análisis en un laboratorio de una porción de tejido tomada de una zona donde se sospecha la presencia de crecimiento anormal de células.

Bipolar disorder/trastorno maníaco-depresivo   Enfermedad psicológica caracterizada por cambios extremos en el estado de ánimo entre depresión y euforia o manía.

Bladder/vejiga   Órgano muscular hueco que funciona como reservorio de orina.

Blizzard/ventisca   Tormenta de nieve con vientos de 35 millas (56 km) por hora o más.

Blood alcohol concentration (BAC)/concentración de alcohol en la sangre   La cantidad de alcohol en la sangre de un individuo expresada en forma de porcentaje.

Body composition/composición corporal   La relación entre la grasa corporal y los tejidos magros, incluyendo músculos, huesos, agua y tejidos conjuntivos como ligamentos, cartílago y tendones.

Body language/lenguaje corporal   Comunicación no verbal a través de gestos, expresiones faciales y comportamientos.

Body mass index (BMI)/índice de masa corporal (IMC)   La relación entre peso y estatura.

Brain stem/médula oblonga o bulbo raquídeo   Tallo de fibras y células nerviosas de 3 pulgadas (7.6 cm) de largo que conecta la espina dorsal con el resto del cerebro.

Bronqui/bronquios   Conductos que conectan la tráquea con los pulmones.

Bulimia nervosa/bulimia   Trastorno en el que ciclos de comer en exceso se suceden de alguna forma de purga o limpieza del trayecto digestivo.

C

Calories/calorías   Unidades de calor.

Cancer/cáncer   Crecimiento anormal y descontrolado de las células.

Capillaries/capilares   Vasos que transportan la sangre entre las arteriolas y otros vasos pequeños llamados vénulas.

Carbohydrate loading/almacenamiento de carbohidratos   Almacenar glicógeno extra en los músculos.

Carbohydrates/carbohidratos Almidones y azúcares presentes en el alimento.

Carbon monoxide/monóxido de carbono Gas venenoso inodoro e incoloro, presente en el humo de cigarrillo, que pasa a la sangre a través de los pulmones.

Carcinogens/carcinógenos Sustancias que causan cáncer.

Cardiac muscle/músculo cardíaco Un tipo especial de tejido estriado que forma las paredes del corazón.

Cardipulmonary resucitacion (CPR)/resucitación cardiopulmonar (RCP) Una técnica para salvar vidas en la que se fuerza al corazón a bombear sangre al cuerpo por medio de la aplicación de presión.

Cardiorespiratory endurance/resistencia cardiovascular La capacidad del corazón, los pulmones y los vasos sanguíneos para enviar energía y oxígeno a los tejidos del organismo durante largos períodos de actividad vigorosa.

Cardiovascular diseases (CVDs)/enfermedades cardiovasculares Trastornos de salud que afectan el corazón y los vasos sanguíneos.

Cardiovascular failure/insuficiencia cardíaca Situación en la que el corazón no bombea sangre.

Carjacking/secuestro de un auto Robar o secuestrar un auto por la fuerza.

Carotid pulse/pulso carotídeo El latido cardíaco que se siente a ambos lados del cuello.

Cartilage/cartílago Tejido conjuntivo fuerte y flexible.

Cerebellum/cerebelo La segunda parte del cerebro en tamaño.

Cerebral palsy/parálisis cerebral Un grupo de trastornos neurológicos no progresivos que resultan de daños al cerebro antes de nacer, durante el parto, en el período neonatal o en la primera infancia.

Cerebrum/cerebro La parte más grande y más compleja del encéfalo.

Cervix/cérvix El cuello del útero.

Chemotherapy/quimioterapia El uso de medicamentos en el tratamiento del cáncer.

Child abuse/maltrato infantil Daño físico, incluyendo abuso sexual, o daño emocional que se hace a un niño o niña.

Chlamydia/clamidia Infección causada por una bacteria que afecta la vagina en las mujeres y la uretra en los hombres.

Chlorofluorocarbons (CFCs)/clorofluorocarbonos Compuestos del cloro, el flúor y el carbón.

Cholesterol/colesterol Sustancia semejante a la grasa que se produce en el hígado de todos los animales y, como consecuencia, presente únicamente en alimentos de origen animal.

Chorionic villi sampling/biopsia de vellosidades coriónicas Examen en el que se extrae una pequeña muestra de membrana del corion, una capa de tejido que se desarrolla en la placenta.

Choroid/coroides La capa media de la pared del globo ocular.

Chromosomes/cromosomas Estructuras diminutas dentro del núcleo de las células que contienen información sobre los rasgos hereditarios.

Chyme/quimo Mezcla cremosa y líquida de alimento y jugos gástricos.

Circumcision/circuncisión Procedimiento quirúrgico por el que se extirpa el prepucio del pene.

Cirrhosis/cirrosis Trastorno en el que se destruye el tejido del hígado y es reemplazado por tejido fibroso.

Clinical psychologist/psicólogo clínico Psicólogo o psicóloga que diagnostica y trata los trastornos emocionales y de comportamiento, pero no puede recetar medicamentos.

Clique/camarilla Grupo de amigos pequeño y restringido, cuyos miembros suelen venir de medios similares o compartir gustos, y que excluye a otros que considera ajenos a su círculo.

Closure/cierre La conclusión de una de las partes más intensas del proceso de duelo.

Cluster of suicides/suicidios múltiples Proliferación de suicidios que ocurren dentro de un período corto de tiempo e involucran a varias personas de la misma escuela o comunidad.

Codependents/codependientes Personas que se preocupan demasiado con el problema de adicción de otro y sienten el impulso de arreglarlo o controlarlo.

Cognition/entendimiento La capacidad de razonar y deducir soluciones abstractas.

Commitment/compromiso Una promesa o voto.

Communication/comunicación Proceso por el cual uno envía mensajes y recibe mensajes de otros.

Compromise/acuerdo Arreglo en el que cada persona cede algo para lograr una solución que satisfaga a todos.

Confidentiality/confidencialidad Respetar la privacidad de ambas partes y mantener en secreto los detalles.

Confirmatory test/análisis de confirmación Prueba altamente eficaz utilizada para confirmar los resultados de un ELISA (EIA) positivo.

Conflict/conflicto Cualquier desacuerdo, lucha o pelea.

Conflict resolution/resolución de conflictos Proceso dar solución a un conflicto por medio de la cooperación y la búsqueda de soluciones en común.

Congenital/congénito Que está presente al nacer.

Congestive heart failure/insuficiencia cardíaca congestiva Debilitamiento lento y progresivo del corazón debido a la sobrecarga.

Conservation/conservación   Preocupación por preservar el medio ambiente.

Constructive criticism/crítica constructiva   Comentarios hechos sin hostilidad que señalan problemas y potencialmente pueden ayudar a alguien a cambiar.

Contaminant/contaminante   Sustancia que echa a perder o infecta.

Cool-down/enfriamiento   Actividad que se inicia para reducir gradualmente la actividad.

Cooperation/cooperación   Trabajar en conjunto para beneficio de todos.

Coordination/coordinación   La capacidad para usar juntas y bien dos o más partes del cuerpo, o de usar los sentidos junto con las partes del cuerpo.

Cornea/córnea   Lente principal del ojo que realiza la mayor parte de la tarea de enfocar.

Crisis/crisis   Un cambio extremo en la vida de una persona.

Crisis center/centro de emergencias   Establecimiento equipado para manejar emergencias y para orientar a personas que necesitan ayuda.

Cross-contamination/contaminación cruzada   La propagación de bacterias de uno a otro alimento.

Cross-training/entrenamiento combinado   Combinar varias rutinas de ejercicio para ejercitar distintos sistemas del cuerpo.

Culture/cultura   Las creencias, costumbres y comportamientos colectivos de un grupo.

Custody/custodia   Una decisión legal sobre quién tiene la responsabilidad de tomar decisiones que afectan a los niños y quién tiene la responsibilidad física de cuidarlos.

Cystitis/cistitis   Infección bacteriana de la vejiga que ocurre con mayor frecuencia en las mujeres.

D

Dandruff/caspa   Trastorno en que se cae la capa más superficial de células de piel muertas del cuero cabelludo.

Date rape/violación durante una cita   La violación que ocurre entre dos personas que están saliendo juntas.

Defense mechanisms/mecanismos de defensa   Estrategias que se usan para hacer frente a sentimientos y situaciones muy fuertes o estresantes.

Deforestation/deforestación   La destrucción de los bosques.

Delayed grief response/Reacción tardía del duelo   La postergación de las etapas más intensas del duelo.

Delirium tremens (DTs)/delirium tremens   Los dramáticos efectos físicos y psicológicos del síndrome de abstinencia del alcohol.

Depressants/depresores   Drogas que tienden a desacelerar el sistema nervioso central.

Depression/depresión   Sentimientos de desamparo, desesperanza y tristeza.

Dermis/dermis   La capa interna y gruesa de la piel.

Desertification/desertificación   La transformación de praderas y campos de lluvia o regadío en zonas de condiciones desérticas.

Designated drivers/conductores designados   Personas en un contexto social que deciden no tomar para así poder conducir un auto y evitar riesgos para ellos y para otros.

Designer drugs/drogas ilegales de preparado especial   Sustancias sintéticas cuyo fin es imitar los efectos de los narcóticos y alucinógenos.

Detachment/desapego   El proceso de desligarse o dejar de estar involucrado en la adicción de otro, rehusando a que esa adicción controle nuestra vida.

Detoxification/desintoxicación   El proceso de limpiar el cuerpo de drogas.

Developmental task/tarea del desarrollo   Algo que debe ocurrir en una etapa en particular para que la persona continúe su crecimiento para convertirse en un adulto sano y maduro.

Diabetes/diabetes   Enfermedad crónica que afecta el modo en que las células del cuerpo convierten el alimento en energía.

Diaphragm/diafragma   Músculo que separa la cavidad torácica de la cavidad abdominal.

Digestion/digestión   La descomposición física y química del alimento para su uso por las células del cuerpo.

Disability/incapacidad   Cualquier impedimento físico o mental que limita la actividad normal, incluyendo, ver, oír, caminar o hablar.

Distress/aflicción   Tensión negativa.

Domestic violence/violencia doméstica   Cualquier acto de violencia que involucre a miembros de una misma familia.

Drug watches/agrupaciones vecinales antidrogas   Esfuerzos comunitarios organizados en los que residentes de un vecindario tratan de impedir la compraventa y el consumo de drogas patrullando, vigilando, denunciando y de otras formas.

Drug-Free School Zones/zonas libres de drogas alrededor de las escuelas   Áreas dentro de los 1,000 pies de distancia de una escuela señalizadas con letreros, dentro de las cuales aquel que sea hallado vendiendo drogas recibe penas particularmente severas.

E

Electrocution/electrocución   Muerte que resulta de una descarga eléctrica de alto voltaje que pasa por el cuerpo.

Electrolytes/electrólitos   Nutrientes que se cargan de electricidad al ser sumergidos en una solución.

Elimination/eliminación   La expulsión de alimento sin digerir o desechos corporales.

ELISA (EIA)/ELISA Prueba que detecta la presencia de anticuerpos del VIH en la sangre.

Embryo/embrión Racimo de células en desarrollo que se forma después de la implantación.

Emetic/emético Un agente que induce el vómito.

Emotional abuse/maltrato emocional Patrón de comportamiento que atenta contra el desarrollo emocional y la autovaloración de un niño o niña.

Emotional initmacy/intimidad emocional La capacidad de vivir una relación cariñosa y afectuosa con otra persona con quien puedes compartir tus sentimientos más intimos.

Emotional maturity/madurez emocional Estado en el que las capacidades mentales y emocionales de un individuo se han desarrollado plenamente.

Emotions/emociones Sentimientos.

Empathy/empatía La capacidad para imaginar y comprender cómo se siente otra persona.

Empty-nest syndrome/síndrome del nido vacío Sentimientos de desesperación y soledad que suceden cuando los hijos se van de la casa y entran en la edad adulta.

Enabling/posibilitar Tratar de proteger a una persona que tiene problemas con el alcohol o las drogas para que no tenga que enfrentar las consecuencias de su problema de adicción.

Endocrine glands/glándulas endócrinas Estructuras de secreción interna que producen hormonas.

Enriched food/alimentos enriquecidos Alimento al cual se le agregan los nutrientes que ha perdido durante el procesamiento.

Environment/medio ambiente La suma total de lo que te rodeaótu familia, el lugar adonde te has criado, el lugar donde vives ahora y la totalidad de tus experiencias.

Epidemic/epidemia Brote de una enfermedad infecciosa que afecta a una población numerosa.

Epidemiology/epidemiología El estudio científico de las epidemias.

Epidermis/epidermis La capa delgada exterior de la piel.

Epilepsy/epilepsia Trastorno del sistema nervioso que se caracteriza por ataques recurrentesóepisodios repentinos de actividad eléctrica descontrolada en el cerebro.

Escalate/escalar Avanzar a una situación que no es sana e incluso puede ser peligrosa para todas las partes involucradas.

Ethanol/etanol El tipo de alcohol que se encuentra en las bebidas alcohólicas.

Euphoria/euforia Sentimiento temporario de bienestar intenso o felicidad que puede verse sucedido por un "bajón" o derrumbe anímico completo.

Eustress/estrés positivo Tensión benéfica.

Exploited/explotado Utilizado para beneficio de otro.

Extensors/extensores Músculos que abren una articulación.

External auditory canal/canal auditivo externo Un conducto de más o menos 1 pulgada (2.5 cm) de largo.

F

Fallopian tubes/trompas de Falopio Un par de trompas con extensiones similares a dedos que atraen al óvulo.

Family counseling/terapia familiar Terapia para restaurar las relaciones sanas en una familia.

Famine/hambruna Escasez generalizada de alimento.

Fatigue/fatiga Tercera etapa de la respuesta al estrés que se manifiesta en un sentimiento de cansancio que reduce el nivel de actividad.

Fatty liver/hígado graso Trastorno en el que se acumula en el hígado grasa que no puede ser descompuesta.

Feedback/retroalimentación Mensajes de otros que nos indican lo que piensan sobre quiénes somos y cómo somos.

Fermentation/fermentación La acción química de la levadura sobre los azúcares.

Fertilization/fertilización La unión de una célula reproductiva masculina con una femenina.

Fetal alcohol syndrome/síndrome de alcoholismo fetal Trastorno en el que un feto se ha visto afectado en forma negativa mental y físicamente por la ingestión de mucho alcohol por parte de su madre durante el embarazo.

Fetus/feto Nombre que se le da al embrión desde la octava semana hasta el nacimiento.

Fibrillation/fibrilación El latido rápido e ineficaz del corazón en una de dos cámaras llamadas ventrículos.

Fire extinguisher/extintor de incendios Aparato portátil que apaga pequeños incendios al lanzar sustancias químicas que extinguen el fuego.

First aid/primeros auxilios La atención médica inmediata y temporaria que se presta a alguien que se ha enfermado o lesionado.

Flexibility/flexibilidad La capacidad de mover una parte del cuerpo a través de todo un espectro de movimiento.

Fexors/flexores Músculos que cierran una articulación.

Follicles/folículos Pequeños sacos o bolsas de la piel.

Food additives/aditivos Sustancias que se añaden a los alimentos con el propósito de obtener un efecto deseado.

Food allergy/alergia alimenticia Trastorno en el que el sistema inmune del cuerpo reacciona exageradamente a ciertos alimentos.

Foodborne illness/intoxicación alimenticia
Enfermedad causada por los alimentos.

Fortification/fortificación El proceso de añadir nutrientes que no están presentes por naturaleza.

Foster care/acogimiento familiar Bajo la guía y supervisión de una familia encabezada por padres o una padre o madre que no tiene relación sanguinea con el niño.

Friendship/amistad Una relación significativa entre dos personas basada en el cariño, la consideración y la confianza.

Frostbite/congelación Condición que ocurre cuando se congela el tejido del cuerpo.

G

Gametes/gametos Células reproductivas que producen las gónadas.

Gangrene/gangrena La muerte de tejido en alguna parte del cuerpo.

Gastric juices/jugos gástricos Secreciones de la capa interior del estómago que contienen pepsina, y ácido hidroclorídrico.

Gateway drugs/drogas precursoras Drogas que a menudo conducen al consumo serio y peligroso de drogas.

Generativity/capacidad de generar Volver la atención más allá de uno mismo en el presente y empezar a ocuparse de las generaciones futuras.

Generic/genérico Versión más barata de un medicamento que puede reemplazar a un medicamento de marca.

Genes/genes Pequeños segmentos de las moléculas de ADN (ácido desoxirribonucleico).

Genital herpes/herpes genital Llagas similares a ampollas en la zona genital.

Genital warts/verrugas genitales Verrugas rosadas o rojizas con una textura similar a la coliflor que aparecen en la zona genital.

Glucose/glucosa Azúcar simple que representa la principal fuente de energía del cuerpo.

Glycogen/glucógeno Sustancia similar al almidón.

Goal/meta Objetivo que quieres lograr y para el cual hay que planificar y trabajar.

Gonads/gónadas Los ovarios y los testículos.

Gonorrhea/gonorrea Enfermedad de transmisión sexual causada por bacterias que afectan la membrana mucosa genital, principalmente en el revestimiento de la uretra en los hombres y en el cuello del útero y la vagina en las mujeres.

Greenhouse effect/efecto invernadero
Desaceleración del ritmo al que la tierra despide calor, lo cual causa un aumento en la temperatura de la tierra.

Grief reaction/reacción al duelo La totalidad de la respuesta de un individuo a una pérdida significativa.

H

Halfway houses/establecimientos de transición
Entidades de tratamiento continuado que ofrecen alojamiento, asesoramiento y reuniones de apoyo a quienes se están recuperando de una adicción severa.

Hallucinogens/alucinógenos Drogas que alteran el estado de ánimo, los pensamientos y las percepciones sensitivas, incluyendo la vista, el oído, el olfato y el tacto.

Hardy personality/personalidad robusta Un tipo de personalidad que parece poder mantener un buen estado de salud pese a sufrir estrés grave o incluso traumático.

Hashish/hachís Resina color café oscuro que se obtiene de la punta del cáñamo.

Hazardous wastes/residuos peligrosos Cualquier sustancia que sea explosiva, corrosiva, inflamable o tóxica para la vida humana u otras formas de vida.

Health/salud La combinación del bienestar físico, mental-emocional y social.

Health care facility/establecimiento de atención médica Cualquier lugar atendido por profesionales de la salud y equipado para prestar servicios de salud.

Health-care providers/prestadores de servicios de salud Profesionales entrenados en el campo de los servicios de salud.

Health consumer/consumidor de servicios de salud Persona que utiliza productos o servicios de salud.

Health insurance/seguro médico Plan para cubrir una parte o la totalidad de los gastos asociados al tratamiento médico.

Health literacy/educación sobre salud La capacidad de un individuo para obtener, interpretar y comprender información básica relacionada con la salud, y de utilizar tal información y servicios con el fin de promover su salud y bienestar.

Health maintenance organization HMO)/organización para el mantenimiento de la salud Un grupo de médicos de distintas especialidades que trabajan juntos para prestar servicios médicos a los socios de la organización.

Health skills/recursos de salud Instrumentos y estrategias específicos que conducen a decisiones mejores y más informadas en lo que concierne a la salud.

Heat cramps/calambres Espasmos musculares que resultan de la pérdida de grandes cantidades de sal y agua a través de la transpiración.

Heat exhaustion/golpe de calor Calentamiento excesivo del cuerpo que se manifiesta por piel fría y húmeda y síntomas de choque.

Hemodialysis/hemodiálisis Técnica por la cual se limpia la sangre de desechos con un riñón artificial.

Hemoglobin/hemoglobina La parte de la sangre que lleva oxígeno.

Heredity/herencia   Todos los rasgos y propiedades que se transmiten biológicamente de padres a hijos.

Hernia/hernia   Protuberancia de un órgano o tejido a través de un área débil del músculo.

Hiatal hernia/hernia hiatal   Trastorno en el que parte del estómago sobresale a través de una abertura en el diafragma.

Hierarchy of needs/jerarquía de necesidades   Lista categorizada de las necesidades esenciales para el crecimiento y desarrollo humano, presentadas en orden ascendente desde las más básicas hasta las que producen mayor satisfacción y sentimiento de realización.

HIV reactive/VIH positivo   Infectado con el VIH.

Homicide/homicidio   El asesinato intencional de un ser humano por otro.

Hormones/hormonas   Sustancias químicas producidas por glándulas de secreción internas que regulan la actividad de distintas células del organismo.

Hostility/hostilidad   El uso intencional de comportamiento poco amable o antipático.

Human immunodeficiency virus (HIV)/virus de inmunodeficiencia humana (VIH)   Virus que ataca el sistema inmune del cuerpo.

Hunger/hambre   Impulso natural que nos protege de la inanición.

Hurricane/huracán   Tormenta fuerte con lluvia y vendavales.

Hydration/hidratación   El proceso de agregar fluidos al cuerpo.

Hypertension/hipertensión   Presión arterial alta.

Hypochondria/hipocondria   Preocupación por el cuerpo y miedo a supuestas enfermedades que son inexistentes.

Hypothermia/hipotermia   Condición en que la temperatura del cuerpo baja a niveles peligrosos.

I

"I" message/mensaje "yo"   Declaración en la que alguien expresa sus sentimientos usando el pronombre "yo".

Illegal drugs/drogas ilegales   Drogas que se compran ilícitamente en la calle.

Illicit drug use/consumo ilegal de drogas   El consumo o venta de cualquier sustancia ilegal o prohibida.

Immunity/inmunidad   Las defensas naturales del cuerpo contra la infección.

Immunization/vacunación   Programa por el cual se inmuniza contra una enfermedad a una comunidad u otra población numerosa.

Impaired glucose tolerance (IGT)/Alteración en la tolerancia a la glucosa   Trastorno en el que los niveles de azúcar en la sangre son más altos que lo normal, pero no tan altos como para ser clasificados como diabetes.

Incontinence/incontinencia   La incapacidad del cuerpo para controlar la vejiga y la eliminación de desechos.

Indigestion/indigestión   Malestar y ardor en la boca del estómago.

Infatuation/amor desmedido   Sentimientos de pasión exagerada por otra persona.

Infectious disease/enfermedad infecciosa   Enfermedad causada por organismos que entran en el cuerpo humano y se multiplican.

Infertility/infertilidad   La incapacidad de una mujer para quedar embarazada.

Ingestion/ingestión   La introducción de alimento en el cuerpo.

Inhalants/inhalantes   Sustancias con vapores que se huelen y se aspiran para inducir un estado de alucinación.

Inpatient treatment/tratamiento de pacientes internados   Atención médica o psicológica durante la cual una persona permanece en un establecimiento médico o de rehabilitación.

Insulin/insulina   Hormona que se produce en el páncreas y que ayuda al cuerpo a transformar glucosa en energía.

Integrity/entereza   Sentimiento de integridad y satisfacción.

Integumentary system/sistema integumentario   El sistema corporal que incluye la piel, el cabello, las uñas, las glándulas sebáceas y las glándulas sudoríparas.

Internal conflicts/conflictos internos   Luchas dentro de uno mismo.

Interpersonal conflicts/conflictos interpersonales   Desacuerdos entre grupos de cualquier tamaño, ya sean dos personas o dos países.

Intervention/intervención   La interrupción del ciclo continuo de adicción antes de que el adicto o el alcohólico toque fondo.

Intoxication/ebriedad   Disminución de la capacidad física y mental como resultado del consumo de alcohol.

Intravenous (IV) drugs/drogas intravenosas   Drogas que se inyectan en las venas.

Isokinetic exercise/ejercicio isoquinético   Actividad que implica resistencia a lo largo de un espectro completo de movimiento.

Isometric exercise/ejercicio isométrico   Actividad que usa la tensión muscular para mejorar la fuerza muscular con poco o ningún movimiento de la parte del cuerpo.

Isotonic exercise/ejercicio isotónico   Actividad que combina la contracción muscular con movimientos repetitivos.

L

Labyrinth/laberinto   Oído interno.

Lacrimal gland/lagrimal   La glándula encargada de producir lágrimas.

Larynx/laringe   Órgano encargado de la voz.

Latency/latencia   Etapa en la que el virus está presente pero inactivo.

Leukoplakia/leucoplasia   Manchas gruesas, blanquecinas y apergaminadas presentes en de la boca de quienes mascan tabaco y que pueden evolucionar hacia el cáncer de boca.

Lifestyle activities/actividades del estilo de vida   Formas de actividad física, incorporadas a la rutina diaria normal o al esparcimiento, que promueven la buena salud a lo largo de la vida.

Lifestyle factors/factores del estilo de vida   Hábitos y comportamientos personales relacionados con el modo de vida que afectan el nivel de salud.

Ligaments/ligamentos   Cordones resistentes de tejido fibroso y algo elástico que unen los extremos de los huesos a la altura de la articulación.

Linoleic acid/ácido linoleico   Ácido graso esencial que es fundamental para el crecimiento y la salud de la piel, pero que no se produce en el cuerpo.

Lipid/lípido   Sustancia grasosa que no se disuelve en agua.

Look-alike drugs/drogas de imitación   Drogas que se fabrican de manera tal que se parezcan a drogas ilegales específicas.

Lymph/linfa   Fluido amarillo transparente que rellena los espacios alrededor de las células del cuerpo.

Lymphocytes/linfocitos   Un tipo de glóbulo blanco que protege al organismo contra los patógenos.

M

Mainstream smoke/humo directo   El humo que exhala el fumador.

Malignant/maligno   Canceroso.

Manipulation/manipulación   Forma solapada o deshonesta de controlar o influir en los demás.

Marijuana/marihuana   La planta del cáñamo (cannabis) que se fuma, se come o se toma por sus efectos intoxicantes.

Marital adjustment/adaptación al matrimonio   La forma en que las personas se ajustan o se adaptan entre sí y al matriomio.

Mastication/masticación   El proceso de mascar.

Mediator/mediador   Persona que ayuda a otros a resolver cuestiones para satisfacción de ambas partes.

Meditation/mediación   Proceso en el que personas específicamente entrenadas ayudan a otras a resolver sus conflictos de manera pacífica.

Medicaid/Medicaid   Programa de ayuda para asistencia médica destinado a personas de todas las edades que no tienen los recursos para financiar su atención médica.

Medical history/historial clínico   Información completa y amplia sobre vacunaciones y enfermedades pasadas de un paciente.

Medicare/Medicare   Programa de seguro de salud accesible a personas de 65 años de edad o más y a aquellos que reciben beneficios por incapacidad a través del seguro social.

Medicine misuse/mal uso de medicamentos   Utilizar un medicamento para un fin distinto al que tiene.

Medicines/medicamentos   Sustancias que, al ser ingeridas o introducidas en el cuerpo, ayudan a prevenir o curar enfermedades u otros problemas médicos.

Megadoses/megadosis   Grandes cantidades de suplementos nutricionales.

Melanin/melanina   El pigmento que da su coloración a la piel, el cabello y el iris de los ojos.

Melanoma/melanoma   Un tipo frecuentemente mortal de cáncer de la piel.

Menopause/menopausia   El detenimiento permanente de la ovulación y la menstruación.

Menstrual cycle/ciclo menstrual   El tiempo que transcurre entre el comienzo de un periodo menstrual y el inicio del siguiente.

Mental disorder/trastorno mental   Enfermedad de la mente que puede afectar los pensamientos, sentimientos y comportamientos de una persona, impidiéndole llevar una vida feliz, sana y productiva.

Mental health/salud mental   Tener una actitud general positiva, sentirse cómodo con uno mismo y los demás, y ser capaz de enfrentar los desafíos y las demandas de la vida.

Mental retardation/retardo mental   Capacidad intelectual inferior al promedio presente desde el nacimiento o la primera infancia y asociada a dificultades en el aprendizaje y la adaptación social.

Metabolism/metabolismo   El proceso por el cual el cuerpo obtiene energía del alimento.

Metastasis/metástasis   La propagación del cáncer desde el lugar donde se originó a otras partes del cuerpo.

Minerals/minerales   Sustancias inorgánicas que el cuerpo no puede producir pero que actúan como catalizadores, regulando muchos procesos vitales del cuerpo.

Miscarriage/aborto espontáneo   Pérdida espontánea de un embarazo.

Modeling/imitar   Copiar los comportamientos de aquellos a quienes uno está expuesto.

Mucous membranes/membranas mucosas   Revestimiento suave semejante a la piel de muchas partes del cuerpo.

Muscle cramp/calambre muscular   Espasmo o contractura súbita de un músculo.

Muscle tone/tono muscular   La tensión natural de las fibras musculares.

Muscular endurance/resistencia muscular   La capacidad de los músculos para realizar tareas físicas difíciles durante un período de tiempo sin fatigarse.

Muscular strength/fuerza muscular   La cantidad de fuerza que puede ejercer un músculo.

N

Narcotics/narcóticos   Drogas derivadas de la planta del opio que tienen un efecto sedante.

Neglect/descuido   No proveer para las necesidades físicas y emocionales de una niño o niña.

Negotiation/negociación   Proceso en el que se hacen concesiones recíprocas para llegar a un acuerdo.

Nephrons/nefrones   Las unidades funcionales de los riñones.

Neurologist/neurólogo   Médico especializado en los trastornos orgánicos del cerebro y el sistema nervioso.

Neurons/neuronas   Células nerviosas.

Neutrophils/neutrófilos   Los fagocitos principales involucrados en el proceso de fagocitosis.

Nicotine/nicotina   La droga adictiva presente en los cigarrillos.

Nicotine substitutes/sustitutos de la nicotina   Formas manufacturadas de nicotina que envían pequeñas cantidades de la droga al organismo de quien las usa mientras él o ella está intentando dejar el hábito del tabaco.

Nicotine withdrawal/síndrome de abstinencia de la nicotina   El proceso que ocurre cuando se deja de consumir nicotina, una droga adictiva.

Nongonococcal urethritis/uretritis no gonocóxica   Infección causada por varios tipos diferentes de organismos similares a las bacterias que infectan la uretra en los hombres y el cuello del útero en las mujeres.

Noninfectious diseases/enfermedades no infecciosas   Enfermedades que no son transmitidas por medio de un patógeno.

Nutrient supplements/suplementos nutricionales   Píldoras, polvos, líquidos y otros nutrientes sintéticos.

Nutrient-dense/de alto valor nutritivo   Alimentos ricos en nutrientes en relación a su contenido calórico.

nutrients/nutrientes   Sustancias presentes en el alimento que el cuerpo necesita para ejercer adecuadamente funciones como crecer, reconstituirse y disponer de una provisión de energía.

Nutrition/nutrición   Proceso por el cual el cuerpo incorpora y utiliza los alimentos.

O

Obesity/obesidad   Exceso de grasa o tejido adiposo en el cuerpo.

Occupational Safety and Health Administration (OSHA)/Departamento de Seguridad y Sanidad Laboral   Agencia federal responsable de promover condiciones seguras y sanitarias en el lugar de trabajo.

Ossicles/huesillos del oído   Tres huesillos móviles unidos entre sí.

Ossification/osificación   El proceso por el que se forman, renuevan y reparan los huesos.

Osteoarthritis/osteoartritis   Enfermedad que afecta principalmente las articulaciones que soportan peso de las rodillas y caderas, causando molestias y dolores, especialmente al moverse.

Otosclerosis/otoesclerosis   Trastorno hereditario en el que un sobrehueso impide el movimiento de los huesillos del oído.

Outpatient surgical facility/establecimiento de cirugía para pacientes ambulatorios   Lugar adonde se opera a pacientes que son dados de alta el mismo día.

Outpatient treatment/tratamiento de pacientes ambulatorios   Atención médica y psicológica en una institución para alguien que quiere dejar el alcohol y las drogas.

Ova/óvulos   Células reproductivas femeninas.

Ovaries/ovarios   Glándulas sexuales femeninas que contienen los óvulos y producen hormonas sexuales femeninas.

Overdose/sobredosis   Reacción grave o hasta mortal a la ingestión de una gran cantidad de droga.

Overexertion/esfuerzo excesivo   Ejercitar el cuerpo en exceso.

Overload/sobrecarga   Ejercitar el cuerpo en forma más exigente que lo normal.

Over-the-counter (OTC) medicines/medicamentos sin receta   Remedios que se pueden comprar sin receta médica.

Ovulation/ovulación   El proceso de liberar un óvulo maduro cada mes.

P

Pancreas/páncreas   Glándula que cumple funciones en dos sistemasóel digestivo y el endócrino.

Paranoia/paranoia   Suspicacia irracional o recelo hacia los demás.

Parasites/parásitos   Organismos que viven en o dentro de otro organismo y obtienen su alimento de él.

Parathyroid glands/glándulas paratirodes   Estructuras que producen la hormona paratiroides, que regula el equilibrio de calcio y fósforo del organismo.

Particulates/partículas   Pequeños fragmentos suspendidos de materia que son transportados por el aire.

Passive/pasivo   El que renuncia, cede o retrocede sin hacer valer sus derechos y necesidades.

Passive immunity/inmunidad pasiva   La inmunidad temporaria que un recién nacido obtiene de su madre.

Passive smoke/humo indirecto   Humo de cigarrillo, cigarro o pipa que inhalan los no fumadores, y también el humo que permanece en un ambiente cerrado una vez que el fumador ha terminado de fumar.

Pasteurized/pasteurizado   Sometido a un proceso de calentamiento para destruir o retrasar el crecimiento de patógenos.

Peer mediators/mediadores paritarios   Estudiantes entrenados para ayudar a otros estudiantes a encontrar formas justas de arreglar sus diferencias.

Peer pressure/presión del grupo de pares   El control y la influencia que pueden ejercer sobre ti las personas de tu misma edad.

Peers/grupo de pares   Personas de la misma edad que comparten intereses similares.

Penis/pene   Órgano en forma de tubo que se une al cuerpo justo encima de los testículos.

Peptic ulcer/úlcera péptica   Llaga en el revestimiento interno del trayecto digestivo.

Periodontal disease/enfermedad periodontal   Inflamación de las estructuras periodontales.

Periodontium/periodonto   La área que rodea los dientes.

Perishable/perecedero   Que puede echarse a perder.

Peristalsis/peristalsis   Una serie de contracciones musculares involuntarias.

Personal identity/identidad personal   Los factores que nos hacen únicos y diferentes a todos los demás.

Personality/personalidad   Conjunto complejo de características que nos hace únicos y diferentes a todo los demás.

Personality disorders/trastornos de la personalidad   Una variedad de enfermedades psicológicas que afectan la capacidad de una persona para relacionarse con los demás.

Phagocytosis/fagocitosis   El proceso por el cual los fagocitos rodean y destruyen los patógenos.

Pharynx/faringe   Garganta.

Phobias/fobias   Miedos irracionales.

Physical activity/actividad física   Cualquier forma de movimiento, ya sea intencional, como en el caso de los deportes y el entretenimiento, o incidental, como en el caso de realizar las tareas hogareñas.

Physical fitness/buen estado físico   La capacidad de realizar fácilmente las tareas diarias y tener suficiente energía de reserva para responder a demandas inesperadas.

Physical maturity/madurez física   Estado en el cual el cuerpo y todos sus órganos han alcanzado un nivel completo de desarrollo.

Pituitary gland/glándula pituitaria   Estructura que regula y controla la actividad de todas las otras glándulas endócrinas.

Placenta/placenta   Capa exterior de células del embrión con tejido materno rico en sangre.

Planned pregnancy/embarazo planeado   Tomar la decisión de quedar encinta antes de concebir.

Plaque/placa dental   Película pegajosa e incolora que actúa sobre el azúcar formando ácidos que destruyen el esmalte dental e irritan las encías.

Plasma/plasma   El líquido en el que están suspendidos los demás componentes de la sangre.

Platelets/plaquetas   Células que previenen la pérdida de sangre.

Platonic friendship/amistad platónica   Una relación con un miembro del sexo opuesto en la que hay afecto pero no hay actividad sexual.

Pleurisy/pleuresía   Inflamación de la membrana interna que reviste los pulmones y la cavidad torácica.

Pneumonia/neumonía   Grave inflamación de los pulmones.

Poison/veneno   Una sustancia, ya sea sólida, líquida o gaseosa, que causa daño, enfermedad o la muerte al ser introducida en el cuerpo.

Poison control center/centro de control de intoxicaciones   Línea telefónica que funciona las 24 horas y provee asesoramiento sobre cómo tratar a las víctimas de envenenamiento.

Power/potencia   La capacidad de ejercer fuerza con mucha rapidez.

Preferred provider organization (PPO)/plan de salud   Un tipo de seguro de salud en el que los prestadores de servicios médicos acuerdan cobrar menos a los socios del plan.

Prejudice/prejuicio   Sentimiento negativo hacia alguien o hacia algo que no está basado en la experiencia sino más bien en estereotipos.

Prescription medicines/medicamentos con receta   Remedios que no pueden ser usados en forma segura sin la aprobación por escrito de un médico acreditado.

Pressure point/punto de presión   Uno de varios puntos a lo largo de la arteria mayor que provee de sangre a una extremidad afectada.

Prevention/prevención   Practicar hábitos sanos para mantenerse bien y libre de enfermedades y otros malestares.

Primary care physician/médico de cabecera   Un profesional de la medicina que provee la atención de salud primaria.

Priorities/prioridades Aquellas metas, tareas o actividades que uno juzga más importantes que otras.

Priorities/prioridades Aquellas cosas que están en primer lugar en cuanto a su importancia.

Profound deafness/sordera profunda Pérdida del oído tan severa que la persona afectada no puede beneficiarse del uso de amplificación mecánica como la de un audífono.

Progression/progresión Aumento gradual del esfuerzo necesario para lograr un nivel de estado físico más alto.

Proteins/proteínas Nutrientes que ayudan a producir y mantener los tejidos del cuerpo.

Psychiatric social worker/trabajador social para casos psiquiátricos Alguien especializado en casos psiquiátricos que trabaja en un hospital psiquiátrico, clínica de salud mental o agencia de servicios familiares y provee asesoramiento y tratamiento a personas con problemas emocionales.

Psychiatrist/psiquiatra Médico especializado en el diagnóstico y tratamiento de trastornos mentales que puede recetar medicamentos.

Psychoactive drugs/drogas psicoactivas Sustancias químicas que afectan el sistema nervioso central e interfieren con el funcionamiento normal del cerebro.

Psychologists/psicólogos Profesional con título doctoral especializado en el diagnóstico y tratamiento de trastornos emocionales.

Psychosomatic response/respuesta psicosomática Trastorno físico que resulta del estrés más bien que de una lesión o enfermedad.

Puberty/pubertad La etapa en la que hombres y mujeres adquieren la capacidad física de reproducirse.

Public health/salud pública Esfuerzo comunitario para controlar y promover el bienestar de la población.

Pulp/pulpa El tejido vivo situado dentro de los dientes.

Q

Quackery/curanderismo Un tipo de fraude médico.

R

Rabies/rabia Enfermedad viral del sistema nervioso que eventualmente conduce a la locura y la muerte.

Random violence/violencia al azar Violencia cometida sin ninguna razón en particular.

Rape/violación Relación sexual forzada.

Reaction time/tiempo de reacción La velocidad del movimiento tan pronto una persona se da cuenta de que debe moverse.

Rechanneling/reorientación Transferir o recanalizar tus energías.

Recommended Dietary Allowances (RDA)/Raciones Dietéticas Recomendadas (RDR) Las cantidades de nutrientes que previenen deficiencias y excesos en la mayoría de las personas saludables.

Recovery/recuperación Aprender a vivir sin alcohol ni drogas.

Recycling/reciclaje El tratamiento de la basura de forma que pueda volver a usarse, y la conciencia de que tales prácticas existen.

Reflex/reflejo Respuesta espontánea del cuerpo a un estímulo.

Refusal skills/técnicas para rehusarse Habilidades que te ayudan a rehusarte cuando te instan a participar en comportamientos poco seguros o poco sanos.

Rehydration/rehidratación Restaurar los líquidos que el cuerpo ha perdido.

Relapses/recaídas Deslices en la recuperación, o retornos periódicos a la bebida y el consumo de drogas.

Relationship/relación Vínculo o conexión entre las personas.

Relaxation response/respuesta a la relajación Estado de reposo profundo que puede alcanzarse al practicar regularmente una o más técnicas de relajación.

Repetitive motion injury/lesión por uso repetido Daño a los tejidos causado por la reiteración prolongada de movimientos.

Rescue breathing/asistencia respiratoria de emergencia Respiración artificial.

Resilience/flexibilidad La capacidad de adaptarse de forma efectiva y recuperarse de una desilusión, una dificultad o una crisis.

Resistance/resistencia La segunda etapa de la respuesta al estrés, cuando el cuerpo busca reparar el daño sufrido a raíz del hecho estresante y volver a su estado normal.

Respiration/respiración El intercambio de gases entre el cuerpo y el medio ambiente.

Respiratory failure/insuficiencia respiratoria Estado en el que el aire no puede llegar a los pulmones.

Resting heart rate/frecuencia cardíaca basal La cantidad de veces que late el corazón en un minuto cuando está en reposo.

Retina/retina Membrana sensible a la luz en la que la córnea y el cristalino proyectan las imágenes.

Rheumatoid arthritis/artritis reumatoidea Inflamación destructiva e incapacitante de las articulaciones.

Risk factors/factores de riesgo Actos o comportamientos que representan un riesgo potencial para la salud.

Road rage/furia del conductor Cuando se combinan la ira intensa y el acto de conducir un vehículo.

Role/papel   La función o papel que juegas en una relación.

Rubella/rubéola   Erupción semejante a la del sarampión.

S

Schizophrenia/esquizofrenia   Serio trastorno mental que significa "mente dividida".

Sclera/esclerótica   La capa externa blanca y resistente del ojo.

Sebaceous glands/glándulas sebáceas   Estructuras de la piel que producen una secreción aceitosa llamada sebo.

Sedentary lifestyle/estilo de vida sedentario   Estilo de vida que requiere poco movimiento o ejercicio.

Self-actualization/autorrealización   El esfuerzo por llegar a ser lo mejor posible.

Self-control/autocontrol   La capacidad para usar la sensatez en lugar de las emociones.

Self-directed/por voluntad propia   Tomar decisiones correctas en cuanto al comportamiento cuando no hay adultos que hagan cumplir las reglas.

Self-esteem/autoestima   La confianza y valoración que uno siente respecto de sí mismo.

Semen/semen   Líquido espeso que contiene espermatozoides y otras secreciones del órgano reproductivo masculino.

Sex characteristics/características sexuales   Los rasgos relacionados con el sexo.

Sexual assault/agresión sexual   Cualquier ataque sexual intencional contra otra persona.

Sexually transmitted diseases (STDs)/enfermedades de transmisión sexual (ETS)   Enfermedades infecciosas que se contagian a través del contacto sexual.

Shock/choque   La imposibilidad del sistema cardiovascular de mantener un flujo adecuado de sangre circulando por los órganos vitales del cuerpo.

Sibling/hermano   Hermano o hermana.

Side effects/efectos secundarios   Reacciones no buscadas a los medicamentos.

Sidestream smoke/corriente de humo   El humo que sale del tabaco que se está quemando.

Situation/situación   La circunstancia o evento previo a un accidente.

Skeletal muscles/músculos del esqueleto   Los músculos estriados pegados a los huesos que causan los movimientos del cuerpo.

Smoke detector/detector de humo   Alarma que suena ante la presencia de humo.

Smokeless tobacco/tabaco sin humo   Tabaco que se aspira por la nariz o se masca.

Smooth muscles/músculos lisos   El tipo de músculo que se encarga de mover los órganos internos.

Somatoform disorder/trastorno somatoforme   Enfermedad o trastorno en el que una persona se queja de síntomas para los cuales no se puede hallar una causa física.

Specialist/especialista   Médico que ha recibido formación adicional en un área particular de la medicina.

Specificity/especificidad   Principio que establece que determinados ejercicios y actividades mejoran ciertas áreas del estado físico relacionadas con la salud.

Speed/velocidad   La capacidad de trasladarse una distancia o completar un movimiento del cuerpo en un periodo corto de tiempo.

Sperm/espermatozoides   Células reproductivas masculinas.

Spousal abuse/maltrato conyugal   Maltrato doméstico dirigido a un cónyuge.

Sprain/torcedura   Lesión de los tejidos que rodean a una articulación.

Stereotype/estereotipo   Opinión exagerada o demasiado simplificada acerca de todo un grupo de personas, frecuentemente basada en la raza, la religión o la orientación sexual.

Sterility/esterilidad   Trastorno en el que una persona es incapaz de reproducirse.

Stillbirth/parto de un feto muerto   Nacimiento de un bebé muerto.

Stimulant/estimulante   Droga que aumenta la actividad del sistema nervioso central, el corazón y otros órganos.

Strain/distensión   Condición en la que los músculos han trabajado en exceso.

Strep throat/inflamación de la garganta   Infección bacteriana de la garganta.

Stress/estrés   Las demandas y reacciones del cuerpo y la mente ante las exigencias diarias.

Stress tolerance/tolerancia al estrés   La cantidad de estrés que puedes sobrellevar antes de llegar al punto en que el estrés es demasiado.

Stressor/factor estresante   Cualquier estímulo que produce una respuesta de estrés.

Stroke/accidente cerebrovascular   Interrupción del flujo de sangre a cualquier parte del cerebro.

Substance abuse/abuso de sustancias   Uso innecesario o impropio de sustancias químicas sin un propósito médico.

Suicide/suicidio   Quitarse la propia vida.

Support group/grupo de apoyo   Reunión formal o informal de personas que se encuentran y comparten experiencias, sentimientos y confianza mutua.

Sweat glands/glándulas sudoríparas   Estructuras dentro de la piel que secretan tranpiración a través de conductos hacia los poros en la superficie de la piel.

Synergistic effect/effecto sinérgico   La interacción de dos o más medicamentos que resulta en un efecto mayor que cuando se toman las medicinas independientemente una de la otra.

Synthetic drugs/drogas sintéticas Sustancias químicas producidas artificialmente en un laboratorio.

Syphilis/sífilis Una ETS que ataca muchas partes del cuerpo y es causada por una pequeña bacteria llamada espiroqueta.

T

Tar/alquitrán Líquido espeso, pegajoso y oscuro que se produce al quemar tabaco.

Tartar/sarro dental Sustancia dura como una costra.

Tendinitis/tendinitis Inflamación de un tendón.

Tendons/tendones Cuerdas fibrosas que unen el músculo con el hueso o con otros músculos.

Testes/testículos Dos glándulas pequeñas que producen espermatozoides.

Testosterone/testosterona Hormona sexual masculina.

Therapeutic communities/comunidades terapéuticas Centros de tratamiento donde residen los pacientes.

Thyroid gland/glándula tiroides Estructura que produce hormonas que regulan el metabolismoóel uso de nutrientes por las célulasóla producción de calor corporal y el crecimiento de los huesos.

Time management skills/técnicas de administración del tiempo Estrategias específicas para planificar y utilizar el tiempo de forma efectiva y sana.

Tinnitus/tiniteo Trastorno en el que se oyen retintineos, zumbidos, silbidos, siseos y otros sonidos en la ausencia de sonido externo.

Tolerance/tolerancia Aceptar las diferencias de otros y permitirles ser como son sin expresar desaprobación.

Tolerance/tolerancia Situación en la que el cuerpo se acostumbra al efecto de un medicamento.

Tornado/tornado Tormenta de viento fuerte y giratorio.

Trachea/tráquea Conducto para el aire.

Training/entrenamiento Programa formal de preparación física para participar en un deporte.

Transitions/transiciones Cambios críticos que ocurren en todas las etapas de la vida.

Transmission/transmisión Propagación.

Trichomoniasis/tricomoniasis Infección vaginal que puede llevar a infecciones de la uretra y la vejiga.

Tuberculosis (TB)/tuberculosis (TB) Infección bacteriana altamente contagiosa que casi siempre afecta los pulmones.

Tumors/tumores Masas de tejido.

Type A personality/personalidad del Tipo A Tipo de personalidad competitiva y orientada a los logros que es la más propensa a desarrollar enfermedades cardíacas.

Type B personality/personalidad del Tipo B Tipo de personalidad apacible y no competitiva que es menos propensa a sufrir enfermedades cardíacas.

U

Ultrasound/ecografía o estudio de ultrasonido Examen en el que se utilizan ondas de sonido para proyectar imágenes de luz en una pantalla.

Umbilical cord/cordón umbilical Tubo por el que pasan nutrientes y oxígeno desde la sangre de la madre hacia la sangre del embrión.

Undernutrition/malnutrición No consumir suficientes nutrientes esenciales o calorías para el funcionamiento normal del organismo.

Underweight/bajo peso Estar por debajo del peso normal un 10 por ciento o más.

Unit pricing/precio por unidad Estrategia para establecer el costo relativo de un producto basándose en el costo por unidad estándar, como una onza o gramo.

Ureters/uréteres Tubos que conectan los riñones con la vejiga.

Urethra/uretra El tubo que va desde la vejiga hacia el exterior del cuerpo.

Urethritis/uretritis Inflamación de la uretra.

Urine/orina Material de desecho líquido.

Uterus/útero Órgano muscular pequeño en forma de pera, aproximadamente del tamaño de un puño.

V

Vaccine/vacuna Preparación que contiene patógenos debilitados o muertos y provee inmunidad al estimular al cuerpo a producir anticuerpos para ese patógeno.

Vagina/vagina Conducto muscular y elástico que se extiende desde el útero hasta el exterior del cuerpo.

Vaginitis/vaginitis Inflamación común de los genitales femeninos.

Values/valores Creencias y normas de comportamiento que crees importantes.

Vegans/vegetalistas Vegetarianos que sólo consumen alimentos de origen vegetal.

Vehicular safety/seguridad vehicular Obedecer las reglas del tránsito, así como utilizar el sentido común y el buen criterio.

Veins/venas Los vasos que regresan al corazón la sangre desoxigenada desde los órganos y tejidos del cuerpo.

Venom/ponzoña Sustancia venenosa secretada por una serpiente u otro animal.

Violence/violencia El uso de fuerza física para dañar o maltratar a otra persona o personas.

Virus/virus El agente infeccioso más pequeño que se conoce.

Vitamins/vitaminas Compuestos que ayudan a regular varios procesos vitales, incluyendo la digestión, la absorción, el metabolismo y el uso de otros nutrientes.

W

Warm-up/precalentamiento Actividad que prepara los músculos para el trabajo por venir.

Weight cycling/oscilación de peso El ciclo de perder peso, ganarlo, volver a adelgazar y recuperar peso.

Wellness/bienestar Estado general de contento, o de salud total.

Withdrawal/síndrome de abstinencia El proceso que ocurre cuando una persona deja de consumir un medicamento u otra sustancia de la cual es fisiológicamente dependiente.

X

Xiphoid process/apéndice xifoides Extremo inferior del esternón que se proyecta hacia abajo hasta el punto donde el esternón se toca con las costillas.

Z

Zygote/cigota Célula que resulta de la unión de un óvulo y un espermatozoide.

Index

obstacles, 267
relationships and, 485, 499–500
skills, 10, 29. *See also* Marriage
Community
effort against drugs, 595
relationships, 260
resources, 33
services, 289
Compensation, 204
Competition, 83
Compliments, 269
Comprehensive Drug Abuse Prevention
and Control Act of 1970, 519
Compression, 85
Compromise, 261, 291
Computerized tomography (CT), 375
Confidentiality, 323
Confirmatory test, 664
Conflict, 83, 316–19
building and recognition, 317–18
gang, 327–28
internal, 317
interpersonal, 316
in marriage, 499
resolution, 320–23, 496
Congenital heart disease, 397
Congestive heart failure, 680
Conjunctivitis, 175
Conservation, 734–35
Constipation, 420
Constructive criticism, 190, 268
Consumer Information Center (CIC),
715
Consumer Product Safety Commission
(CPSC), 715
Contaminant, 151
Controlled Substances Act. *See*
Comprehensive Drug Abuse
Prevention and Control Act of
1970
Cool-down, 64
Cooperation, 261
Coordination, 74, 76
COPD. *See* Chronic obstructive
pulmonary disease (COPD)
Copper, 110
Corn, 344
Cornea, 172
Coronary angiography, 681
Coronary bypass surgery, 682
Corticosterone, 379
Counseling. *See also* Mediation
abuse, 333
codependency, 612
family, 290
genetic, 467
grief, 231
HIV-positive testing, 665
rape victims, 763
Counselors, 251
Cowper's glands, 438–39
CPR. *See* Cardiopulmonary resuscitation
(CPR)
Crack, 582
Cramps
heat, 789
menstrual, 445
muscle, 84
Crisis center, 288
Crista, 178

Cross-contamination, 153
Cross-training, 62
Cryptococcosis, 666
Culture, 14–15
communication and differences in,
268
family traditions and, 278
food and, 97
transition to adulthood and, 301
Curfews, 307
Cushing's disease, 381
Cyberknife, 687
Cystic fibrosis, 466
Cystitis, 428
Cytomegalovirus (CMV), 667

D

Dairy products, in diet, 114–15
Dandruff, 166
Date rape, 331–32, 762
Dating, open, in foods, 125
Dating relationships, 301–3
abuse in, 331–32, 552, 762
Making Responsible Decisions, 480
on-line, 486
Deafness
conductive, 178
profound, 695
sensorineural, 179
Death, 7
smoking and, 528–29
stages of grief, 231
Decibel (dB), 177
Decisions
abstinence, 21, 484
conflict and, 317
drinking, 554
food, 98–99
making, 35–36. *See also* Alcohol;
Anger; Codependency; Colds,
common; Dating relationships;
Diabetes; Driving; Emergencies;
Family; Friendship; Genital herpes;
Head injuries; Health Plan; HIV,
Human immunodeficiency virus
(HIV); Lactose intolerance;
Medicine; Muscular dystrophy;
Perfectionism; Refusal skills;
Responsibility; Safety; Smoking;
Social changes; Suicide; Voice;
Water pollution
sexual activity, 483–84
Defense mechanisms, 204
Defibrillator, 397
Deforestation, 732–33
Dehydration, 86, 146
Delayed grief response, 231
Delirium tremens (DTs), 565
Dementia, 505
Dendrite, 365
Denial, 204, 229
Dental hygienist, 706
Deoxyribonucleic acid (DNA), 164,
461–62
Dependability, 262
Dependence, 577
Depressants, 550, 582
Depression, 229
clinical, 241
teen years and, 243

Dermatologist, 705
Dermis, 341–42
Desertification, 733
Designated driver, 559
Designer drugs, 590
Detachment, 612
Detoxification, 605
Developmental stages, 468–71. *See also*
Erikson, Erik; Puberty
Developmental task, 468
during adolescence, 481–82, 719
of adulthood, 495–97
Diabetes, 116, 689–92
Making Responsible Decisions, 691
Diabetes mellitus, 381
Diaphragm, 401
Diaphyses, 346
Diarrhea, 420
Diastolic pressure, 396
Diet, 136
fad, 139–40
pills, 141
training, 145
Dietary Guidelines, 112
Dietitian, 706
Digestion, 412–13, 418
Digestive system, 103
care, 417
functions, 412
problems, 418–23
structure, 413–16
Dilation, 460
Dinner, 120
Disability, 694
Disasters, natural, 751–53
Discipline, parenthood and, 500–501
Diseases, 381, 399, 405
addiction as a, 610
degenerative, 374–76
eye, 175
infectious. *See* Infectious diseases
lifestyle, 148
older adulthood, 505
periodontal, 169
prevention and medicines, 513
Dislocation, 86, 350
Distress, 215
Diuretics, 515
Divorce, 285–86
DNA. *See* Deoxyribonucleic acid (DNA)
Domestic violence, 286–87, 565
Dopamine, 206
Down syndrome, 466
Drinking. *See also* Alcohol
binge, 562
driving and, 554, 557–59
long-term effects of, 559–61
physical effects of, 555–57, 559–60
short-term effects of, 555–59
signs of, 564
Driving
alcohol and, 557–59
marijuana and, 588
Driving, alcohol and, 564, 755
Drug Enforcement Administration
(DEA), 584
Drug-Free School Zones, 593
Drugs. *See also* Addiction; Designer
drugs; Look-alike drugs;
Psychoactive drugs

personality and, 195
Hernia, 357, 440
Heroin, 584
Herpes
    genital, 487, 648–49
    Making Responsible Decisions, 648
Hiatal hernia, 419
Hierarchy of needs, 191–95
HIV, Human immunodeficiency virus
        (HIV), 399, 486, 576, 621, 651,
        658–59, 763
    Making Responsible Decisions, 661
    prevention, 668
    symptoms, 664
    testing, 663–65
    transmission, 659–61
    vaccine, 513
HIV infection, 165, 661
    abstinence and, 669
    symptoms, 664
    vaccine research, 667
HMO (Health Maintenance
        Organization), 708
Hodgkin's disease, 399, 685
Homeless population, 192
Homicide, 7, 324, 552
Homocysteine, 680
Honesty, 262
Horizontal Gaze Nystagmus, 557
Hormones, 104, 377, 436, 443
    endocrine, 444
    puberty and, 478
Hostility, 200, 205. See also Feud
Human papilloma virus (HPV), 648
Hunger, 97
    vs. appetite, 99
Hurricane, 752
Hydration, 80
Hydrocarbons, 727
Hydrochloric acid, 414–15
Hydrocortisone, 379
Hygiene, personal, 165, 169, 439, 444
    disease prevention and, 635
Hypertension, 677, 678–79
Hypochondria, 240
Hypothalamus, 369
Hypothermia, 87, 556

I

Ibuprofen, 515
Ice, 85
Idealization, 204
Identity, 267, 482. See also Maturity
    establishment of individual, 496–97
Ileum, 415
Illegal drugs, 575
Illness, family problems and, 284
"I" message, 264
Immune deficiency, 399
Immune response, 624–26
    stress and, 222
Immune system, 624, 658. See also
        Acquired immune deficiency
        syndrome (AIDS); T cells
    aging, 504
    diabetes and, 691
    nonspecific resistance, 624–25
    specific resistance, 625–26
Immunity, 624, 632–33, 643
Immunization, 12, 513, 630, 633–35

Impaired glucose tolerance (IGT), 691
Impetigo, 344
Implantation, 454–55
Impotence, 441
Incontinence, 428
Incus, 177
Indigestion, 418
Industrial wastes, 729
Infancy, 469
Infection. See also Lymphatic system;
        White blood cells
    respiratory system, 403
Infectious diseases. See also under
        individual diseases
    causes, 620–22
    prevention, 632–35, 773
    risk reduction of, 622
    skin and, 162
    transmission, 623
Infertility, 446–47
Inflammatory response, 625
Influenza, 628
Information, 32–33
    AIDS and HIV, 668
Ingestion, 413
Ingredients list, 122–23
Inhalants, 589
Injuries, 84–86, 350, 352
    head and spinal cord, 373–74
    muscles, 357
    prevention and equipment, 88–89
Inner ear, 177
Inpatient treatment, 606–7
Insulin, 380, 416, 690–92
Insurance, health, 707–8. See also
        Health Plan
Integrity, 505
Integumentary system, 162–65, 340–44.
        See also Skin
Internal conflicts, 317
Internist, 705
Interpersonal conflicts, 316
Intervention, 604
Intimacy, emotional, 497
Intolerance, food, 155
Intoxication, 550–51
Intravenous (IV) drugs, 659
Iodine, 110, 381
Iris, 172
Iron, 109–10, 390, 398
Irradiation, food, 153
Isokinetic exercise, 58
Isometric exercise, 58
Isotonic exercise, 58

J

Jejunum, 415
Joints, 348
    arthritis, 692–93
    injuries to, 350

K

Keratin, 165
Kidneys, 388, 425. See also Nephritis;
        Uremia
    alcohol and, 557
    artificial. See Hemodialysis
    failure, 429
    fluid intake, 425–26

stones, 428
Kübler-Ross, Elizabeth, 229

L

Labeling
    claims, 123–25
    dating on, 125
    medicine, 520
    nutrition panel on food, 121
Laboratory technician, 706
Labyrinth, 177
Laceration, 772
Lacrimal gland, 171
Lactobacilli, 621
Lactose intolerance, 155, 422
    Making Responsible Decisions, 422
Landfills, 731
Langerhans, Paul, 380
Large intestine, 415
Larynx, 402
Laser surgery, 174
Late adulthood, 504–5
Latency, 664
Lead, 728
Legumes, 116
Lens, 172
Less/more, label definition, 124
Leukemia, 398, 687
Leukoplakia, 535
Lice, 166
    pubic, 650
Licensing boards, 715
Life cycle, 494
Lifestyle
    activities, 61, 72–73
    diseases, 148
    factors, 8
    sedentary vs. nonsedentary, 54
Ligaments, 348
Light, label definition, 124
Limbs, artificial, 351
Limits, setting, 500–501
    expressions of physical attraction,
        644
Linoleic acid, 105
Lipase, 416
Lipids, 105, 341
Listening skills and techniques, 29,
        265–66. See also
        Communication
Liver, 416. See also Hepatitis
    effects of alcohol on, 555–57,
        559–60
Lobes, 401
Longevity, 8
Look-alike drugs, 590
Loss, 228–31
Love, 199
    family, 281
    parents' unconditional, 501
Loyalty, 262
LSD, 584, 585
Lunch, 120
Lungs, 388, 401
    cancer, 534–35
    effect of alcohol on, 556
    smoking and, 530
Lymph, 393–94, 683
Lymphatic system, 393–94, 396, 626
    problems, 399

Credits

© Aaron Haupt; 526
© Aaron Haupt/Stock Boston/PNI; 154T
© Aaron Haupt/Stock Boston; 275
© Aaron Haupt/Photo Researchers; 455T
© John Henley/The Stock Market; 212, 479
© Michal Heron/The Stock Market; 429
© Ken Highfill/Photo Researchers; 777R
© Kevin Horan/Tony Stone Images; 579
Susan Hunt; 463
© Robert Huntzinger/The Stock Market; 661, 213T, 496, 540, 758L
© Richard Hutchings/Photo Researchers; 213T, 496, 540, 758L
© IFA/Leo deWys Inc. NY; 215
© Image Club Graphics; 71B, 213B
© Institut Pasteur/CNRI/PHOTOTAKE; 15
© Jacobsen/Index Stock Imagery; 141L
© Jasmine/PNI; 12R, 208
© Johns Hopkins Children's Center, courtesy of the Carson Scholars Fund; 369
© William Johnson/Stock Boston; 71M, 78
© Jump Run Productions/The Image Bank; 640
© Henryk Kaiser/Leo de Wys Inc.; 619B, 660TL
© Dr. Michael Klein/Peter Arnold; 693B
© Bruce Kliewe/The Picture Cube; 743T
© David Klutho/Allsport USA; 219, 223
© L. Kolvoord/The Image Works; 217M
© J. Koontz/The Picture Cube; 338
© Bob Krist/Corbis; Interior of CNN Room
© Mehau Kulyk, Science Source/Photo Researchers; 364 background, 667, 682
© Dr. Dennis Kunkel/PHOTOTAKE; 620M, 621B
© Susan Lapides; 469T, 609R, 731
© Calvin Larsen/Photo Researchers; 527B
© Ken Lax/Photo Researchers; 493B
© Andrew M. Levine/Photo Researchers; 587L
© Rob Lewine/The Stock Market; 226TR
© David Lissy/Leo de Wys Inc. N.Y.; 586
© Andy Lyons/Allsport USA; 372, 376, 503
© Rafael Macia/Photo Researchers; 593
© Stephen Marks/The Image Bank; 634T
© Doug Martin; 386, 768
© Doug Martin, courtesy of Dr. Clayton N. Hicks; 160
© Court Mast/FPG International LLC; 238
© Tom McCarthy/Leo de Wys Inc.; 675
© Tom & DeeAnn McCarthy/The Stock Market; 758R
© Patti McConville/The Image Bank; 753
© Tom McHugh/Photo Researchers; 727B
© Will & Deni McIntyre/Photo Researchers; 500, 656, 706
© Mednet/PHOTOTAKE; 635
© Peter Menzel/Stock Boston; 718
© Lawrence Migdale/Photo Researchers; 277M, 751
© Bill Miles/The Stock Market; 648
© Roy Morsch/The Stock Market; 220R, 277BR
© Prof. P. Motta, Science Source/Photo Researchers; 339T, 436, 442, 693T
© Mugshots/The Stock Market; 482
© Bob Mullinex; 70, 510
© Larry Mulvehill/Photo Researchers; 773
© Dr. Gopal Murti, Science Source/Photo Researchers; 454
© Joseph Nettis/Photo Researchers; 332B
© Joseph Nettis/Stock Boston/PNI; 306
© NIBSC, Science Source/Photo Researchers; 659
© Richard T. Nowitz/Photo Researchers; 565, 769B
© Michael Paras/International Stock; 600

© Alfred Pasieka, Science Source/Photo Researchers; xM, 387, 650T
© Jose Pelaez/The Stock Market; 226TL, 435M
© Brent Petersen/The Stock Market; 198B
© Petit Format/Nestle/Photo Researchers; 457
© Mark D. Phillips/Photo Researchers; 411T
© David Phillips/Photo Researchers; 464L
© Phyllis Picardi/International Stock; 131T
© Picture Perfect; 403, 591–592
© Noah Poritz/Photo Researchers; 629
© James Prince/Photo Researchers; 495T
© Patrick Ramesy/International Stock; 94
© Alon Reininger/Leo de Wys Inc. N.Y.; 657T
© Claude Revy, Jean/PHOTOTAKE; 684
© D. Richardson/Custom Medical Stock Photo; 462
© Tim Rollins; 13
© Marc Romanelli/The Image Bank; 445, 625, 685B (girl)
© Martin M. Rotker/Photo Researchers; 560B
© Rouchon/Explorer/Photo Researchers; 143
© R. Rowan/Photo Researchers; 389
© Nancy Santullo/The Stock Market; 787
© Chuck Savage/The Stock Market; 61 row 1
© Karelle Scharff; 326, 594
© B. Seitz/Photo Researchers; 622B
© Blair Seitz/Photo Researchers; 703B
© Frank Siteman/Stock Boston; 477B
© SIU/Photo Researchers; 560T
© Ariel Skelley/The Stock Market; 277T
© A. Sofianopoulos/Ace Photo Agency/PHOTOTAKE; 511T
© St. Bartholomew's Hospital, Science Source/Photo Researchers; 680
© Stock Image/Zephyr Images; 71T
© SuperStock; 279, 297
© Karl H. Switak; 777B
© Tektoff-Merieux, CNRI, Science Photo Library/Custom Medical Stock Photo; 619T
© Telegraph Colour Library/FPG International; 131B, 131M, 226BL, 229, 413L, 574, 583, 587R, 599, 601T, 623B, 676–677
© Sheila Terry, Science Source/Photo Researchers; 530L, 774T
© Terry Wild Studio; 8, 45T 57T, 142, 217T, 275T, 308, 368T, 419, 446, 513
© Jay Thomas/International Stock; 368B
© Arthur Tilley/FPG International; 453T
© Geoff Tompkinson, Science Source/Photo Researchers; 511B, 618
© USDA, Science Source/Photo Researchers; 660TR
© Vanessa Vick/Photo Researchers; 277BL, 669
© E. H. Wallop/The Stock Market; 61 row 2R
© Westerman/International Stock; 226ML
© Keith Wood/Tony Stone Images; 184
© Yellow Dog Productions/The Image Bank; 439
© Robert Zappalorti/Photo Researchers; 777M

ILLUSTRATIONS

Matt Meadows; 341
Judith Tulenko Morley; 346, 347, 348
Network Graphics; 172
Betsy Paley; 392
Felipe Passalacqua; 349
Rolin Graphics Inc.; 413R, 426
Charles S. Scogins; 355, 356T, 366
Gretchen Shields; 780, 781, 782, 783, 784